碾压混凝土拱坝研究与实践

刘光廷　著

黄河水利出版社

内 容 提 要

本书为清华大学刘光廷教授十余年来为发展软岩上碾压混凝土拱坝设计进行的科研成果。共选收论文100篇,内容涉及混凝土温度断裂、压剪断裂、三维曲面断裂、随机应力及不均质体强度等方面的应用基础理论研究,碾压混凝土拱坝新结构、混凝土双轴徐变、累计温度及自重徐变仿真设计、湿热传导、水管冷却、裂隙岩体渗流、软岩渗流及饱和软岩强度折减等研究成果。书中阐述的基本理论和方法以及碾压混凝土拱坝新结构等都是作者本人及其指导研究生的创新性成果,其中很多已经得到工程实践的检验,并且得到了国内外广泛的赞誉。

本书可供水利、土木、力学等方面的科研人员和工程技术人员使用,也可供高等院校师生参考。

图书在版编目(CIP)数据

碾压混凝土拱坝研究与实践/刘光廷著.—郑州:黄河水利出版社,2004.10

ISBN 7-80621-841-6

Ⅰ.碾… Ⅱ.刘… Ⅲ.混凝土坝:碾压土坝:拱坝-研究 Ⅳ.TV642.4

中国版本图书馆CIP数据核字(2004)第102910号

出 版 社:黄河水利出版社

地址:河南省郑州市金水路11号　　邮政编码:450003

发行单位:黄河水利出版社

发行部电话及传真:0371-6022620

E-mail:yrcp@public.zz.ha.cn

承印单位:河南省瑞光印务股份有限公司

开本:787mm×1 092mm　1/16

印张:50.25

字数:1 160千字　　印数:1—2 000

版次:2004年10月第1版　　印次:2004年10月第1次印刷

书号:ISBN 7-80621-841-6/TV·372　　定价:138.00元

本书组织委员会

主任委员	周厚贵	孙　役	杜　彬	
副主任委员	李鹏辉	谭先春	戴西辉	
委　　员	周瑞忠	刘　宁	杨占宇	陈润发
	陈凤岐	燕　乔	高　虎	胡　昱
	王章忠	刘元秀	严　冰	靳宏文
	张佑明	戴　勇	邓凤玲	沙保卫
	焦修刚	叶源新	徐增辉	邓兰秋

前 言

多年来,我国一直为水利水电建设工程投资大、建设周期长、发挥效益慢、工程缺陷多等问题所困扰。在水利水电建设中采用新结构、新材料、新工艺和新的设计方法以缩短建设周期、降低工程造价、提前发挥效益,尤其是减少工程缺陷已成为亟待解决的重大课题。

20世纪70年代初,国外首先将水泥用量少、压实工艺简单的碾压混凝土成功地引入大体积混凝土坝工程建设上,实践表明,大仓面混凝土准备工作量减少,施工速度快,单价低。为此,世界各国纷纷采用,目前已建成的碾压混凝土坝有200多座。80年代我国在福建坑口首次采用碾压混凝土工艺筑重力坝,在短短的10多年内,迅速发展,遍及全国,先后在坑口、铜街子、岩滩、水口、大广坝、观音阁、桃林口、江垭、大朝山等,直到高206m的龙滩等主体工程都采用了碾压混凝土重力坝。

1988年,南非修建了50m高碾压混凝土重力拱坝,平面拱可减少混凝土水平层面连接削弱的缺陷。1989年修建70m高重力拱坝,径向设诱导短缝,水泥用量减少58~60kg/m^{3}混凝土,绝热温升降低9~13℃,坝体降温时温度诱导缝仍然扩大形成上下游贯穿裂缝,整体浇筑带来较多梁向裂缝。1990年我国普定修建75m高碾压混凝土重力拱坝,混凝土浇筑连续三年,沿拱轴每60m设置有可重复灌浆设施,利用诱导缝释放应力,以便在拱坝降温过程灌浆。1991年水利部推荐清华大学水利系向设计单位介绍碾压混凝土成层结构研究和温泉堡碾压混凝土拱坝(高49m)方案,采用了30m间隔的横缝,仓面小影响施工工艺,层间缺陷少。1994年,清华大学水利系在水利部贷款资助下,研究人工短缝释放应力,设计了世界上第一座碾压混凝土薄拱坝即溪柄一级碾压混凝土薄拱坝,施工速度快,1995年完工即蓄水。1997年,沙牌碾压混凝土拱坝(拱坝高117.5m,深层垫座14.5m)开工修建,采用2条横缝和2条横向诱导缝的分缝形式。1998年,清华大学水利系研究人工短缝和铰结拱,并设计了在高寒软基强震条件下的新疆石门子109m高的碾压混凝土拱坝,2000年10月提前蓄水。1999年在甘肃修建80m高的龙首混合坝型的碾压混凝土坝(拱坝+重力坝),采用周边缝和诱导缝结合的分缝形式,施工速度快,2001年4月底下闸蓄水。

碾压混凝土技术虽然发展迅速,但国内外还来不及建立一套与新工艺和新材料相适应的新的设计思想和新的结构形式,使碾压混凝土筑坝技术的进一步发展受到传统的结构形式和设计方法的限制。例如:由于碾压混凝土容易出现层间缺陷,国外往往采用加大剖面(加大工程量)的办法而不是改变传力方式来保证重力坝稳定安全。甚至对适合修建拱坝的地方也采用加大工程量改为重力坝,这不仅加大施工强度和增加对设备的投入,而且增加造价、影响建造工期。20世纪90年代初,国内外一直很少建造工程量小的碾压混凝土拱坝,更没有修建碾压混凝土薄拱坝的先例。我国具备修建拱坝条件的坝址很多,如何通过改进结构形式和设计方法,既保留拱坝在结构上超载能力大、层间缺陷对安全影响小、工程量少的特点,又引用碾压混凝土水泥用量少、大仓面施工、准备工作量少、快速施工的特点，是坝工界关注的重大课题。

为了发展碾压混凝土拱坝新结构，1988年清华大学水利系研究多裂隙体强度压剪断裂和温度断裂，提出用稳定人工短缝释放应力的碾压混凝土拱坝新结构，得到电力部勘测设计院支持，建议工程检验。1991年为温泉堡碾压混凝土拱坝提供含水平缺陷结构内应力及边缘应力奇异性研究，含横缝拱坝变形传力及坝踵水平短缝的拱坝应力重分布研究，碾压混凝土拱坝施工期及运行期仿真组合应力研究。1993年在水利部工程贷款支持下，水利部重点项目基金和国家自然科学基金科研经费资助下清华大学水利系研究设计了国际上第一座碾压混凝土薄拱坝（溪柄工程，高63.5m）。研究提供成层结构应力、三维裂缝、弯曲断裂、温度断裂及应变强度因子等35篇重要刊物文章，提出人工短缝释放应力及止裂新结构，进行三维累计仿真设计计算及工程设计。在缺乏拌和起重运输设备条件下大部分拱坝仍用大仓面无缝快速施工，仅1995年上半年即完成坝体碾压混凝土，当年拦蓄50年一遇洪水，为增加发电效益又连续三年超校核水位蓄水。由于施工期设备不足，间歇时间长，坝体曾有两个高程的层间缺陷，进行了灌浆处理，未出现径向约束裂缝，10年来安全运行。

1998年在新疆自治区及昌吉州领导及清华大学985基金支持下，清华大学水利系进一步研究设计了国际上第一座高寒强震地区软岩地基上高百米以上碾压混凝土拱坝，进一步提供坝体抗冻、防裂、人工缝减震、适应软岩大变位“柔性拱”，软岩和混凝土多轴徐变和随机徐变应力，研究“铰接拱”结构提前蓄水，研究非定常渗流区和饱和岩体强度折减，混凝土湿热传导及工程浸水冷却等问题，提供64篇文章，获发明专利3项及实用新型专利1项，进行仿真参数测定设计计算及工程监测以修正工程措施。碾压混凝土施工速度快，混凝土浇筑仅11个月（未计入冬季严寒停工期）即开始蓄水春灌，15个月完成百米高混凝土拱坝的碾压。

碾压混凝土材料和工艺在国内发展很快，大大促进了碾压混凝土拱坝的实施，本书介绍作者1988年以来进行的碾压混凝土拱坝研究并公开发表的成果和直接指导研究生进行碾压混凝土拱坝新结构的应用基础和设计应用研究的工作内容。

应该着重指出的是，这些碾压混凝土拱坝的研究和实践工作是与水利部原副部长何璟同志的大力倡导以及水利部和电力部的扶持分不开的，水利部原科技司司长李春敏同志的支持，尤其是原电力部王圣培同志的直接参与，使我们渡过了许多难关，我们将永志不忘。

作　者

2004年5月

目 录

前 言

绪 论

碾压混凝土薄拱坝结构研究…………(3)
高寒、强震、成层软弱砾岩(弹模 4 000MPa)基础上的石门子碾压混凝土拱坝………(10)

一、多裂隙体及混凝土的应力和压剪断裂、温度断裂、止裂及应力释放结构

弹性力学问题的第二类边界积分方程
——边界元法及其二维基本解…………(17)
弹性力学问题的第二类边界积分方程
——边界元法的三维基本解…………(27)
The Strength of a Finite Body with Multiple Cracks…………(35)
The Synthetic Deformation modulus and the Synthetic Poisson's Ratio of multiple-Crack Bodies…………(48)
An Analytic-Fictitious Boundary Forces Method for Calculating Multi-Crack Problem in Arbitrary Region with Mixed Mode Boundaries…………(57)
Study on the Curved and Branch Cracks in Massive Concrete Structures…………(67)
Study on Boundary Multiple Crack and the Stability of Horizontal Cracks in Concrete Cravity Dam…………(74)
缝内含有不同导温介质时的稳定温度断裂研究…………(84)
The Analytic-Numerical Solution for Thermal Crack Problems and Crack Prevention of RCAD…………(90)
Fracture Problem of Multiple Crack Body Under Harmonic Thermal Load and the Stability of Cracks in RCAD…………(102)
Thermally Stressed Multiple Systems in Steady State…………(112)
稳定热流场中温度断裂子域的解析数值解…………(126)
多裂隙体的稳定热断裂(张开型)问题…………(132)
Harmonic Thermal Fracture of Multiple Crack System and the Stability of Cracks in RCC Arch Dam…………(140)
混合边界多裂隙体在简谐变温场作用下的断裂问题(张开型)…………(154)
Study on Steady-Thermal Fracture with Different Conductive Material Filled in Crack…………(162)

含有绝热裂缝的有限自由板在稳定温度场作用下的断裂分析…………………………(170)
Fictitious Thermal Source (FTS) Method in Solving Harmonic Temperature Field Problem …………………………………………………………………………(179)
Singular Integral Equation Groups For 3-D Crack Problems in Finite Body …………(187)
三维热传导问题的间接边界元法……………………………………………………(194)
不连续位移超奇异积分方程法解三维多裂纹问题…………………………………(199)
位移不连续边界元法解多裂纹体的裂缝扩展………………………………………(206)
三维椭圆裂纹前沿非法平面内扩展的可能性研究…………………………………(212)
Solution of Periodic Heat Conduction by Indirect Boundary Element Method Based on Fictitious Heat Source …………………………………………………………(216)
Continuous Near-Tip Fields For A Dynamic Crack Propagating in a Power-Law Elastic-Plastic Material …………………………………………………………(225)
Three-dimensional Stress and Displacement Fields Near an Elliptical Crack Front ………………………………………………………………………………………(234)

二、(不确定性问题)随机应力及不均质体强度

大体积混凝土结构温度场的随机有限元算法………………………………………(255)
Spectral Stochastic Finite Element Analysis of Periodic Random Thermal Creep Stress in Concrete ………………………………………………………………(262)
Research on Nonstationary Random Thermal Creep Stresses in Mass Concrete Structures …………………………………………………………………………(272)
大体积混凝土结构随机温度徐变应力计算方法研究………………………………(284)
混凝土结构的随机温度及随机徐变应力……………………………………………(296)
非平稳温度场影响下混凝土结构的随机徐变应力…………………………………(310)
混凝土结构温度徐变应力的首次超越可靠度………………………………………(318)
Time-Dependent Reliability Assessment for Mass Concrete Structures ……………(326)
Experiments and Simulation on the Propagation of the Juncture Crack Between Gravel and Mortar ……………………………………………………………(345)
用随机骨料模型数值模拟混凝土材料的断裂………………………………………(351)
地震动随机场变界展开法……………………………………………………………(356)
地震动随机场投影展开法……………………………………………………………(361)
拱坝地震动随机响应分析……………………………………………………………(366)
子费用模糊估算的水电工程总造价概率估计………………………………………(371)
工程项目投资费用的随机—模糊估算方法研究……………………………………(377)
二维混凝土随机骨料模型研究………………………………………………………(383)
三维混凝土骨料随机投放算法研究…………………………………………………(390)
数值计算中的一种无网格方法研究…………………………………………………(398)

三、碾压混凝土拱坝新结构、仿真计算及参数测定

Finite Element Analysis of Accumulated Stresses Due To Dead Weight in Rcc Dams ……… (411)
Numerical Procedure for Thermal Creep Stress in Mass Concrete Structures ……… (420)
Numerical-Experimental Analysis of the Cracks in Massive Concrete Under Compression-Shear Conditions ……… (430)
混凝土、砂浆早期温度断裂韧性实验研究 ……… (436)
混凝土绝热温升测试仪的研制及其应用……… (442)
碾压混凝土拱坝坝体应力的简化计算……… (447)
成层弹性介质的二维基本解……… (454)
整体碾压混凝土拱坝工艺及温度场仿真计算……… (461)
含灌浆横缝碾压混凝土拱坝仿真应力和双轴强度判别……… (468)
含横缝碾压混凝土拱坝的变形和应力重分布……… (475)
缝端奇异边界单元和界面裂缝的应力强度因子计算……… (482)
溪柄碾压混凝土薄拱坝的研究……… (488)
溪柄碾压混凝土薄拱坝运行期位移预测和实测……… (497)
Research and Practice on Xi-Bing Roller Compacted Concrete Thin Arch Dam ……… (502)
碾压混凝土坝非稳定温度场计算预测与工程实测的比较……… (516)
层体边界元法在二维层体断裂分析中的应用……… (522)
三维热弹性力学问题的混合边界元法……… (527)
碾压混凝土坝的等效连续本构模型……… (533)
水管冷却效应的有限元子结构模拟技术……… (539)
阶梯形变截面圆拱和圆环稳定计算的有效方法……… (546)
拱坝河谷自由场反应……… (550)
拱坝河谷三维地震动分析……… (554)
碾压混凝土拱坝设人工短缝的应力释放及止裂作用……… (562)
石门子碾压混凝土拱坝温度场实测与仿真计算……… (569)
混凝土双轴压缩徐变试验初步研究……… (574)
老化黏弹性蠕变本构方程中的热力学条件……… (579)
考虑温度对于弹模影响效应的大体积混凝土施工期应力计算……… (585)
自生体积变形试验方法研究及应用……… (592)
RCC Arch Dams: Chinese Research and Practice ……… (597)
RCC Arch Dam Structure on the Taxi River and Water Storage Measure During Construction ……… (606)
Research and Practice of Roller-Compacted Concrete Arch Dams ……… (617)
碾压混凝土拱坝的铰结拱研究……… (628)
裂缝在压剪条件下的应力场和扩展能……… (634)

碾压混凝土重力坝结构改进和仿真应力…………(639)
柔性拱和软弱地基上的碾压混凝土拱坝…………(646)
侧约束对拱坝坝体应力和位移的影响…………(652)
Microstudy on Creep of Concrete at Early age Under Biaxial Compression …………(658)
无限域波动问题的有限元模型…………(666)
软化砂砾岩上的拱坝新结构…………(671)

四、湿热传导和干裂问题

石门子碾压混凝土拱坝采用聚氨酯硬质泡沫保温保湿的效果分析…………(681)
混凝土湿热传导与湿热扩散特性试验研究(Ⅰ)
——试验设计原理…………(684)
混凝土湿热传导与湿热扩散特性试验研究(Ⅱ)
——试验成果及其分析…………(695)
混凝土等温传湿过程的试验研究…………(701)
Experimental Study on Surface Cracking of Early-age Concrete …………(708)
Study on Mass Diffusivity of Concrete Under Isothermal Condition …………(718)
节理岩体的渗透系数与应变、应力的关系 …………(727)
岩体裂隙渗流水力特性的试验研究…………(733)
被自由面穿过排水孔的数值模拟方法…………(738)
改进的单元渗透矩阵调整法求解无压渗流场…………(744)
饱和非饱和三维多孔介质非稳定渗流分析…………(749)
饱和模型非定常渗流的数值求解方法…………(755)
饱和软岩受压硬化、强度折减及本构模型 …………(760)
低渗透饱和岩石加载时体积弹模与孔隙液压关系…………(766)
复杂应力状态下的饱和体本构模型及内力变化…………(774)
软弱地基上的碾压混凝土拱坝应力与位移分析…………(781)
软岩多轴流变特性及其对拱坝的影响…………(787)

绪　论

碾压混凝土薄拱坝结构研究

1 碾压混凝土坝的发展

碾压混凝土筑坝近期在国内外发展很快，它仓面大，减少模板灌浆工作量，工艺简单，水泥用量少，不依靠浇筑块表面散热的连续快速施工大大加快主体坝工的进度。因此，尽管它目前尚存在层间缺陷降低了坝体抗剪能力，但国内外常不惜加大剖面增加工程量（如日本百米高的玉川坝）以克服坝体抗剪能力下降的缺点来换取碾压混凝土简易快速施工的方便，并得到良好的经济效益。我国水利工程也存在投资大、发挥效益慢的问题，因此碾压混凝土快速施工引进后，从坑口工程修建到现在十多年间就迅速发展遍及全国。从碾压混凝土材料到工艺都取得了一定的经验。

由于碾压混凝土材料和工艺的迅速发展中，来不及同时发展与之相适应的新结构和新设计方法，进一步提高层间质量、防渗和耐久性，到目前为止仍采用加大工程量的方法来保持重力结构的安全，采用20世纪初以来重力坝设计计算和强度判别方法，加大工程量和安全系数。当前实践中，人们希望通过改进技术而不增加工程量来保证坝体安全，加快工程进度，对于适合拱坝条件的地方，希望保留拱坝在结构上超载能力大、工程量小的优点，却又同时引用碾压混凝土减少温控快速施工的优点。为此，1988年我们曾结合多裂隙体及含缺陷结构强度、弯曲裂缝及温度断裂研究探索柔性工程结构，释放水压及温度应力，同时保持拱坝整体强度。1993年溪柄工程设计时，国内外已建和在建的碾压混凝土拱坝有4座，最早是南非两座碾压混凝土重力拱坝，坝高50m和70m，拱坝未设径向横缝，仅用径向诱导缝灌浆以消除拱坝温度应力，蓄水冷却后温度应力沿诱导缝拉成上下游贯穿缝，最大缝宽达2～3mm，凿槽灌浆止漏，小缝宽0.1mm难灌浆，漏水量达2～3.5L/s。梁为重力剖面，拱整体作用被破坏仍可挡水。1990年我国普定修建75m碾压混凝土厚拱坝，模仿南非工程设置改进的诱导缝，普定气候好、建材条件好、施工质量好，设计上工程量较大，为降低温升，放慢浇筑上升速度，未显示快速施工的优点，混凝土浇筑延续三年。沿拱轴60m设置的诱导缝，蓄水后坝体出现贯穿裂缝，缝不发生在预定的诱导缝位置，须进行灌浆修补。1991年水利部推荐我们向设计单位介绍碾压混凝土成层结构研究和温泉堡碾压混凝土拱坝（高49m）设计方案，采用了30m间距横缝，拱坝两侧上部增设诱导缝各一条，拱坝厚度小，30m仓面小，混凝土中水泥用量较多（抗冻要求）层间间歇短，容易满足层间结合要求，因此缺陷少，坝体混凝土质量良好，但横缝准备工作量大，运输平仓碾压有干扰，冬季寒冷停工，三年完成拱坝浇筑，碾压混凝土施工速度快的优点不明显。

1993年，在水利部工程贷款支持下、水利部和国家自然科学基金科研经费资助下研究设计了国际上第一座碾压混凝土薄拱坝——福建省溪柄工程，坝高63.5m，厚高比0.189，坝址气温较高，年平均温度19℃，多雨，冬季枯水季短。拱坝修建在节理发育的砂岩上，拱座基岩渗水严重。设计按常规进行4～5m深坝基固结灌浆以及一排3m间距帷幕灌浆向左岸延伸 10m 及向右岸延伸 40m 以阻止绕渗，由于右岸灌浆后仍然渗流量较大，帷幕增加到 1.5m 间距，渗流消减。溪柄碾压混凝土薄拱坝用低热 425# 水泥，低绝热温升混凝土（12℃），后期高强度（高掺粉煤灰及石粉）混凝土及高抗渗涂料 XYPEX，外力作用下多裂隙相互影响及裂缝边界影响的解析数值解和有限元近似取值，内力分布及缝端应力强度因子和应变强度因子判别用于工程，采用人工短缝新结构释放上游坝肩和下游拱冠的温度和水压拉应力，在缝端小范围用高韧性材料止裂以保持缝的稳定。研制等温绝热仪较精确测定施工期不同温度条件下的混凝土绝热温升过程，利用改变部分骨料降低混凝土膨胀系数等仿真参数。考虑碾压混凝土层间缺陷研究成层弹性介质基本解及数值方法，研究成层碾压混凝土结构的应力重分布和边界剪应力集中。研制高精度双轴徐变仪，施工期温度和自重组合累计徐变应力，施工期未到运行期应力及三维仿真计算，进行含人工短缝溢流孔等构造的拱坝边缘及内应力设计。研制低热低膨胀率、高强混凝土，对含人工短缝拱坝下部 2/3 高度内不设横缝冬季浇筑，气温升高后上部 1/3 坝高留中央横缝用混凝土塞成拱提前拦洪，工程缺少必要的施工设备（1m^3 混凝土搅拌机一台，固定起重缆索一条，无备用设备），但施工速度快，1995 年年内碾压混凝土浇筑到坝顶，当年汛期拦 30 年一遇洪水，汛后完成溢流坎及坝顶结构。为了增加发电量，又于 1997、1999、2000 年连续超校核水位蓄水，坝体安全运行。薄拱坝 1997 年已接近稳定变场，至今已运行 6 年未出现约束裂缝，由于施工设备不足，层间曾超要求间歇，而未处理，坝体有水平缝，灌浆队伍更换，部分固结灌浆孔未灌以及帷幕孔未进行。1996 年蓄水时多处漏水，补灌浆后坝肩渗漏不明显，坝体因较薄，未设排水孔及廊道，背面仍有少量渗点。施工期进行温度预测计算和工程实测比较效果良好，实测人工短缝张开＜1mm 时缝端槽钢后面应变为 37μ，保持稳定，坝顶位移实测和计算预测变化相同。工程验收（2002 年 6 月）结论是："设计是成功的"。

2002 年 6 月 2 日溪柄电站工程验收结论：

溪柄一级水库大坝是水利部批准列为"八五"期间重点攻关的科研示范坝，是世界第一座碾压混凝土薄拱坝。清华大学水电系及水电设计研究所通过研究施工期和运行期大仓面坝体温度应力和组合应力变化规律、温度断裂和组合应力作用下裂缝的延伸稳定，首次提出了释放应力的人工短缝措施，并在工程中得以应用，实践证明短缝保持稳定。1996 年 4 月大坝导流洞封堵验收，1996 年 9 月第一台机组并网发电，1996 年 8 月大坝经受非常洪水位的考验，此后还长时间持续高水位运行，全坝至今没有出现约束裂缝，证明设计是成功的。溪柄一、二级电站各工程项目已全部按设计要求完成，各分部、各单位工程质量合格，投入试生产 5 年，运行管理工作已走上正轨，工程档案资料整理完毕。本验收委员会一致认为：该工程已具备竣工验收条件，同意通过验收，正式交付使用。

2　碾压混凝土薄拱坝布置及剖面设计

坝轴线布置在"S"形河谷的下拐点处，右岸拱座在凸出的山脊上，左岸拱座在两条山沟之间，上游的山沟即 F2 断层，F2 断层产状 N48°E/SE∠NW47°，倾角较陡，倾向下游，坝基深层处与 F2 断层相交，对坝体稳定没有影响。通过 F2 断层的渗水问题采用帷幕灌浆处理坝区枢纽布置见图 1，上游剖面展示图见图 2。

碾压混凝土薄拱坝坝顶高程 644m，最大坝高 63.5m（不包括 1 米的防浪墙），坝底宽 12m，宽高比 0.189，坝顶弧线长 95.5m，坝顶宽 4m。坝体外轮廓为简单的同心圆拱，在坝顶处的外半径为48m,内半径为44m,圆心角为114°。坝顶挑流式溢流坎布置在坝轴线偏左岸侧,自桩号0+18.55~0+49.55m,溢流前缘长31米(包括两条各1m的边墩),共五孔,每孔净宽5m。由于下游河床较窄,中间三孔沿径向收缩,挑距35m,两侧孔出口缩窄成2m,改变挑距为30m,堰顶最大单宽流量$14m^3/s$,挑坎末端最大单宽$35m^3/s$,但入水单宽$70m^3/s$,预计未来最大冲坑深约20m。设消力池坝高12m,抬高后尾水深18m,溢洪堰设四个中墩和两个边墩。闸门设门槽,宽0.5m,深0.25m,原设计正常挡水位(坝顶)以上自由溢流,坝预留闸门位置,以备提高水位的可能。运行期业主为提高调节库容,加五扇闸门。闸墩门槽上游侧设1m宽人行桥,桥面高程645m,门槽下游侧与坝顶齐平设工作桥,宽4m,桥面高程645m。溢流前缘外半径为49.65m,挑流坎处内半径为39m(距圆心中心),溢流坝顶高程为639m。

为施工方便,薄拱坝外形采用简单的无倒坡的同心圆拱,在拱上游两坝肩设置人工短缝和下游两坝肩采用局部加厚加贴角的方式形成双曲拱受力。由于整体碾压混凝土拱坝温度应力相对较大,为经济起见尽量不进行人工温控措施,主要利用冬春季12月~次年3月低温季节碾压快速施工,这时月平均气温(混凝土入仓温度)10~16℃,较年平均气温19℃低3~8℃,以降低坝体温度。在大坝浇筑过程中,后期气温升高,超过设计要求,从高程610m往上开始埋设冷却水管,平行于坝轴线方向呈折线弧形布置。冷却水管对碾压工艺有干扰。

从585m高程往上在拱上游两坝肩拱座设置止水的人工折缝,止水以防压力水深入坝内,人工短缝折45°转向坝体低应力区,缝端设置16号槽钢止裂,并埋设止水、灌浆盒与灌浆管,为运行期冷却后灌浆提供条件,改善稳定条件:自高程590~620m之间,坝体下游面拱冠附近设置三条短缝,缝沿径向,高程610m以下的径向缝深为2m,610m以上的径向缝深为1.5m。仿真计算表明:人工短缝可释放水压荷载作用下的拉力区,也释放了整体拱上下游面的温度应力,尤其是拱向应力,具体说来就是设置人工短缝后,沿拱坝上游坝肩宏观拉应力大大下降为微压,下游拱冠拉应力也大大下降。缝内设灌浆系统目的是运行期需要时也可以利用灌浆改变作用力方向,以增强拱座稳定。实测表明:在超高水位下运行时人工短缝张开<1mm,止裂措施后面实测应变<37μ,止裂效果好,人工缝保持稳定。

坝体620m高程以上河谷较宽,混凝土浇筑时间延长后,气温上升,在拱中部设一条灌浆横缝,自633m高程以上横缝上游预留孔作膨胀混凝土塞,作为铰接拱保持拱向传力,改善拱座应力,横缝待坝体冷却后灌浆。

碾压混凝土按90天强度设计,强度保证率85%,标号为C15,配制强度17.9MPa。在590m高程以下采用二级配,590m高程以上采用最大粒径为6cm的三级配混凝土。相应的水泥($425^{\#}$)用量分别为$75kg/m^3$和$65kg/m^3$,粉煤灰用量分别为$120kg/m^3$和$105kg/m^3$,木钙掺量均为0.25%。实测混凝土全级配绝热温升12℃。实测全级配粉砂岩骨料混凝土$\alpha=8.5$,坝体中下部温度应力较大部位细骨料用石灰石代替,以降低混凝土膨胀系数($\alpha=6.0$)。拱坝上游面用1.5m厚二级配混凝土R $90200^{\#}$,其他部分为三级配混凝土R $90150^{\#}$。混凝土配合比试验见表1。由于测定强度比设计要求高,施工中降低碾压混凝土水泥用量5kg,相应降低混凝土绝热温升为11℃,增大常态混凝土的水胶比便于人工振捣，见表 2。

在拱坝上游面设计刷涂 XYPEX 防渗涂料，形成防渗膜，以改善坝面防渗性能。经室内试验表明：防渗涂料垂直渗入混凝土约 2cm 深，混凝土抗渗标号由 S_4 提高到 S_8，而且新老涂层连接良好。

泄水孔

泄水孔设在高程 620m 坝右岸端头处，孔口尺寸为高 1.5m，宽 1m，出口为 1.2m×1.0m，最大泄流量为 26m^3/s。泄水孔长 9.42m，闸室长 4.58m，下游泄槽长 12m。泄水孔全长 26m，全部建在基岩上，泄水孔采用 200$^{\#}$ 常态混凝土，与拱坝坝体碾压混凝土连接处设 2mm 厚的紫铜片止水两边各伸出 20cm。泄水孔顶板厚 1m，底板及边墙厚 0.7m，泄水孔出口前 1.52m 处埋设一通气孔，直径 38mm，由闸室平台上通出孔外。

泄水孔进口设一道静水启闭的工作闸门，上游坝面上埋设轨道，启闭机安装在坝顶上的启闭机框架平台上，平台高程 648.13m，检修平台高程 644m。

泄水孔出口设一道动水启闭的弧形工作闸门，启闭机安装在 625.2m 高程的闸室平台上，弧形闸门铰轴中心高程 621.6m，桩号 0+008m（坝轴线处的桩号 0+000），闸室边墙厚 0.6m，埋设启闭导轨。

泄槽底板厚 0.3m，边墙高 1.8m，厚 0.4m，自桩号 0+014.5～0+019 为扩散渐变段，由矩形泄槽变为梯形泄槽，边坡 1:0.5。泄槽底部基岩上开挖纵、横向卵石排水沟，断面为0.15m×0.15m。

泄水孔钢筋混凝土施工，未震捣出现蜂窝及孔洞，拆模后填补了混凝土，蓄水后作反灌处理止漏。

表 1　混凝土配合比试验

混凝土种类	设计标号	水胶比	级配	S（%）	木钙掺量（%）	$C:F$	材料用量							
							水泥	粉煤灰	砂	小石	中石	大石	水	木钙（固）
碾压混凝土	R90 150	0.51	三	32	0.25	28:62	65	105	680	469	469	625	87	0.425
		0.51	二	35	0.25	38:62	75	120	724	727	727		100	0.488
常态混凝土	R90 150	0.70	三	31	0.25	80:20	137	34	638	461	307	768	120	0.428
			二	35	0.25	80:20	171	43	680	683	683		150	0.535
	R90 200	0.60	三	29	0.25	80:20	160	40	589	312	312	780	120	0.500
			二	33	0.25	80:20	200	50	630	692	692		150	0.625

表 2

混凝土标号	设计标号	水胶比	S（%）	木钙掺量（%）	石子级配	材料用量							性能													
					小石:中石:大石	水	水泥	粉煤灰	砂	小石	中石	大石	C:F	Vc(s)或slump（cm）	湿容重（kg/m³）	抗压强度（MPa）7d	抗压强度（MPa）28d	抗压强度（MPa）90d	抗拉强度（MPa）7d	抗拉强度（MPa）28d	抗拉强度（MPa）90d	静压弹模 ×10⁴MPa 28d	静压弹模 ×10⁴MPa 90d	极限拉伸 ×10 90d	凝结时间 初凝	凝结时间 终凝
碾压混凝土	150 R90	0.50	32	0.25	30:30:40	87	70	105	676	468	468	624	40:60	8.6(s)	2 490	6.8	13.4	22.0	0.43	1.02	1.77	1.83	2.86	0.76	16:18	23:24
	150 R90	0.50	35	0.25	50:50	100	80	120	719	725	725		40:60	7.0(s)	2 467	6.6	14.6	23.9	0.45	1.02	1.57	1.52	2.10	0.71	16:48	28:36
常态混凝土	150 R90	0.62	30	0.25	30:20:50	120	150	38	609	463	300	771	80:20	4.0	2 470	10.3	18.8	26.4	0.83	1.66	2.39				21:36	27:12
	150 R90	0.62	35	0.25	50:50	150	194	48	668	674	674		80:20	6.4	2 412	10.7	17.5	25.0	0.82	1.58	1.98	2.12	2.61			
	200 R90	0.54	23	0.25	30:20:50	120	170	44	561	470	313	704	80:20	4.6	2 403	13.5	23.9	32.7	1.15	2.18	2.47					
	200 R90	0.54	33	0.25	50:50	150	222	56	620	683	603		80:20	5.6	2 445	12.3	21.7	29.2	1.02	1.86	2.48	2.35	3.24		21:28	26:10

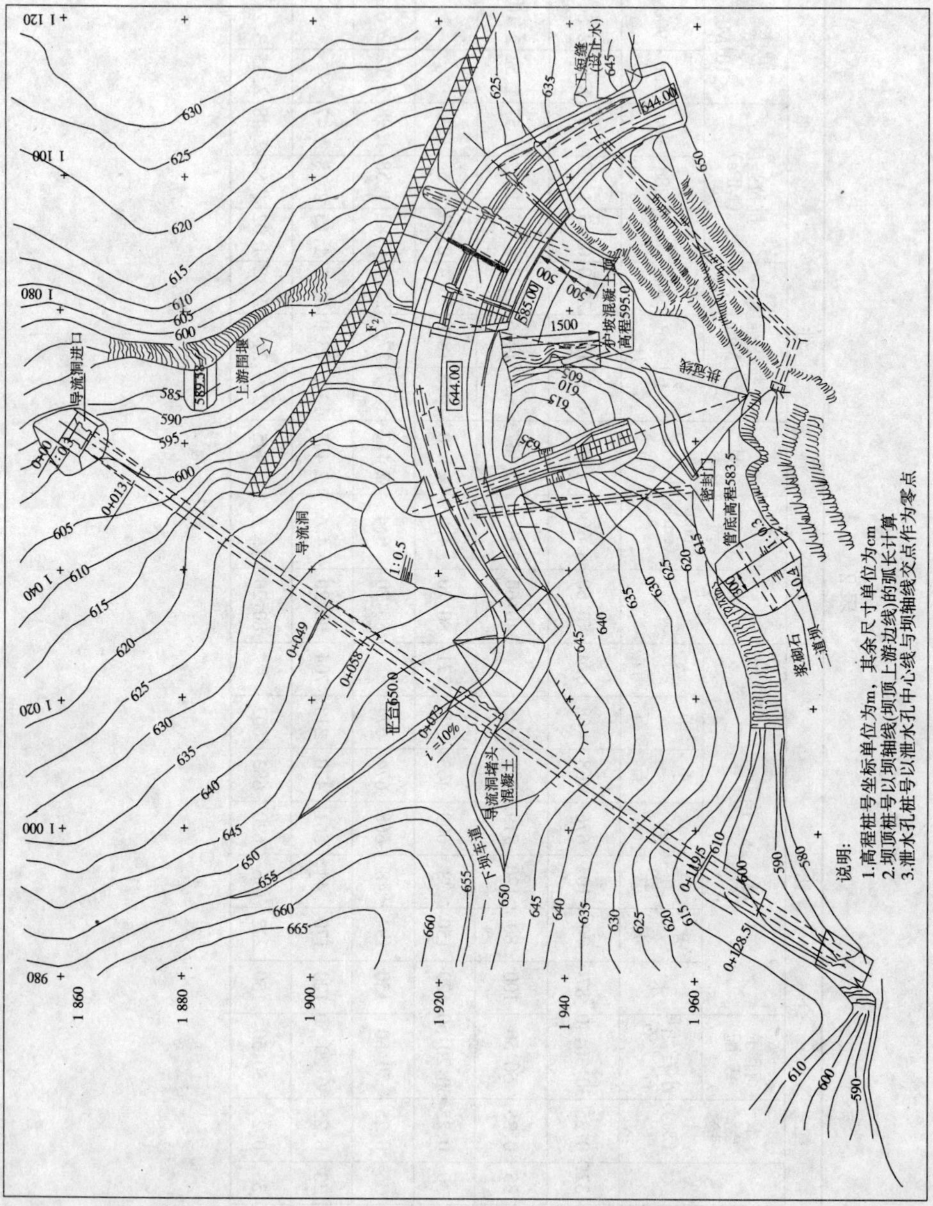
导流洞进口
上游围堰
导流洞
平台650.0
导流洞堵头混凝土
下坝车道
护坡混凝土高程595.0
人工短缝(设止水)
管底高程583.5
浆砌石
二道坝
说明:
1.高程桩号坐标单位为m，其余尺寸单位为cm
2.坝顶桩号以坝轴线(坝顶上游边线)的弧长计算
3.泄水孔桩号以泄水孔中心线与坝轴线交点作为零点

图1 坝区枢纽布置图

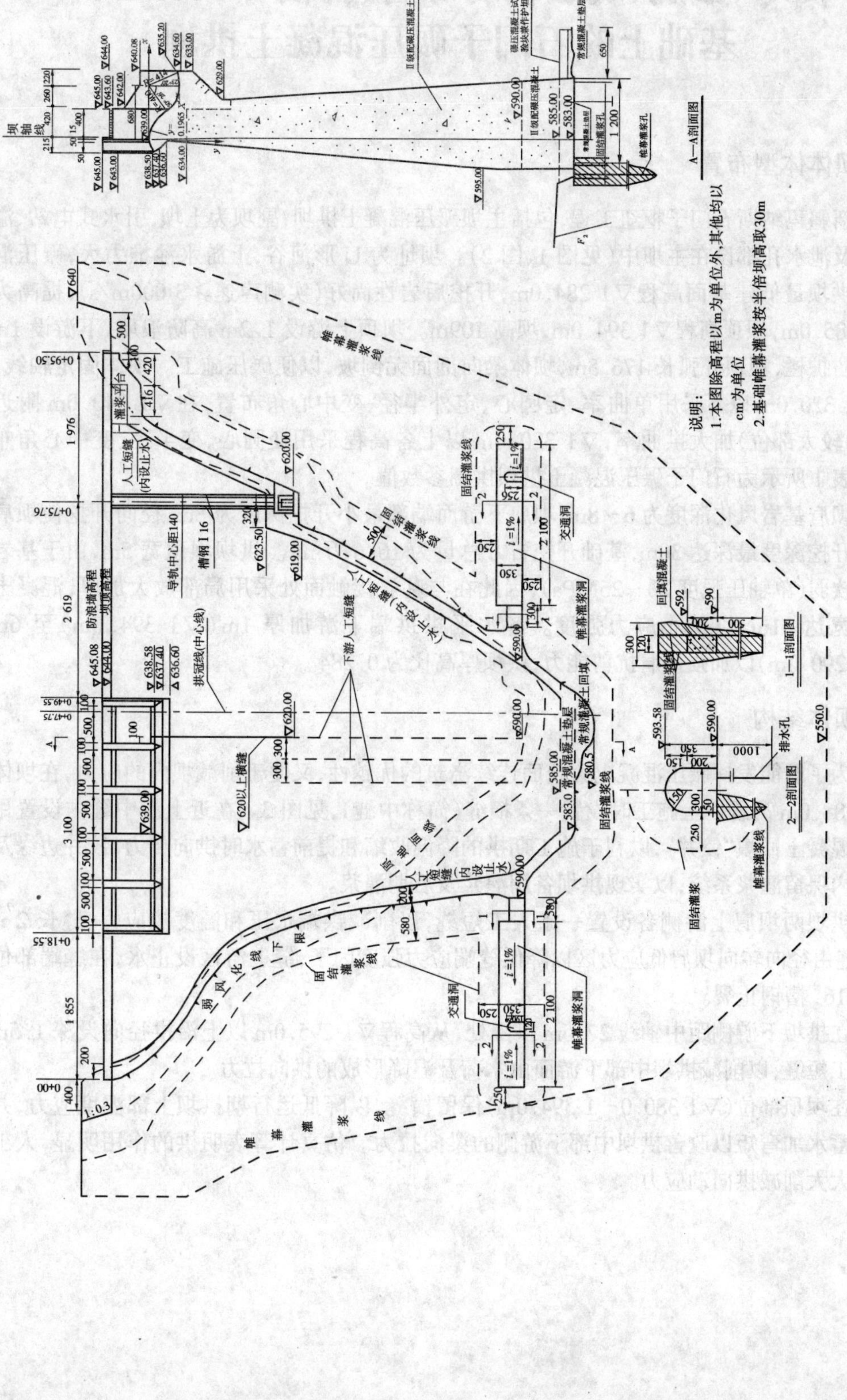

说明：
1.本图除高程以m为单位外，其他均以cm为单位
2.基础锥幕灌浆按半倍坝高取30m

图 2 上游展示图

高寒、强震、成层软弱砾岩(弹模 4 000MPa)基础上的石门子碾压混凝土拱坝

1　坝体体型布置

新疆玛纳斯石门子枢纽工程,包括主坝碾压混凝土拱坝,副坝为土坝,引水式电站、溢洪道及泄水孔都设在主坝中(见图 1、图 2)。坝址为 U 形河谷,上游水沙推力大,碾压混凝土拱坝最低建基面高程▽1 284.0m,开挖后岩性尚好(实测声速≥3 000m/s),提高为▽1 285.0m,坝顶高程▽1 394.0m,坝高 109m。坝顶上游设 1.2m 高防浪墙,下游设 1m 高的防护栏,坝顶外弧长 176.5m,坝体梁向剖面无倒坡,以便碾压施工。坝体固定轴线,在▽1 320.0m 以下采用单曲率、定圆心、定外半径、变中心角布置,在▽1 340.0m 附近(应力较大部位)加大拱曲率,▽1 320.0m 以上各高程采用变圆心、变半径、变中心角布置。表 1 所示为石门子碾压混凝土拱坝拱圈参数值。

坝肩基岩风化深度为 6~8m,坝肩下游面端部最小开挖深度为 8m,径向开挖使坝肩上游开挖深度最深达 30m,基础开挖石方总量为 16.6 万 m^3。拱坝坝顶宽 5m,由于基岩比较软弱(单轴压强度 20~25MPa),因此在与基岩接触面处采用局部放大加厚,混凝土坝底宽达 31m,以减小应力强度。各水平拱拱端下游加厚 1m(▽1 394.0m)至 6m(▽1 290.0m)以加强拱肩抗剪能力,拱坝厚高比为 0.284。

2　坝体结构

为了既能发挥碾压混凝土大仓面连续浇筑的优越性,又便于削减坝内的应力,在坝体▽1 288.0m 高程以上施工时设置一条横缝(简称中缝),见图 3。在近上游中缝内设置用膨胀混凝土回填"铰井",以利于施工期拱的降温收缩和提前蓄水时拱向传力,铰井边缘及中缝内保留灌浆系统,以实现拱坝备用灌浆及后期灌浆。

拱坝两坝肩上游侧各设置一条人工短缝,以削减拱端水压和温度拉应力,缝长 2~4m,缝由径向转向坝肩低应力区以降低缝端应力强度因子,缝上游区设止水,在缝端部位埋设 16# 槽钢止裂。

在拱坝下游侧距中轴线 27.5m 拱圈处,从高程▽1 295.0m 以上沿拱径向设深 1.5m 的人工短缝,以削减拱坝中部下游面由水荷及温降形成的拱向拉力。

在坝顶部位(▽1 380.0~1 394.0m)保留横缝,以降低运行期拱坝上部温度应力,并利用蓄水加弯矩以改善拱坝中部下游侧的梁向拉力。仿真计算表明拱的作用明显,人工缝也大大削减拱向动应力。

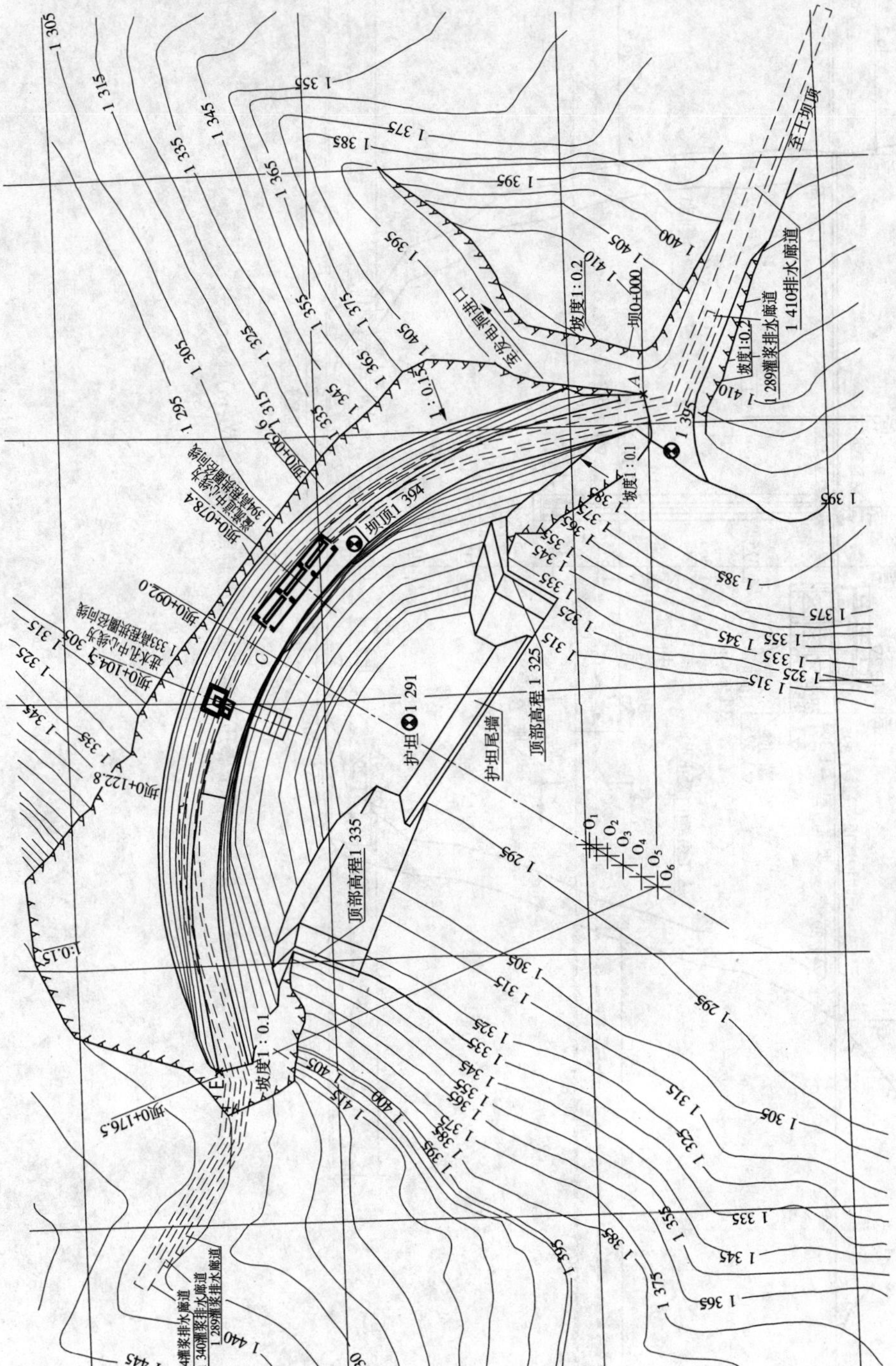

图 1 新疆石门子碾压混凝土拱坝平面图

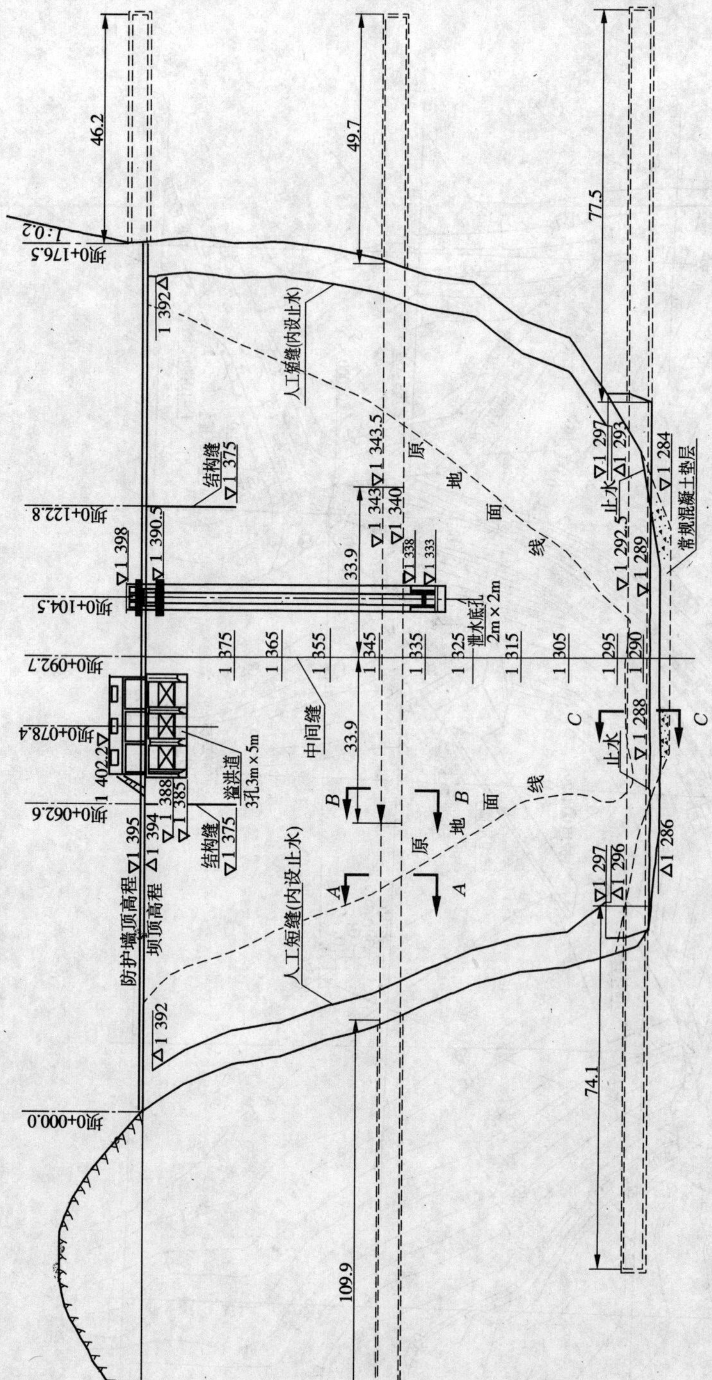

图 2 新疆石门子碾压混凝土拱坝上游展示图(单位:m)

表 1　石门子碾压混凝土拱坝拱圈参数值

单位 高程	左圆心角 (°)	右圆心角 (°)	总圆心角 (°)	外半径 (m)	内半径 (m)	贴坡厚 (m)	贴坡角 (°)	圆心位置 (m)
▽1 290	23.2	34.5	57.7	84.00	53.00	5.0	16.2	84.0
▽1 300	38.3	42.0	80.3	84.00	58.81	4.5	20.0	84.0
▽1 320	44.5	49.1	93.6	84.00	66.00	3·5	20.0	84.0
▽1 340	50.5	54.8	104.8	83.60	69.43	2.5	22.8	84.0
▽1 355	54.5	56.5	111.0	83.10	71.47	2.0	20.8	85.5
▽1 375	55.9	56.3	112.2	86.24	78.01	2.0	20.6	91.8
▽1 394	58.7	53.0	111.7	90.88	85.88	1.0	20.0	99.5

注:表中圆心位置是指与过拱冠梁上游坝踵垂线的距离。

主坝坝顶布置三孔溢洪道,每孔宽 5m、高 3m。单宽流量 $11m^3/s$(设计)~$14m^3/s$(校核)。溢流时,挑坎处的水平流速>10m/s,使下溢水流离开下游坝体。在校核洪水流量 $212.39m^3/s$ 下泄时,下游水面(高程▽1 319.0m)及消力池混凝土底板表面(▽1 290.0m)计算挑距分别为 31.8m、38.4m,相应的冲刷深度为 16.4m、21.8m,小于下游水垫深 29m。整体动床模型试验验证溢洪道下泄 $216.3m^3/s$ 时,冲刷深度为 14m,挑距为 34m,与计算接近。

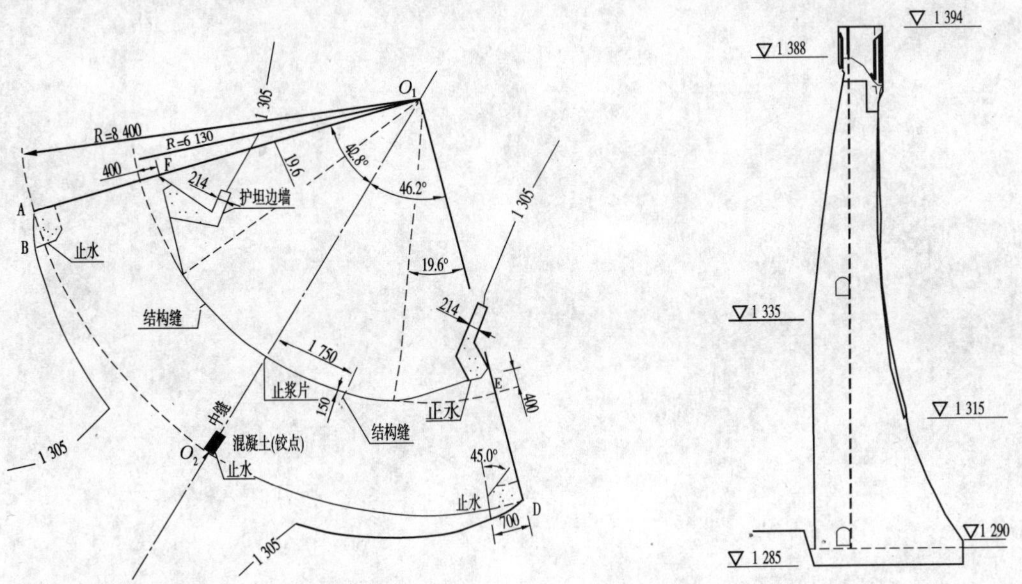

图 3　拱坝平面构造及溢流剖面图

主坝中心线的右侧布置泄水孔,泄水孔中心线与拱坝中心线的平面夹角采用 9°,使泄流时水流射向主流河道,水流可平顺流入左岸二级电站明渠。孔底坎高程为▽1 333.0m,孔口尺寸为 2m×2m。施工过程中,当导流洞堵塞后,可由此下泄来水;运行期可以用来泄洪;检修时,可以用来放空水库;不发电时,可以用此孔泄放下游所需用水,必要时还可用于冲沙。

根据规划要求，泄水孔在库水位为▽1 339.0m时，可下泄流量30m³/s。

泄水孔进口安设一扇平面检修门。检修门平时可放在▽1 390.5m的检修平台上，高水位时也可在坝顶用启闭机操作闸门启闭。检修平台以上不再设置闸门轨道和门槽。

泄水孔出口孔口尺寸为高1.6m、宽2.0m，保证孔内水流处于有压状态。设置一扇钢弧形门，用螺杆式启闭机操作闸门启闭。因闸门小，自重甚轻，靠自重不能关紧闸门，因此用螺杆加压关紧。

研究表明，饱和砾岩受压前期刚度加大，但强度下降达30%～50%。为了减少基岩遇水软化，在两岸坝肩岩体内布置两排间距2m的帷幕灌浆孔及一排排水孔，由勘测结果看出基础渗透率低(1Lu)，灌浆主要削减裂隙、断层渗流。不稳定渗流分析表明，在消除裂隙和断层渗流后有压渗流影响范围只有上游15m岩层，帷幕后可望得到部分非饱和岩基区，它提高了稳定安全度。为了防止沿右岸J3夹层和F6断层滑动的不稳定体和左岸J3和F5、F3断层滑动的不稳定体的滑移，在右岸上游沿F3做井字形抗滑键，在坝体下游垂直可能滑动面做4条抗滑洞，结合通往▽1 340.0m和▽1 289.0m廊道的沿断层设置交通洞，洞顶底扩挖填混凝土和灌浆，以加强抗剪能力。

一、多裂隙体及混凝土的应力和压剪断裂、温度断裂、止裂及应力释放结构

弹性力学问题的第二类边界积分方程

——边界元法及其二维基本解

摘　要　本文导出了以单位集中不连续位移(第二类边界)产生的场为基本解的两种边界积分方程——直接法和间接法边界积分方程,按 Hadamard 主值存在,进行高阶奇异积分并给出了二维问题的两个基本解,与通常的第一类直接法和间接法相比,第二类方法对处理裂纹等不连续结构面较为有利。

关键词　弹性力学　积分方程　边界元法　不连续位移　基本解

边界元法中以单位集中力作用下的应力场为基本解(即著名的 Kelvin 解)的方法,本文称为第一类直接法和间接法。本文提出的第二类直接法和间接法是以单位集中不连续位移(或集中位错)产生的应力场和位移场作为基本解,它们可以直接模拟不连续结构面,便于解决含裂纹的结构问题。

文献[1,2]曾对二维问题直接将边界用折线代替,得到的就是本文所述的间接法中的最简单的二维常单元情形。第二类方法与第一类方法是完全平行的,因此对其他问题也可以作类似的推广,其数值技术也可以利用第一类方法的成果。

1　合成位移和集中位移的概念

合成位移:考虑曲面上点 M(见图1),当曲面上有沿法线 n 方向的位移 $U_n(Q)$ 时(Q 表示曲面上任意一点),以 M 为内点的曲面某一部分区域 S 的合成位移定义为

$$U_n^* = \int_S U_n(Q)\mathrm{d}S(Q)$$

同样与 n 垂直的某一方向 t 的合成位移定义为

$$U_t^* = \int_S U_t(Q)\mathrm{d}S(Q)$$

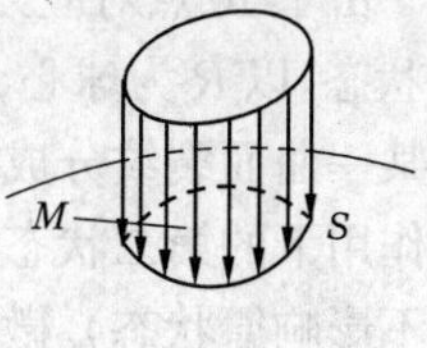

图1

集中位移:当 S 很小时,S_0 上的各点位移可视为均布,用点 M 上的值 $U_n(M)$、$U_t(M)$ 代表。令:$U_n(M)S_0 = C_n$(常数),$U_t(M)S_0 = C_t$(常数),S_0 为 S 的面积,则集中位移定义为

$$\hat{U}_n(M) = \lim_{S\to 0}\int_S U_n(Q)\mathrm{d}S(Q) = \lim_{S\to 0}\frac{C_n}{S_0}\int_S \mathrm{d}S(Q) = C_n$$

$$\hat{U}_t(M) = \lim_{S\to 0}\int_S U_t(Q)\mathrm{d}S(Q) = C_t$$

集中位移是合成位移值不变时令 $S\to 0$ 的极限值。当 $C_n = 1$ 及 $C_t = 1$ 时,称为单位

本文选自《清华大学学报(自然科学版)》1988 年第 2 期,作者还有林潮熙。

法向集中位移和单位切向集中位移。

与集中位移相对应，通常的位移 $U_n(Q)$、$U_t(Q)$ 可以看做“分布位移”，显然单位集中位移是分布为 $\delta(M)$ 的分布位移。

不连续位移：考虑三维连续体中有一闭合裂纹，裂纹面积为 S，令裂纹张开，则裂纹面上各点就有法向不连续位移 $D_n(Q)$，切向不连续位移 $D_{t_1}(Q)$、$D_{t_2}(Q)$。

$$D_i(Q) = D_i(Q)^+ - D_i(Q)^- \qquad (i = n, t_1, t_2)$$

即不连续位移为上下裂纹面位移之差。

同样，合成不连续位移定义为上下裂纹面合成位移之差。令合成不连续位移值不变，再令裂纹面积 $S \to 0$ 即得到集中不连续位移。

2 第二类直接法的边界积分方程

设一弹性域 V，边界为 $S = S_t + S_u$，S_t 为应力边界，S_u 为位移边界(见图2)。为简单计不考虑体力作用，只考虑 S 上作用着面力 t_j。

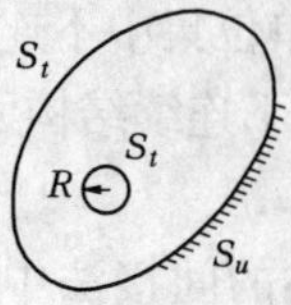

图2

把 V 看做无限域的一部分，在无限域的 V 内任一点 R 作用着单位集中法向不连续位移 $D_n = 1$(作用面的法线方向为 n)和单位集中切向不连续位移 $D_{t_1} = 1$、$D_{t_2} = 1$，n、t_1、t_2 三个方向互相正交。不失一般性，以 n、t_1、t_2 建立坐标系 x_3、x_2、x_1。无限域内在 i 向不连续位移下任一点 Q 的 j 方向位移为 $\overline{U}_{ji}(Q,R)$。切除 V 以外的无限体部分，需要在 S 上将内力换算为面力 $\overline{T}_{ji}(Q,R)$，以维持 V 内的变形值。为了利用Betti定理建立积分方程，可以将 $\overline{T}_{ji}(Q,R)$ 和 R 点所加的一对“集中力”看成第一组力，相应的位移为第一组位移；把实际 S 上的面力 t_j(外荷载，包括位移边界上的作用力)看做第二组力，其位移 u_j 为第二组位移。

由于 R 点对应力和位移来说都是奇点，把 R 点集中不连续位移看做当 $\varepsilon \to 0$ 时的极限状态。以 R 为球心，以 ε 为半径作一微球，球体被通过 R 点且在 R 点法向为 n(即 i 方向)的某一曲面裂纹分成两半球，这时裂纹面上作用着的是分布不连续位移和分布力(第二组力作用下的第二状态也可以看做有此小裂纹，但应注意要将“未开裂应力”加上，则裂纹并不影响原状态)。微球内部记为 V_ε，表面记为 S_ε。

挖掉微球，利用Betti定理得

$$\int_{S+S_\varepsilon} t_j(Q)\overline{U}_{ji}(Q,R)\mathrm{d}S(Q) = \int_{S+S_\varepsilon} u_j(Q)\overline{T}_{ji}(Q,R)\mathrm{d}S(Q) \tag{1}$$

当 $\varepsilon \to 0$，即 $S_\varepsilon \to 0$ 时，下列极限值存在：

$$\lim_{S_\varepsilon \to 0}\int_{S_\varepsilon} t_j(Q)\overline{U}_{ji}(Q,R)\mathrm{d}S(Q) = t_j(R)\delta_{ji} \tag{2}$$

$$\lim_{S_\varepsilon \to 0}\int_{S_\varepsilon} u_j(Q)\overline{T}_{ji}(Q,R)\mathrm{d}S(Q) = 0 \tag{3}$$

式中：

$$\delta_{ji} = \begin{cases} 0 & (j \neq i) \\ 1 & (j = i) \end{cases}$$

上两式的简单证明如下：由于 ε 充分小，第二状态下的位移 $u_j(Q)$ 和应力 $t_j(Q)$ 在式(2)、式(3) 中可看做是常量 $u_j(R)$、$t_j(R)$，移至积分号外，故只须考虑 $\overline{U}_{ji}(Q,R)$、$\overline{T}(Q,R)$ 的积分值。注意第二组力包括挖掉微球后代替内力的外力。微球被裂纹分成两半球后，在裂纹面上加均布不连续位移(即上下表面相对位移)，不考虑微球内各点变形即假定微球是刚性球，上半球面 S_ε^+ 上各点位移与裂纹上表面相同，下半球面 S_ε^- 上各点位移与裂纹下半面相同，因此

$$\int_{S_\varepsilon}\overline{U}_{ji}(Q)\mathrm{d}S(Q)=\int_{S_\varepsilon^+}\overline{U}_{ji}(Q)\mathrm{d}S(Q)-\int_{S_\varepsilon^-}\overline{U}_{ji}(Q)\mathrm{d}S(Q)$$

就是上下表面合成的不连续位移，当 $j=i$ 时其值等于 1，当 $j\neq i$ 时其值等于 0。在 $\varepsilon\to 0$ 的情况下，微球的刚性假设是精确的，因此式(2) 成立。对式(3)，根据物理意义，R 点集中不连续位移相应的一对集中力自成平衡，故式(3) 也成立。

当 R 点在边界 S 的光滑点上时，式(2) 的面积分只在半个微球面上进行，其积分值应为 $\frac{1}{2}t_j(R)\delta_{ji}$，当 R 点在 S 之外时，不需要挖微球，式(2) 极限值等于零。综上所述，式(1) 可写为

$$C_{ji}(R)t_j(R)=\int_S u_j(Q)\overline{T}_{ji}(Q,R)\mathrm{d}S(Q)-\int_S t_j(Q)\overline{U}_{ji}(Q,R)\mathrm{d}S(Q) \tag{4}$$

式中：

$$C_{ji}(R)=\begin{cases}0 & (R\text{ 在 }S\text{ 外})\\ \frac{1}{2}\delta_{ji} & (R\text{ 在 }S\text{ 上})\\ \delta_{ji} & (R\text{ 在 }S\text{ 内})\end{cases}$$

当 R 在 S 上时，式(3) 的极限值是：当 $i\neq j$ 时等于 0(因为 i,j 是正交坐标系中的坐标方向)，而当 $i=j$ 时极限值不存在，这时边界积分方程(4) 中第一个积分在通常意义下或在 Cauchy 意义下都是发散的。但可证明，利用 Hadamard 主值，该方程是可解的。

方程(4) 就是所要求的第二类直接法方程。它是高阶奇异积分方程，根据已知的边界条件可由该方程求出边界上的应力和位移，进而求得内部应力(也可用此方程)。通常边界条件较复杂，只能用各种数值解法。上述讨论及方程(4) 对二维问题也适用，不同的是用微圆代替微球，用二维基本解代替三维基本解。

3　第二类间接法的边界积分方程

有一弹性域 V，边界为 $S=S_t+S_u$，将 V 看成弹性无限域的一部分，在此无限域中，V 内作用着体力 $f_k(T)$，令 S 上有法向和切向不连续位移 $D_n(Q)$、$D_{t_1}(Q)$、$D_{t_2}(Q)$(见图3)，采用上节同样的坐标系，根据叠加原理，V 内任一点 M 的位移和应力为

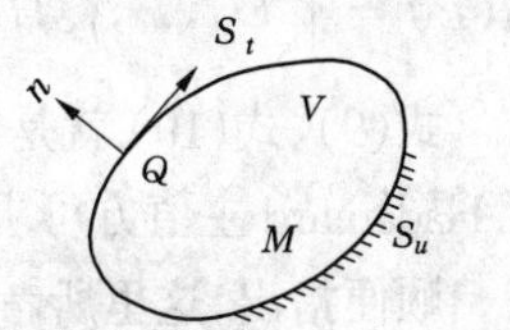

图 3

$$u_i(M)=\int_S\overline{U}_{ik}(M,Q)D_k(Q)\mathrm{d}S(Q)+\int_V U_{ik}(M,T)f_k(T)\mathrm{d}V(T) \tag{5}$$

$$\sigma_{ij}(M)=\int_S \overline{B}_{ijk}(M,Q)D_k(Q)\mathrm{d}S(Q)+\int_V B_{ijk}(M,T)f_k(T)\mathrm{d}V(T) \tag{6}$$

式中：$U_{ik}(M,T)$ 为 Kelvin 位移解；$\overline{B}_{ijk}(M,Q)$ 为 S 上 Q 点给出单位法向($k=n$)或切向($k=t_1$ 或 $k=t_2$)集中不连续位移时 V 内 M 点的应力；B_{ijk} 为 Kelvin 应力解。

不连续位移 $D_k(Q)$ 是未知函数。一旦求得 $D_k(Q)$，就可由上两式求任一点应力和位移。

为了求 $D_k(Q)$，利用边界条件：

$$u_i\mid_{Q\in S_u}=\overline{u}_i(Q)\qquad t_i\mid_{Q\in S_t}=\overline{t}_i(Q) \tag{7}$$

将 M 点移至边界 S 上记为 P，式(5)、式(6) 形式上成为

$$\overline{u}_i(P)=\int_S \overline{U}_{ik}(P,Q)D_k(Q)\mathrm{d}S(Q)+\int_V U_{ik}(P,T)f_k(T)\mathrm{d}V(T) \tag{8}$$

$$\overline{t}_i(P)=\int_S \overline{T}_{ik}(P,Q)D_k(Q)\mathrm{d}S(Q)+\int_V T_{ik}(P,T)f_k(T)\mathrm{d}V(T) \tag{9}$$

式中：$T_{ik}(P,T)$ 为 Kelvin 应力解。

式(8)、式(9) 中的体积分内被积函数都是已知量，两个面积分为奇异积分。与上节相同，在 P 点作半微球进行分析，然后取极限。这时面积分分为半微球部分和原边界部分，后者是常义积分，故只考察前者。

$$\int_{S_\varepsilon^-}\overline{U}_{ik}(P,Q)D_k(Q)\mathrm{d}S(Q)\qquad 及\int_{S_\varepsilon^-}\overline{T}_{ik}(P,Q)D_k(Q)\mathrm{d}S(Q)$$

由于 ε 充分小，$D_k(Q)$ 可看做常量，用球心处值 $D_k(P)$ 代表并提出积分号外，而 $\overline{U}_{ik}$、$\overline{T}_{ik}$ 的积分在上一节已考察过了。根据上一节有：

$$\lim_{\varepsilon\to 0}\int_{S_\varepsilon^-}\overline{U}_{ik}(P,Q)D_k(Q)\mathrm{d}S(Q)=\frac{1}{2}\delta_{ik}D_k(P)$$

$$\lim_{\varepsilon\to 0}\int_{S_\varepsilon^-}\overline{T}_{ik}(P,Q)D_k(Q)\mathrm{d}S(Q)=0$$

于是，式(8) 应改为

$$\overline{u}_i(P)=\int_S \overline{U}_{ik}(P,Q)D_k(Q)\mathrm{d}S(Q)+\int_V U_{ik}(P,T)f_k(T)\mathrm{d}V(T)+\frac{1}{2}\delta_{ik}D_k(P) \tag{10}$$

式(9)、式(10) 就是第二类间接法的边界积分方程，也是高阶奇异积分方程，必须进行 Hadamard 主值方可求解。应用分片插值技术就可导出第二类边界元间接法。

顺便指出，这里所考察的边界点都假定为光滑点。对不光滑点，应修改式(4) 中的 C_{ji} 值及式(10) 中最后一项系数值，处理技术与第一类方法一样，可参看文献[6]。

4 二维问题的基本解

4.1 法向不连接位移基本解

如图 4 所示，长 $2a$ 的平面裂纹，给出上、下表面法向(即 y 方向) 均布不连续位移 D_y，无限域的位移场和应力场可写为[1,2]

$$\left.\begin{aligned}
u_x &= D_y[-(1-2\nu)f'_x - yf''_{xy}] \\
u_y &= D_y[2(1-\nu)f'_y - yf''_{yy}] \\
\sigma_{xx} &= 2GD_y[f''_{yy} + \varphi yf'''_{yyy}] \\
\sigma_{yy} &= 2GD_y[f''_{yy} - yf'''_{yyy}] \\
\sigma_{xy} &= 2GD_y[-yf'''_{xyy}]
\end{aligned}\right\} \quad (11)$$

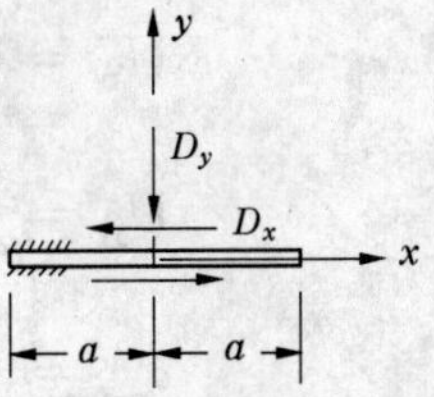

图 4

式中：f'_x 等表示对 f 求偏导数；ν 为泊松比；G 为剪切弹模。

函数 f 及其偏导数的表达式如下：

$$\left.\begin{aligned}
f(x,y) &= \frac{-1}{4\pi(1-\nu)}\Big[y\Big(\arctan\frac{y}{x-a} - \arctan\frac{y}{x+a}\Big) - \\
&\quad (x-a)\ln\sqrt{(x-a)^2+y^2} + (x+a)\ln\sqrt{(x+a)^2+y^2}\Big] \\
f'_x &= \frac{1}{4\pi(1-\nu)}\Big[\ln\sqrt{(x-a)^2+y^2} - \ln\sqrt{(x+a)^2+y^2}\Big] \\
f'_y &= \frac{-1}{4\pi(1-\nu)}\Big[\arctan\frac{y}{x-a} - \arctan\frac{y}{x+a}\Big] \\
f'_{xy} &= \frac{1}{4\pi(1-\nu)}\Big[\frac{y}{(x-a)^2+y^2} - \frac{y}{(x+a)^2+y^2}\Big] \\
f''_{xx} = -f''_{yy} &= \frac{1}{4\pi(1-\nu)}\Big[\frac{x-a}{(x-a)^2+y^2} - \frac{x+a}{(x+a)^2+y^2}\Big] \\
f'''_{xyy} = -f'''_{xxx} &= \frac{1}{4\pi(1-\nu)}\Big\{\frac{(x-a)^2-y^2}{[(x-a)^2+y^2]^2} - \frac{(x+a)^2-y^2}{[(x+a)^2+y^2]^2}\Big\} \\
f'''_{yyy} = -f'''_{xxy} &= \frac{2y}{4\pi(1-\nu)}\Big\{\frac{x-a}{[(x-a)^2+y^2]^2} - \frac{x+a}{[(x+a)^2+y^2]^2}\Big\}
\end{aligned}\right\} \quad (12)$$

令裂纹面上的合成不连续位移 $\overline{D}_y = D_y 2a = 1$，则 $D_y = 1/2a$。代入上述各式再令 $a \to 0$，可得出基本解，即单位法向不连续位移作用下的位移场和应力场为

$$\left.\begin{aligned}
U_{xy} &= \lim_{a\to 0}\Big\{\frac{1}{2a}[-(1-2\nu)f'_x - yf''_{xy}]\Big\} \\
U_{yy} &= \lim_{a\to 0}\Big\{\frac{1}{2a}[2(1-\nu)f'_y - yf''_{yy}]\Big\} \\
\sigma_{xxy} &= \lim_{a\to 0}\Big\{\frac{1}{2a}2G[f''_{yy} + yf'''_{yyy}]\Big\} \\
\sigma_{yyy} &= \lim_{a\to 0}\Big\{\frac{1}{2a}2G[f''_{yy} - yf'''_{yyy}]\Big\} \\
\sigma_{xyy} &= \lim_{a\to 0}\Big\{\frac{1}{2a}2G[-yf'''_{xyy}]\Big\}
\end{aligned}\right\} \quad (13)$$

各分量最后一个下标 y 表示不连续位移的方向。

运用罗必塔法则，可求出 a 趋近于零时的 $\frac{f'_x}{a}$、$\frac{f'_y}{a}$、$\frac{f''_{xy}}{a}$、$\frac{f''_{xx}}{a}$、$\frac{f'''_{xyy}}{a}$、$\frac{f'''_{yyy}}{a}$ 的极限。这时不考虑 $y=0$、$|x| \leqslant a$ 线段上的点，因为对这些点，上述极限一般不存在。把求得的极限值代入式(13)，得

$$\left.\begin{aligned}
U_{xy} &= \frac{x}{4\pi(1-\nu)}\left[\frac{1-2\nu}{x^2+y^2}-\frac{2y^2}{(x^2+y^2)^2}\right]\\
U_{yy} &= \frac{y}{4\pi(1-\nu)}\left[\frac{-2(1-\nu)}{x^2+y^2}+\frac{x^2-y^2}{(x^2+y^2)^2}\right]\\
\sigma_{xxy} &= \frac{2G}{4\pi(1-\nu)}\left[\frac{-(x^2-y^2)}{(x^2+y^2)^2}+2y^2\frac{(4x^2-y^2)}{(x^2+y^2)^3}\right]\\
\sigma_{yyy} &= \frac{2G}{4\pi(1-\nu)}\left[\frac{-(x^2-y^2)}{(x^2+y^2)^2}-2y^2\frac{(4x^2-y^2)}{(x^2+y^2)^3}\right]\\
\sigma_{xyy} &= \frac{2G}{4\pi(1-\nu)}\frac{-2xy}{(x^2+y^2)^2}
\end{aligned}\right\} \tag{14}$$

4.2　切向不连续位移基本解

在给出裂纹上、下表面均布切向不连续位移 D_x 后(见图 4),无限域位移场和应力场为[1,2]

$$\left.\begin{aligned}
u_x &= D_x[2(1-\nu)f'_y - yf''_{xx}]\\
u_y &= D_x[(1-2\nu)f'_x - yf''_{xy}]\\
\sigma_{xx} &= 2GD_x[2f''_{xy} + yf'''_{xyy}]\\
\sigma_{yy} &= 2GD_x[-yf'''_{xyy}]\\
\sigma_{xy} &= 2GD_x[2f''_{yy} + yf'''_{yyy}]
\end{aligned}\right\} \tag{15}$$

与法向不连续位移情况类似,令 $D_x = 1/2a$,代入式(15),令 $a \to 0$ 取极限,得如下基本解:

$$\left.\begin{aligned}
U_{xx} &= \frac{y}{4\pi(1-\nu)}\left[\frac{-2(1-\nu)}{x^2+y^2}-\frac{x^2-y^2}{(x^2+y^2)^2}\right]\\
U_{yx} &= \frac{x}{4\pi(1-\nu)}\left[\frac{-(1-2\nu)}{x^2+y^2}-\frac{2y^2}{(x^2+y^2)^2}\right]\\
\sigma_{xxx} &= \frac{2G}{4\pi(1-\nu)}\frac{6xy}{(x^2+y^2)^2}\\
\sigma_{yyx} &= \frac{2G}{4\pi(1-\nu)}\frac{-2xy}{(x^2+y^2)^2}\\
\sigma_{xyx} &= \frac{2G}{4\pi(1-\nu)}\left[\frac{-(x^2-y^2)}{(x^2+y^2)^2}+2y^2\frac{(4x^2-y^2)}{(x^2+y^2)^3}\right]
\end{aligned}\right\} \tag{16}$$

各分量最后一个下标 x 表示切向不连续位移的作用。

4.3　关于积分 $\int_S u_j(Q)\overline{T}_{ji}(Q,R)\mathrm{d}S(Q)$

R 点在边界 S 上,为了简单起见,先考虑只取 R 点附近一段曲线进行积分,此曲线很短可看做直线,并且 $u_j(Q)$ 看做常量 $u_j(R)$。不失一般性,把 R 点作为坐标原点,该段长 $2a$ 直线放在 x 轴上,考虑如下两个积分:

$$\int_{-a}^{a}\overline{T}_{yy}(Q,R)\mathrm{d}x, \qquad \int_{-a}^{a}\overline{T}_{xx}(Q,R)\mathrm{d}x$$

令 $y = 0$,由式(14) 得

$$T_{yy}\mid_{y=0}=\frac{2G}{4\pi(1-\nu)}\frac{-1}{x^2}\qquad T_{xx}\mid_{y=0}=\frac{2G}{4\pi(1-\nu)}\frac{-1}{x^2}$$

因而有：

$$\int_{-a}^{a}\overline{T}_{yy}\mathrm{d}x=\int_{-a}^{a}\overline{T}_{xx}\mathrm{d}x=\int_{-a}^{a}\frac{-2G}{4\pi(1-\nu)}\frac{1}{x^2}\mathrm{d}x$$

$$=\lim_{\varepsilon\to 0}\frac{-2G}{4\pi(1-\nu)}\left[\int_{-a}^{-\varepsilon}\frac{1}{x^2}\mathrm{d}x+\int_{\varepsilon}^{a}\frac{1}{x^2}\mathrm{d}x=\lim_{x\to 0}\frac{2G}{4\pi(1-\nu)}\left(\frac{2}{a}-\frac{2}{\varepsilon}\right)\right.$$

可见积分在 Cauchy 主值意义下是发散的。

根据 Hadamard 主值的定义[3]：

$$P\int_a^b\frac{f(x)\mathrm{d}x}{(x-u)^{n+1}}=\lim_{\varepsilon\to 0}\left\{\int_a^{u-\varepsilon}\frac{f(x)\mathrm{d}x}{(x-u)^{n+1}}+\int_{u+\varepsilon}^{b}\frac{f(x)\mathrm{d}x}{(x-u)^{n+1}}-H_n(u,\varepsilon)\right\}\tag{17}$$

式中：P 表示 Hadamard 主值；当 $n=0$ 时，$H_0=0$，与 Cauchy 主值定义一致；当 n 为正整数时，则

$$H_n(u,\varepsilon)=\sum_{i=0}^{n-1}\frac{f^{(i)}(u)}{i!}\left\{\frac{1-(-1)^{n-i}}{(n-i)\varepsilon^{n-i}}\right\}\tag{18}$$

于是有（注意 $u=0,f=\dfrac{-2G}{4\pi(1-\nu)},H_n=\dfrac{-2G}{4\pi(1-\nu)}\dfrac{2}{\varepsilon}$）： (19)

$$P\int_{-a}^{a}\overline{T}_{yy}\mathrm{d}x=P\int_{-a}^{a}\overline{T}_{xx}\mathrm{d}x$$

$$=\lim_{\varepsilon\to 0}\left[\int_{-a}^{-\varepsilon}\frac{-2G}{4\pi(1-\nu)}\frac{1}{x^2}\mathrm{d}x+\int_{\varepsilon}^{a}\frac{-2G}{4\pi(1-\nu)}\frac{1}{x^2}\mathrm{d}x-H_n\right]$$

$$=\frac{2G}{4\pi(1-\nu)}\frac{2}{a}$$

可见 Hadamard 主值存在。

现在对 S 不是直线而是光滑曲线（见图 5），$u_j(Q)$ 不是均布的情况证明 Hadamard 主值存在。

仍然把 R 作为原点，由式(14) 中第 4 式代入下述积分，得

$$I=\int_S u_y(Q)\overline{T}_{yy}(Q,R)\mathrm{d}S$$

$$=\frac{-2G}{4\pi(1-\nu)}\int_S u_y(x,y)\left[\frac{1}{x^2+y^2}-\frac{2y^2}{(x^2+y^2)^2}+2y^2\frac{(4x^2-y^2)}{(x^2+y^2)^3}\right]\mathrm{d}S\tag{20}$$

在奇点(0,0) 处：

$$\lim_{x\to 0}\frac{y(x)}{x}=\frac{\mathrm{d}y}{\mathrm{d}x}\Big|_{x=0}=0$$

$$\lim_{x\to 0}\frac{y(x)}{x^2}=\frac{1}{2}y''\Big|_{x=0}\qquad 有限值$$

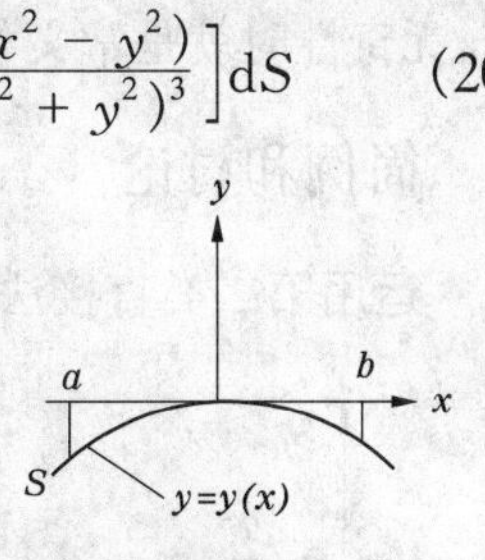

图 5

考察式(20) 后两项被积函数的奇异性（利用上两式），则

$$\lim_{x\to 0}\frac{2y^2}{(x^2+y^2)^2}=\lim_{x\to 0}\frac{2\left(\dfrac{y}{x^2}\right)^2}{\left[1+\left(\dfrac{y}{x}\right)^2\right]^2}=2\left(\frac{y''}{2}\right)^2\qquad 有限值$$

$$\lim_{x\to 0}\frac{2y^2(4x^2-y^2)}{(x^2+y^2)^3}=\lim_{x\to 0}2\frac{4\left(\frac{y}{x^2}\right)^2-\left(\frac{y}{x}\right)^4}{\left[1-\left(\frac{y}{x}\right)^2\right]^3}=8\left(\frac{y''}{2}\right)^2\qquad\text{有限值}$$

可见式(20)后两项积分的奇性可以消除。

式(20)第一项积分写为

$$I_1=\int_S u_y(x,y)\frac{1}{x^2+y^2}\mathrm{d}S$$
$$=\int_a^b\frac{1}{x^2}\left[u_y(x,y)\frac{1}{1+\frac{y^2}{x^2}}\sqrt{1+y'^2}\right]\mathrm{d}x$$

记　$$G(x)=u_y(x,y)\frac{1}{1+\frac{y^2}{x^2}}\sqrt{1+y'^2}\qquad(G\text{ 为有界函数})$$

则　$$I_1=\int_a^b\frac{1}{x^2}G(x)\mathrm{d}x$$

由式(18)可得此积分的 Hadamard 主值为

$$P\int_a^b\frac{1}{x^2}G(x)\mathrm{d}x=\lim_{\varepsilon\to 0}\left\{\int_a^{-\varepsilon}\frac{1}{x^2}G(x)\mathrm{d}x+\int_\varepsilon^b\frac{1}{x^2}G(x)\mathrm{d}x-H_1(0,\varepsilon)\right\}$$

这里:$H_1(0,\varepsilon)=G(0)\frac{2}{\varepsilon}$,见式(17),将上式右边两个积分进行分部积分,得

$$P\int_a^b\frac{1}{x^2}G(x)\mathrm{d}x=\lim_{\varepsilon\to 0}\left\{-\frac{G(x)}{x}\bigg|_a^{-\varepsilon}+\int_a^{-\varepsilon}\frac{G'(x)}{x}\mathrm{d}x-\frac{G(x)}{x}\bigg|_\varepsilon^b+\int_\varepsilon^b\frac{G'(x)}{x}\mathrm{d}x-G(0)\frac{2}{\varepsilon}\right\}$$
$$=\lim_{\varepsilon\to 0}\left\{\int_a^{-\varepsilon}\frac{1}{x}G'(x)\mathrm{d}x+\int_\varepsilon^b\frac{1}{x}G'(x)\mathrm{d}x\right\}+\frac{G(a)}{a}-\frac{G(b)}{b}$$

右端极限值是$\int_a^b\frac{G'(x)}{x}\mathrm{d}x$ 的 Cauchy 主值,它是存在的[4]。

因此,高阶奇异积分可以在 Hadamard 主值意义下进行,在一阶奇性时就是 Cauchy 积分,无奇性时就是常义积分,故后两者是 Hadamard 积分的特例。

5　简例和讨论

运用第二类直接法解滑开型 Griffith 裂纹问题。

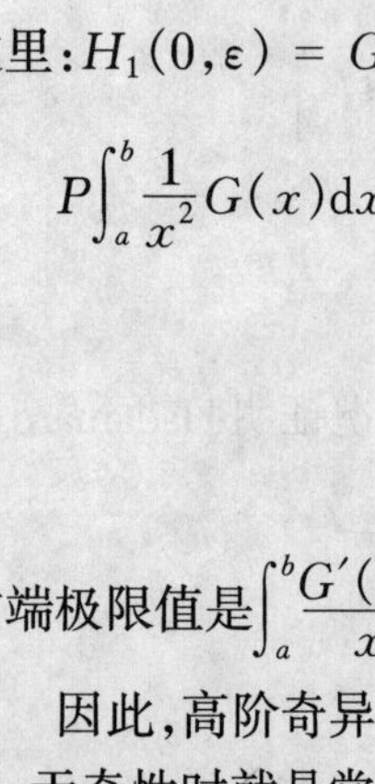

图 6

无限平面内有一长 $2b$ 的裂纹(见图6),其上、下表面作用着均布剪力 q,裂纹表面只有 x 向位移 u_x,根据直接法边界积分方程(4)得

$$\frac{1}{2}t_x(R)=\int_{-b}^b u_x(Q)\overline{T}_{xx}(Q,R)\mathrm{d}x-\int_{-b}^b t_x(Q)\overline{U}_{xx}(Q,R)\mathrm{d}x$$

由式(16)中第一式可知,在 $y=0$ 上,$\overline{U}_{xx}=0$,故第二项积分为零,上式成为:

$$\frac{1}{2}t_x(R) = \int_{-b}^{b} u_x(Q)\overline{T}_{xx}(Q,R)\mathrm{d}x$$

由式(16)中第五式得到集中不连续位移作用于原点时 x 轴上任一点切向应力：

$$\sigma_{xyx}\mid_{y=0} = \frac{-G}{2\pi(1-\nu)}\frac{1}{x^2}$$

当单位切向集中不连续位移作用于 x 轴上的 R 点(坐标为 x_i)时，x 轴上 Q 点(坐标为 x)的应力由上式得

$$\overline{T}_{xx}(x,x_i) = \frac{-G}{2\pi(1-\nu)}\frac{1}{(x_i-x)^2}$$

因此
$$\frac{1}{2}t_x(x_i) = \frac{-G}{2\pi(1-\nu)}\int_{-b}^{b} u_x(x_S)\frac{1}{(x_i-x)^2}\mathrm{d}x$$

将边界$(-b,b)$等分为 N 个单元，设每个单元内的位移为常量(常单元)，用该单元(编号为 j)的中点值 u_j 来代替(相应的坐标值为 x_j)。由上式得

$$\frac{1}{2}q = \frac{-G}{2\pi(1-\nu)}\sum_{j=1}^{N} u_j\int_{x_j-a}^{x_j+a}\frac{1}{(x_i-x)^2}\mathrm{d}x$$

左边是由各单元边界条件 $t_x \equiv q$ 得到的，右边 $a = b/N$ 是半个单元长度。

当 $j \neq i$ 时，可求得积分

$$I_{ji} = \int_{x_j-a}^{x_j+a}\frac{1}{(x_i-x)^2}\mathrm{d}x = \frac{2a}{(x_i-x_j)^2-a^2}$$

当 $j = i$ 时，上式为高阶奇异积分，其 Hadamard 主值已由式(19)得出

$$I_{ii} = \int_{x_i-a}^{x_i+a}\frac{1}{(x_i-x)^2}\mathrm{d}x = \frac{2}{a}$$

可见上式在 $j = i$ 时正好适用。

联解$\frac{1}{2}q$ 与 I_{ji} 两表达式，得出 N 个线性方程为

$$\frac{q\pi(1-\nu)}{2G} = \sum_{j=1}^{N} u_j\frac{a}{(x_i-x_j)^2-a^2}\quad(i = 1,2,\cdots,N)$$

令裂纹长度 $2b = 2$，分别划分单元数为：3,5,7,9,11,15,19,25,35 进行计算，部分结果见表 1，原点位移$\frac{U_0G}{q(1-\nu)}$的收敛情况见图 7(精确解可参考文献[5])。

表 1　原点精确解 $u_0 = 1$ 的相对数值计算位移 u_x

单元数 N	$x = 0$	$x = 0.4$	$x = 0.8$
3	1.178 1	—	—
5	1.104 5	1.030 8	0.773 1
15	1.033 9	0.953 6	0.657 3
25	1.020 2	0.938 6	0.634 1
35	1.014 4	0.932 2	0.624 2
精确解	1.000 0	0.916 5	0.600 0

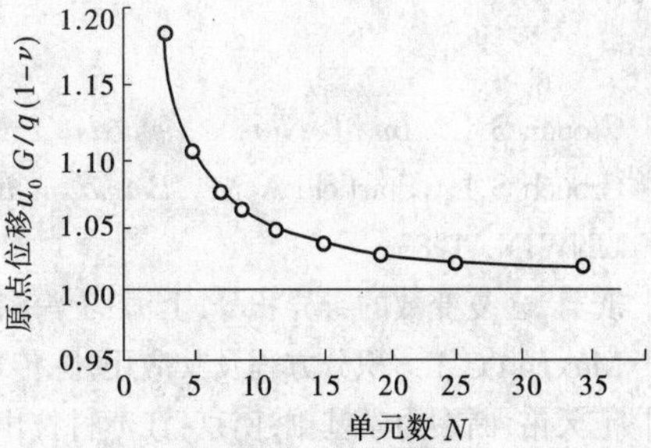

图 7　原点位移收敛图

计算表明,常单元虽然简单,裂纹周边位移用 10 个单元一般误差已降到 10% 以内,误差分布为中部小、两端大。但对裂纹前缘,常单元模式比较粗糙,很难直接用来计算应力强度因子。但是,如果只用常单元程序来估算应力强度因子,只要对常单元计算结果作一简单的修正,也可以得到有用的结果。虽然对该例裂纹表面相对位移精确解是按 $C\sqrt{2\bar{x}b+\bar{x}^2}$ 规律变化的,但一般情况下,裂纹前缘位移是按 $C\sqrt{\bar{x}}$ 规律变化,因此将常单元结果按 $C\sqrt{\bar{x}}$ 规律向裂纹尖端外推。以 $b=1$ 的裂纹划分等距 11 个单元为例算应力强度因子 K_{II}。缝端第一个常单元计算值通常与实际相差太远,将它舍弃,由第二个单元 u_* 外推,即位移在 $\bar{x}=0\sim4b/11$ 范围内按 $C\sqrt{\bar{x}}$ 变化($\bar{x}$ 为局部坐标)。计算 K_{II},也用较简略的方法:按 $\bar{x}=-\varepsilon(\varepsilon>0)$ 处的应力 $\sigma_{12}(-\varepsilon)$ 推求,即按下式:

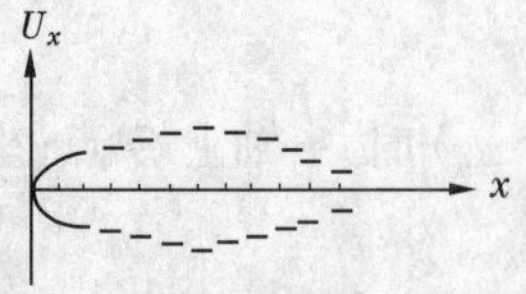

图 8　裂纹面的不连续位移值

$$K_{\mathrm{II}}=\sigma_{12}(-\varepsilon)\sqrt{2\pi\varepsilon}$$

计算 σ_{12} 时,各常单元贡献计算公式已如前述,"修正单元"的贡献为

$$\sigma'_{12}(-\varepsilon)=\frac{Gu_*}{2\pi(1-\nu)}\frac{1}{\sqrt{4a}}\int_0^{4a}\frac{\sqrt{\bar{x}}}{(\bar{x}+\varepsilon)^2}\mathrm{d}\,\bar{x}$$

$$=\frac{Gu_*}{2\pi(1-\nu)}\frac{1}{\sqrt{4a}}\left[\frac{-\sqrt{4a}}{\varepsilon+4a}+\frac{1}{\sqrt{\varepsilon}}\arctan\sqrt{\frac{4a}{\varepsilon}}\right]$$

修正结果为 $K_{\mathrm{II}}=1.073\sqrt{\pi}$,与精确解 $K_{\mathrm{II}}=\sqrt{\pi}$ 相比误差为 7.3%。显然,采用高阶单元或特殊缝端单元等可进一步改善精度。

在任意形状域及任意分布的多裂纹问题中,本文方法可直接以实际裂纹面不连续位移作未知量(间接法)裂纹上下表面的点只作为一个点处理,未知量少,且避免了第一类方法处理一般裂缝的困难。迄今为止第一类方法(主要是直接法)还没有比较简便的方法计算一般多裂纹问题。早期方法曾近似将裂纹张开按多连域求解,则张开过大影响精度,太小又引起方程病态甚至奇异。其他如 T. A. Cruse 补充方程法,或子域法计算量浩大。格林函数法虽然效率高,但目前只能处理二维单个裂纹问题。本文方法解断裂力学问题将是一种有前途的方法。

参 考 文 献

[1] Crouch S. L.. *Int. J. Num. Methods*, Engng. 10, 1976, 301～343

[2] Crouch S. L., Starfield A. M.. *Boundary Element Method in Solid Mechanics*. London George Allen and UNWIN, 1983

[3] 龚昇. 多复变数的奇异积分. 上海:上海科技出版社, 1982

[4] Михлин С. Г.. 积分方程及其应用. 陈传璋,卢鹤绂译. 上海:商务印书馆, 1960

[5] 范天佑. 断裂力学基础. 南京:江苏科技出版社, 1978

[6] Hartmann F.. *New Developments in Boundary Element Methods* (*Brebbiaed.*) Butter Worths Pub, London, 1980, 367～379

弹性力学问题的第二类边界积分方程

——边界元法的三维基本解

摘　要　本文运用Hankel变换导出了三维弹性静力学问题的第二类边界积分方程,一边界元法的两组基本解,以这两组基本解为核的边界积分方程是高阶奇异积分方程可以在Hadamard主值意义下求解。

用断裂力学分析多裂纹体对研究工程结构有重要意义,水工大体积混凝土在施工期间常出现一些裂缝,这些裂缝破坏了结构整体性,有些甚至危及运行期工程结构的安全。因此,研究多裂隙体的受力后工作状态,应力重分布和裂缝在结构受力时的稳定性是我国水电"七五"期间重要研究项目之一。已有研究表明,硬化混凝土存在着许多初始微裂缝,加载后的力学性能也和这些裂缝的开展过程密切相关,因此对混凝土强度的研究也和多裂隙体研究密切相关。

含多裂隙的工程结构用有限元和普通边界元解三维多裂隙问题,要得到工程可用精度,计算量异常浩大,用集中不连续位移的第二类边界积分方程——边界元法[1]对处理裂纹等不连续面较为有利。文献[1]中已经给出第二类边界积分方程及二维基本解,本文给出三维基本解。

第二类间接法的边界积分方程为[1]

$$\left.\begin{aligned}\overline{u}_i(P) &= \int_s \overline{U}_{ik}(P,Q)D_k(Q)\mathrm{d}s(Q)+\int_v U_{ik}(P,T)f_k(T)\mathrm{d}v(T)\\ \overline{t}_i(P) &= \int_s \overline{T}_{ik}(P,Q)D_k(Q)\mathrm{d}s(Q)+\int_v T_{ik}(P,T)f_k(T)\mathrm{d}v(T)\end{aligned}\right\} \tag{1}$$

式中:v 为解域;s 为 v 的边界;$\overline{u}_i$、$\overline{t}_i$ 为边界已知位移和面力;f_k 为体力荷载;D_k 为不连续位移;U_{ik}、T_{ik} 为Kelvin解(位移和应力);$\overline{T}_{ik}$、$\overline{U}_{ik}(P,Q)$ 分别为 Q 点 K 方向作用一单位集中不连续位移(作用面法向即 s 的法向)时 P 点 i 方向的应力和位移,即应力基本解和位移基本解。示察积分核 $\overline{T}_{ik}$ 可见该方程有高阶奇异性,应当在Hadamard主值意义下积分。

1　三维基本解(I)—— 法向不连续位移

三维无限域中,在原点作用着单位法向集中不连续位移(张开为正),作用面为 xy 平面(r,θ),求位移和应力基本解。对于这个轴对称问题用柱坐标,归结为下列方程[2,3]:

$$\nabla^2\nabla^2\phi = 0 \tag{2}$$

本文选自第五届全国断裂学术会议论文集(一),1988年5月,作者还有林潮熙。

$$\nabla^2 = \partial^2/\partial r^2 + \partial/r\partial r + \partial^2/\partial z^2$$

式中：ϕ 为位移函数。

位移和应力：

$$\left.\begin{aligned} u_r &= -\partial^2\phi/\partial r\partial z \\ u_x &= 2(1-\nu)\nabla^2\phi - \partial^2\phi/\partial z^2 \\ \sigma_{rr} &= 2\mu\partial/\partial z(\nu\nabla^2\phi - \partial^2\phi/\partial r^2) \\ \sigma_{\theta\theta} &= 2\mu\partial/\partial z(\nu\nabla^2\phi - (1/r)\partial\phi/\partial r) \\ \sigma_{zz} &= 2\mu\partial/\partial z[(2-\nu)\nabla^2\phi - \partial^2\phi/\partial z^2] \\ \sigma_{rz} &= 2\mu\partial/\partial z[(1-\nu)\nabla^2\phi - \partial^2\phi/\partial z^2] \end{aligned}\right\} \tag{3}$$

式中：ν 为泊松比；μ 为剪切弹模。

引进零阶 Hankel 变换：

$$G(\xi,z) = \int_0^\infty r\phi(r,z)J_0(\xi r)\mathrm{d}r \tag{4}$$

方程(2)化为：

$$(\mathrm{d}^2/\mathrm{d}z^2 - \xi^2)^2 G(\xi,z) = 0 \tag{5}$$

通解：
$$G(\xi,z) = (A+Bz)\mathrm{e}^{-\xi z} + (C+Dz)\mathrm{e}^{\xi z} \tag{6}$$

式中：A、B、C、D 是 ξ 的函数，由边界条件确定。

求出 $G(\xi,z)$ 后，作 Hankel 反变换得 $\phi(r,z)$ 按式(3)得位移和应力。位移和应力用 $G(\xi,z)$ 表示如下：

$$\left.\begin{aligned} u_r &= \int_0^\infty \xi^2 G'_z(\xi,z)J_1(\xi,r)\mathrm{d}\xi \\ u_z &= \int_0^\infty [(1-2\nu)G_z''(\xi,z) - 2(1-\nu)\xi^2 G(\xi,z)]\xi J_0(\xi r)\mathrm{d}\xi \\ \sigma_{zz} &= 2\mu\int_0^\infty [(1-\nu)G'''(\xi,z) - 2(2-\nu)\xi^2 G_z'(\xi,z)]\xi J_0(\xi r)\mathrm{d}\xi \\ \sigma_{rz} &= 2\mu\int_0^\infty \nu G''_z(\xi,z) + (1-\nu)\xi^2 G(\xi,z)\xi^2 J_1(\xi r)\mathrm{d}\xi \\ \sigma_{rr} &= 2\mu\int_0^\infty [\nu G'''_z(\xi,z) + (1-\nu)\xi^2 G_z'(\xi,z)]\xi J_0(\xi r)\mathrm{d}\xi - u/r\int_0^\infty \xi^2 G'_z(\xi,z)J_1(\xi r)\mathrm{d}\xi \\ \sigma_{\theta\theta} &= 2\mu\int_0^\infty [\nu G'''_z(\xi,z) - \xi^2 G_z'(\xi,z)]\xi J_0(\xi r)\mathrm{d}\xi + u/r\int_0^\infty \xi^2 G'_z(\xi,z)J_1(\xi r)\mathrm{d}\xi \end{aligned}\right\} \tag{7}$$

式中：G'_z、G_z''、G_z''' 为对 z 的一、二、三阶偏导数；J_0、J_1 为零阶和一阶 Bessel 函数。

现边界条件为

$$\sqrt{r^2+z^2} \to \infty, \sigma_{ij} = 0 \tag{8}$$

$$z = 0 \text{ 时 } \sigma_{rz} = 0 \tag{9}$$

$$u_z = \frac{1}{2}\delta(r) \tag{10}$$

$\delta(r)$ 为二维 Dirac δ 函数，$\delta(r)=\lim\limits_{a\to 0}\delta_a(r)$。

$$\delta_a(r)=\begin{cases}0, & \text{当 } r>a\\ 1/\pi a^2, & \text{当 } r\leqslant a\end{cases}$$

由条件(8)、式(6)得 $C=D=0$，则

$$G(\xi,z)=(A+Bz)\mathrm{e}^{-\xi z} \tag{11}$$

即

$$G_z'(\xi,z)=[(A+Bz)(-\xi)+B]\mathrm{e}^{-\xi z} \tag{12}$$

$$G_z''(\xi,z)=[(A+Bz)\xi^2-2B\xi]\mathrm{e}^{-\xi z} \tag{13}$$

$$G_z'''(\xi,z)=[(A+Bz)(-\xi^3)+3B\xi^2]\mathrm{e}^{-\xi z} \tag{14}$$

代入式(7)第四式，由边界条件式(9)得

$$\sigma_{rz}\mid_{z=0}=0=2\mu\int_0^\infty[\nu(A\xi^2-2B\xi)+(1-\nu)A\xi^2]\xi^2J_1(\xi r)\mathrm{d}\xi$$

得

$$\beta(\xi)=1/2\nu A\xi(\xi) \tag{15}$$

同样：

$$u_z\mid_{z=0}=\int_0^\infty A\xi^3(1-1/\nu)J_0(\xi r)\mathrm{d}\xi \tag{16}$$

边界条件式(10)进行零阶 Hankel 变换，利用式(16)：

$$A=1/4\pi\frac{1}{1-1/\nu}\xi^{-2}$$

因此

$$B=1/8\pi\nu\frac{1}{1-1/\nu}\xi^{-1} \tag{17}$$

回代入式(7)得位移和应力基本解为

表达式

$$I(m,n)=\int_0^\infty\xi^m e^{-\xi z}J_n(\xi r)\mathrm{d}\xi \tag{18}$$

$$\left.\begin{aligned}
u_z(r,z)&=1/4\pi\frac{1}{1-1/\nu}[(1-1/\nu)I(1,0)-z/2\nu I(2,0)]\\
u_r(r,z)&=1/4\pi\frac{1}{1-1/\nu}[(-1+1/2\nu)I(1,1)-z/2\nu I(2,1)]\\
\sigma_{zz}(r,z)&=2\mu(1/4\pi)\frac{1}{1-1/\nu}[(1/2\nu)I(2,0)+z/2\nu I(3,0)]\\
\sigma_{rr}(r,z)&=2\mu(1/4\pi)\frac{1}{1-1/\nu}[(1/2\nu)I(2,0)-z/2\nu I(3,0)+\\
&\qquad 1/2\nu(1-1/2\nu)I(1,1)+1/2\nu(z/2\nu)I(2,1)]\\
\sigma_{\theta\theta}(r,z)&=2\mu(1/4\pi)\frac{1}{1-1/\nu}[(5/2-\nu-1/2\nu)I(2,0)+(1-\nu)z/(2r)I(3,0)+\\
&\qquad 1/2\nu(-1+1/2\nu)I(1,1)-1/2rz/2\nu I(2,1)]\\
\sigma_{rz}(r,z)&=2\mu/4\pi\frac{1}{1-1/\nu}z/2\nu I(3,1)
\end{aligned}\right\} \tag{19}$$

2 三维基本解(Ⅱ)—— 切向不连续位移

三维无限域中原点处作用单位切向不连续位移,作用面法向仍是正轴,这是原点处圆盘裂纹其上、下表面作用着均布不连续切向移位,当其半径趋于零时的极限情况(裂纹平面向 x 轴为正方向移动)。这不是轴对称问题可用 Muki 解法[3,5],对周向进行有限 Fourier 变换,对径向仍进行 Hankel 变换。问题归结为下列方程组在边界条件下求解:

$$\left.\begin{aligned}\nabla^2\nabla^2\phi &= 0\\ \nabla^2\Psi &= 0\end{aligned}\right\}\tag{20}$$

式中:ϕ、Ψ 为位移函数。

位移和应力:

$$\left.\begin{aligned}
u_r &= -\partial^2\phi/\partial r\partial z + (2/r)\partial\phi/\partial\theta\\
u_\theta &= -(1/r)\partial\phi/\partial\theta\partial z - 2\partial\Psi/\partial r\\
u_z &= 2(1-\nu)\nabla^2\phi - \partial^2\phi/\partial z^2\\
\sigma_{rr} &= 2\mu[\partial/\partial z(\nu\nabla^2\phi - \partial^2\phi/\partial r^2) + (2/r)\partial^2\Psi/\partial\theta\partial r - (2/r^2)\partial\Psi/\partial\theta]\\
\sigma_{zz} &= 2\mu\{\partial/\partial r[(2-\nu)\nabla^2\phi - \partial^2\phi/\partial z^2]\}\\
\sigma_{\theta\theta} &= 2\mu[\partial/\partial z(\nu\nabla^2\phi - (1/r)\partial\phi/\partial r - (1/r^2)\partial^2\phi\partial\theta^2) -\\
&\quad (2/r)\partial^2\Psi/\partial\theta\partial r + (2/r^2)\partial\Psi/\partial\theta]\\
\sigma_{rz} &= 2\mu[\partial/\partial r(1-\nu)\nabla^2\phi - \partial^2\phi/\partial z^2 + (1/r)\partial^2\Psi/\partial\theta\partial z]\\
\sigma_{\theta z} &= 2\mu\{(1/r)\partial/\partial\theta[(1-\nu)\nabla^2\phi - \partial^2\Psi/\partial z^2] - \partial^2\Psi/\partial r\partial z\}\\
\sigma_{r\theta} &= 2\mu[(1/r)\partial^2/\partial\theta\partial z(\theta/r - \partial\phi/\partial r) - 2\partial^2\Psi/\partial r^2 - \partial^2\Psi/\partial z^2]
\end{aligned}\right\}\tag{21}$$

将 ϕ 和 Ψ 展成以下级数:

$$\left.\begin{aligned}\phi(r,\theta,z) &= \sum_{m=0}^{\infty}\phi_m(r,z)\cos m\theta\\ \Psi(r,\theta,z) &= \sum_{m=0}^{\infty}\Psi_m(r,z)\sin m\theta\end{aligned}\right\}\tag{22}$$

代入式(20)进行 m 阶 Hankel 变换:

$$(\mathrm{d}^2/\mathrm{d}z^2 - \xi^2)G_m(\xi,z) = 0$$

$$(\mathrm{d}^2/\mathrm{d}z^2 - \xi^2)H_m(\xi,z) = 0$$

通解是:$G_m(\xi,z) = (A_m + B_m z)\mathrm{e}^{-\xi z} + (C_m + D_m z)\mathrm{e}^{\xi z}$

$$H_m(\xi,z) = E_m\mathrm{e}^{-\xi z} + F_m\mathrm{e}^{\xi z}$$

系数 $A_m \sim F_m$ 由边界条件定,求出 G_m、H_m 后进行 Hankel 反变换由式(22)定 ϕ,Ψ 代入式(21)得位移和应力。

$$
\left.\begin{aligned}
u_r &= \frac{1}{2}\sum_{m=0}^{\infty}[U_{m+1} - V_{m-1}]\cos m\theta \\
u_\theta &= \frac{1}{2}\sum_{m=0}^{\infty}[U_{m+1} + V_{m-1}]\sin m\theta \\
u_z &= \sum_{m=0}^{\infty}\left\{\int_0^\infty [(1-2\nu)G_m'' - 2(1-\nu)\xi G_m]\xi J_m(\xi r)\mathrm{d}\xi\right\}\cos m\theta \\
\sigma_{rr} &= 2\mu\sum_{m=0}^{\infty}\left\{\int_0^\infty [\nu G_m''' + (1-\nu)\xi^2 G_m']\xi J_m(\xi r)\mathrm{d}\xi - (m+1)/2rU_{m+1} - \right. \\
&\quad \left.(m-1)/(2r)V_{m-1}\right\}\cos m\theta \\
\sigma_{zz} &= 2\mu\sum_{m=0}^{\infty}\left\{\int_0^\infty [(1-\nu)G_m''' - (2-\nu)\xi^2 G_m']\xi J_m(\xi r)\mathrm{d}\xi\right\}\cos m\theta \\
\sigma_{\theta\theta} &= 2\mu\sum_{m=0}^{\infty}\left\{\int_0^\infty \nu(G_m''' - \xi^2 G_m')\xi J_m(\xi r)\mathrm{d}\xi + (m+1)/(2r)U_{m+1} + \right. \\
&\quad \left.(m-1)/(2r)V_{m-1}\right\}\cos m\theta \\
\sigma_{rz} &= \mu\sum_{m=0}^{\infty}\left\{\int_0^\infty [\nu(G_m''' + (1-\nu)\xi^2 G_m + H_m']\xi^2 J_{m+1}(\xi r)\mathrm{d}\xi - \right. \\
&\quad \left.\int_0^\infty [\nu G_m'' + (1-\nu)\xi^2 G_m - H_m']\xi^2 J_{m-1}(\xi r)\mathrm{d}\xi\right\}\cos m\theta \\
\sigma_{\theta z} &= \mu\sum_{m=0}^{\infty}\left\{\int_0^\infty [\nu G_m'' + (1-\nu)\xi^2 G_m + H_m']\xi^2 J_{m+1}(\xi r)\mathrm{d}\xi + \right. \\
&\quad \left.\int_0^\infty [\nu G_m'' + (1-\nu)\xi^2 G_m - H_m']\xi^2 J_{m-1}(\xi r)\mathrm{d}\xi\right\}\sin m\theta \\
\sigma_{r\theta} &= 2\mu\sum_{m=0}^{\infty}\left\{\int_0^\infty H_m\xi^3 J_m(\xi r)\mathrm{d}\xi - (m+1)/(2r)U_{m+1} + (m-1)/(2r)V_{m-1}\right\}\sin m\theta
\end{aligned}\right\}\tag{23}
$$

式中：G_m'、G_m''、G_m'''、H_m' 表示 G_m、H_m 对 z 的各阶导数。

$$U_{m+1} = \int_0^\infty [G_m' + 2H_m]\xi^2 J_{m+1}(\xi r)\mathrm{d}\xi$$

$$V_{m-1} = \int_0^\infty [G_m' - 2H_m]\xi^2 J_{m-1}(\xi r)\mathrm{d}\xi$$

边界条件是：

$$\sqrt{r^2 + z^2} \to \infty,\ \sigma_{ij} = 0 \quad (\text{应力有界}) \tag{24}$$

$$z = 0, u_r = \frac{1}{2}\delta(r)\cos\theta \tag{25}$$

$$z = 0, u_\theta = -\frac{1}{2}\delta(r)\sin\theta \tag{26}$$

$$z = 0, \sigma_z = 0(\text{反对称}) \tag{27}$$

式(25)、式(26)为圆盘裂纹上、下表面在 x 方向相对位移令其半径趋于零得到的(如图1)。再由式(23)前两式可见只需要取 G_1, H_1(即 $m = 1$)作解答,记为 G, H 相应所有下标 m 可略去,简化式(23)。

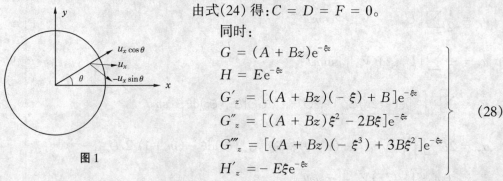

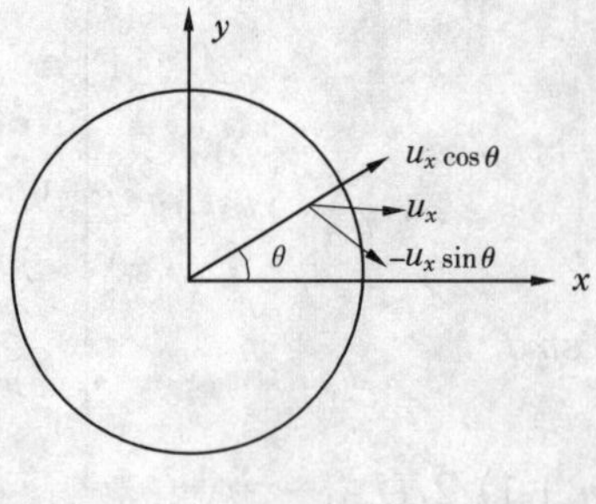

图 1

由式(24)得:$C = D = F = 0$。

同时:

$$\left.\begin{aligned}
&G = (A + Bz)e^{-\xi z}\\
&H = Ee^{-\xi z}\\
&G'_z = [(A + Bz)(-\xi) + B]e^{-\xi z}\\
&G''_z = [(A + Bz)\xi^2 - 2B\xi]e^{-\xi z}\\
&G'''_z = [(A + Bz)(-\xi^3) + 3B\xi^2]e^{-\xi z}\\
&H'_z = -E\xi e^{-\xi z}
\end{aligned}\right\} \tag{28}$$

由边界条件和式(23)、式(28)可求出 A、B、E:

$$\left.\begin{aligned}
&A = 1/8\pi\frac{1-2\nu}{1-\nu}\xi^{-2}\\
&B = 1/8\pi(\frac{1-2\nu}{1-\nu}-2)\xi^{-1}\\
&E = 1/8\pi\xi^{-1}
\end{aligned}\right\} \tag{29}$$

回代得应力和位移基本解:

$$\left.\begin{aligned}
&u_r(r,\theta,z) = \frac{1}{2}\cos\theta\left\{z/8\pi\frac{1}{1-\nu}[I(2,2) - I(2,0)] + (1/2\pi)I(1,0)\right\}\\
&u_\theta(r,\theta,z) = \frac{1}{2}\sin\theta\left\{z/8\pi\frac{1}{1-\nu}[I(2,2) + I(2,0)] - (1/2\pi)I(1,0)\right\}\\
&u_z(r,\theta,z) = \frac{1}{2}\cos\theta\left\{z/4\pi\frac{1}{1-\nu}I(2,1) + I/4\pi\frac{1-2\nu}{1-\nu}I(1,1)\right\}\\
&\sigma_{rz}(r,\theta,z) = \mu\cos\theta(\nu/8\pi)\left\{\frac{-z}{1-\nu}I(3,2) + (\frac{3-2\nu}{1-\nu} - 1/\nu)I(2,2) +\right.\\
&\qquad\left.\frac{z}{1-\nu}I(3,0) - (\frac{3-2\nu}{1-\nu} - 1/\nu)I(2,0)\right\}\\
&\sigma_{\theta z}(r,\theta,z) = \mu\sin\theta(\nu/8\pi)\left\{\frac{-z}{1-\nu}I(3,2) + (\frac{3-2\nu}{1-\nu} - 1/\nu)I(2,2) -\right.\\
&\qquad\left.\frac{z}{1-\nu}I(3,0) - (\frac{3-2\nu}{1-\nu} - 1/\nu)I(2,0)\right\}\\
&\sigma_{r\theta}(r,\theta,z) = \mu/(4\pi)\sin\theta\{I(2,1) + (2/r)(1/1-\nu)I(2,2)\}\\
&\sigma_{zz}(r,\theta,z) = \mu/(4\pi)\cos\theta\{-2z/(1-\nu)I(3,1)\}\\
&\sigma_{rr}(r,\theta,z) = \mu/4\pi\cos\theta\left\{\frac{z}{1-r}I(3,1) - \frac{2}{1-\nu}(2,1) - 2z/\nu\frac{I}{1-\nu}(2,2)\right\}\\
&\sigma_{\theta\theta}(r,\theta,z) = \mu/(4\pi)\cos\theta\left\{\frac{-2\nu}{1-\nu}I(2,1) - z/r\frac{1}{1-\nu}I(2,2)\right\}
\end{aligned}\right\} \tag{30}$$

3 函数 $I(m,n)$ 的计算

$$I(1,0) = z(r^2 + z^2)^{-3/2}$$

$$I(1,1) = r(r^2 + z^2)^{-3/2}$$

由文献[2]查到,当 $n > -1$ 时,$I(m,n)$ 可用超几何级数表示为[2]

$$I(m,n)=\frac{2^m r^n \Gamma(\frac{m+n+1}{2})\Gamma(1+\frac{m+n}{2})}{(r^2+z^2)^{(m+n+1)/2}\Gamma(n+1)\Gamma(\frac{1}{2})}$$

$$_2F_1(\frac{m+n+1}{2};\frac{n-m}{2};1+n;\frac{r^2}{r^2+z^2})$$

其中： $_2F_1(r+m,\alpha,r,x)=(1-x)^{-1}\alpha J_m[\alpha-m,r,x/(x-1)]$

J_m 为 m 次 Jacobi 多项式。

$$I(1,2)=\frac{2r^2\Gamma(2)\Gamma(5/2)}{(r^2+z^2)^2\Gamma(3)\Gamma(\frac{1}{2})}\quad {}_2F_1(2,\frac{1}{2},3,\frac{r^2}{r^2+z^2})$$

由超几何级数的二倍公式[4]：

$$_2F_1[\alpha,\beta,(\alpha+\beta+1)/2,x]={}_2F_1[\alpha/2;\beta/2;(\alpha+\beta+1)/2,4x(1-x)]$$

得 $$I(1,2)=3/2\frac{r^2}{(r^2+z^2)^2}F_1(4;1;3;\frac{1}{2}[1\pm\sqrt{1-r^2/(r^2+z^2)}]$$

$$=\frac{3r^2}{(r^2+z^2)^2}\left(1+\sqrt{1-\frac{r^2}{r^2+z^2}}\right)^{-1}J_1\left(0,3,\frac{1-\sqrt{1-\frac{r^2}{r^2+z^2}}}{-1-\sqrt{1-\frac{r^2}{r^2+z^2}}}\right)$$

$$=\frac{r^2}{(r^2+z^2)^2}\left(1+\sqrt{1-\frac{r^2}{r^2+z^2}}\right)^{-2}\left(1-\frac{z}{\sqrt{r^2+z^2}}\right)$$

同样可求得

$$I(2,0)=\frac{2}{(r^2+z^2)^{3/2}}(1-3/2\frac{r^2}{r^2+z^2})$$

$$I(2,1)=\frac{3rz}{(r^2+z^2)^{5/2}}$$

$$I(2,2)=\frac{3r^2}{(r^2+z^2)^{5/2}}$$

$$I(3,0)=\frac{3z(2z^2-3r^2)}{(r^2+z^2)^{7/2}}$$

$$I(3,1)=\frac{3r(4z^2-r^2)}{(r^2+z^2)^{7/2}}$$

$$I(3,2)=\frac{15r^2z}{(r^2+z^2)^{7/2}}$$

4 结论

将以上计算结果代入基本解整理后可得以下两种基本解。

(1) 法向不连续位移作用下的基本解：

$$\left.\begin{aligned}
u_r &= c[(-1+1/2\nu)r/\rho^3-(3/2\nu)rz^2/\rho^5]\\
u_z &= c[(1-2/\nu)z/\rho^3+(3/2\nu)r^2z/\rho^5]\\
\sigma_{rr} &= \mu c/\nu\rho^7[-2(1-\nu)\rho^4+15r^2z^2]\\
\sigma_{\theta\theta} &= \mu c/\nu\rho^5[(1-4\nu)r^2-2(1-\nu)z^2]\\
\sigma_{zz} &= \mu c/\nu\rho^7[-r^4-8r^2z^2+8z^4]\\
\sigma_{zr} &= \mu c/\nu\rho^7[12rz^3-3r^3z]
\end{aligned}\right\}\qquad(31)$$

(2) 切向不连续位移作用下的基本解：

$$\left.\begin{aligned}
u_r &= c_1\cos\theta[6zr^2/\rho^5+2(1-2\nu)z/\rho^3]\\
u_\theta &= c_1\sin\theta(1-2\nu)(-2z)/\rho^3\\
u_z &= c_1\cos\theta[(1-2\nu)2r/\rho^3+6z^2r/\rho^5]\\
\sigma_{rr} &= 2\mu c_1\cos\theta(6zr/\rho^5-30r^3z/\rho^7)\\
\sigma_{\theta\theta} &= 2\mu c_1\cos\theta(1-2\nu)6zr/\rho^5\\
\sigma_{zx} &= 2\mu c_1\cos\theta[6zr/\rho^5-30rz^3/\rho^7]\\
\sigma_{r\theta} &= 2\mu c_1\sin\theta(-6\nu rz/\rho^5)\\
\sigma_{\theta z} &= 2\mu c_1\sin\theta(-6\nu z^2)/\rho^5\\
\sigma_{rx} &= 2\mu c_1\cos\theta[(2+2\nu)1/\rho^3-30z^2r^2/\rho^7]
\end{aligned}\right\}\qquad(32)$$

式中：$\rho=(r^2+z^2)^{1/2}$；$c=1/4\pi[-\nu/(1-\nu)]$，$c_1=1/16\pi\cdot 1/(1-\nu)$；$\nu$ 为泊松比；μ 为剪切弹模。

将上述结果代入柱坐标弹性方程及本文边界条件可以验证本文结果。

边界元插值函数的选取同第一类边界元，第二类边界元可直接模拟不连续结构面尺外边界，计算量较小，配合特殊单元来提高精度，则对多裂纹体、含弱面的结构、尤其对计算量和存储急需改进的三维问题，本文三维基本解提供有利应用条件。

参 考 文 献

[1] 刘光廷，林潮熙. 弹性力学问题的第二类边界积分方程——边界元法及其二维基本解. 清华大学学报，1988(2)

[2] Sneddon I. N.. 富利叶变换. 何衍睿，张燮译. 北京：科学出版社，1958

[3] 范天佑. 断裂力学基础. 南京：江苏科学技术出版社，1978

[4] 小各正雄，桥本英典. 特殊函数. 钱端壮译. 上海：上海科技出版社，1962

[5] Muki R.. *Progress in Solid Mechanics*. Vol. (ed. by Sneddon, I. N. and Hill. R)1960

THE STRENGTH OF A FINITE BODY WITH MULTIPLE CRACKS

Abstract This paper presented an analytical-numerical solution of a finite body with multiple cracks. According to the Bueckner method and based on the solution for the integral equation system of fracture series, we proposed a direct method considering interaction between boundary and cracks —"Virtual loading method". Instead of repeated loading and tedious computing of non-equilibrium stresses on the boundaries, a direct analytical solution including virtual loads is used, by which the more accurate results are obtained and less computing time is needed.

1 Introduction

Cracks always happen during the construction or operation of the concrete structures. It is necessary to distinguish which of them would propagate under loading and bring damage or danger to the structures. The cracks and joints also exist in the rock foundation. As a supporting body of structures, the states of rock mass are specially concerned in engineering. Since not only the deformation of foundation will affect the stress distribution in structure, but also the propagation of cracks in rock mass, penetration and even sliding of rock mass will cause the collapse of structure.

It is a long time since the studies on cracks have introduced to the field of strength of the metal, and recently also of concrete materials, rocks, etc. Scholars paid more attention to the failure mechanism near the crack tip, the capacity of preventing propagation of crack (fracture toughness) and established the failure criteria. However the studies on the propagating energy (Stress Intensity Factor) of the loaded body with multiple cracks in general are far from plenty. The SIF calculated from the stresses and displacements field with a single crack in infinity is quite different from that which happens in practice in engineering. For instance cracks may happen near by or even run across each other in a concrete block. It is very difficult to find a rock foundation with only a single crack or joint. The experimental results have shown that in the multiple cracked body there is quite a variation of average deformation modulus between tension and compression. The stress-strain relationship also changes with the directions of loading. And therefore usual descriptions of mechanical behavoir of cracked body-nonlinear, etc. in the physical or numeric-mathematical models are not suitable. It is necessary to study the strength and deformation of multiple crack body for recent engineering

本文选自《Engineering Fracture Mechanics》1989 年 4 月，作者还有 Zhou Ruizhong。

requirement.

2 "Released Stress" on the Crack Surface

Stress distribution in the multiple crack body with arbitrary size and shape under loading can be obtained by two corresponding equivalent load systems; noncracked body subjected to boundary loading and multiple crack body with the crack faces subjected to a pressure equal to the crack line stress (released stress) of prescribed noncracked body with boundary loading. The calculations should be continued until the boundary conditions of the crack faces and outer boundary are satisfied. Since the singularity of stress exists at the end of crack, the stress of noncracked body at the crack end is relative very small. SIFs mainly depend on the "released stress" of crack faces (Bueckner method). According to the Bueckner method, the SIF of any crack in a multiple crack body can be calculated from releasing the stress at the crack location.

The boundary collocation method offered by B. Gross and J. E. Srawley is more convenient and accurate for the stress calculation in various complicate boundaries at arbitrary distributed cracks location. The general solution of stress function in least square boundary collocation of discrete type can be used for determining the values of released stress at the cracks location of noncracked body. It can be written as:

$$\phi = {}_1\phi_0 + {}_2\phi_0 + {}_1\phi_1 + {}_2\phi_1 + {}_1\overline{\phi}_0 + {}_2\overline{\phi}_0 + {}_1\phi_m + {}_2\phi_m + \phi_c^*$$

where ϕ_c^* is the eigen function corresponding to body force and thermo-variation. When these two kinds of load are not considered ϕ_c^* is neglected, then we have:

$$
\begin{aligned}
{}_1\phi_0 &= C_{01} r^2 + C_{02} r^2 \ln r + C_{03} + C_{04} \ln r \\
{}_2\phi_0 &= (C'_{01} r^2 + C'_{02} r^2 \ln r + C'_{03} + C'_{04} \ln r)\theta \\
{}_1\phi_1 &= (C_{11} r^3 + C_{12} \frac{1}{r} + C_{13} r + C_{14} r \ln r)\cos\theta \\
{}_2\phi_1 &= (C'_{11} r^3 + C'_{12} \frac{1}{r} + C'_{13} r + C'_{14} r \ln r)\sin\theta \\
{}_1\overline{\phi}_0 &= (\overline{C}_{01} r + \overline{C}_{02} r \ln r)\theta\cos\theta \\
{}_2\overline{\phi}_0 &= (\overline{C}_{01} r + \overline{C}_{02} r \ln r)\theta\sin\theta \\
{}_1\phi_m &= \sum_{m=2}^{n} (C_{m1} r^{m+2} + C_{m2} r^m + C_{m3} r^{-m+2} + C_{m4} r^{-m})\cos m\theta \\
{}_2\phi_m &= \sum_{m=2}^{n} (C'_{m1} r^{m+2} + C'_{m2} r^m + C'_{m3} r^{-m+2} + C'_{m4} r^{-m})\sin m\theta
\end{aligned}
\tag{1}
$$

Take the symmetric case for example. In order to increase the precision of solution, the conditional number Cond $[A] = \| A \| \cdot \| A^{-1} \|$ of Matrix $[A]$ should be minimum. We chose the following expression of stress function.

$$\Phi(r,\theta) = C_{01} r^2 + C_{02} r^2 \ln r + C_{03} + C_{04} \ln r + \left(C_{05} r^3 + C_{06} \frac{1}{r} + C_{07} r + C_{08} r \ln r \right)\cos\theta +$$

$$(C_{09} r + C_{10} r \ln r) \theta \sin\theta + \sum_{m=2}^{m} \left[C_{m1} \left(\frac{r}{D}\right)^{m+2} + C_{m2} \left(\frac{r}{D}\right)^{m} + C_{m3} \left(\frac{r}{D}\right)^{-m+2} + \right.$$

$$\left. C_{m4} \left(\frac{r}{D}\right)^{-m} \right] \cos m\theta \tag{2}$$

where D is arbitrary constant, then we have:

$$\frac{\partial \Phi}{\partial r} = 2C_{01} r + C_{02}(2\ln r + 1)r + C_{04} \frac{1}{r} + \left[3C_{05} r^2 - C_{06} \frac{1}{r^2} + C_{07} + C_{08}(\ln r + 1)\right]\cos\theta +$$

$$\left[C_{09} + C_{10}(\ln r + 1)\right]\theta\sin\theta + \sum_{m=2}^{n} \left[C_{m1} \left(\frac{r}{D}\right)^{m+1} \left(\frac{m+2}{D}\right) + C_{m2} \left(\frac{r}{D}\right)^{m-1} \left(\frac{m}{D}\right) + \right.$$

$$\left. C_{m3} \left(\frac{r}{D}\right)^{1-m} \left(\frac{2-m}{D}\right) - C_{m4} \left(\frac{r}{D}\right)^{-m-1} \frac{m}{D} \right] \cos m\theta$$

$$\frac{\partial \Phi}{\partial \theta} = - \left(C_{05} r^3 + C_{06} \frac{1}{r} + C_{07} r + C_{08} r \ln r \right) \sin\theta + (C_{09} r + C_{10} r \ln r)\sin\theta + \theta\cos\theta) -$$

$$\sum_{m=2}^{n} \left[C_{m1} \left(\frac{r}{D}\right)^{m+2} + C_{m2} \left(\frac{r}{D}\right)^{m} + C_{m3} \left(\frac{r}{D}\right)^{-m+2} + C_{m4} \left(\frac{r}{D}\right)^{-m} \right] m \sin m\theta$$

stress components in polar coordinate are:

$$\sigma_r = \frac{1}{r} \frac{\partial \Phi}{\partial r} + \frac{1}{r^2} \frac{\partial^2 \Phi}{\partial \theta^2}$$

$$= 2C_{01} + C_{02}(2\ln r + 1) + C_{04} \frac{1}{r^2} + \left[2C_{05} r - 2C_{06} \frac{1}{r^3} + C_{08} \frac{1}{r}\right]\cos\theta +$$

$$C_{09} \frac{1}{r}\cos\theta + C_{10} \frac{1}{r}(\theta\sin\theta + \ln r\cos\theta) - \sum_{m=2}^{n} \left[C_{m1} \left(\frac{r}{D}\right)^{m} \frac{1}{D^2}(m-2)(m+1) + \right.$$

$$C_{m2} \left(\frac{r}{D}\right)^{m-2} \frac{q}{D} m(m-1) + C_{m3} \left(\frac{r}{D}\right)^{-m} \frac{1}{D^2}(m+2)(m+1) +$$

$$\left. C_{m4} \left(\frac{r}{D}\right)^{-m-2} \frac{1}{D^2} m(m+1) \right] \cos m\theta$$

$$\sigma_\theta = \frac{\partial^2 \Phi}{\partial r^2} = 2C_{01} + C_{02}(3 + 2\ln r) - C_{04} \frac{1}{r^2} + \left(6C_{05} r + 2C_{06} \frac{1}{r^3} + C_{08} \frac{1}{r}\right)\cos\theta +$$

$$C_{10} \frac{1}{r}\theta\sin\theta + \sum_{m=2}^{n} \left[C_{m1} \frac{(m+2)(m+1)}{D^2} \left(\frac{r}{D}\right)^{m} + C_{m2} \frac{m(m-1)}{D^2} \left(\frac{r}{D}\right)^{m-2} + \right.$$

$$\left. C_{m3} \frac{(2-m)(1-m)}{D^2} \left(\frac{r}{D}\right)^{-m} + C_{m4} \frac{m(m+1)}{D^2} \left(\frac{r}{D}\right)^{-m-2} \right] \cos m\theta$$

$$\tau_{r\theta} = - \frac{\partial}{\partial r} \left(\frac{1}{r} \frac{\partial \phi}{\partial \theta}\right) = \left(2C_{05} r - 2C_{06} \frac{1}{r^3} + C_{08} \frac{1}{r}\right)\sin\theta - C_{10} \frac{1}{r}(\sin\theta + \theta\cos\theta) +$$

$$\sum_{m=2}^{n} \left[\frac{C_{m1}}{D^2}(m+1) \left(\frac{r}{D}\right)^{m} + \frac{C_{m2}}{D^2}(m-1) \left(\frac{r}{D}\right)^{m-2} + \frac{C_{m3}}{D^2} \left(\frac{r}{D}\right)^{-m}(1-m) + \right.$$

$$\left. \frac{C_{m4}}{D^2}(-m-1) \left(\frac{r}{D}\right)^{-m-2} \right] m \sin m\theta \tag{3}$$

stress function ϕ must also satisfy the boundary condition, the main vector is:

$$X^* + iY^* = \int_{AB} [x^*(s) + iy^*(s)]ds = -i\left[\frac{\partial \phi}{\partial x} + i\frac{\partial \phi}{\partial y}\right]_A^B$$

where $x^*(s)$ and $y^*(s)$ are boundary load components in x, y direction respectively. Also

$$\left.\begin{aligned}\left(\frac{\partial\phi}{\partial y}\right)_B &= \left(\frac{\partial\phi}{\partial y}\right)_A + \int_A^B x^*(s)\mathrm{d}s \\ \left(\frac{\partial\phi}{\partial x}\right)_B &= \left(\frac{\partial\phi}{\partial x}\right)_A + \int_A^B y^*(s)\mathrm{d}s\end{aligned}\right\} \tag{4}$$

$$\frac{\mathrm{d}\phi}{\mathrm{d}s} = \frac{\partial\phi}{\partial x}\cdot\frac{\mathrm{d}x}{\mathrm{d}s} + \frac{\partial\phi}{\partial y}\frac{\mathrm{d}y}{\mathrm{d}s} = -\frac{\mathrm{d}x}{\mathrm{d}s}\int_A^B y^*(s)\mathrm{d}s + \frac{\mathrm{d}y}{\mathrm{d}s}\int_A^B x^*(s)\mathrm{d}s$$

Integrate by parts, we have

$$[\phi]_A^B = \int_A^B (x - x_B)y^*(s)\mathrm{d}s + \int_A^B (y_B - y)x^*(s)\mathrm{d}s \tag{5}$$

The initial condition may be taken such as $(\partial\phi/\partial y)_A = (\partial\phi/\partial x)_A = [\phi]_A = 0$ without losing generality. $(\partial\phi/\partial x)$and $((\partial\phi/\partial y)$ are known as following:

$$\begin{aligned}\frac{\partial\phi}{\partial x} &= \frac{\partial\phi}{\partial r}\cdot\frac{\partial r}{\partial x} + \frac{\partial\phi}{\partial\theta}\cdot\frac{\partial\theta}{\partial x} \\ &= 2C_{01}r\cdot\sin\theta + C_{02}(2\ln r + 1)r\cdot\cos\theta + C_{04}\frac{1}{r}\cos\theta + C_{05}r^2(1 + 2\cos^2\theta) - \\ &\quad C_{06}\frac{1}{r^2}\cos2\theta + C_{07} + C_{08}(\cos^2\theta + \ln r) - C_{09}\sin^2\theta + C_{10}\sin\theta(\theta\cos\theta - \ln r\cdot\sin\theta) + \\ &\quad \sum_{m=2}^{n}\left\{C_{m1}\left(\frac{r}{D}\right)^{m-1}\frac{1}{D}[(m+1)\cos(m-1)\theta + \cos(m+1)\theta] + \right. \\ &\quad C_{m2}\left(\frac{r}{D}\right)^{m-1}\frac{1}{D}[m\cdot\cos(m-1)\theta] + C_{m3}\left(\frac{r}{D}\right)^{-m+1}\frac{1}{D}[(1-m)\cos(m+1)\theta + \\ &\quad \left.\cos(m-1)\theta] - C_{m4}\left(\frac{r}{D}\right)^{-m-1}\frac{1}{D}[m\cdot\cos(m+1)\theta]\right\}\end{aligned}$$

$$\begin{aligned}\frac{\partial\phi}{\partial y} &= \frac{\partial\phi}{\partial r}\cdot\frac{\partial r}{\partial y} + \frac{\partial\phi}{\partial\theta}\cdot\frac{\partial\theta}{\partial y} \\ &= 2C_{01}r\cdot\sin\theta + C_{02}(1 + 2\ln r)r\cdot\sin\theta + C_{04}\frac{1}{r}\sin\theta + C_{05}r^2\cdot\sin2\theta - \\ &\quad C_{06}\frac{1}{r^2}\sin2\theta + C_{08}\frac{1}{2}\sin2\theta + C_{09}[\theta + \frac{1}{2}\sin2\theta] + C_{10}(\theta\cdot\ln r + \ln r\cdot\frac{1}{2}\sin2\theta + \theta\cdot\sin^2\theta) + \\ &\quad \sum_{m=2}^{n}\left\{C_{m1}\left(\frac{r}{D}\right)^{m+1}\frac{1}{D}[\sin(m+1)\theta - (m+1)\sin(m-1)\theta] + \right. \\ &\quad C_{m3}\left(\frac{r}{D}\right)^{-m+1}\frac{1}{D}[(1-m)\sin(m+1)\theta - \sin(m-1)\theta] - C_{m4}\left(\frac{r}{D}\right)^{-m-1}\frac{1}{D}[m\cdot\sin(m+1)\theta] - \\ &\quad \left.C_{m2}\left(\frac{r}{D}\right)^{m-1}\frac{1}{D}[m - \sin(m-1)\theta]\right\}\end{aligned} \tag{6}$$

Since the loads on boundary $x^*(s)$ and $y^*(s)$ are given, ϕ^*, $(\partial\phi^*/\partial x)$, $(\partial\phi^*/\partial y)$ on boundary points are defined. According to weighted residual technique, ϕ exactly satisfies the control equation and residual on boundary can be written as:

$$R_i = \phi(r_i, \theta_i) - \phi^*(r_i, \theta_i)$$

$$R_{i+m} = \frac{\partial\phi}{\partial x}(r_i, \theta_i) - \frac{\partial\phi^*}{\partial x}(r_i, \theta_i)$$

$$R_{i+2m} = \frac{\partial\phi}{\partial y}(r_i,\theta_i) - \frac{\partial\phi^*}{\partial y}(r_i,\theta_i)\ (i = 1,2,\cdots,m) \tag{7}$$

let function $I(C_i) = \int_s R^2 ds$, $I(C_i)$ become minimum when $\partial I/\partial C_i = 0$, from which a group of linear equations with unknown C_i may be expressed by matrix $\{R\}$

$$\{R\} = \{A\}\{C\} - \{B\}$$

where $\{B\}$ are known vectors on the right side of equations and $\{C\}$ are unknown coefficients to be determined. Then extreme condition should be:

$$[A]^T[A]\{C\} = [A]^T\{B\} \tag{8}$$

All unknowns can be solved by (8) and then the stress components are given by (3).

3 Cracks, Singular Integral Eguation Group with its Numerical Method

The discontinued displacement function of the upper and lower crack faces can be written as:

$$g(t) = -\frac{2Gi}{1+k}\{[u^+(t,0) - u^-(t,0)] + i[\nu^+(t,0) - \nu^-(t,0)]\} \tag{9}$$

where:

$$t \in (a_j, b_j),\ (j = 1,2,\cdots,N)$$

$$k = \begin{cases} 3 - 4\nu & \text{(plane strain)} \\ 3 - \nu/1 + \nu. & \text{(plane stress)} \end{cases}$$

For Riemann-Hilbert boundary value problem

$$2G(u + i\nu) = k\phi(z) - \omega(\bar{z}) - (z - \bar{z})\overline{\phi(z)}$$

$$(\phi(z) = \phi'(z), \Omega(z) = \omega'(z))$$

$$g'(t) = -\frac{i}{1+k}\{[k\phi(t) + \Omega(t)]^+ - [k\phi(t) + \Omega(t)]^-\}$$

In local coordinate, Muskhelishvilis' stress function may be defined as:

$$\left.\begin{aligned} \phi(z_k) &= \frac{1}{2\pi}\int_{-l_k}^{l_k}\frac{g'_k(t)}{t - z_k}dt \\ \Psi(z_k) &= \frac{1}{2\pi}\int_{-l_k}^{l_k}\left(\frac{\overline{g'_k(t)}}{t - z_k} - \frac{tg'_k(t)}{(t - z_k)^2}\right)dt \end{aligned}\right\} \tag{10}$$

where $z_k = e^{-i\alpha_k}(z - z_k^0)$. We transform the coordinate reference from local to general, and consider all of the cracks. The stress function can be written in the form:

$$\left.\begin{aligned} \phi(z) &= \frac{1}{2\pi}\sum_{k=1}^{n}\int_{-l_k}^{l_k}\frac{g'_k(t)}{t - z_k}dt \\ \Psi(z) &= \frac{1}{2\pi}\sum_{k=1}^{n}\int_{-l_k}^{l_k}\left[\frac{\overline{g'_k(t)}}{t - z_k} - \frac{\overline{T_k e^{i\alpha_k}}}{(t - z_k)^2}\cdot g'_k(t)\right]dt \end{aligned}\right\} \tag{11}$$

The singular integral equation system with N cracks can be written in the forms see Fig. 1:

$$\int_{-l_k}^{l_k}\frac{g'_n(t)}{t - x}dt + \sum_{k=1}^{n}{}'\int_{-l_k}^{l_k}[G'_k(t)k_{nk}(t,x) + \overline{g'_k(t)}L_{nk}(t,x)dt = \pi f_n(x) \tag{12}$$

$$|x| < l_n, n = 1,2,\cdots,N$$

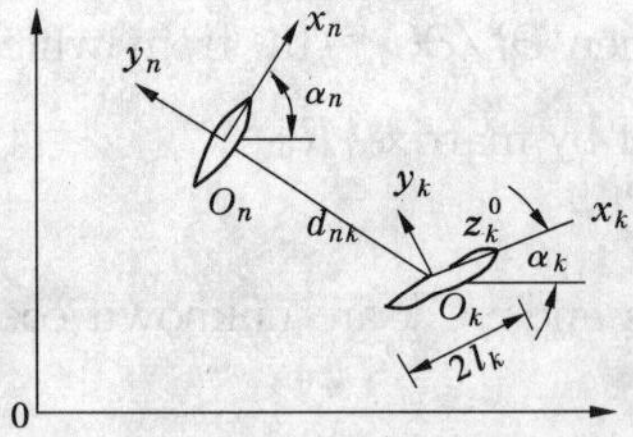

Fig. 1　Coordinate of crack system

where the prime in $\sum_{k=1}^{n}{}'$ represents the influence comes from all other cracks (except itself). The kernel functions are:

$$k_{nk}(t,x) = \frac{e^{i\alpha_k}}{2}\left(\frac{1}{T_k - x_n} + \frac{e^{-2i\alpha_n}}{\overline{T_k} - \overline{x_n}}\right)$$

$$L_{nk}(t,x) = \frac{e^{-i\alpha_k}}{2}\left(\frac{1}{\overline{T_k} - \overline{x_n}} \times \frac{T_k - x_n}{(\overline{T_k} - \overline{x_n})^2} \cdot e^{-2i\alpha_k}\right)$$

where $x_n = xe^{i\alpha_n} + z_n^0$, $f_n(x)$ is the released stress on crack faces given in above section. Let $\eta = t/l$, $\zeta = x/l$, formula (12) can be written in dimensionless form:

$$\int_{-1}^{1}\frac{g'(\eta)}{\eta - \xi}d\eta + \sum_{k=1}^{n}{}'\int_{-1}^{1}[g'(\eta)k(\eta,\xi) + \overline{g'(\eta)}L(\eta,\xi)]d\eta = \pi f(\xi) \quad |\xi| < 1 \tag{13}$$

Now define $g'(\eta) = U(\eta)/\sqrt{1-\eta^2}$, and use Gauss-Chebyshev quadraurture.

$$\int_{-1}^{1}\frac{g'(\eta)}{\eta - \xi}d\eta = \frac{\pi}{M}\sum_{m=1}^{M}\frac{U(\eta_m)}{\eta_m - \xi_r}$$

$$\int_{-1}^{1}g'(\eta)k(\eta,\xi)d\eta = \frac{\pi}{M}\sum_{m=1}^{M}k(\eta_m,\xi_r)U(\eta,m)$$

$$\int_{-1}^{1}\overline{g'(\eta)}L(\eta,\xi)d\eta = \frac{\pi}{M}\sum_{m=1}^{M}L(\eta_m,\xi_r)\overline{U(\eta,m)}$$

where

$$\eta_m = \cos\frac{2m-1}{2M}\pi \quad (m = 1,2,\cdots,M)$$

$$\xi_r = \cos\frac{\pi_r}{M} \qquad (r = 1,2,\cdots,m-1)$$

M is the number of the interpolate points, for physical condition exists

$$\sum_{m=1}^{n}U(\eta_m) = 0$$

Eq. (13) becomes

$$\frac{1}{M}\left\{\sum_{m=1}^{n}\frac{U(\eta_m)}{\eta_m - \xi_r} + \sum_{k=1}^{N}{}'\sum_{m=1}^{M}[k(\eta_m,\xi_r)U(\eta_m) + L(\eta_m,\xi_r)\overline{U}(\eta_m)]\right\} = f(\xi_r) \tag{14}$$

Solve the linear equation system for inter-polate points on every crack. Unknowns $U(\eta_m)$ at each point can be obtained. Then the strength factor other values at crack end are further given.

There is another useful Fredholm method for solving Caushy singular integral equation when concentrated forces on crack $P - iQ$ act at a distance S from the origin of coordinate, we have

$$[\phi(t) + \Omega(t)]^+ + [\phi(t) + \Omega(t)]^- = 2(P - iQ)\delta(t - s)$$

$$[\phi(t) - \Omega(t)]^+ + [\phi(t) - \Omega(t)]^- = 0$$

the single value condition of displacement is considered

$$\phi(z)=\Omega(z)=-\frac{P-iQ}{2\pi}\frac{\sqrt{a^2-s^2}}{(z-s)\sqrt{z^2-a^2}}$$

where a is the half length of the crack. Along the direction of angle α to the $x-$axis of crack face, the stress components at z point under local coordinate can be written as:

$$\begin{aligned}\sigma'_y-i\tau'_{xy}&=\phi(z)+\overline{\phi(z)}+e^{-2i\alpha}[\Omega(\bar{z})-\overline{\phi(z)}+(z-\bar{z})\overline{\phi'(z)}]\\&=\frac{-(P-iQ)}{2\pi}\sqrt{a^2-s^2}\{G(z)+e^{-2i\alpha}\,\overline{G(z)}\}-\frac{P+iQ}{2\pi}\sqrt{a^2-s^2}\times\\&\quad\{\overline{G(z)}(1-e^{-2i\alpha})+e^{-2i\alpha}(z-\bar{z})\overline{G'(z)}\}\end{aligned}\qquad(15)$$

where

$$G(z)=\frac{1}{\sqrt{z^2-a^2}(z-s)};\ G'(z)=\frac{a^2+sz-2z^2}{(z-s)^2\sqrt{(z^2-a^2)^3}}$$

when P and Q are the unit forces, stress components σ'_y, τ'_{xy} are the weighted function of the integral equation. By superposition the equations we have the form:

$$P_n(s_n)-iQ_n(s_n)+\sum_{k=1}^{N}{}'\int_{-l_k}^{l_k}[P_k(s_k)-iQ_k(s_k)]C_{nk}(s_k,s_n)ds_k+$$
$$\sum_{k=1}^{N}{}'\int_{-l_k}^{l_k}[P_k(s_k)+iQ_k(s_k)]D_{nk}(s_k,s_n)ds_k=p_n(s_n)-iq_n(s_n)\qquad(16)$$

where n, k represent the nth and kth crack; s_k and s_n denote the distances between the interpolate nodes and crack centre; p_n, q_n are known loads; P_n, Q_n, P_k and Q_k are the unknowns to be solved.

From Eqs. (15) and (16) the weighted functions are:

$$C_{nk}(s_k,s_n)=\frac{-\sqrt{a^2-s_k^2}}{2\pi}\{G(t_{kn},s_k)+e^{2i(\alpha_k-\alpha_n)}\,\overline{G(t_{kn},s_k)}\}$$

$$D_{nk}(s_k,s_n)=\frac{-\sqrt{a^2-s_k^2}}{2\pi}\{\overline{G(t_{kn},s_k)}[1-e^{2i(\alpha_k-\alpha_n)}]+e^{2i(\alpha_k-\alpha_n)}\cdot(t_{kn}-\bar{t}_{kn})G'(t_{kn},s_k)\}$$

$$t_{kn}=(z_{k0}+s_n e^{i\alpha_n}-z_k^0)e^{-i\alpha_k}\qquad(17)$$

Eq. (16) has a more convenient form then solving the singular integral equations. The SIF may be obtained after unknown forces are solved.

$$K_{\mathrm{I}}^{\pm}=-\frac{1}{\sqrt{\pi l_n}}\int_{-l_n}^{l_n}P_n(s_n)\frac{\sqrt{l_n\pm s_n}}{\sqrt{l_n\mp s_n}}ds_n$$

$$K_{\mathrm{II}}^{\pm}=-\frac{1}{\sqrt{\pi l_n}}\int_{-l_n}^{l_n}Q_n(s_n)\frac{\sqrt{l_n\pm s_n}}{\sqrt{l_n\mp s_n}}ds_n$$

4 The Fictitious Stress Method Considering the Interaction Between Boundary and Cracks

The previous analysis is defined in infinite domain, or if the distance between crack and boundary is more than 5 times the crack length, the error will be less than 3.4%. Otherwise a noticeable error may be caused. In order to satisfy the definite boundary condition, method of loading of nonequilibrium boundary stress is usually used. The progress carries on until the error tends to zero. For the solution of engineering precision, much computer time has to be spent in such repeated superposition and less accurate results are obtained. And therefore we would like to suggest the following direct fictitious stress (or virtual load) method.

Multiple crack body with arbitrary boundary loads can be resolved as in Fig. 2. Where the first part is a common elastic problem only. The second part can also be reduced as in Fig. 3.

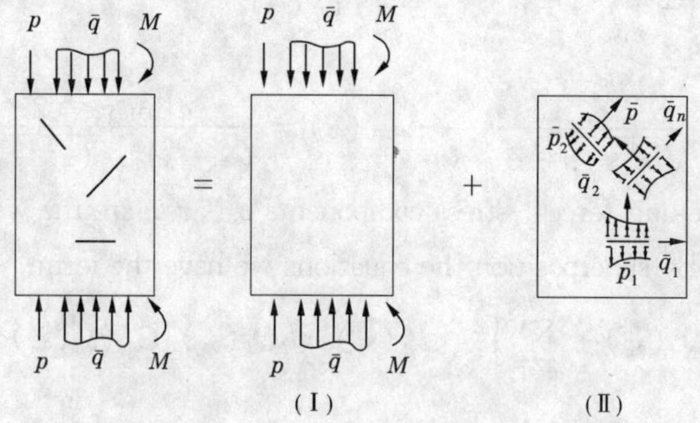

Fig. 2 Reduction of calculating conditions

Fig. 3 (Ⅲ) is taken as a fundamental solution for an infinite body. Suppose that there are proper normal force $N(s)$ and shear force $T(s)$ (fictitious load) acting on the original boundary as shown in Fig. 3 (Ⅳ). They have the same magnitude but are opposite in direction with the forces on the similar original boundaries cutting down from the infinite body of Fig. 3 (Ⅲ). Fictitious loads were unknowns and were solved together with other unknowns.

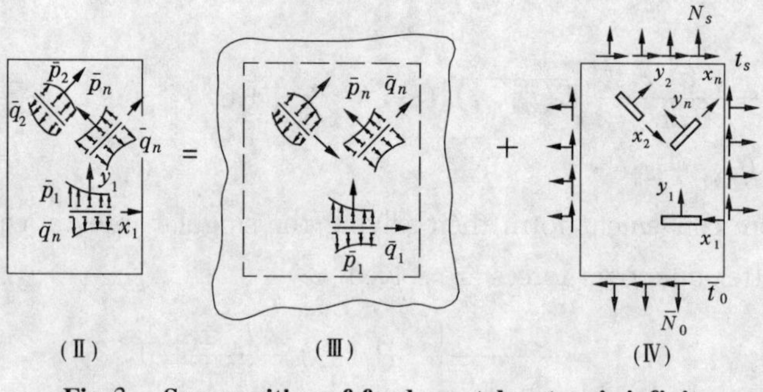

Fig. 3 Superposition of fundamental system is infinity

Let's divide the boundary into L segments. The two ends of node on the jth segment are written as a_j and b_j. The segments are so short that one can replace equivalently the fictitious forces $N(s)$ and $T(s)$ on a_jb_j by the strength of load $N_j(\xi)$ and $T_j(\xi)$ or $N_j(\eta)$ and $T_j(\eta)$ over the corresponding length. Where ξ, η are the location of arbitrary boundary point. Now by Fredholm integral equations we have:

(1) At each point of crack surface:

$$P_n(s_n) + \sum_{k=1}^{M}{}' \int_{-l_k}^{l_k} P_k(s_k) f_{nn,nk}(s_k, s_n) \mathrm{d}s_k + \sum_{k=1}^{N}{}' \int_{-l_k}^{l_k} Q_k(s_k) f_{nt,nk}(s_k, s_n) \mathrm{d}s_k +$$
$$\sum_{j=1}^{L} \int_{a_j}^{b_j} N_j(\xi) H_{nn,n\xi}(\xi, s_n) \mathrm{d}\xi_j + \sum_{j=1}^{L} \int_{a_j}^{b_j} T_j(\xi) H_{nt,n\xi}(\xi, s_n) \mathrm{d}\xi_j = p_n(s_n)$$
$$Q_n(s_n) + \sum_{k=1}^{N}{}' \int_{-l_k}^{l_k} P_k(s_k) f_{tn,nk}(s_k, s_n) \mathrm{d}s_k + \sum_{k=1}^{N}{}' \int_{-l_k}^{l_k} Q_k(s_k) f_{tt,nk}(s_k, s_n) \mathrm{d}s_k +$$
$$\sum_{j=1}^{L} \int_{a_j}^{b_j} N_j(\xi) H_{tn,n\xi}(\xi, s_n) \mathrm{d}\xi_j + \sum_{j=1}^{L} \int_{a_j}^{b_j} T_j(\xi) H_{tt,n\xi}(\xi, s_n) \mathrm{d}\xi_j = q_n(s_n)$$
$$(k = 1, 2, \cdots, N,\ \xi \in s,\ |s_n| < l_n,\ |s_k| < l_k) \tag{18}$$

(2) At each point of boundary

$$C_{nj} N_n(\xi) + \sum_{\substack{j=1 \\ j \neq n}}^{L} \int_{a_j}^{b_j} N_j(\eta) H_{nn,\xi\eta}(\eta, \xi) \mathrm{d}\eta_j + \sum_{\substack{j=1 \\ j \neq n}}^{L} \int_{a_j}^{b_j} T_j(\eta) H_{nt,\xi\eta}(\eta, \xi) \mathrm{d}\xi_j +$$
$$\sum_{k=1}^{N} \int_{-l_k}^{l_k} P_k(s_k) f_{nn,\xi s_k}(s_k, \xi) \mathrm{d}s_k + \sum_{k=1}^{n} \int_{-l_k}^{l_k} Q_k(s_k) f_{nn,\xi s_k}(s_k, \xi) \mathrm{d}s_k = \eta_n(\xi)$$
$$C_{nj} T_n(\xi) + \sum_{\substack{j=1 \\ j \neq n}}^{L} \int_{a_j}^{b_j} N_j(\eta) H_{tn,\xi\eta}(\eta, \xi) \mathrm{d}\eta_j + \sum_{\substack{j=1 \\ j \neq n}}^{L} \int_{a_j}^{b_j} T_j(\eta) H_{tt,\xi\eta}(\eta, \xi) \mathrm{d}\eta_j +$$
$$\sum_{k=1}^{N} \int_{-l_k}^{l_k} P_k(s_k) f_{tn,\xi s_k}(s_k, \xi) \mathrm{d}s_k + \sum_{k=1}^{N} \int_{-l_k}^{l_k} Q_k(s_k) f_{tt,\xi s_k}(s_k, \xi) \mathrm{d}s_k = t_n(\xi)$$
$$\tag{19}$$

where $f_{nn}, f_{nt}, f_{tn}, f_{tt}$ are the normal and shear forces at corresponding node caused by unit force acting on the point of crack face, i. e. the weighted function obtained from the previous section; $H_{nn}, H_{nt}, H_{tn}, H_{tt}$ are the normal and shear forces at corresponding node caused by unit force acting on the point of boundary.

$$C_{nj} = \begin{cases} \dfrac{1}{2} & \text{on the smooth boundary} \\ \dfrac{\theta}{2\pi} & \text{on corner of boundary with the internal angle } \theta \end{cases}$$

$p_n(s_n), q_n(s_n), n_n(\xi), t_n(\xi)$ are known. H_{nn}, H_{nt}, H_{tn}, H_{tt} may be given from Riemann boundary value problem by substituting

$$\phi(z) = -\frac{s}{z - z_0};\quad s = \frac{Q + iP}{2\pi(1 + k)};\quad \Omega(z) = \frac{k}{z - z_0} + \frac{\overline{s}(\overline{z} - z_0)}{(z - z_0)^2}$$

into:

$$\begin{aligned} \sigma_x &= \mathrm{Re}[2\phi(z) - \overline{x}\phi'(z) - \Psi'(z)] \\ &= \mathrm{Re}[3\phi(z) - \overline{\Omega}(z) + (z - \overline{z})\phi'(z)] \\ \sigma_y &= \mathrm{Re}[2\phi(z) + \overline{z}\phi'(z) + \Psi'(z)] \\ &= \mathrm{Re}[\phi(z) + \overline{\Omega}(z) - (z - \overline{z})\phi'(z)] \\ \tau_{xy} &= \mathrm{Im}[\overline{z}\phi'(z) + \Psi'(z)] \end{aligned}$$

$$= \mathrm{Im}[-\phi(z) - \overline{\Omega}(z) - (z - \overline{z})\phi'(z)] \tag{20}$$

when the acting point of force is taken to be the origin, the results can be represented in polar coordinates (as shown in Fig.4).

$$\sigma_r = \frac{-(3+\nu)}{4\pi} Q \frac{\cos\theta}{r} - \frac{3(1+\nu)}{4\pi} P \frac{\sin\theta}{r}$$

$$\sigma_\theta = \frac{(1-\nu)}{4\pi} Q \frac{\cos\theta}{r} + \frac{(1+\nu)}{4\pi} P \frac{\sin\theta}{r}$$

$$\tau_{xy} = \frac{(1-\nu)}{4\pi} Q \frac{\sin\theta}{r} - \frac{(1-\nu)}{4\pi} P \frac{\cos\theta}{r} \tag{21}$$

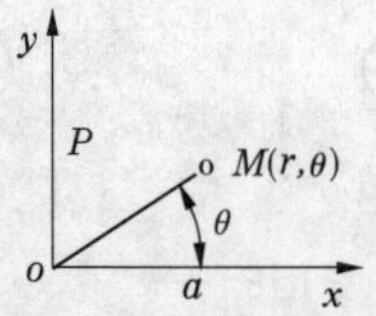

Fig.4　Stress components in polar coordinates under concentrated load

Formulae (20) and (21) will give at least a linear equation group of $(2\times N\times M+2\times L)$ orders, and therefore all unknowns are determined. Furthermore, formulae (20) and (21) will reduce to the form of (17) if the cracks are far from the boundary. When the cracks are located far from each other, they give little effect to each other, and therefore the presentation of these cracks brings a change to stress condition only in a small area beyond the crack tip.

5　Examples

Based on the previous equation group, program [BCMCI-VL] was provided. We examine the example of quadrilateral (as shown in Fig.5), containing 5 cracks with the same interval of 3.0cm ($\Delta h = 3.0$cm) and 1.5cm, and compare it with experimental results.

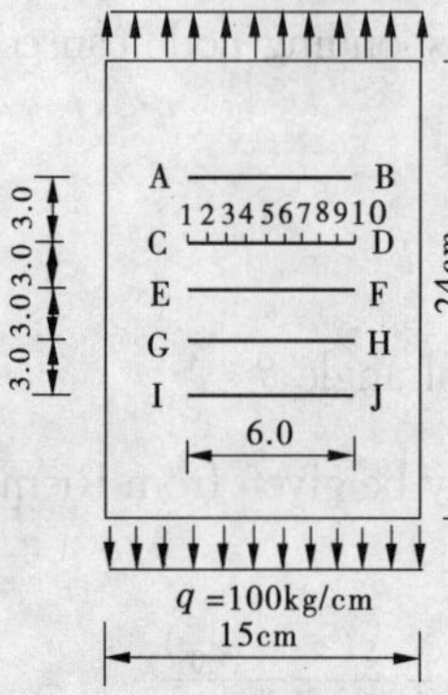

Fig.5　Calculating example

Ten items of stress function are taken into consideration. The power series are considered with $4\times 9 = 36$ items. The highest power is $(r/b)^{12}$, number of unknown coefficients are 46. The coefficients of the stress function ϕ are solved and shown in Table 1. In Table 2 the released stresses along cracks CD and EF are listed. It is found that these five cracks give interference to each other. The factors of stress intensity at crack end are given in Table 3.

The values of stress intensity factor measured by the coherent-light-shadow spot method and solved by an analytic numerical method have a good agreement with deviation less than 3%.

Values in Table 2 show that the maximum of calculating error of the 46 item series for the present example is about 1.36% for σ_y. There is a slightly crashing tendency of crack surface along the x direction. Repeat the calculation of five cracks with reduced interval of 1.5cm, SIFs of which are shown in Table 4.

Table 1 Results of the coefficients of the stress function ϕ

No.	1	2	3	4	5	6	7	8
item	r^2	$r^2 \ln r$	C_{03}	$\ln r$	$r^3 \cos\theta$	$1/r \cos\theta$	$r\cos\theta$	$r \ln r \cos\theta$
coefficient	12.137 8	−1.490 4	11 982.065 2	−1 040.978 1	0.027 7	−2 441.549 8	−890.446 1	−22.099 5
No.	9	10	11	12	13	14	15	16
item	$r\theta \sin\theta$	$r \ln r\theta$ $\sin\theta$	$\cos 2\theta$ $(r/D)^4$	$\cos 2\theta$ $(r/D)^2$	$\cos 2\theta$ $(r/D)^0$	$\cos 2\theta$ $(r/D)^{-2}$	$\cos 3\theta$ $(r/D)^5$	$\cos 3\theta$ $(e/D)^3$
coefficient	−263.468 7	105.475 9	1 043.730 6	−27.938 6	−1 426.130 7	99.098 7	−687.299 5	507.481 2
No.	17	18	19	20	21	22	23	24
item	$\cos 3\theta$ $(r/D)^{-1}$	$\cos 3\theta$ $(r/D)^{-3}$	$\cos 4\theta$ $(r/D)^6$	$\cos 4\theta$ $(r/D)^4$	$\cos 4\theta$ $(r/D)^{-2}$	$\cos 4\theta$ $(r/D)^{-4}$	$\cos 5\theta$ $(r/D)^7$	$\cos 5\theta$ $(r/D)^5$
coefficient	671.840 7	88.081 4	12.557 6	397.063 5	−492.182 5	−115.447 2	118.038 1	−156.297 2
No.	25	26	27	28	29	30	31	32
item	$\cos 5\theta$ $(r/D)^{-3}$	$\cos 5\theta$ $(r/D)^{-5}$	$\cos 6\theta$ $(r/D)^8$	$\cos 6\theta$ $(r/D)^6$	$\cos 6\theta$ $(r/D)^{-4}$	$\cos 6\theta$ $(r/D)^{-6}$	$\cos 7\theta$ $(r/D)^9$	$\cos 7\theta$ $(r/D)^7$
coefficient	284.377 9	34.620 5	−32.070 3	−35.182 5	−71.184 8	12.438 6	29.008 7	−65.909 3
No.	33	34	35	36	37	38	39	40
item	$\cos 7\theta$ $(r/D)^{-5}$	$\cos 7\theta$ $(r/D)^{-7}$	$\cos 8\theta$ $(r/D)^{10}$	$\cos 8\theta$ $(r/D)^8$	$\cos 8\theta$ $(r/D)^{-6}$	$\cos 8\theta$ $(r/D)^{-8}$	$\cos 9\theta$ $(r/D)^{11}$	$\cos 9\theta$ $(r/D)^9$
coefficient	−20.510 0	−12.315 0	−39.847 6	113.254 8	20.705 4	3.581 2	20.006 3	−55.166 3
No.	41	42	43	44	45	46		
item	$\cos 9\theta$ $(r/D)^{-7}$	$\cos 9\theta$ $(r/D)^{-9}$	$\cos 10\theta$ $(r/D)^{12}$	$\cos 10\theta$ $(r/D)^{10}$	$\cos 10\theta$ $(r/D)^{-8}$	$\cos 10\theta$ $(r/D)^{-10}$		
coefficient	−5.852 9	−0.395 9	−3.571 4	9.666 0	0.587 1	0.006 6		

Table 2 Released stresses along cracks CD and EF

Crack	Stress component	No. of point								
		1	2	3	4	5	6	7	8	9
CD	σ_x	−0.435	−0.560	−0.642	−0.695	−0.805	−0.726	−0.628	−0.519	−0.402
	σ_y	100.339	100.775	100.921	101.184	101.462	101.229	101.012	100.727	100.388
EF	σ_x	−1.044	−1.051	−1.071	−1.100	−1.112	−1.079	−0.999	−0.907	−0.847
	σ_y	100.506	100.639	100.853	101.059	101.160	101.101	100.910	100.688	100.545

Note. 1. stress unit kg/cm^2, $\tau_{xy} \equiv 0$. $\Delta h = 3cm$;

2. Location of points 1~9 are shown in Fig. 5. They are Chebyshev points of interpolated value.

Table 3 Factors of stress intensity of five cracks (interval between cracks $\Delta h = 3.0cm$)

SIF / Crack	Left end K_I ($kg/cm^{3/2}$)	Right end K_I ($kg/cm^{3/2}$)	Average value ($kg/cm^{3/2}$)	Compared to EF (%)
AB	281.560	281.455	281.507	147.9
CD	200.349	200.044	200.196	105.2
EF	190.250	190.302	190.276	100
GH	200.027	200.416	200.221	105.2
IJ	281.534	281.707	281.620	147.9

Similar crack poblems have been studied by scholars with experimental methods, since mathematic difficulty has always happened with analytic solutions of multiple cracks with an engineering boundary. For example the parallel cracks in steel plate have been studied by Dr

Isida M with the moire method, two conclusions of whom have been widely accepted in engineering:

(1) The strength of multiple crack body with iso-length parallel cracks under tension is higher than that of the single crack body. The smaller the interval Δh between the cracksis, the stronger the strength of the multiple crack bodyis.

(2) Crack could be considered as independently if the interval Δh between cracks is longer than half crack length a. It is known that SIF for a single crack length $2a = 6$cm in infinity under unit axial tension of 100 kg/cm^2 as Fig. 5 is:

$$K_1 = \sigma_x \sqrt{\pi a} = 306.998(\text{kg/cm}^{3/2})$$

S. I. F. for a single center crack plate as Fig. 5 is:

$$K_1 = F \cdot \sigma_x \sqrt{\pi a} = 344.452(\text{kg/cm}^{3/2})$$

Comparing these K_1 values with those in Tables 3 and 4, We can Conclude:

Table 4 Stress intensity factor of five cracks (interval between cracks $\Delta h = 1.5$cm)

SIF Crack	Average value (kg/cm$^{3/2}$)	Compared to EF (%)
AB	238.393	147.1
CD	167.792	103.5
EF	162.084	100
GH	167.781	103.5
IJ	238.469	147.1

(1) In the multiple parallel cracks body, the most dangerous area is the two outer crack tip region. SIFs of outer cracks is 47% larger than the center one.

(2) As in Fig. 5, the maximum SIFs of five cracks is 281.120kg/cm$^{3/2}$ but SIFs of the single crack under the same condition is 344.452kg/cm$^{3/2}$. As the interval Δh of five cracks reduces from 3 to 1.5cm, the maximum SIFs draw down to 238.469kg/cm$^{3/2}$. These confirm the first conclusion of Dr Isida, i. e. the strength of multiple crack body is stronger than that of single crack body under the same condition, and the smaller the interval Δh between the cracksis, the stronger the strength of the multiple crack bodyis.

(3) In Table 3, $\Delta h = 3.0\text{cm} = a$ the interval of cracks is equal to the half length of crack. But the interaction among cracks remains noticeable. The difference of SIFs between an outer crack and a crack at center is about 47%. It seems that the second conclusion of Dr Isida may be somewhat lower.

(4) If we take off two outer cracks A B, IJ from quadrilateral in Fig. 5, and calculate the values of SIFs again (shown in Table 5). Compare Tables 3,4 and 5, it is found that K_1 value decreases with the removal of two outer cracks and decreases also whenever 2 cracks are inserted into the remained 3 cracks (Δh becomes into 1.5cm), either change of crack number or rearrangement of crack position may cause the change of stressfield and K_1 value even

under simple tension condition.

Table 5 Stress intensity factors of three cracks ($\Delta h = 3.0$cm)

SIF Crack	Average value K_2 ($kg/cm^{3/2}$)	Compared to EF (%)
CD	257.95	126.5
EF	203.89	100
GH	258.01	126.5

In general the multiple crack problem is quite different from the problems of single crack. Sometimes it will make a mistaken sketch for arbitrary separated cracks or under complicated loads if we replace multiple crack by simplified single crack.

6 Few Ending Words

The mixed solution by analytic and numerical method for finite multiple crack body is given in this paper. Based on the solutions of the integral equation series the "fictitious load method" considering the interaction between boundary and cracks is suggested. The simple calculation offers an accurate results which has a good agreement with checking experiment. In comparing with common finite element method, the mixed method gives more accurate results, and spends less computing time CPU, about half CPU time of FEM for calculating the previous example, also the mixed method reduced a lot of the work on datum preparation and element division. Finally some mechanical behaviors on the strength of the multiple crack quadrilateral were discussed for practical purposes.

THE SYNTHETIC DEFORMATION MODULUS AND THE SYNTHETIC POISSON'S RATIO OF MULTIPLE-CRACK BODIES

Abstract In the present paper the results from theoretical solutions of multiple cracks are compared with the experimental. The synthetic modulus of deformation and the synthetic Poisson's ratio of a multiple-crack body were studied. The existence of series cracks in the material and the behaviors of cracks during different loading have a very important effect on the macro-mechanical properties of material.

1 Introduction

Cracks in concrete structures and joint cracks in rock bodies may have the mechanical properties of the "multiple-crack body". Even so there are parallel cracks in some given directions in the multiple-crack body, the strength and deformation of the loaded body are quite different from those in an isotropic elastic-plastic body or those in an anisotropic body. For example, when a load is acted in the direction perpendicular to the cracks, the magnitude of the total deformation of stretching and that of pressing are different, i.e. the synthetic deformation modulus is related not only to the direction of the principal stress axes, but also to the kind of loading. For the rock foundation with many joint cracks and the structure with multiple cracks, the numerical method and Fredholm treatment for the Cauchy singular integral equation have been greatly developed in recent years[1~4]. Nevertheless, the research on stress analysis and crack opening analysis of multiple-crack bodies can not cope with the need of engineering problems. So the "virtual loading method" was proposed for the stress analysis of the finite multiple-crack bodies. This method takes into account the interference among the cracks and between the cracks and the boundary when the integral equation is being solved. In addition, the stress intensity factor of each crack, the stress distribution, the deformation and the strength can also be given directly. The "virtual loading method" is accurate. Tedious repeated computing of opposite load caused by the unequilibrium boundary forces can be avoided, and thus less CPU time is needed. This paper is based on the comparison of the analytical and the numerical solution with experiments. The stress distribution, the deformation, the intensity factor, the synthetic modulus and the Poisson's ratio in a squareboard with parallel cracks subjected to uniaxial tension were studied. The re-

本文选自《Engineering Fracture Mechanics》1990 年第 4 期,作者还有 Zhou Ruizhong。

sults show that the cracks have important effects on the macro-mechanical properties of materials. This method is also used in the analysis of the cases involving irregular crack patterns.

2 Calculation and Experiments on the Finite Body With Multiple Cracks

(1) The tension test is carried out on a plexiglass rectangular board with 5 parallel cracks, as shown in Fig. 1. Related calculation is done using the method in ref. [5], and the analytical and the numerical solutions are given as follows:

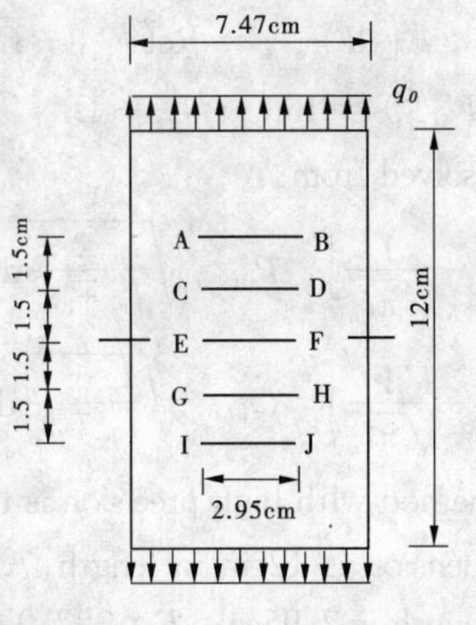

Fig. 1 Rectangular board with 5 parallel cracks (plexiglass)

(a) At the points on the crack surface:

$$P_{n(s_n)} + \sum_{k=1}^{N}{}' \int_{-l_k}^{l_k} P_{k(s_k)} f_{nn,nk(s_k,s_n)}, \mathrm{d}s_k + \sum_{k=1}^{N}{}' \int_{-l_k}^{l_k} Q_{k(s_k)} f_{nt,nk}(s_k, s_n) \mathrm{d}s_k + \sum_{j=1}^{L} \int_{a_j}^{b_j} N_{j(\xi)} H_{nn,n\xi(\xi,s_k)} \mathrm{d}\xi_j + \sum_{j=1}^{L} \int_{a_j}^{b_j} T_{j(\xi)} H_{nt,n\xi(\xi,s_n)} \mathrm{d}\xi_j = p_n(s_n) \tag{1}$$

$$Q_{n(s_n)} + \sum_{k=1}^{N}{}' \int_{-l_k}^{l_k} P_{k(s_k)} f_{tn,nk(s_k,s_n)} \mathrm{d}s_k + \sum_{k=1}^{N}{}' \int_{-l_k}^{l_k} Q_{k(s_k)} f_{tt,nk(s_k,s_n)} \mathrm{d}s_k + \sum_{j=1}^{L} \int_{a_j}^{b_j} N_{j(\xi)} H_{tn,n\xi(\xi,s_n)} \mathrm{d}\xi_j + \sum_{j=1}^{L} \int_{a_j}^{b_j} T_{j(\xi)} H_{tt,n\xi(\xi,s_n)} \mathrm{d}\xi_j = q_{n(s_n)}$$

$$k = 1,2,\cdots,N \quad | s_n | < l_n, \quad | s_k | < l_k \quad \xi_j \in s_j \tag{2}$$

(b) At the points on the boundary:

$$C_{nj} N_{n(\xi)} + \sum_{\substack{j=1 \\ j\neq n}}^{L} \int_{a_j}^{b_j} N_{j(n)} H_{nn,\xi\eta(\eta,\xi)} \mathrm{d}\eta_j + \sum_{\substack{j=1 \\ j\neq n}}^{L} \int_{a_j}^{b_j} T_{j(\eta)} H_{nt,\xi\eta(\eta,\xi)} \mathrm{d}\eta_j + \sum_{k=1}^{N} \int_{-l_k}^{l_k} P_{k(s_k)} f_{nn,\xi_k(s_k,\xi)} \mathrm{d}s_k + \sum_{k=1}^{N} \int_{-l_k}^{l_k} Q_{k(s_k)} f_{nt,\xi_k(s_k,\xi)} \mathrm{d}s_k = n_{n(\xi)} \tag{3}$$

$$C_{nj} T_{n(\xi)} + \sum_{\substack{j=1 \\ j\neq n}}^{L} \int_{a_j}^{b_j} N_{j(\eta)} H_{tn,\xi\eta(\eta,\xi)} \mathrm{d}\eta_j + \sum_{\substack{j=1 \\ j\neq n}}^{L} \int_{a_j}^{b_j} T_{j(\eta)} H_{tt,\xi\eta(\eta,\xi)} \mathrm{d}\eta_j + \sum_{k=1}^{K} \int_{-l_k}^{l_k} P_{k(s_k)} f_{tn,\xi_k(s_k,\xi)} \mathrm{d}s_k + \sum_{k=1}^{N} \int_{-l_k}^{l_k} Q_{k(s_k)} f_{tt,\xi_k(s_k,\xi)} \mathrm{d}s_k = t_{n(\xi)} \tag{4}$$

In which, f_{nn}, f_{nt}, f_{tn}, f_{tt} are normal and shear stresses at each point caused by the unit force acting on boundary point.

$$C_{nj} = \begin{cases} 1/2 & \text{at the smooth boundary point} \\ \theta/2\pi & \text{at the boundary corner point, } \theta \text{ is the internal angle} \end{cases}$$

For H_{nn}, H_{nt}, H_{tn} and H_{tt}, they can be represented by the Riemann Boundary Value solution:

$$\left.\begin{aligned} \sigma_x &= \mathrm{Re}(2\phi_{(z)} - \bar{z}\phi'_{(z)} + \Psi'_{(z)}) = \mathrm{Re}(3\phi_{(z)} - \overline{\Omega}_{(z)} + (z - \bar{z})\phi'_{(z)}) \\ \sigma_y &= \mathrm{Re}(2\phi_{(z)} + \bar{z}\phi'_{(z)} + \Psi'_{(z)}) = \mathrm{Re}(\phi_{(z)} + \overline{\Omega}_{(z)} - (z - \bar{z})\phi'_{(z)}) \\ \tau_{xy} &= \mathrm{Im}(\bar{z}\phi'_{(z)} + \Psi'_{(z)}) = \mathrm{Im}(-\phi_{(z)} + \overline{\Omega}_{(z)} - (z - \bar{z})\phi'_{(z)}) \end{aligned}\right\} \quad (5)$$

Thus the intensity factor can be solved from:

$$\left.\begin{aligned} K_{\mathrm{I}}^{\pm} &= -\frac{1}{\sqrt{\pi l_n}}\int_{-l_n}^{l_n} P_{n(s_n)}\sqrt{\frac{l_n \pm s_n}{l_n \mp s_n}}\,\mathrm{d}s_n \\ K_{\mathrm{II}}^{\pm} &= -\frac{1}{\sqrt{\pi l_n}}\int_{-l_n}^{l_n} Q_{n(s_n)}\sqrt{\frac{l_n \pm s_n}{l_n \mp s_n}}\,\mathrm{d}s_n \end{aligned}\right\} \quad (6)$$

In addition, the simple caustic method with high precision is used to find K_{I} in the experiment. The plexiglass sample dimension is 12cm in length, 7.47cm in width, 0.314cm in thickness, and the actual crack length is 2.95cm, $E=287.0\mathrm{kg/mm^2}$, $\mu=0.4$.

On the basis of Maxwell-Neumann Optics Law, the relationship between transmission and reflection is:

$$\left.\begin{aligned} C_{\mathrm{r}} - C_{\mathrm{t}} &= -\frac{\mu}{2E} \\ C_{\mathrm{r}}/C_{\mathrm{t}} &= \frac{1}{2}\left(\frac{Z_{\mathrm{ot}}}{Z_{\mathrm{or}}}\right)\left(\frac{\lambda_{\mathrm{t}}}{\lambda_{\mathrm{r}}}\right)^{1.5} q_{\lambda}^{2.5} \end{aligned}\right\} \quad (7)$$

in which C_{r} and C_{t} are stress optics constants, $\lambda_{\mathrm{t}} = (Z_{\mathrm{i}} + Z_{\mathrm{ot}})/Z_{\mathrm{i}}$, $\lambda_{\mathrm{r}} = (Z_{\mathrm{i}} + Z_{\mathrm{or}})/Z_{\mathrm{i}}$, $q_{\lambda} = D_{\mathrm{r}}/D_{\mathrm{t}}$, D_{r} and D_{t} are diameters of reflex and through caustic circles. Then we obtained $C_{\mathrm{r}}=12.014\times10^{-4}\mathrm{mm^2/kg}$, $C_{\mathrm{t}}=5.046\times10^{-4}\mathrm{mm^2/kg}$ by the test.

Generally, the figure on the T screen is clear, steady and with high precision. From the T screen the intensity factor can be calculated by:

$$K_{\mathrm{I}} = 0.0934\,\frac{1}{C_t \cdot d \cdot Z_{\mathrm{ot}}} \cdot \frac{1}{\lambda_{\mathrm{t}}^{3/2}}(D_{\mathrm{t}}^{\max})^{2.5} \quad (8)$$

The results of observation and analysis are shown in Table 1 (referring to Figs. 2, 3 and 4). It is concluded that they are in good agreement.

(2) The comparison of the analytical solution with the experiment of the displacement on the concrete board with multiple cracks by the laser speckle method.

Table 1 The comparison experiment results with results of calculations

Item order	Loading (kg/cm^2)		D_t^{max} (mm)	$(D_t^{max})^{2.5}$	K_I ($kg/mm^{3/2}$)	Experiment K_I ($kg/cm^{3/2}$)	Calculation K_I ($kg/cm^{3/2}$)
1	19.56	AB	7.65	162.05	1.137	35.95	38.87
		CD	6.72	117.16	0.822	26.00	27.69
2	41.20	AB	10.45	353.18	2.478	78.35	81.86
		CD	9.14	252.84	1.774	56.10	58.32
3	60.72	AB	12.63	566.54	3.975	125.71	120.65
		CD	10.98	399.36	2.802	88.62	85.95
4	83.50	AB	13.99	732.58	5.140	162.54	165.92
		CD	12.30	530.91	3.725	117.79	118.20

Speckle technique has been widely used in the research on fracture mechanics of concrete materials. This method can be used to the displacement measurement with the accuracy of 10^{-6}m.

The concrete sample with cracks whose dimensional ratio is 1:0.55:2:4 as shown in Figs. 5 and 6 (No. 400# cement:water:sand:cobble stone) was made in a special model. The internal cracks (for tension test) was made by burying plastic strips 0.5mm in thickness. After curiling sample surface was finished and washed by organic solvent. Then the surface was precoated and was sprayed with copper powder. The distinct speckle stripes pattern was obtained as in Fig. 7. At the same time, 16 samples were made to determine the elastic modulus and the Poisson's ratio. The actual compressive strength of the sample is 124.7kg/cm^2, $E = 1.942 \times 10^5 kg/cm^2$ and $\mu = 0.171$. The sample size with cracks is 24cm × 15cm × 3cm, and the crack length is 2a = 6cm. Because of the symmetry of the sample, the displacement at the center point is zero if the sample is loaded by uniform pulling forces. Hence the deformation at each point can be calculated by deducting from its displacement the measured displacement at the center (as the rigid-body translation).

In the linear elastic test, $q_0 = 8.89$kg/cm, which should be amplified to $q_0 = 100$ kg/cm according to the proportion of the measured displacement. After the conversion of the displacement, the experimental results at 13 points on line MN is shown in Fig. 8 as the dotted line.

Under the same condition, the analytical and the numerical calculations were done by using formulas (1) ~ (6), in which 10 terms of the transcendental function of the stress function were taken, and 36 terms of the power series were used, among which the highest power was $(r/d)^{12}$ so there were 46 unknowns.

The displacement on line MN is shown in Fig. 9 as the solid line. When comparing in Fig. 9, it is found that the inhomogeneity of concrete material and the deduction of the rigid-body translation has little effect on the displacement, but the error in the second direction is somewhat larger. Hence for the intensity factors and the displacements in the body with

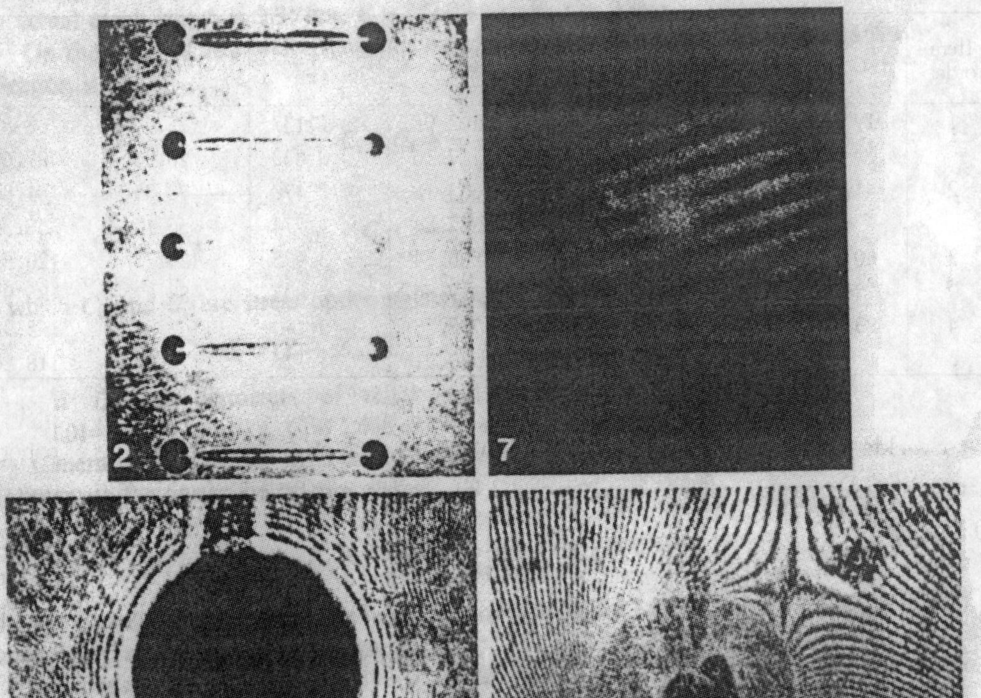

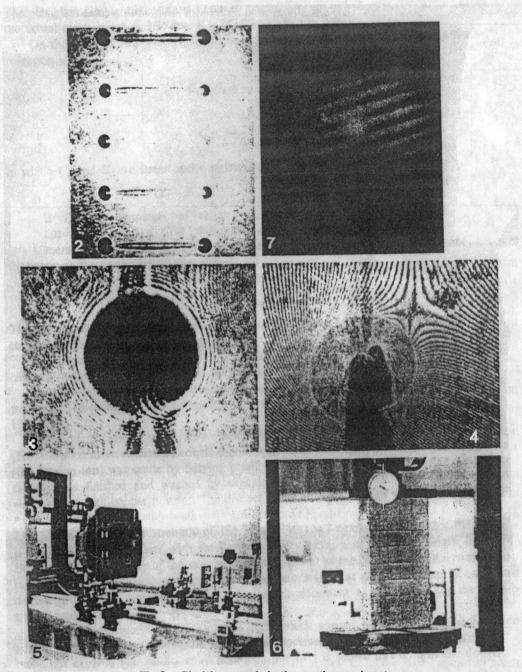

Fig. 2　Plexiglass sample in the caustic experiment

Fig. 3　Through caustic circle

Fig. 4　Reflex caustic circle

Fig. 5　Speckle experiment

Fig. 6　Speckle sample (made of concrete)

Fig. 7　Speckle stripes

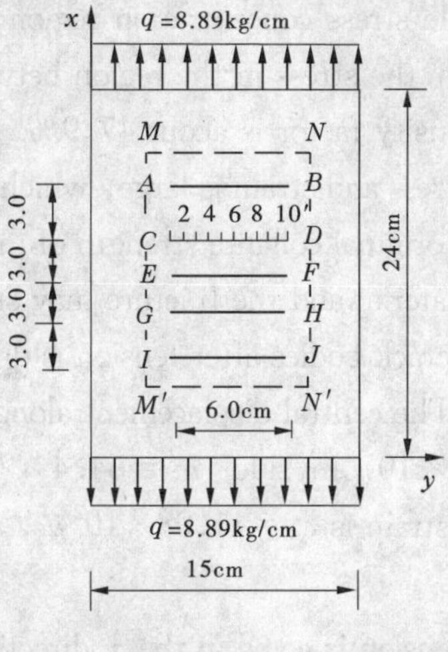

Fig. 8 Speckle sample (concrete)

cracks the theory and the experiment can verify each other.

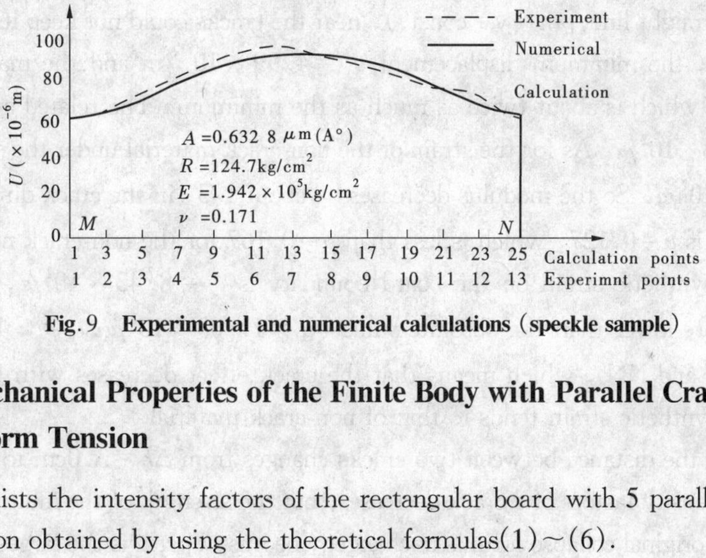

Fig. 9 Experimental and numerical calculations (speckle sample)

3 The Mechanical Properties of the Finite Body with Parallel Cracks Subjected to Uniform Tension

Table 2 lists the intensity factors of the rectangular board with 5 parallel cracks under uniform tension obtained by using the theoretical formulas(1)~(6).

Table 2 The intensity factors of the rectangular board with 5 parallel cracks (Fig. 8)

SIF cracks	Left K_I ($kg/cm^{3/2}$)	Right K_I ($kg/cm^{3/2}$)	Average K_I ($kg/cm^{3/2}$)	Percent (%)
AB	281.560	281.455	281.500	147.9
CD	200.349	200.044	200.196	105.2
EF	190.250	190.302	190.276	100
GH	200.027	200.416	200.221	105.2
IJ	281.534	281.707	281.620	147.9

We noted:

(1) It can be seen that the internal stress in the cracked body is not quite uniform. The

crack tip is in the biaxial tensile stress concentration region, which make failure easier for brittleness materials. Moreover, the stress in the region between cracks is slightly compressive. The difference in the intensity factor is about 47.9%. At the tips of the outer cracks AB and IJ, the range of high stress and strain is large, which is becoming smaller toward the center of the board. Hence the original collapse strength of multiple-crack body is much lower than that of homogeneous material and the fracture may start near the outer cracks.

(2) Line MN in multiple-crack bodies after tension is different from that in a non-crack body (still in a straight line). The central displacement along line MN is larger than that on both sides (central: $u' = 95.6 \times 10^{-6}$ m, side: $u' = 64.4 \times 10^{-6}$ m), the difference is about 1/2 u'. The related synthetic strain is $\epsilon_{x'} = 11.08 \times 10^2 \mu\epsilon$, and for the non-crack material, $\epsilon_x = 5.55 \times 10^2 \mu\epsilon$.

So it is found that when tension is acted in the x direction, the synthetic elastic modulus of materials decreases about by half, and when compression is acted it still remains the same.

(3) The straight line, nn' (y = const.), near the cracks could not keep its original state after stretching, the minimum displacement $v' = 4.99 \times 10^{-6}$ m and the maximum one is 8.23×10^{-6} m, which is about twice as much as the minimum. The related synthetic strain is $\epsilon_{y'} = -1.408 \times 10^2 \mu\epsilon$. As for the strain of the non-crack material under the same condition $\epsilon_{y'} = -0.93 \times 10^2 \mu\epsilon$. So the modulus decreases by about 1/3 (in the crack direction) and its Poisson's ratio is $\mu = 0.127$, which is less than $\mu = 0.167$ for the non-crack material.

(4) The synthetic strain on the board boundary is $\epsilon_x = 8.43 \times 10^2 \mu\epsilon$, $\epsilon_y = -1.0 \times 10^2 \mu\epsilon$, which are lower than the absolute value ($\epsilon_x = 11.03 \times 10^2 \mu\epsilon$, $\epsilon_y = -1.41 \times 10^2 \mu\epsilon$) along lines MN and NN′, which means that the crack effect decreases with increasing distance and the synthetic strain tends to that of non-crack material.

(5) When the distance between two cracks changes from $\Delta h = 3.0$cm to $\Delta h = 1.5$cm, the absolute intensity factors of a crack decreases, but the strength of the multiple-crack body increases. The original collapse form is unchanged, because k_1 still is the largest for the outer cracks AB and IJ.

While the outer cracks AB and IJ no longer exist, the intensity factors tend to be more uniform. The changes in the crack number and the distance between them also cause the change in the values of the boundary displacement and its distribution.

4 The Synthetic Mechanical Properties of the Crack Subjected to Compressive and Shearing Forces in the finite multiple-Crack(Skew Cracks)

In the special case with the above-mentioned parallel-cracked board loaded by the uniform compression on both ends, the negative k_1 could not cause the collapse because of the same deformation on the two crack surface, the strength of the multiple-crack body has not been changed. The synthetic strain is the same as that of the non-crack body.

However, when the board with parallel inclined cracks is loaded by uniform pressure on its ends (Fig. 10) and the cracks subjected to compressive and shearing forces if they could not get closed, the same method can be used to calculate the boundary displacement in the inclined crack body. Moreover, while the cracks are getting closed, the Mohr-Coulomb rule ($\tau = 6nf + c$) is used in computation. Thus we obtained the average strains $\epsilon_{x'} = 650\mu\rho$, $\epsilon_{y'} = 111\mu\epsilon$, $\gamma = 0.170$.

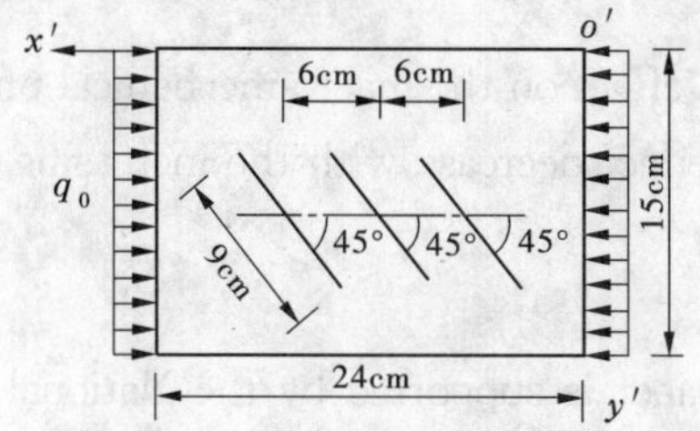

Fig. 10 Skew cracks in the compressive and shearing state

It is found that the deformation u' on the boundary point ($o'y'$) is different from that on the horizontal cracks. The deformation is unsymmetrical with respect to the central axis, the boundary displacement on the skew-cracked body subjected to compressive and shearing forces is less than that of the parallel-cracked body subject to tension. The synthetic strain of the skew-cracked board is $\epsilon_x = 6.50 \times 10^2 \mu\epsilon$, which is less than that the body with 3 horizontal cracks and tends to the non-crack material. Its synthetic deformation modulus $E_x = 1.54 \times 10^5 \text{kg/cm}^2$ is somewhat less than that of the non-crack material

$$E_x = 1.8 \times 10^5 \text{kg/cm}^2$$

The synthetic horizontal strain at o'x' boundary point is $\epsilon_y = 1.11 \times 10^2 \mu\epsilon$ and for the non-crack material $\epsilon_y = 0.93 \times 10^2$, Poisson's ratio is $\mu = 0.170$ which is much closer to the non-crack material $\mu = 0.167$ (much higher than that of the board with 3 cracks $\mu = 0.133$).

In the multiple-crack body subjected to compression, its synthetic mechanical properties is similar to that of the non-crack material when the crack is at right angle to the load direction, and it will be similar to that of unisotropic materials, whose elastic modulus is reduced, but the strength is different.

5 Conclusions

(1) For the multiple-crack body, analytical-numerical solution in this paper is in good agreement with the results of the caustic, speckle test, and hence they verify the theoretical results. They show that the macro-mechanical properties are affected by micro-cracks (deformation, synthetic deformation modulus, synthetic Poisson's ratio and strength).

(2) The body with cracks in some direction displays anisotropism. For example, when a board is stretched and crack is at right angle to the loading direction, its synthetic modulus

($F_x = 9.02 \times 10^4$ kg/cm^2) is about half of the non-crack board ($E_x = E_y = 1.8 \times 10^5$ kg/cm^2), and its Poisson's ratio ($\mu = 0.127$) is much less than that of the non-crack board ($\mu = 0.167$). The crack number, the distance between cracks, the crack length, the loading direction and the kind of load can affect the material deformation, distribution, the synthetic modulus, the synthetic Poisson's ratio and the strength.

(3) In the inclined-crack body subjected to compression, its synthetic mechanical properties is somewhat similar to that of anisotropic materials, but their collapse strengths are different.

(4) Micro-cracks have great effect on the macro-mechanical properties of the material in the region near cracks, and the effect decrease with the increasing distance.

Acknowledgment

The research work of this paper is supported by the National Natural Science Foundation(N. S. F.)of China.

References

[1] V. V. Panasyuk et al.. *A general method of solution of two-dimensional problems in the theory of cracks*. Engng Fracture Mech. 9,481~497,1977

[2] P. S. Theocarls, N. I. Ioakimidis. *Numerical integration methods for solution of singular integral equations*. Q. Appl. Math. 4,173~183,1977

[3] N. I. Ioakimidis. *A new singular integral equation for the classical crack problem in plane and anti-plane elasticity*. Int. J. Fracture 21, 115~122,1983

[4] Y. Z. Chen. Engng Fracture Mech. 12,767,1984

[5] G. T. Liu ,R. Z. Zhou. *The strength of finite body with multiple cracks*. Int. Conf. on Fracture and Damage of Concrete and Rock, Vienna, Austria (4~6 July 1988)

AN ANALYTIC-FICTITIOUS BOUNDARY FORCES METHOD FOR CALCULATING MULTI-CRACK PROBLEM IN ARBITRARY REGION WITH MIXED MODE BOUNDARIES

Abstract In present paper the more accurate analytic solution with considering interference among the cracks and boundaries are used for the weighting factors of stress relaxation. The unknown fictitious forces on boundary elements and on crack surfaces are used as basic parameter. Matrix represented in fictitious forces can be determined by known outer and inner (crack-faces) boundary conditions. The SIF, stress and displacement fields are obtained from solved fictitious forces. Examples are illustrated, and the effectiveness of this method-accuracy and reducing the time of computer are confirmed.

1 Introduction

Compared with the other numerical methods, the boundary element method has its advantages. But it is difficult for BEM to discribe the stress near the crack tips. The analytical solutions can easily give the stress near the crack tips, but it is difficult to satisfy the boundary conditions in engineering. In this paper, the combination of an analytical solution and fictitious boundary forces method was introduced with high precision and reducing computer time.

Suppose there is a crack C_3 in the arbitrary plane domain A. (Fig. 1) The boundary of domain A is divided into displacement boundary C_1 and stress boundary C_2 respectively. The stress and displacement fields in domain A and the SIF at the crack tips can be obtained by the following method.

2 Fictitious Boundary Element Force Method [1]

In the case of no crack C_3, suppose that we have an infinite plane Ω_1 which has the same material and thickness as domain A. In Ω_1, we take domain A' which has the same form with domain A. Correspondingly, the boundary of A' is divided into two parts, C'_1 and C'_2. Then N line segments are used to replace the boundary of A' (Fig. 2), and every line segment is taken as a boundary element.

The uniform distributed normal and tangential fictitious forces are loaded to each ele-

本文选自 EISEIVER Applied Science 1989 年出版的《Fracture of Concrete and Rock Recent Developments》一书，作者还有 Chi Yuan。

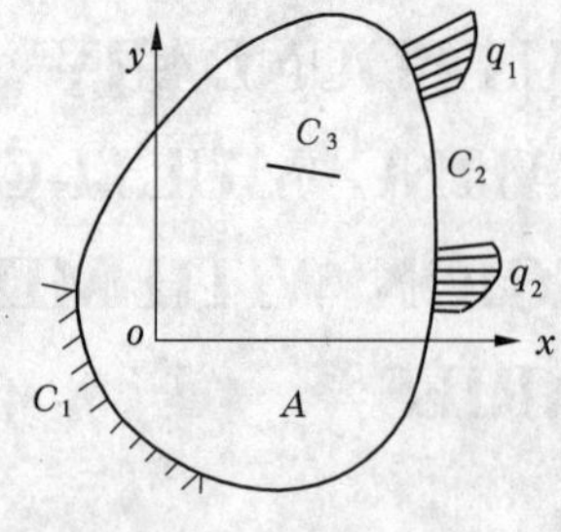

Fig. 1

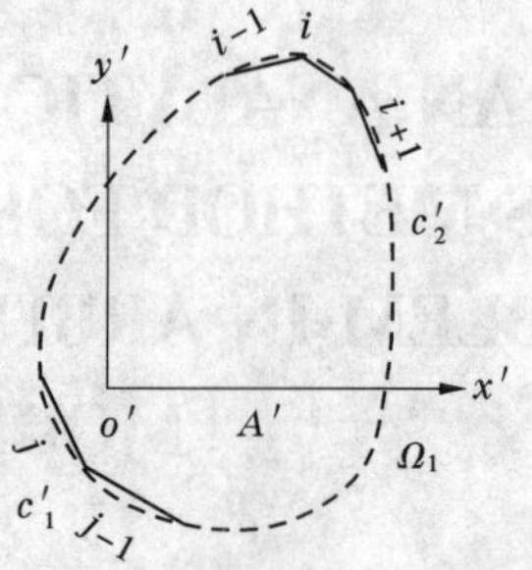

Fig. 2

ment(Fig. 3). P_n^i and P_s^i represent the normal and tangential fictitious forces respectively, the superscript i indicates the element number. These fictitious forces are the unkowns of the problem. Under the action of the fictitious forces on the boundary A', the corresponding displacement and stress fields, which take P_n^i and P_s^i as the paramaters will be produced in the infinite plane Ω_1. These fields can be obtained from ordinary transform of Kelvin's Solution of plane problem: When an uniform distributed force is loaded on line segment in infinite plane and the local coordinate system coincides with the segment (Fig. 4), the concentrated forces at point ξ can be expressed as follows:

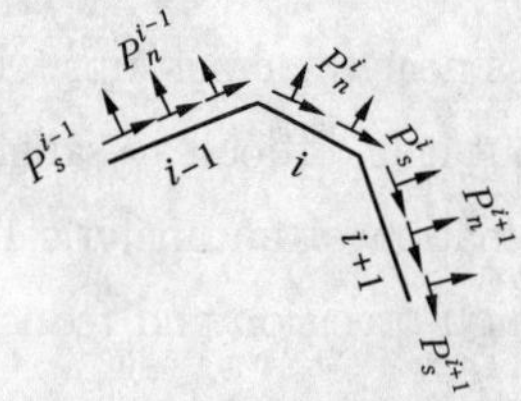

Fig. 3

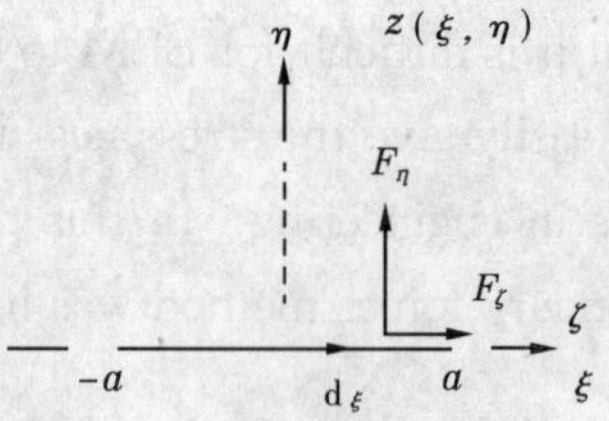

Fig. 4

$$F_\zeta = P_\zeta \mathrm{d}\xi \qquad F_\eta = P_\eta \mathrm{d}\xi$$

Substituting above expressions into Kelvin's Solution and integrating which with respect to ξ in the interval $-$a and a, the displacement and stress due to the force loaded along the segment $[-a, a]$ in local coordinate at any point $z(\zeta, \eta)$ can be written as: (plane strain problem)

$$u_\zeta = \frac{P_\zeta}{2G}[(3-4\mu)f + \eta f_\eta] + \frac{P_\eta}{2G}[-\eta f_\zeta]$$

$$u_\eta = \frac{P_\eta}{2G}[(3-4\mu)f - \eta f_\eta] + \frac{P_\zeta}{2G}[-\eta f_\zeta] \tag{1}$$

$$\sigma_\zeta = P_\zeta[(3-2\mu)f_\zeta + \eta f_{\zeta\eta}] + P_\eta(2\mu f_\eta + \eta f_{\eta\eta})$$

$$\sigma_\eta = P_\zeta[-(1-2\mu)f_\zeta - \eta f_{\zeta\eta}] + P_\eta[2(1-\mu)f_\eta - \eta f_{\eta\eta}]$$

$$\tau_{\zeta\eta} = P_\zeta[2(1-\mu)f_\eta + \eta f_{\eta\eta}] + P_\eta[(1-2\mu)f_\zeta - \eta f_{\zeta\eta}] \tag{2}$$

where f_ζ and f_η indicate the partial derivative of the function f with respect to ζ and η; μ is the Poisson' ratio and G is the shear modulus.

$$f=\int_{-a}^{+a}\{-\frac{1}{4\pi(1-\mu)}\ln[(\zeta-\xi)^2+\eta^2]^{1/2}\}\mathrm{d}\xi$$

$$=\frac{-1}{4\pi(1-\mu)}\{\eta(\arctan\frac{\eta}{\zeta-a}-\arctan\frac{\eta}{\zeta+a})-(\zeta-a)\ln\sqrt{(\zeta-a)^2+\eta^2}+(\zeta+a)\ln\sqrt{(\zeta+a)^2+\eta^2}\}+\frac{a}{2\pi(1-\mu)}$$

When the line segment (element) is located at any position in the ensemble coordinate system(Fig. 5), where xoy is the ensemble system and ζ_η is the local system. β is the angle between the local and ensemble system. The displacements and stresses at any point $z(x, y)$ can be expressed as follow:

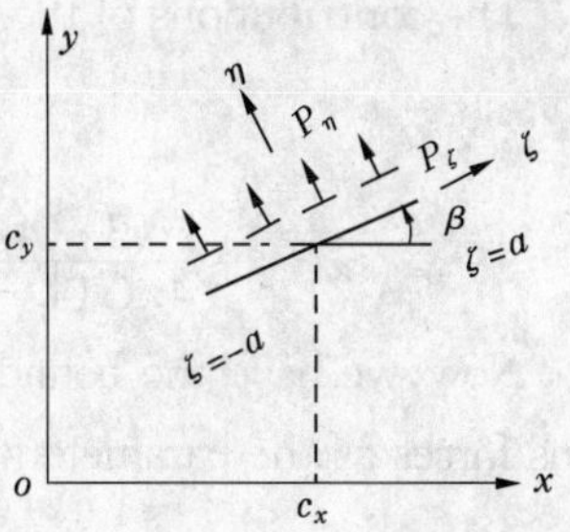

Fig. 5

$$u_x=\frac{p_\zeta}{2G}[(3-4\mu)\cos\beta F_1+\eta(\sin\beta F_2+\cos\beta F_3)]+\frac{p_\eta}{2G}[-(3-4\mu)\sin\beta F_1-\eta(\cos\beta F_2-\sin\beta F_3)]$$

$$u_y=\frac{p_\zeta}{2G}[(3-4\mu)\sin\beta F_1-\eta(\cos\beta F_2-\sin\beta F_3)]+\frac{p_\eta}{2G}[(3-4\mu)\cos\beta F_1-\eta(\sin\beta F_2+\cos\beta F_3)] \qquad (3)$$

$$\sigma_x=p_\zeta[F_2+2(1-\mu)(\cos2\beta F_2-\sin2\beta F_3)+\eta(\cos2\beta F_4+\sin2\beta F_5)]+p_\eta[F_3-(1-2\mu)(\sin2\beta F_2+\cos2\beta F_3)+\eta(\sin2\beta F_4-\cos2\beta F_5)]$$

$$\sigma_y=p_\zeta[F_2-2(1-\mu)(\cos2\beta F_2-\sin2\beta F_3)-\eta(\cos2\beta F_4+\sin2\beta F_5)]+p_\eta[F_3+(1-2\mu)(\sin2\beta F_2+\cos2\beta F_3)-\eta(\sin2\beta F_4-\cos2\beta F_5)]$$

$$\tau_y=p_\zeta[2(1-\mu)(\sin2\beta F_2+\cos2\beta F_3)+\eta(\sin2\beta F_4-\cos2\beta F_5)]+p_\eta[(1-2\mu)(\cos2\beta F_2-\sin2\beta F_3)-\eta(\cos2\beta F_4+\sin2\beta F_5)] \qquad (4)$$

where $F_1=f(\zeta,\eta)$, $F_2=f_\zeta(\zeta,\eta)$
$F_3=f_\eta(\zeta,\eta)$, $F_4=f_{\zeta\eta}(\zeta,\eta)$, $F_5=f_{\zeta\zeta}(\zeta,\eta)$

Since the boundary A′ is discretezated by many line segments, the various quantities at the midpoint of each element can be obtained by the superposition of two parts of contribution. One part is the contribution from the fictitious forces loaded on the other elements and the other is the contribution from the fictitious forces loaded on itself.

The contribution by the fictitious forces loaded on element j to the midpoint of element i can be expressed as:

tangential surface force :

$$\sigma_s^i=(\sigma_y^{ij}-\sigma_x^{ij})\sin\beta^i\cos\beta^i+\tau_{xy}^{ij}(\cos^2\beta^i-\sin^2\beta^i) \qquad (5)$$

normal surface force:

$$\sigma_n^i=\sigma_x^{ij}\sin^2\beta^i-2\tau_{xy}^{ij}\sin\beta^i\cos\beta^i+\sigma_y^{ij}\cos^2\beta^i$$

tangential displacement:

$$u_s^i = u_x^{ij}\cos\beta^i + u_y^{ij}\sin\beta^i \tag{6}$$

normal displacement:

$$u_n^i = -u_x^{ij}\sin\beta^i + u_y^{ij}\cos\beta^i$$

The contributions of the fictitious forces on the elements itself can be written as follows:

$$\sigma_s^i = \frac{1}{2}p_s^i \qquad \sigma_n^i = \frac{1}{2}p_n^i \tag{7}$$

$$u_s^i = -\frac{(3-4\mu)}{4\pi G(1-\mu)}a^i \ln a^i p_s^i \qquad u_n^i = -\frac{(3-4\mu)}{4\pi G(1-\mu)}a^i \ln a^i p_n^i \tag{8}$$

Now, we have the boundary stress and displacement expressions, which take the fictitious forces as the parameters.

3 Analytical Solution for Crack-Surface-Loaded Problem

Suppose, there is a crack with length $2a$ in an infinite domain Ω_2 and let the local axis ox coincides with the crack (Fig. 6) when the crack surfaces are loaded at point $x = s$ with two pair of forces P and Q, the displacements and stresses at any point $z(x, y)$ in Ω_2 can be expressed as the complex functions [2] (plane strain problem)

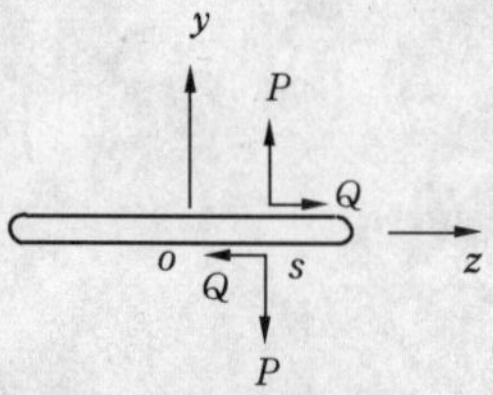

Fig. 6

$$\sigma_y - i\tau_{xy} = \phi(z) + Q(\bar{z}) + (z - \bar{z})\overline{\phi'(z)}$$

$$\sigma_y + \sigma_x = 4\mathrm{Re}\phi(z)$$

$$2G(u_x + iu_y) = (3-4\mu)\phi(z) - \omega(\bar{z}) - (z - \bar{z})\overline{\phi(z)} \tag{9}$$

where $\phi(z) = Q(z) = \dfrac{(P - iQ)\sqrt{a^2 - s^2}}{2\pi(z - s)\sqrt{z^2 - a^2}}$

$$\phi(z) = \int \phi(z)\mathrm{d}z = -\frac{P - iQ}{2\pi i}\ln\left\{\frac{\sqrt{s^2 - a^2}}{z - s}\left[\sqrt{s^2 - a^2} + \sqrt{z^2 - a^2}\right] + s\right\}$$

in which a non-essential complex constant has been omitted.

Then:

$$\sigma_y - i\tau_{xy} = \frac{(P - iQ)\sqrt{a^2 - s^2}}{\pi}\mathrm{Re}\left[\frac{1}{\sqrt{z^2 - a^2}(z - s)}\right] + \frac{(P + iQ)\sqrt{a^2 - s^2}}{\pi}iy\left[\frac{a^2 + sz - 2z^2}{(z - s)^2(z^2 - a^2)^{3/2}}\right] \tag{10}$$

$$\sigma_y + \sigma_x = 2\mathrm{Re}\left[\frac{(P - iQ)\sqrt{a^2 - s^2}}{\pi}\frac{1}{\sqrt{z^2 - a^2}(z - s)}\right] \tag{11}$$

$$2G(u_x + iu_y) = \frac{P - iQ}{2\pi i}\left\{-(3-4\mu)\ln\left[\frac{\sqrt{s^2 - a^2}}{z - s}(\sqrt{s^2 - a^2} + \sqrt{z^2 - a^2}) + s\right] + \ln\left(\left[\frac{\sqrt{s^2 - a^2}}{\bar{z} - s}(\sqrt{s^2 - a^2} + \sqrt{\bar{z}^2 - a^2}) + S\right]\right\} +$$

$$iy\frac{(P+iQ)\sqrt{a^2-s^2}}{\pi}\left[\frac{1}{\sqrt{z^2-a^2}(z-s)}\right] \tag{12}$$

For notational convenience, we may rewrite (10), (11) and (12) briefly:

$$\left.\begin{aligned}\sigma_y - i\tau_{xy} &= G_1(P,Q,z,s)\\ \sigma_y+\sigma_x &= G_2(P,Q,z,s)\\ 2G(u_x+iu_y) &= G_3(P,Q,z,s)\end{aligned}\right\}$$

When arbitrary distributed fictitious forces are exerted on crack surface (Fig. 7), at the point $(\zeta,0)$ the concentrated forces are

$$P(\zeta)=F_n(\zeta)\mathrm{d}\zeta \qquad Q(\zeta)=F_s(\zeta)\mathrm{d}\zeta$$

The stresses and displacements integrated along the crack in local system take the forms:

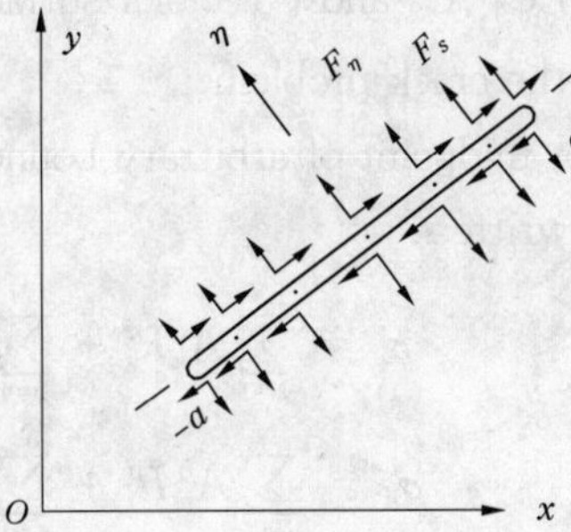

Fig. 7

$$\sigma_\eta - i\tau_{\zeta\eta} = \int_{-a}^{+a} G_1(F_n(\zeta)\mathrm{d}\zeta\cdot F_s(\zeta)\mathrm{d}\zeta\cdot\zeta+i\eta\cdot\zeta) \tag{13}$$

$$\sigma_\eta+\sigma_\zeta = \int_{-a}^{+a} G_2(F_n(\zeta)\mathrm{d}\zeta\cdot F_s(\zeta)\mathrm{d}\zeta\cdot\zeta+i\eta\cdot\zeta) \tag{14}$$

$$2G(u_\zeta+iu_\eta) = \int_{-a}^{+a} G_3(F_n(\zeta)\mathrm{d}\zeta\cdot F_s(\zeta)\mathrm{d}\zeta\cdot\zeta+i\eta\cdot\zeta) \tag{15}$$

Using Gauss integration formula:

$$\int_{-1}^{+1} f(x)\mathrm{d}x = \sum_{k=1}^{n}\lambda_k^{(n)} f(\xi_k^{(n)}) \tag{16}$$

where $\xi_k^{(n)}$ are the coordinates of Gauss points of order n; $\lambda_k^{(n)}$ are the corresponding Gauss weights.

and transforming the upper and lower limits of (13)~(15), we obtain:

$$\sigma_\eta - i\tau_{\zeta\eta} = a\sum_{k=1}^{n} G_1[F_n(a\xi_k^{(n)})\lambda_k^{(n)}\cdot F_s(a\xi_k^{(n)})\lambda_k^{(n)}\cdot\zeta+i\eta,\zeta] \tag{17}$$

$$\sigma_\eta+\sigma_\zeta = a\sum_{k=1}^{n} G_2[F_n(a\xi_k^{(n)})\lambda_k^{(n)}\cdot F_s(a\xi_k^{(n)})\lambda_k^{(n)}\cdot\zeta+i\eta,\zeta] \tag{18}$$

$$2G(u_\zeta+iu_\eta) = a\sum_{k=1}^{n} G_3[F_n(a\xi_k^{(n)})\lambda_k^{(n)}\cdot F_s(a\xi_k^{(n)})\lambda_k^{(n)}\cdot\zeta+i\eta,\zeta] \tag{19}$$

Now, we have expressed the displacements and stresses in local system as the functions of the distributed fictitious forces at Gauss points in the crack.

Using the coordinate transformation, we obtain the corresponding stress and displacement expressions in the ensemble coordinate system.

The distributed forces exerted on the crack surfaces give the effects to themselves, which can be obtained with the boundary equilibrium conditions.

$$\sigma_n(a\xi_k^{(n)}) = F_n(a\xi_k^{(n)}),\quad \sigma_s(a\xi_k^{(n)}) = F_s(a\xi_k^{(n)}) \tag{20}$$

The fictitious boundary forces method also gives us the stresses and displacements at crack-position C'_3 in Ω_1. Superposing two infinite plane Ω_1 and Ω_2, we obtain the stresses and displacements produced by both the fictitious unkown boundary forces and unkown cracksurface forces. If the superposed stresses or displacements satisfy the boundary conditions on C_1、C_2 and C_3(crack surface) we can say that the derived solution is the real solution of the crack problem.

For midpoint of arbitrary boundary element i, the stresses (σ) and displacements (u) can be written:

$$\sigma_s^i = \sum_{j=1}^{N} A_{ss}^{ij} P_s^j + \sum_{j=1}^{N} A_{sn}^{ij} P_n^j - \sum_{h=1}^{L} C_{ss}^{ih} F_s^h - \sum_{h=1}^{L} C_{sn}^{ih} F_n^h \tag{21}$$

$$\sigma_n^i = \sum_{j=1}^{N} A_{ns}^{ij} P_s^j + \sum_{j=1}^{N} A_{nn}^{ij} P_n^j - \sum_{h=1}^{L} C_{ns}^{ih} F_s^h - \sum_{h=1}^{L} C_{nn}^{ih} F_n^h \tag{22}$$

$$u_s^i = \sum_{j=1}^{N} B_{ss}^{ij} P_s^j + \sum_{j=1}^{N} B_{sn}^{ij} P_n^j - \sum_{h=1}^{L} D_{ss}^{ih} F_s^h - \sum_{h=1}^{L} D_{sn}^{ih} F_n^h \tag{23}$$

$$u_n^i = \sum_{j=1}^{N} B_{ss}^{ij} P_s^j + \sum_{j=1}^{N} B_{nn}^{ij} P_s^j - \sum_{h=1}^{L} D_{ns}^{ih} F_s^h - \sum_{h=1}^{L} D_{nn}^{ih} F_n^h \tag{24}$$

$$\sigma_s^h = \sum_{j=1}^{N} A_{ss}^{hj} P_s^j + \sum_{j=1}^{N} A_{sn}^{hj} P_n^j - F_s^h \tag{25}$$

$$\sigma_n^h = \sum_{j=1}^{N} A_{ns}^{hj} P_s^j + \sum_{j=1}^{N} A_{nn}^{hj} P_n^j - F_n^h \tag{26}$$

where A, C are stress-influence coefficients; B, D are diplacement-influence coefficients; P_n^j, P_s^j are fictitious forces exerted on boundary element j; F_n^h, F_s^h are fictitious forces exerted at Gauss point h in crack element; A_{sn}^{ij} means shear (s) stress in element i caused by unit normal (n) force on j element; C_{sn}^{ih} means shear (s) stress in boundary element i caussed by unit normal (n) force at Gauss point h in crack; N, L are the numbers of midpoint in boundary and Guass point in crack respectively.

For the crack of open type, the crack surface is free. (The stresses on crack-surface in Ω_2 and Ω_1 are same in magnitude and opposite in direction.) The stresses on the crack surface keep zero (or released completely).

$\sigma_s^h = 0$, $\sigma_n^h = 0$, $(h = 1, 2, \cdots, L)$ in Eqs. (25), (26)

4 Calculation of SIF

Since the fictitious unknown forces on crack surface are solved from illustrated equations. SIF of crack can easy be determined by stress relaxation of the crack, which gives the singular stress field beyond the crack tips. For example at $+a$:

$$K_{\mathrm{I}}^{+} - iK_{\mathrm{II}}^{+} = 2(2\pi)^{1/2} \lim_{z \to a} (z - a)^{1/2} \phi(z) = \left[\frac{a + s}{\pi a (a - s)}\right]^{1/2} (P - iQ) \tag{27}$$

Substituting $P(\zeta) = F_n(\zeta)\mathrm{d}\zeta$, $Q(\zeta) = F_s(\zeta)\mathrm{d}\zeta$, $s = \zeta$, and integrating Eq. (27) along the carck, we have:

$$K_{\mathrm{I}}^{+} - iK_{\mathrm{II}}^{+} = \int_{-a}^{a}\left[\frac{a+\zeta}{\pi a(a-\zeta)}\right]^{1/2}[F_n(\zeta) - F_s(\zeta)]\mathrm{d}\zeta \tag{28}$$

The more accurate Jacobi-chebyshev integration was used to calculate Eq. (28), which contains singular kernel $\sqrt{\frac{1+x}{1-x}}$, $(x\to 1)$.

5 Example of Single Crack Problem

Suppose that there is a rectangular plate with a center crack (Fig. 8), $b = 15.0$cm and $h = 12.0$cm. Uniformly distributed forces ($q = 100$kN) are exerted on side AB and side DC. The results for different crack length $2a = 4.5$cm and $2a = 6.0$cm are shown in Table 1. In this problem the Gauss integrating order is 7 and the numbers of the boundary elements are 26 and 40 respectively.

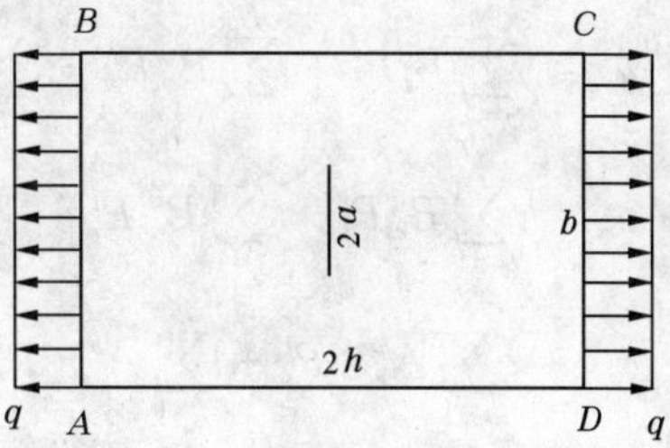

Fig. 8

For displacement boundary problem, we take the same structure for the example. The elastic modulus of the material is $E = 1\ 000.0$kN/cm^2 and the Poisson's ratio $\mu = 0.3$. Suppose that displacements on AB and CD are constant and $u_n = 0.5$cm, $u_s = 0$cm, the results are show in Table 2.

Table 1 The K_{I} for stress boundary problem ($K_{\mathrm{II}} = 0$) (unit: kN /cm$^{3/2}$)

Crack length	26 elemeats	40 elemeats	Boundary collocation[3]
4.5	269	270	276
6.0	324	326	337

Table 2 The K_{I} for mixed boundary problem ($K_{\mathrm{II}} = 0$) (unit: kN /cm$^{3/2}$)

Crack length	40 elemeats	Boundary collocation[3]
4.5	89	88
6.0	102	102

When the number of element is 40 and Gauss integration order is 7, the total unknowns in equations are $40\times 2 + 7\times 2 = 94$.

The error of the boundary collocation method results in Table 1 and Table 2 is about 1%[3].

6 The Solution of Multi-Crack Problem in Finite Domain with Mixed Boundary Conditions

The similar method can be used to derive the stresses and displacements in multi-crack body. Suppose that there is a finite domain A with M cracks C_3, C_4, $\cdots$, C_{M-2}. Correspondingly, let Ω_2 contain C_3, Ω_3 contain C_4, $\cdots$, Ω_{M+1} contain C_{M+2}, The M different arbitray fictitious crack forces are exerted on each crack surface. Using the coordinate transformations, and superposing the $M+1$ infinite planes $\Omega_1, \Omega_2, \cdots, \Omega_{M+1}$, we obtain at any point of boundaries and cracks the stresses and displacements caused by the fictitious boundary forces and M different arbitrary distributed fictitious crack forces. The superposing procedure can be expressed as follow:

$$\begin{aligned}
\sigma_s^i &= \sum_{j=1}^{N} A_{ss}^{ij} P_s^j + \sum_{j=1}^{N} A_{sn}^{ij} P_n^j - \sum_{k=1}^{M}\sum_{h=1}^{L} C_{ss}^{i,hk} F_s^{hk} - \sum_{k=1}^{M}\sum_{h=1}^{L} C_{sn}^{i,hk} F_n^{hk} \\
\sigma_n^i &= \sum_{j=1}^{N} A_{ns}^{ij} P_s^j + \sum_{j=1}^{N} A_{nn}^{ij} P_n^j - \sum_{k=1}^{M}\sum_{h=1}^{L} C_{ns}^{i,hk} F_s^{hk} - \sum_{k=1}^{M}\sum_{h=1}^{L} C_{nn}^{i,hk} F_n^{hk} \\
u_s^i &= \sum_{j=1}^{N} B_{ss}^{ij} P_s^j + \sum_{j=1}^{N} B_{sn}^{ij} P_n^j - \sum_{k=1}^{M}\sum_{h=1}^{L} D_{ss}^{i,hk} F_s^{hk} - \sum_{k=1}^{M}\sum_{h=1}^{L} D_{sn}^{i,hk} F_n^{hk} \\
u_n^i &= \sum_{j=1}^{N} B_{ns}^{ij} P_s^j + \sum_{j=1}^{N} B_{nn}^{ij} P_n^j - \sum_{k=1}^{M}\sum_{h=1}^{L} D_{ns}^{i,hk} F_s^{hk} - \sum_{k=1}^{M}\sum_{h=1}^{L} D_{nn}^{i,hk} F_n^{hk} \\
\sigma_s^{hm} &= \sum_{j=1}^{N} A_{ss}^{hm,j} P_s^j + \sum_{j=1}^{N} A_{sn}^{hm,j} P_n^j - F_s^{hm} - \sum_{k\neq m}^{M}\sum_{h=1}^{L} C_{ss}^{hm,hk} F_s^{hk} - \sum_{k\neq m}^{M}\sum_{h=1}^{L} C_{sn}^{hm,hk} F_n^{hk} \\
\sigma_n^{hm} &= \sum_{j=1}^{N} A_{ns}^{hm,j} P_s^j + \sum_{j=1}^{N} A_{nn}^{hm,j} P_n^j - F_n^{hm} - \sum_{k\neq m}^{M}\sum_{h=1}^{L} C_{ns}^{hm,hk} F_s^{hk} - \sum_{k\neq m}^{M}\sum_{h=1}^{L} C_{nn}^{hm,hk} F_n^{hk} \qquad (29)
\end{aligned}$$

where M is number of cracks; m is the numeral order of cracks; hk or hm is the hth Gauss point on k or m crack surface.

The SIF at the every tips of the cracks can be similarly calculated by stress-relaxation of solved forces on the corresponding crack face. For SIF at kth crack, we use F_s^{hk}, F_n^{hk} which act on the crack surface in Ω_{k+1} infinite plane.

7 Numerical Examples for Multi-Crack Porblem

Example 1: Two uniform distributed normal forces are exerted on the left and right of a plate respectively, and the other two sides of the plate are free (Fig. 9). Two cases, the plate with 3 cracks and 5 cracks are discussed, 26 boundary elements and 7-order Gauss integration are use. The SIFs are shown in Table 3.

Table 3 Comparison of K_{I} value with reference [4]

Crack	3 cracks The method	[4]	5 cracks The method	[4]
AB			289	281
CD	264	258	194	200
EF	196	204	185	190
GH	264	258	194	200
IJ			289	281

Example 2: A finite plate contains two non-parallel cracks. The left and right of the plate are loaded with two uniform distributed normal forces (Fig. 10). The SIFs. are shown in Table 4.

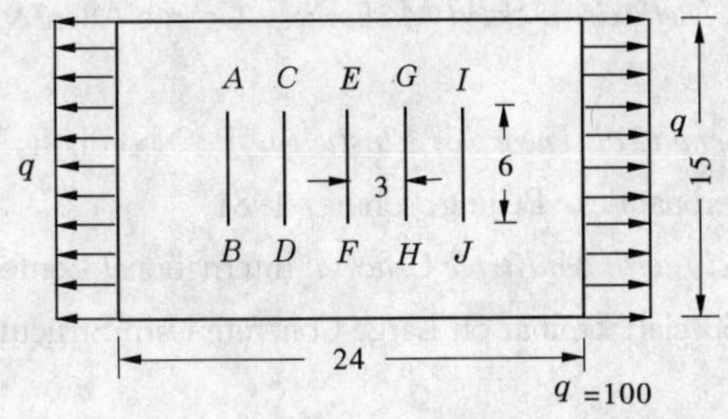

Fig. 9

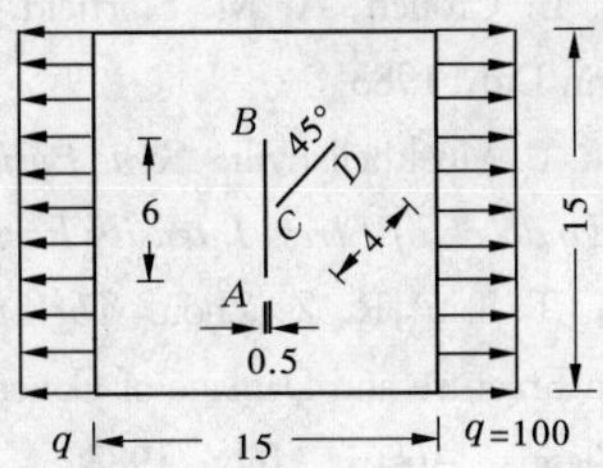

Fig. 10

Table 4 K_{I} and K_{II} at each crack tip

Point number	A	B	C	D
K_{I}	402	306	102	222
K_{II}	7.79	−8.99	87.7	−147

In the case of parallel cracks problem in example 1, the same regularity of SIF is given. The values of SIF. at outer cracks are greater than that at central cracks, since the existance of outer cracks induces a reduction to the released quantities of the central cracks.

From example 2, the existance of crack *AB* greatly reduces the value of K_{I} and K_{II} of crack *CD* at the tip *C*, which is near by the center of crack *AB*. From the point of view of released stress(table 5), there are quite different pattern of stress-releasing in both sides of Gauss point 4 on crack *AB*. The released value have an extreme value near point *C*.

Table 5 Released stress at Gauss points

Gauss	points	1	2	3	4	5	6	7
AB	F_n	126.9	133.1	147.9	184.3	67.81	78.18	91.62
	F_s	−0.44	−0.71	−2.74	31.08	9.31	−11.69	−16.13
CD	F_n	11.07	24.13	49.25	81.62	97.59	98.99	96.91
	F_s	−14.75	−45.60	−41.14	−47.11	−58.49	−64.42	−65.55

For crack *CD*, the normal released value increases gradually from point *C* to point *D*, the influence of crack *AB* to the tip *D* is comparatively weaker.

The method developed in present paper can be used to solve the multicrack problem in finite plate with complex boundary conditions conveniently, and give out the stress displacement fields in the domain, and SIF at the crack tips. The interference among the cracks and the various boundaries are taken into account. A few number of elements can give out the numerical results of good accuracy. The engineering requirement can be met satisfactrily using the micro-computer.

References

[1] S. L. Crouch, A. M. Starfield. *Boundary Element Methods in Solid Mechanics*. George Allen & Unwin Ltd, 1983

[2] N. I. Muskhelishvili. *Some Basic Problems of Mathematical Theory of Elasticity*. P. Noordhoff, 1953

[3] *Handbook of Stress Intensity Factors*. Institute of Aeronautics. Beijing, China. 1981

[4] G. T. Liu ,R. Z. Zhou. *The Strength of Finite Body with Mulitiple Cracks*. International Conference on Fracture and Damage of Concrete and Rock and Special Seminar on Large Conerete Dam Structure on Vienna. Austria. July, 1988

STUDY ON THE CURVED AND BRANCH CRACKS IN MASSIVE CONCRETE STRUCTURES

Abstract For engineering purpose an improved analytic-numerical method for determining the strength of the finite body with curved and branch cracks is proposed in present paper by introducing singular element of high order displacement function near the crack tip into the second kind of boundary integral equation. Therefore, the disadvantages of dividing region with increasing large amount of element nodes in the ordinary boundary element method disappear. The prescribed method shows an easier and more efficient way for the strength and safety analyses of structures containing complicated cracks, and with greatly reducing of computer time.

Three simple examples are illustrated and compared with known analytical solution. They are in good agreement. The maximum deviation of results is less than 2%. The present method has an evident advantage in solving problems of complicated engineering region with curved or branch cracks.

1 Introduction

Various shapes of cracks (including curved and branch cracks) usually happen in Concrete Structures. Since most of them are under complex stress conditions (normal and shear stress). The typical analytical solution for crack surface load in infinity given by Muskhelishvili is suitable for straight fracture only. For Ordinary Boundary Element Method, Kelvin's solution has been used as a foundamental solution for the crack problem[1], by which the body is divided into subdomains consisting all the cracks surface as its boundaries and thus evidently increased the numbers of boundary elements and computing time, especially for the crack-group problems.

Following the idea of discontinuous displacement presented by Crouch[2], G. T. Liu and C. X. Lin[3] also gave the solution of second kind boundary integral equation. The stress and displacement field were obtained by point discontinuous displacement method, which reduces the number of elements for the avoidance of dividing into subdomains. It was used in solving multiple cracks problem successfully.

In present paper the former mentioned principle[3] is developed for the curved and branch crack analysis in finite region. The indirect boundary element method is used with high order singular element at crack tip. Numerical examples are illustrated for comparing

本文选自《Proceedings from the lnternational Conference on Daml Fracture》, Boulder, Colorado, USA. Sep. 11~13, 1991, 作者还有 Lin Guoyu。

with the known results and also for the investigation of complicated crack (such as curved, branch crack) in engineering practice. Results of high precision and evident reduction of computing time is confirmed.

2 Fundamental Solution

Considering a crack in plane with coordinate $x_1 x_2$ (Fig. 1), the crack length is $2a$ with upper surface of crack $x_2 = 0^+$ and lower surface of crack $x_2 = 0^-$, discontinuous displacement $D_i\ (i = 1,2)$ is defined as shear and normal displacement differences of crack surfaces, that is

$$D_1 = u_1(x, 0^-) - u_1(x, 0^+)$$
$$D_2 = u_2(x, 0^-) - u_2(x, 0^+)$$

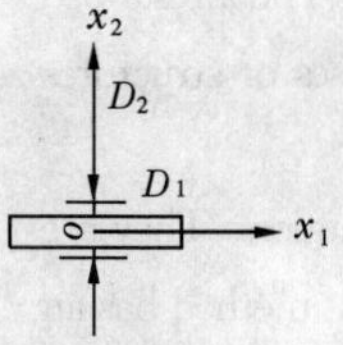

Fig. 1

Let $D_1 2a = 1$, $D_2 2a = 1$ and $a \to 0$, we have the stress and displacement field (fundamental solution) under point discontinuous displacement.

(1) Stresses and displacement field induced by normal discontinuous displacement

$$\left.\begin{aligned}
u_1^2 &= \frac{x_1}{4\pi(1-\upsilon)}\left[\frac{1-2\upsilon}{x_1^2+x_2^2} - \frac{2x_2^2}{(x_1^2+x_2^2)^2}\right] \\
u_2^2 &= \frac{x_2}{4\pi(1-\upsilon)}\left[-\frac{2(1-\upsilon)}{x_1^2+x_2^2} + \frac{x_1^2-x_2^2}{(x_1^2+x_2^2)^2}\right] \\
\sigma_{11}^2 &= \frac{2G}{4\pi(1-\upsilon)}\left[-\frac{x_1^2-x_2^2}{(x_1^2+x_2^2)^2} + \frac{2x_2^2(3x_1^2-x_2^2)}{(x_1^2+x_2^2)^3}\right] \\
\sigma_{22}^2 &= \frac{2G}{4\pi(1-\upsilon)}\left[-\frac{x_1^2-x_2^2}{(x_1^2+x_2^2)^2} - \frac{2x_2^2(3x_1^2-x_2^2)}{(x_1^2+x_2^2)^3}\right] \\
\sigma_{12}^2 &= \frac{2G}{4\pi(1-\upsilon)}\left[-\frac{x_1 x_2}{(x_1^2+x_2^2)^2}\right]
\end{aligned}\right\} \quad (1)$$

(2) Stresses and displacement field induced by shear discontinuous displacement

$$\left.\begin{aligned}
u_1^1 &= \frac{x_2}{4\pi(1\ \upsilon)}\left[-\frac{2(1-\upsilon)}{x_1^2+x_2^2} - \frac{x_1^2-x_2^2}{(x_1^2+x_2^2)^2}\right] \\
u_2^1 &= \frac{x_1}{4\pi(1-\upsilon)}\left[-\frac{(1-2\upsilon)}{x_1^2+x_2^2} - \frac{2x_2^2}{(x_1^2+x_2^2)^2}\right] \\
\sigma_{11}^1 &= \frac{2G}{4\pi(1-\upsilon)}\frac{6x_1^2x_2^2}{(x_1^2+x_2^2)^2} \\
\sigma_{22}^1 &= \frac{2G}{4\pi(1-\upsilon)}\left[-\frac{2x_1^2x_2^2}{(x_1^2+x_2^2)^2}\right] \\
\sigma_{12}^1 &= \frac{2G}{4\pi(1-\upsilon)}\left[-\frac{x_1^2-x_2^2}{(x_1^2+x_2^2)^2} - \frac{2x_2^2(3x_1^2-x_2^2)}{(x_1^2+x_2^2)^2}\right]
\end{aligned}\right\} \quad (2)$$

where υ is Poisson's ratio; G is shear elastic modulus u_i^k is displacement of point (x_1, x_2) in ith direction caused by the point discontinuous displacement in kth direction; σ_{ij}^k is the stress component of point (x_1, x_2) caused by point discontinuous in kth direction at original point.

3 The Second Kind(Indirect)Boundary Integral Equation

Suppose that S is an elastic region bounded by Boundary $\Gamma(\Gamma=\Gamma_t+\Gamma_u+\Gamma_c)$. Γ_t, Γ_u, Γ_c are mixed boundary conditions with forces and displacements loading on the outer boundary and crack surfaces respectively (Fig. 2). Consider S as a part of infinite elastic plane and assume that $D_i(Q)$ are components of applied discontinuous displacement in Γ, where Q is an arbitrary point on Γ. Based on the principle of superposition and the fundamental solution of Eq. (1) - (2) and in the case of absence body force, the displacement and stress of point M in the domain are

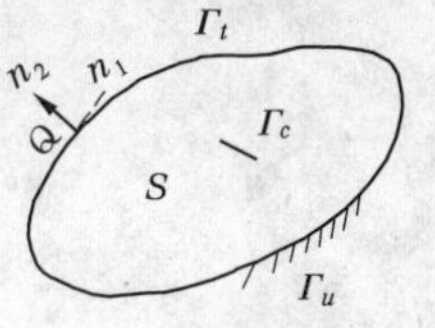

Fig. 2

$$u_s(M) = \int_\Gamma u_i^k(M,Q)D_k(Q)\mathrm{d}\Gamma(Q)$$

$$\sigma_{ij}(M) = \int_\Gamma B_{ij}^k(M,Q)D_k(Q)\mathrm{d}\Gamma(Q) \qquad (3)$$

where: $u_i^k(M,Q)$ and $B_{ij}^k(M,Q)$ are the components of displacement and stress of point M caused by unit discontinuous displacement in kth direction at point Q, respectively; $D_k(Q)$ is the distributing function of discontinuous displacement. The boundary conditions are

$$u_i|_{Q\in\Gamma_u} = \overline{u}_i(Q), \qquad t_i|_{Q\in\Gamma_t} = \overline{t}_i^t(Q), \qquad t_i|_{Q\in\Gamma_c} = t_i^c(Q) \qquad (4)$$

where, $\overline{u}_i(Q)$ are the components of displacement on the boundary Γ_u; $\overline{t}_i^t(Q)$, $\overline{t}_i^c(Q)$ are components of forces acting on the boundary Γ_t and Γ_c, respectively.

Suppose that P is an arbitrary segments or point on Γ, in Eqs. (3), when $M \to P$, we obtain boundary integral equation of second kind (indirect method):

$$\overline{u}_i(P) = \int_\Gamma u_i^k(P,Q)\, D_k(Q)\, d\Gamma(Q) + C_{ik}(P)\delta_{ik}D_k(P)$$

$$\overline{t}_i(P) = \int_\Gamma T_i^k(P,Q)\, D_k(Q)\, \mathrm{d}\Gamma(Q) \qquad (5)$$

where, $T_i^k(P,Q)$ is the ith component of traction at point P caused by point discontinuous displacement in kth direction at point Q. For smooth boundary point P, $C_{ik}(P)=0.5$, δ is Derac δ function.

4 Special Element Formulation

In order to give an more accurately model of the singular behaviour near the crack tip, discontinuous displacement D_j in the jth direction of the elements adjacent to the crack tip can be represented by

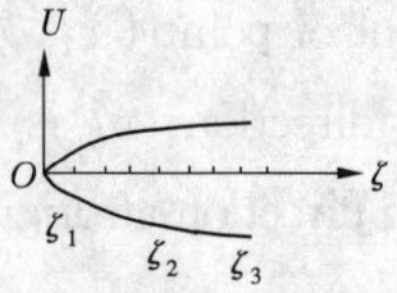

Fig. 3

$$D_j = \sum_{i=1}^{n} N_i D_j^i \qquad (i = 1,2,\cdots,n; j = 1,2) \tag{6}$$

where:

$$N_i = \Big(\prod_{\substack{k=1\\k\neq i}}^{n} \frac{\zeta - \zeta_k}{\zeta_i - \zeta_k}\Big)\sqrt{\frac{\zeta}{\zeta_i}}$$

O in Fig. 3 is crack tip and ζ is the distance from arbitrary point to crack tip. In the case of $n=2$,

$$N_1 = \frac{(\zeta - \zeta_3)}{(\zeta_1 - \zeta_2)}\sqrt{\frac{\zeta}{\zeta_1}}$$

$$N_2 = \frac{(\zeta - \zeta_1)}{(\zeta_2 - \zeta_1)}\sqrt{\frac{\zeta}{\zeta_2}}$$

In the case of $n=3$,

$$N_1 = \frac{(\zeta - \zeta_2)(\zeta - \zeta_3)}{(\zeta_1 - \zeta_2)(\zeta_1 - \zeta_3)}\sqrt{\frac{\zeta}{\zeta_1}}$$

$$N_2 = \frac{(\zeta - \zeta_1)(\zeta - \zeta_3)}{(\zeta_2 - \zeta_1)(\zeta_2 - \zeta_3)}\sqrt{\frac{\zeta}{\zeta_2}}$$

$$N_3 = \frac{(\zeta - \zeta_1)(\zeta - \zeta_2)}{(\zeta_3 - \zeta_1)(\zeta_3 - \zeta_2)}\sqrt{\frac{\zeta}{\zeta_3}}$$

5 Stress Intensity Factor

The stress intensity factor can be written as:

$$K_{\mathrm{I}} = \lim_{\zeta\to 0} \frac{\sqrt{2\pi}G}{4(1-\upsilon)} \frac{D_2(\zeta)}{\sqrt{\zeta}}$$

$$K_{\mathrm{II}} = \lim_{\zeta\to 0} \frac{\sqrt{2\pi}G}{4(1-\upsilon)} \frac{D_1(\zeta)}{\sqrt{\zeta}} \tag{7}$$

where, $D_2(\zeta)$ and $D_1(\zeta)$ denote normal and shear discontlnuous displacements respectively.

Substitute the above expression of D into Eqs. (7). In the case of $n=2$, we have

$$K_{\mathrm{I}} = \frac{\sqrt{2\pi}G}{4(1-\upsilon)} \frac{\zeta_1\zeta_2}{\zeta_1 - \zeta_2}(\zeta_2^{-3/2}D_2^2 - \zeta_1^{-3/2}D_2^1)$$

$$K_{\mathrm{II}} = \frac{\sqrt{2\pi}G}{4(1-\upsilon)} \frac{\zeta_1\zeta_2}{\zeta_1 - \zeta_2}(\zeta_2^{-3/2}D_1^2 - \zeta_1^{-3/2}D_1^1)$$

D_j^1 and D_j^2 are the jth component of the first and second element adjacement to crack tip. Similarly, we can easily write the formulation of stress intensity factor in $n=3$ case.

6 Numerical Examples

6.1 Simple Circular Arc Crack Problem in an Infinite Plate (Fig. 4)

In this example an infinite plate with an arc crack under biaxial uniform tension was analyzed by present method. A series of analysis were performed with changing the arc angle α. The stress intensity factors K_{I} and K_{II} obtained from the present analysis were rewritten as $F_{\mathrm{I}}=K_{\mathrm{I}}/\sigma\sqrt{\pi c}$ and $F_{\mathrm{II}}=K_{\mathrm{II}}/\sigma\sqrt{\pi c}$. In Fig. 5, the calculated results are compared with the analytical solution. They are in good agreement. The computing time on microcomputer were less than 1 min for each case of arc crack.

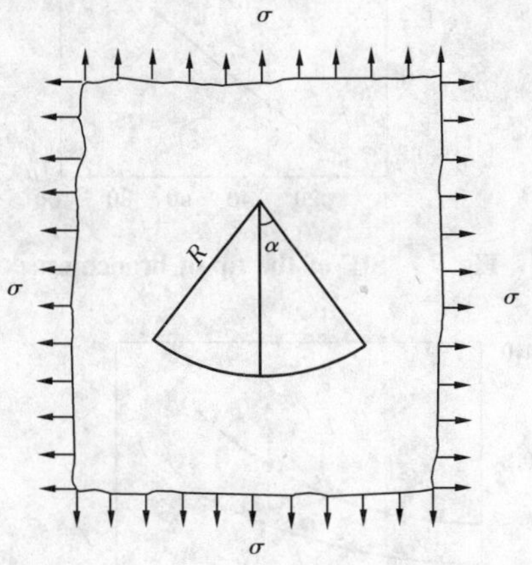

Fig. 4

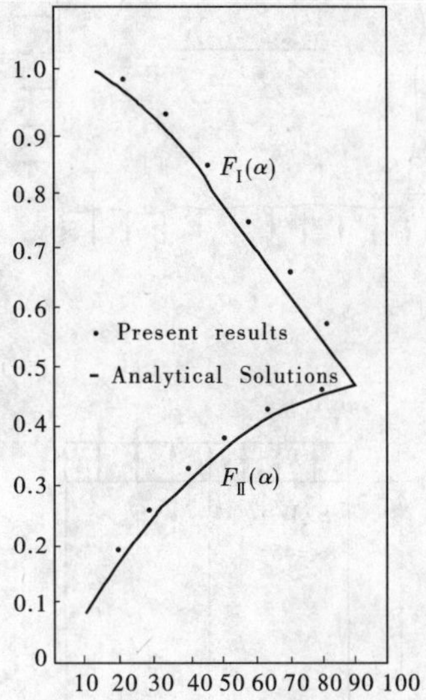

Fig. 5 **SIF of the tip of branch crack**

6.2 A Forked Crack with Three Branches (Fig. 6)

The problem of the forked crack with three branches in an infinite plate is considered in this example. The plate is loaded under biaxial uniform tension $\sigma_{xx}^{\infty}=\sigma_{yy}^{\infty}=\sigma$, $\sigma_{xy}^{\infty}=0$ and $b/a=0.5$ angle α changes between 0° and 90°, the calculated SIF values at two crack tips A and B are expresses as

$$K_{\mathrm{I}}^{A}=F_{\mathrm{I}}^{A}(\alpha)\sigma(\pi a)^{1/2}$$
$$K_{\mathrm{I}}^{B}=F_{\mathrm{I}}^{B}(\alpha)\sigma(\pi a)^{1/2}$$
$$K_{\mathrm{II}}^{B}=F_{\mathrm{II}}^{B}(\alpha)\sigma(\pi a)^{1/2}$$

$F_{\mathrm{I}}^{A}(\alpha)$, $F_{\mathrm{I}}^{B}(\alpha)$ and $F_{\mathrm{II}}^{B}(\alpha)$ values are shown in Fig 7. In these simple cases the deviations between results of present method and that given by Y. K. chaung[4] are negligible.

6.3 A Center Arc Crack in Finite Plate

A center arc crack in a rectangular plate under uniform tensile stress σ is shown in Fig. 8, where R and 2α denote the radius and open angle of arc crack respectively, results are shown in Fig. 9 for $\alpha=\pi/4(45°)$ and $H/W=2$ with various R/W from 0.1~0.8. The SIF is normalized by following expression.

The results of this simple case are in good agreement with the analysis given from the combination of BEM and FEM by Dr. Miyazaki[5] etc.

The proposed method in present paper is suitable for the analysis of the multiple cracks

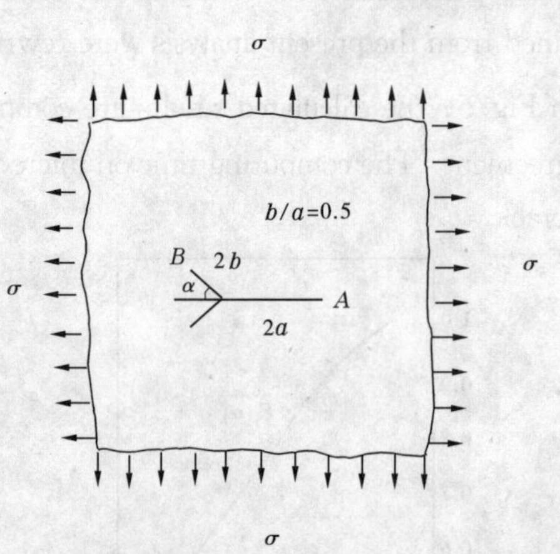

Fig. 6

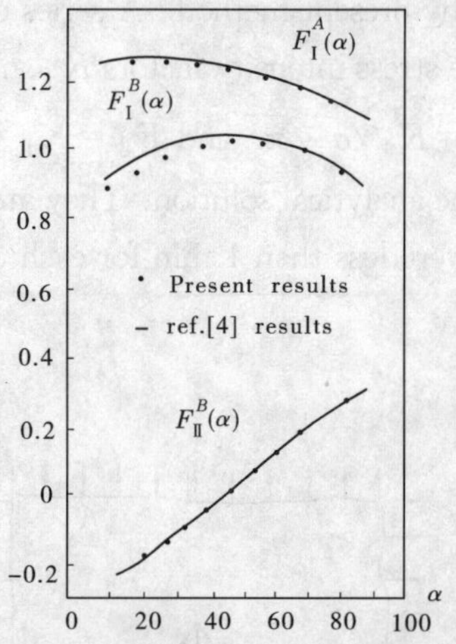

Fig. 7　SIF of the tip of branch cracks

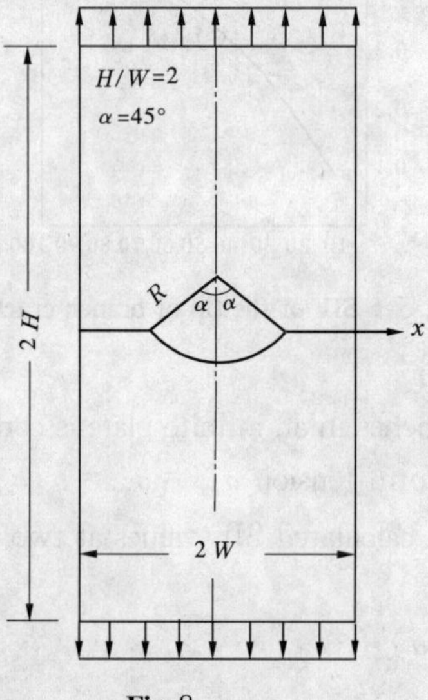

Fig. 8

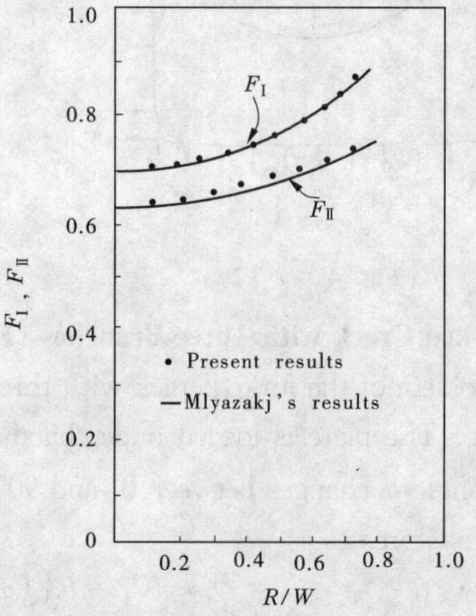

Fig. 9　SIF of arc crack in finite body

in complicated boundary conditions with high precision and reduction of computing time.

$$F_{\mathrm{I}} = K_{\mathrm{I}} / \frac{\sigma \sqrt{\pi R} \sin\alpha}{1 + \sin^2 \alpha /2}$$

$$F_{\mathrm{II}} = K_{\mathrm{II}} / \frac{\sigma \sqrt{\pi R} \sin\alpha}{1 + \sin^2 \alpha /2}$$

7 Conclusion

(1) Curved and branch cracks were usually occured in massive concrete of hydraulic structures (such as concrete dam) under complicated stress (normal and shear stress) conditions. In order to estimate the stability of crack and safety of structures, the boundary integral equation of second kind (indirect method) together with the special element adjacent to

crack tip are introduced in the present paper. It has been successfully and effectively used in fracture analysis of complicated shape crack in infinite or finite body.

(2) The numerical practices show that the proposed method has the advantages of economic computing time and fewer data of preparation in comparing with finite element method and ordinary boundary element method, especially in the case of multiple complicated in shape cracks.

(3) Compared the present results with the convincible analytical solutions or numerical solutions of high precision in simple condition, we can easily come to the conclusion that the present method has a good precision which is enough to meet the engineering requirment.

References

[1] T. A. *Cruse. 2 and 3-D problems of fracture mechanics*. In Development in BEM—1(1979), 79~119

[2] S. L. Crouch. *Solution of plane elasticity problems by the displacement discontinuity method*. Int. Journal. of Num. Meth. Eng., Vol. 10, 301~363, 1976

[3] G. T. Liu, C. X. Lin. *The second kind of boundary integral equation-Boundary element method of elastic problems with its 2-D fundamental solution*. Journal of Tsinghua Univ., Vol. 28, No. 2. 1988. (Report on the 4 - th conf. of Hydraulic Eng. society of China 1986)

[4] Y. K. Chaung etc.. *Solutions of branch crack problems in plane elasticity by using a new integral equation approach*. Eng. Fract. Mech., Vol. 28, N. L, 31~41, 1987

[5] N. Miyazaki etc.. *Stress intensity factor analysis by combination of boundary element and finite element methods*. Eng. Fracture Mech., Vol. 36, No. 1 61~67, 1990

STUDY ON BOUNDARY MULTIPLE CRACK AND THE STABILITY OF HORIZONTAL CRACKS IN CONCRETE CRAVITY DAM

Abstract The observation data show that most of the cracks in massive concrete start from the boundaries of the structures, and propagate after operation. In present paper the analytical solutions for the concentrated loads acting on the surfaces of the semi-infinite fracture in infinite region were used together with boundary fictitious force method. The analytic-nu-merical method considering the influence among the boundaries and crack tips was given for solving the boundary multi-crack problem. It is suitable for various boundary supporting conditions with high precision and reduction of computing time. For illustration, the state of horizontal cracks located near the upstream and downstream regions of the gravity dam were studied with complicate stress conditions: tension-shear, or compression-shear and hydraulic pressure in cracks.

1 Introduction

Cracks often occur in massive concrete of the hydraulic structures during its construction. Statistical data showed that in some cases the number of cracks in one dam can reach several hundreds. In order to keep the rigidity and safety of the structure the restoration is required. The restoration process is usually expensive and takes long time. It is neccesary to analyse the stabilities of the cracks and to distinguish which one would propagate and bring damage to the structure under loading.

One of the most common cracks and defects in concrete dam is the horizontal cracks between concrete layers. This paper presents an analytical-numeric method (ANM) for solving boundary multi-crack problems. The Boundary Fitted (colocated) Method (BFM) is mainly effective for single crack. The FEM., even with singular elements, will not be suitable to the multiple cracks located colse to each other and surrounded with unsymmetric stress-field beyond the crack tips, the computing time for FEM, greatly increases in the case of crack groups, which leads to a great difficulty in practice.

2 Analytical-Numeric Method (ANM) for Boundary Multi-Crack

Assume an arbitrary finite region A which consists of displacement boundary C_1 and stress boundary C_2. Cracks C_3 and C_4 intersect the boundary (See Fig. 1). This problem can be solved through the following procedure:

Let infinite region Ω_1 have the same physical properties as region A. The region sur-

本文选自《Proceedings from the International conference on Dam Fracture》, Boulder, Colorado, USA. Sep. 11～13, 1991, 作者还有 Lin Guoyu。

rounded by the imaginary line is assumed to be an equivelant of region A (See Fig. 2). Apply a fictitious force distribution P_n and P_s to the imaginary boundary. Let $z(\zeta,\eta)$ be an arbitrary point in ζ, η local coordinates of infinity as showing in Fig. 3, then $F_\zeta = P_\zeta \,\mathrm{d}\zeta$ and $F_\eta = P_\eta \,\mathrm{d}\zeta$.

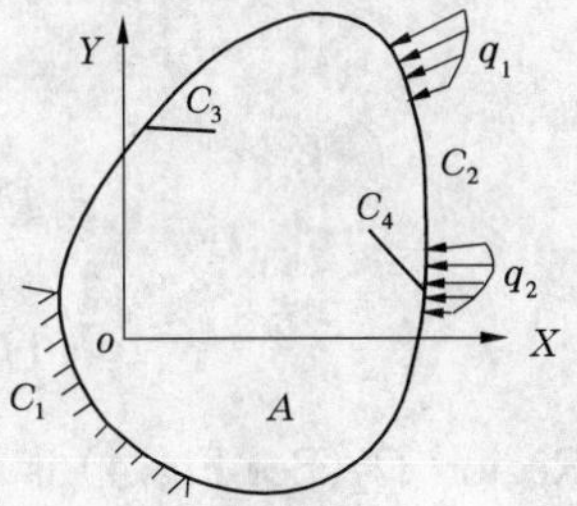

Fig. 1

Consequently the stress field and displacement field is obtained by integrating the Kelvin solution[1,2]:

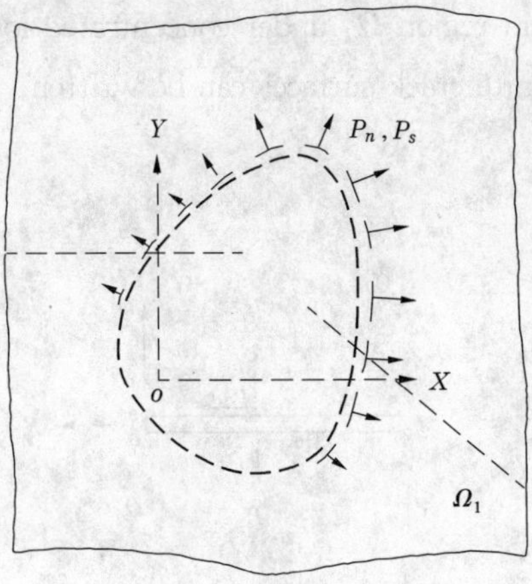

Fig. 2

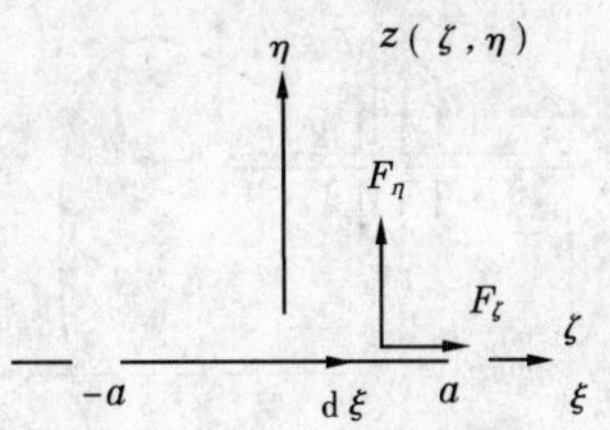

Fig. 3

$$U_\zeta = \frac{P_\zeta}{2G}[(3-4\upsilon)f + \eta f'_{\eta}] + \frac{P_\eta}{2G}[-\eta f'_{\zeta}]$$

$$U_\eta = \frac{P_\eta}{2G}[(3-4\upsilon)f - \eta f'_{\eta}] + \frac{P_\zeta}{2G}[-\eta f'_{\zeta}] \tag{1}$$

$$\sigma_\zeta = P_\zeta[(3-2\upsilon)f'_{\zeta} + \eta f'_{\zeta\eta}] + P_\eta[2\upsilon f'_{\eta} + \eta f'_{\eta\eta}]$$

$$\sigma_\eta = P_\zeta[-(1-2\upsilon)f'_{\zeta} - \eta f'_{\zeta\eta}] + P_\eta[2(1-\upsilon)f'_{\eta} - \eta f'_{\eta\eta}]$$

$$\tau_{\zeta\eta} = P_\zeta[2(1-\upsilon)f'_{\eta} + \eta f'_{\eta\eta}] + P_\eta[(1-2\upsilon)f'_{\zeta} - \eta f'_{\zeta\eta}] \tag{2}$$

where υ is Poisson ratio; G is shearing modulus; f'_{ζ} and $f'_{\zeta\eta}$ represent the partial derivatives with respect to ζ and ζ,η respectively.

$$f = \int_{-a}^{a} g(\zeta-\xi,\eta)\,\mathrm{d}\xi \qquad \left(g = -\frac{1}{4\pi(1-\upsilon)}\ln(\zeta^2+\eta^2)^{\frac{1}{2}}\right)$$

$$= \frac{1}{4\pi(1-\upsilon)}\left[\eta\left(\arctan\frac{\eta}{\zeta-a} - \arctan\frac{\eta}{\zeta+a}\right) - (\zeta-a)\ln\sqrt{(\zeta-a)^2+\eta^2} + (\zeta+a)\ln\sqrt{(\zeta+a)^2+\eta^2} + \frac{a}{2\pi(1-\upsilon)}\right.$$

The effect of the fictitious force of the element to itself $\zeta=0$ and $\eta \to 0^-$ can be written as:

$$\sigma_s^i = \frac{1}{2}P_s^i$$

$$\sigma_n^i = \frac{1}{2} P_n^i \tag{3}$$

$$U_s^i = -\frac{(3-4\upsilon)}{4\pi G(1-\upsilon)} a^i \ln a^i \cdot P_s^i$$

$$U_n^i = -\frac{(3-4\upsilon)}{4\pi G(1-\upsilon)} a^i \ln a^i \cdot P_n^i \tag{4}$$

Region Ω_2 (See Fig.4) is an infinite region with same physical property as region A. A semi-infinite crack from $x=-\infty$ to $x=0$ in local coordinate x_3, y_3 exists in region Ω_2. The end of crack coincides with crack C_3. The above problem can be simplified as shown in Fig. 5. The distributions of the stress and displacement in region Ω_2 under concentrated load P and Q acting on the arbitrary points $-s$ of semi-infinite crack surfaces can be written:

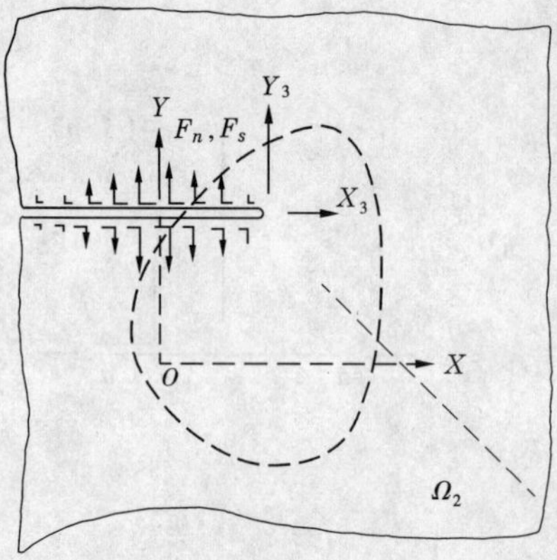

Fig. 4

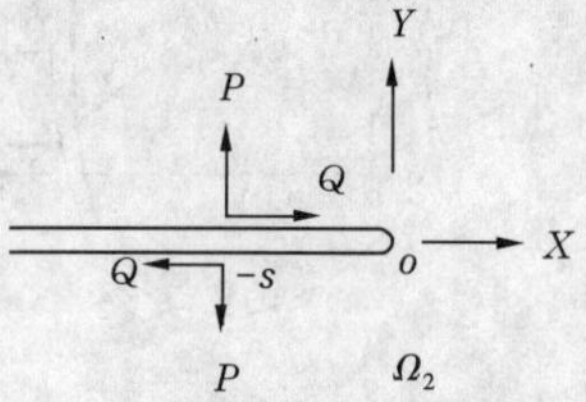

Fig. 5

$$\sigma_y + \sigma_x = 2\mathrm{Re}\left[\frac{(P-iQ)\sqrt{s}}{\pi} \cdot \frac{1}{\sqrt{Z}(Z+s)}\right]$$

$$\sigma_y - i\tau_{xy} = \frac{(P-iQ)\sqrt{s}}{\pi}\mathrm{Re}\left[\frac{1}{\sqrt{Z}(Z+s)}\right] - \frac{(P+iQ)\sqrt{s}}{\pi} iy\left[\frac{s+3Z}{2(Z+s)^2 Z^{\frac{3}{2}}}\right] \tag{5}$$

$$2G(U_x + iU_y) = \frac{(P-iQ)}{2\pi i}\left\{-(3-4\upsilon)\ln\frac{Z-b+2i\sqrt{bZ}}{Z+b} + \ln\frac{\overline{Z}-b+2i\sqrt{b\overline{Z}}}{\overline{Z}+b}\right\} - iy\frac{(P+iQ)\sqrt{s}}{\pi}\left[\overline{\frac{1}{\sqrt{Z}(Z+s)}}\right] \tag{6}$$

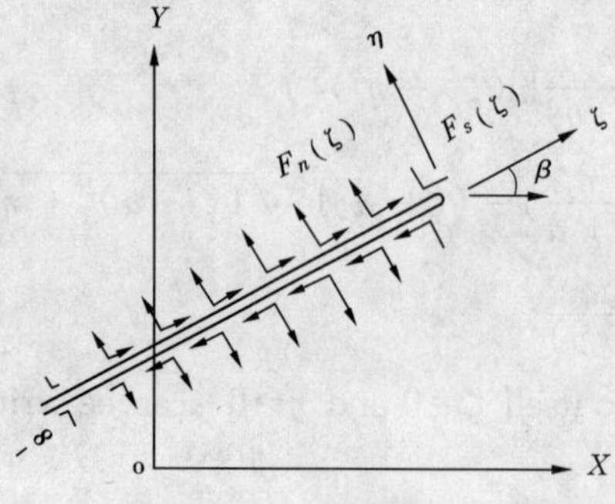

Fig. 6

where $z = x + iy$; G represents the shearing modulus and υ is Poisson Ratio.

Consider that $P(\zeta) = F_n(\zeta)\mathrm{d}\zeta$ and $Q(\zeta) = F_s(\zeta)\mathrm{d}\zeta$ (Fig.6). Where F_n and F_s are the forces distributed on the surface of the semi-infinite crack with one end coincided with crack C_3. The distributions of stress end displcement in local coordinate within region Ω_2 (including the locations of Boundary A and Semi-infinite crack C_4) under F_n, F_s can be obtained by integrating over the semi-infinite crack C_3.

Hence:

$$\sigma_\eta + \sigma_\zeta = \int_{-\infty}^{0} G_1[F_n(\zeta)d\zeta, F_s(\zeta)d\zeta, \zeta + i\eta, \zeta] \tag{7}$$

$$\sigma_\eta - i\tau_{\zeta\eta} = \int_{-\infty}^{0} G_2[F_n(\zeta)d\zeta, F_s(\zeta)d\zeta, \zeta + i\eta, \zeta] \tag{8}$$

$$2G(U_\zeta + iU_\eta) = \int_{-\infty}^{0} G_3[F_n(\zeta)d\zeta, F_s(\zeta)d\zeta, \zeta + i\eta, \zeta] \tag{9}$$

If the fictitious distribution forces on C_3 crack surfaces satisfy:

$$F_n(\zeta) = 0, \qquad F_s(\zeta) = 0 \qquad (-\infty < \zeta < -b,\ b > 0)$$

formulae(7),(8),(9) can be written in Gauss integration form:

$$\sigma_\eta + \sigma_\zeta = \frac{b}{2}\sum_{K=1}^{n} G_1\{F_n[\frac{b}{2}(\xi_K^{(n)} - 1)] \cdot \lambda_K^{(n)}, F_s[\frac{b}{2}(\xi_K^{(n)} - 1)] \cdot \lambda_K^{(n)}, \zeta + i\eta, \zeta\} \tag{10}$$

$$\sigma_\eta - i\tau_{\zeta\eta} = \frac{b}{2}\sum_{K=1}^{n} G_2\{F_n[\frac{b}{2}(\xi_K^{(n)} - 1)] \cdot \lambda_K^{(n)}, F_s[\frac{b}{2}(\xi_K^{(n)} - 1)] \cdot \lambda_K^{(n)}, \zeta + i\eta, \zeta\} \tag{11}$$

$$2G(U_\zeta + iU_\eta) = \frac{b}{2}\sum_{K=1}^{n} G_3\{F_n[\frac{b}{2}(\xi_K^{(n)} - 1)] \cdot \lambda_K^{(n)}, F_s[\frac{b}{2}(\xi_K^{(n)} - 1)] \cdot \lambda_K^{(n)}, \zeta + i\eta, \zeta\} \tag{12}$$

where $\xi_K^{(n)}$ is the coordinate of Gaussian point $\xi_K^{(n)} \in [-1, 1]$ in nth order Gauss integration; $\lambda_K^{(n)}$ is the weight of Gauss integration.

Noticing that the forces applied to the crack surfaces are distributive forces, the stress of the Gauss point on the crack surfaces can be obtained from the boundary equilibrium conditions.

$$\sigma_s[\frac{b}{2}(\xi_K^{(n)} - 1)] = F_s[\frac{b}{2}(\xi_K^{(n)} - 1)] \tag{13}$$

$$\sigma_n[\frac{b}{2}(\xi_K^{(n)} - 1)] = F_n[\frac{b}{2}(\xi_K^{(n)} - 1)] \tag{14}$$

The distributions of stress and displacement (discribed by a function of ficticious force) along the location of boundary A and the semi-infinite crack C_3 induced by fictitious distributive force F_n, F_s applied to the semi-infinite crack whose one end coincides with C_4 in region Ω_3(Fig. 7) can be derived by the same procedure as above.

Assume the cracks C_3, C_4 grow infinitely along the imaginary lines in Ω_1 respectively (Fig. 2) and keep constant the forces existing on the cutting surfaces of the cracks. Hence the stress and displacement in the other part of region Ω_1 remain unchanged. A distributive force which keeps the stress field and displacement field unchanged exists on the surfaces of the cracks. Quite similar, in region Ω_2, crack grows infinitely along the imaginary line

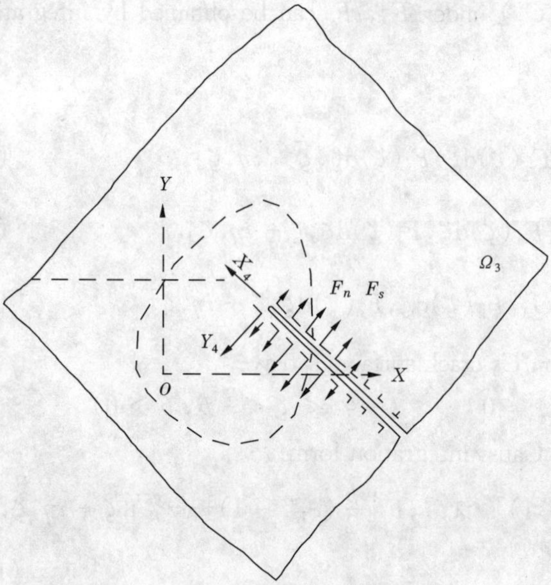

Fig. 7

which contains crack C_4 and in region Ω_3, crack grows infinitely along the imaginary line which contains crack C_3 and the respective crack surface forces remain unchanged.

Since regions Ω_1, Ω_2 and Ω_3 have a same boundary, their interior force and boundary force can be superposed. The stress and displacement field of the combination of crack surface distributive forces and boundary forces can be obtained by superposing region Ω_1, Ω_2 and Ω_3.

Let F_n, F_s represent the unknown fictitious forces on crack surface, P_n, P_s represent the unknown boundry fictitious forces. Converting above solutions from local coordinates to a unitive coordinate, we obtain the stress and displacement induced by the combination of crack surface fictitious force and boundary fictitious force. The resullts by solving the equation groups which satisfy C_1, C_2, C_3, C_4 boundary conditions are given as:

$$\sigma_s^i = \sum_{j=1}^{N} A_{ss}^{ij} P_s^j + \sum_{j=1}^{N} A_{sn}^{ij} P_n^j - \sum_{K=1}^{M}\sum_{h=1}^{L} C_{ss}^{i,hk} F_s^{hk} - \sum_{K=1}^{M}\sum_{h=1}^{L} C_{sn}^{i,hk} F_n^{hk} \tag{15}$$

$$\sigma_n^i = \sum_{j=1}^{N} A_{ns}^{ij} P_s^j + \sum_{j=1}^{N} A_{nn}^{ij} P_n^j - \sum_{K=1}^{M}\sum_{h=1}^{L} C_{ns}^{i,hk} F_s^{hk} - \sum_{K=1}^{M}\sum_{h=1}^{L} C_{nn}^{i,hk} F_n^{hk} \tag{16}$$

$$U_s^i = \sum_{j=1}^{N} B_{ss}^{ij} P_s^j + \sum_{j=1}^{N} B_{sn}^{ij} P_n^j - \sum_{K=1}^{M}\sum_{h=1}^{L} D_{ss}^{i,hk} F_s^{hk} - \sum_{K=1}^{M}\sum_{h=1}^{L} D_{sn}^{i,hk} F_n^{hk} \tag{17}$$

$$U_n^i = \sum_{j=1}^{N} B_{ns}^{ij} P_s^j + \sum_{j=1}^{N} B_{nn}^{ij} P_n^j - \sum_{K=1}^{M}\sum_{h=1}^{L} D_{ns}^{i,hk} F_s^{hk} - \sum_{K=1}^{M}\sum_{h=1}^{L} D_{nn}^{i,hk} F_n^{hk} \tag{18}$$

$$\sigma_s^{hm} = \sum_{j=1}^{N} A_{ss}^{hm,j} P_s^j + \sum_{j=1}^{N} A_{sn}^{hm,j} P_n^j - F_s^{hm} - \sum_{\substack{K=1\\K\neq m}}^{M}\sum_{h=1}^{L} C_{ss}^{hm,hk} F_s^{hk} - \sum_{\substack{K=1\\K\neq m}}^{M}\sum_{h=1}^{L} C_{sn}^{hm,hk} F_n^{hk} \tag{19}$$

$$\sigma_n^{hm} = \sum_{j=1}^{N} A_{ns}^{hm,j} P_s^j + \sum_{j=1}^{N} A_{nn}^{hm,j} P_n^j - F_n^{hm} - \sum_{\substack{K=1\\K\neq m}}^{M}\sum_{h=1}^{L} C_{ns}^{hm,hk} F_s^{hk} - \sum_{\substack{K=1\\K\neq m}}^{M}\sum_{h=1}^{L} C_{nn}^{hm,hk} F_n^{hk} \tag{20}$$

where: N is the total number of boundary elements; M is the total number of cracks; L is the total number of integration points on the crack surfaces; A, C are stress transmission factor; B, D are displacement transmission factor; P_n^j, P_s^j represent fictitious forces applied to element j; F_n^h, F_s^h, represent fictitious surface forces applied to number h Gauss point on the crack surface; σ_s^i, σ_n^i represent the surface force applied to the centre of element i in local coordinate; U_s^i, U_n^i represent the displacements of the central point of element i in local coordinate; σ_s^h, σ_n^h represent the stress of number h Gauss point on the crack surface in local coordinate; hk and hm represent number h integration point on number k and m crack respectively.

Substitute the known boundary conditions (including force conditions on the semi-infinite cracks beyone the cracks C_3 and C_4, See Fig. 1) into the left sides of equations (15)~(20). Solved the equation groups, we obtain the boundary and crack surface fictitious parameters and then also the stress field and displacement field of region A.

3 Calculation of Stress Intensity Factor (SIF)

Boundary fictitious forces and crack surface forces can be obtained by solving equations (15)~(20). Cracks with surfaces applied by fictitious forces exist independently in their respective infinite region. The singular stress fields in the ends of thess cracks exist in the same infinite region only. The stress at the same location in the other region are finite quantities and dose not affect the SIF. Applied concentrated forces P, Q to point $x = -s$ on a semi-infinite crack (Fig. 3), the SIF of the crack can be written as[1]:

$$K_{\mathrm{I}} - iK_{\mathrm{II}} = \sqrt{\frac{2}{\pi}}\frac{1}{\sqrt{s}}(P - iQ) \tag{21}$$

Substitute $F_n(\zeta)\mathrm{d}\zeta$ and $F_s(\zeta)\mathrm{d}\zeta$ for P and Q respectively and let $s = -\zeta$, and then integrate $\mathrm{d}\zeta$ along the semi-infinite crack. We have:

$$K_{\mathrm{I}} - iK_{\mathrm{II}} = \sqrt{\frac{2}{\pi}}\int_{-\infty}^{0}\frac{1}{\sqrt{-\zeta}}[F_n(\zeta) - iF_s(\zeta)]\mathrm{d}\zeta \tag{22}$$

4 Example

In order to compare the results easily, the simple example used here has been already solved by BFM.

Assume a square plate containing a lateral crack and with stress boundary condition Fig. 8.

Length of each side: 20cm;

Length of the crack: 5.0cm;

Distributed load in side AB and DC: $q = 10$ kN/cm^2;

The results given by BFM in reference (4) are $K_{\mathrm{I}} = 65.0\mathrm{kN/cm^{3/2}}$, $K_{\mathrm{II}} = 0$. BFM has a result with good precision for single crack plate during sim-

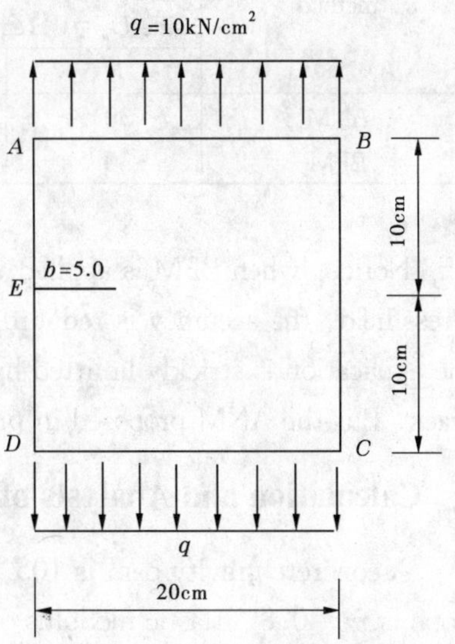

Fig. 8

ple force condition. The deviation of results obtained by prescribed method and BFM is less than 1%.

Results given by the proposed in present paper method is shown in Table 1.

Table 1 K_{I} caused by various fictitious force region of crack (FFRC)

(unit: $kN/cm^{3/2}$)

Length of FFRC outside the plate	K_{I} by FFRC outside the plate					K_{I} by FFRC inside the plate	K_{I} Total
	$-6b\sim-5b$	$-5b\sim-4b$	$-4b\sim-3b$	$-3b\sim-2b$	$-2b\sim-b$	$-b,0$	
$0\times b$	/					54.8	54.8
$1b$					16.8	42.3	59.1
$3b$			2.7	5.5	15.0	39.8	63.0
$5b$	1.3	1.9	3.0	5.3	14.4	38.5	64.4

From Table 1, in the region outside the engineering finite region, the farther a section apart from the end of a crack, the less the contribution of crack surface fictitious force to K_{I}. However, let's compare to the value given by BFM. The difference is about 3% when the length of the fictitious force area outside the crack is $3b$ and is less than 1% when the length is $5b$. Hence, in engineering practice, $5b$ should be used as the length of fictitious force area outside the crack.

In Table 2 the comparisions of other simple cases are shown in. Figs. 9, 10 (outside length of $5b$ is taken in considering).

Table 2 K_{I} given by ANM in comparision with BFM

method	Fig. 8 Loading by normal displacement of upper and lower side $U_n=0.1$cm		Fig. 9		Fig. 10	
	K_{I}	K_{II}	K_{I}	K_{II}	K_{I}	K_{II}
ANM	30.9	0	46.1	−26.0	78.9	0
BFM	30.1	0	47.6	−22.6	76.7	0

Notice: when BFM is applied to an oblique crack (See Fig. 9), with the unsymmetric stress field, the accuracy is reduced due to the increasing of the polynomial coefficent, and the application is strickly limitted by the dimensions of the structure and the location of the crack. But the ANM proposed in present paper dose not have such problems.

5 Calculation and Analysis of Horizontal Cracks in A Gravity Dam

A concrete gravity dam is 105.5m high. Upstream water depth is 100m. Downstream slope is $m=0.8$. Elastic modulus of the dam and rock foundation are $E=2.3\times10^7\mathrm{kN/m^2}$ respectively. Poissons ratio is $\upsilon=0.167$. Density of concrete dam is $\gamma=24.0\mathrm{kN/m^3}$.

Loads consist of:

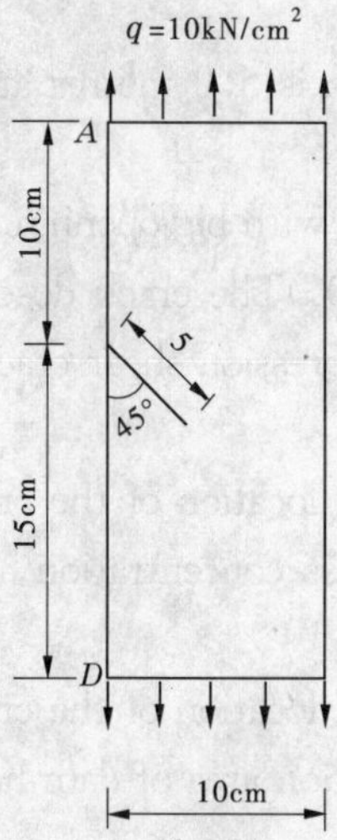

Fig. 9

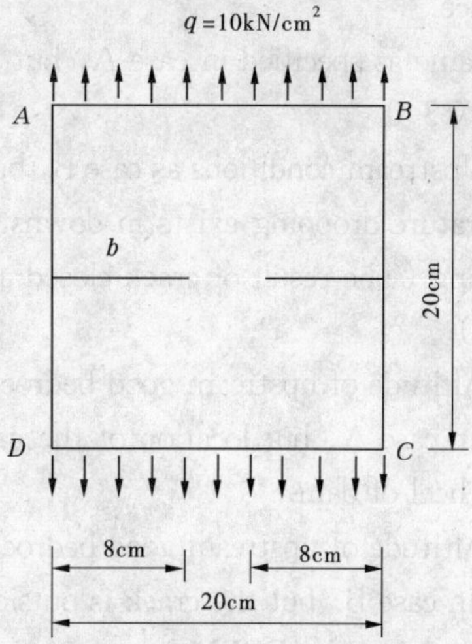

Fig. 10

a) weight of the dam;

b) hydro-static pressure on upstream surface;

c) hydro-static pressure on upstream foundation;

d) hydro-static pressure acting on the upstream crack surface.

Boundary supporting conditions as showed in Fig. 11.

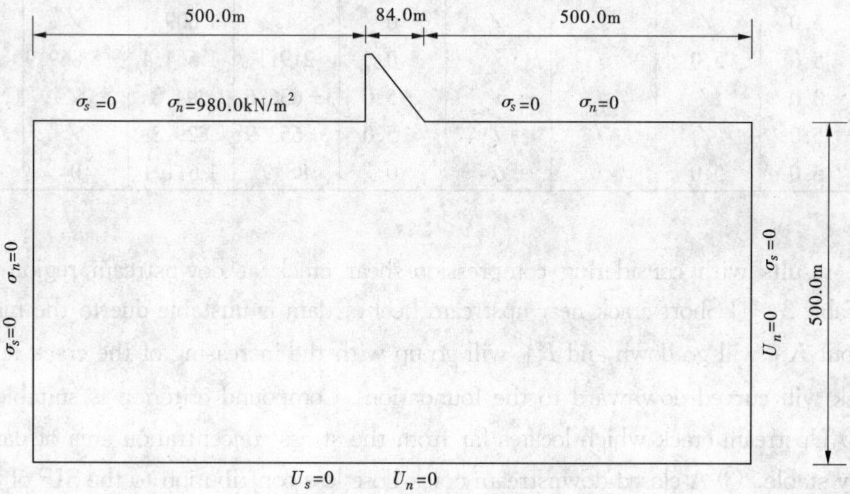

Fig. 11

where: U_n, U_s are displacements in normal and tangential direction respectively.

σ_n, σ_s, are surface forces in normal and tangential direction respectively.

Calculate and analyze the following cases:

A. The elevation of upstream good rock foundation is $\nabla 0.0$. A 3.0 meters long horizontal crack exists in the stress concentration region where the elevation is $\nabla 3.0$ in upstream dam surface.

B. Same as specified in case A, but the length of the crack is 5.0 metres at the same elevation ▽3.0.

C. Upstream conditions as case B, but a 5-metre-long crack with big openning produced by temperature dropping exists in downstream at altitude ▽3.0. The crack dose not close after loading (The result of crack closed after loading i. e. Compression-shear crack is given in (F)*.).

D. Altitude of upstream good bedrock is ▽ −5.0, size and location of the crack are as specified in case A, but location of the carck is outside the stress concentration area of the upstream heel of dam.

E. Altitude of upstream good bedrock is ▽ −5.0, size and location of the crack are as specified in case B. but the crack is outside the stress concentration area of dam heel.

Results given by DBEMC program are shown in Table 3.

Table 3 SIF of each case (unit: $kN/m^{3/2}$)

case	upstream crack length	down-stream crack length	hydro-pressure on upstream crack sur-face	compres-sion -shear state	altitude of upstream bedrock	K_I upstream crack	K_{II} upstream crack	K_I down-stream crack	K_{II} downstream crack
A	3.0	/	√	/	0	187.4	1 206.0	/	/
B	5.0	/	√	/	0	84.2	1 609.1	/	/
C	5.0	5.0	√	/	0	219.1	1 664.4	−5 869.9	3 239.2
D	3.0	/	√	/	−5.0	−636.6	394.8	/	/
E	5.0	/	√	/	−5.0	−653.9	829.3	/	/
F*	5.0	5.0	√	√	0	88.9	1 611.1	0	621.9

F* results with considering compression-shear crack at downstream region of dam. From Table 3, ① Short crack near upstream heel of dam is unstable due to the higher K_I value, but K_I will go down and K_{II} will go up with the increasing of the crack length. So the crack will curved downward to the foundation. Compound criterion is suitable for this case. ② Upstream crack which locates far from the stress concentration area of dam heel is normally stable. ③ A closed downstream crack dose less contribution to the SIF of upstream crack. But an open crack makes the ends of either upstream crack or downstream crack more serious. So it is also profitable to restore downstream open cracks. ④ Taking compression-shear resistance on the crack surface into account in case of closed crack can greatly reduce the K_{II} value and make the study more tallying with the engineering practice.

6 Conclusions

The Analytic-Numerical method for boundary multiple crack problem presented in this paper is simple in principle. It is applicable to more complex engineering boundary conditions and support conditions. In order to acheive high precision to meet engineering requirements, the proposed method takes interferences between all arbitrary distributed cracks and interferences between cracks and boundary into account. For simple loading and single crack problem, BFM can give a good results of high precision and shows in good agreement with the results given by ANM proposed in present paper. Compared with FEM, the ANM has the advantages of higher precision and less computing time. The prescribed method was used in studying the gravity dam with defects, and offered a quick effective criterion for the stability of cracks in dam.

This study was supported by N. S. F. of China.

References

[1] S. L. Crouch, A. M. Stanfield. *Boundary element methods in solid mechanics*. George Allen and Unwin Ltd., 1983

[2] G. T. Liu, Y. Chi. *An Analytic-Fictitious Boundary Forces method for calculating malti-crack Problem in Arbitrary Region With Mixed Mode Boundaries*. Fracture of concrete and rock, recent development, Elsevier Applied Science, London and New York, 1989

[3] H. Tada, P. C. Paris, G. R. Irwin. *The stress analysis of cracks, handbook*, Del. Research Corp. Hellertown, Pa, 1973

[4] *Aeronautics Research Institute of China*. Handbook of S. I. F, Science Press of China, 1981

缝内含有不同导温介质时的稳定温度断裂研究

摘　要　针对水工混凝土工程实际中常常遇到张开型裂缝或缝内含有与混凝土和岩石不同导热介质的材料,引入等效热导率,以确定热断裂解,即求解含缝体的温度场、应力场或应力强度因子。等效热导率可用两块平行板,中间有不同厚度的间隔或不同的导热介质时的实验量测而得。解析结果和实验结果吻合良好。对某实际工程的计算结果表明,由充满导热介质的裂缝干扰稳定温度场而引起的应力强度因子远小于裂缝面绝热假定引起的应力强度因子值。

关键词　水工结构　混凝土水工结构　裂缝　温度场　热导率

水工大体积混凝土中,常遇到一些张开型裂缝,需要搞清哪些裂缝会影响结构的安全。实测表明,混凝土坝中裂缝的开展往往受许多因素的影响,其中温度是主要的因素之一。在稳定温度场作用下,热流主要流向是坝上下游方向,顺坝轴方向的裂缝及灌浆缺陷区的存在破坏了结构的连续性,阻止了热流的通过,打乱了原有的温度场,其结果又反过来使结构在缝端产生应力集中,增加了裂缝开展的可能性。计算中怎样考虑裂缝和温度场的相互影响,一直是人们比较关心的问题。

以往的研究者多将缝面视为绝热[1~4],这宜于材料热导率相对空气很高且缝宽较大的情况,导致相当大的 S.I.F 值,但它和水工大体积混凝土内含裂缝的实际情况不符。J.R.Baber曾假设缝面的导热量与温度梯度成某种比例关系,研究了不完全传热时的情形[1]。实际上这种传热量与缝内介质及缝宽密切相关,因此固定的比例关系难以确定。实际上,当缝宽不大时,在裂缝中含有空气或其他介质夹层,热量可通过对流、辐射和传导多种方式传播,它与缝中介质传热能力和缝宽有关。本文假定:缝中含有与周围结构不同的导热介质,可用综合等效热导率来近似,然后求解受张开裂缝干扰的温度场及温度应力。等效热导率可由两块中间含有不同厚度的导热介质的方板来模拟。

1　裂缝内含有部分导热介质时的无限大板的稳定温度场及应力场

1.1　温度场

假设无限平板中含有长为$2a$、宽为$2b$的张开裂缝(见图1)垂直于裂缝方向有热流量 q 通过。平板的热导率为 k_1,缝内介质的热导率为 k_2。假设裂缝在平面上为一长轴是 $2a$、短轴为 $2b$ 的椭圆,则可借助于保角变换求解温度场及温度应力。取映射函数

$$z = R\left(\xi + \frac{1}{\xi}\right) \tag{1}$$

本文选自《清华大学学报(自然科学版)》1990 年第 2 期,作者还有张国新。

其中：$R=\dfrac{a+b}{2}$，$m=\dfrac{a-b}{a+b}$。该函数将 z 平面上的椭圆映射成 ξ 平面上的单位圆。

在 ξ 平面上，设单位圆外、内的温度分别为 $T_1(\rho,\beta)$、$T_2(\rho,\beta)$，其中：$\xi=\rho e^{i\beta}$。则

$$\left.\begin{aligned}&\frac{\partial^2 T_1}{\partial\rho^2}+\frac{1}{\rho}\frac{\partial T_1}{\partial\rho}+\frac{1}{\rho^2}\frac{\partial^2 T_1}{\partial\beta^2}=0 \quad (\rho\geqslant 1)\\&\frac{\partial^2 T_2}{\partial\rho^2}+\frac{1}{\rho}\frac{\partial T_2}{\partial\rho}+\frac{1}{\rho_2}\frac{\partial^2 T_2}{\partial\beta^2}=0 \quad (\rho< 1)\\&T_1=T_2 \quad k'_1\frac{\partial T_1}{\partial\rho}=k'_2\frac{\partial T_2}{\partial\rho} \quad (\rho=1)\\&\qquad T_1=Rq\rho\sin\beta \qquad (\rho=\infty)\end{aligned}\right\} \quad (2)$$

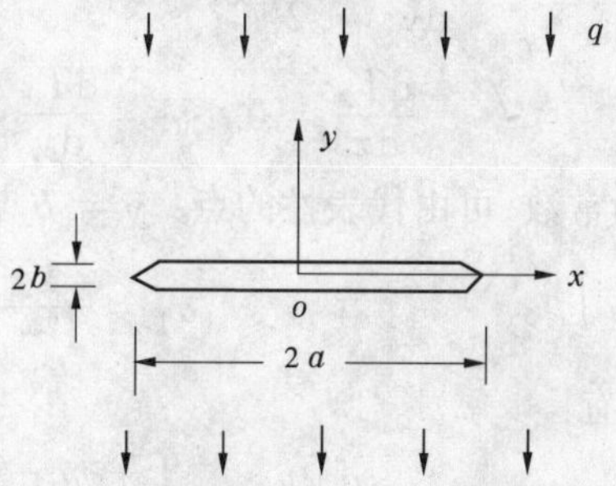

图 1 稳定热流通过含裂缝的无限平板

其中：k'_2、k'_1 是映射后圆内外的热导率。

假设变换后的热导率仍为常数，且其比例为

$$k'_2/k'_1=a_0k_2/k_1=a_0a_0$$

用分离变量法求解方程(2)得

$$T_1=qR\left(\rho+\frac{a_1}{\rho}\right)\sin\beta \qquad (\rho\geqslant 1) \tag{3}$$

由式(1)可得逆变换式

$$\xi=\frac{1}{a+b}\left(z+\sqrt{z^2-a^2+b^2}\right) \tag{4}$$

用式(4)将式(3)变换到 z 平面得

$$T_1(x,y)=\frac{q}{2}\left[(1+a_1)A\sin\frac{1}{2}\theta+(1-a_1)y\right]$$

其中：

$$A=\left[(x^2-y^2-a^2+b^2)^2+4x^2y^2\right]^{1/4}$$

$$\theta=\arcsin 2xy/A^2=\arccos(x^2-y^2-a^2+b^2)/A^2$$

在椭圆周边上有：$T_1(x,y)\Big|_{\frac{x^2}{a^2}+\frac{y^2}{b^2}=1}=\dfrac{q}{2}\left[(1+a_1)\dfrac{a}{b}+(1-a_1)\right]y$

由上式及椭圆内部的温度分布为线性的事实得

$$T_2(x,y)=\frac{q}{2}\left[(1+a_1)\frac{a}{b}+(1-a_1)\right]y$$

$$y\leqslant b \qquad |x|\leqslant\sqrt{a^2\left(1-\frac{y^2}{b^2}\right)}$$

根据裂缝表面热流连续的条件，即由 $k_1\dfrac{dT_1}{dn}=k_2\dfrac{dT_2}{dn}$ 可得出如上各式中的 a_1 值，因为

$$\frac{dT}{dn}=\cos(n,x)\frac{dT}{dx}+\cos(n,y)\frac{dT}{dy}$$

在椭圆边界上：

$$\cos(n,x)=\frac{b\sqrt{b^2-y^2}}{\sqrt{b^4-(b^2-a^2)y^2}} \qquad \cos(n,y)=\frac{ay}{\sqrt{b^4-(b^2-a^2)y^2}}$$

$$\frac{dT_1}{dx} = \frac{q}{2}\left[(1+a_1)\frac{\sqrt{b^2-y^2}(b^2-a^2)y}{(a^2-b^2)y^2+b^4}\right]$$

$$\frac{dT_1}{dy} = \frac{q}{2}\left[(1+a_1)\frac{b}{a}\frac{b^2a^2-a^2y^2-b^2y^2+b^4}{(a^2-b^2)y^2+b^4}+(1-a_1)\right]$$

$$\frac{dT_2}{dx} = 0 \qquad \frac{dT_2}{dy} = \frac{q}{2}\left[(1+a_1)\frac{1+m}{1-m}+(1-a_1)\right]$$

a_1 为常数,可由代表性的点：$y = b$ 求得

$$a_1 = \frac{1-m-2a_0}{1-m+2a_0 m} \qquad a_0 = \frac{k_2}{k_1}$$

因此有：

$$T_1(x,y) = \frac{q}{2}\left[\left(1+\frac{1-m-2a_0}{1-m+2a_0 m}\right)A\sin\frac{\theta}{2}+\left(1-\frac{1-m-2a_0}{1-m+2a_0 m}\right)y\right] \tag{5}$$

1.2　**应力场**

由式(5) 表述的温度场在 ξ 平面上可写成如下形式：

$$T_1(\xi,\bar{\xi}) = \frac{qRi}{2}\left[(\bar{\xi}-\xi)+a_1\left(\frac{1}{\xi}-\frac{1}{\bar{\xi}}\right)\right] \tag{6}$$

由文献[2] 给出的缝面自由条件：

$$F_1(\sigma)+\overline{F}_1(\sigma)-\frac{\sigma^2}{W'(\sigma)}[\overline{w}(\sigma)F'_1(\sigma)+w'(\sigma)F_2(\sigma)]$$

$$= \frac{Ea}{2}\left[T_1(\xi,\bar{\xi})-\frac{\xi^2}{\overline{w}'(\xi)}\int\frac{\partial T_1}{\partial\xi}\overline{w}'(\xi)d\bar{\xi}\right]_{\xi=\sigma} \tag{7}$$

式中：$\sigma = e^{i\theta}$,单位圆上的点；$w(\xi) = R\left(\xi+\frac{m}{\xi}\right)$；$F_1(z) = \varphi'(z)$，$F_2(z) = \psi'(z)$、$\Phi(z)$、$\Psi(z)$ 为 Muskhelishvili 应力函数；E 为弹性模量；a 为线膨胀系数。

将式(6) 代入式(7),并取共轭得

$$F_1(\sigma)+\overline{F}_1(\sigma)-\left[\frac{\sigma^2+m}{(\sigma^2-m)\sigma}\overline{F}_1(\sigma)+\frac{1-m\sigma^2}{\sigma^2-m}\overline{F}_2(\sigma)\right]$$

$$= -\frac{EaqRi\sigma^3}{4(\sigma^2-m)}\left[(1+2a_1)-\frac{a_1+m}{\sigma^2}+\frac{(2+a_1)m}{\sigma^4}\right] \tag{8}$$

假设：$F_1(\xi) = a_1\xi+\sum_{k=0}^{\infty}a_{-k}\xi^{-k}$　　　$F_2(\xi) = b_1\xi+\sum_{k=1}^{\infty}b_{-k}\xi^{-k}$

代入式(8),并利用柯西积分得

$$F_1(\xi) = -\frac{1}{4}EaqRi\frac{1}{\xi^2-m}\left(\xi^3+\frac{a_1 m}{\xi}\right)$$

$$F_2(\xi) = \frac{1}{4}EaqRi\frac{(a_1+m)\xi}{(\xi^2-m)^3}[\xi^4-2(1+m+m^2)\xi^2+m^2]$$

将式(4) 代入上两式后得

$$\Phi(z) = \frac{Eaqi}{8m}\left[(a_1-m)z-(a_1+m)\sqrt{z^2-(a+b)^2 m}-\right.$$

$$\left.\frac{a_1+m}{2}\frac{(a+b)^2 m}{\sqrt{z^2-(a+b)^2 m}}\right.$$

$$\Psi(z) = \frac{Eaqi}{8m}\left[(a_1 - m) - \frac{z(m + a_1)}{\sqrt{z^2 - (a+b)^2 m}} + \frac{(m + a_1)(a+b)^2 mz}{2[z^2 - (a+b)m]^{3/2}}\right]$$

将其代入：$\sigma_x + \sigma_y = 4\mathrm{Re}\Phi(z)$

$$\sigma_y - \sigma_x + 2i\tau_{xy} = 2[\bar{z}\Phi'(z) + \Psi(z)] - Ea\int \frac{\partial T(z,\bar{z})}{\partial \bar{z}}\mathrm{d}z$$

得

$$\sigma_x = -\frac{Eaq}{16}(a_1 + m)(a+b)^2\left\{\frac{3}{A}\sin\frac{\theta}{2} + \left[x^2 + y^2 - \frac{(1+m^2)}{2}(a+b)^2\right]\frac{1}{A^3}\sin\frac{3}{2}\theta\right\}$$

$$\sigma_y = \frac{Eaq}{16}(a_1 + m)(a+b)^2\left\{\left[x^2 + y^2 - \frac{(1+m^2)}{2}(a+b)^2\right]\frac{1}{A^3}\sin\frac{3}{2}\theta - \frac{1}{A}\sin\frac{1}{2}\theta\right\}$$

$$\tau_{xy} = \frac{Eaq}{16}(a_1 + m)(a+b)^2\left\{\frac{1}{A}\cos\frac{\theta}{2} + \left[x^2 + y^2 - \frac{(1+m^2)}{2}(a+b)^2\right]\frac{1}{A^3}\cos\frac{3}{2}\theta\right\}$$

最后，缝端应力强度因子可表示为

$$K_{\mathrm{I}} = 0$$

$$K_{\mathrm{II}} = \frac{Eaq}{8\sqrt{a}}\sqrt{\pi}(1 + a_1 m)(a+b)^2 \tag{9}$$

2 数值结果与实验验证

对含绝热裂缝板的研究可知，裂缝干扰温度场的范围不大[4]。对 10cm × 10cm × 2cm 的环氧树脂板进行实验。板中间开一 4cm 长的直缝（见图 2），温度边界条件见图 2，前后两面用透明保温材料作等温场绝热（$\partial T/\partial n \simeq 0$）。用反射式光弹仪进行拍照，得到不同缝宽时的等色线照片。

由缝端等色线照片知，缝端椭圆状等色线的轴与 x 轴成大概 45° 的角，沿这个方向取不同的距离 r 的等色线值，可以确定应力强度因子。缝端应力可由下式表示：

$$\sigma_x = -\frac{K_{\mathrm{II}}}{\sqrt{2\pi r}}\left[\sin\frac{1}{2}\theta\left(2 + \cos\frac{1}{2}\theta\cos\frac{3}{2}\theta\right)\right]$$

$$\sigma_y = \frac{K_{\mathrm{II}}}{\sqrt{2\pi r}}\left(\sin\frac{1}{2}\theta\cos\frac{1}{2}\theta\cos\frac{3}{2}\theta\right)$$

$$\tau_{xy} = \frac{K_{\mathrm{II}}}{\sqrt{2\pi r}}\left[\cos\frac{1}{2}\theta\left(1 - \sin\frac{1}{2}\theta\sin\frac{3}{2}\theta\right)\right]$$

将 $\theta = 45°$ 代入上式，并由主应力公式得

$$\sigma_1 - \sigma_2 = 0.631\frac{K_{\mathrm{II}}}{\sqrt{r}}$$

令 $N = \dfrac{0.631}{\sqrt{r}}$，得

$$\sigma_1 - \sigma_2 = NK_{\mathrm{II}}$$

根据实验结果作出的$(\sigma_1 - \sigma_2) \sim N$ 曲线的斜率即是K_{II} 值，由式(9) 所得数值结果与实验结果的比较见图 3，两者吻合良好，精度满足工程需要。

实验中环氧树脂的物理特性为

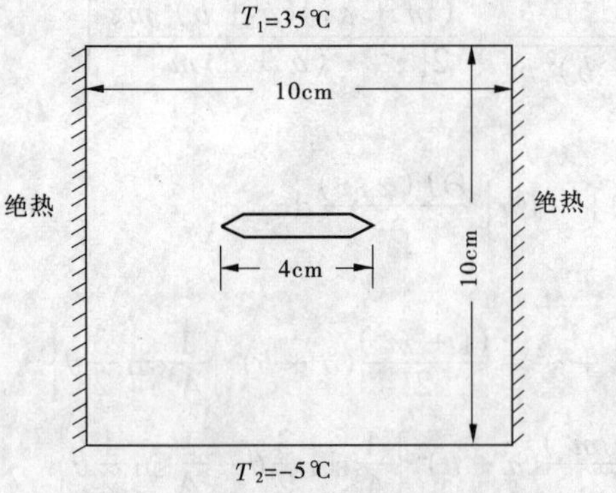

图 2　含裂缝的环氧板的热断裂实验

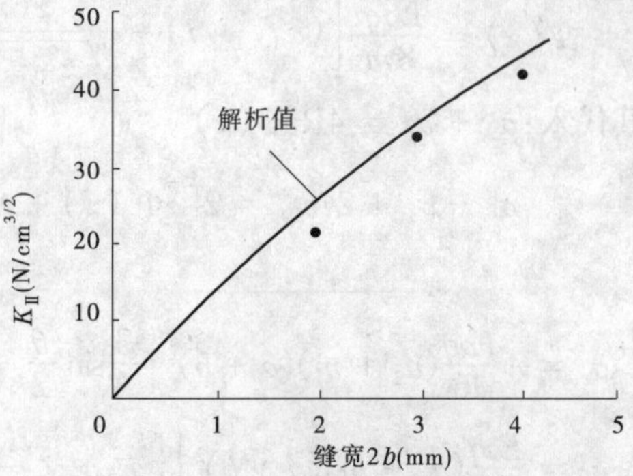

图 3　数值结果和实验结果的比较

线膨胀系数 $a = 68 \times 10^{-6}\text{K}^{-1}$；

弹性模量 $E = 3.4 \times 10^5 \text{N/cm}^2$；

热导率 $k_1 = 0.2\text{W/(m·k)}$；

缝内介质热导率 $k_2 = 0.03\text{W/(m·k)}$；

边界温差 $T_1 - T_2 = 40\text{K}$。

工程实例：某混凝土拱坝的一个坝段，内含平行于坝轴线方向的裂缝，缝宽 2mm；坝厚 20m；上下游坝面温差为 15K。

材料常数：$E = 25 \times 10^5 \text{N/cm}^2$，$a = 1 \times 10^{-5}$，$k_1 = 2.4\text{W/(m·K)}$。

缝内空气热导率：$k_2 = 0.03\text{W/(m·K)}$。

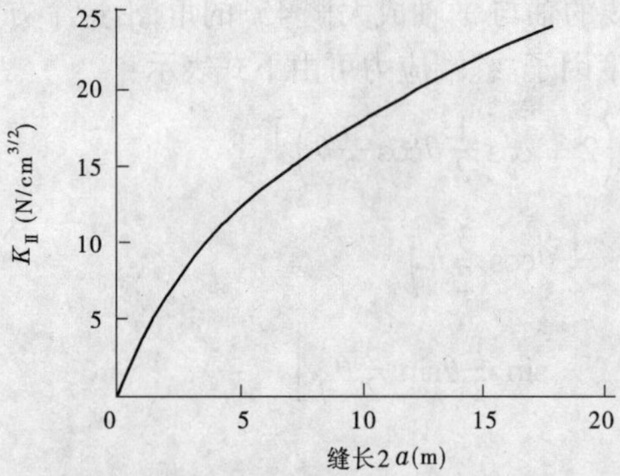

图 4　不同缝长时的 K_{II} 值　（缝宽：2mm）

根据式(9)，不同缝长时的应力强度因子见图 4。

由图 4 可以看出，当混凝土坝内缝宽为 2mm 时(灌浆缺陷)，应力强度因子 K_{II} 小于 $30\text{N/cm}^{3/2}$。对于一般的混凝土坝而言，通常裂缝宽度很小。$b/a < 0.000\,2$。因而由于裂缝干扰稳定温度场而引起的应力强度因子不大。同条件下，若裂缝面按绝热考虑[4]，则应力强度因子 $K_{\text{II}} = 610\text{N/cm}^{3/2}$，影响很大。而裂缝面绝热条件和工程混凝土裂缝实际情况相差太远。

3　结论

(1)当垂直于热流方向的裂缝干扰温度场时，含裂缝板内只产生Ⅱ型应力强度因子。

(2)由式(9)算出的应力强度因子值与实验值吻合良好，表明它有较好的精度。

(3)混凝土坝内裂缝一般很窄，由裂缝干扰温度场而引起的应力强度因子不大，不宜按绝热面来考虑裂缝影响,它过分夸大了应力强度因子 K_{II} 值。

参 考 文 献

[1] Florence A L, Goodier J N. *Thermal Stresses due to Disturbance of Uniform Heat Flow by an Insulated Ovaloid Hole*. Journal of Applied Mechanics, 1960, 12: 635

[2] Nowinski J L, *Theory of Thermoelastisity with Applications*. Netherlad, Sijthoff & Noordhoff International Publishers, 1973, 349~357

[3] Panasyuk V V, Savruk M P, Datsyshyn A P. *A General Method of Solution of Two-dimensional problems in the Theroy of Cracks*. Engineering Fracture Mechanics, 1977, 9: 481~497

[4] 张国新,刘光廷. 含有绝热裂缝的有限自由板在稳定温度场作用下的断裂分析. 水利水运科学研究,1989(1):96~105

THE ANALYTIC-NUMERICAL SOLUTION FOR THERMAL CRACK PROBLEMS AND CRACK PREVENTION OF RCAD

Abstract In order to study the stability of cracks in Roll Compacted Arch Dam (RCAD), and the preventive measures from unexpected thermocracks. The method of fictitious thermal sources and fictitious forces for solving thermal fracture problem is introduced in present paper. A group of boundary singular integral equations, in which the fictitious forces on the boundaries and on the crack surfaces are taken as foundamental unknowns, is proposed. The stress fields of a tyipical arch in RCAD under different load-combination of water pressure and thermal load was calculated by using the method mentioned above. The results of stress redistribution and state of the stability of cracks during crack emergence in dam were also given. The stress distribution of RCAD can be improved by artificial short joints (with water stops) located in the upstream abutments which will lead to the prevention of cracks in arch dam during operation.

1 Introduction

More attention has been paid to Roll Compacted Dam (RCD) in recent years for its simple technology and high speed of construction. Up to date, all the RCD in China are gravity dams. But engineers attempt to built dam more economically through Rolled Compacted Arch Dam (RCAD). How to make a good design of RCAD, in which unexpected cracks will not happen after the temperature drop of dam body, is a difficult problem. In order to simplify the technology of construction and keep the rigidity of Arch Dam during operation, no vertical constructional joint with grouting systems will be left in RCAD. The temperature of block raises up by hydration heat in the initial stage of construction, and drops down-ward during the long period of operation under the effect of the surrounding temperature change of water and atmosphere. All the contraction of dam will be entirely restrained by rock foundation and especially in horizontal arch direction, and thus the emergence of serious cracks is almost inevitable. However what will happen with these cracks after stress redistribution? Can we build a RCAD without unexpected cracks or with good quality? In present paper solution of thermal crack was introduced, and stability of multiple crack in arch dam during mechanical and thermal load was discussed, and finally engineering measures for building RCAD with good quality were proposed.

本文选自《Proceedings from the International Conference on Dam Fracture》, Boulder, Colorado, USA. Sep. 11～13, 1991, 作者还有 Zhang Guoxin。

2 The Method of Thermal Fracture Analysis

The thermal fracture problem of mutiple cracks body with mixed mode boundary conditions (See Fig. 1) can be divided into following three parts: Ⅰ. The displacements and stress distribution on the boundaries and in the region (with no cracks) of engineering project caused by fictitious loads $N(s) - iT(s)$ acting on the boundary lines of the same project in an infinite plane with no cracks. Ⅱ. The displacement and stress distribution on the boundaries and in the region of the engineering project caused by fictitious boundary thermal sources $H(s)$ located on the boundary of the same project in an infinite plane with no cracks. Ⅲ. The displacement and stress distribution on the boundaries and in the region of the engineering project caused by the released stressess $N^c(s) - iT^c(s)$ on the crack surfaces in an infinite region with multiple cracks. Let the displacements and stresses caused by the combination of fictitious loads $N(s) - iT(s)$, thermal loads $H(s)$ and releasing forces $N^c(s) - iT^c(s)$ on crack surfaces satisfy the boundary conditions of original problem and stress-free condition on the crack surfaces (opentype), the fictitious loads and releasing stresses of cracks can be determined by solving equation groups and then the SIF of every crack tips and stress field in engineering region can also be obtained.

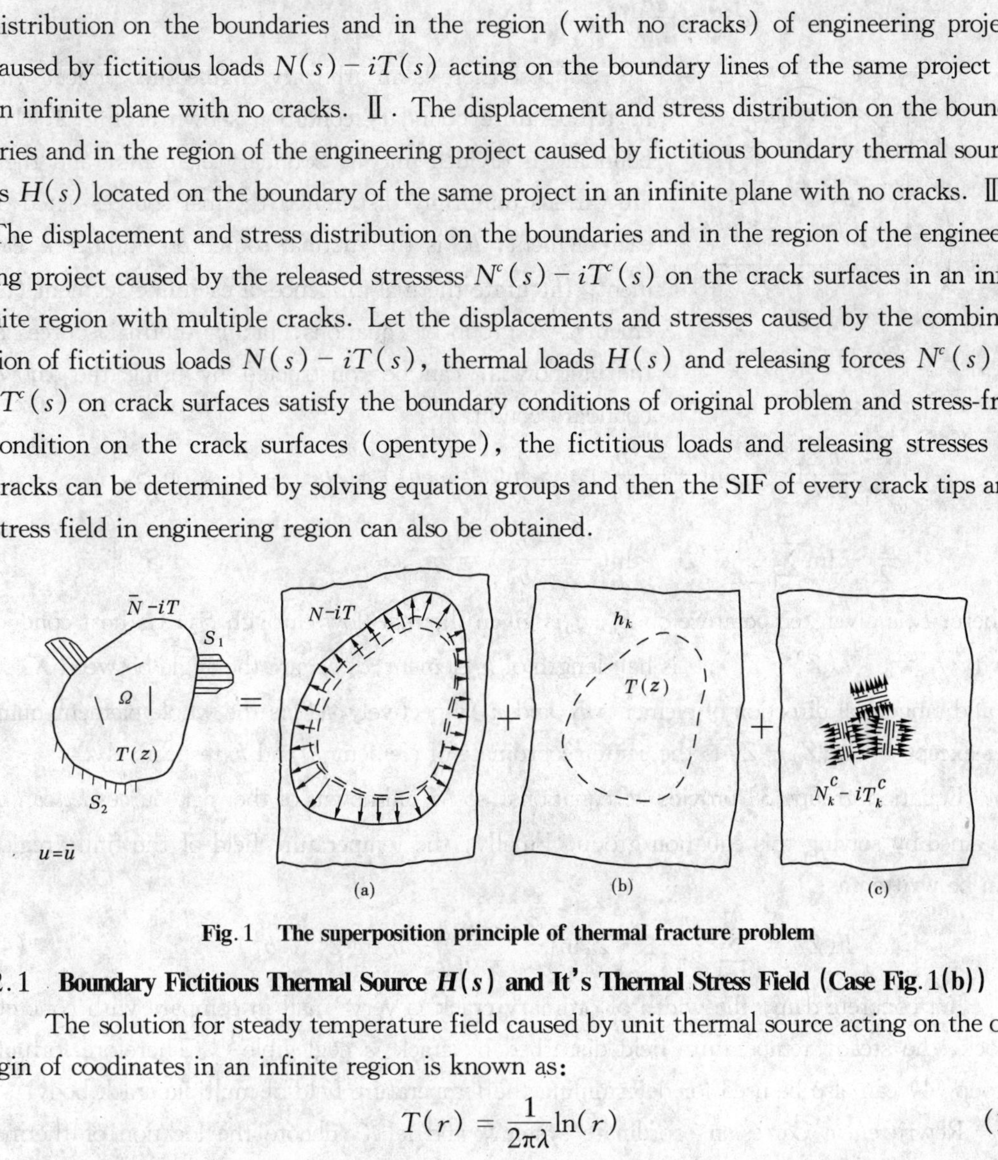

Fig. 1 The superposition principle of thermal fracture problem

2.1 Boundary Fictitious Thermal Source $H(s)$ and It's Thermal Stress Field (Case Fig. 1(b))

The solution for steady temperature field caused by unit thermal source acting on the origin of coodinates in an infinite region is known as:

$$T(r) = \frac{1}{2\pi\lambda}\ln(r) \tag{1}$$

where: r is the distance apart from the point thermal source; λ is the heat conductivity; α, E are linear expansion parameter and elastic modulus respectively.

The thermal stress and displacement in this infinite plane with no cracks can also be written as:

$$\left.\begin{aligned} U_r^* &= -\frac{\alpha(1+\nu)}{2\pi\lambda}\left(\frac{r}{2}\ln r - \frac{r}{4}\right), U_\theta^* = 0 \\ \sigma_{rr}^* &= \frac{\alpha E}{4\pi\lambda}\left(\ln r - \frac{1}{2}\right) \\ \sigma_{\theta\theta}^* &= \frac{\alpha E}{4\pi\lambda}\left(\ln r + \frac{1}{2}\right) \end{aligned}\right\} \tag{2}$$

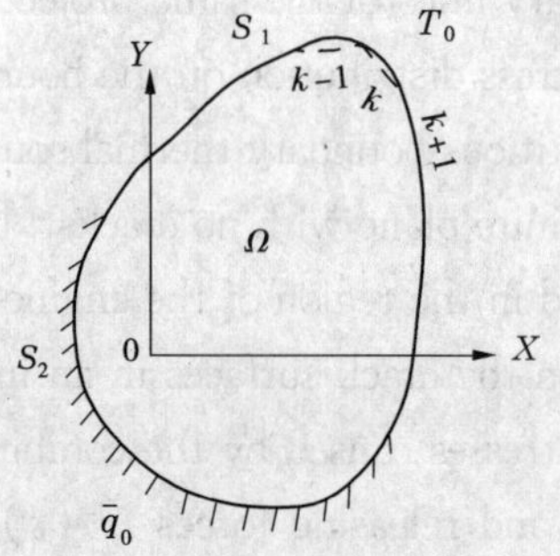

Fig. 2

Suppose there is an arbitrary engineering project with its temperature boundary condition shown as Fig. 2. The boundary is divided into M boundary elements, and there are various uniformly distributed thermal sources acted on each element, h_k is the thermal source on number k element. Integrate thermal influence of each line segment (element). A group of equations, taking thermal sources as the unknowns, can be constructed by using the known boundary conditions:

$$\left.\begin{aligned} &\sum_{k=1}^{M}\frac{h_k}{2\pi\lambda}\mathrm{Re}[t_{kn}\ln(\frac{t_{kn}-b_k}{t_{kn}+b_k}) - b_k\ln(t_{kn}^2 - b_k^2) + 2b_k] = \overline{T}_{on}, \text{ on } S_1 \\ &\frac{1}{2} - \mathrm{Im}\sum_{k=1}^{M}\frac{h_k}{2\pi}\mathrm{e}^{-i(a_k - a_n)}\ln(\frac{t_{kn}-b_k}{t_{kn}+b_k}) = \overline{q}_{on}, \qquad \text{on } S_2 \end{aligned}\right\} \tag{3}$$

where: T_0 is given temperature on S_1; q_0 is given thermal flow through S_2; λ is heat conductivity; $t_{kn} = \mathrm{e}^{-ia_k}(Z_n^0 - Z_k^0)$; b_k is half length of k element; a_k, a_n are the angle between X axis and tangential direction of elements K and n respectively; M' is the whole element number except $k = n$; $Z_n^0 - Z_k^0$ is the center coordinate of element n and k respectively.

Equation group (3) provids M equations, so M unknowns of thermal sources h_k can be obtained by solving this equation group. Finally, the temperature field of the finite region can be written as:

$$T(Z) = \sum_{k=1}^{M}\frac{h_k}{2\pi\lambda}\mathrm{Re}\left[Z_k\ln\left(\frac{Z_k - b_k}{Z_k + b_k}\right) - b_k\ln(Z_k^2 - b_k^2) + 2b_k\right] \tag{4}$$

For concrete dam, the width of ordinary crack is very small in compare with concrete block, the steady temperature field disturbed by crack is neglegible[1]. Therefore formula group (4) can also be used for determining the temperature field of multiple crack body.

Rewritten in Cartesion coordinate system, and let C denote the location of thermal source.

The stress and displacement of arbitrary point Z in α direction induced by the thermal source $H(s)$ distributed on the boundary of the problem are expressed respectively:

$$
\left.\begin{aligned}
U^T + iV^T &= \frac{\alpha(1+\nu)}{8\pi\lambda}\int_\Gamma -[(Z-c(s))\cdot\ln(Z-c(s)) + (Z-c(s))\cdot \\
&\quad \ln(\overline{Z}-\overline{c}(s)) - (Z-c(s))]H(s)\cdot e^{-i(a-a(s))}ds \\
\sigma_x^T + \sigma_y^T &= \frac{\alpha E}{4\pi\lambda}\int_\Gamma H(s)[\ln(Z-c(s)) + \ln(\overline{Z}-\overline{c}(s))]ds \\
\sigma_y^T - \sigma_x^T + 2i\tau_{xy}^T &= \frac{\alpha E}{4\pi\lambda}\int_\Gamma \frac{\overline{Z}-\overline{c}(s)}{Z-c(s)}H(s)e^{-2i(a-a(s))}ds
\end{aligned}\right\} \quad (5)
$$

2.2 The Stress and Displacement Field of an Infinite Plane with no Cracks Caused by Fictitious Load (Case Fig. 1(a))

The stress functions caused by a point load $Q=\frac{F_x+iF_y}{2(1+æ)}$ located at $Z=c$ in an infinite plane (Fig. 3) are known[2]

$$
\left.\begin{aligned}
\psi(Z) &= -Q\ln(Z-c) \\
\Psi(Z) &= æ\overline{Q}[\ln(Z-c)+1] + Q\cdot c\cdot\frac{1}{Z-c}
\end{aligned}\right\} \quad (6)
$$

where: $æ=\begin{cases} 3-4\nu & \text{plane strain} \\ \dfrac{3-\nu}{1+\nu} & \text{plane stress} \end{cases}$

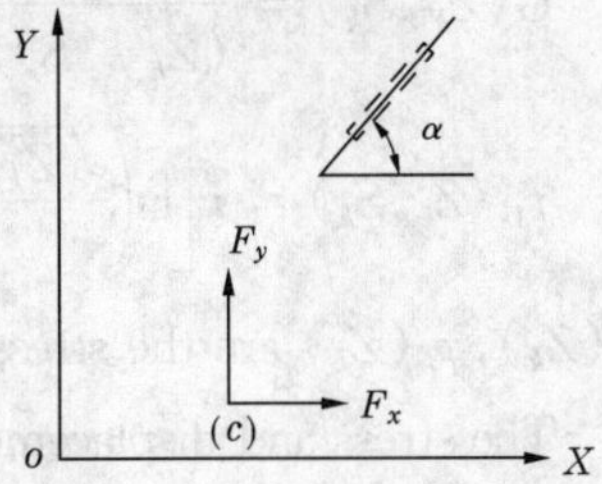

Fig. 3 Point load acted on an infinite plane

The stress and displacement of arbitrary point $Z(x,y)$ in the direction of angle α in respect to X axis caused by distributed load $Q(s)$ on boundary are given as:

$$
\left.\begin{aligned}
\sigma_y^e - i\tau_{xy}^e &= \int_\Gamma\left\{-Q(s)\left[\frac{1}{Z-C(s)} - æe^{2i(a-a(s))}\frac{1}{\overline{Z}-\overline{C}(s)}\right]-\right. \\
&\quad \left.\overline{Q}(s)\left[\frac{1}{\overline{Z}-\overline{C}(s)} + e^{-2i(a-a(s))}\frac{(Z-C(s))}{(\overline{Z}-\overline{C}(s))^2}\right]\right\}ds \\
\sigma_x^e + i\tau_y^e &= \int_\Gamma\left\{-2Q(s)\frac{1}{Z-C(s)} - 2\overline{Q}(s)\frac{1}{\overline{Z}-\overline{C}(s)}\right\}ds \\
U^e + iV^e &= \frac{1}{2\mu}\int_\Gamma e^{ia(s)}\left\{-æQ(s)[\ln(Z-C(s)) + \ln(\overline{Z}-\overline{C}(s)) + 1] + \right. \\
&\quad \left.\overline{Q}(s)\cdot\frac{Z-C(s)}{\overline{Z}-\overline{C}(s)}\right\}ds
\end{aligned}\right\} \quad (7)
$$

where: Γ is the whole boundary of the problem.

2.3 The Displacement and Stress Field Induced by the Distributed Load on Crack Surface (Case Fig. 1(c))

Suppose there is a pair of point force $P=F_x-iF_y$ on the crack surfaces at a distance S apart form the original local coordinate system (Fig. 4), we have:[3,4]

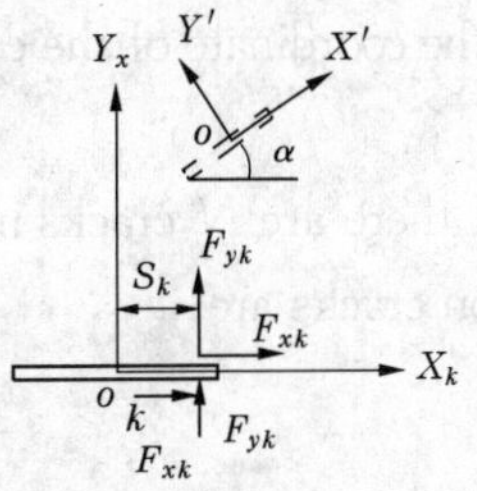

Fig. 4

$$\Phi(Z) = \Omega(Z) = -\frac{P}{2\pi}\frac{\sqrt{a^2 - s^2}}{(Z - s)\sqrt{Z^2 - a^2}} \tag{8}$$

Since distributed forces $P_k(S_k) = F_y(S_k) - iF_x(S_k)$ act on the surface of number k crack, we have:

$$\left.\begin{aligned} \varphi_k(Z_k) &= -\frac{1}{2\pi}\int_{-a_k}^{a_k} P_k(S_k) f_1(Z_k, S_k)\mathrm{d}S_k \\ \psi_k(Z_k) &= -\frac{1}{2\pi}\int_{-a_k}^{a_k} [\overline{P_k(S_k)} f_{1k}(Z_k, S_k) - \\ &\quad Z_k P_k(S_k)\sqrt{a_k^2 - S_k^2}\, G(Z_k, S_k)\mathrm{d}S_k \end{aligned}\right\} \tag{9}$$

where:

$$\left.\begin{aligned} G(Z_k, S_k) &= \frac{1}{(Z_k - S_k)\sqrt{Z_k^2 - a_k^2}} \\ f_{1k}(Z_k, S_k) &= i\left[\ln\left(\frac{\sqrt{Z_k^2 - a_k^2} + i\sqrt{a_k^2 - S_k^2}}{Z_k - S_k} - \frac{S_k i}{\sqrt{a_k^2 - S_k^2}}\right) - \ln\left(1 + \frac{S_k}{\sqrt{S_k^2 - a_k^2}}\right)\right] \end{aligned}\right\}$$

$\varphi_k(Z_k), \varphi_k(Z_k)$ are the stress functions in local coordinate system.

The stress and displacement at arbitrary point Z in the direction α with respect to X axis are:

$$\left.\begin{aligned} \sigma_y^k - i\tau_{xy}^k &= \int_{-a_k}^{a_k} P_k(S_k) C_k(S_k, Z)\mathrm{d}S_k + \int_{-a_k}^{a_k} \overline{P_k(S_k)} D_k(S_k, Z)\mathrm{d}S_k \\ U^k + iV^k &= \frac{\mathrm{e}^{i(a_k - a)}}{4\mu\pi}\left\{\int_{-a_k}^{a_k} P_k(S_k)[\overline{f_{1k}(Z_k, S_k)} - æ f_{1k}(Z_k, S_k)]\mathrm{d}S_k + \right. \\ &\quad \left.\int_{-a_k}^{a_k} \overline{P_k(S_k)}(Z_k - \overline{Z}_k)\sqrt{a_k^2 - S_k^2}\,\overline{G(Z_k, S_k)}\mathrm{d}S_k\right\} \end{aligned}\right\} \tag{10}$$

where:

$$C_k = -\frac{1}{2\pi}\sqrt{a_k^2 - S_k^2}[G(Z_k, S_k) + \mathrm{e}^{2i(a_k - a)}\,\overline{G(Z_k, S_k)}]$$

$$D_k = -\frac{1}{2\pi}\sqrt{a_k^2 - S_k^2}\left\{\overline{G(Z_k, S_k)}[1 - \mathrm{e}^{2i(a_k - a)}] + \mathrm{e}^{2i(a_k - a)}(Z_k - \overline{Z}_k)\,\overline{G'(Z_k, S_k)}\right\}$$

$$Z_k = (Z - Z_k^0)\mathrm{e}^{-ia_k}$$

Z_k^0 is the coordinate of the central point of crack k; a_k is the angle between crack k and X axis.

If there are N cracks in region, the displacement and stress caused by the total released force on cracks are:

$$\left.\begin{aligned} \sigma_y^c - i\tau_{xy}^c &= \sum_{k=1}^{N}[\sigma_y^k - i\tau_{xy}^k] \\ U^c + iV^c &= \sum_{k=1}^{M}[U^k + iV^k] \end{aligned}\right\} \tag{11}$$

where, the upper mark c denotes the stress and displacement induced by fictitious load on the crack surface.

3 The Boundary Equation Group of Thermal Fracture Problem

The stress and displacement field in region Ω induced by fictitious boundary loads, thermal loads and released fictitious forces on crack surfaces can be determined by using the method illustrated in Fig. 1. Let point Z in region approach to P_0 on S_1 or Q_0 on S_2 and point C_0 on crack surfaces respectively, then a group of boundary integral equations satisfying the boundary condition and free condition of crack surfaces can be obtained as:

$$\left.\begin{aligned}&\sigma_n^e(P_0)-i\sigma_t^e(P_0)+\sigma_n^T(P_0)-i\sigma_t^T(P_0)+\sigma_n^c(P_0)-i\sigma_t^c(P_0)=\overline{N}(P_0)-i\overline{T}(P_0)\\&U^e(Q_0)+iV^e(Q_0)+U^T(Q_0)+iV^T(Q_0)+U^c(Q_0)+iV^c(Q_0)=\overline{U}(Q_0)+i\overline{V}(Q_0)\\&\sigma_{yk}^e(C_0)-i\tau_{xyk}^e(C_0)+\sigma_{yk}^T(C_0)-i\tau_{xyk}^T(C_0)+\alpha_{yk}^c(C_0)-i\tau_{xyk}^c(C_0)=0\end{aligned}\right\}\tag{12}$$

where: the upper mark e, T, c, denote the stress and displacement induced by fictitious boundary loads, thermal loads and fictitious forces on crack surfaces respectively; P_0, Q_0 are the points on boundary S_1 and S_2 respectively; C_0 is the point on crack surfaces.

Solved singular integral equations (12), the fictitious boundary loads and the fictitious forces on crack surfaces can be obtained, and then the stress field and the displacement field can also be obtained. The S.I.F. at every crack tips can be calculated as following:

$$K_n^{\mathrm{I}}-iK_n^{\mathrm{II}}=-\frac{1}{\sqrt{\pi a_n}}\int_{-a_n}^{a_n}[F_y(S_n)-iF_x(S_n)]\sqrt{\frac{a_n\pm S_n}{a_n\mp S_n}}\,\mathrm{d}S_n\tag{13}$$

Results of numerical example by the proposed method in present paper were compared with the experimental results of 12cm×10cm×0.6cm epoxy plate with 4cm long edge crack and restrained top and bottom of the plate during uniformly temperature drop of 20℃.

They are in good agreement both the SIF value and iso-shear (lsochromatic) stress curves.

Calculating result: $K_{\mathrm{I}}=14.10\mathrm{MPa\cdot cm^{1/2}}$ $K_{\mathrm{II}}=0.0\mathrm{MPa\cdot cm^{1/2}}$

Experimental result: $K_{\mathrm{I}}=14.85\mathrm{MPa\cdot cm^{1/2}}$ $K_{\mathrm{II}}=0.32\mathrm{MPa\cdot cm^{1/2}}$

4 Engineering Application(Release the Thermal Stress in RCAD)

An experimental RCAD is designed with no transverse joints along the axis of dam. In order to simplify the concrete technology, the surface of roll compacted layers will not be treated specially. The effect of the cantilever of arch dam is weak. In the extreme case the structure is considered as many horizontal arch layers individually, the stability of cracks happened in dam and the result of artificial cracks for improving stress distribution is analysised qualitatively. An plan arch in the RCAD is illustrated in Fig. 5. The temperature of arch is 29℃ (for zero stress condition). The final steady temperature in operation are: upstream

12℃, downstream 16℃. The initial gradient of temperature in both sides of rock foundation is about 1℃/50m. The inner temperature of rock foundation at 100m deep remains constant (18℃) before and after pounding. The temperature of the ground surface of the mountain is 16℃ (average) before pounding, and in upstream side (reservoir) temperature changes to 12℃ after pounding. The water pressure on this arch is 80m during the normal high water level of reservoir.

For numerical analysis, the boundaries of arch and abutment in Fig. 5 were divided into 51 boundary elements and prescribed method was used to solve the problem easily with the aid of microcomputer only. Different cases were calculated for comparison:

(1) Water pressure only.

(2) Thermal load only.

(3) Water pressure and thermal load.

(4) Stress redistribution in arch after the emergence of the cracks at both sides of upstream abutment induced by the same water pressure and thermal load.

(5) Stress redistribution in arch after the emergence of the crack at the downstream arch crown induced by water pressure and thermal load.

The calculating results are shown in Fig. 6～Fig. 16. Where σ_1 is the first (maximum) principle stress; σ_2 is the second (minimum) principle stress.

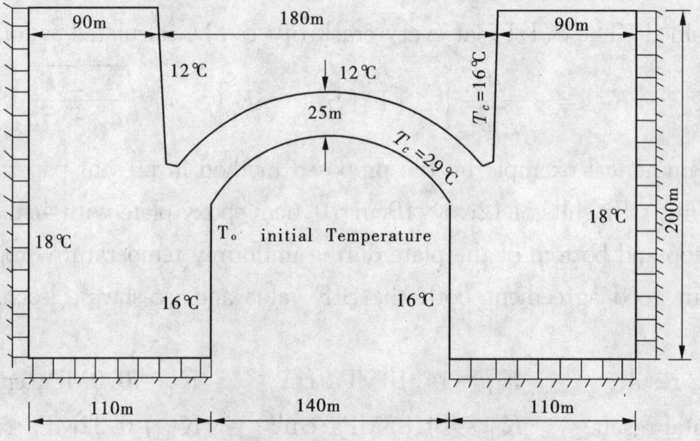

Fig. 5

5 Discussions

(1) The stresses in arch induced by water pressure keep the same distribution with ordinary case (Figs. 6, 7). Tension stress with low level occurs near the upstream abutments, the angle between the first principle stress and x axis is about 50℃, which is just the same as the tangential direction of the arch abutment. All the other parts of the arch are under compression stress. The maximum compression stress occurs at both sides of the down stream abutments. The compression stress in a small zone exceeds −5MPa. Therefore the

water load will not bring any important crack in this project.

(2) If the arch dam is cooled down before lifting water level (Figs. 8, 9), almost all the arch will be set under unfavourate region of tension stress. The maximum tension stress at the downstream of the arch crown is about 3.9MPa, which has the same direction with x axis. The maximum tension stress areas in arch locate at the upstream abutments with a small area of stress exceeding 5.0MPa. It can be seen that cracks would happen at the downstream of arch crown and the upstream abutments, if the temperature of arch dropped before pounding.

(3) The supperposition of stress induced by water pressure and thermal load makes a great reduction of the tension stress area as compared with the condition of thermal load only, and also reduction of the magnitude of stresses except those near the upstream arch abutment (Figs. 10, 11). The maximum tension stress decreases from 3.9MPa to 2.5MPa at downstream crown, and increases up to 7MPa at the upstream arch abutments with reducing the area of tension stress. Since the maximum tensile stress of arch always happens in the upstream arch abutments either due to water load or thermal load, there would happen the fractures more easier after operation.

(4) Let the cracks of 2.5m long emerge in both sides of upstream abutments after long period operation of arch dam, the stress redistributions are shown in Fig. 12, Fig. 13, the state of stresses is improved significantly. The tensile stress zones at two upstream abutments almost disappear and the maximum tensile stress at the downstream crown goes down to 0.5 MPa, all other parts of arch laid under the pressure state. The stress-relaxation caused by cracks emerged in the upstream abutments is very sensitive to the thermal stress. The cracks in the upstream abutments bring a little increasing of compression stress to the downstream abutment only. So that, the "earlier" pounding (pounding before the end of construction) would give the advantages to the stress distribution in dam. It decreases the depth of tensile stress zone in the upstream abutment and can prevent the emergence of cracks in the downstream arch crown. Therefore the short artificial joint (about 3.0m long with water stops) in the upstream arch abutments with the measure of earlier pounding will keep the RCAD in good quality (under the normal constructing technology).

(5) In practice the cracks happened in downstream arch crown of RCAD (experimental coffer-dam in China) without artificial engineering measures. The cracks propagate from downstream to ward upstream and perpendicular to the arch axis. Analytic-numerical calculations show the same results of crack propagation. The variation of SIF in different crack length at the downstream crown were traced. The curve (Fig. 16) shows that SIF decrease to 6~8MPa·$cm^{1/2}$ and crack stops after the depth of crack reaches 9.0m. If the artificial joint is made on the downstream crown, it needs about 10m long. The cross section is weakened by 2/5. The stress redistributions in dam with 10m long crack in the downstream crown are shown in Fig. 14, Fig. 15. Comparing Fig. 10 and Fig. 14, it can be seen that the

tensile stress zone did not disappear after the crack emergence in the downstream crown. They transfered to the both sides of crown only, the tensile stress with high level still existed near downstream crown, the tensile stress at two upstream abutments remained at high level of 4.0MPa. The cracks in these places are still inavoidable and so the cracks or artifical joint in the downstream crown could not improve the stress distribution in arch.

(6) The proposed analytic-numerical solution for thermal crack in present paper offers an easy and effective method for the analysis of thermal crack engineering, which is important problem for RCAD.

This study was supported by N.S.F. of China

unit of stress in figures: 0.1 MPa

− pressure + tension

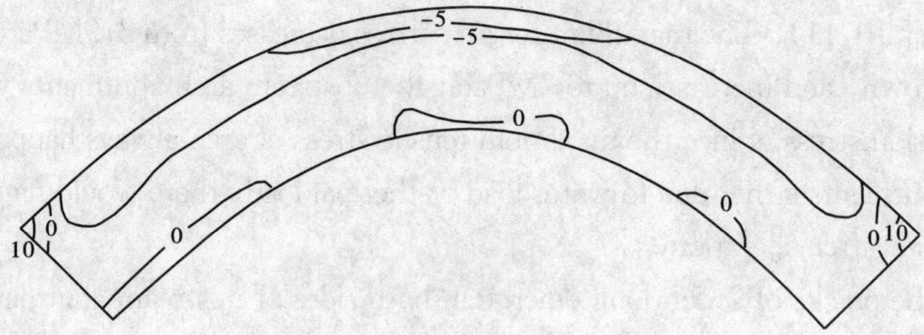

Fig.6 σ_1 (water pressure)

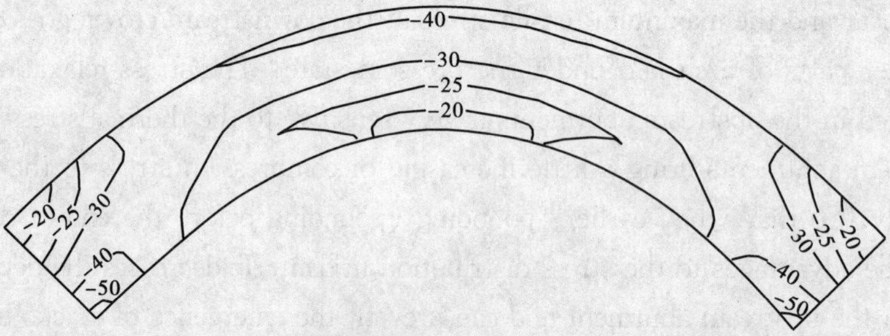

Fig.7 σ_2 (water pressure)

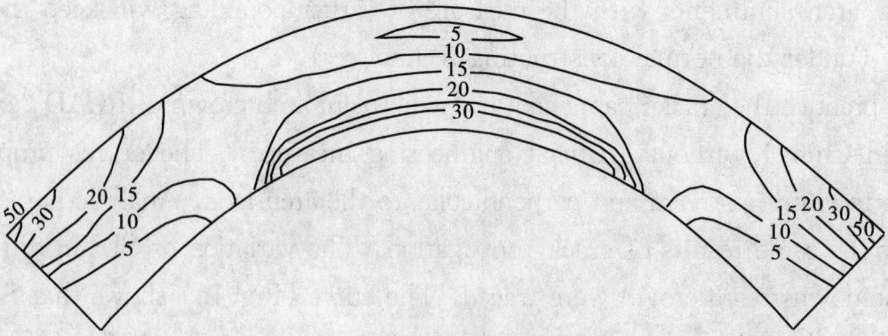

Fig.8 σ_1 (temperature drop)

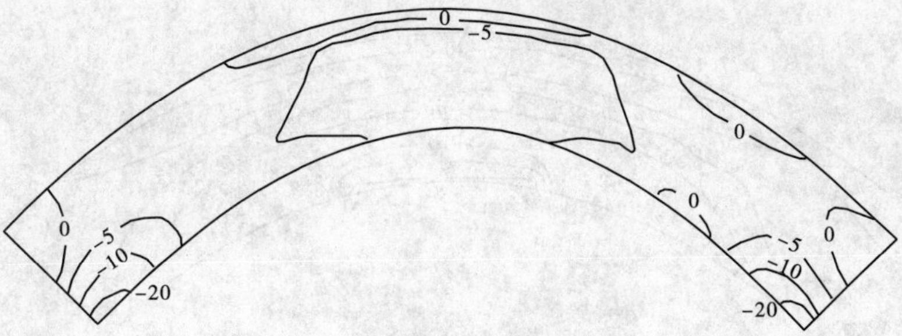

Fig. 9 $\boldsymbol{\sigma}_2$ **(temperature drop)**

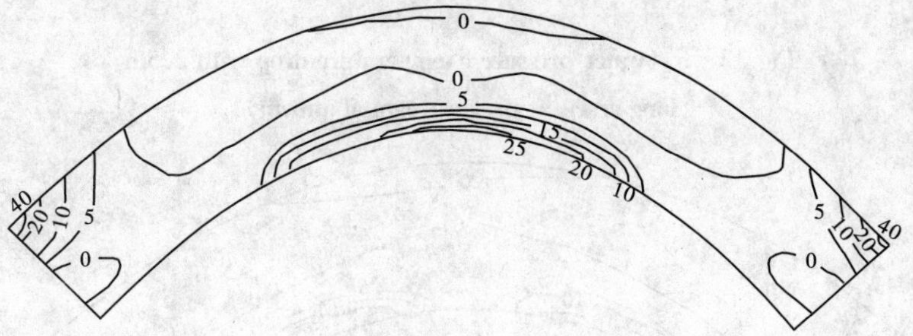

Fig. 10 $\boldsymbol{\sigma}_1$ **(water pressure + temperature drop)**

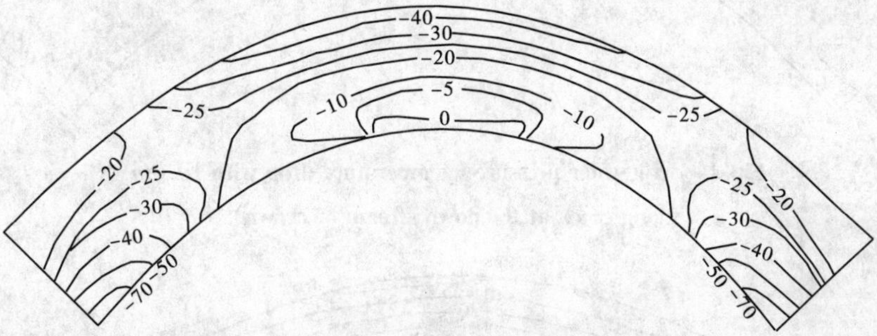

Fig. 11 $\boldsymbol{\sigma}_2$ **(water pressure + temperature drop)**

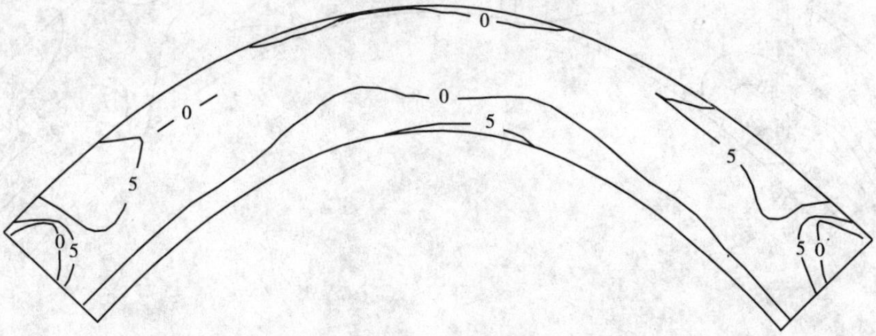

Fig. 12 $\boldsymbol{\sigma}_1$ **(water pressure + temperature drop with 2.5m long crack at the upstream abutment)**

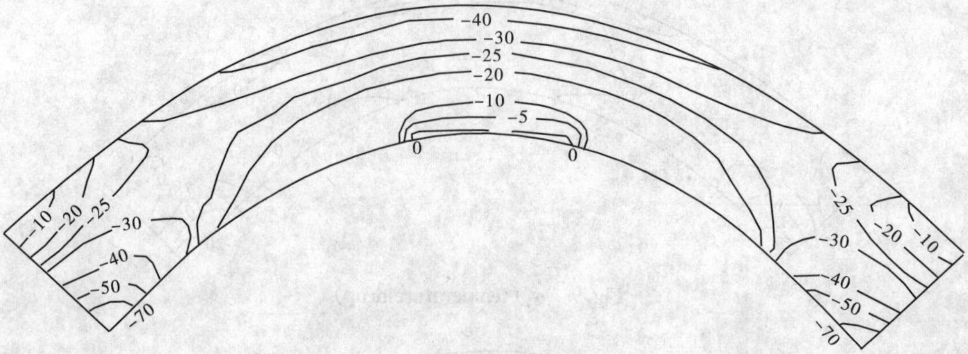

Fig. 13　σ_2 (water pressure + temperature drop with 2.5m long crack at the upstream abutment)

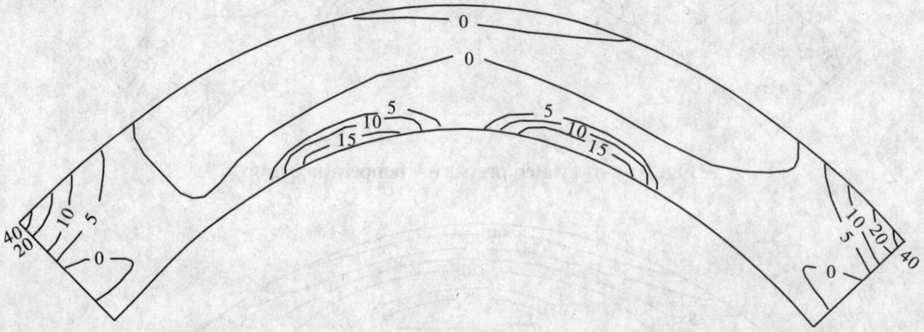

Fig. 14　σ_1 (water pressure + temperature drop with 10.0m long crack at the down stream of crown)

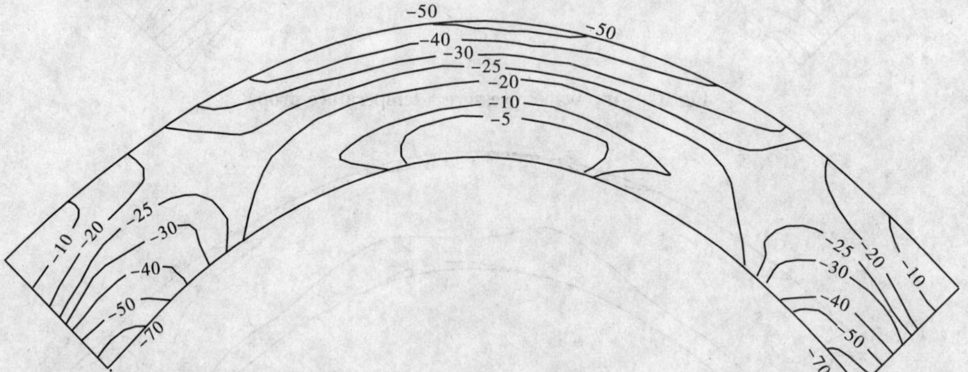

Fig. 15　σ_2 (water pressure + temperature drop with 10.0m long crack at the down stream of crown)

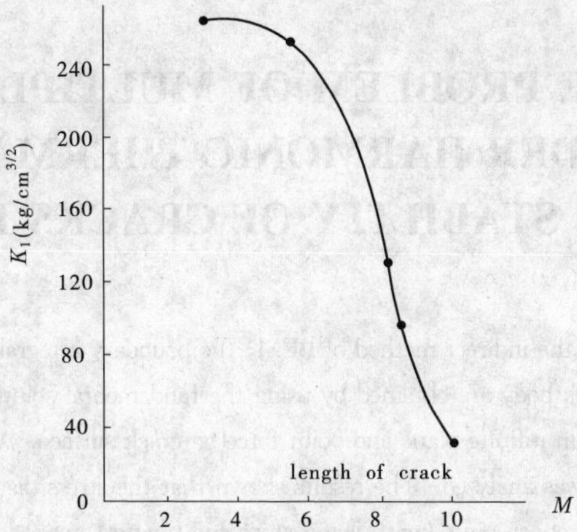

Fig. 16 Relationship between SIF and depth of fracture near the downstream arch crown

References

[1] Guangting Liu ,Guoxin Zhang. *Steady thermal fracture analysis of finite body with crack filled with conductive material*. Fracture of Concrete and Rock Recent Development, pp. 730~737, Elsevier Applied Science, London and New York 1989

[2] Green A. E. ,Zerna W.. *Theoretical elasticity*. Oxfored at the Clarendon Press, 1954

[3] Yizhou Chen. *General case of multiple crack problems in an infinit plate*. Eng. Fracture Mechanics, Vol. 20, No. 4, 1984

[4] Guangting Liu, Yuan Chi. *An analytic-fictitious boundary forces method for calculating multi-crack problem in arbitrary region with mixed mode boundaries*. Fracture of Concrete and Rock Recent Development, pp. 91~100, Elsevier Applied Science, London and New York. 1989

FRACTURE PROBLEM OF MULTIPLE CRACK BODY UNDER HARMONIC THERMAL LOAD AND THE STABILITY OF CRACKS IN RCAD

Abstract According to the indirect method of BEM, the boundary integral equations for fracture problem of multiple crack body are obtained by using the fundamental solutions of harmonic thermoelasticity, point load in infinite plane and point force on crack surface. As an example, a horizontal arch of a RCAD was analysed. The results shown that the stress distribution of RCAD can be improved by artificial short joints (with water stops and fracture stops) located on the upstream of abutments. Since the cracks on the downstream of crown would extend easily during February to April, so the water pressure should be kept during that time.

1 Introduction

Cracks are the main diseases of massive concrete structure. They usually happen on the surface of structure because of the temperature difference between the interior part and external surface of the concrete block and the shrinkage effect. During the high temperature seasons, the temperature in the structure is usually lower than outside because of the heat conduction delay and therefore the tenssion stress should occor inside the concrete, it leads to the extending of crack into the structure. The cracks open and close periodically with the variations of the temperature of atmosphere and water. Some of the cracks develop step by step after a period of temperature variation, at last they become penetrating cracks and which may bring danger to the dam. For example, the similar situation was happened in one of the buttress dam in China, Fontana dam [Abraham I J, et al., 1979.] and Hautefage dam (Buosheng Liu, 1981.). The calculation results also show the fact that the periodical temperature variation of water and atmosphere is an important factor for the extending of cracks. So the study on the fracture problems of multiple crack body under harmonic thermal load is important in engineering practice.

Generally, thermal stresses are induced by the thermal deformation and restraint of structure. When the restraint is weakened with the emergence of cracks, the thermal stresses decrease or disappear. The tenssion stresses in RCAD can also be reduced by the artificial short joints on upstream abutment. In the present paper the problem is solved by means of indirect method of BEM. A calculation example of RCAD is given and the stability of crack is discussed.

本文选自《International Symposium on Roller Compacted Concrete Dams》1991 年 11 月，作者还有 Zhang Guoxin。

2 Harmonic Temperature Field

During operation, dam is laid under the influence of harmonic temperature variation of water and atmosphere, the temperature in the dam also variates periodically. The boundary condition of harmonic heat conduction problem can be simplified as shown in Fig. 1. Where, the temperature on boundary Γ_1 is known as $T(\zeta,t)=\overline{T}_0(\zeta)+\overline{f}(\zeta)\sin\omega t+\overline{g}(\zeta)\cos\omega t$, the heat flow through Γ_2 is: $-\lambda\dfrac{\partial T}{\partial n}=\overline{q}_0(\eta)+\overline{q}_1(\eta)\sin\omega t+\overline{q}_2(\eta)\cos\omega t$.

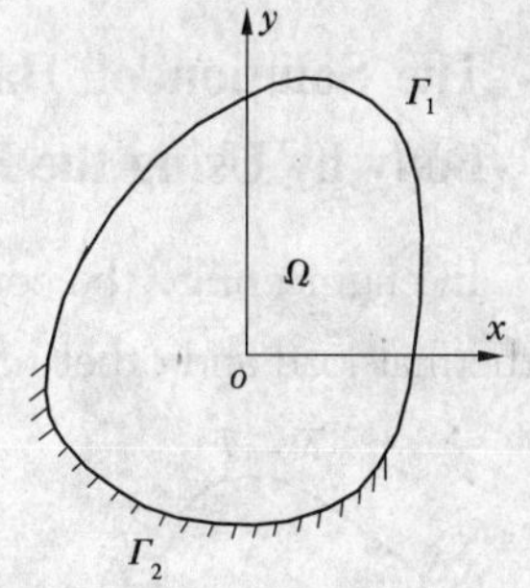

Fig. 1 Boundary condition of head conduction

According to indirect method of BEM, the boundary integral equations in which fictitious thermal sources are taken as the basic unknowns can be obtained by using the fundamental solution of harmonic temperature field (Guoxin Zhang, Guangting Liu, 1990.10):

$$\left.\begin{aligned}
\overline{T}_0(\zeta) &= \int_\Gamma h(s)\frac{1}{2\pi\lambda}\ln(r_{\zeta s})\mathrm{d}s \\
\overline{f}(\zeta) &= \int_\Gamma\left[\frac{q_1(s)}{4\lambda}\mathrm{Im}H_0^{(1)}\left(r_{\zeta s}\sqrt{\frac{\omega i}{a}}\right)-\frac{q_2(s)}{4\lambda}\mathrm{Re}H_0^{(1)}\left(r_{\zeta s}\sqrt{\frac{\omega i}{a}}\right)\right]\mathrm{d}s \\
\overline{g}(\zeta) &= \int_\Gamma\left[\frac{q_1(s)}{4\lambda}\mathrm{Re}H_0^{(1)}\left(r_{\zeta s}\sqrt{\frac{\omega i}{a}}\right)+\frac{q_2(s)}{4\lambda}\mathrm{Im}H_0^{(1)}\left(r_{\zeta s}\sqrt{\frac{\omega i}{a}}\right)\right]\mathrm{d}s \\
\overline{q}_0(\eta) &= \frac{1}{2}h(\eta)-\frac{1}{2\pi}\int_\Gamma h(s)\frac{a}{an_\eta}[\ln(r_{\eta s})]\mathrm{d}s \\
\overline{q}_1(\eta) &= \frac{1}{2}q_1(\eta)-\frac{1}{4}\int_\Gamma\left\{q_1(s)\frac{a}{an_\eta}\left[\mathrm{Im}H_0^{(1)}\left(r_{\eta s}\sqrt{\frac{\omega i}{a}}\right)\right]-q_2(s)\frac{a}{an_\eta}\left[\mathrm{Re}H_0^{(1)}\left(r_{\eta s}\sqrt{\frac{\omega i}{a}}\right)\right]\right\}\mathrm{d}s \\
\overline{q}_2(\eta) &= \frac{1}{2}q_2(\eta)-\frac{1}{4}\int_\Gamma\left\{q_1(s)\frac{a}{an_\eta}\left[\mathrm{Re}H_0^{(1)}\left(r_{\eta s}\sqrt{\frac{\omega i}{a}}\right)\right]+q_2(s)\frac{a}{an_\eta}\left[\mathrm{Im}H_0^{(1)}\left(r_{\eta s}\sqrt{\frac{\omega i}{a}}\right)\right]\right\}\mathrm{d}s
\end{aligned}\right\} \tag{1}$$

where: ζ is a point on boundary Γ_1; η is a point on boundary Γ_2; $h(s), q_1(s), q_2(s)$ are distributed steady thermal source, amplitude of sine thermal source and amplitude of cosine thermal source respectively; λ is thermal conductivity; n_η is the out normal direction of point η; r_{zs} is the distance between point z to the integral point s; $H_0^{(1)}(z)$ is the first kind of Hankel function with 0 order.

By means of numerical, equation (1) can be solved, thus the steady thermal source $h(s)$, the amplitudes of harmonic thermal source $q_1(s)$ and $q_2(s)$ are obtained, then the temperature field can be written as:

$$\begin{aligned}
T(z,t) = \frac{1}{4\lambda}\int_\Gamma\Bigg\{&\frac{2}{\pi}h(s)\ln(r_{zs})+q_1(s)\left[\cos\omega t\,\mathrm{Re}H_0^{(1)}\left(r_{zs}\sqrt{\frac{\omega i}{a}}\right)+\sin\omega t\,\mathrm{Im}H_0^{(1)}\left(r_{zs}\sqrt{\frac{\omega i}{a}}\right)\right]+ \\
&q_2(s)\left[\cos\omega t\,\mathrm{Im}H_0^{(1)}\left(r_{zs}\sqrt{\frac{\omega i}{a}}\right)-\sin\omega t\,\mathrm{Re}H_0^{(1)}\left(r_{zs}\sqrt{\frac{\omega i}{a}}\right)\right]\Bigg\}\mathrm{d}s
\end{aligned} \tag{2}$$

3　The Solution of Harmonic Thermal Fracture Problem of Multiple Crack Body by Using the Fictitious Force Method

In engineering, the boundary condition of structure with multiple cracks under harmonic thermal load and other mechanical load can be simplified as shown in Fig. 2.

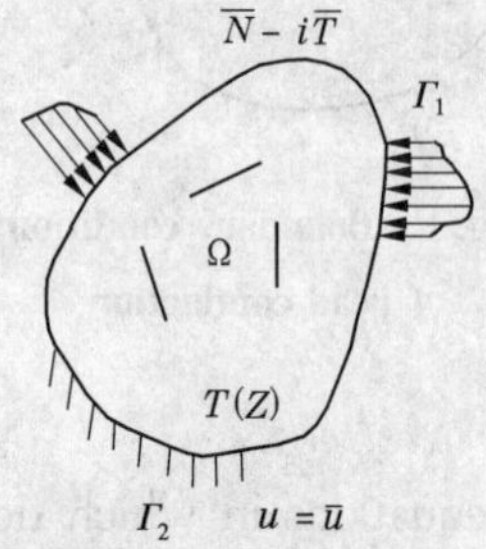

Fig. 2　Multiple crack problem

where: the displacements are known as $u = \overline{u}$ on Γ_1; the force distributions are known on Γ_2.

There are N cracks in region Ω, the length of number k crack is $2a_k$. Suppose fictitious distributive forces act on crack surfaces, the fictitious force on crack k is $P_k(s_k, t)$. The boundary of structure is also loaded by fictitious force $Q(s, t)$. Thus the structure is acted by three kinds of load: ① fictitious force on crack surfaces; ② the fictitious force on the boundary of structure; ③ thermal load.

3.1　Fundamental Solutions

(1) The stresses and displacements at point z in α direction induced by a point force $Q = \dfrac{F_x + iF_y}{2\pi(1+æ)}$ at point s in an infinite plane can be obtained by Kelvin solution:

$$\left.\begin{aligned} \sigma_y^* - i\tau_{xy}^* &= -Q\left(\frac{1}{z-s} - æ\mathrm{e}^{-2i\alpha}\frac{1}{\overline{z}-\overline{s}}\right) - \overline{Q}\left[\frac{1}{\overline{z}-\overline{s}} + \mathrm{e}^{-2i\alpha}\frac{(z-s)}{(\overline{z}-\overline{s})^2}\right] \\ u^* + iv^* &= \frac{\mathrm{e}^{-i\alpha}}{2\mu}\left\{-æQ[\ln(z-s) + \ln(\overline{z}-\overline{s}) + 1] + \overline{Q}\frac{z-s}{\overline{z}-\overline{s}}\right\} \end{aligned}\right\} \tag{3}$$

(2) According to the stress function (Yizhou Chen, 1983), the stresses and displacements at point z in the direction of α caused by a point force $P = F_y - iF_x$ acted on point s on crack surface are:

$$\begin{aligned} \sigma_y^{*c} - i\tau_{xy}^{*c} = &\frac{1}{2\pi}\sqrt{a^2 - s^2}\{P[G(z,a) + \mathrm{e}^{2i\alpha}\overline{G(z,s)}] + \\ &\overline{P}[\overline{G(z,s)}(1-\mathrm{e}^{2i\alpha}) + \mathrm{e}^{2i\alpha}(z-\overline{z})\overline{G'(z,s)}]\} \\ u^{*c} + iv^{*c} = &\frac{\mathrm{e}^{i\alpha}}{4\mu\pi}\{P[\overline{f_1(z,s)} - æf_1(z,s)] + \overline{P}(z-\overline{z})\sqrt{a^2-s^2}\,\overline{G(z,s)}\} \end{aligned} \tag{4}$$

where:

$$G(z,s) = 1/(z-s)\sqrt{z^2 - a^2},$$

$$\begin{aligned} f_1(z,s) = i[&\ln((\sqrt{z^2-a^2} + i\sqrt{a^2-s^2})/(z-s) - si/\sqrt{a^2-s^2}) - \\ &\ln(1 + s/\sqrt{s^2-a^2})] \end{aligned}$$

(3) The stresses and displacements induced by steady and harmonic thermal source $q = h + q_1\sin\omega t + q_2\cos\omega t$ at point s can be obtained by solving thermoelastic problem using the temperature field caused by a steady and harmonic point thermal source (Guoxin Zhang, Guangting Liu, 1990.10):

$$
\left.\begin{aligned}
\sigma_y^{*T} - i\tau_{xy}^{*T} &= \frac{a_l E}{8\lambda}\left\{\frac{h}{\pi}\left[\ln\frac{z-s}{\bar{z}-\bar{s}} + e^{-2ia}\frac{z-s}{\bar{z}-\bar{s}}\right] + \sigma_r(r) + \sigma_\theta(r) + \right.\\
&\qquad \left. e^{-2ia}\frac{z-s}{\bar{z}-\bar{s}}[\sigma_\theta(r) - \sigma_r(r)]\right\}\\
u^{*T} + i\nu^{*T} &= e^{-ia}\frac{a_l(1+\nu)}{8\lambda}\{-h(z-s)[\ln(z-s)(\bar{z}-\bar{s}) - 1] + \\
&\qquad \frac{2(z-s)}{r}[\cos\omega t(q_1 \mathrm{Re}U_0(r) + q_2 \mathrm{Im}U_0(r)) + \\
&\qquad \sin\omega t(q_1 \mathrm{Im}U_0(r) - q_2 \mathrm{Re}U_0(r))]\}
\end{aligned}\right\} \quad (5)
$$

where:

$$
\sigma_r(r) = -\cos\omega t[q_1 \mathrm{Re}S_0(r) + q_2 \mathrm{Im}S_0(r)] - \sin\omega t[q_1 \mathrm{Im}S_0(r) - q_2 \mathrm{Re}S_0(r)]
$$

$$
\begin{aligned}
\sigma_\theta(r) = &\cos\omega t[q_1 \mathrm{Re}(S_0(r) - H_0^{(1)}(r)) + q_2 \mathrm{Im}(S_0(r) - H_0^{(1)}(r))] + \\
&\sin\omega t[q_1 \mathrm{Im}(S_0(r) - H_0^{(1)}(r)) + q_2 \mathrm{Re}(S_0(r) - H_0^{(1)}(r))]
\end{aligned}
$$

$$
\begin{aligned}
U_0(r) = &\left(1 + \frac{2i}{\pi}\ln\frac{\sqrt{\frac{\omega i}{a}}}{2} + \frac{2i}{\pi}\gamma\right)\sum_{k=0}^{\infty} A_k \frac{r^{2k+1}}{2k+2} + \frac{2i}{\pi}\sum_{k=0}^{\infty} A_k \frac{r^{2k+1}}{2k+2}\ln r - \\
&\frac{2i}{\pi}\sum_{k=1}^{\infty} A_k \frac{r^{2k+1}}{2k+2}\sum_{m=1}^{k}\frac{1}{m} - \frac{2i}{\pi}\sum_{k=0}^{\infty} A_k \frac{r^{2k+1}}{(2k+2)^2}
\end{aligned}
$$

$$
\begin{aligned}
S_0(r) = &\left[1 + \frac{2i}{\pi}\left(\ln\frac{\sqrt{\frac{\omega i}{a}}}{2} + \gamma\right)\right]\sum_{k=0}^{\infty} A_k \frac{r^{2k}}{2k+2} - \frac{2i}{\pi}\sum_{k=0}^{\infty} A_k \frac{r^{2k}}{(2k+2)^2} + \\
&\frac{2i}{\pi}\sum_{k=0}^{\infty} A_k \frac{r^{2k}}{2k+2}\ln r - \frac{2i}{\pi}\sum_{k=1}^{\infty} A_k \frac{r^{2k+1}}{2k+2}\sum_{m=1}^{k}\frac{1}{m}
\end{aligned}
$$

3.2 Boundary Integral Equations

The stresses and displacements at point z in region Ω in the direction of α and time t caused by the combination of thermal source $h(s) + q_1(s)\sin\omega t + q_2(s)\cos\omega t$ and distributive force $Q(s)$ on the boundary of the region and the fictitious forces on crack surfaces can be obtained by the integration of formulae (3), (4) and (5) along the boundary of the region and crack surfaces, they are:

$$
\begin{aligned}
\sigma_y(z,t) - i\tau_{xy}(z,t) = &\int_\Gamma \{\sigma_y^*[Q(s,t),z] - i\tau_{xy}^*[Q(s,t),z]\}\mathrm{d}s + \\
&\sum_{k=1}^{N}\int_{-a_k}^{a_k}\{\sigma_y^{*c}[P_k(s_k,t),z] - i\tau_{xy}^{*c}[P_k(s_k,t),z]\}\mathrm{d}s_k + \\
&\int_\Gamma \{\sigma_y^{*T}[q(s_k,t),z] - i\tau_{xy}^{*T}[q(s,t),z]\}ds
\end{aligned}
$$

$$
\begin{aligned}
u(z,t) + i\nu(z,t) = &\int_\Gamma \{u^*[Q(s,t),z] + i\nu^*[Q(s,t),z]\}\mathrm{d}s + \\
&\sum_{k=1}^{N}\int_{-a_k}^{a_k}\{u^{*c}[P_k(s_k,t),z] + i\nu^{*c}[P_k(s_k,t),z]\}\mathrm{d}s_k +
\end{aligned}
$$

$$\int_{\Gamma}\{u^{*T}[q(s_k,t),z]+i\nu^{*T}[q(s,t),z]\}\mathrm{d}s \tag{6}$$

Suppose the known displacements on the boundary Γ_1 is $\overline{u}(\eta)+i\overline{\nu}(\eta)$, the external force on Γ_2 is $N(\xi)-iT(\xi)$, the surfaces of all the cracks are free. Let z in the first formula of equation (6) approach to ξ on Γ_2 and ζ_n on the surface of crack n infinitely, and let z in the second formula of equation (6) approach to η on Γ_1, a group of equations solving the problem can be obtained as:

$$\begin{aligned}N(\xi,t)-iT(\xi,t)=&-\frac{i}{2}Q(\xi,t)+\int_{\Gamma}\{\sigma_y^*[Q(s,t),\xi]-i\tau_{xy}^*[Q(s,t),\xi]\}\mathrm{d}s+\\&\sum_{k=1}^{N}\int_{-a_k}^{a_k}\{\sigma_y^{*c}[P_k(s_k,t),\xi]-i\tau_{xy}^{*c}[P_k(s_k,t),\xi]\}\mathrm{d}s_k+\\&\int_{\Gamma}\{\sigma_y^{*T}[q(s_k,t),\xi]-i\tau_{xy}^{*T}[q(s,t),\xi]\}\mathrm{d}s\\\overline{u}(\eta,t)+i\overline{\nu}(\eta,t)=&\int_{\Gamma}\{u^*[Q(s,t),\eta]+i\nu^*[Q(s,t),\eta]\}\mathrm{d}s+\\&\sum_{k=1}^{N}\int_{-a_k}^{a_k}\{u^{*c}[P_k(s_k,t),\eta]+i\nu^{*c}[P_k(s_k,t),\eta]\}\mathrm{d}s_k+\\&\int_{\Gamma}\{u^{*T}[q(s_k,t),\eta]+i\nu^{*T}[q(s,t),\eta]\}\mathrm{d}s\end{aligned} \tag{7}$$

$$\begin{aligned}O=&\frac{1}{2}P_k(\zeta_n,t)+\int_{\Gamma}\{\sigma_y^*[Q(s,t),\zeta_n]-i\tau_{xy}^*[Q(s,t),\zeta_n]\}\mathrm{d}s+\\&\sum_{k=1}^{N}\int_{-a_k}^{a_k}\{\sigma_y^{*c}[P_k(s_k,t),\zeta_n]-i\tau_{xy}^{*c}[P_k(s_k,t),\zeta_n]\}\mathrm{d}s_k+\\&\int_{\Gamma}\{\sigma_y^{*T}[q(s_k,t),\zeta_n]-i\tau_{xy}^{*T}[q(s,t),\zeta_n]\}\mathrm{d}s\end{aligned}$$

Equation group (7) is the integral equation for solving fracture problem of multiple crack body under harmonic thermal load and other mechanical loads. The equations can be solved by BEM, and then the fictitious forces on boundary and crack surface can be obtained. The stresses and displacements can be calculated by formula (6). The SIF at every crack tips can be calculated as following:

$$K_{n\mathrm{I}}^{\pm}(t)-iK_{n\mathrm{II}}^{\pm}(t)=-\frac{1}{\sqrt{\pi a_n}}\int_{-a_n}^{a_n}P_n(s_n,t)\sqrt{\frac{a_n\pm s_n}{a_n\mp s_n}}\mathrm{d}s_n \tag{8}$$

4 Engineering Application

An experimental roll compacted arch dam was designed with the consideration of limit state. It is difficult to enssure the quality of connection between layers. An arch and its boundary condition is shown in Fig. 3. The maximum temperature before cooling in the arch is 29℃ and the maximum water head above the arch is 80.0m. The temperature of water in the reservoir is $Tu=13.5+3.5\sin\omega(t-4)$, the temperture of atmosphere is $Td=16.7+$

$9.7\sin\omega(t-4)$. Where $\omega = 2\pi/12$. The following problems are calculated and analysed by using the method presented in this paper: ① the influence of short artificial joints at the upstream abutments to the improvement on stress distribution in arch. ② The stability of cracks on the downstream of crown and limit of temperature in arch in order to enssure the stability of crack.

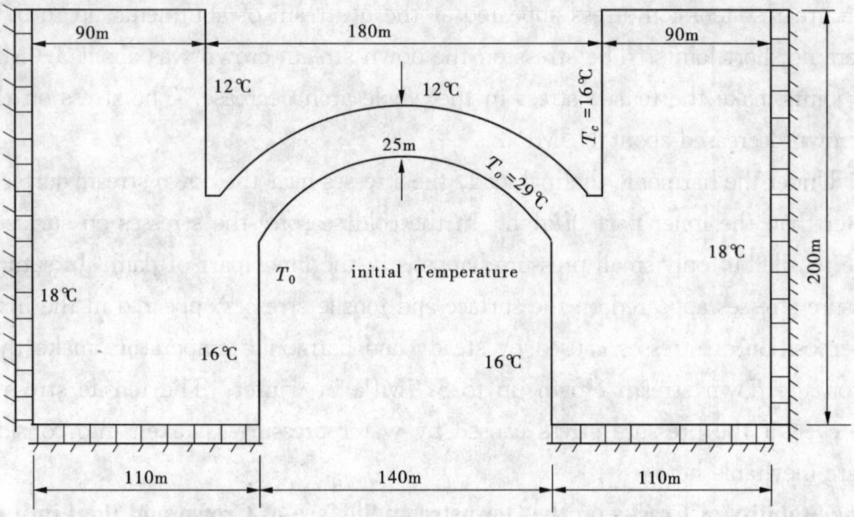

Fig. 3 Boundary condition of arch

4.1 The Improvement on Stress Distribution in Arch by the Short Artificial Joints

In order to improve the stress distribution of dam, two short artificial joints with length of 3.0m(with water stop and fracture stop) were made on both sides of upstream abutments. The stresses in arch direction of controlling points on two abutments and crown before and after the joints were made are shown in Table 1.

Table 1 The stresses at some controlling points of arch with and without artificial joints

(unit: MPa)

		water pressure		steady thermal load		harmonic thermal load	
		no joint	joint	no joint	joint	no joint	joint
abutment	up	-3.9	-3.5	-0.8	-0.3	0.6	0.6
	mid	-2.5	-2.9	1.6	0.9	-0.2	-0.3
	down	-1.4	-2.6	3.2	1.7	2.4	2.0
crown	up	0.8	0	5.0	0	1.1	0
	mid	-2.5	-3.2	0.8	1.0	-0.2	0
	down	-5.0	-5.2	-1.4	-2.1	0	0.8

It can be seen from Table 1:

(1) If there were no artificial joints, most area of the arch was in pressure state in arch direction except a small corner near the upstream abutments under water pressure. After the

joints were made, the tensile stresses in this small area on the upstream of abutments disappeared and the pressure stresses at the down stream of crown increased about 1.2MPa, which is beneficial to the reduction of tensile stresses casued by temperature load.

(2) Higher tensile stresses appeared on the upstream area of two abutments and down stream of crown and most part of the arch was in tensile stresses. Under steady thermal load, the greatest tenssion stress appeared at the upstream of abutments up to 5.0MPa if there were no short joints. The stress on the down stream crown was about 3.0MPa. The artificial joints make the tensile stress in the whole arch decrease. The stress on the down stream crown decreased about 1.5MPa.

(3) Under the harmonic thermal load, the stresses near the down stream surface of dam are greater than the inner part of arch. In the cold season, the stresses on surface are remarkable tensile but only small pressure happens in the inner part of dam. In summer time the pressure stresses appeared on the surface and tensile stresses appeared in the inner part. The superposition of stresses caused by steady and harmonic temperature make the tensile stresses on the down stream crown up to 3.7MPa in winter. The tensile stress remains 1.1MPa even if the pressure stress caused by water pressure is taken into consideration. Cracks are inevitable here.

4.2 The Stability of Cracks on the Downstream Surface of Crown and the Limit of Highest Temperature of Dam During Construction

Although the tensile stresses on downstream crown decreased enormously after the consideration of artificial joints at the upstream abutments, there remains tensile stresses of high level during the seasons and especially when the water level is lower. In order to study the stability of cracks on the downstream surface of crown, the variation of SIF to time with different temperature limitation of dam, different water level and different length of cracks were analysed by means of the method presented in this paper, the results are shown in Fig. 4 to Fig. 6.

It can be seen from Fig. 4 to Fig. 6 that when the maximum temperature in dam is $T_m = 29℃$, as long as the water head above the arch is greater than 40.0m the cracks on the surface of downstream crown keep stable. The reservior can not be emptied in all the seasons, otherwise the crack will propagate through the dam.

When the maximum temperature of dam is limited to $T_m = 24℃$, water pressure is still needed for the stability of cracks. If the highest temperature in dam decreases to 20.0℃, water pressure is needed only during January to June. In the other seasons, the reservior can be emptied.

The prescribed requirements can hardly be satisfied during the construction. Since the thermal stress is very sensitive to thermal expansion α_1 (in the example of present paper, thermal expansion $\alpha_1 = 0.000\ 01$), so it is better to use the concrete with lower thermal expansion (for instance $\alpha_1 = 0.000\ 006$) for the safety of dam.

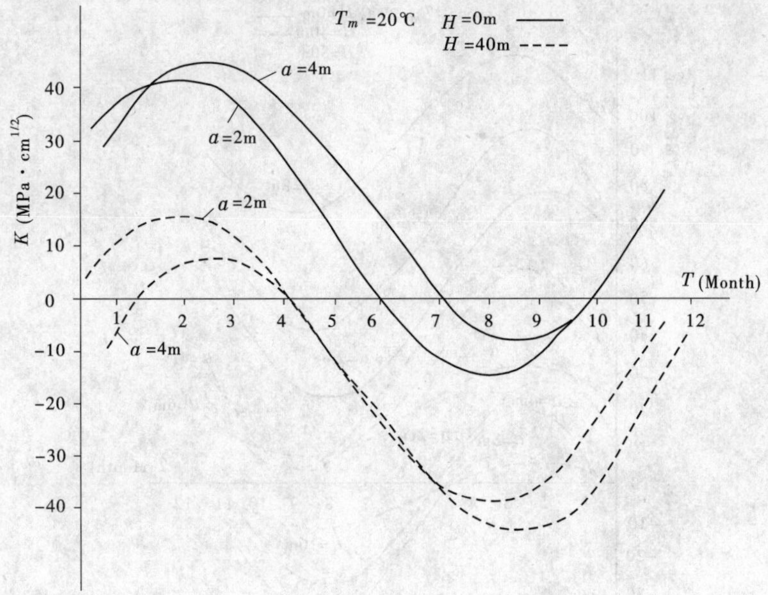

Fig. 4 The SIF of crack on downstream crown when $T_m = 20$℃

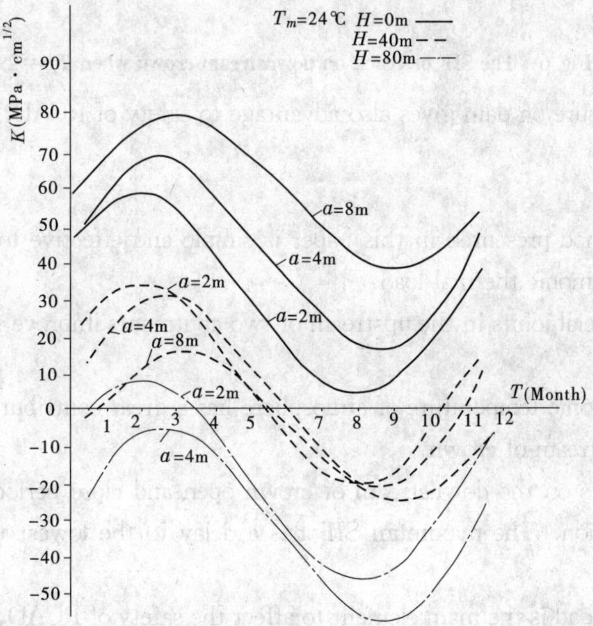

Fig. 5 The SIF of crack on downstream crown when $T_m = 24$℃

It can also be seen from Fig. 4 to Fig. 6 that the SIF variates periodically, the maximum value of SIF has a phase-delay with respect to the lowest temperature of atmosphere, and the longer the crack, the longer the delay time. The maximum SIF usually happend during February to April for 2～8m long crack. So that it is not suitable to empty the reservior in these time. The effect of water pressure for the prevention of cracks is obvious. Keeping a

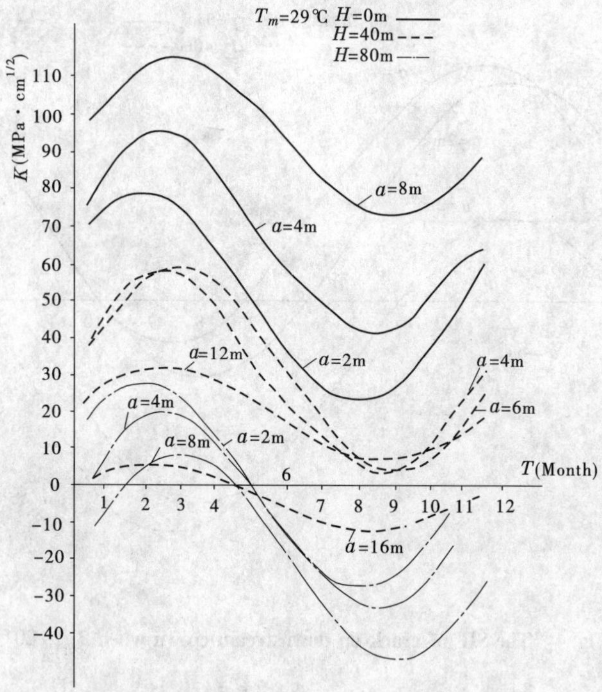

Fig. 6　The SIF of crack on downstream crown when T_m = 29℃

certain water pressure on dam gives also advantage to safety of RCAD.

5 Conclusions

(1) The method presented in this paper is simple and effective to solve multiple crack problem under harmonic thermal load.

(2) The artificial joints in the upstream of two abutments improve the stress distribution effectively.

(3) The harmonic temperature of atmosphere has a great contribution to the increase of SIF on the downstream of crown.

(4) The cracks on the downstream of crown open and close periodically because of the temperature variation. The maximum SIF has a delay to the lowest temperature of atmosphere.

(5) Thermal load is the main element to affect the safety of RCAD, the concrete material with possible lowest thermal expansion should be used for RCAD.

(6) Water pressure prevents the extension of cracks on downstream crown where the observation should be kept during operation for the safety of RCAD.

References

[1] Abrabam I. J. ,Sloan R. C. . 13*th International Congress on Large Dams*. International Commission on Large Dams, Vol 1,1979,pp. 1~24

[2] Buosheng Liu. *The Serious Destruction of Four Dams in French*. Hydraulic Electricity in Abroud, 1981,5,pp. 20~27

[3] Guoxin Zhang, Guangting Liu. *Fictitious Thermal Source (F. T. S) Method in Solving Harmonic Temperature Field Problem*. Proceedings of International Symposium on Pumped Storage Development, Beijing, China. 1990. 10, pp. 196~203

[4] Yizhou Chen. *General Case of Multiple Crack Problems in an Infinite Plate*. Engl. Fracture Mechanics, Vol. 20 No. 4, 1984

THERMALLY STRESSED MULTIPLE SYSTEMS IN STEADY STATE

Abstract This work is concerned with formulating the steady state linear thermoelastic problem for bodies with finite dimensions and multiple cracks. A superposition scheme is used so that the finite body problem is divided into three component problems involving the infinite region. The first and second component problems are concerned, respectively, with prescribing displacements/tractions and thermal disturbance in an infinite region at the site that conforms to the boundary of the finite body. The third component problem corresponds to an infinite region with cracks subjected to the negative of the tractions obtained from the mechanical and thermal loadings. Upon adding all three component problems, the mechanical and thermal boundary conditions of the original problem with multiple free surface cracks are recovered.

Numerical results are obtained for edge crack, three parallel cracks and three inclined cracks along the sides of an equilateral triangle, In all cases, a steady state temperature difference is maintained either uniformly over or across the specimen with fixed edges. Constant contours of shear stress are calculated and they matched well with the corresponding isochromatics observed in experiments.

1 Introduction

Multiple cracking is common to many materials used in the construction of building and dam structures[1-3]. Changes in the environment temperature could cause failure by fracture. The interaction of cracks can be complex, particularly when they are clustered closely together giving rise to highly non-symmetrical distribution of stresses and/or strains. Effective stress solutions would be a prerequisite for predicting the potential failure behavior of multiple cracks. Previous works[4~10] on this subject have dealt mostly with mechanical loads or thermal loads applied to bodies containing a single crack. One of the main objectives of this work is to develop an effective analytical procedure for determining the stress states in finite bodies weakened by multiple cracks under thermally induced stresses. Comparisons are then made with the corresponding isochromatics observed experimentally.

Mode Ⅰ and Ⅱ thermal stress intensity factor[11] solutions are also obtained, the combination of which would determine the condition of crack initiation provided that the fracture toughness of the material is known. Details on mixed mode fracture are not within the scope

本文选自 Elsevier Science Publishers B. V. 1992 年出版的《Theoretical and Applied Fracture Mechanics》一书，作者还有 G. X. Zhong。

of this investigation.

2 Preliminary Consideration on Thermal Disturbance

Within the framework of linear thermoelasticity, the temperature field can be determined independent of the stresses. Referring to the two-dimensional region Λ of (x, y) which is enclosed by the surface Σ that consists of two portions Σ_1 and Σ_2 on which the following conditions prevail

$$T(x,y) = T_n^0, \text{ on } \Sigma_1, \; q(x,y) = q_n^0, \text{ on } \Sigma_2 \tag{1}$$

Refer to the schematic in Fig. 1(a). Suppose that the boundary Σ is divided into segments $1, 2, \cdots, k-1, k, k+1, \cdots, m$ as shown in Fig. 1(b) such a different uniformly distributed heat sources are applied. For a steady thermal source h_k referred to the kth segment, the fundamental governing equations are given by

$$\sum_{k=1}^{m} \frac{1}{2\pi\lambda} h_k \mathrm{Re}\left[t_{kn} \log\left(\frac{t_{kn} - d_k}{t_{kn} + d_k}\right) - b_k \log(t_{kn}^2 - d_k^2) + 2d_k \right] = T_n^0, \text{ on} \sum\nolimits_1$$

$$\frac{1}{2} - \mathrm{Im}\left[\sum_{k=1}^{m^*} \frac{1}{2\pi} h_k \exp\{-i(\beta_k - \beta_n)\} \log\left(\frac{t_{kn} - d_k}{t_{kn} + d_k}\right)\right] = q_n^0, \text{ on} \sum\nolimits_2 \tag{2}$$

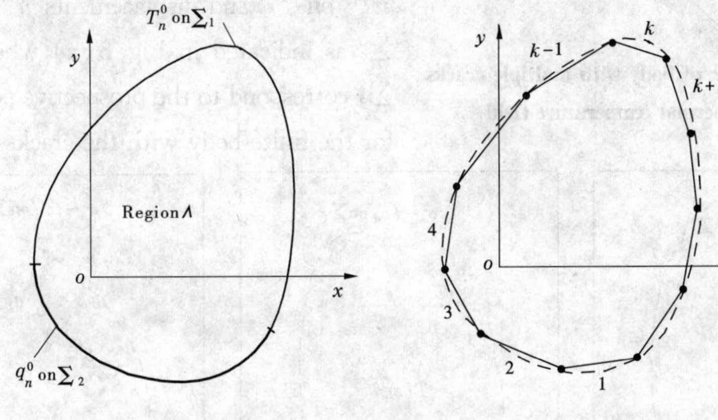

(a) Smooth boundary (b) Segmented boundary

Fig. 1 Mixed thermal boundary conditions on body without cracks

with λ being the heat conductivity, m^* refers to the total number of segments except for $k = n$. In Eq. (2),

$$t_{kn} = (z_n^0 - z_k^0)\exp(-i\beta_k) \tag{3}$$

Here, z stands for the complex variable $x + iy$ and z_n^0 and z_k^0 locate the center of segment n and k, respectively. The angles between the x-axis and tangential direction of segment k and n are given by β_k and β_n while d_k designates the half length of element k.

The first of Eq. (2) contains m expressions in terms of the m heat sources h_k. This leads to the temperature field for a finite region:

$$T(z)=\sum_{k=1}^{m}\frac{1}{2\pi\lambda}h_k\mathrm{Re}\left[z_k\log\left(\frac{z_k-d_k}{z_k+d_k}\right)-d_k\log(z_k^2-d_k^2)+2d_k\right] \tag{4}$$

3 Formulation of Mixed Boundary Value Problem

Now, let the region Λ in Fig. 2 contain p number of cracks $L_1, L_2, \cdots, L_p$ whose ends are $a_j b_j (j=1,2,\cdots,p)$. Interaction between the cracks and the temperature field in Eq. (4) is neglected [12]. Surrounding Λ is the surface $\Sigma=\Sigma_1+\Sigma_2$ with tractions $\sigma_n^0-i\tau_n^0$ specified on Σ_1 and displacements $u_n^0+iv_n^0$ on Σ_2 Values of z on Σ are denoted by s. The finite body problem will be divided into three infinite body problems whose solutions are readily available from the complex function theory[13]. They can be stated briefly as follows:

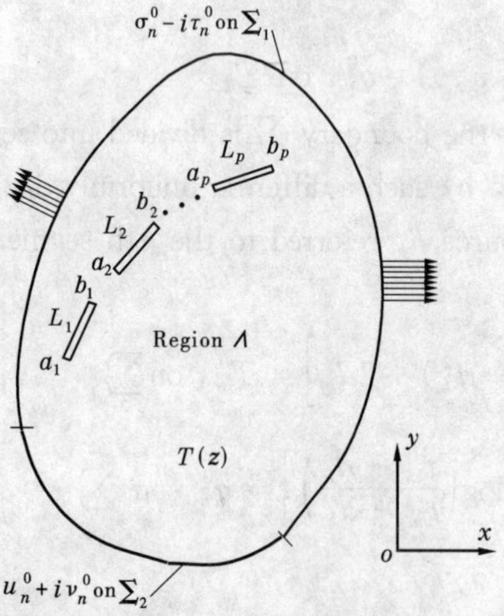

Fig. 2 Schematic of body with multiple cracks in nonisothermal temperature field

(1) Infinite region with tractions $\sigma_n^{(1)}-i\tau_n^{(1)}$ on Σ_1 and displacements $u_n^{(1)}+iv_n^{(1)}$ on Σ_2 as indicated in Fig. 3(a) where Σ_1 and Σ_2 correspond to the prospective portion of Σ for the finite body with the cracks absent.

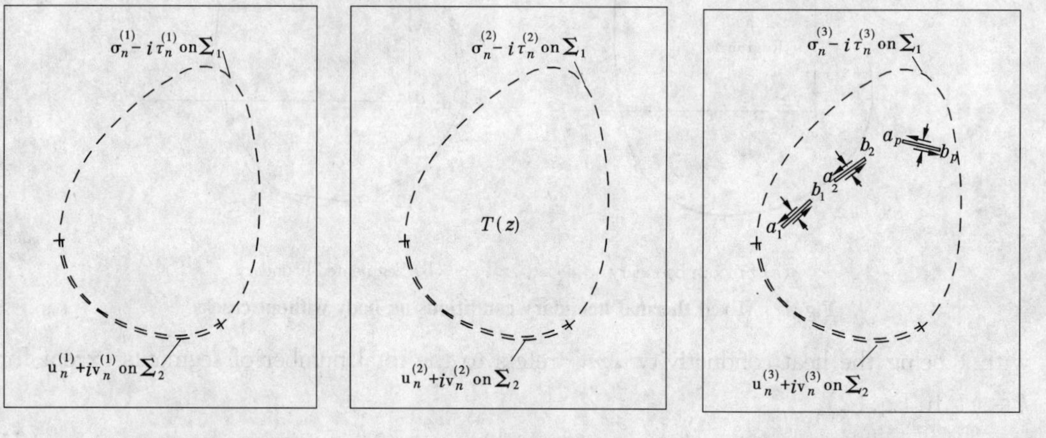

(a) Mechanical load effect (b) Thermal disturbance (c) Influence of cracks

Fig. 3 Infinite domain component problems accounting for disturbance from thermal load and cracks

(2) The tractions $\sigma_n^{(2)}-i\tau_n^{(2)}$ on Σ_1 and displacements $u_n^{(2)}+iv_n^{(2)}$ are obtained from distributed thermal source $H(s)$ in the infinite region on Σ for the finite body without cracks. Fig. 3(b).

(3) The tractions $\sigma_n^{(3)}-i\tau_n^{(3)}$ on Σ_1 and displacements $u_n^{(3)}+iv_n^{(3)}$ on Σ_2 in Fig. 3(c) are determined together with tractions applied to the cracks $L_j (j=1,2,\cdots,p)$ that are the

nega tive of those induced at the prospective crack sites from mechanical and thermal load.

The superposition of the foregoing three infinite domain problems yields the original boundary value problem with free surface cracks $L_1, L_2, \cdots, L_p$ as shown in Fig. 2. In what follows, each of the component problems will be discussed separately and the superscripts (1), (2) and (3) will be used to identify the three problems in Figs. 3(a), 3(b) and 3(c), respectively.

3.1 Arbitrary Tractions Inside Infinite Region with no Cracks

The concentrated load solution given in [13] can be used to generate arbitrary tractions applied to the interior of an infinite domain. Referring to Fig. 4(a) for a complex point force $P = F_x + iF_y$ applied at $z = c$, the complex functions take the forms

$$\phi(z) = -\frac{P}{2(1+k)}\log(z-c),\ \Psi(z) = \frac{k\overline{P}}{2(1+k)}[\log(z-c)+1] + \frac{P}{2(1+k)}\frac{c}{z-c} \tag{5}$$

in which $k = 3-4\nu$ for plane strain and $(3-\nu)/(1+\nu)$ for plane stress. The stresses can be obtained from

$$\begin{aligned}\sigma_x + \sigma_y &= 4\mathrm{Re}[\phi'(z)] \\ \sigma_y - \sigma_x + 2i\tau_{xy} &= 2[\bar{z}\phi''(z) + \psi'(z)]\end{aligned} \tag{6}$$

and the displacements from

$$2\mu(u_x + iv_y) = k\phi(z) - z\overline{\phi}'(z) - \overline{\psi}(z) \tag{7}$$

where bar denotes complex conjugate.

Let $P = Q(s)\,ds$ and use the concentrated load as a Green's function. The stresses and displacements at a point, say z, due to distributed forces $Q(s)$ on Σ making an angle β with the x-axis as in Fig. 4(b) can be obtained by integration:

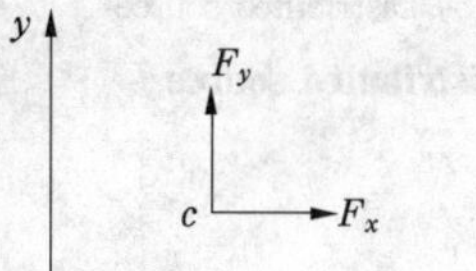

(a) Point forces

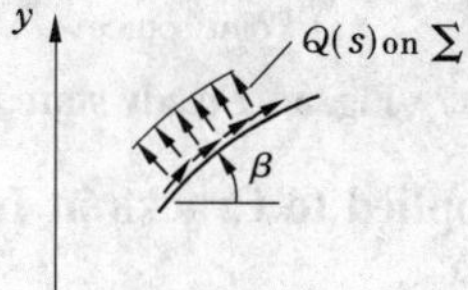

(b) Distributed tractions

Fig. 4 Isolated point forces and tractions on inclined boundary

$$\sigma_x^{(1)} + \sigma_y^{(1)} = -\frac{2}{1+k}\int_{\Sigma}\mathrm{Re}\left[\frac{Q(s)}{z-c(s)}\right]ds$$

$$\begin{aligned}\sigma_y^{(1)} - i\tau_{xy}^{(1)} = -\frac{1}{2(1+k)}\int_{\Sigma}\Big\{&Q(s)\left[\frac{1}{z-c(s)} - \frac{k\exp\{2i[\beta-\beta(s)]\}}{\bar{z}-\bar{c}(s)}\right] + \\ &\overline{Q}(s)\left[\frac{1}{\bar{z}-\bar{c}(s)} - \frac{[z-c(s)]\exp\{-2i[\beta-\beta(s)]\}}{[\bar{z}-\bar{c}(s)]^2}\right]\Big\}ds\end{aligned} \tag{8}$$

and

$$u_x^{(1)} + iv_y^{(1)} = \frac{1}{4\mu(1+k)}\int_{\Sigma} \exp[-i\beta(s)]\Big\{-kQ(s)\{\log[z-c(s)] + \log[\overline{z}-\overline{c}(s)]+1\} + \overline{Q}(s)\frac{z-c(s)}{\overline{z}-\overline{c}(s)}\Big\}\mathrm{d}s \tag{9}$$

Here, Σ designates the surface on which the tractions $Q(s)$ are applied.

3.2 Thermal Stresses and Displacements in Infinite Region without Cracks

Referring to Fig. 3(b) or Fig. 5(a), the point heat source h_k may be used to generate the result for a distributed thermal source $H(s)$ over Σ, Fig. 5(b). The corresponding stresses are

$$\sigma_x^{(2)} + \sigma_y^{(2)} = \frac{\alpha E}{2\pi\lambda}\int_{\Sigma} H(s)\mathrm{Re}\{\log[z-c(s)]\}\mathrm{d}s$$

$$\sigma_y^{(2)} - \sigma_x^{(2)} + 2i\tau_{xy}^{(2)} = \frac{\alpha E}{4\pi\lambda}\int_{\Sigma} H(s)\exp\{-2i[\beta-\beta(s)]\}\frac{\overline{z}-\overline{c}(s)}{z-c(s)}\mathrm{d}s \tag{10}$$

and the displacements take the forms

$$u_x^{(2)} + iv_y^{(2)} = -\frac{\alpha(1+\nu)}{8\pi\lambda}\int_{\Sigma} H(s)[z-c(s)][2\,\mathrm{Re}\{\log[z-c(s)]\}-1]\exp\{-i[\beta-\beta(s)]\}\mathrm{d}s \tag{11}$$

where α is the linear coefficient of thermal expansion.

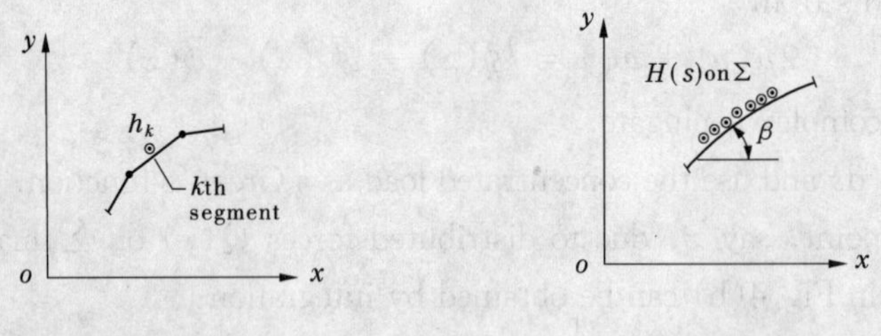

(a) Point source (b) Distributed source

Fig. 5 Steady state thermal point and distributed source

3.3 Tractions Applied to Cracks in Infinite Region

The solution[13]

$$\Phi(z) = \Omega(z) = -\frac{P}{2\pi i}\frac{\sqrt{a^2-s^2}}{(z-s)\sqrt{z^2-a^2}} \tag{12}$$

corresponds to an infinite region with a crack of length $2a$ subjected to a pair of point force $P = F_x + iF_y$ at $z = s$ as shown in Fig. 6(a). It can be used to obtain the function $\Phi(z)$ or $\phi'(z)$ and $\Psi(z)$ or $\psi'(z)$ for arbitrary tractions $R(s)$ applied on the crack by knowing that[13]

$$\Psi(z) = -\Phi(z) - z\Phi'(z) + \overline{\Omega}(z) \tag{13}$$

By letting $P = R(s)\,\mathrm{d}s$ or $P_j = R_j(s_j)\mathrm{d}s_j$ for the jth crack, then $\Phi_j(z_j)$ and $\Psi_j(z_j)$ can be obtained by integrating over the line cracks with ends $-a_j$ to a_j. Referring to a local coordinate system (x_j, y_j) centered on the crack, the results may be written as

$$\Phi_j(z_j) = -\frac{1}{2\pi i}\int_{-a_j}^{a_j} R_j(s_j)G(z_j, s_j)\sqrt{a_j^2 - s_j^2}\,\mathrm{d}s_j$$

$$\Psi_j(z_j) = \frac{1}{2\pi i}\int_{-a_j}^{a_j} [R_j(s_j) - \overline{R}_j(\overline{s}_j)]G(z_j, s_j)\sqrt{a_j^2 - s_j^2}\,\mathrm{d}s_j + \frac{z_k}{2\pi i}\int_{-a_j}^{a_j} R_j(s_j)G'(z_j, s_j)\sqrt{a_j^2 - s_j^2}\,\mathrm{d}s_j \quad (14)$$

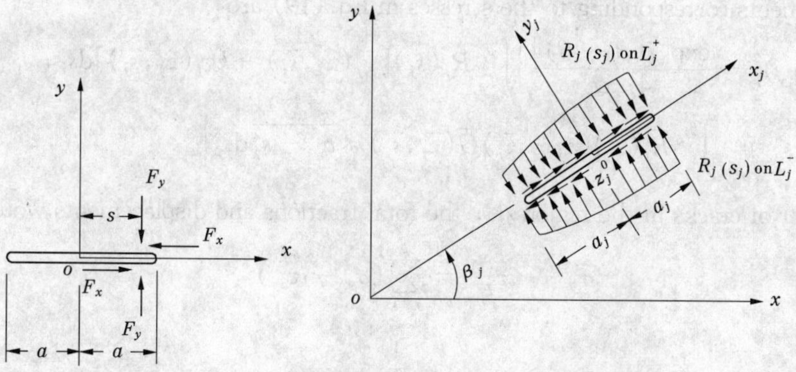

(a) Isolated forces (b) Surface tractions

Fig. 6 Point forces and tractions on a finite length crack

in which $R_j(s_j)$ stand for tractions applied to the upper surface L_j^+ and lower surface L_j^- of the crack in Fig. 6(b). In Eq. (14), G and G' stand for

$$G(z_j, s_j) = \frac{1}{(z_j - s_j)\sqrt{z_j^2 - a_j^2}}, G'(z_j, s_j) = \frac{a_j^2 + s_j z_j - 2z_j^2}{(z_j - s_j)^2(z_j^2 - a_j^2)^{3/2}} \quad (15)$$

Eq. (14) can be integrated with reference to z_j giving

$$\phi_j(z_j) = -\frac{1}{2\pi i}\int_{-a_j}^{a_j} R_j(s_j)g(z_j, s_j)\mathrm{d}s_j$$

$$\psi_j(s_j) = -\frac{1}{2\pi i}\int_{-a_j}^{a_j}\left[\overline{R}_j(\overline{s}_j)g_j(z_j, s_j) - z_j R_j(s_j)\sqrt{a_j^2 - s_j^2}G(z_j, s_j)\right]\mathrm{d}s_j \quad (16)$$

The function $g_j(z_j, s_j)$ is given by

$$g_j(z_j, s_j) = i\left\{\log\left[\frac{\sqrt{z_j^2 - a_j^2} + i\sqrt{a_j^2 - s_j^2}}{z_j - s_j} - \frac{is_j}{\sqrt{a_j^2 - s_j^2}}\right] - \log\left[1 + \frac{s_j}{\sqrt{s_j^2 - a_j^2}}\right]\right\} \quad (17)$$

Making use of Eqs. (6) and (16), the normal and shear combination on the crack L_j that makes an angle β with the x-axis as in Fig. 6(b) becomes

$$(\sigma_y - i\tau_{xy})_j = \int_{-a_j}^{a_j} R_j(s_j)A_j(s_j, z)\mathrm{d}s_j + \int_{-a_j}^{a_j}\overline{R}_j(\overline{s}_j)B_j(s_j, z)\mathrm{d}s_j \quad (18)$$

Note that

$$A_j = -\frac{1}{2\pi i}\sqrt{a_j^2 - s_j^2}\{G(z_j, s_j) + \overline{G}(\overline{z}_j, \overline{s}_j)\exp[2i(\beta_j - \beta)]\}$$

$$B_j = -\frac{1}{2\pi i}\sqrt{a_j^2 - s_j^2}\{\overline{G}(\overline{z}_j,\overline{s}_j)\{1 - \exp[2i(\beta_j - \beta)]\} +$$
$$(z_j - \overline{z}_j)\overline{G}'(\overline{z}_j,\overline{s}_j)\exp[2i(\beta_j - \beta)]\} \quad (19)$$

As shown in Fig. 6(b), z_j^0 locates at the center of the crack L_j and the angle β_j, it follows that

$$z_j = (z - z_j^0)\exp(-i\beta_j) \quad (20)$$

The displacements corresponding to the stresses in Eq. (19) are

$$(u_x + iv_y)_j = \frac{\exp[i(\beta_j - \beta)]}{4\mu\pi i}\left\{\int_{-a_j}^{a_j} R_j(s_j)[\overline{g}_j(\overline{z}_j,\overline{s}_j) - kg_j(z_j,s_j)]ds_j + \right.$$
$$\left.\int_{-a_j}^{a_j} \overline{R}_j(\overline{s}_j)(z_j - \overline{z}_j)\overline{G}(\overline{z}_j,\overline{s}_j)\sqrt{a_j^2 - s_j^2}ds_j\right\} \quad (21)$$

For p number of cracks in the region Λ, the total tractions and displacements would be

$$\sigma_y^{(3)} - i\tau_{xy}^{(3)} = \sum_{j=1}^{p}(\sigma_y - i\tau_{xy})_j \quad (22)$$

and

$$u_x^{(3)} + iv_y^{(3)} = \sum_{j=1}^{m}(u_x + iv_y)_j \quad (23)$$

This completes the solution for the problem in Fig. 3(c).

4 Governing Singular Integral Equations

Returning to the original problem in Fig. 2, the final solution may now be obtained by adding those found from the three component problems in Figs. 3(a) to 3(c) inclusive. If $\sigma_n^0 - i\tau_n^0$ denote the tractions specified on Σ_1, then the sum of Eqs. (8), (10) and (22) must satisfy

$$\sum_{k=1}^{3}[\sigma_n^{(k)} - i\tau_n^{(k)}] = \sigma_n^0 - i\tau_n^0 \text{ on } \Sigma_1 \quad (24)$$

Similarly, the displacements $u_n^0 - iv_n^0$ specified on Σ_2 must be enforced. That is, the sum of Eqs. (9), (11) and (23) must yield

$$\sum_{k=1}^{3}[u_n^{(k)} + iv_n^{(k)}] = u_n^0 + iv_n^0 \text{ on } \Sigma_2 \quad (25)$$

Finally, the free surface crack condition requires that

$$\sum_{k=1}^{3}[\sigma_y^{(k)} - i\tau_{xy}^{(k)}]_j = 0, \text{ on } L_j(j = 1,2,\cdots,p) \quad (26)$$

Eqs. (24) to (26) inclusive yield $p+2$ equations solving for the $p+2$ unknowns with $Q_1(s)$ on Σ_1 and $Q_2(s)$ on Σ_2 while $H(s)$ is the thermal source on Σ and $R_j(s_j)$ with $j=1,2,\cdots,p$. These equations can be solved numerically to obtain the stress and displacements in the region Λ in accordance with the mechanical and thermal boundary conditions specified on Σ.

5 Discussion of Results

Numerical results will be calculated for three examples and in each case, the epoxy plate specimen would be fixed at the opposing edges and a uniform temperature drop would be applied. Isochromatics are also obtained for a fringe value of $f = 1.32$ MPa·cm. The mechanical and thermal properties of the specimen are given in Table 1.

Table 1 Mechanical and thermal properties of epoxy plate specimen

Young's modulus $E \times 10^4$ (MPa)	Poisson's ratio ν	Heat conductivity $\lambda \times 10^{-4}$ (m^2/h)	Coefficient of thermal expansion $\alpha \times 10^{-5}$ (K^{-1})
3.95	0.34	5.0	6.8

Calculated will also be the crack tip stress intensity factors K_1 and K_2 which can be combined into the complex form[14]:

$$K_1 - iK_2 = -\frac{1}{\sqrt{\pi a_j}}\int_{-a_j}^{a_j} (\sigma_y - i\tau_{xy})_j \sqrt{\frac{a_j + s_j}{a_j - s_j}} \mathrm{d}s_j \tag{27}$$

In Eq. (27), $(\sigma_y - i\tau_{xy})_j$ refer to a system of local coordinates (x_j, y_j) in Fig. 6(b) for the jth crack.

5.1 Edge Crack

Consider an epoxy plate with dimensions 12cm × 10cm × 0.6cm as shown in Fig. 7. It contains an edge crack of 4cm in length and is constrained from displacements at the upper and lower edges Σ_2 while the sides Σ_1 are stress free. A uniform temperature drop of 20K is applied. Fig. 8 gives the constant shear stress contours around the crack and their distribution agrees well with the isochromatics in Fig. 9. To be expected is the increase in shear stress as the crack tip is approached. The numbers 23, 46, …, 82 refer to magnitudes of the shear stress contours in units of MPa. A comparison of the calculated and measured stress intensity factors K_1 and K_2 according to Eq. (27) is also made. The agreement is good as indicated by the results in Table 2. A slight degree of asymmetry prevailed in the experiment as indicated by the non-zero but small K_2 value.

Table 2 Analytical and experimental values of K_j ($j = 1, 2$) in MPa·$cm^{\frac{1}{2}}$ for an edge crack experiencing a uniform temperature drop of 20 K

Analysis		Experiment	
K_1	K_2	K_1	K_2
14.10	0.0	14.85	0.32

5.2 Three Parallel Cracks

The configuration of three parallel cracks a_jb_j ($j = 1, 2, 3$), each of length 2.5cm, is shown in Fig. 10. They are spaced 2cm apart in a plate of 12cm × 6cm × 0.6cm so that the

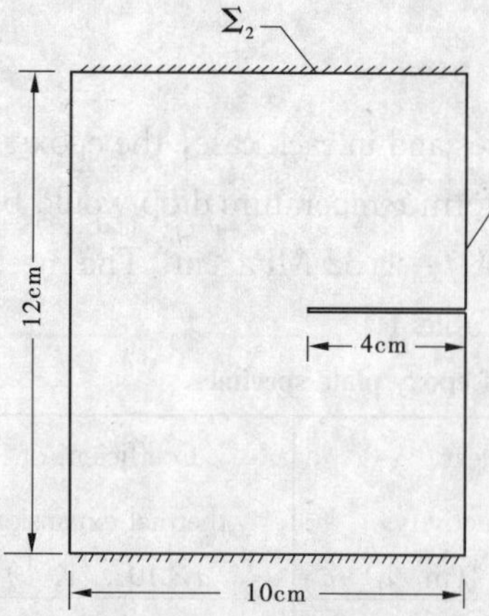

Fig. 7 **Edge crack in plate with constrained edges: uniform temperature drop 20K**

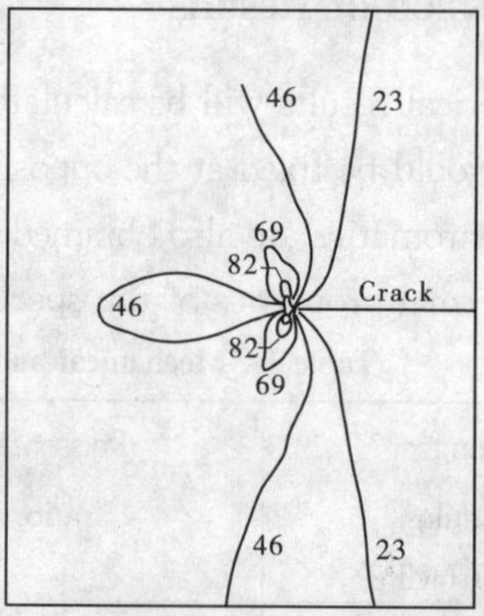

Fig. 8 **Constant shear stress contours: edge crack**

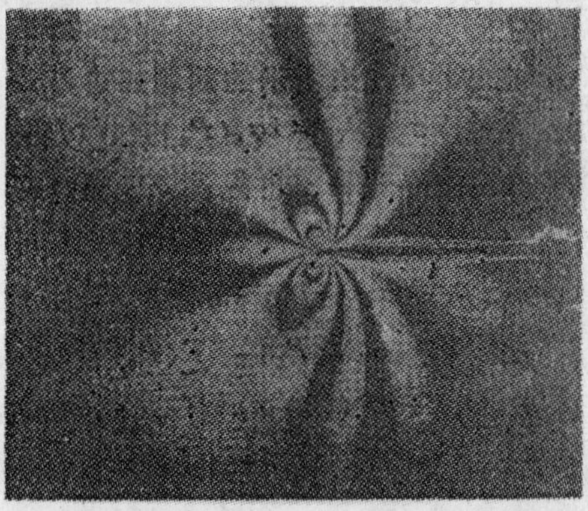

Fig. 9 **Isochromatics around edge crack subjected to 20 K uniform temperature drop**

center crack $a_2 b_2$ coincides with the middle of the plate. By fixing the plate at both edges Σ_2, the system is subjected to a uniform temperature drop of 25K. The other two edges Σ_1 are stress free. Displayed in Fig. 11 are the constant shear stress contours which are symmetric about the middle crack. Again, the contours close to the crack tip are more intensified. The corresponding isochromatics can be found in Fig. 12 and the resemblance to the analytical results in Fig. 11 is apparent. Summarized in Table 3 are the stress intensity factors for the six(6) crack tips $a_j b_j$ ($j = 1,2$). Positive K_1 refers to crack opening and positive K_2 to a relative displacement of the crack surfaces so that upper surface move to the right and lower surface to the left. This convention applies to the left and right crack tips. Referring to Fig. 10, for example, the sign for K_2 at a_1 is opposite to that at a_3 as K_2 at b_1 to that at b_3. This is because a temperature drop causes the material to contract but the fixed edges would tend to restrain such a motion. Therefore, the lower surface of $a_1 b_1$ facing the fixed edge would tend to move outward relative to its upper surface that would move inward. The convention, therefore, yield a positive K_2 at a_1 and negative K_2 at b_1. The same applies to the ends a_3 and b_3 as shown by the results in Table 3. Asymmetry effect is small because both a_1b_1 and a_3b_3 are sufficiently far away from the fixed edge while $K_2=0$ for the middle crack a_2b_2 because of symmetry. Good agreement is seen between the analytical and experimental results.

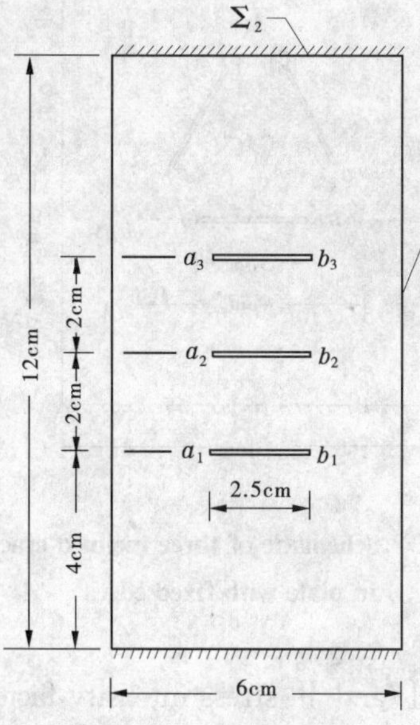

Fig. 10 Three parallel cracks in plate with fixed edges

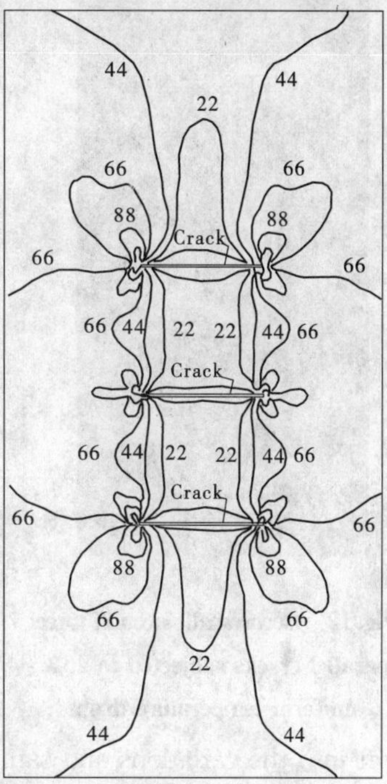

Fig. 11 Constant shear stress contours: three parallel cracks

Table 3 Analytical and experimental values of $K_j\,(j=1.2)$ in $\mathrm{MPa\cdot cm^{\frac{1}{2}}}$ for three parallel cracks undergoing a uniform temperature drop of 25K

Stress intensity factor type	Crack tip location					
	a_1	b_1	a_2	b_2	a_3	b_3
Analytical						
K_1	9.38	9.38	7.75	7.75	9.38	9.38
K_2	0.74	−0.74	0	0	−0.74	0.74
Experimental						
K_1	9.12	9.16	7.48	7.41	9.04	8.98
K_2	0.67	−0.72	0	0	−0.68	0.61

5.3 Inclined Cracks on Sides of Equilateral Triangle

Depicted in Fig. 13 are three cracks $a_jb_j\,(j=1,2,3)$ of equal length 3cm and they are centered on the sides of an equilateral triangle. One of the cracks a_1b_1 is parallel to the plate 12cm×10cm×0.6cm with two of the edges fixed on Σ_2. Temperature drops of 20K and

30K are applied to the free surface plate edges Σ_1 next to cracks a_2b_2 and a_3b_3, respectively. Displayed in Figs. 14 and 15 are, respectively, the constant shear stress contours and the corresponding isochromatics. The agreement is good.

Fig. 12 Isochromatic around three parallel cracks subjected to 25K uniform temperature drop

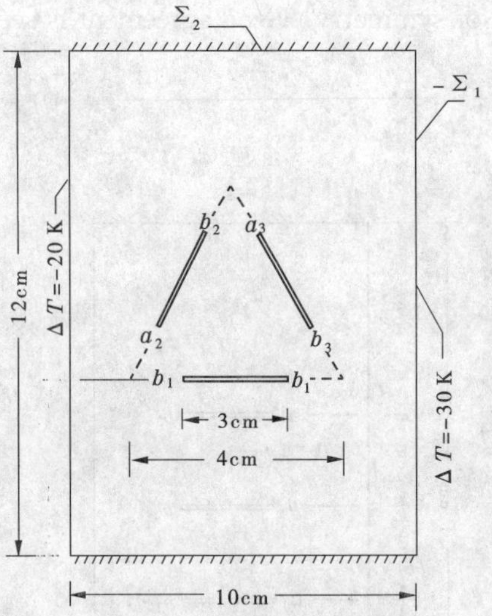

Fig. 13 Schematic of three inclined cracks in plate with fixed edges

Insight into the variations and signs of the Mode Ⅰ and Ⅱ stress intensity factors can be gained by keeping in mind that the left side of the plate in Fig. 13 contracts less than the right side. Moreover, those crack surfaces nearest to the wall would experience less contraction. The horizontal temperature gradient and vertical wall constraint effect would add for crack a_2b_2 and oppose one another for the crack a_3b_3. Although the relative physical displacements of the crack a_1b_1 being parallel to the fixed edge in Fig. 13 are similar to the crack a_1b_1 in Fig. 10, the sign for K_2 at a_1 and b_1 are opposite. This is because the direction of a_1 to b_1 in Fig. 13 corresponds to that of b_1 to a_1 in Fig. 10. Since the problem has no symmetry, all the stress intensity factors are different as indicated in Table 4.

Table 4 Analytical and experimental values of $K_j\ (j=1,2)$ in MPa·cm$^{\frac{1}{2}}$ for three inclined cracks subjected to a temperature gradient

Stress intensity factor type	Crack tip location					
	a_1	b_1	a_2	b_2	a_3	b_3
Analytical						
K_1	11.09	11.61	0.464	2.510	2.29	−0.036
K_2	−0.06	0.18	−5.74	3.98	−3.49	−5.00
Experimental						
K_1	9.85	10.74	0.29	—	—	0.0
K_2	−0.13	0.22	−5.87	—	—	−5.30

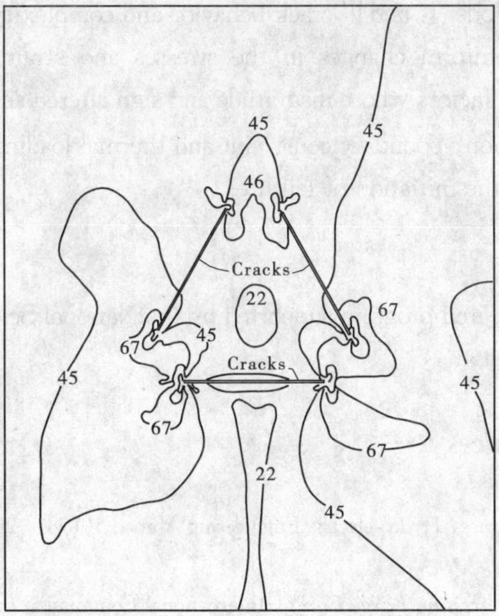

Fig. 14 Constant shear stress contours around three inclined cracks

Fig. 15 Isochromatics around three inclined cracks subjected to a horizontal temperature gradient

Mode 1 effect dominated for crack $a_1 b_1$ because the gradient of material displacement is normal to the crack plane. As it is expected, the K_j-factors at b_2 and a_1 would be larger than those at a_3 and b_3, respectively. This is because the thermal gradient and edge constraint effect add at a_2 and b_2 and subtract at a_3 and b_3. The signs for K_2 at opposing crack ends are opposite for all of the cases discussed except for a_3 and b_3 where K_2 are both negative. This is because the fixed edge constraint dominates at a_3 and temperature gradient contraction controls at b_3. Agreement with the experimentally determined K_j-factors is satisfactory at those locations where measurements were made as indicated in Table 4.

6 Conclusions

Superposition is used to formulate the problem of multiple cracks in bodies with finite dimensions by application of solutions for infinite body problems that are more readily obtained. Both mechanical and thermal loading are considered. Neglected in the analysis is the interaction of the cracks with the temperature field. That is, the disturbance due to the change in the thermal conductivity of the cracks is not accounted for. Such an effect may or may not be negligible depending on the application[5,6,12].

Constant shear stress contours are obtained and they agreed well with experimentally measured isochromatics for three specific example problems. Crack tip stress intensity factors advocated in the linear elasstic fracture mechanics are also determined for systems with multiple cracks that exhibit the combined effect of Mode Ⅰ and Ⅱ crack behavior and complexity of the non-symmetric stress conditions. Nonuniform changes in the stresses and strains around the cracks are exhibited from K_1 and K_2 factors whose magnitude and sign altered according to the specimen geometry, crack formation, boundary constraint and thermal loading condition. Their combination would determine the initiation of failture.

Acknowledgment

The work in this paper is the result of a research program supported by the National Science Foundation in the People's Republic of China.

References

[1] B. S. Liu. *The seriously damage of four dams in France*. Hydro-electric Engineering Abroad 5(1981) 20 ~27

[2] I. J. Abraham , R. C. Sloan. *13th International Congress on Large Dams*. International Commission on Large Dams, Vol. 1, pp. 1~24, 1979

[3] Z. G. Liu, Z. B. Zhou , L. W. Yuan. *Calculation of vertical crack propagation on the upstream face of the Zhexi single buttress dam*, J. Hydraulic Eng. 5(1990)29~36

[4] Y. Z. Chen. *General case of multiple crack problems in an infinite plate*. Eng. Fract. Mech. 20(4) (1984) 591~598

[5] G. C. Sih , R. C. Bolton. *Prediction of thermally induced fracture from notch and crack front*. Theoret. Appl. Fract. Mech. 5 (1986)125~132

[6] G. C. Sih , C. K. Chen. *Growth of crack caused by temperature gradients with change in surface insulation*. Theoret. Appl. Fract. Mech. 5(1986)101~107

[7] R. Z. Zhou , G. T. Liu. *The synthetic deformation modulus and the synthetic Poisson's ratio of multiple crack bodies*. Eng. Fract Mech. 35(4/5)(1990)731~738

[8] G. T. Liu , Y. Chi. *An analytic-fictitious boundary forces method for calculating multi-crack problem in arbitrary region with mixed mode boundaries*. Fracture of Concrete and Rock, Recent Developments (Elsevier: Barking, UK, 1989) pp. 91~100

[9] V. V. Panasyuk, M. P. Savruk , A. P. Datsyshyn. *A general method of solution of two dimensional problem in the theory of cracks*, Eng. Fract. Mech. 9(1977)481~497

[10] G. X. Zhang , G. T. Liu. *The fracture analysis of a finite plate with thermally insulated Griffith crack in steady thermo-field*. J. Nonjing Hydraulic Res. Inst. (1990)85~96

[11] G. C. Sih. *On the singular character of themal stresses near a crack tip*, J. Appl. Mech. 29, (1962) pp. 587~589

[12] G. T. Liu , G. X. Zhang. *Steady thermal fracture analysis of finite body with crack filled with conductive material*. Fracture of Concrete and Rock, Recent Developments (Elsevier: Barking, UK, 1989) pp. 737~746

[13] N. I. Muskhelishvili. *Some Basic Problems of Mathematical Theory of Elasticity* (Noordhoff: The Netherlands, 1953)

[14] G. C. Sih, P. C. Paris, F. Erdogan. *Crack tip stress intensity factors for plane extension and plate bending problems*. J. Appl. Mech. 29(1962)306~312

稳定热流场中温度断裂子域的解析数值解

摘　要　本文介绍了将粗网格有限元与有限含裂缝子域已知边界位移时的解析数值解相结合求解多裂隙体稳定热断裂问题的方法。计算实例表明:该方法精度好,计算工作量少。

复杂的水工大体积混凝土结构的热应力计算常采用有限元法。当结构内含裂缝时(尤其有较多裂缝或较密集裂隙区时)既使用奇异单元计算应力场和应力强度因子,也要用密集网格计算以满足工程精度要求[1,2],这给本来就需要大量节点的结构计算(如拱坝)更增加了困难,大大增加了计算时间和费用,也增大数据准备工作量。实践中有时因超出计算机容量而使计算难以进行,缝端应力场的不对称性也增加了应力强度因子定值的困难,并影响取值精度。

由于缝端的奇异场影响范围较小,因而考虑了宏观裂缝影响的粗网格有限元计算结果中,远离缝端的节点位移可保持较好的精度。故可将整体结构的粗网格有限元法与含裂缝局部区域的解析数值解相结合,求解热断裂问题。即用粗网格对含裂缝的整体结构进行网格剖分,并用有限元法计算,再沿裂缝周围切出某个含裂缝的子域,将用粗网格计算所得的该子域边界上的节点位移作为该子域的已知边界位移,利用本文的解析数值方法进行计算,这样既可提高应力变化率大的缝端应力场和应力强度因子的数值精度,也可避免用大量密集单元,从而节省计算工作量和费用。

设一已知边界约束和边界温度的结构(见图 1),结构内含多条裂缝。在裂缝的外部取含裂缝的子域作为温度断裂子域,用通常粗网格单元对整个含缝结构进行剖分计算出子域周界上各节点的位移及温度值,用解析数值解形式建立含裂缝子域内位移、应力及温度分布和子域边界节点位移及温度的关系式。当该式所表达的位移和粗网格有限元计算所得的子域边界节点位移一致时,获得正确解。

实践中,当裂缝不很长时,可将含裂缝子域 K 划分成 8 个奇异单元(见图 2),即可得到较高精度的子域周边位移值。将这些奇异单元直接并入整体粗网格单元进行结构计

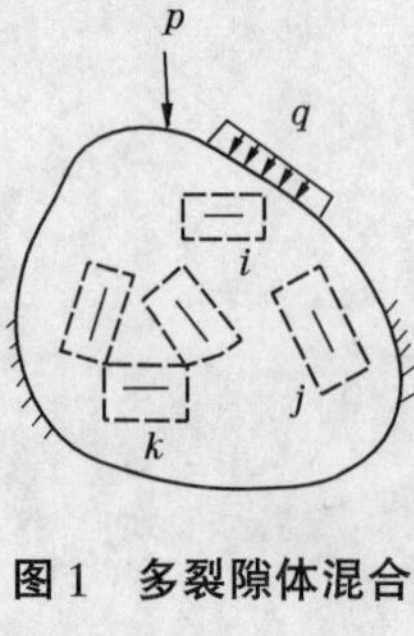

图 1　多裂隙体混合边界问题

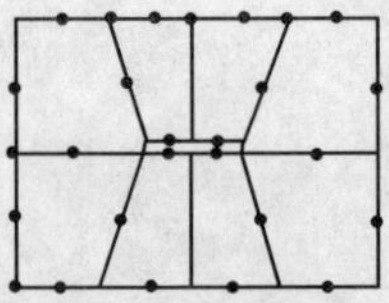

图 2　子域网格划分

本文选自《水利学报》1991 年第 6 期,作者还有张国新。

算,得到子域周边节点的位移和周边及内部节点的温度值,作为该温度断裂子域的边界条件,再把该子域作为已知边界位移和温度分布的第2类基本问题求解,取得子域内应力分布及应力强度因子。实践表明:用这种方法解多裂缝体问题,在保证精度的前提下,可大大节省计算工作量。

1 温度分布

由文献[4]可知:通常混凝土坝中裂缝宽($2b$,为mm以下量级)远小于缝长($2a$),不论缝内充填水、土或空气,对稳定温度场干扰均很小。因此,由裂缝干扰温度场引起的K_{I}、K_{II}也很小,为此本文暂不考虑裂缝对温度场的干扰。平面稳定温度场和变化缓慢的不稳定温度场可用简单多项式近似表示为

$$T(x,y)=\sum_{j=0}^{4}\sum_{k=0}^{j}\alpha_{jk}x^{j-k}y^{k}=\sum_{m=1}^{15}\alpha_m\varphi_m(x,y) \tag{1}$$

式中:α_{jk}为15个待定系数,可由子域周边和内部若干插值点(大于20个)的坐标及相应温度求解如下最小二乘法方程而得

$$[A]\{\alpha\}=\{d\}$$

其中:$\alpha_{ij}=\sum_{k=1}^{M}\varphi_i(x_k,y_k)\varphi_j(x_k,y_k)$;$d_i=\sum_{k=1}^{M}T_k\varphi_i(x_k,y_k)$;$M$为插值点总数;$\varphi_i$为插值基函数,即$x^{j-k}y^{k}$。

2 位移场逼近

子域(见图2)的位移$\{u\}$由3部分组成:①子域中不含裂缝时周边节点作用虚拟位移时引起的位移场$\{\overline{u}\}$;②子域内温度场引起的位移场$\{u_t\}$;③为保证缝面自由条件在缝面加反力后引起的位移场$\{u_c\}$,即

$$\{u\}=\{\overline{u}\}+\{u_t\}+\{u_c\} \tag{2}$$

当子域内部总的位移函数$\{u\}$在边界上的值和粗网格有限元法求得的子域边界位移值相同时,为正确解,可在边界上取若干插值点(包括已有有限元节点)用最小二乘法拟合求解。

2.1 无裂缝子域在虚拟边界位移及温度场作用下的应力函数和应力

取应力函数形式:

$$\Phi(z)=\sum_{k=1}^{\infty}a_kz^{k}\quad \Psi(z)=\sum_{k=1}^{\infty}b_kz^{k} \tag{3}$$

式中:$a_k=a_k^R+ia_k^I$,$b_k=b_k^R+ib_k^I$为待定复系数。

由上式及其导函数可求得应力场为[3]

$$\sigma'_x+\sigma'_y=4\mathrm{Re}\sum_{k=1}^{\infty}(a_k^R+ia_k^I)^4kz^{k-1}-\gamma\sum_{j=0}^{4}\sum_{k=0}^{j}\alpha_{jk}x^{j-k}y^{k}$$

$$\sigma'_y-\sigma'_x+2\tau'_{xy}=2\Big[z\sum_{k=1}^{\infty}k(k-1)a_kz^{k-2}+\sum_{k=1}^{\infty}b_kkz^{k-1}\Big]-$$

$$\gamma\sum_{j=0}^{4}\sum_{k=0}^{j}\left(\frac{1}{2}\right)^{j}(-i)^{k}a_{jk}\sum_{m=0}^{j-k}\sum_{R=0}^{k}C_{j-k}^{m}(-1)^{n}C_{n}^{k}Z^{j-m-n-1}\times$$
$$\bar{z}^{m+n+1}\frac{(j-m-n)}{(m+n+1)} \tag{4}$$

2.2　裂缝表面施加反力 $-\sigma'_y\mid_{y=0,\,|x|\leqslant a}$ 和 $-\tau'_{xy}\mid_{y=0,\,|x|\leqslant a}$ 时的无限域应力函数

无限域内含裂缝 $2a$，由式(4)求出裂缝位置的正应力 σ'_y 和切应力 τ_{xy}，反号加到裂缝表面，由柯西积分法求出其应力函数为

$$\Phi_2(\xi)=\sum_{k=1}^{\infty}D_k\sum_{j=0}^{NT}C_k^j\left(\frac{1}{\xi}\right)^{k-2j}$$
$$\Psi_2(\xi)=\sum_{k=1}^{\infty}\overline{D}_k\sum_{j=0}^{NT}C_k^j\left(\frac{1}{\xi}\right)^{k-2j}+$$
$$\frac{1+\xi^2}{\xi^2-1}\sum_{k=1}^{\infty}D_k\sum_{j=0}^{NT}C_k^j(k-2j)\left(\frac{1}{\xi}\right)^{k-2j} \tag{5}$$

式中：　$NT=\mathrm{INT}\left[\frac{(k+1)}{2}\right]-1$，$\mathrm{INT}\left(\frac{k+1}{2}\right)$为取整函数。

$$\mathrm{INT}\left(\frac{k+1}{2}\right)=\begin{cases}k/2,k\ \text{为偶数时}\\(k-1)/2,k\ \text{为奇数时,}\end{cases}\quad\gamma=\begin{cases}E\alpha(1-\upsilon)\\E\alpha\end{cases}$$

$$D_k=\frac{1}{k}\left(\frac{a}{2}\right)^k\{-[k(k+1)a_k^R+kb_k^R]+i[k(k-1)a_k^I+kb_k^I]+(d_k^b+id_k^c)\}$$

$$d_k^b+id_k^c=\begin{cases}\dfrac{\gamma}{2}\Big[a_{k0}+\sum\limits_{j=0}^{k}\left(\dfrac{1}{2}\right)^k(-i)^j a_{kj}\sum\limits_{m=0}^{k-j}\sum\limits_{m=0}^{j}C_{k-j}^m\times\\ C_n^j(-1)^n\dfrac{k-m-n}{m+n+1}\Big]\quad(k\leqslant5)\\0\qquad\qquad(k>5)\end{cases}$$

$$\xi=\begin{cases}(z+\sqrt{z^2-a^2})/a\quad(x\geqslant0)\\(z-\sqrt{z^2-a^2})/a\quad(x<0)\end{cases}$$

2.3　含裂缝子域的总的位移分布函数

将式(3)和式(5)叠加，可得子域内总的应力函数，由此可得整个平面的位移为

$$u+i\upsilon=\frac{1}{2\mu}\Big[\sum_{k=1}^{\infty}(e_k^1a_k^R+e_k^2a_k^I+e_k^5)+\sum_{k=0}^{\infty}(e_k^3b_k^R+e_k^4b_k^I)+$$
$$\beta\int T(z,\bar{z})\mathrm{d}z+u_0+i\upsilon_0 \tag{6}$$

式中：u_0、υ_0 为坐标原点的位移。

$$\beta=\begin{cases}\alpha(1+\nu)/[2(1-\nu)],\ \text{平面应变}\\\alpha(1+\nu)/2,\ \text{平面应力}\end{cases}$$

$$e_k^1=æz^k-kz\bar{z}^{k-1}-(k-1)\left(\frac{a}{2}\right)^k\Big[æ\sum_{j=0}^{NT}C_k^j\left(\frac{1}{\xi}\right)^{k-2j}-\sum_{j=0}^{NT}C_k^j\left(\frac{1}{\bar{\xi}}\right)^{k-2j}\Big]\pm$$
$$(k+1)\left(\frac{a}{2}\right)^k\frac{2iy}{\sqrt{\bar{z}^2-a^2}}\sum_{j=0}^{NT}C_k^j(k-2j)\left(\frac{1}{\bar{\xi}}\right)^{k-2j}$$

$$e_k^2 = i\left\{æz^k + kz\bar{z}^{k-1} + (k-1)\left(\frac{a}{2}\right)^k \sum_{j=0}^{NT}\left[æ\left(\frac{1}{\xi}\right)^{k-2j} - \left(\frac{1}{\bar{\xi}}\right)^{k-2j}\right]C_k^j \mp \right.$$
$$\left.(k-1)\left(\frac{a}{2}\right)^k \frac{2iy}{\sqrt{\bar{z}^2 - a^2}} \sum_{j=0}^{NT} C_k^j (k-2j)\left(\frac{1}{\bar{\xi}}\right)^{k-2j}\right\}$$

$$e_k^3 = -\bar{z}^k - \left(\frac{a}{2}\right)^k\left[æ\sum_{j=0}^{NT} C_k^j\left(\frac{1}{\xi}\right)^{k-2j} - \sum_{j=0}^{NT} C_k^j\left(\frac{1}{\bar{\xi}}\right)^{k-2j}\right] \mp$$
$$\left(\frac{a}{2}\right)^k \frac{2iy}{\sqrt{\bar{z}^2 - a^2}} \sum_{j=0}^{NT} C_k^j (k-2j)\left(\frac{1}{\bar{\xi}}\right)^{k-2j}$$

$$e_k^4 = i\left\{\bar{Z}^k + \left(\frac{a}{2}\right)^k\left[æ\sum_{j=0}^{NT} C_k^j\left(\frac{1}{\xi}\right)^{k-2j} - \sum_{j=0}^{NT} C_k^j\left(\frac{1}{\bar{\xi}}\right)^{k-2j}\right] \mp \right.$$
$$\left.\left(\frac{a}{2}\right)^k \frac{2iy}{\sqrt{\bar{z}^2 - a^2}} \sum_{j=0}^{NT} C_k^j (k-2j)\left(\frac{1}{\bar{\xi}}\right)^{k-2j}\right\}$$

$$e_k^5 = (d_k^d + id_k^c)\frac{1}{k}\left(\frac{a}{2}\right)^k \sum_{j=0}^{NT}\left[æC_k^j\left(\frac{1}{\xi}\right)^{k-2j} - C_k^j\left(\frac{1}{\bar{\xi}}\right)^{k-2j}\right] \mp$$
$$\left.\frac{2iy}{\sqrt{\bar{z}^2 - a^2}} C_k^j (k-2j)\left(\frac{1}{\bar{\xi}}\right)^{k-2j}\right]$$

$x \geqslant 0$ 时,取上边符号;$x < 0$ 时,取下边符号。

将式(6)改写成

$$u + iv = \sum_{m=1}^{\infty} e_m a_m + u_r + iv_r + u_0 + iv_0 \tag{7}$$

式中:$e_{4(k+1)+j} = e_k^j$; $a_{4(k-1)+1} = a_k^R$; $a_{4(k-1)+2} = a_k^I$; $a_{4(k-1)+3} = b_k^R$; $a_{4(k-1)+4} = b_k^I$; $u^T + iv^T = \sum_{k=1}^{\infty} \frac{1}{2\mu} e_k^5 + \beta\int T(z,\bar{z})\mathrm{d}z$。

3 应力函数系数 a_k、b_k 及应力强度因子

由整体结构粗网格有限元计算得到子域周边的各节点位移和温度值。根据精度要求,再在子域周边布置 Me 个插值节点,由插值法求出这些节点的位移及温度值,代入式(7),取其前 $4M$ 项,利用最小二乘法拟合,可得如下方程:

$$[K]\{a\} = \{d\} \tag{8}$$

式中:
$$K_{ij} = \sum_{k=1}^{Me} e_i(z_k) e_j(z_k),\ (i,j = 1,2,\cdots 4M);$$
$$d_i = \sum_{k=1}^{Me}[u_T(z_k) + iv_T(z_k) + u_0 + iv_0]e_i(z_k)$$

求解式(8),可得未知系数 a_k、b_k。由于 a_k、b_k 随 k 的增大收剑很快,通常只取前6至8项即可达到相当精度。根据精度的要求,Me 可任定,当 a_k、b_k 的项数一定时,增加 Me 可提高边界上位移和温度的拟合精度,从而提高 a_k、b_k 的精度。系数 a_k、b_k 一经求出,即可求出整个位移场及应力场,应力强度因子可由下式确定。

$$K_{\mathrm{I}}^{\pm}-iK_{\mathrm{II}}^{\pm}=\begin{cases}-2\sqrt{\dfrac{\pi}{a}}\sum\limits_{k=1}^{M}D_k\sum\limits_{j=0}^{NT}C_k^j(k-2j) & (x=-a\text{ 时})\\ -2\sqrt{\dfrac{\pi}{a}}\sum\limits_{k=1}^{M}D_k\sum\limits_{j=0}^{NT}C_k^j(-1)^{k-2j+1}(k-2j) & (x=a\text{ 时})\end{cases}$$

4　精度考核

设无限板内含 $2a=2$m 的裂缝，无穷远处拉力 $P=0.1$MPa。以裂缝为中心取 6m × 4m 的有限板，以解析解所得边界位移为基本边界条件。比较解析解、密网格的有限元法(144 单元)、解析解的边界位移值用断裂子域解析数值解求解以及粗网格(24 单元) 计算子域边界位移用断裂子域解析数值求解。这 4 种方法所得若干节点位移、应力强度因子比较如表 1 所示。

表 1　部分点位移不同计算方法比较

项　目		计算方法			
		解析解	密网格有限元	精确边界位移 + 断裂子域解	粗网格有限元 + 断裂子域解
缝端位移 (m)	u	0.480 2E − 04	0.419 1 E − 04	0.480 2E − 04	0.479 0E − 04
	v	0.00	− 0.378 0E − 09	0.154 0E − 09	− 0.287 6E − 08
缝面上某点位移 (m)	u	0.485 1E − 04	0.452 1E − 04	0.485 1E − 04	0.483 8E − 04
	v	0.242 3E − 04	0.227 4E − 04	0.242 3E − 04	0.242 6E − 04
应力强度因子 (MPa · cm$^{1/2}$)	K_{I}	17.24	16.51	17.24	17.75
	K_{II}	0.0	0	− 0.2E − 04	5.8E − 03

由表 1 可以看出，将精确边界位移代入断裂子域计算所得结果与解析解完全一致，说明该断裂子域具有很高的精度。当用断裂子域配合有限元计算时，只需很少的单元(24 个) 即可达到很高的精度(0.17%)。而用密网格的有限元法计算时，即使网格划得很密，也很难达 到此精度(由文献[4]可见，在含裂缝板的1/4范围内布置215个节点计算，精度为 0.75%)。对含多裂缝结构，尤其有多种荷载，包括温度、渗压等体积力作用时，本文提出的用网格有限元和子域解析解相结合的方法都能适应，而且可用较少工作量和机时得到高精度结果。

5　算例

一个 12cm × 10cm 平板内含有 3 条沿等边三角形分布的裂缝，缝长 3cm，上下两面 y 方向固定，用粗网格有限单元法配合断裂子域计算当温度均匀下降 10℃ 时的断裂应力场及各缝端的应力强度因子。

网格划分见图 3，共 54 个单元，179 个节点，先用有限单元法算出各节点的位移，再代入断裂子域计算、计算结果见等应力图(见图 4)，应力强度因子见表 2。

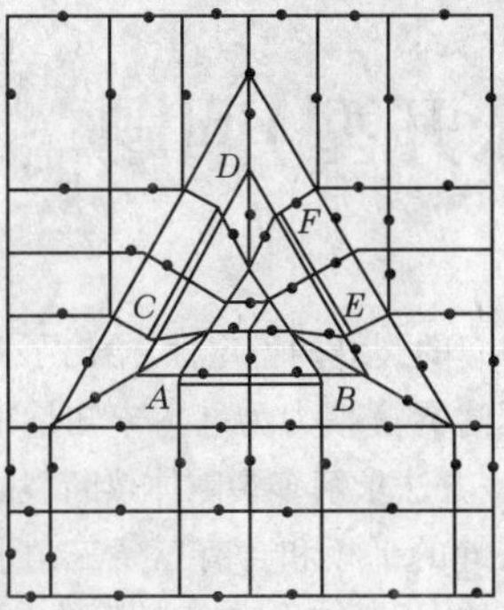

图 3　三角形分布裂缝的单元划分

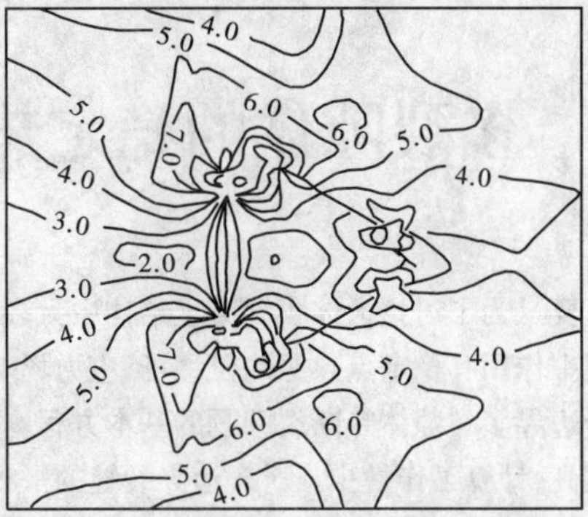

图 4　等剪应力图　(单位:MPa)

表 2　各缝端应力强度因子　(单位:MPa · cm$^{1/2}$)

应力强度因子	点		号			
	A	*B*	*C*	*D*	*E*	*F*
K_{I}	9.33	9.33	1.36	0.87	1.34	0.92
K_{II}		0.07	−4.23	−4.46	4.21	4.43

由以上结果可以看出,含有 3 条三角形分布裂缝的平板,两端约束,均匀温降时,水平裂缝只产生 Ⅰ 型应力强度因子,与水平方向夹角为 60° 的两条缝,其缝端可同时产生 Ⅰ、Ⅱ 两种类型的应力强度因子,且 Ⅱ 型应力强度因子较 Ⅰ 型大。水平缝两端的应力强度因子较倾斜缝大,因此破坏时将沿水平缝拉开。这个结果与观察统计结果吻合。

由计算示例可知,用解析裂缝子域的解析数值法解决平面断裂问题工作量要节省很多,含 3 条裂缝的板的温度断裂问题只要 100 多个节点即能得到精度好的结果。用 ELXSI 机只需 40s 多,用断裂子域配合通用数值方法来解决复杂荷载多裂缝温度断裂问题精度高、机时少,优越性是明显的。

参 考 文 献

[1] 姚敬之. 奇异变单元与等参数单元结合的有限元法. 水利学报,1981(5):35~47
[2] 周瑞忠. 多裂纹体断裂理论及其在高拱坝破坏问题中的应用. 清华大学工学博士论文,1988
[3] Nowinskj, I. L.. *Theory of Thermoelastisity with Applications*. Netherlands, 1978
[4] Мусхелдшвлщ, Н. И.. 数学弹性力学的几个基本问题. 赵惠元译. 北京:科学出版社,1958
[5] 刘光廷,张国新. 缝内含有不同导温介质时的稳定温度断裂研究. 清华大学学报,1990,30(2):15~21

多裂隙体的稳定热断裂(张开型)问题

摘　要　为了讨论大体积混凝土结构中大多数由温度变化引起的裂缝的稳定性,给出了无限平板中作用有稳定点热源的位移场、应力场基本解,构造出以边界虚拟力为基本未知量求解混合边界多裂隙体热断裂问题的基本方程。数值计算表明,该方法求解多裂隙体热断裂问题精度高,计算工作量少。对含边界裂缝的平板、含三条平行裂缝的平板和含有三条三角形分布的裂缝的平板在稳定温度荷载作用下进行了实验和计算互校,两者结果吻合良好。

关键词　混凝土结构　大坝多裂隙体　热断裂　虚拟力

施工期的裂缝在运行期造成严重危害的例子国际国内都有。如法国 Tala 坝和 Hautefage 坝[1]的破坏中,温度荷载起了重要作用。美国 Fontana 坝[2]的裂缝每过一个冬季即向前扩展,表明了温度荷载对裂缝扩展的影响。国内某大头坝的劈头裂缝在大坝运行 7 年之后,沿支墩严重开裂,危及坝体安全[3]。研究表明:后期危害性裂缝往往由施工期裂缝发展而来,而温度荷载是裂缝扩展的主要因素之一。当然不是所有裂缝都有发展并危及结构安全,需要判别裂缝的稳定性。

国内 15 座典型拱坝调查[3]表明:坝体裂缝常以群缝的形式出现,最多竟达 3 300 多条。在裂缝的扩展中,各裂缝相互影响。有的裂缝相距很近或离边界很近,因此不宜按传统的无限域或半无限域的单缝考虑。对于多裂缝问题,使用有限单元法因缝端密网格要求大量单元而给计算带来困难。不对称应力分布也给应力强度因子取值带来困难。本文提供解析数值法研究多裂隙体热断裂问题并和热断裂实验结果进行互校。

以往多裂隙体的研究多限于外力荷载[4~7],热断裂研究也以单缝、缝面绝热为主[7,8]。本文研究的多裂隙体混合边值热断裂问题可按图 1 的方式分解为 3 部分:① 不含裂缝的无限域在原问题的边界处作用有虚拟荷载 $T^e(s)+iN^e(s)$ 时引起该处及域内的位移和应力;② 不含裂缝的无限体在原边界处作用有虚拟边界热源 $H(s)$ 时在该处及域内引起的应力和位移;③ 无限含裂缝体在原裂缝部位作用有虚拟裂缝释放应力 $N^e(s)-iT^e(s)$ 时在原边界及域内引起的位移和应力。令在虚拟荷载 $T(s)+iN(s)$、温度荷载 $H(s)$ 及裂缝释放应力 $N^e(s)-iT^e(s)$ 的联合作用下满足原问题的边界条件及缝面条件,求出边界虚拟荷载和缝面释放应力,从而进一步求出各缝端应力强度因子和应力场。

1　边界虚拟热源 $H(s)$ 及温度场

研究表明[9],由于实际工程中的裂缝宽度相对很小,当缝内含有某种导热介质(如水、空气等)时,裂缝对稳定温度场干扰很小,可忽略不计。

设稳定热传导问题的边界条件见图2。将其边界按虚线所示划分成 M 个边界单元。假设在每个单元上作用有常分布热源,第 k 单元的热源为 h_k,则利用稳定点热源作用时的热

本文选自《清华大学学报(自然科学版)》1991 年第 2 期,作者还有张国新。

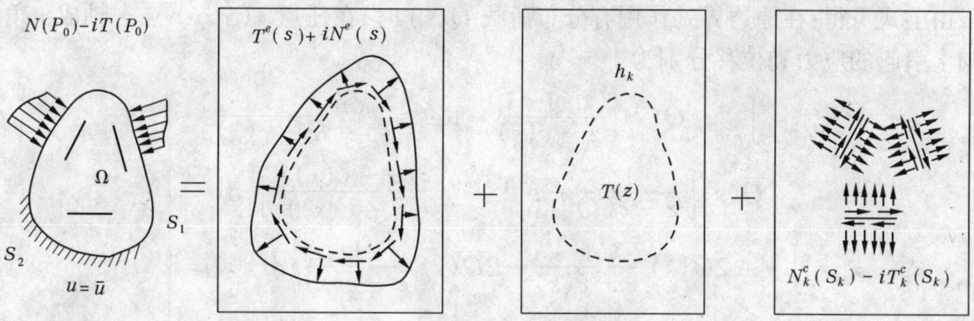

图 1　热断裂问题的叠加原理

传导问题基本解可以构造出一组以边界热源为基本未知量的方程组：

$$\sum_{k=1}^{M}\frac{h_k}{2\pi\lambda}\mathrm{Re}\left[t_{kn}\ln\left(\frac{t_{kn}-b_k}{t_{kn}+b_k}\right)-b_k\ln(t_{kn}^2-b_k^2)+2b_k\right]=\overline{T}_{0n}$$

在 S_1 上，$n=1,2,\cdots,M_1$

$$\frac{1}{2}-\mathrm{Im}\sum_{k=1}^{M'}\frac{h_k}{2\pi}\mathrm{e}^{-i(a_k-a_m)}\ln\left(\frac{t_{km}-b_k}{t_{km}+b_k}\right)=\overline{q}_{0m}\qquad(1)$$

在 S_2 上，$m=1,2,\cdots,M_2$

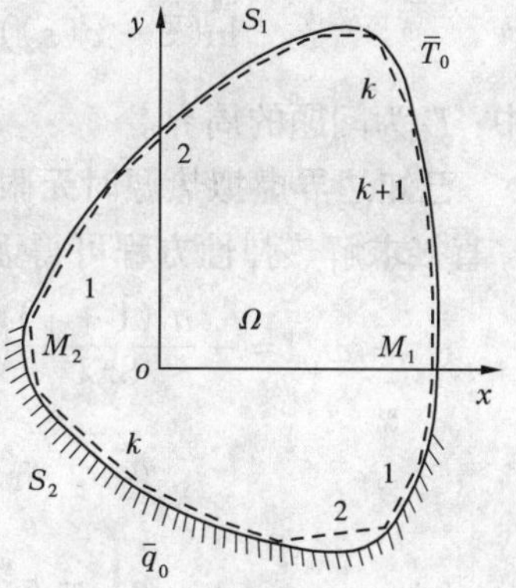

图 2　稳定热传导问题的边界条件及边界元划分

式中：$M_1+M_2=M$；$\overline{T}$ 为 S_1 上的已知温度；λ 为热导率；$\overline{q}$ 为 S_2 上的已知热流量；$t_{kn}=\mathrm{e}^{-ia_k}(Z_n^0-Z_k^0)$；$Z_k^0$、$Z_n^0$ 为第 k、n 边界单元的形心坐标；b_k 为第 k 边界单元的半长；M' 为除去 $k=n$ 之外的 M 的余集；a_k、a_n 为第 k 和第 n 单元的切向与坐标 x 轴的夹角。

方程组(1) 提供 M 个方程，可解 M 个未知边界热源 h_k，最后温度场 $T(z)$ 表示为

$$T(z)=\sum_{k=1}^{M}\frac{h_k}{2\pi\lambda}\mathrm{Re}\left[z_k\ln\left(\frac{z_k-b_k}{z_k+b_k}\right)-b_k\ln(z_k^2-b_k^2)+2b_k\right]\qquad(2)$$

2　混合边值热断裂问题的奇异积分方程组

2.1　无限域无裂纹体有虚拟荷载时的应力场位移场

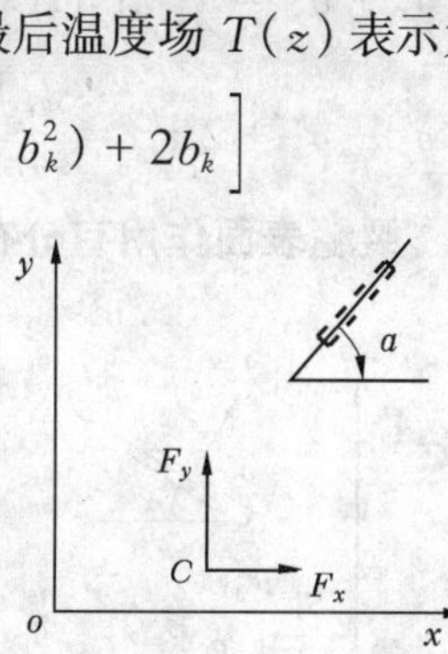

图 3　无限域中作用有集中荷载

无限域 $z_0=c$ 点作用有集中荷载 $Q=(F_x+iF_y)/[2\pi(1+R)]$ 时的应力函数为(见图 3)[10]

$$\varphi(z)=-Q\ln(z-c)$$

$$\psi(z)=R\overline{Q}[\ln(z-c)+1]+Qc/(z-c)$$

式中：R 为 Muskhelishivily 常数。

$$R=\begin{cases}3-4\nu & \text{平面应变}\\(3-\nu)/(1+\nu) & \text{平面应力}\end{cases}$$

由上式可得:在原边界处作用有分布荷载 $Q(s)$ 时,在任意 $z(x,y)$ 与 x 轴成 α 角的方向上引起的应力和位移分别为

$$\left.\begin{aligned}\sigma_y^e - i\tau_{xy}^e &= \int_\Gamma \Big\{ -Q(s)\Big[\frac{1}{z-c(s)} - R e^{-2i(\alpha-\alpha(s))}\frac{1}{\overline{z}-\overline{c}(s)}\Big] - \\ &\quad \overline{Q}(s)\Big[\frac{1}{\overline{z}-\overline{c}(s)} + e^{-2i(\alpha-\alpha(s))}\frac{(z-c(s))}{(\overline{z}-\overline{c}(s))^2}\Big]\Big\}ds \\ \sigma_x^e + \sigma_y^e &= \int_\Gamma \Big\{-2Q(s)\frac{1}{z-c(s)} - 2\overline{Q}(s)\frac{1}{\overline{z}-\overline{c}(s)}\Big\}ds \\ u^e + iv^e &= \frac{1}{2\mu}\int_\Gamma e^{-i\alpha(s)}\{-RQ(s)[\ln(z-c(s)) + \\ &\quad \ln(\overline{z}-\overline{c}(s)) + 1] + \overline{Q}(s)\frac{z-c(s)}{\overline{z}-\overline{c}(s)}\Big\}ds\end{aligned}\right\} \tag{3}$$

式中:Γ 为问题的周界。

2.2　已知边界虚拟热源时无限域无裂纹体的温度应力及位移

直接求解热弹性方程可得无限域内稳定点热源作用时的应力场及位移场:

$$u^* + iv^* = -\frac{a_l(1+\nu)}{8\pi\lambda}[(z-c)\ln(z-c) + (z-c)\ln(\overline{z}-\overline{c}) - (z-c)]$$

$$\sigma_x^* + \sigma_y^* = \frac{a_l E}{4\pi\lambda}[\ln(z-c) + \ln(\overline{z}-\overline{c})]$$

$$\sigma_y^* - \sigma_x^* + 2i\tau_{xy}^* = \frac{a_l E}{4\pi\lambda}\frac{\overline{z}-\overline{c}}{z-c}$$

当周界上有分布热源 $H(s)$ 时,任意点 z 在 α 方向上的应力和位移分别为

$$\left.\begin{aligned}u^h + iv^h &= \frac{a_l(1+\nu)}{8\pi\lambda}\int_\Gamma -[(z-c(s))\ln(z-c(s)) + \\ &\quad (z-c(s))\ln(\overline{z}-c(s)) - (z-c(s))]H(s)e^{-i(\alpha-\alpha(s))}ds \\ \sigma_x^h + \sigma_y^h &= \frac{a_l E}{4\pi\lambda}\int_\Gamma H(s)[\ln(z-c(s)) + \ln(\overline{z}-\overline{c}(s))]ds \\ \sigma_y^h - \sigma_x^h + 2i\tau_{xy}^h &= \frac{a_l E}{4\pi\lambda}\int_\Gamma \frac{\overline{z}-\overline{c}(c)}{z-c(s)}H(s)e^{-2i(\alpha-\alpha(s))}ds\end{aligned}\right\} \tag{4}$$

2.3　裂缝表面作用有分布荷载时的位移场、应力场

在缝面上离原点为 s 的集中力 $P = F_y - iF_x$ 的作用下(见图4),求解 Riemann－Hilbert 问题,并将位移单值条件代入得到应力函数

$$\Phi(z) = \Omega(z) = -\frac{P}{2\pi}\frac{\sqrt{a^2-s^2}}{(z-s)\sqrt{z^2-a^2}}$$

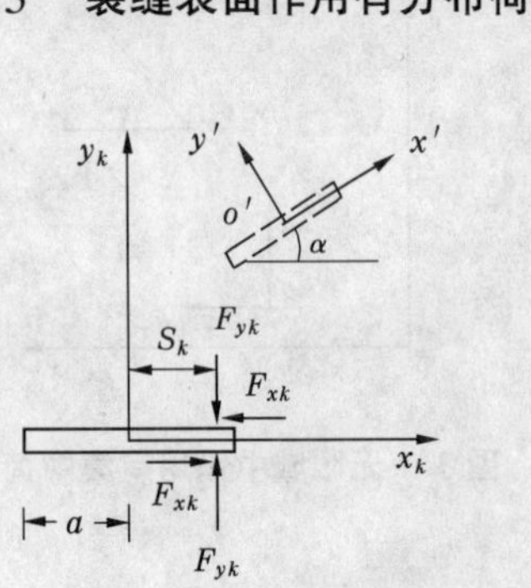

图4　无限域中的裂缝

由上式可以求出,当在第 k 条裂缝上作用有分布力 $P_k(S_k) = F_y(S_k) - iF_x(S_k)$ 时局部坐标系下的应力函数为

$$\left.\begin{aligned}\varphi_k(z_k) &= -\frac{1}{2\pi}\int_{-a_k}^{a_k} P_k(S_k)f_1(z_k,S_k)\mathrm{d}S_k \\ \psi_k(z_k) &= -\frac{1}{2\pi}\int_{-a_k}^{a_k}[\overline{P_k(S_k)}f_{1k}(z_k,S_k) - \\ &\qquad z_kP_k(S_k)\sqrt{a_k^2-S_k^2}G(z_k,S_k)]\mathrm{d}S_k\end{aligned}\right\} \tag{5}$$

式中:$G(z_k,S_k) = 1/(z_k - S_k)\sqrt{z_k^2 - a_k^2}$

$$G'(z_k,S_k) = (a_k^2 + S_kz_k + 2z_k^2)/(z_k - S_k)^2(\sqrt{z_k^2 - a_k^2})^3$$

$$f_{1k}(z_k,S_k) = i\left[\ln\left(\frac{\sqrt{z_k^2-a_k^2}+i\sqrt{a_k^2-S_k^2}}{z_k-S_k} - \frac{S_ki}{\sqrt{a_k^2-S_k^2}}\right) - \ln\left(1+\frac{S_k}{\sqrt{S_k^2-a_k^2}}\right)\right]$$

由式(5)可得任意点 z 在与 x 轴成 α 角的方向上的应力和位移:

$$\left.\begin{aligned}\sigma_y^k - i\tau_{xy}^k &= \int_{-a_k}^{a_k} P_k(S_k)C_k(S_k,z)\mathrm{d}S_k + \int_{-a_k}^{a_k}\overline{P_k(S_k)}D_k(S_k,z)\mathrm{d}S_k \\ u^k + iv^k &= \frac{\mathrm{e}^{i(ak-a)}}{4\mu\pi}\left\{\int_{-a_k}^{a_k} P_k(S_k)[\overline{f_{1k}(z_k,S_k)} - Rf_{1k}(z_k,S_k)]\mathrm{d}S_k + \right. \\ &\qquad \left.\int_{-a_k}^{a_k}\overline{P_k(S_k)}(z_k-\overline{z}_k)\sqrt{a_k^2-S_k^2}\,\overline{G(z_k,S_k)}\mathrm{d}S_k\right\}\end{aligned}\right\} \tag{6}$$

$$C_k = -\frac{1}{2\pi}\sqrt{a_k^2-S_k^2}[G(z_k,S_k) + \mathrm{e}^{2i(ak-a)}\overline{G(z_k,S_k)}]$$

$$D_k = -\frac{1}{2\pi}\sqrt{a_k^2-S_k^2}\{\overline{G(z_k,S_k)}[1-\mathrm{e}^{2i(ak-a)}] + \mathrm{e}^{2i(ak-a)}(z_k-\overline{z}_k)\overline{G'(z_k,S_k)}\}$$

式中:$z_k = (z - z_k^0)\mathrm{e}^{-iak}$;$z_k^0$ 为第 k 条裂缝的中点坐标。

如果有 N 条裂缝,则由总的裂缝释放应力引起的位移和应力为

$$\left.\begin{aligned}\sigma_y^c - i\tau_{xy}^c &= \sum_{k=1}^{N}[\sigma_y^k - i\tau_{xy}^k] \\ u^c + iv^c &= \sum_{k=1}^{N}[u^k + iv^k]\end{aligned}\right\} \tag{7}$$

式中:上角标 c 表示由裂缝表面分布荷载引起的应力和位移。

3 奇异积分方程组

若将图 1 中左边所示问题的边界分为两部分:已知边界位移 $u(Q_0) = \overline{u}(Q_0)$;已知边界应力 $\sigma_n(P_0) - i\sigma_t(P_0) = N(P_0) - iT(P_0)$。并认为裂缝为张开裂缝,缝面自由。则令在虚拟边界荷载、热荷载、缝面虚拟释放力共同作用下满足原问题的边界条件和缝面自由条件。由式(3)、式(4)、式(7) 可得一组积分方程:

$$\left.\begin{aligned}&\sigma_n^e(P_0)-i\sigma_t^e(P_0)+\sigma_n^h(P_0)-i\sigma_t^h(P_0)+\sigma_n^c(P_0)-i\sigma_t^c(P_0)\\&\qquad=N(P_0)-iT(P_0)\\&u^e(Q_0)+iv^e(Q_0)+u^h(Q_0)+iv^h(Q_0)+u^c(Q_0)+iv^c(Q_0)\\&\qquad=\bar{u}(Q_0)+i\bar{v}(Q_0)\\&\sigma_{yk}^e(C_0)-i\tau_{xyk}^e(C_0)+\sigma_{yk}^h(C_0)-i\tau_{xyk}^h(C_0)+\sigma_{yk}^c(C_0)-i\tau_{xyk}^c(C_0)\\&\qquad=0\end{aligned}\right\}\tag{8}$$

式中:上角标 e、c、h 分别表示由边界虚拟荷载、温度荷载和缝面虚拟力引起的各量;P_0、Q_0、C_0 分别表示边界 S_1、S_2 和缝面上的点。

解奇异积分方程组,求出边界虚拟荷载和缝面虚拟力,则可得整个应力场和位移场。缝端应力强度因子由下式求得

$$K_{\mathrm{I}}^n-iK_{\mathrm{II}}^n=-\frac{1}{\sqrt{\pi a_n}}\int_{-a_n}^{a_n}\left[F_y(S_n)-iF_x(S_n)\right]\sqrt{\frac{a_n\pm S_n}{a_n\mp S_n}}\,\mathrm{d}S_n$$

4 计算实例及与实验结果的比较

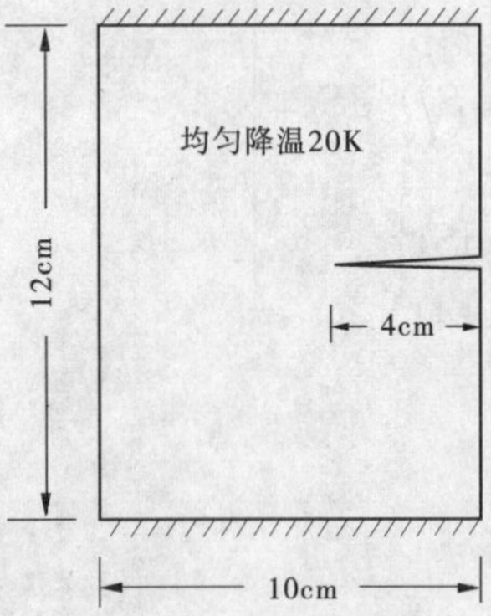

图 5 带边缝的环氧板

4.1 含边缝的环氧板均匀温降 20K 时的结果比较

取 12cm×10cm×0.6cm 的环氧板在侧面沿 x 轴开一个 4cm 长的边缝,上下两边固定约束,两侧面自由(见图 5)。

实测环氧树脂的材料常数为

弹性模量:$E=3.95\times10^3\mathrm{MPa}$

泊松比:$\nu=0.34$

条纹值:$f=1.32\mathrm{MPa\cdot cm}$

导温系数:$a=1.39\times10^{-7}\mathrm{m^2/s}$

膨胀系数:$0.68\times10^{-5}\,1/\mathrm{K}$。

计算结果的等应力差图与实验结果的等色线图见图 6、图 7。应力强度因子为

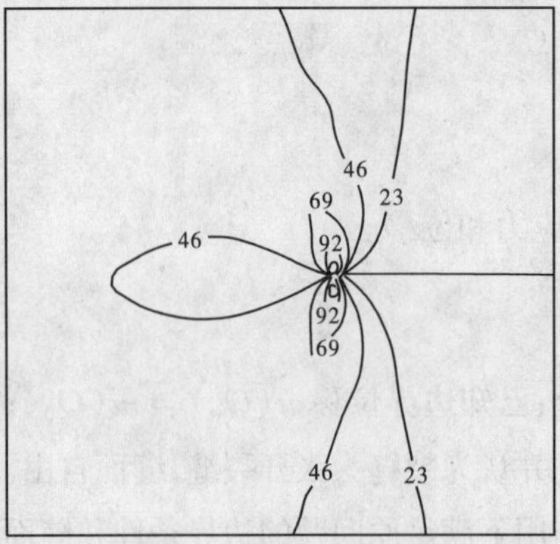

图 6 计算等应力差图

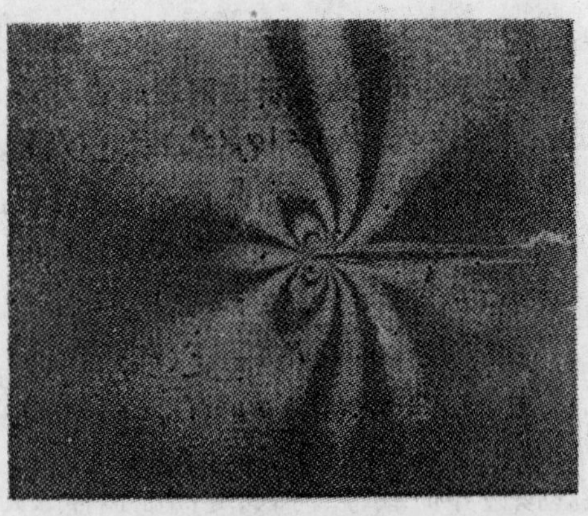

图 7 均匀温降 20K 时的实验等色线照片

计算值：$K_{\mathrm{I}} = 14.10\mathrm{MPa}\cdot\mathrm{cm}^{1/2}$，$K_{\mathrm{II}} = 0\mathrm{MPa}\cdot\mathrm{cm}^{1/2}$

实验值：$K_{\mathrm{I}} = 14.85\mathrm{MPa}\cdot\mathrm{cm}^{1/2}$，$K_{\mathrm{II}} = 0.32\mathrm{MPa}\cdot\mathrm{cm}^{1/2}$

4.2　含有 3 条平行裂缝平板的热断裂问题

含有 3 条平行裂缝的平板见图 8，均匀温降 25K 时，各缝端应力强度因子的计算结果和实验值比较见表 1。计算结果的等应力差曲线和实验结果的等色线见图 9、图 10。

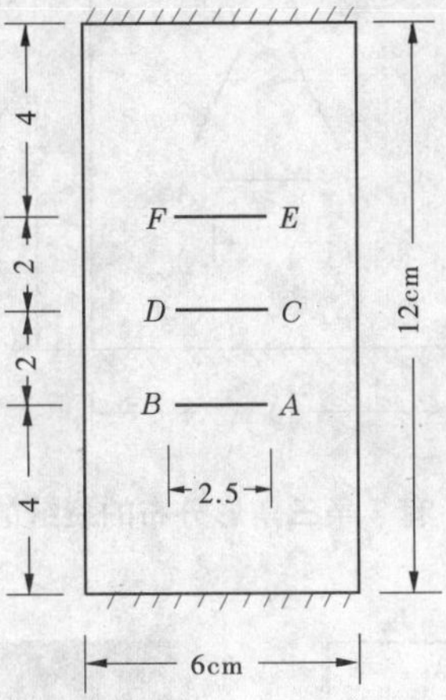

图 8　有 3 条平行缝的平板

表 1　均匀温降 25K 时的应力强度因子　（单位：$\mathrm{MPa}\cdot\mathrm{cm}^{1/2}$）

点号		A	B	C	D	E	F
实验	K_{I}	9.12	9.16	7.48	7.41	9.04	8.98
	K_{II}	0.67	−0.72	0	0	−0.68	0.61
计算	K_{I}	9.38	9.38	7.75	7.75	9.38	9.38
	K_{II}	0.74	−0.74	0	0	−0.74	0.74

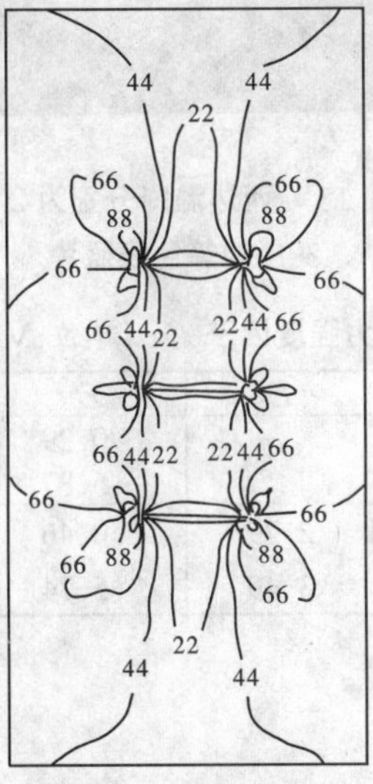

图 9　计算等应力差图

图 10　实验等色线照片

4.3　含有3条三角形分布裂缝的矩形平板在稳定温度场作用下的热断裂问题

含3条三角形分布裂缝的矩形平板试件两侧分别温降20、30K时(见图11),用本文方法所得等应力差曲线见图12,实验照片见图13。相应的缝端应力强度因子比较见表2。

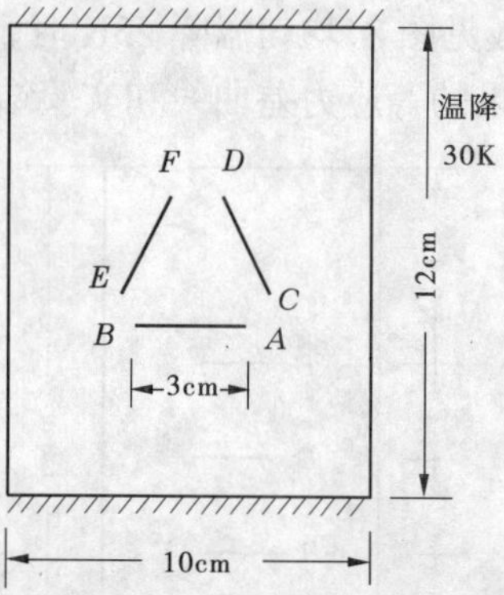

图11　有3条三角形分布的裂缝的平板

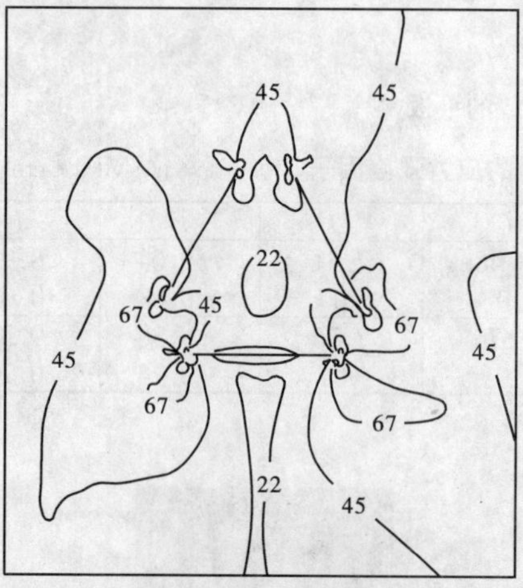

图12　两边温降分别为20、30K的计算结果

图13　两边温降分别为20、30K的等色线照片

表2　两侧分别温降20、30K时的应力强度因子　(单位:MPa · $cm^{1/2}$)

点号		A	B	C	D	E	F
实验	K_I	9.85	10.74	0		0.29	
	K_{II}	0.13	−0.22	5.30		−5.87	
计算	K_I	11.09	11.61	−0.04	2.29	0.46	2.51
	K_{II}	0.06	−0.18	5.00	3.49	−5.74	−3.98

注:由于实验中温降时固端条件未能准确模拟,K_I 数值偏小。

5　结论

(1)本文提出的虚拟热源和虚拟荷载法相结合求解多裂隙体热断裂问题的方法,概念明确。将3个实例的计算结果和实验结果进行了比较,两者相近,可相互验证。计算精度好,省机时,求解3条裂缝的热断裂问题只需机时30～50s CPU (ELXSI 机)。

(2)在固定边界及温度荷载作用下,多条裂缝相互影响的结果使应力强度因子降低,如含有3条中心裂缝的平板的最大缝端应力强度因子比含有1条等长裂缝板的低22.6%。表明多条裂缝的相互影响使结构刚度降低。

(3)含多条平行裂缝的固端平板的温降荷载作用下,靠近约束边界的裂缝的应力强度因子最大,它和应力边界条件不同,仍有Ⅱ型应力强度因子产生。

参 考 文 献

[1] 刘泊生译. 法国四座拱坝的严重破坏情况. 国外水利水电,1981(5):20～27

[2] Abraham I J, Sloan R C. 13*th Int Congr on Large Dams*. Int Common Large Dams, Vol.1,1979.1～24

[3] 刘振国,周筑宝,袁龙蔚. 柘溪大头坝迎水面垂直裂缝扩展过程研究. 水利学报. 1989(1):29～36

[4] 陈宜周. 无限平板中的多裂纹问题. 西北工业大学学报, 1984,2(4):367～374

[5] Zhou Ruizhong, Liu Guangting. *The Synthetic Deformation Modulus and The Synthetic Poisson's Ratio of Multiple Crack Bodies*. Int Conf on Fracture and Damage of Concrete and Rock and Special Seminar on Large Concrete Dam Structure, July 1988, Vienna Austria

[6] Liu Guangting, Chi Yuan. *An Analytic-Fictitious Boundary Forces Method for Calculating Multi-Crack Problem in Arbitrary Region with Mixed Mode Boundaries*. Int Conf Recent Development on the Fracture of Concrete and Rock, Sept 1989, University of Wales College of Cardiff, U K

[7] Panasyuk V V, Savruk M P, Datsyshyn A P. *A General Method of Solution of Two Dimensional Problems in the Theory of Cracks*. Eng Fract Mech, 1977,9:481～497

[8] 张国新,刘光廷. 含有绝热裂缝的有限自由板在稳定温度场作用下的断裂分析. 水利水运科学研究,1989(1):86～96

[9] 刘光廷,张国新. 缝内含有不同导温介质时的稳定温度断裂研究. 清华大学学报,1990,30(2):15～21

[10] Green A E, Zerna W. *Theoretical Elasticity*. London: Oxford University Press,1954

HARMONIC THERMAL FRACTURE OF MULTIPLE CRACK SYSTEM AND THE STABILITY OF CRACKS IN RCC ARCH DAM

Abstract This work is concerned with formulating the harmonic state linear thermoelastic problem for bodies with finite dimension and multiple cracks. The fundamental solutions for temperature and stress fields caused by a point harmonic heat source in an infinite plane are presented. The boundary integral equations are obtained by the superposition of displacements and stresses caused by the prescribing displacements/tractions and thermal disturbance in an infinite region on the site that conforms to the boundary of the finite body, and that in an infinite region with cracks subjected to the negative tractions obtained from the mechanical and thermal loadings.

A numerical result is obtained for two inclined cracks in a rectangular plate. The convergency of the method is examined. As an example of engineering application, a horizontal arch with cracks in a RCC arch dam in south China is analyzed. The variations of SIF at the tip of cracks with the changes of environmental temperature and water level are given. It shows that the stress distribution in the arch can be improved by artificial short joints located at upstream of the abutment, and the water pressure should be kept constant during February～April for the consideration of stability of cracks.

1 Introduction

Multiple cracks are common to many materials used in the construction of buildings and dam structures. Change of the environment temperature is the main factor affecting the stability of cracks. The cracks on the surface of structure open and close periodically with the variation of atmospheric temperature, which can be simplified as harmonic; some develop step-by-step after a period of temperature variation, finally bringing potential danger to the construction[1~3]. The interaction of cracks may be complex, particularly when they are clustered closely together giving rise to highly non-symmetrical distribution of stress and/or strain, and also giving rise to stress intensity factor. Previous work[4~11] on this subject has dealt mostly with mechanical loads or thermal loads applied to bodies with single crack or steady thermal loads applied to a multiple crack system. The main objective of the present study is to develop an effective method for determining the stress state in finite bodies weakened by multiple cracks and SIF at the tip of cracks under harmonic temperature variation. The method was used to analyze the stress distribution of an arch dam and to evaluate the stability of cracks in the dam. The results show a high dependence of crack stability on the temperature variation and water pressure applied on the upstream surface of dam.

本文选自《Engineering Fracture Mechanics》1996 年第 5 期，作者还有 G. X. ZHANG, Y. WU。

2 Harmonic Temperature Field

Usually the width of a crack in a mass of concrete is very small (<2mm) compared with the structure, so the disturbance caused by the surface insulation of the crack can be neglected [12].

Within the framework of linear thermoelasticity, the temperature field can be determined independent of the stresses. Referring to the two-dimensional region Ω of $z(x, y)$, which is enclosed by the surface Γ that consists of two portions Γ_1 and Γ_2 (See Fig. 1), on which the following conditions prevail:

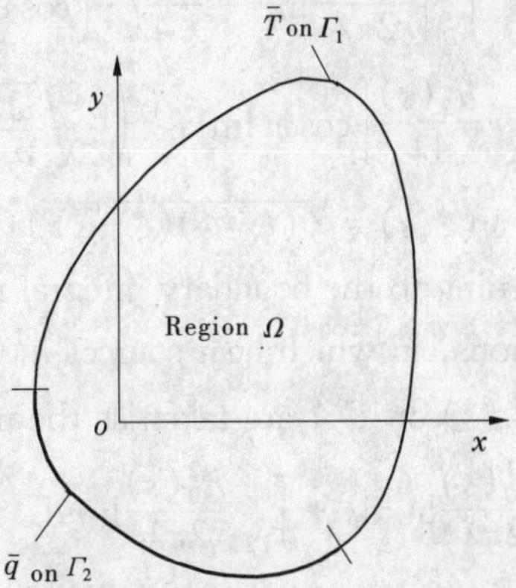

Fig. 1 Boundary condition of heat conduction

$$T(\xi_1, t) = \overline{T}_0(\xi) + \overline{f}(\xi)\sin\omega t + \overline{g}(\xi)\cos\omega t\,(\Gamma_1) -$$
$$\lambda \frac{\partial T}{\partial n} = \overline{q}_0(\eta) + \overline{q}_1(\eta)\sin\omega t + \overline{q}_2(\eta)\cos\omega t\,(\Gamma_2) \tag{1}$$

where λ is the heat conductivity, $\overline{T}_0(\xi)$ is the steady temperature and $\overline{f}(\xi), \overline{g}(\xi)$ stand for the amplitude of temperature variation, respectively. $\overline{q}_0(\eta)$ is the steady heat flow, $\overline{q}_1(\eta)$, $\overline{q}_2(\eta)$ are the amplitude of heat flow variation.

The fundamental solution of the steady and harmonic point heat source can be used to generate the temperature field in the infinite domain. Suppose a point heat source $P = h_0 + h_1\sin\omega t + h_2\cos\omega t$ applied at $z = c$, the fundamental solution of temperature field can be written as [13]:

$$T^*(r, t) = \frac{1}{2\pi\lambda}\ln r + \frac{h_1}{4\lambda}\left[\cos\omega t\,\mathrm{Re}\,H_0^{(1)}\left(r\sqrt{\frac{\omega}{a}i}\right) + \sin\omega t\,\mathrm{Im}H_0^{(1)}\left(r\sqrt{\frac{\omega}{a}i}\right)\right] +$$
$$\frac{h_2}{4\lambda}\left[\cos\omega t\,\mathrm{Im}\,H_0^{(1)}\left(r\sqrt{\frac{\omega}{a}i}\right) - \sin\omega t\,\mathrm{Re}H_0^{(1)}\left(r\sqrt{\frac{\omega}{a}i}\right)\right] \tag{2}$$

Note that:

$H_0^{(1)}(z)$ is the first kind of Hankel function with zero order.

The temperature field caused by the distributed heat source $h_0(s) + h_1(s)\sin\omega t + h_2(s)\cos\omega t$ applied on the boundary Γ can be obtained by the integration of Eq. (2) along boundary Γ:

$$T(z, t) = \int_\Gamma \left\{\frac{h_0(s)}{2\pi\lambda}\ln r + \frac{h_1(s)}{4\lambda}\left[\cos\omega t\,\mathrm{Re}H_0^{(1)}\left(r\sqrt{\frac{\omega}{a}i}\right) + \sin\omega t\,\mathrm{Im}H_0^{(1)}\left(r\sqrt{\frac{\omega}{a}i}\right)\right] +\right.$$
$$\left.\frac{h_2(s)}{4\lambda}\left[\cos\omega t\,\mathrm{Im}H_0^{(1)}\left(r\sqrt{\frac{\omega}{a}i}\right) - \sin\omega t\,\mathrm{Re}H_0^{(1)}\left(r\sqrt{\frac{\omega}{a}i}\right)\right]\right\} ds \tag{3}$$

where $r=r(z,s)=\sqrt{(z-s)(\overline{z}-\overline{s})}$. Suppose ξ is a point on Γ_1, consider the limit of $z\to\xi$, then Eq. (3) can be written as:

$$T(\xi,t)=\int_{\Gamma}\left\{\frac{h_0(s)}{2\pi\lambda}\ln r+\frac{h_1(s)}{4\lambda}\left[\cos\omega t\,\mathrm{Re}H_0^{(1)}\left(r\sqrt{\frac{\omega}{a}}i\right)+\sin\omega t\,\mathrm{Im}H_0^{(1)}\left(r\sqrt{\frac{\omega}{a}}i\right)\right]+\frac{h_2(s)}{4\lambda}\left[\cos\omega t\,\mathrm{Im}H_0^{(1)}\left(r\sqrt{\frac{\omega}{a}}i\right)-\sin\omega t\,\mathrm{Re}H_0^{(1)}\left(r\sqrt{\frac{\omega}{a}}i\right)\right]\right\}\mathrm{d}s \tag{4}$$

where $r=r(\xi,s)=\sqrt{(\xi-s)(\overline{\xi}-\overline{s})}$.

According to the boundary integral method and Eq. (1)~Eq. (4), the boundary integral equations, in which heat sources $h_0^1(s)$, $h_1^1(s)$, $h_2^1(s)$ on boundary Γ_1, and $h_0^2(s)$, $h_1^2(s)$, $h_2^2(s)$ on Γ_2, are taken as the unknowns, are given by:

$$\left\{\begin{aligned}
&\int_{\Gamma1}\frac{h_0^1(s)}{2\pi\lambda}\ln r\,\mathrm{d}s+\int_{\Gamma2}\frac{h_0^2(s)}{2\pi\lambda}\ln r\,\mathrm{d}s=\overline{T}_0(\xi)\\
&\int_{\Gamma1}\left[\frac{h_1^1(s)}{4\lambda}\mathrm{Im}H_0^{(1)}\left(r\sqrt{\frac{\omega}{a}}i\right)-\frac{h_2^1(s)}{4\lambda}\mathrm{Re}H_0^{(1)}\left(r\sqrt{\frac{\omega}{a}}i\right)\right]\mathrm{d}s+\\
&\quad\int_{\Gamma2}\left[\frac{h_1^2(s)}{4\lambda}\mathrm{Im}H_0^{(1)}\left(r\sqrt{\frac{\omega}{a}}i\right)-\frac{h_2^2(s)}{4\lambda}\mathrm{Re}H_0^{(1)}\left(r\sqrt{\frac{\omega}{a}}i\right)\right]\mathrm{d}s=\overline{f}(\xi)\\
&\int_{\Gamma1}\left[\frac{h_1^1(s)}{4\lambda}\mathrm{Re}H_0^{(1)}\left(r\sqrt{\frac{\omega}{a}}i\right)+\frac{h_2^1(s)}{4\lambda}\mathrm{Im}H_0^{(1)}\left(r\sqrt{\frac{\omega}{a}}i\right)\right]\mathrm{d}s+\\
&\quad\int_{\Gamma2}\left[\frac{h_1^2(s)}{4\lambda}\mathrm{Re}H_0^{(1)}\left(r\sqrt{\frac{\omega}{a}}i\right)+\frac{h_2^2(s)}{4\lambda}\mathrm{Im}H_0^{(1)}\left(r\sqrt{\frac{\omega}{a}}i\right)\right]\mathrm{d}s=\overline{g}(\xi)
\end{aligned}\right. \tag{5}$$

$$\left\{\begin{aligned}
&\frac{1}{2}h_0(\eta)-\int_{\Gamma1}\mathrm{Im}\left[\frac{h_0^1(s)}{2\pi}\frac{1}{\eta-s}\mathrm{e}^{i(\beta\eta-\beta s)}\right]\mathrm{d}s-\int_{\Gamma2}\mathrm{Im}\left[\frac{h_0^2(s)}{2\pi}\frac{1}{\eta-s}\mathrm{e}^{i(\beta\eta-\beta s)}\right]\mathrm{d}s=\overline{q}_0(\eta)\\
&\frac{1}{2}h_1(\eta)-\int_{\Gamma1}\left\{\frac{h_1^1(s)}{4}\frac{\partial}{\partial n_\eta}\left[\mathrm{Im}H_0^{(1)}\left(r\sqrt{\frac{\omega}{a}}i\right)\right]-\frac{h_2^1(s)}{4}\frac{\partial}{\partial n_\eta}\left[\mathrm{Re}H_0^{(1)}\left(r\sqrt{\frac{\omega}{a}}i\right)\right]\right\}\mathrm{d}s-\\
&\quad\int_{\Gamma2}\left\{\frac{h_1^2(s)}{4}\frac{\partial}{\partial n_\eta}\left[\mathrm{Im}h_0^{(1)}\left(r\sqrt{\frac{\omega}{a}}i\right)\right]-\frac{h_2^2(s)}{4}\frac{\partial}{\partial n_\eta}\left[\mathrm{Re}H_0^{(1)}\left(r\sqrt{\frac{\omega}{a}}i\right)\right]\right\}\mathrm{d}s=\overline{q}_1(\eta)\\
&\frac{1}{2}h_2(\eta)-\int_{\Gamma1}\left\{\frac{h_1^1(s)}{4}\frac{\partial}{\partial n_\eta}\left[\mathrm{Re}H_0^{(1)}\left(r\sqrt{\frac{\omega}{a}}i\right)\right]-\frac{h_2^1(s)}{4}\frac{\partial}{\partial n_\eta}\left[\mathrm{Im}H_0^{(1)}\left(r\sqrt{\frac{\omega}{a}}i\right)\right]\right\}\mathrm{d}s-\\
&\quad\int_{\Gamma2}\left\{\frac{h_1^2(s)}{4}\frac{\partial}{\partial n_\eta}\left[\mathrm{Re}H_0^{(1)}\left(r\sqrt{\frac{\omega}{a}}i\right)\right]-\frac{h_2^2(s)}{4}\frac{\partial}{\partial n_\eta}\left[\mathrm{Im}H_0^{(1)}\left(r\sqrt{\frac{\omega}{a}}i\right)\right]\right\}\mathrm{d}s=\overline{q}_2(\eta)
\end{aligned}\right. \tag{6}$$

in which ξ is a point on Γ_1 and η is a point on Γ_2, β_η is the angle between the normal direction of point η on Γ and the x-axis.

Eqs. (5) can be solved numerically to obtain the distributed heat sources $h_0(s)$、$h_1(s)$、$h_2(s)$ on Γ_1 and Γ_2, then the temperature field can be given by Eq. (3).

3 Fundamental Solutions

Now, let the region Ω in Fig. 2 contain p cracks $l_1, l_2, \cdots, l_p$ whose ends are $a_j b_j$ ($j=$

$1,2,\cdots,p)$. The surface of the cracks are free of traction. Surrounding Ω is the surface Γ with traction specified on Γ_1 and displacements specified on Γ_2. The heat source $h_0(s)+h_1(s)\sin\omega t+h_2(s)\cos\omega t$ obtained from the section above is also applied on the surface Γ.

In order to form the integral equations which are needed to solve the problem, three kinds of fundamental solution should be used.

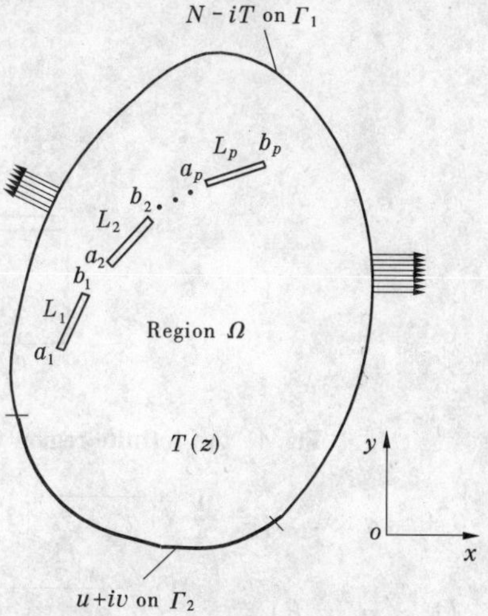

Fig. 2 Multiple crack problem

3.1 Static Mechanical Fundamental Solution for An Infinite Continuity Region

For a complex point force $p=F_x+iF_y$ applied at $z=c$, the stresses and displacements in $x-y$ coordinate system at a point z in the direction β (See Fig. 3) can be obtained by the Kelvin solution[14]:

$$\sigma_{x_1}^{*(1)}+\sigma_{y_1}^{*(1)}=-\frac{2}{1+\text{æ}}\mathrm{Re}\left[\frac{P}{z-c}\right]$$

$$\sigma_{y_1}^{*(1)}-iT_{x_1y_1}^{*(1)}=-\frac{1}{2(1+\text{æ})}\left\{P\left[\frac{1}{z-c}-\frac{\text{æ}\exp\{2i\beta\}}{\overline{z}-\overline{c}(s)}\right]+\overline{P}\frac{1}{\overline{z}-\overline{c}}-\frac{(z-c)\exp\{2i\beta\}}{(\overline{z}-\overline{c})^2}\right\} \tag{7}$$

and

$$u_{x_1}^{*(1)}+iv_{y_1}^{*(1)}=\frac{1}{4\mu(1+\text{æ})}\exp(-i\beta)\left\{-\text{æ}P[\lg(z-c)+\lg(\overline{z}-\overline{c})+1]+\overline{P}\frac{z}{\overline{z}-\overline{c}}\right\} \tag{8}$$

3.2 Solution Caused by A Point Force Acted on Crack Surface

For an infinite region with a crack of length $2a$ subjected to a pair of point force $P=F_y-iF_x$ at $z=s$ shown in Fig. 4, the stresses and displacements in $x-y$ coordinate system at point z in the direction of α can be expressed as

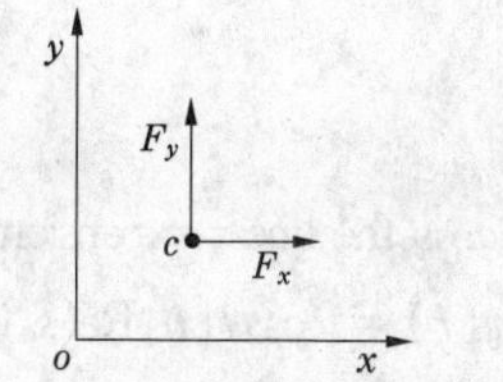

Fig. 3 Point force applied at $z=c$

$$\left.\begin{aligned}u_{x'}^{*(2)}(z,a)+iv_{y'}^{*(2)}(z,a)&=\frac{e^{i\beta}}{4\mu\pi}\{P[\overline{f_1}(z,a,s)-\text{æ}f_1(z,a,s)]\times\\&\qquad\overline{P}(z-\overline{z})\sqrt{a^2-s^2}\,\overline{G(z,a,s)}\}\\ \sigma_{y'}^{*(2)}(z,a)-i\tau_{x'y'}^{*(2)}(z,a)&=PC(z,a,s,\beta)+\overline{P}D(z,a,s,\beta)\end{aligned}\right\} \tag{9}$$

where

$$G(z,a,s)=1/(z-s)\sqrt{z^2-a^2}$$

$$f_1(z,a,s)=i\left[\ln\left(\frac{\sqrt{z^2-a^2}+i\sqrt{a^2-s^2}}{z-s}-\frac{si}{\sqrt{a^2-s^2}}\right)-\ln\left(1+\frac{s}{\sqrt{s^2-a^2}}\right)\right]$$

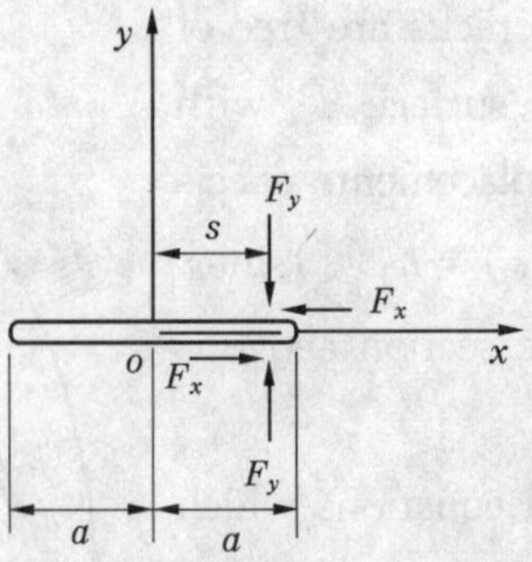

Fig. 4　An infinite region with a crack subjected to a pair of point force

$$C(z,a,s,\beta)=\frac{1}{2\pi}\sqrt{a^2-s^2}\left[G(z,a,s)+e^{-2i\beta}\overline{G(z,a,s)}\right]$$

$$D(z,a,s,\beta)=-\frac{1}{2\pi}\sqrt{a^2-s^2}\left[\overline{G(z,a,s)}(1-e^{-2i\beta})+e^{-2i\beta}(z-\bar{z})\overline{G'(z,a,s)}\right]$$

3.3　Fundamental Solution of Thermoelasticity

By solving the thermoelastic problem in $x-y$ coordinate system, the stresses and displacement induced by point thermal source $q=h_0+h_1\sin\omega t+h_2\cos\omega t$ at point $z=s$ can be written as:

$$u^{*(3)}(z,\beta,t)+iv^{*(3)}(z,\beta,t)=-e^{-i\beta}\frac{\alpha(1+\mu)}{4\pi\lambda}h_0(z-s)(\ln r-\frac{1}{2})+e^{-i\beta}\frac{\alpha(1+\mu)}{4\lambda}\times$$
$$\frac{z-s}{r}\{\cos\omega t[h_1\mathrm{Re}U_0(r)+h_2\mathrm{Im}U_0(r)]+$$
$$\sin\omega t[h_1\mathrm{Im}U_0(r)-h_2\mathrm{Re}U_0(r)]\}$$

$$\sigma_{y'}^{*(3)}(z,\beta,t)-i\tau_{x'y'}^{*(3)}(z,\beta,t)=\frac{\alpha E}{8\lambda}\left\{\frac{h_0}{\pi}\left[\ln\frac{z-s}{\bar{z}-\bar{s}}+e^{2i\beta}\frac{z-s}{\bar{z}-\bar{s}}\right]+\sigma_r(r)+\sigma_0(r)+\right.$$
$$\left.e^{-2i\beta}\frac{z-s}{\bar{z}-\bar{s}}[\sigma_0(r)-\sigma_r(r)]\right\}\qquad(10)$$

where α_i is the linear expansion.

$$\sigma_0(r)=\cos\omega t[h_1\mathrm{Re}(s_0(r)-H_0^{(1)}(r))+h_2\mathrm{Im}(s_0(r)-H_0^{(1)}(r))]+$$
$$\sin\omega t[h_1\mathrm{Im}(s_0(r)-H_0^{(1)}(r))-h_2\mathrm{Re}(s_0(r)-H_0^{(1)}(r))]$$
$$\sigma_r(r)=-\cos\omega t[h_1\mathrm{Re}(s_0(r))+h_2\mathrm{Im}(s_0(r))]-\sin\omega t[h_1\mathrm{Im}(s_0(r))-h_2\mathrm{Re}(s_0(r))]$$
$$u_0(r)=\left(1+\frac{2i}{\pi}\ln\left(\sqrt{\frac{\omega i}{a}}/2\right)+\frac{2i}{\pi}\gamma\right)\sum_{k=0}^{\infty}A_k\frac{r^{2k+1}}{2k+2}+\frac{2i}{\pi}\sum_{k=0}^{\infty}A_k\frac{r^{2k+1}}{2k+2}\ln r-$$
$$\frac{2i}{\pi}\sum_{k=1}^{\infty}A_k\frac{r^{2k+1}}{2k+2}\sum_{m=1}^{\infty}\frac{1}{m}-\frac{2i}{\pi}\sum_{k=0}^{\infty}A_k\frac{r^{2k+1}}{(2k+2)^2}$$
$$S_0(r)=\left[1+\frac{2i}{\pi}\ln\left(\sqrt{\frac{\omega}{a}}i/2\right)+\gamma\right]\sum_{k=0}^{\infty}A_k\frac{r^{2k}}{2k+2}-\frac{2i}{\pi}\sum_{k=0}^{\infty}A_k\frac{r^{2k}}{(2k+2)^2}+$$
$$\frac{2i}{\pi}\sum_{k=0}^{\infty}A_k\frac{r^{2k}}{2k+2}\ln r-\frac{2i}{\pi}\sum_{k=1}^{\infty}A_k\frac{r^{2k}}{2k+2}\sum_{m=1}^{\infty}\frac{1}{m}$$

where γ is the Euler constant.

4 Boundary Integral Equations

Returning to the original problem in Fig. 2, suppose distributed fictitious forces $Q^1(s,t)$, $Q^2(s,t)$ are applied on Γ_1 and Γ_2, respectively, and $P_k(s_k,t)$ is acted on the surface of kth crack. The fictitious distributed thermal source $q(s,t)=q^1(s,t)+q^2(s,t)$ has already been obtained from Eq. (5) and Eq. (6). The stresses and displacements at a point z in region Ω can be defined as:

$$u(z,\beta,t)+iv(z,\beta,t)=\int_\Gamma\{u^{*(1)}[Q(s,t,z,\beta)]+iv^{*(1)}[Q(s,t,z,\beta)]\}\mathrm{d}s+\sum_{k=1}^{N}\int_{-a_k}^{a_k}\{u^{*(2)}[P_k(s_k,t),z,\beta]+iv^{*(2)}[P_k(s_k,t),z,\beta]\}\mathrm{d}s+\int_\Gamma\{u^{*(3)}[q(s,t)],z,\beta,t]+iv^{*(3)}[q(s,t),z,\beta,t)]\}\mathrm{d}s \tag{11a}$$

$$\sigma_y(z,\beta,t)-i\tau_{xy}(z,\beta,t)=\int_\Gamma\{\sigma_y^{*(1)}[Q(s,t),z,\beta]\}-i\tau_{xy}^{*(1)}[Q(s,t),z,\beta]\}\mathrm{d}s+\sum_{k=1}^{N}\int_{-a_k}^{a_k}\{\sigma^{*(2)}[P_k(s_k,t),z,\beta]-i\tau_{xy}^{*(2)}[P_k(s_k,t),z,\beta]\}\mathrm{d}s+\int_\Gamma\{\sigma_y^{*(3)}[q(s,t),z,\beta,t]-i\tau_{xy}^{*(3)}[q(s,t),z,\beta,t)]\}\mathrm{d}s \tag{11b}$$

Note that $Q(s,t,z,\beta)=Q^1(s,t,z,\beta)+Q^2(s,t,z,\beta)$.

Now suppose the known displacement on Γ_1 is $\overline{u}(\eta,t)+i\overline{v}(\eta,t)$, where $\overline{u}(\eta,t)$ and $\overline{v}(\eta,t)$ denote the normal and tangent displacements at point η, respectively, and the known traction on Γ_2 is $N(\xi,t)-iT(\xi,t)$, in which $N(\xi,t)$ and $T(\xi,t)$ are the normal and tangent tractions at point ξ, respectively, the surface of crack keeps free. Let z in Eq. (11a) close towards the point η on the boundary Γ_1 infinitely; one integral equation that satisfies the known displacement condition on boundary Γ_1 can be given as:

$$\overline{u}(\eta,t)+i\overline{v}(\eta,t)=\int_r\{u^{*(1)}[Q(s,t),\eta,\beta_{\eta s}]+iv^{*(1)}[Q(s,t),\eta,\beta_{\eta s}]\}\mathrm{d}s+\sum_{k=1}^{N}\int_{-a_k}^{a_k}\{u^{*(2)}[P_k(s_k,t),\eta,\beta_{\eta k}]+iv^{*(2)}[P_k(s_k,t),\eta,\beta_{\eta k}]\}\mathrm{d}s+\int_r\{u^{*(3)}[q(s,t),\eta,\alpha_{\eta s},t]+iv^{*(3)}[q(s,t),\eta,\beta_{\eta s},t]\}\mathrm{d}s \tag{12a}$$

Let z in Eq. (11b) close to the point ξ on the boundary Γ_2 infinitely; a singalarity arises when the integral points coincide with point ξ, and by means of the Cauchy integral formula, an integral equation that satisfies the boundary condition on boundary Γ_2 can be written as:

$$N(\xi,t)-iT(\xi,t)=-\frac{i}{2}Q^2(\xi,t)+\int_\Gamma\{\sigma_y^{*(1)}[Q(s,t),\xi,\beta_{\xi s}]+i\tau_{xy}^{*(1)}[Q(s,t),\xi,\beta_{\xi s}]\}\mathrm{d}s+$$

$$\int_{\Gamma}\{\sigma^{*(3)}[q(s,t),\xi,\beta_{\xi s},t]-i\tau_{xy}^{*(3)}[q(s,t),\xi,\beta_{\xi k},t]\}\mathrm{d}s+$$

$$\sum_{k=1}^{N}\int_{-a_k}^{a_k}\{\sigma_y^{*(2)}[P_k(s_k,t),\xi,\beta_{\xi k}]-i\tau_{xy}^{*(2)}[P_k(s_k,t),\xi,\beta_{\xi k}]\}\mathrm{d}s \qquad (12b)$$

Another singular integral equation that satisfies the traction free condition on the surface of nth crack can be obtained using the method mentioned above as

$$O=\frac{1}{2}P_n(\xi_n,t)+\int_{\Gamma}\{\sigma_y^{*(1)}[Q(s,t),\xi_n,\beta_{ns}]-i\tau_{xy}^{*(1)}[Q(s,t),\xi_n,\beta_{ns}]\}\mathrm{d}s+$$

$$\int_{\Gamma}\{\sigma^{*(3)}[q(s,t),\xi_n,\beta_{ns},t]-i\tau_{xy}^{*(3)}[q(s,t),\xi_n,\beta_{ns},t]\}\mathrm{d}s+$$

$$\sum_{k=1}^{N}\int_{-a_k}^{a_k}\{\sigma_y^{*(2)}[P_k(s_k,t),\xi_n,\beta_{nk}]-i\tau_{xy}^{*(2)}[P_k(s_k,t),\xi_n,\beta_{nk}]\}\mathrm{d}s \ (n=1,2,\cdots,p) \qquad (12c)$$

where $\beta_{\eta s}=\beta_\eta-\beta_s$.

Eqs. (12a) ~ (12c) inclusive yield $p+2$ equations solving the $p+2$ unknows with $Q^1(s)$ on Γ_1 and $Q^2(s)$ on Γ_2 while $q(s,t)$ is the thermal source on Γ and $P_j(s,t)$ with $j=1,2,\cdots,p$. These equations can be solved numerically to obtain the stresses and displacements in region Ω in accordance with the mechanical and harmonic thermal boundary conditions specified on Γ.

The stress intensity factors K_{I} and K_{II} at the tip of nth crack can also be calculated by:

$$K_{n\mathrm{I}}^{\pm}(t)-iK_{n\mathrm{II}}^{\pm}(t)=-\frac{1}{\sqrt{\pi a_n}}\int_{-a_n}^{a_n}P_n(s_n,t)\sqrt{\frac{a_n\pm s_n}{a_n\mp s_n}}\mathrm{d}s_n \qquad (13)$$

Take a plate with the dimension of 10cm × 10cm as an example to examine the convergency of the method (See Fig. 5). There are two cracks with length $2a=2.0$cm in the plate, one is a horizontal crack and the other has a 45° angle with horizontal direction. The top and the bottom of the plate were mechanically fixed. The temperature variation on the left side is $\Delta T=20\sin 6.28\ t$ K and the temperature change on right side remains 0. By means of the method described above, the stress intensity factors, with different number of boundary elements and crack elements, at the tips of every crack are calculated. The variation of SIF at point A and C along with the number of elements is shown in Fig. 6. It can be seen from Fig. 6 that when the total elements number more than 30, the stress intensity factors K_{I} at point A and C are near the steady values. That means the method proposed in this paper has a good convergency.

5 Engineering Application

An experimental RCC arch dam was designed in China. Take a horizontal arch as an example to study the stress distribution and the stability of cracks by means of the method pre

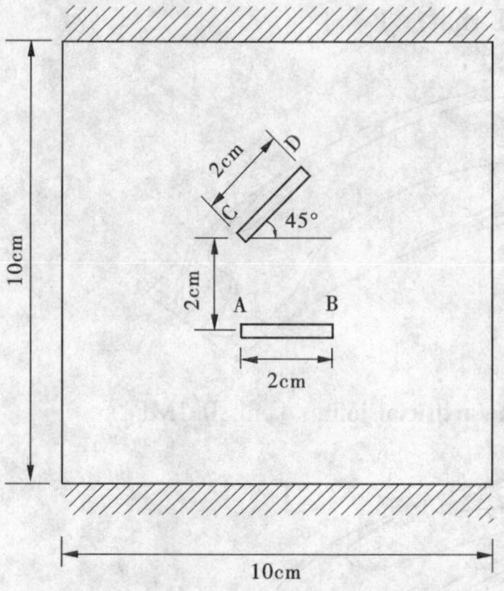

Fig. 5 **Example of convergency test**

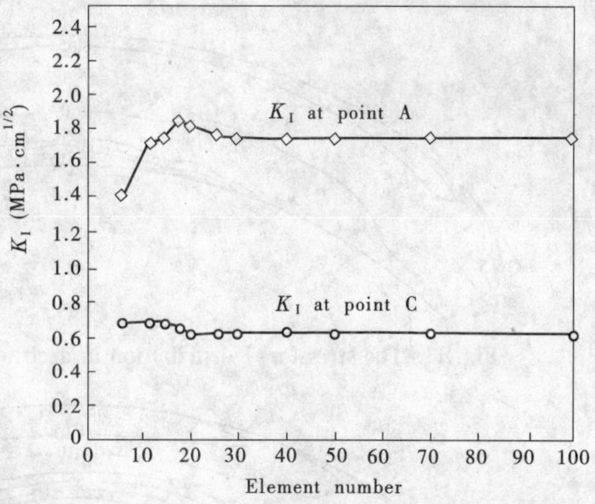

Fig. 6 **Convergency test**

sented in this paper. The boundary condition is shown in Fig. 7. The maximum temperature before cooling is 29℃ and the maximum water pressure is 8.0MPa. The temperature on the upstream surface of the arch is $T_u = 13.5 + 3.5\sin\omega(t-4)$℃, the temperature on downstream surface of the arch is $T_d = 16.7 + 9.7\sin\omega(t-4)$℃, where $\omega = 2\pi/12$. The following problems are calculated and analyzed: ① the influence of short artificial joints at the upstream abutments on the improvement of the stress distribution in the arch; ② the stability of cracks on the downstream surface of crown and the limited maximum temperature in the arch.

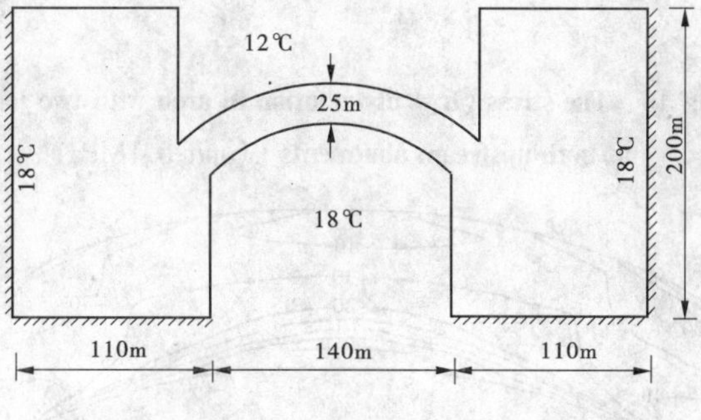

Fig. 7 **Boundary condition**

5.1 The Improvement on the Stress Distribution in the Arch by the Short Artificial Joints

In order to improve the stress distribution in the arch dam two short watertight artificial joints of length 3.0m were made at both sides of the upstream abutment with one joint of length 2.0m at the crown of the downstream surface. The stress distributions in the arch before and after the artificial joints were made, under water and thermal load in January, are shown in Fig. 8～Fig. 13. The comparison of stresses in the arch direction at some points is given in Table 1.

It can be seen from Fig. 8 to Fig. 13 and Table 1 that:

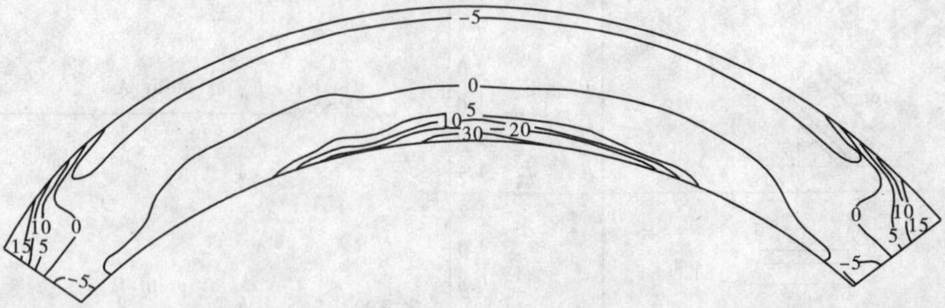

Fig. 8 The stress(σ_1) distribution in arch with no artificial joint (unit: 0.1MPa)

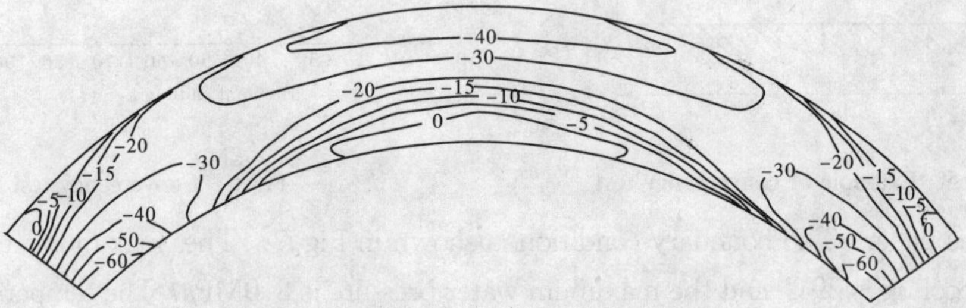

Fig. 9 The stress (σ_2) distribution in arch with no artificial joint (unit: 0.1MPa)

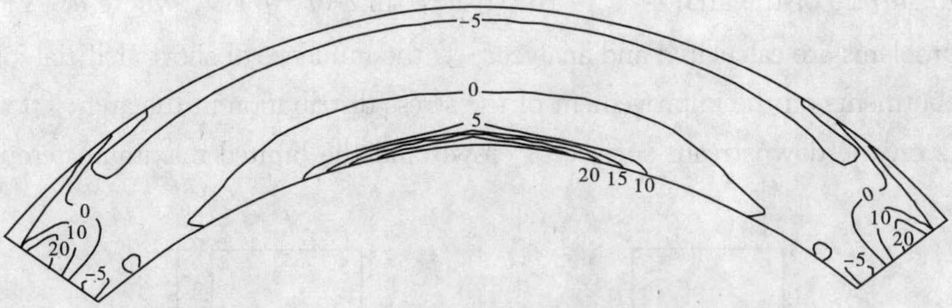

Fig. 10 The stress (σ_1) distribution in arch with two joints at both upstream abutments (unit: 0.1MPa)

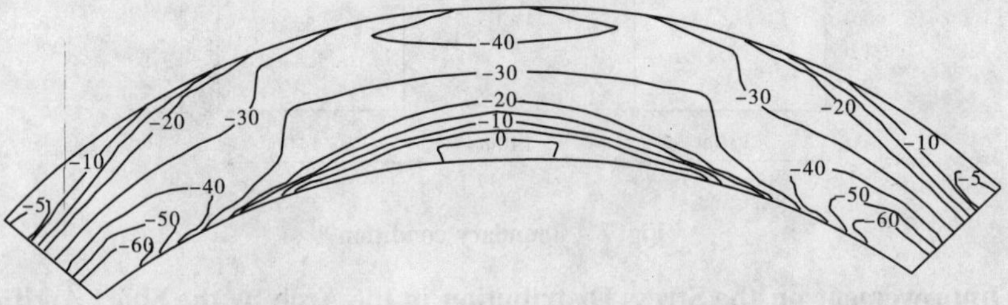

Fig. 11 The stress (σ_2) distribution in arch with two joints at both upstream abutments (unit: 0.1MPa)

(1) If there are no artificial joints, the first principal stress in most areas of the arch is tensile stress, especially in the upstream areas of both abutments and the area near the crown of the downstream surface. The maximum tensile stress at both abutments is up to 6.9MPa, and the maximum tensile stress on the downstream surface is about 4.2MPa. Cracks are in-

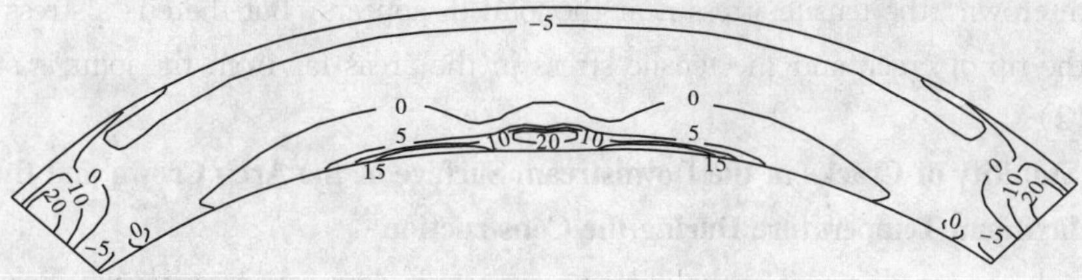

Fig. 12 The stress (σ_1) distribution in arch with joints at upstream abutments and a joint at the downstream crown (unit: 0.1MPa)

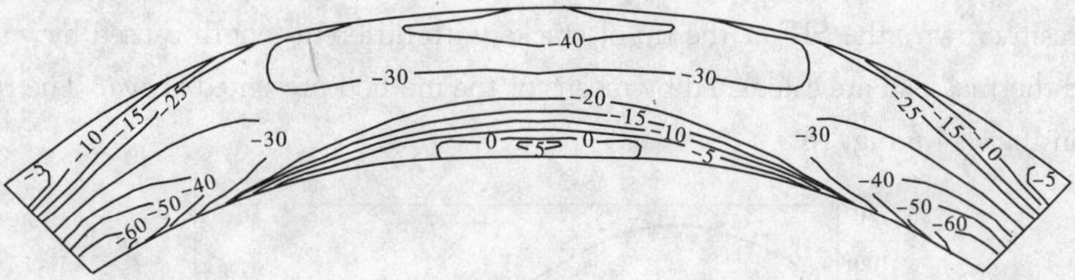

Fig. 13 The stress (σ_2) distribution in arch with joints at both upstream abutments and a joint at the downstream crown (unit: 0.1MPa)

evitable in these areas. The second principal stress in almost all of the arch is compressive; the maximum compressive stress on the downstream surface of both abutments is more than 6.0MPa. After the artificial joints are made at both sides of the upstream abutment, almost all the tensile stresses near the upstream surface of both abutments disappear, and the tensile stress on the downstream surface of crown decreases from 4.2~2.1MPa.

Table 1 The comparison of σ_1 at some points in the arch with and without artificial joints at the upstream of the two abutments

Load		Water pressure		Static thermal load		Harmonic thermal load		Sum	
		No joints	Joints	No joints	Joints	No joints	Joints	No joints	Joints
Crown	Upstream surface	-3.9	-3.5	-0.8	-0.3	0.6	0.6	-4.1	-3.2
	Middle	-2.5	-2.9	1.6	0.9	-0.2	-0.3	-1.1	-2.3
	Downstream surface	-1.4	-2.6	3.2	2.7	2.4	2.0	4.2	2.1
Abutment	Upstream surface	0.8	0	5.0	0	1.1	0	6.9	0
	Middle	-2.5	-3.2	0.8	1.0	-0.2	0	-1.9	-2.2
	Downstream surface	-5.0	-5.2	-1.4	-2.1	0	0.8	-6.4	-6.5

(2)Although two artificial joints at both upstream abutments decrease the first principal stress on the downstream surface, the tensile stress on the crown of downstream surface is still about 2.0MPa; cracks will occur here in winter. After an artificial joint is made at the downstream crown, the tensile stress near the joint disappears, but there is a stress concentration at the tip of crack and the tensile stress in the areas far from the joint is still large (See Fig. 12).

5.2 The Stability of Cracks at the Downstream Surface of the Arch Crown and the Limited Maximum Temperature During the Construction

Although the tensile stress at the downstream crown decreases enormously after the consideration of artificial joints, there is still a tensile stress concentration at the crack tip and the stability of the crack is still a problem. In order to study the stability of the crack on the downstream crown, the SIF at the tip of cracks with different length caused by water pressure and thermal load are calculated by means of the method presented above. The results are shown in Fig. 14～Fig. 16.

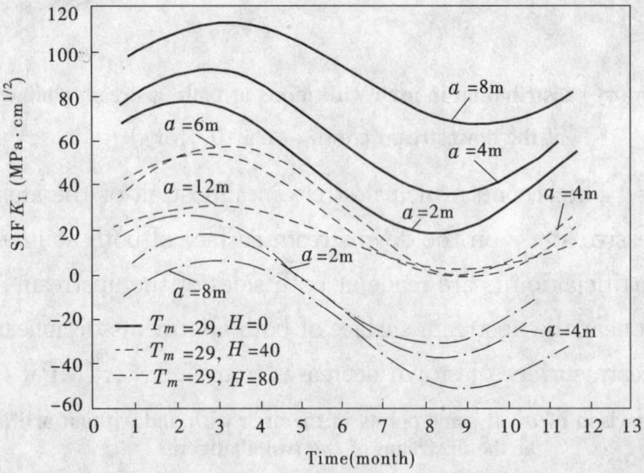

Fig. 14 The SIF at the tip of crack on downstream crown with maximum initial temperature $T_m = 29$℃

It can be seen from these results that the SIF at crack tip changes periodically with the variation of seasonal temperature. The maximum SIF does not occur in January when the atmospheric temperature is the lowest, it has a phase delay compared with the temperature. This delay is related to the length of crack. The longer the crack is, the bigger the delay. When the crack is 2m long, the maximum SIF occurs in February, while if the crack is 8m long, the maximum SIF occurs in March～April. So, the crack in the inner part may extend during this period. The amplitude of variation of SIF is also related to the length of crack. The shorter the crack is, the bigger the amplitude of variation. In contrast, the amplitude of SIF decreases when the length of crack increases. For example, when the length is 2m, the amplitude of variation of SIF is 29MPa·cm$^{1/2}$, and when the crack length is 8m the amplitude reduces to 22MPa·cm$^{1/2}$. The reason for the reduction is that if the crack becomes longer, the crack tip is far away from the downstream reaches and the change of temperature reduces.

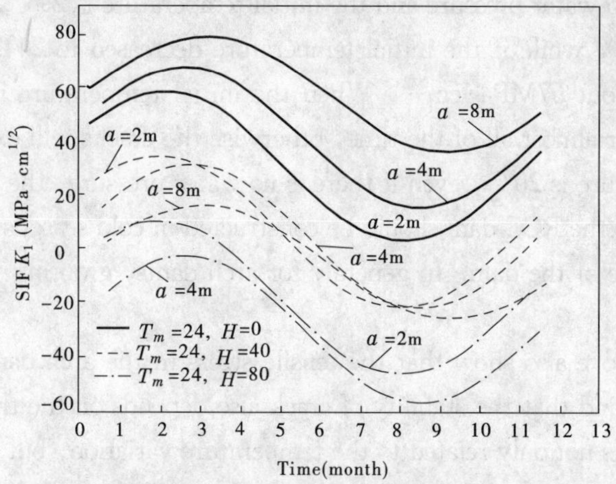

Fig. 15 The SIF at the tip of crack on downstream crown with maximum initial temperature T_m = 24℃

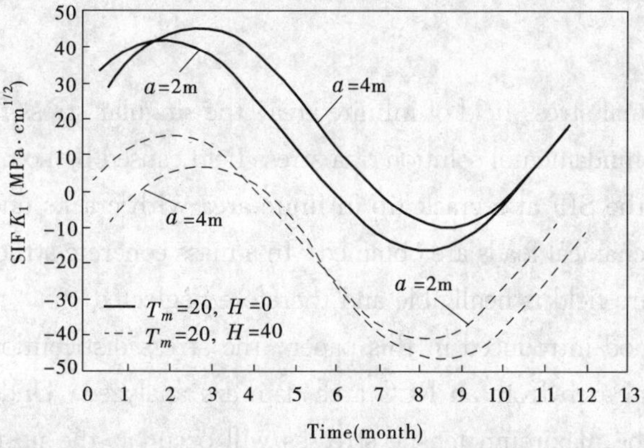

Fig. 16 The SIF at the tip of crack on downstream crown with maximum initial temperature T_m = 20℃

Pressure stress occurs in the arch because of the water pressure. This stress is in the arch direction. So the water load is of benefit to the stability of cracks in the downstream surface of arch. For example, when the initial temperature is 29℃, the crack cannot remain stable if there is no water pressure. The longer the crack is , the greater the SIF. While the water pressure is loaded, for example, when there is 40m water head on the upstream surface of the arch, the SIF at the crack tip will decrease along with an increase in the crack length. This means that the extension of crack will stop after a period of propagation, so the crack is stable. In general, the SIF at the crack tip reaches a maximum in late winter to early spring. So, the water level should be maintained at a certain height in order to prevent penetrating cracks from occurring in the dam.

The SIF of crack in the downstream reaches of the arch dam is also related to the initial temperature. The higher the temperature, the greater the SIF. For example, for a 4m long crack, if there is no water pressure and the initial temperature is 29℃, the maximum SIF is about 95MPa·cm$^{1/2}$, while if the initial temperature decreased to 24℃, the maximum SIF would reduce to about 67MPa·cm$^{1/2}$. When the initial temperature is 29℃, the reservoir cannot be empty for almost all of the time, otherwise the cracks will extend unstably. When the initial temperature is 20℃, even if there is no water pressure, the cracks will not extend except in April. So the RCC dam should be constructed in cold seasons in order to reduce the highest temperature of the dam. In general, for arch dams, grouting should also be done in cold seasons.

The results above also show that the tensile stress in the arch dam is mainly caused by the thermal stress and that the stability of crack also depends on the thermal stress. Because the thermal stress is not only related to the temperature variation, but also related to the linear coefficient of expansion of the material, and it is sensitive to the linear expansion coefficient. So, materials with smaller thermal expansion coefficients should be selected to construct the RCC dam.

6 Conclusions

Using the thermal stress field of infinite area, the singular stress field of a plane including cracks, and the fundamental solution of a stress field caused by point load, the solution of the stress field and the SIF at a crack tip in finite area with cracks under harmonic thermal load and general mechanical loads are obtained. In a mass concrete structure, the influence of cracks on temperature field is negligible and therefore neglected.

Using the method introduced in this paper, the stress distribution and the stability of cracks in a horizontal arch from an RCC arch dam are analyzed. Under the water pressure and thermal load, the maximum tensile stresses will occur at the upstream surface of both abutments and the downstream reaches of the arch crown. In order to prevent the dam from irregular and penetrating cracks occurring, watertight artificial short joints with crack resistance have been installed. The result shows that the tensile stresses in the upper reaches of both abutments can be eliminated by the artificial joints, but in the middle part of the downstream surface, only the tensile stress near the joints is eliminated. Cracks may still occur in other parts. So, more artificial joints should be put in the downstream reaches. The stability of cracks in the downstream reaches not only depends on the change of temperature, but also depends on the water pressure. Measures should be taken to decrease the highest temperature of the dam and material with small thermal expansion should be used in dam construction in order to cut down the thermal stress. Furthermore, the water level should be kept to a certain height in late winter and early spring to prevent penetrating cracks from occurring in the dam.

References

[1] B.S. Liu. *The serious damage of four dams in France*. Hydro－electric Engineering Abroad 5,20～27, 1981

[2] I.J. Abraham, R.C. Sloan. *13th International Congress on Large Dams*. International Commission on Large Dams. Vol.1, pp.1～24,1979

[3] Z.G. Liu, Z.B. Zhou ,L.W. Yuan. *Calculation of vertical crack propagation on the upstream face of the Zhexi single buttress dam*. J.Hydraulic Engng 5,29～36,1990

[4] Y.Z. Chen. *General case of multiple crack problems in an infinite plate*. Engng Fracture Mech. 20, 591～598,1984

[5] G.C. Sih ,R.C. Bolton. *Prediction of thermally induced fracture from notch and crack front*. Theoret. Appl. Fracture Mech. 5, 125～132,1986

[6] G.C. Sih ,*C.K. Chen*. *Growth of crack caused by temperature gradients with change in surface insulation*. Theoret. Appl. Fracture Mech. 5, 101～107,1986

[7] R.Z. Zhou, G.T. Liu. *The synthetic deformation modulus and the synthetic Possion's ratio of multiple crack bodies*. Engng Fracture Mech. 35,4/5,731～738,1990

[8] G.T. Liu, Y. Chi. *An analytic-fictitious boundary forces method for calculating multi-crack problem in arbitrary region with mixed mode boundaries*, in Fracture of Concrete and Rock, Recent Developments, pp.91～100. Elsevier, U.K,1989

[9] V.V. Panasyuk, M.P. Savruk, A.P. Datsyshyn. *A general method of solution of two-dimensional problem in the theory of cracks*. Engng Fracture Mech. 9,481～497,1977

[10] G.X. Zhang, G.T. Liu. *The fracture analysis of a finite plate with thermally insulated Griffith crack in steady thermo-field*. J.Nonjing Hydraulic Res. Inst. 1,85～96,1990

[11] G.C. Sih. *On the singular character of thermal stresses near a crack tip*. J.Appl. Mech.29, 587～589,1962

[12] G.T. Liu, G.X. Zhang. *Study on steady thermal fracture with different conductive material filled in crack*. Fracnure of Concrete and Rock, Recent Developments ,1989

[13] G.X. Zhang, G.T. Liu. *Fictificious Thermal Source (F.T.s) Method in Solving Harmonic Temperature Field Problem*. Proc. Int. Symp. on Pumped Storage Development, Beijing, China (16～19 October 1990)

[14] G.X. Zhang, G.T. Liu. *Thermally stressed multiple systems in steady state*. Theoret. Fracture Mech. 17,6～81 ,1992

混合边界多裂隙体在简谐变温场作用下的断裂问题(张开型)

摘　要　给出了无限平面作用有简谐变化的点热源时的位移场、应力场基本解。用间接法构造出混合边值多裂隙体在简谐变温场作用下的热断裂问题的边界积分方程,并离散求解。数值结果表明,该方法求解多裂隙体的简谐热断裂问题精度好,计算工作量少。文中计算了含边界裂缝的平板、含三条平行裂缝的平板在简谐变温场作用下缝端应力强度因子的变化过程,并与实验结果进行了比较,两者吻合良好。

关键词　多裂隙体　简谐变温场　热断裂　虚拟力

在混凝土结构施工中,尽管采取了许多昂贵的温控措施,坝体裂隙仍然是不可避免的[1],温度变化又是运行期影响坝体裂缝稳定的重要因素。国内外都有施工期裂缝在运行期受变温场、水压及自重作用而危及坝体安全的例子,如法国的 Tola 坝和 Hautefage 坝[2]、美国的 Fontana 坝[3]等。实测和计算都表明:裂缝冬季张开,夏季闭合,每过一个冬季即向前扩展一段,表明了周期性变化的温度场对裂缝扩展的影响。国内某大头坝的劈头裂缝在坝体运行 7 年后,沿支墩严重开裂,危及坝体安全。研究表明:后期裂缝的扩展是由施工期裂缝发展而来,而周期性变化的温度场是裂缝扩展的主要因素之一[4]。

以往非定常热荷载作用下的断裂研究,多以含单缝的特殊结构如圆环、圆筒、半无限体等为主[5~8],在处理方式上往往是在时间方向上差分,即把时间分成若干时段,求出每个时段的温度分布,再由各时刻的温度场求出应力场及应力强度因子。这种方法对于求解热冲击等初值问题及无变化规律的非定常热应力及热断裂问题是有效的,但对于简谐变化的热荷载作用的断裂问题,这种方法在计算上有一定的困难。对于一般结构来讲,简谐变化的边界热荷载,从开始作用到结构中每一点的温度及应力都周期性变化需要较长的一段时间,尤其是像混凝土坝这样的大型结构,从坝体建成到坝内每点都做简谐变化往往需要几年时间,相应的计算也需要同样长的时间,这样就需要大量的计算时段,无疑是不经济的。因此,在求解多裂隙体简谐热断裂方面,以往的方法尚有以下两点不足:①缺乏求解该问题的一般方法;②即使是单缝问题,求解起来也很不经济。

在周期性(简谐)变化的边界温度作用下,结构内部的温度也同样做相同周期的变化,不同的是不同点的温度变化幅度及相位不同。根据这一事实,可以求解非定常热传导问题的边值问题,从而将整个结构的温度场用一个包含时间简谐函数的式子统一描述,进一步可求解热断裂问题。本文独立推导出了简谐变化的点热源作用下的平面温度场、应力场及位移场基本解,并用这几个基本解及 K 场解、缝面作用有一对力时的基本解,根据边界元法中间接法原理构造出求解多裂隙体热断裂问题的边界积分方程。借助于边界离散技术,可以很方便地求出整个应力场及缝端应力强度因子。

本文选自《应用力学学报》1993 年第 2 期,作者还有张国新。

1　温度场

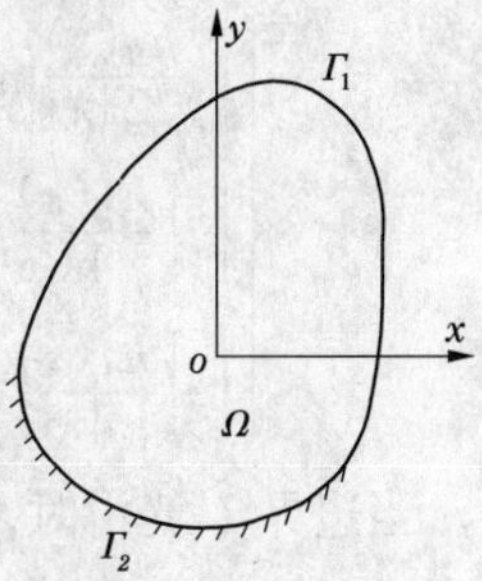

图1　简化模型

大体积含裂缝混凝土结构,通常裂缝宽度很小(<2mm),可不考虑裂缝对温度场的影响[9],因此可简化为无缝体的热传导问题,见图1。无内热源时,基本方程和边界条件为

$$\left.\begin{aligned}&\frac{\partial T(z,t)}{\partial t} = a\overline{V}^2 T(z,t) \quad (\text{域 }\Omega\text{ 内})\\&\overline{T} = \overline{T}_0 + \overline{f}\sin\omega t + \overline{g}\cos\omega t - \quad (\Gamma_1\text{ 上})\\&\lambda\frac{\partial T(z,t)}{\partial n} = \overline{q}_0 + \overline{q}_1\sin\omega t + \overline{q}_2\cos\omega t \quad (\Gamma_2\text{ 上})\end{aligned}\right\}\quad(1)$$

式中:$T(z,t)$为温度场;z为域Ω内的点;a为导温系数;t为时间;λ为热导率;n为边界法向;$\overline{T}_0$、$\overline{f}$、$\overline{g}$分别为边界Γ_1上的已知稳定温度、正弦变化及余弦变化的温度变幅;$\overline{q}_0$、$\overline{q}_1$、$\overline{q}_2$分别为边界Γ_2上的已知稳定热流、正弦变化及余弦变化的热流量变幅。

式(1)中稳定温度场部分的基本解即为拉普拉斯方程基本解。简谐变温场部分的基本解为[10]

$$\begin{aligned}T^*(r,t) = {}&\frac{1}{2\pi\lambda}\ln r + \frac{h_1}{4a}\left[\cos\omega t\,\mathrm{Re}H_0^{(1)}\left(r\sqrt{\frac{\omega}{a}}i\right) + \sin\omega t\,\mathrm{Im}H_0^{(1)}\left(r\sqrt{\frac{\omega}{a}}i\right)\right] +\\&\frac{h_2}{4\lambda}\left[\cos\omega t\,\mathrm{Im}\,H_0^{(1)}\left(r\sqrt{\frac{\omega}{a}}i\right)\sin\omega t\,\mathrm{Re}H_0^{(1)}\left(r\sqrt{\frac{\omega}{a}}i\right)\right]\end{aligned}\quad(2)$$

式中:$H_0^{(1)}(z)$为零阶一类Mankel函数;$h_1 = \cos\omega t_0$,$h_2 = \sin\omega t_0$。

将式(2)表示在复平面内,并令在$z = s$点作用有点热源,则式中的$r = \sqrt{(z-s)(\overline{z}-\overline{s})}$。

假设在域Ω的周界Γ上作用有虚拟热源$h_0(s) + h_1(s)\sin\omega t + h_2(s)\cos\omega t$,$S\in\Gamma$,则由边界积分方程的间接法[11],可以推导出域$\Omega$内任意一点$z$在$t$时刻的温度为

$$\begin{aligned}T(z,t) = \int_r\Bigg\{&\frac{h_0(s)}{2\pi\lambda}\ln r + \frac{h_1(s)}{4\lambda}\left[\cos\omega t\,\mathrm{Re}H_0^{(1)}\left(r\sqrt{\frac{\omega}{a}}i\right) + \sin\omega t\,\mathrm{Im}H_0^{(1)}\left(r\sqrt{\frac{\omega}{a}}i\right)\right] +\\&\frac{h_2(s)}{4\lambda}\left[\cos\omega t\,\mathrm{Im}H_0^{(1)}\left(r\sqrt{\frac{\omega}{a}}i\right) - \sin\omega t\,\mathrm{Re}H_0^{(1)}\left(r\sqrt{\frac{\omega}{a}}i\right)\right]\Bigg\}\mathrm{d}s\end{aligned}\quad(3)$$

设ξ为Γ_1上的点,考虑$z\to\xi$的极限,则式(3)变为

$$\begin{aligned}T(\xi,t) = \int_r\Bigg\{&\frac{h_0(s)}{2\pi\lambda}\ln r + \frac{h_1(s)}{4\lambda}\left[\cos\omega t\,\mathrm{Re}\,H_0^{(1)}\left(r\sqrt{\frac{\omega}{a}}i\right) + \sin\omega t\,\mathrm{Im}H_0^{(1)}\left(r\sqrt{\frac{\omega}{a}}i\right)\right] +\\&\frac{h_2(s)}{4\lambda}\left[\cos\omega t\,\mathrm{Im}H_0^{(1)}\left(r\sqrt{\frac{\omega}{a}}i\right) - \sin\omega t\,\mathrm{Re}H_0^{(1)}\left(r\sqrt{\frac{\omega}{a}}i\right)\right]\Bigg\}\mathrm{d}s\end{aligned}\quad(4)$$

式中:$r = r(\xi,s) = \sqrt{(\xi-s)(\overline{\xi}-s)}$。

将Γ_1上的边界条件$\overline{T}(\xi,t) = \overline{T}_0(\xi) + \overline{f}(\xi)\sin\omega t + \overline{g}(\xi)x\cos\omega t$代入上式,可得以下方程:

$$\begin{cases}\int_{r}\frac{h_{0}(s)}{2\pi\lambda}\ln r\mathrm{d}s=\overline{T}_{0}(\xi)\\ \int_{r}\left[\frac{h_{1}(s)}{4\lambda}\mathrm{Im}H_{0}^{(1)}\left(r\sqrt{\frac{\omega}{a}i}\right)-\frac{h_{2}(s)}{4\lambda}\mathrm{Re}H_{0}^{(1)}\left(r\sqrt{\frac{\omega}{a}i}\right)\right]\mathrm{d}s=\overline{f}(\xi)\\ \int_{r}\left[\frac{h_{1}(s)}{4\lambda}\mathrm{Re}H_{0}^{(1)}\left(r\sqrt{\frac{\omega}{a}i}\right)+\frac{h_{2}(s)}{4\lambda}\mathrm{Im}H_{0}^{(1)}\left(r\sqrt{\frac{\omega}{a}i}\right)\right]\mathrm{d}s=\overline{g}(\xi)\end{cases}\tag{5}$$

当边界 Γ 光滑时，将式(4) 在 ξ 点对其外法线方向 n_{ξ} 微分，得到 ξ 点法向的热流量，即 $q(\xi,t)=-\lambda\frac{\partial T(\xi,t)}{\partial n_{\xi}}$，用 Γ_2 上的点 η 代替 ξ，并求其柯西积分主值，然后将 η 点的边界条件代入得另一组方程：

$$\begin{cases}\frac{1}{2}h_{0}(\eta)-\int_{r}\mathrm{Im}\left[\frac{h_{0}(s)}{2\pi}\frac{1}{\eta-s}\mathrm{e}^{i(a_{\eta}-a_{s})}\right]\mathrm{d}s=\overline{q}_{0}(\eta)\\ \frac{1}{2}h_{1}(\eta)-\frac{1}{2}h_{2}(\eta)-\int_{r}\left\{\frac{h_{1}(s)}{4}\frac{\partial}{\partial n_{\xi}}\left[\mathrm{Im}H_{0}^{(1)}\left(r\sqrt{\frac{\omega}{a}i}\right)\right]-\right.\\ \left.\qquad\frac{h_{2}(s)}{4}\frac{\partial}{\partial n_{\eta}}\left[\mathrm{Re}H_{0}^{(1)}\left(r\sqrt{\frac{\omega}{a}i}\right)\right]\right\}\mathrm{d}s=\overline{q}_{1}(\eta)\\ \frac{1}{2}h_{1}(\eta)-\frac{1}{2}h_{2}(\eta)-\int_{r}\left\{\frac{h_{1}(s)}{4}\frac{\partial}{\partial n_{\eta}}\left[\mathrm{Re}H_{0}^{(1)}\left(r\sqrt{\frac{\omega}{a}i}\right)\right]-\right.\\ \left.\qquad\frac{h_{1}(s)}{4}\frac{\partial}{\partial n_{\eta}}\left[\mathrm{Im}H_{0}^{(1)}\left(r\sqrt{\frac{\omega}{a}i}\right)\right]\right\}\mathrm{d}s\end{cases}\tag{6}$$

式中：$r=\sqrt{(\eta-s)(\overline{\eta}-\overline{s})}$。

用边界元法将方程(5)、(6) 离散，联立求解，即可求出边界 Γ 上的虚拟稳定热源 $h_0(s)$、虚拟简谐热源变幅 $h_1(s)$、$h_2(s)$，然后代入式(4) 即可求出整个温度场[10]。

2 热弹性断裂问题的基本解

2.1 无限连续弹性介质的静力基本解

(1) 由 Kelvin 解，可以求出当在无限介质中 c 点作用有集中荷载 $Q=\frac{F_x+iF_y}{2\pi(1+\lambda)}$ 时在 α 方向引起的位移及应力为

$$\begin{cases}u^{*c}(z,\alpha)+iv^{*c}(z,\alpha)=\frac{\mathrm{e}^{-i\alpha}}{2\mu}\left\{\lambda Q[\ln(z-c)(\overline{z}-\overline{c})+1]+\overline{Q}\frac{z-c}{\overline{z}-\overline{c}}\right\}\\ \sigma_{y}^{*c}(z,\alpha)+i\tau_{xy}^{*c}(z,\alpha)=-Q\left[\frac{1}{z-c}-\lambda\mathrm{e}^{-2i\alpha}\frac{1}{\overline{z}-\overline{c}}\right]-\overline{Q}\left[\frac{1}{\overline{z}-\overline{c}}+\mathrm{e}^{-2i\alpha}\frac{z-c}{(\overline{z}-\overline{c})^{2}}\right]\end{cases}\tag{7}$$

(2) 设无限域中含有长为 $2a$，方向与 x 轴重合的张开缝，则当在缝面上 s 点作用有一对自平衡的集中荷载 $P=F_y^c-iF_x^c$ 时，任一点 z 在 α 方向的位移和应力为[12]

$$\begin{cases}u^{*c}(z,\alpha)+iv^{*c}(z,\alpha)=\frac{\mathrm{e}^{i\alpha}}{4\mu\pi}\{P[\overline{f}_{1}(z,a,s)-\alpha_{l}f_{1}(z,a,s)]+\\ \qquad\overline{P}(z-\overline{z})\sqrt{a^{2}-s^{2}}G(z,a,s)\}\\ \sigma_{y}^{*c}(z,\alpha)-i\tau_{xy}^{*c}(z,\alpha)=PC(z,a,s,\alpha)+\overline{P}D(z,a,s,\alpha)\end{cases}\tag{8}$$

其中:

$$G(z,a,s) = 1/(z-s)\sqrt{z^2-a^2}$$

$$f_1(z,a,s) = i[\ln(\frac{\sqrt{z^2-a^2}+i\sqrt{a^2-s^2}}{z-s} - \frac{si}{\sqrt{a^2-s^2}}) - \ln(1+\frac{s}{\sqrt{s^2-a^2}})]$$

$$C(z,a,s,\alpha) = \frac{1}{2\pi}\sqrt{a^2-s^2}[G(z,a,s)+e^{-2i\alpha}\overline{G(z,a,s)}]$$

$$D(z,a,s,\alpha) = -\frac{1}{2\pi}\sqrt{a^2-s^2}[\overline{G(z,a,s)}(1-e^{-2i\alpha})+e^{-2i\alpha}(z-\bar{z})\overline{G'(z,a,s)}]$$

2.2 无限介质中热弹性基本解

由热弹性问题的基本方法,可以求出在 $z=s$ 点作用有点热源 $q = h_0 + h_1\sin\omega t + h_2\cos\omega t$ 时引起的 α 方向的位移和应力为

$$\begin{aligned} u^{*T}(z,\alpha,t) + iv^{*T}(z,\alpha,t) = & -e^{-i\alpha}\frac{\alpha_l(1+\nu)}{4\pi\lambda}h_0(z-s)(\ln r - \frac{1}{2}) + \\ & e^{-i\alpha}\frac{\alpha_l(1+\nu)}{4\lambda}\frac{z-s}{r}\{\cos\omega t[h_1\mathrm{Re}U_0(r)+h_2\mathrm{Im}U_0(r)] + \\ & \sin\omega t[h_1\mathrm{Im}U_0(r) - h_2\mathrm{Re}U_0(r)]\} \end{aligned} \tag{9}$$

$$\begin{aligned} \sigma_y^{*T}(z,\alpha,t) - i\tau_{xy}^{*T}(z,\alpha,t) = & \frac{\alpha_l E}{8\lambda}\{\frac{h_0}{\pi}[\ln\frac{z-s}{\bar{z}-\bar{s}} + e^{-2i\alpha}\frac{\bar{z}-\bar{s}}{z-s}] + \\ & \sigma_r(r)+\sigma_0(r)+e^{-2i\alpha}\frac{z-s}{\bar{z}-\bar{s}}[\sigma_0(r)-\sigma_r(r)]\} \end{aligned}$$

式中:α_l 为线胀系数。

$$\begin{aligned} \sigma_0(r) = & \cos\omega t[h_1\mathrm{Re}(s_0(r)-H_0^{(1)}(r)) + h_2\mathrm{Im}(s_0(r)-H_0^{(1)}(r))] + \\ & \sin\omega t[h_1\mathrm{Im}(s_0(r)-H_0^{(1)}(r)) - h_2\mathrm{Re}(s_0(r)-H_0^{(1)}(r))] \end{aligned}$$

$$\sigma_r(r) = -\cos\omega t[h_1\mathrm{Re}(s_0(r)+h_2\mathrm{Im}(s_0(r))] - \sin\omega t[h_1\mathrm{Im}(s_0(r)) - h_2\mathrm{Re}(s_0(r))]$$

$$\begin{aligned} U_0(r) = & \left[(1+\frac{2i}{\pi}\ln\left(\sqrt{\frac{\omega}{a}}i/2\right)+\frac{2i}{\pi}r\right]\sum_{k=0}^{\infty}A_k\frac{r^{2k+1}}{2k+2} + \frac{2i}{\pi}\sum_{k=0}^{\infty}A_k\frac{r^{2k+1}}{2k+2}\ln r - \\ & \frac{2i}{\pi}\sum_{k=0}^{\infty}A_k\frac{r^{2k+1}}{2k+2}\sum_{m=1}^{k}\frac{1}{m} - \frac{2i}{\pi}\sum_{k=0}^{\infty}A_k\frac{r^{2k+1}}{(2k+2)^2} \end{aligned}$$

$$\begin{aligned} S_0(r) = & \left[1+\frac{2i}{\pi}\ln\left(\sqrt{\frac{\omega}{a}}i/2\right)+r\right]\sum_{k=0}^{\infty}A_k\frac{r^{2k}}{2k+2} - \frac{2i}{\pi}\sum_{k=0}^{\infty}A_k\frac{r^{2k}}{(2k+2)^2} + \\ & \frac{2i}{\pi}\sum_{k=0}^{\infty}A_k\frac{r^{2k}}{2k+2}\ln r - \frac{2i}{\pi}\sum_{k=1}^{\infty}A_k\frac{r^{2k}}{2k+2}\sum_{m=1}^{k}\frac{1}{m} \end{aligned}$$

3 边界积分方程

令在边界 Γ 上作用有分布荷载 $Q(s,t)$,$s\in\Gamma$,在第 k 条裂缝的缝面上作用有分布虚拟力 $P_k(S_k,t)$,S_k 为第 k 条缝面上的点,则域 Ω 内的位移和应力为[10]

$$u(z,\alpha,t) + iv(z,\alpha,t) = \int_\Gamma\{u^{*c}[Q(s,t),z,\alpha] + iv^{*c}[Q(s,t),z,\alpha]\}ds +$$

$$\sum_{k=1}^{N}\int_{-a_k}^{a_k}\{u^{*c}[P_k(s_k,t),z,\alpha]+iv^{*c}[P_k(s_k,t),z,\alpha]\}\mathrm{d}s+$$

$$\int_{\Gamma}\{u^{*T}[q(s,t)],z,\alpha,t]+iv^{*T}[q(s,t),z,\alpha,t)]\}\mathrm{d}s \qquad (10)$$

$$\sigma_y(z,\alpha,t)-i\tau_{xy}(z,\alpha,t)=\int_{\Gamma}\{\sigma_y^{*c}[Q(s,t),z,\alpha]-i\tau_{xy}^{*c}[Q(s,t),z,\alpha]\}\mathrm{d}s+$$

$$\sum_{k=1}^{N}\int_{-a_k}^{a_k}\{\sigma_y^{*c}[P_k(s_k,t),z,\alpha]-i\tau_{xy}^{*c}[P_k(s_k,t),z,\alpha]\}\mathrm{d}s+$$

$$\int_{\Gamma}\{\sigma_y^{*T}[q(s,t),z,\alpha,t]-i\tau_{xy}^{*T}[q(s,t),z,\alpha,t]\}\mathrm{d}s$$

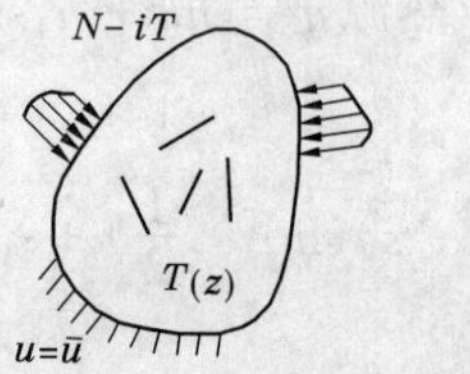

图 2　多裂隙体的边界条件

令边界 Γ_1 上的已知位移为 $\overline{u}(\eta,t)+i\overline{v}(\eta,t)$，其中 $\overline{u}(\eta,t)$ 和 $\overline{v}(\eta,t)$ 分别为 η 点的切向位移和法向位移；令边界 Γ_2 上的已知外力为 $N(\xi,t)-iT(\xi,t)$，其中 $N(\xi,t)$ 和 $T(\xi,t)$ 分别为 ξ 点的法向外力和切向外力，各缝面自由(见图 2)。令式(10)第一式中 z 无限趋近于边界 Γ_1 上的 η 点，则可得到一个满足 Γ_1 上已知位移的边界积分方程：

$$\overline{u}(\eta,t)+i\overline{v}(\eta,t)=\int_{\Gamma}\{u^{*c}[Q(s,t),\eta,\alpha_{\eta s}]+iv^{*c}[Q(s,t),\eta,\alpha_{\eta s}]\}\mathrm{d}s+$$

$$\sum_{k=1}^{N}\int_{-a_k}^{a_k}\{u^{*c}[P_k(s_k,t),\eta,\alpha_{\eta k}]+iv^{*c}[P_k(s_k,t),\eta,\alpha_{\eta k}]\}\mathrm{d}sx+$$

$$\int_{\Gamma}\{u^{*T}[q(s,t),\eta,\alpha_{\eta s},t]+iv^{*T}[q(s,t),\eta,\alpha_{\eta s},t]\}\mathrm{d}s \qquad (11a)$$

令式(10)第二式中的 z 无限趋近于边界 Γ_2 上的 ξ 点和第 n 条裂缝缝面上的 ξ_n 点，则当积分点 s 与 ξ 点重合，积分点 s_k 与 ξ_k 重合时，式中的积分核出现奇异，求出积分在 s 点及 ξ_n 点的主值再代入式(10)中的第二式，可得两个方程：

$$N(\xi,t)-iT(\xi,t)=-\frac{i}{2}Q(\xi,t)+\int_{\Gamma}\{\sigma_y^{*e}[Q(s,t),\xi,\alpha_{\xi s}]-i\tau_{xy}^{*e}[Q(s,t),\xi,\alpha_{\xi s}]\}\mathrm{d}s+$$

$$\int_{\Gamma}\{\sigma_y^{*T}[q(s,t),\xi,\alpha_{\xi s},t]-i\tau_{xy}^{*T}[q(s,t),\xi,\alpha_{\xi s},t]\}\mathrm{d}s+$$

$$\sum_{k=1}^{N}\int_{-a_k}^{a_k}\{\sigma_y^{*c}[P_k(s_k,t),\xi,\alpha_{\xi s_k}]-i\tau_{xy}^{*c}[P_k(s_k,t),\xi,\alpha_{\xi s_k}]\}\mathrm{d}s_x \qquad (11b)$$

$$O=\frac{1}{2}Pn(\xi_n,t)+\int_{\Gamma}\{\sigma_y^{*e}[Q(s,t),\xi_n,\alpha_{\xi_n s}]-i\tau_{xy}^{*e}[Q(s,t),\xi_n,\alpha_{\xi_n s}]\}\mathrm{d}s+$$

$$\int_{\Gamma}\{\sigma_y^{*T}[q(s,t),\xi_n,\alpha_{\xi_n s},t]-i\tau_{xy}^{*T}[q(s,t),\xi_n,\alpha_{\xi_n s},t]\}\mathrm{d}s+$$

$$\sum_{k=1}^{N}\int_{-a_k}^{a_k}\{\sigma_y^{*c}[P_k(s_k,t),\xi_n,\alpha_{\xi_n s_k}]-i\tau_{xy}^{*c}[P_k(s_k,t),\xi_n,\alpha_{\xi_n s_k})]\}\mathrm{d}s_x \qquad (11c)$$

其中：$\alpha_{\xi s}=\alpha_{\xi}-\alpha_s$。

方程(11a)、(11b)、(11c)即构成求解多裂隙体热断裂问题的边界积分方程组。其中(11a)中的第三项,(11b)、(11c)中的第二项积分为已知值,不含未知量,可移到自由项一边,将这三个方程联立用边界元法离散求解,可得到边界分布虚拟力 $Q(s,t)$ 和缝面分布虚拟力 $P_k(s_k,t)$,然后可用公式(10)求出各点各时刻的位移、应力。各缝端各时刻的应力强度因子可由下式求得[13]:

$$K_{n\mathrm{I}}^{\pm}(t) - iK_{n\mathrm{II}}^{\pm}(t) = -\frac{1}{\sqrt{na_n}}\int_{-a_n}^{a_n} P_n(s_n,t)\sqrt{\frac{a_n \pm s_n}{a_n \mp s_n}}\mathrm{d}s_n \tag{12}$$

取一 10cm×10cm 的矩形板(见图3),板内含有两条长为 $2a = 2\mathrm{cm}$ 的缝,一条为水平缝,另一条与水平方向成 45° 夹角。板的上下两端固定,左边施加 $\Delta T = 20°\sin 6.28t$ 的变化温度,右边温度为 0℃,用本文方法,取不同数目的边界单元和缝面单元计算。当相位 $\omega t = \frac{2\pi}{8}$ 时,水平缝 A 端和倾斜缝 C 端的Ⅰ型应力强度因子随单元数的变化见图4。

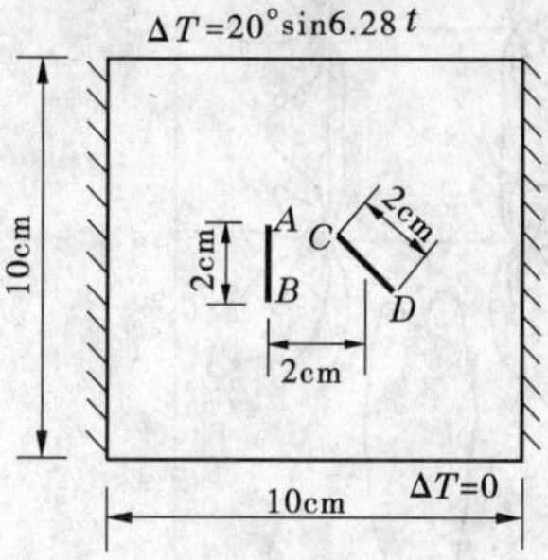

图3　含双缝的平板

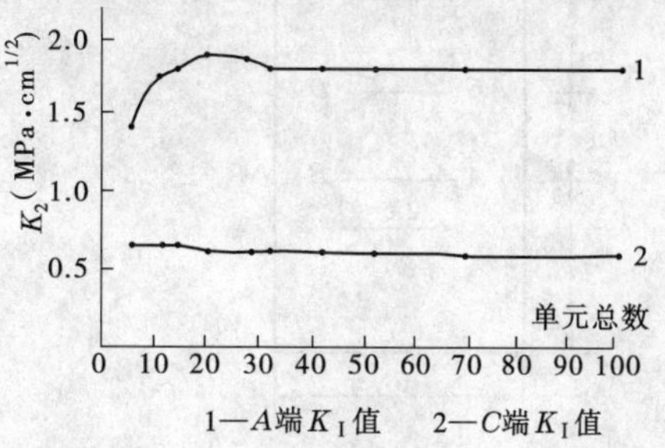

图4　A、C 两缝端 K_{I} 随单元数目的变化

由图4可以看出,当单元总数到达40左右时,计算结果接近稳定值,随着单元数目的增多,K_{I} 值基本保持不变,计算结果也表明:当单元数目达到一定值后,各缝端各时刻的应力强度因子即趋于稳定值不再随单元数目的变化而变化。由此可以看出,本文方法具有较好的收敛性。

4　计算实例及与实验结果(详见另文)的比较

4.1　含单条边缝的环氧树脂板在简谐变温场作用下的断裂问题

含有一条边界裂缝的环氧板,板的尺寸及边界条件如图5,在均匀温降20℃的基础上再在裂缝的一边施加变幅为20℃,周期为0.5小时的简谐变温场。取40个边界单元5个裂缝单元计算,应力强度因子随时间变化的实验结果与计算结果比较见图6。

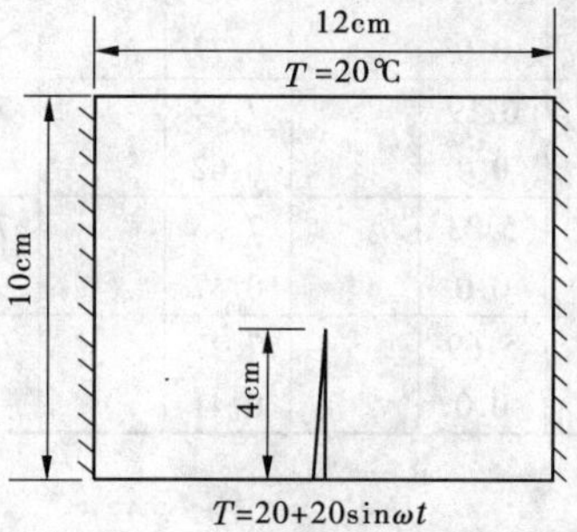

图5　单缝环氧试件

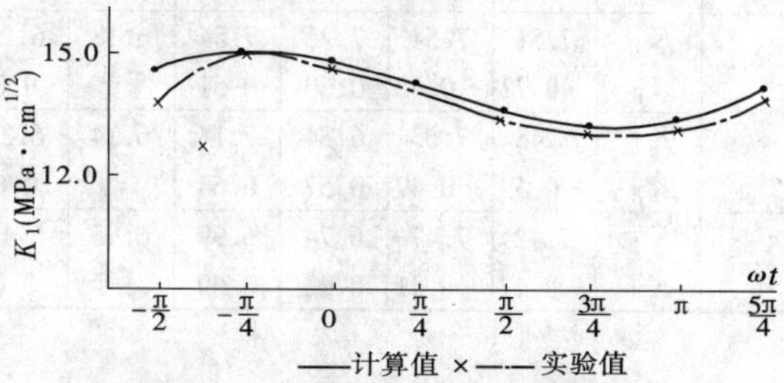

图6　K_{I} 的实验结果与计算结果比较

4.2　含有三条平行裂缝的环氧平板在简谐变温场作用下的断裂问题

取一含有三条平行裂缝的平板见图 7。板的上下两端固定，在均匀温降 20℃，周期为 0.5 小时的简谐变温场，取 40 个边界单元，每条裂缝取 8 个边界单元进行计算。$\omega t=\frac{\pi}{4}$ 时的等应力差图见图 8，各缝端不同时刻应力强度因子的实验值和计算值比较见表 1。

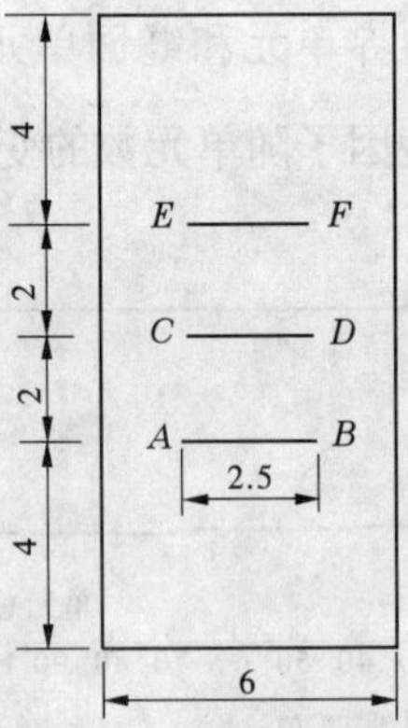

图 7　含有三条平行裂缝的试件

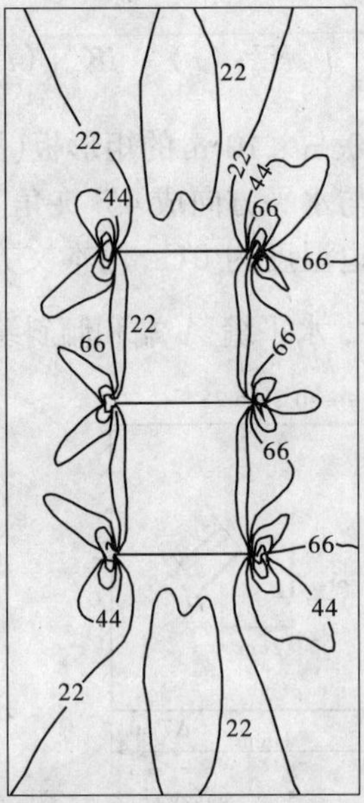

图 8　$\omega t=\frac{\pi}{4}$ 时的等应力差曲线（计算结果）

表 1　各缝端不同时刻应力强度因子的实验值和计算值的比较　（单位：$MPa\cdot cm^{1/2}$）

项目		A		B		C		D		E		F	
		实验	计算	实验	计算	实验	计算	实验	计算	实验	计算	实验	计算
$-\frac{\pi}{2}$	K_{I}	7.37	7.41	7.14	7.17	6.01	6.10	6.07	5.86		7.41		7.17
	K_{II}	−0.38	−0.47	0.31	0.63		0.0	0.0	0.0		0.47		−0.63
$-\frac{\pi}{4}$	K_{I}	7.40	7.36	7.82	7.57	6.09	6.05	6.47	6.24		7.36		7.57
	K_{II}	−0.49	−0.62	0.36	0.49		0.0	0.0	0.0		0.62		−0.49
0	K_{I}	7.45	7.36	8.16	7.97	6.17	6.06	6.75	6.60		7.36		7.97
	K_{II}	−0.64	−0.76	0.42	0.36		0.0	0.0	0.0		0.76		−0.36
$\frac{\pi}{4}$	K_{I}	7.48	7.42	8.34	8.12	6.25	6.12	6.80	6.73		7.42		8.12
	K_{II}	−0.77	−0.82	0.47	0.31		0.0	0.0	0.0		0.82		−0.31
$\frac{\pi}{2}$	K_{I}	7.56	7.49	7.83	7.94	6.28	6.18	6.52	6.57		7.49		7.94
	K_{II}	−0.81	−0.77	0.54	0.37		0.0	0.0	0.0		0.77		−0.37
$\frac{3}{4}\pi$	K_{I}	7.51	7.54	7.25	7.54	6.18	6.22	6.12	6.19		7.54		7.54
	K_{II}	−0.72	−0.62	0.60	0.51		0.0	0.0	0.0		0.62		−0.51
π	K_{I}	7.48	7.53	6.84	7.14	6.14	6.21	5.87	5.83		7.53		7.14
	K_{II}	−0.59	−0.47	0.57	0.64		0.0	0.0	0.0		0.47		−0.64
$\frac{5}{4}\pi$	K_{I}	7.42	7.47	6.74	6.99	6.05	6.16	5.83	5.69		7.47		6.99
	K_{II}	−0.47	−0.41	0.42	0.69		0.0	0.0	0.0		0.41		−0.69

由图 6 和表 1 可以看出，缝端因力强度因子也随着边界温度周期性变化。应力强度因

子的最大值不发生在边界温度最低的时刻,而是有一定的滞后,滞后时间的长短取决于材料的导温系数及缝端离开变温边界的距离。由图 8 及表 1 可以看出,有三条平行裂缝时,靠近约束边界的裂缝的应力强度因子最大,且有 Ⅱ 型应力强度因子产生。由实验结果和计算结果的比较可以看出,两者吻合良好。

5　结语

(1) 本文提出的虚拟热源法和虚拟力法相结合求解混合边界多裂隙体在简谐变温场作用下的热断裂问题的方法概念明确,计算精度好。针对两种试件进行了实验和计算的相互验证,两者吻合较好。本方法省机时,求解含三条裂缝的平板的简谐热断裂问题只需要 40 个边界单元和 24 个裂缝单元即可取得较好的精度,CPU 工作时间只需 60s(ELASI 机)。由于数据处理工作量小,可用一般的微机进行计算。

(2) 两端固定含有多条裂缝的平板,靠近约束边界的裂缝的缝端应力强度因子最大,且有 Ⅱ 型应力强度因子产生,其结果使该处裂缝较易扩展。

参 考 文 献

[1] 国内典型混凝土坝裂缝情况调查与分析.水利水电科学研究院结构材料所研究报告.1988.7

[2] 刘泊生译.法国四座拱坝的严重破坏情况.国外水利水电,1981(5):20~27

[3] Abrabam I J, Sloan R C. *13th International Congress on Lange Dams*. International Commission on Large Dams. Vol.1,1979,1~24

[4] 涂传林,谯常忻.柘溪大坝裂缝问题.混凝土坝技术,1988(1)

[5] Emery A F, Neighbors P K, et al.. *Stress Intensity Factors in Edge-Cracked Plate Subjected to Transient Thermal Singularities*. Journal of Pressure Verssele Technology, Transactions of the ASME, 1977. 11:100~111

[6] Delale F, Kolluri S P. *Fracture of Thickwalled Cylinders Subjected to Transient Thermal Stresses*. Journal of Thermal Stresses, Vol.8,1985:225~248

[7] Naotake Noda, Naobumi Sumi. *Stress Intensity Factor for Transient Thermal Stress of a This Plste With a Griffith Crack*. Journal of Thermal Stress, Vol.8,1985:173~182

[8] Herman F Nied. *Thermal Shock Fracture in an Edge-Cracked Plate*. Journal of Thermal Stresses, Vol. 6,1985:217~229

[9] 刘光廷,张国新.缝内含有部分导热介质时的稳定温度断裂研究.清华大学学报,1990,30(2):15~21

[10] Gaoxin Zhang, Guangting Liu. *Fictitious Thermal Source (F. T. S) Method in Solving Marmonic Temperature Field Problem*. Proceeding of International Symposium on Pumped Storage Development, Beijing, China,1990,10:196~203

[11] 田中正隆,等.边界单元法基础与应用.郎德宏译.北京:煤炭工业出版社,1987

[12] Yizhou Chen. *General Case of Multiple Crack Problems in an Infinite Plate*. Engineering Fracture Machanics. Vol.20,No.4,1984

[13] Rizhong zhou, Guangting Liu. *The Synthetic Deformation Modulus and Synthetic Poisson's Ratio of Multiple Crack Bodies*. International Conferenee on Fracture and Damage of Concrete and Rock, Vienna Austnia, July 4~6,1988

STUDY ON STEADY-THERMAL FRACTURE WITH DIFFERENT CONDUCTIVE MATERIAL FILLED IN CRACK

Abstract The empty cracks (filled with air) or cracks filled with different heat conductive material from rock and concrete (water or soil) usually happen in engineering practice. In present paper an equivalent heat conductive coefficient is used in determining thermo-crack solution, i. e., temperature field or stress field or S. I. F induced by cracks filled with air or soft materials. The equivalent heat conductive coefficient can be determined from experimental method by two concrete (or rock) plate with various thickness of material placing between them. The comparison of analytic and experimental results shows a good agreement with each other. An engineering example shows that the S. I. F caused by the temperature field disturbed by crack is small in the fracture analysis of concrete structures.

1 Introduction

Cracks of open type usually happen in engineering. It is necessary to distinguish which of them will be dangerous to the structure. Observations in situ show that the fractures in concrete dam usually induced from the composition of various factors among them the thermal factor is one of the most important factor. Homogenious temperature-drop of arch dam leads to an increasing of cracks in the upstream abutment. In winter, new horizental cracks are always induced to the down-stream face of dam. In the steady temperature field in dam, heat flows from down stream up to the reservoir. Cracks and grouting defects along the axis of dam not only cause the discontinuity of the structure, but also make a resistance to heat flow which in return causes the stress concentration. Therefore, relation between cracks in concrete and temperature change has been an attractive problem.

The former studies used to consider the cracks as heat insulator[1~4], this assumption is suitable only for the case that the heat conductivity of structure material is much greater than that of the material in cracks, and the cracks are very wide. It seems a little bit far from the engineering practice in concrete dam. J. R. Barber[1] studied the partially conductive problem assuming that the volumn of heat flow across the crack is proportional to the temperature gradient, but the coefficient relating the volumn of heat flow and temperature gradient is difficult to determine since it also relating to the temperature of material in cracks. In fact,

本文选自 ELSEVIER Applied Science 1989 年出版的《Fracture of Concrete and Rock Recent Developments》一书，作者还有 Zhang Guoxin。

there is air or other medium layer in crack and with finite thickness, the heat flow will propagate by convention, radiation and conduction, which is related to the medium in crack and the width of crack. In this paper, it is assumed that the crack is full filled of heat conductive medium, which is different from structure material, and an equivalent heat conductivity is used to simulate the heat propagation through the air layer in crack. Consequently, the solution of temperature and stress field affected by crack of open type can be given by using conformal mapping. The method is suitable for the concrete structure with crack in which medium is full filled. The equivalent coefficient of heat conductivity corresponding to the given crack can be obtained by experimental method in which two plates with the various thickness of air or medium layer between them are used to simulate the real crack.

2 Temperature and Stress Field

2.1 Temperature Field

Suppose that there is an infinte plate (Fig. 1) with an open crack of $2a$ long and $2b$ wide. The heat flow q passes in the direction perpendicular to the crack. The heat conductivity of plate material is k_1 and that of the material in crack is k_2. It is supposed that the crack can be approximated by an ellipse with long axis $2a$ and short axis $2b$. Therefore conformal mapping can be used to calculate the temperature field and stress field. The mapping function used is:

$$Z = R\left(\xi + \frac{m}{\xi}\right) \tag{1}$$

where: $R = \dfrac{a+b}{2}$, $m = \dfrac{a-b}{a+b}$

The above mapping function maps the ellipse on Z-plane into a unit circle on ξ-plane.

On ξ-plane, the temperature on and outside the unit circle is supposed $T_1(\rho,\beta)$, and the temperature in the circle is $T_2(\rho,\beta)$, where $\xi = \rho e^{i\beta}$.

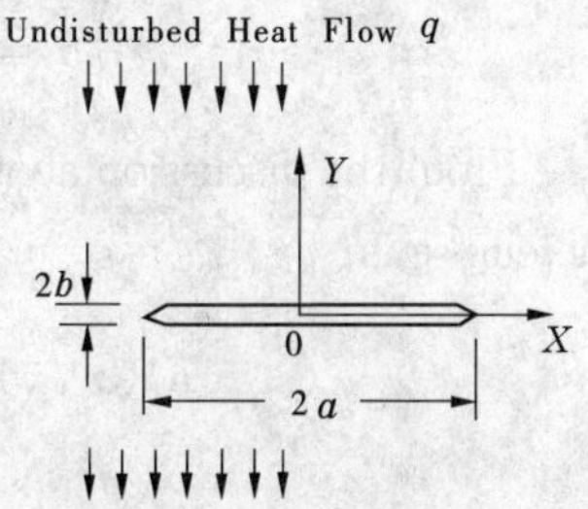

Fig. 1 Heat flow of an infinite plate with an open crack

Consequently, T_1 and T_2 satisfy the following equations and boundary conditions:

$$\left.\begin{aligned}
&\frac{\partial^2 T_1}{\partial\rho^2} + \frac{1}{\rho}\frac{\partial T_1}{\partial\rho} + \frac{1}{\rho^2}\frac{\partial^2 T_1}{\partial\beta^2} = 0 && \rho \geqslant 1\\
&\frac{\partial^2 T_2}{\partial\rho^2} + \frac{1}{\rho}\frac{\partial T_2}{\partial\rho} + \frac{1}{\rho^2}\frac{\partial^2 T_2}{\partial\beta^2} = 0 && \rho < 1\\
&T_1 = T_2 && \rho = 1\\
&k'_1\frac{\partial T_1}{\partial\rho} = k'_2\frac{\partial T_2}{\partial\rho} && \rho = 1\\
&T_1 = Rq\rho\sin\beta && \rho = \infty
\end{aligned}\right\} \tag{2}$$

where, k'_2 and k'_1 are the heat conductivities in and out of the unit circle respectively after mapping on ξ-plane.

It is assumed that the heat conductivities before and after mapping are still constants and the ratio is:

$$\frac{k'_2}{k'_1}=c_0\frac{k_2}{k_1}=c_0 a_0 \tag{3}$$

where k'_1 and k'_2 are heat conductivities of structure material and material in crack respectively.

Solving Eq. (2) by separating variables yields:

$$T_1 = qR(\rho+\frac{a_1}{\rho})\sin\beta \qquad \rho\geqslant 1 \tag{4}$$

By Eq. (1) we can derive the inverse mapping:

$$\xi=\frac{1}{a+b}(Z+\sqrt{Z^2-a^2+b^2}) \tag{5}$$

Mapping Wq. (4) onto Z－plane by formula(5)yields:

$$T_1(x,y) = \frac{q}{2}[(1+a_1)A\sin\frac{1}{2}\theta+(1-a_1)y] \tag{6}$$

where

$$\begin{cases} A = [(x^2-y^2-a^2+b^2)^2+4x^2y^2]^{\frac{1}{4}} \\ \theta = \sin^{-1}\dfrac{2xy}{A^2} = \cos^{-1}\dfrac{x^2-y^2-a^2+b^2}{A^2} \end{cases}$$

From the discussion above, it is obvious that the temperature along the circumference of the ellipse is:

$$T_1(x,y)\Big|_{\frac{x^2}{a^2}+\frac{y^2}{b^2}=1} = \frac{q}{2}[(1+a_1)\frac{a}{b}+(1-a_1)]y \tag{7}$$

According to formula(7), and also the fact that the temperature distribution is the ellipse in linear namely:

$$\begin{cases} T_2(x,y) = \frac{q}{2}[(1+a_1)\frac{a}{b}+(1-a_1)]y \\ y\leqslant b,\ |x|\leqslant\sqrt{a^2(1-y^2/b^2)} \end{cases} \tag{8}$$

Considering the continuity of heat flow on the surface of crack, namely:

$$k_1\frac{\mathrm{d}T_1}{\mathrm{d}n} = k_2\frac{\mathrm{d}T_2}{\mathrm{d}n}$$

we can obtain the value of a_1 in Eqs. (6) and (8).

Because:

$$\frac{\mathrm{d}T}{\mathrm{d}n} = \cos(n,x)\frac{\mathrm{d}T}{\mathrm{d}x}+\cos(n,y)\frac{\mathrm{d}T}{\mathrm{d}y} \tag{9}$$

thus, on the circumference of the ellipse, we have:

$$\cos(n,x) = \frac{b\sqrt{b^2 - y^2}}{\sqrt{b^4 - (b^2 - a^2)y^2}}$$

$$\cos(n,y) = \frac{ay}{\sqrt{b^4 - (b^2 - a^2)y^2}}$$

$$\frac{\mathrm{d}T_1}{\mathrm{d}x} = \frac{q}{2}\left[(1 + a_1)\frac{\sqrt{b^2 - y^2}(b^2 - a^2)y}{(a^2 - b^2)y^2 + b^4}\right] \tag{10}$$

$$\frac{\mathrm{d}T_1}{\mathrm{d}y} = \frac{q}{2}\left[(1 + a_1)\frac{b}{a}\frac{b^2a^2 - a^2y^2 - b^2y^2 + b^4}{(a^2 - b^2)y^2 + b^4} + (1 - a_1)\right]$$

$$\frac{\mathrm{d}T_2}{\mathrm{d}x} = 0$$

$$\frac{\mathrm{d}T_2}{\mathrm{d}y} = \frac{q}{2}\left[(1 + a_1)\frac{1 + m}{1 - m} + 1 - a_1\right]$$

Substituting Eq. (10) into Eq. (9) and $k_1\mathrm{d}T_1/\mathrm{d}n = k_2\mathrm{d}T_2/\mathrm{d}n$, an expression about a_1 is a complicated function of y. Since a_1 is supposed constant, a most representative value of a_1 (at $y = b$) is used. Thus, we have:

$$a_1 = \frac{1 - m - 2a_0}{1 - m + 2a_0 m} \qquad a_0 = \frac{k_2}{k_1} \tag{11}$$

so:

$$T_1(x,y) = \frac{q}{2}\left[(1 + \frac{1 - m - 2a_0}{1 - m + 2a_0 m})A \sin\frac{1}{2}\theta + (1 - \frac{1 - m - 2a_0}{1 - m + 2a_0 m})y\right] \tag{12}$$

2.2 Stress Field

Temperature expression Eq. (6) can be rewritten on ξ-plane as follow:

$$T_1(\zeta,\bar{\zeta}) = \frac{qRi}{2}\left[(\bar{\xi} - \xi) + a_1(\frac{1}{\xi} - \frac{1}{\bar{\xi}})\right] \tag{13}$$

Using the boundary condition on the free crack surface given by reference [2]:

$$F_1(\sigma) + \overline{F}_1(\sigma) - \frac{\sigma^2}{\overline{W}'(\sigma)}[\overline{W}(\sigma)F'_1(\sigma) + W'(\sigma)F_2(\sigma)]$$
$$= \frac{Ea}{2}\left[T_1(\xi,\bar{\xi}) - \frac{\xi^2}{\overline{W}'(\xi)}\int\frac{\partial T_1}{\partial\xi}\overline{W}'(\xi)\mathrm{d}\,\bar{\xi}\right]_{\xi=0} \tag{14}$$

where: $\sigma = \mathrm{e}^{i\theta}$, the points on the circumference of the unit circle.

$F_1(z) = \phi'(z)$, $F_2(z) = \Psi'(z)$, $\phi(z)$, $\Psi(z)$ are Muskhelishvili stress function $W(\xi) = R(\xi + m/\xi)$.

E is the elastic modulus and a is coefficient of expansion. Substituting Eq. (13) into Eq. (14) by rearranging and conjugating, the equation becomes:

$$F_1(\sigma) + \overline{F}_1(\sigma) - \left[\frac{\sigma^2 + m}{(\sigma^2 - m)\sigma}\overline{F}_1(\sigma) + \frac{1 - m\sigma^2}{\sigma^2 - m}\overline{F}_2(\sigma)\right]$$
$$= -\frac{EaqRi\sigma^3}{4(\sigma^2 - m)}\left[(1 + 2a_1) - \frac{a_1 + m}{\sigma^2} + \frac{(2 + a_1)m}{\sigma^4}\right] \tag{15}$$

Suppose:

$$\begin{cases} F_1(\xi) = a_1\xi + \sum_{k=0}^{\infty} a_{-k}\xi^{-k} \\ F_2(\xi) = b_1\xi + \sum_{k=1}^{\infty} b_{-k}\xi^{-k} \end{cases} \tag{16}$$

Substituting Eq. (16) into Eq. (15), multiplying Eq. (15) by $(\sigma^2 - m)\mathrm{d}\sigma/2ni(\sigma - \xi)$, $(\sigma^2 - m)\mathrm{d}\sigma/2ni\sigma^3(\sigma - \xi)$ one after another and then integrating along unit circle, two expressions about $F(\xi)$ which contain the unknowns can be obtained.

Considering the boundary conditions that the stress is zero at infinite and displacement is single-valued, the solutions of simultaneous equations can be expressed as follow:

$$F_1(\xi) = -\frac{1}{4}EaqRi\frac{1}{\xi^2 - m}\left(\xi^3 + \frac{a_1 m}{\xi}\right) \tag{17}$$

and

$$F_2(\xi) = \frac{1}{4}EaqRi\frac{(a_1 + m)\xi}{(\xi^2 - m)^3}[\xi^4 - 2(1 + m + m^2)\xi^2 + m^2] \tag{18}$$

Substituting Eq. (5) into Eq. (17) and Eq. (18) yields:

$$\begin{cases} \phi'(Z) = \frac{Eaqi}{8m}\left[\begin{array}{l}(a_1 - m)Z - (a_1 + m)\sqrt{Z^2 - (a+b)^2 m} - \\ \frac{a_1 + m}{2}\frac{(a+b)^2 m}{\sqrt{Z^2 - (a+b)^2 m}}\end{array}\right] \\ \Psi'(Z) = \frac{Eaqi}{8m}\left[(a_1 - m) - \frac{Z(m + a_1)}{\sqrt{Z^2 - (a+b)^2 m}} + \frac{(m + a_1)(a+b)^2 mZ}{2[Z^2 - (a+b)^2 m]^{3/2}}\right] \end{cases} \tag{19}$$

Substituting Eq. (19) into the following formula:

$$\begin{cases} \sigma_x + \sigma_y = 4\mathrm{Re}\phi'(Z) - EaT \\ \sigma_y - \sigma_x + 2i\tau_{xy} = 2[\overline{Z}\phi''(Z) + \Psi'(Z)] - Ea\int\frac{\partial T(Z,\overline{Z})}{\partial\overline{Z}}\mathrm{d}Z \end{cases} \tag{20}$$

yields:

$$\sigma_x = -\frac{1}{16}Eaq(a_1 + m)(a+b)^2\left\{\frac{3}{A}\sin\frac{1}{2}\theta + \left[x^2 + y^2 - \frac{1}{2}(1 + m^2)(a+b)^2\right]\frac{1}{A^3}\sin\frac{3}{2}\theta\right\}$$

$$\sigma_y = \frac{1}{16}Eaq(a_1 + m)(a+b)^2\left\{\left[x^2 + y^2 - \frac{1}{2}(1 + m^2)(a+b)^2\right]\frac{1}{A^3}\sin\frac{3}{2}\theta - \frac{1}{A}\sin\frac{1}{2}\theta\right\} \tag{21}$$

$$\tau_{xy} = \frac{1}{16}Eaq(a_1 + m)(a+b)^2\left\{\frac{1}{A}\cos\frac{1}{2}\theta + \left[x^2 + y^2 - \frac{1}{2}(1 + m^2)(a+b)^2\right]\frac{1}{A^3}\cos\frac{3}{2}\theta\right\}$$

Finally, the stress intensity factor at the tip of crack can be expressed as:

$$\begin{cases} K_{\mathrm{I}} = 0 \\ K_{\mathrm{II}} = \frac{Eaq}{8\sqrt{a}}\sqrt{n}(1 + a_1 m)(a+b)^2 \end{cases} \tag{22}$$

3 Comparison of the Results of Analytic with Experimental

Studies on temperature field in infinite plate containing heat isolated cracks show that the effective region of temperature field disturbed by crack is within small limits. For experimental check, three epoxy plates of 10cm×10cm×2cm in size and with center crack of 4cm long and 2,3,4mm wide respectively were taken. Make the temperature conditions of T_1, T_2 at boundaries parallel to the center crack, and the heat isolated material at the other two boundaries. Transparent material with very low biaxle refractivity was chosen for front and back protective cover, and almost the same steady temperature field was made in the cover to form heat isolated condition by equal temperature field ($dT/dn = 0$)(See Fig.2). Temperature measurement confirmed the steady distribution of temperature on epoxy plate form T_1 to T_2. The reflective polariscope was used for taking picture and fringe order measurement of the test.

The axis of elliptic-shaped fringes has an angle about 45° to the x − axis. Made a straightline of 45° to x − axis and took the fringe order along this line at different distance r, SIF were determined. The stresses at the tip of crack are:

$$\left.\begin{aligned} \sigma_x &= -\frac{K_{\text{II}}}{\sqrt{2\pi r}}\left[\sin\frac{1}{2}\theta\left(2+\cos\frac{1}{2}\theta\cos\frac{3}{2}\theta\right)\right] \\ \sigma_y &= \frac{K_{\text{II}}}{\sqrt{2\pi r}}\left(\sin\frac{1}{2}\theta\cos\frac{1}{2}\theta\cos\frac{3}{2}\theta\right) \\ \tau_{xy} &= \frac{K_{\text{II}}}{\sqrt{2\pi r}}\left[\cos\frac{1}{2}\theta\left(1-\sin\frac{1}{2}\theta\sin\frac{3}{2}\theta\right)\right] \end{aligned}\right\} \tag{23}$$

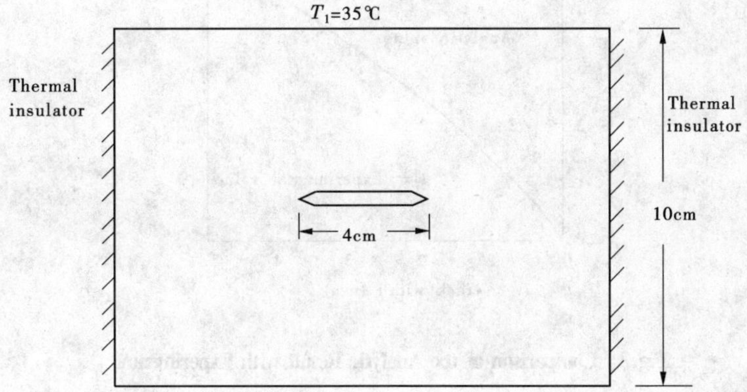

Fig.2 Thermal fracture experiment of epoxy plate with crack

Substituting $\theta = 45°$ into formulas(23) and using the formula of principle stresses, we have:

$$(\sigma_1 - \sigma_2) = 0.631\frac{K_{\text{II}}}{\sqrt{r}} \tag{24}$$

let:

$$N = \frac{0.631}{\sqrt{r}}$$

then

$$\sigma_1 - \sigma_2 = NK_{\mathrm{II}} \tag{24'}$$

Making the curve $(\sigma_1 - \sigma_2)$—N by experimental results, the tangents of curves are taken as K_{II} value. The experimental and analytic-numerical results (formula (22)) were placed together in Fig. 3.

The parameters of epoxy material in present experiment are:

expansion coefficient: $a = 68 \times 10^{-6}$

elastic modulus: $E = 3.4 \times 10^4 \mathrm{kg/cm^2}$

heat-conductive coefficient of epoxy: $k_1 = 0.2\mathrm{W/(m \cdot k)}$

heat-conductive coefficient of material filled in crack: $k_2 = 0.05\mathrm{W/(m \cdot k)}$

in this experiment: $T_1 - T_2 = 40℃$.

It is shown from Fig. 3 that there is a good agreement between the results of analytic and experimental, they are good enough for engineering purpose.

Example: A block of arch dam with crack parallel to the dam axis is considered, the width of the crack is 2mm, the thickness of dam is 20m; the temperature difference of up and down-stream surface of dam is 15℃.

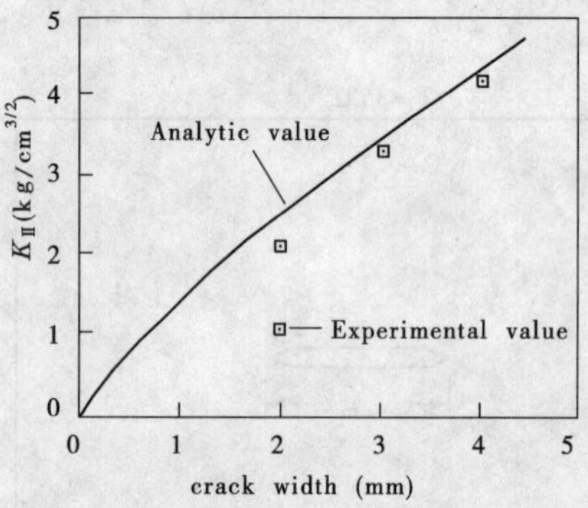

Fig. 3　Comparison of the Analytic Result with Experimental

The material constants are:

$E = 25 \times 10^4 \mathrm{kg/cm^2}$

$a = 0.000\,01$

$k_1 = 2.4\mathrm{W/(m \cdot k)}$

The heat conductivity of air in crack: $k_2 = 0.03\mathrm{W/(m \cdot k)}$.

According to formula(22), the stress intensity factor K_{II} with different crack length a is shown in Fig. 4.

From Fig. 4, when the width of crack in concrete dam is 2mm, the stress intensity fac-

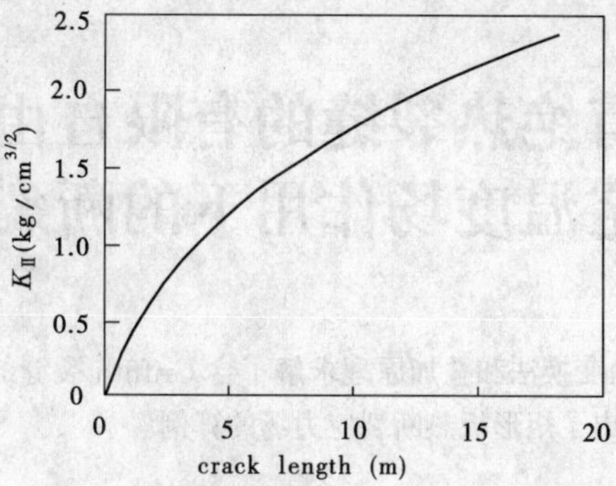

Fig. 4 SIF K_{II} with different crack length (crack width: 2mm)

tor K_{II} is less than $3kg/cm^{3/2}$. For concrete dam, the width of ordinary crack is very small, the ratio $b/a<0.0002$, therefore the stress intensity factor K_{II} caused by steady temperature field disturbed by crack is less than $3kg/cm^{3/2}$, this value is not important. But it increases the SIF at the tip of crack.

4 Conclusions

(1) The stress intensity factor of crack of second kind K_{II} is given for the steady temperature field in structure disturbed by crack.

(2) The analytic results calculated by formula (22) have a good agreement with the experimental results. It is shown that the stress intensity factor K_{II} calculated from the formula has a good precision.

(3) Since the width of ordinary crack in concrete dam is small, the stress intensity factor K_{II} caused by steady temperature field disturbed by cracks is not important. But it increases the SIF at the tip of crack.

References

[1] Florence, A. L., Goodier, J. N.. *Thermal stresses due to disturbance of uniform heat flow by an insulated ovaloid hole*. Journal of Applied Mechanics, 1960, 12, 635~639

[2] Nowinski, J. L. *Theory of Thermoelastisity with Applications*, Netherland, 1978, pp. 349~357

[3] Panasyuk, V. V., Savruk, M. P., Datsyshyn, A. P.. *A general method of solution of two - dimensional problems in the theory of cracks*. Enginearing Frature Mechanics, 1977, Vol. 9, pp. 481~497

[4] Guoxin Zhang, Guangting Liu. *The fracture analysis of a finite plate with thermally isolated Griffith crack in steady thermo-field*. Journal of Nanjing Hydraulic Research Institute. 1989, 1, pp. 96~105

[5] Eckert, E. R. G., Dracke, R. M.. *Analysis of Heat and Mass Transfer*, McGraw-Hill, New York, 1972

含有绝热裂缝的有限自由板在稳定温度场作用下的断裂分析

摘　要　本文用复变保角变换法和叠加原理求解了含 Griffith 裂缝的矩形板,在稳定温度场作用下的热断裂问题,给出了矩形板热断裂应力场的算例。

混凝土结构物在施工期间或运行初期,会产生一些裂缝,这些裂缝在长期运行中能否保持稳定,它对结构的安全是否有影响,是人们非常关心的问题。长期处在温度荷载作用之下运行的水工结构,其裂缝的存在不仅破坏了结构的连续性,还扰乱了热流的传播,从而加剧裂缝端部的应力集中现象和开裂的可能,并将影响到结构的安全。

在拱坝设计中,目前仍将平面稳定温度场的温度应力作为设计依据[1],这就有必要研究当热流受到裂缝干扰时,结构在稳定温度场作用下的断裂问题。A. L. Florence[2] 曾用复变保角变换法及位移单值原理给出了缝端应力强度因子,J. L. Nowinski[3] 给出了热弹性断裂问题在复平面上的一般方程,M. П. Саврук 等[4] 给出了含绝热裂隙体在稳定热流作用下的温度场、应力场的一般积分方程。但已有的研究都取简单的无限体条件,难以直接用于工程。为了逐步引入工程应用,本文提供有限尺寸板含有绝热裂缝时,在稳定温度场作用下的应力场解及断裂强度因子(考虑窄缝内空气导热情况,本文不涉及)。

1　无限含裂纹板的温度场及应力场

无限含裂纹板(见图 1),裂缝长为 $2a$,取裂缝中点为坐标原点。设在无穷远处有垂直于裂缝的热流 q 流过,且无穷远处的温度为 $T|_{y\to\infty} = qy$。则当缝面绝热时(或通过裂缝的导热系数相对很低时),热传导方程为:

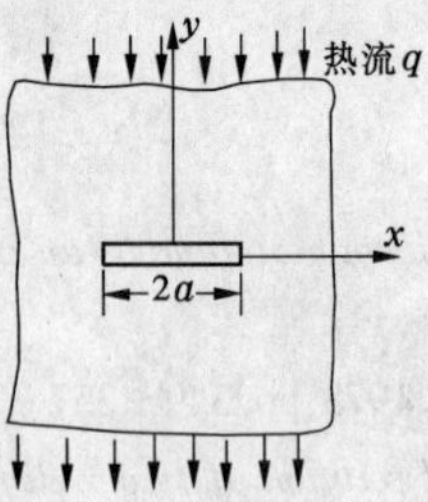

图 1

$$\begin{cases} \dfrac{\partial^2 T}{\partial x^2} + \dfrac{\partial^2 T}{\partial y^2} = 0 & \text{域 } \Omega \text{ 内} \\ T|_{y=\infty} = qy \\ \dfrac{\partial T}{\partial y} = 0 & y = 0,\ |x| \leqslant a \text{ 时} \end{cases} \tag{1}$$

式中:T 为温度;q 为热流梯度。

取映射函数 $$Z = \omega(\xi) = \frac{a}{2}(\xi + \frac{1}{\xi}) \tag{2}$$

则可将 Z 平面上的直缝外域映射成 ξ 平面上的单位圆外,在 ξ 平面上温度为 $T(\rho、\beta)$,$\xi = \rho e^{i\beta}$,则式(1) 变为

本文选自《水利水运科学研究》1989 年第 1 期,作者还有张国新。

$$\begin{cases} \dfrac{\partial^2 T}{\partial \rho^2} + \dfrac{1}{\rho}\dfrac{\partial T}{\partial \rho} + \dfrac{1}{\rho^2}\dfrac{\partial^2 T}{\partial \beta^2} = 0 \\ T = \dfrac{a}{2}\rho q \sin\beta \qquad \rho \to \infty \\ \dfrac{\partial T}{\partial \rho} = 0 \qquad \rho = 1 \end{cases} \tag{3}$$

解方程得

$$T(\rho,\beta) = \frac{a}{2}q(\rho + \frac{1}{\rho})\sin\beta$$

亦即
$$T(\xi,\bar{\xi}) = \frac{q}{4}ai\left[(\bar{\xi} - \xi) + (\frac{1}{\xi} - \frac{1}{\bar{\xi}})\right] \tag{4}$$

设 $F_1(\xi)$、$F_2(\xi)$ 为两个应力函数,且满足

$$\begin{cases} F_1(Z) = \phi'_1(Z) \\ F_2(Z) = \psi'(Z) \end{cases} \tag{5}$$

式中:$\phi_1(Z)$、$\psi(Z)$ 为应力函数。

由文献[2] 知,ξ 平面上单位圆周自由的条件为

$$F_1(\sigma) + \overline{F}_1(\sigma) - \frac{\sigma^2}{\overline{\omega'(\sigma)}}[\overline{\omega}(\sigma)F'_1(\sigma) + \omega'(\sigma)F_2(\sigma)]$$
$$= \frac{E\alpha}{2}\left[T(\xi,\bar{\xi}) - \frac{\xi^2}{\overline{\omega'(\xi)}}\int \frac{\partial T}{\partial \xi}\overline{\omega'(\xi)}\,\overline{d\xi}\right]_{\xi=\sigma} \tag{6}$$

将式(4) 代入式(6) 得

$$F_1(\sigma) + \overline{F}_1(\sigma) + \left[\frac{(1+\sigma^2)\sigma}{\sigma^2 - 1}F'_1(\sigma) + F_2(\sigma)\right]$$
$$= -\frac{E\alpha qai}{8(1-\sigma^2)\sigma}(3 - 2\sigma^2 + 3a^4)$$

取共轭得

$$F_1(\sigma) + \overline{F}_1(\sigma) + \left[\frac{\sigma^2 + 1}{(1-\sigma^2)\sigma} - F'_1(\sigma) + \overline{F}_2(\sigma)\right]$$
$$= -\frac{E\alpha qai}{8(\sigma^2 - 1)}\left(3 - \frac{2}{\sigma^2} + \frac{3}{a^4}\right) \tag{7}$$

设
$$\begin{cases} F_1(\xi) = a_1\xi + \sum\limits_{k=0}^{\infty} a_{-k}\xi^{-k} \\ F_2(\xi) = b_1\xi + \sum\limits_{k=0}^{\infty} b_{-k}\xi^{-k} \end{cases} \tag{8}$$

将式(8) 代入式(7) 并将式(7) 两端同乘以$\dfrac{(\sigma^2 - 1)d\sigma}{2\pi i(\sigma - \xi)}$后,沿单位圆周积分得

$$F_1(\xi)(\xi^2 - 1) = a_1\xi(\xi^2 - 1) + a_0(\xi^2 - 1) + a_{-1}\xi + a_{-2} + \frac{2\overline{a}_1}{\xi} + \frac{\overline{b}_1}{\xi} - \frac{3E\alpha qai}{8}\frac{1}{\xi} \tag{9}$$

在式(7) 两端同乘以$\dfrac{\sigma^2 - 1}{2\pi i\sigma^3}\dfrac{d\sigma}{\sigma - \xi}$ 并沿单位圆周积分得

$$F_1(\xi)(\xi^2-1)=\xi^3\Big[a_1-(a_0+\overline{a}_2+\overline{b}_0-\overline{b}_{-2})\frac{1}{\xi}+\Big(\overline{b}_{-1}+\overline{b}_1+\frac{E\alpha qai}{4}\Big)\frac{1}{\xi^2}+$$
$$(\overline{a}_0+\overline{b}_0)\frac{1}{\xi^3}+\Big(2\overline{a}_1+\overline{b}_1-\frac{3}{8}E\alpha qai\Big)\frac{1}{\xi^4}\Big] \tag{10}$$

比较式(9)、(10)两式,两端均具有相同次幂的系数,引入无穷远处为零和位移单值条件可得

$$F_1(\xi)=-\frac{1}{8}E\alpha qai\,\frac{1}{\xi^2-1}\Big(\xi^3+\frac{1}{\xi}\Big) \tag{11}$$

$$\phi'_1(\xi)=\omega'(\xi)F_1(\xi)=-\frac{1}{16}E\alpha qa^2 i\,\frac{\xi^3+\frac{1}{\xi}}{\xi^2} \tag{11'}$$

同理可得

$$F_2(\xi)=\frac{1}{4}E\alpha qai\Big[\frac{\xi}{(\xi^2-1)^3}\Big](\xi^4-6\xi^2+1) \tag{12}$$

由式(2)可求出逆映射函数

$$\xi=\frac{1}{a}(Z+\sqrt{Z^2-a^2}) \tag{13}$$

将式(13)代入式(11)、式(12)后得

$$\begin{cases}\phi'_1(Z)=-\dfrac{1}{8}E\alpha qi\,\dfrac{2Z^2-a^2}{\sqrt{Z^2-a^2}}\\[2ex]\psi'(Z)=\dfrac{1}{8}E\alpha qi\,\dfrac{Z^2-2a^2}{(Z^2-a^2)\sqrt{Z^2-a^2}}\end{cases} \tag{14}$$

将式(14)代入[3]

$$\begin{cases}\sigma_x+\sigma_y=4\mathrm{Re}\phi'_1(Z)-E\alpha T\\[1ex]\sigma_y-\sigma_x+2i\tau_{xy}=2[\overline{Z}\phi''_1(Z)+\psi'(Z)]-E\alpha\displaystyle\int\frac{\partial T(Z,\overline{Z})}{\partial Z}\mathrm{d}\overline{Z}\end{cases} \tag{15}$$

得

$$\begin{cases}\sigma_y=\dfrac{1}{8}E\alpha qa^2\Big(\dfrac{x^2+y^2-a^2}{A^3}\sin\dfrac{3}{2}\theta-\dfrac{1}{A}\sin\dfrac{1}{2}\theta\Big)\\[2ex]\sigma_x=-\dfrac{1}{8}E\alpha qa^2\Big(\dfrac{x^2+y^2-a^2}{A^3}\sin\dfrac{3}{2}\theta+\dfrac{3}{A}\sin\dfrac{1}{2}\theta\Big)\\[2ex]\tau_{xy}=\dfrac{1}{8}E\alpha qa^2\Big(\dfrac{x^2+y^2-a^2}{A^3}\cos\dfrac{3}{2}\theta+\dfrac{1}{A}\cos\dfrac{1}{2}\theta\Big)\\[2ex]T(x,y)=qA\sin\dfrac{1}{2}\theta\end{cases} \tag{16}$$

其中

$$\begin{cases}A=[(x^2-y^2-a^2)^2+4x^2y^2]^{1/4}\\[1ex]0=\cos^{-1}\Big(\dfrac{x^2-y^2-a^2}{A^2}\Big)=\sin^{-1}\dfrac{2xy}{A^2}\end{cases} \tag{17}$$

2　含裂缝有限体的温度场及应力场

沿 y 向单面传热,两侧面绝热的自由板,上下两个面温度分别为 T_1、T_2,取板的尺寸

为 $2l \times 2h$(见图 2)。

2.1 温度场

由数值计算的结果可知,当 $h \geqslant 4a$、$l \geqslant 4a$ 时,从已有解的无限板中切出一有限板,使此板上下表面的温度为 T_1、T_2,则用无限板的温度场解,作为有限板的温度场的近似解时,其误差小于 3%,故当板的尺寸大于 4 倍缝长时,为简单起见,可取其温度场解的形式与无限板相似

$$\begin{aligned} T(x,y) &= qA\sin\frac{1}{2}\theta + T_0 \\ &= \frac{T_1 - T_2}{2h}A\sin\frac{1}{2}\theta + \frac{T_1 + T_2}{2} \end{aligned} \tag{18}$$

当 $\frac{T_1 + T_2}{2} = 0$、$l = h = 5a$ 时的温度场(见图 3)。

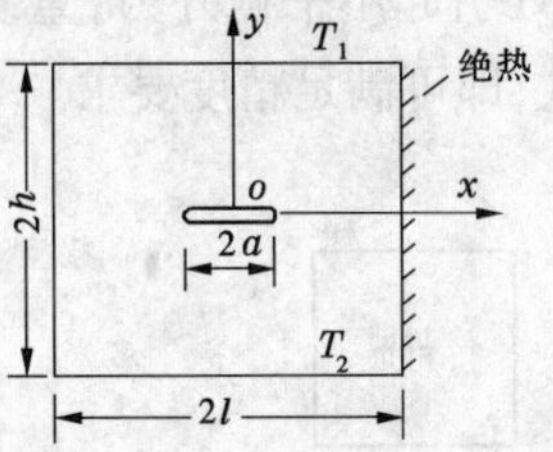

图 2

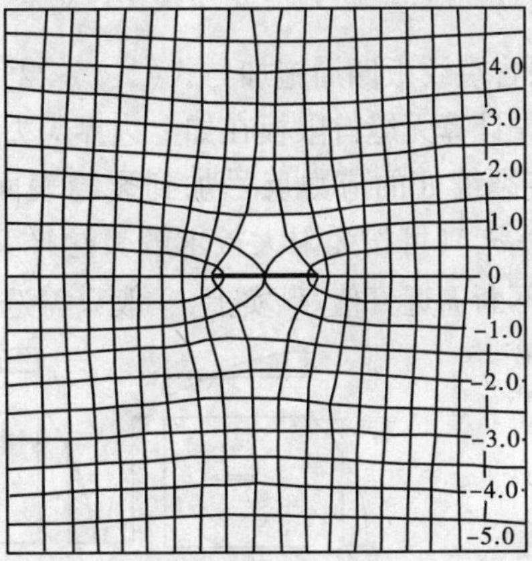

图 3 (单位:$\frac{T}{T_1 - T_2}$)

2.2 应力场

有限含裂纹板的应力场,可为无限含裂纹板的应力场与有限含裂纹板边界处不平衡力作用下产生的应力场的叠加,如取无限含裂纹板的应力场为 σ_{ij}^0,则

$$\begin{cases} \sigma_y^0 = \frac{1}{16}E\alpha a^2\,\frac{T_1 - T_2}{h}\left(\frac{x^2 + y^2 - a^2}{A^3}\sin\frac{3}{2}\theta - \frac{1}{A}\sin\frac{1}{2}\theta\right) \\ \sigma_x^0 = -\frac{1}{16}E\alpha a^2\,\frac{T_1 - T_2}{h}\left(\frac{x^2 + y^2 - a^2}{A^3}\sin\frac{3}{2}\theta + \frac{3}{A}\sin\frac{1}{2}\theta\right) \\ \tau_{xy}^0 = \frac{1}{16}E\alpha a^2\,\frac{T_1 - T_2}{h}\left(\frac{x^2 + y^2 - a^2}{A^3}\cos\frac{3}{2}\theta + \frac{1}{A}\cos\frac{1}{2}\theta\right) \end{cases} \tag{19}$$

将式(11)′ 代入[5]

$$K = K_{\mathrm{I}} - iK_{\mathrm{II}} = 2\left[\frac{\pi}{a}\right]^{1/2}\varphi'(1)$$

得

$$K^0 = K_{\mathrm{I}}^0 - iK_{\mathrm{II}}^0 = -\frac{1}{8}E\alpha\,\frac{T_1 - T_2}{h}a^{2/3}\sqrt{\pi}i \tag{20}$$

从无限板中切取出一有限板,则四周边界上的不平衡力为

$$
\begin{cases}
\sigma_y^0 \mid_{y=h} = \dfrac{1}{16} E\alpha a^2 \dfrac{T_1 - T_2}{h} \left(\dfrac{x^2 + h^2 - a^2}{A^3} \sin \dfrac{3}{2}\theta - \dfrac{1}{A} \sin \dfrac{1}{2}\theta \right) \\
\tau_{xy}^0 \mid_{y=h} = \dfrac{1}{16} E\alpha a^2 \dfrac{T_1 - T_2}{h} \left(\dfrac{x^2 + h^2 - a^2}{A^3} \cos \dfrac{3}{2}\theta + \dfrac{1}{A} \cos \dfrac{1}{2}\theta \right) \\
\sigma_y^0 \mid_{y=h} = - \sigma_y^0 \mid_{y=h} \qquad A = [(x^2 - h^2 - a^2)^2 + 4h^2 x^2]^{1/4} \\
\tau_{xy}^0 \mid_{y=-h} = \tau_{xy}^0 \mid_{y=h} \qquad \theta = \cos^{-1} \dfrac{x^2 - h^2 - a^2}{A^2}
\end{cases}
\tag{21}
$$

$$
\begin{cases}
\tau_{xy}^0 \mid_{x=l} = \dfrac{1}{16} E\alpha a^2 \dfrac{T_1 - T_2}{h} \left(\dfrac{l^2 + y^2 - a^2}{A^3} \cos \dfrac{3}{2}\theta + \dfrac{1}{A} \cos \dfrac{1}{2}\theta \right) \\
\sigma_x^0 \mid_{x=l} = - \dfrac{1}{16} E\alpha a^2 \dfrac{T_1 - T_2}{h} \left(\dfrac{l^2 + y^2 - a^2}{A^3} \sin \dfrac{3}{2}\theta + \dfrac{3}{A} \sin \dfrac{1}{2}\theta \right) \\
A = [(x^2 - y^2 - a^2)^2 + 4l^2 y^2]^{1/4} \qquad \theta = \cos^{-1} \dfrac{l^2 - y^2 - a^2}{A^2}
\end{cases}
\tag{22}
$$

在有限含裂纹板四周施加与式(21)、(22)数值相等、方向相反的外力时,可按图4分解为两步:先计算无缝有限板在如上边界应力作用下的应力场,包括裂缝位置的应力;再切开裂缝将裂缝处的应力反号加到裂缝表面,以满足裂缝自由条件。记前者应力场为 $\sigma_{ij}^{\mathrm{I}a}$,后者为 $\sigma_{ji}^{\mathrm{I}b}$(可按无限大板求解),这样又会在边界处引起不平衡外力,重复如上做法,则可以不断逼近真值。事实上,一般只需迭代1～2次,即可满足精度要求。

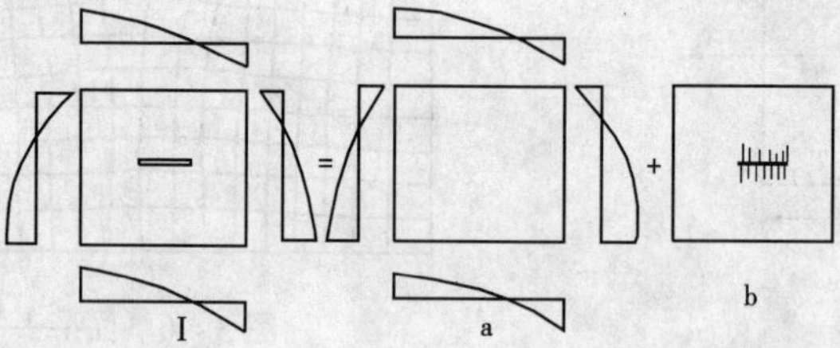

图4

则
$$\sigma_{ij}^{\mathrm{I}} = \sigma_{ij}^{\mathrm{I}a} + \sigma_{ij}^{\mathrm{I}b}$$

为了便于求解,将式(21)展成傅氏级数:

$$
\begin{cases}
\sigma_y^0 \mid_{y=h} = \dfrac{a_0}{2} + \sum\limits_{n=1}^{\infty} a_n \cos \dfrac{n\pi x}{l} \\
\tau_{xy}^0 \mid_{y=h} = \sum\limits_{n=1}^{\infty} b_n \sin \dfrac{n\pi x}{l} + k^0 x \\
\sigma_y^0 \mid_{y=-h} = \sigma_y^0 \mid_{y=h} \qquad k^0 = \dfrac{1}{l} \tau_{xy}^0 \mid_{\substack{x=l \\ y=h}} \\
\tau_{xy}^0 \mid_{y=-h} = \tau_{xy} \mid_{y=h} \\
a_n = \dfrac{2}{l} \int_0^l \sigma_y^0 \mid_{y=h} \cos \dfrac{n\pi x}{l} \mathrm{d}x, \quad b_n = \dfrac{2}{l} \int_0^l \tau_{xy}^0 \mid_{y=h} \sin \dfrac{n\pi x}{l} \mathrm{d}x
\end{cases}
\tag{23}
$$

据式(22)、(23)求出板四周的边界力,反号加到板上,用弹性理论的一般方法可得无裂纹有限板的应力解。

$$\left\{\begin{aligned}
\sigma_x^{Ia} &= \frac{3y}{2h^3}\left[\frac{2}{5}h^2\left(k^0h+\frac{a_0}{2}\right)-l^2\left(k^0h+\frac{a_0}{2}\right)\right]+\frac{3}{2}\frac{1}{h^3}\left(k^0h+\frac{a_0}{2}\right)x^2h-\\
&\frac{1}{h^3}\left(k^0h+\frac{a_0}{2}\right)y^3+\sum_{n=1}^{\infty}\cos\frac{n\pi x}{l}\left[B_n\left(\frac{n\pi}{l}\right)^2\sin\frac{n\pi y}{l}+\right.\\
&\left.C_n\frac{n\pi}{l}\left(2\mathrm{sh}\frac{n\pi y}{l}+\frac{n\pi}{l}y\mathrm{ch}\frac{n\pi y}{l}\right)\right]+\\
&\frac{1}{16}E\alpha\frac{T_1-T_2}{h}a^2\left(\frac{l^2+y^2-a^2}{A^3}\sin\frac{3}{2}\theta+\frac{1}{A}\sin\frac{1}{2}\theta\right)\Big|_{x=l}\\
\sigma_y^{Ia} &= -\left(\frac{1}{2}k^0+\frac{3}{4}\frac{a_0}{h}\right)y+\frac{y^3}{2h^3}\left(k^0h+\frac{a_0}{2}\right)+\\
&\sum_{m=1}^{\infty}-\left(\frac{n\pi}{l}\right)^2\cos\frac{n\pi x}{l}\left[B_n\mathrm{sh}\frac{n\pi y}{l}+C_ny\mathrm{ch}\frac{n\pi y}{l}\right]\\
\tau_{xy}^{Ia} &= \left[-\frac{3}{2}\frac{1}{h^3}\left(k^0h+\frac{a_0}{2}\right)y^2+\left(\frac{1}{2}k^0+\frac{3}{4}\frac{a_0}{h}\right)\right]x+\\
&\sum_{n=1}^{\infty}\frac{n\pi}{l}\sin\frac{n\pi x}{l}\left[B_n\frac{n\pi y}{l}+C_n\left(\mathrm{ch}\frac{n\pi y}{l}+\frac{n\pi}{l}y\mathrm{sh}\frac{n\pi y}{l}\right)\right]
\end{aligned}\right. \tag{24}$$

其中

$$B_n=\frac{\left[\left(\frac{l}{n\pi}\right)^2a_n+\frac{lh}{n\pi}b_n\right]\mathrm{ch}\frac{n\pi h}{l}+\frac{lh}{n\pi}a_n\mathrm{sh}\frac{n\pi h}{l}}{\frac{1}{2}\mathrm{sh}\frac{2n\pi h}{l}-\frac{n\pi h}{l}}$$

$$C_n=\frac{-\frac{l}{n\pi}b_n\mathrm{sh}\frac{n\pi h}{l}-\frac{l}{n\pi}a_n\mathrm{ch}\frac{n\pi h}{l}}{\frac{1}{2}\mathrm{sh}\frac{2n\pi h}{l}-\frac{n\pi}{l}h}$$

有限板沿裂缝切开,则在裂缝表面的不平衡力为

$$\left\{\begin{aligned}
&\tau_{xy}^{Ia}\big|_{y=0}=\left(\frac{1}{2}k^0+\frac{3}{4}\frac{a_0}{h}\right)x+\sum_{n=1}^{\infty}\frac{n\pi}{l}\left(\frac{n\pi}{l}B_n+C_n\right)\sin\frac{n\pi x}{l}\\
&\sigma_y^{Ia}\big|_{y=0}=0
\end{aligned}\right. \tag{25}$$

将此应力反号加到裂缝表面,则裂缝表面外力为(裂缝上表面,法向为$(-y)$向)

$$x_n^{Ib}\big|_{y=0}=\left(\frac{1}{2}k^0+\frac{3}{4}\frac{a_0}{h}\right)x+\sum_{n=1}^{\infty}\frac{n\pi}{l}\left(\frac{n\pi}{l}B_n+C_n\right)\sin\frac{n\pi x}{l} \tag{26}$$

所以,在ξ平面上的裂缝表面有

$$\begin{aligned}
f^{Ib} &= i\int X_n\mathrm{d}s=i\int\left[\left(\frac{1}{2}k^0+\frac{3}{4}\frac{a_0}{h}\right)Z+\sum_{n=1}^{\infty}\frac{n\pi}{l}\left(\frac{n\pi}{l}B_n+C_n\right)\sin\frac{n\pi Z}{l}\right]\mathrm{d}s\\
&= \frac{i}{8}\left(\frac{1}{2}k^0+\frac{3}{4}\frac{a_0}{h}\right)a^2\left(\sigma+\frac{1}{\sigma}\right)^2+i\sum_{n=1}^{\infty}-D_n\frac{l}{n\pi}\cos\frac{n\pi a}{2l}\left(\sigma+\frac{1}{\sigma}\right)
\end{aligned} \tag{27}$$

其中

$$D_n=\frac{n\pi}{l}\left(\frac{n\pi}{l}B_n+C_n\right) \tag{28}$$

由上式得

$$\begin{cases}\phi_1^{Ib}(\xi)=\dfrac{i}{8}ba^2\dfrac{1}{\xi^2}-i\sum\limits_{n=1}^{\infty}D_n\dfrac{1}{n\pi}\sum\limits_{k=1}^{\infty}(-1)^kJ_{2k}\left(\dfrac{n\pi a}{l}\right)\left(\dfrac{1}{\xi}\right)^{2k}\\ \psi^{Ib}(\xi)=-\dfrac{i}{8}ba^2\dfrac{1}{\xi^2}+\dfrac{i}{4}\dfrac{ba^2}{\xi^2}\dfrac{1+\xi^2}{\xi^2-1}+i\sum\limits_{n=1}^{\infty}D_n\dfrac{l}{n\pi}\times\\ \qquad\sum\limits_{n=1}^{\infty}(-1)^kJ_{2k}\left(\dfrac{n\pi a}{l}\right)\left(\dfrac{1}{\xi}\right)^{2k}\left(\dfrac{1}{\xi}\right)^{2k}\left(1-2k\dfrac{\xi^2+1}{\xi^2-1}\right)\end{cases}\tag{29}$$

其中　　$b=\dfrac{1}{2}k^0+\dfrac{3}{4}\dfrac{a_0}{h}$

将式(13)及式(29)代入式(15)(其中 $T=0$)得

$$\begin{cases}\sigma_x^{Ib}=-\left(\dfrac{3}{4}\dfrac{a_0}{h}+\dfrac{1}{2}k^0\right)\Big[3y-\left(\dfrac{5}{2}A-\dfrac{5a^2}{4A}+\dfrac{x^2+y^2}{2A}\right)\sin\dfrac{1}{2}\theta+\\ \qquad\dfrac{1}{4A^3}a^2(x^2+y^2-a^2)\Big]\sin\dfrac{3}{2}\theta+\sum\limits_{n=1}^{\infty}2D_n\dfrac{l}{n\pi}\sum\limits_{k=1}^{\infty}(-1)^kk\times\\ \qquad J_{2k}\left(\dfrac{n\pi a}{l}\right)\left(\dfrac{1}{a}\right)^{2k}\left[\left(H_k+\dfrac{2\sin\frac{1}{2}\theta}{A}\right)\sum\limits_{m=0}^{k}(-1)^mC_{2k}^{2m}E^{2k-2m}F^{2m}-\right.\\ \qquad\left.\left(G_k+\dfrac{2\cos\frac{1}{2}\theta}{A}\right)\sum\limits_{m=0}^{k-1}(-1)^mC_{2k}^{2m+1}E^{2k-2m-1}F^{2m+1}\right]\\ \sigma_y^{Ib}=-\dfrac{1}{4}\left(\dfrac{3}{4}\dfrac{a_0}{h}+\dfrac{1}{2}k^0\right)-4y+\left(2A-\dfrac{1}{A}(a^2-2x^2-2y^2)\right)\sin\dfrac{1}{2}\theta-\\ \qquad\left(\dfrac{a^2(x^2+y^2-a^2)}{A^3}\sin\dfrac{3}{2}\theta\right)+2\sum\limits_{n=1}^{\infty}D_n\dfrac{l}{n\pi}\sum\limits_{k=1}^{\infty}(-1)^kk\times\\ \qquad J_2\left(\dfrac{n\pi a}{l}\right)\left(\dfrac{1}{a}\right)^{2k}\left[\left(\dfrac{2\sin\frac{1}{2}\theta}{A}-H_k\right)\sum\limits_{m=0}^{k}(-1)^mC_{2k}^{2m}E^{2k-2m}F^{2m}+\right.\\ \qquad\left.\left(G_k-\dfrac{2\cos\frac{1}{2}\theta}{A}\right)\sum\limits_{m=0}^{k-1}(-1)^mC_{2k}^{2m+1}E^{2k-2m-1}F^{2m+1}\right]\\ \tau_{xy}^{Ib}=-\dfrac{1}{4}\left(\dfrac{3}{4}\dfrac{a_0}{h}+\dfrac{1}{2}k^0\right)\Big[4x+\left(\dfrac{2}{A}(x^2+y^2)-6A-\dfrac{3a^2}{A}\right)\cos\dfrac{1}{2}\theta+\\ \qquad\dfrac{a^2}{A^3}(a^2-x^2-y^2)\cos\dfrac{3}{2}\theta\Big]-\sum\limits_{n=1}^{\infty}D_n\dfrac{1}{n\pi}\sum\limits_{k=1}^{\infty}(-1)^k2k\times\\ \qquad J_{2k}\left(\dfrac{n\pi a}{l}\right)\left(\dfrac{1}{a}\right)^{2k}\Big[\sum\limits_{m=1}^{k}(-1)^mC_{2k}^{2m}E^{2k-2m}F^{2m}G_k+\\ \qquad\sum\limits_{m=0}^{k-1}(-1)^mC_{2k}^{2m+1}E^{2k-2m-1}F^{2m+1}H_k\Big]\end{cases}\tag{30}$$

其中

$$\begin{cases}G_k=\dfrac{1}{A}\cos\dfrac{1}{2}\theta-\dfrac{4k^0y\sin\theta}{A^2}+\dfrac{1}{A^3}(x^2+y^2-a^2)\cos\dfrac{3}{2}\theta\\ H_k=\dfrac{1}{A}\sin\dfrac{1}{2}\theta+\dfrac{4k^0y\cos\theta}{A^2}+\dfrac{1}{A^3}(x^2+y^2-a^2)\sin\dfrac{3}{2}\theta\\ E=x-A\cos\dfrac{1}{2}\theta\\ F=y-A\sin\dfrac{1}{2}\theta\end{cases}\tag{31}$$

将式(29) 中的第一式代入文献[5] 中的公式

得 $$K = K_{\mathrm{I}} - iK_{\mathrm{II}} = 2\left(\frac{\pi}{a}\right)^{1/4}\phi'(1)$$

$$K^{\mathrm{I}} = K_{\mathrm{I}}^{\mathrm{I}} - iK_{\mathrm{II}}^{\mathrm{I}} = 2(\pi/a)^{1/2}\Big[-\frac{i}{4}\left(\frac{1}{2}k^0 + \frac{3}{4}\frac{a_0}{h}\right)a^2 + i\sum_{n=0}^{\infty}D_n\frac{l}{n\pi}\sum_{k=1}^{\infty}(-1)^k 2kJ_{2k}\left(\frac{n\pi a}{l}\right)\Big] \tag{32}$$

按无限大板求解 σ_{ij}^{lb} 时,满足裂缝边界条件,但在 $x = \pm l$、$y = \pm h$ 处,仍有不平衡边界力,若不满足精度要求,可重复本节第二步。实际上,只需计算 1 ~ 2 次,即可满足。总应力为

$$\sigma_{ij} = \sigma_{ij} + \sum_{m=1}^{n}(\sigma_{ij}^{mb} + \sigma_{ij}^{ma}) \tag{33}$$

$$K = \sum_{m=0}^{n}K^m \tag{34}$$

式中:n 为总的迭代次数;K 为应力强度因子。

3 数值计算实例

取 $10a \times 10a$ 的板,弹模为 E,线胀系数为 α,板的上边温度为 T_1,下边温度为 T_2。用本文所列式(19)、(24)、(30) 和式(33) 进行计算,只需回代一次,即可得到较为精确的结果。板的应力场计算结果见图 5 ~ 图 7。

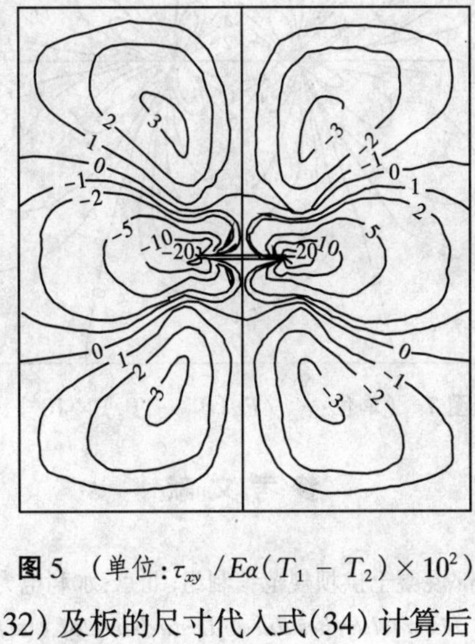

图 5 (单位:$\tau_{xy} / E\alpha(T_1 - T_2) \times 10^2$)

将式(20)、(23) 和式(32) 及板的尺寸代入式(34) 计算后,可得缝端应力强度因子为

$2h = 2l = 10a$ 时:

$$K_{\mathrm{I}} = 0 \quad K_{\mathrm{II}} = 0.043\,22E\alpha(T_1 - T_2)\sqrt{a}$$

$2h = 2l = 5a$ 时:

$$K_{\mathrm{I}} = 0 \quad K_{\mathrm{II}} = 0.081\,252E\alpha(T_1 - T_2)\sqrt{a}$$

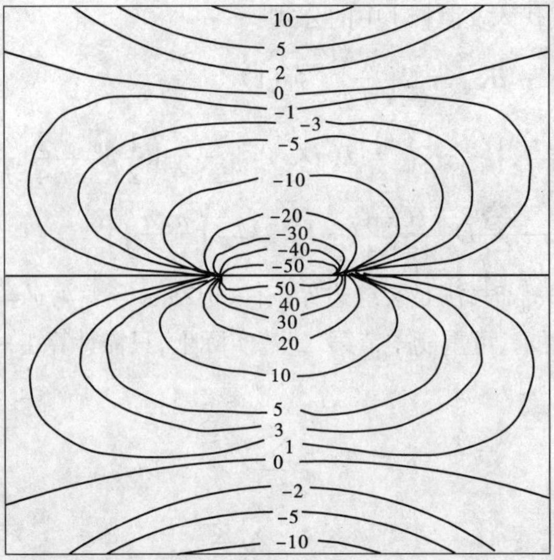

图 6 （单位：τ_{xx} $/E\alpha(T_1 - T_2)\times10^2$）

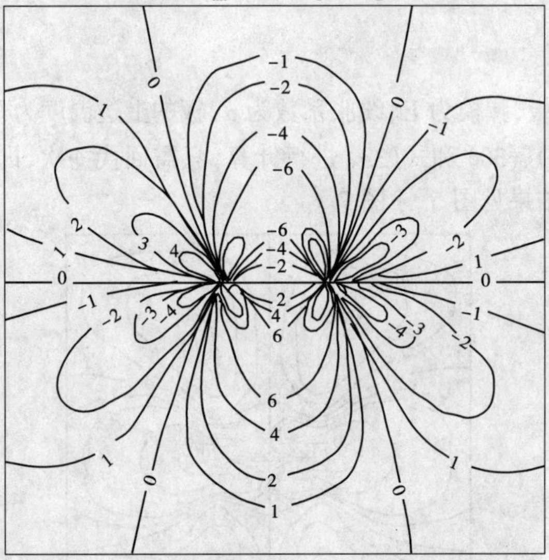

图 7 （单位：τ_{yy} $/E\alpha(T_1 - T_2)\times10^2$）

参 考 文 献

[1] 混凝土拱坝设计规范.水电部混凝土拱坝规范编制组.北京:水利电力出版社,1985

[2] Florence A L, Goodier J N. *Thermalslresses due to Disturbance of Uniform Heat Flow by an Insutaled Ovaloid Hole*. J. of Applied Mechanics, Vol.27, 1960:635～637

[3] Nowinski J L. Theory of *Thermoelasticity with Application*. Netherlands, 1978

[4] Саврук М П, Dачыщин АП, Солтыс И Ф. *Прикладная, Механика*. Том. X_{11}, No.4, 1976, Стр: 89～97

[5] 范天佑.断裂力学基础.南京:江苏科技出版社,1978

FICTITIOUS THERMAL SOURCE (FTS) METHOD IN SOLVING HARMONIC TEMPERATURE FIELD PROBLEM

Abstract In the present paper, the fundamental solution of a temperature field caused by a harmonic point thermal source is presented. A boundary integral method in which fictitious boundary thermal source is taken as the basic unknown is advised for the solution of steady and harmonic temperature field in an arbitrary finite region. Engineering application shows that the advised method gives good results with high precision of temperature field and strongly reduces the calculating works.

1 Introduction

Hydraulic structures (concrete dam, tunnel ect.) are always under the effect of variable temperature of water and air. These variations of temperature play an important part in the arising and development of cracks in the concrete dams or concrete lines of underground tunnels. The damage of four dams in French[1] and the crack growth of Fontana[2] dam in U. S. A showed that a periodical temperature variation of water and air is the main reason for the crack propagation. The observations of cracks happened in the tipical concrete dams in China confirmed also the same reason. The reports of concrete dams in 1960s showed that the surface cracks could be developed to a serious penetrational cracks under the periodical tem perature condition.

According to observation data, the temperature of water and air changes periodically and can be approximated to be harmonic. Considered the difficulty in the analytic method, usually an infinite plane problem with uniaxle heat conduction model was used only for harmonic temperature field. It dose not give the real temperature field under a complicated boundary condition. Recently the finite element method is suitable for all kinds of boundary conditious[3], in order to get high calculating precision for the harmonic condition, F. E. M induces also the enormous preparation work and long computer time. In prensent paper, the fundamental solution for the harmonic temperature field induced by point thermal source was given. Taking the fictitious boundary thermal source as the basic unknown, the fundamental equations for the harmonic temperature field in the structure were also constructed. The practical applications show the benefits of this method with the less calculation work, high precision and saving computer time. Only forty boundary elements are needed for the temperture prediction of a crown profile of arch dam. The common micro-computer is enough to obtain the satisfacto-

本文选自《International Symposium on Pump-Storage Engineering》1990年10月刊,作者还有 Zhang Guoxin。

ry results. Further more, the analytical expression of temperature field provides also the basis for solving thermal fracture problems.

2 Fundamental Equation and Definite Condition

During the operation of the concrete structure, the contribution of hydration heat to the temperature field of structure is negligible, the temperature boundary conditions are divided into two kinds, i. e., 1) boundary on which temperature is known, for example, the upstream surface of dam or the surface of tunnel, its temperature can be taken as the temperatue of water; 2) the boundary on which the state of heat flow is known, for example, thermal insolation boundary (no heat flow). The fundamental equation and boundary condition can be written as (Fig. 1):

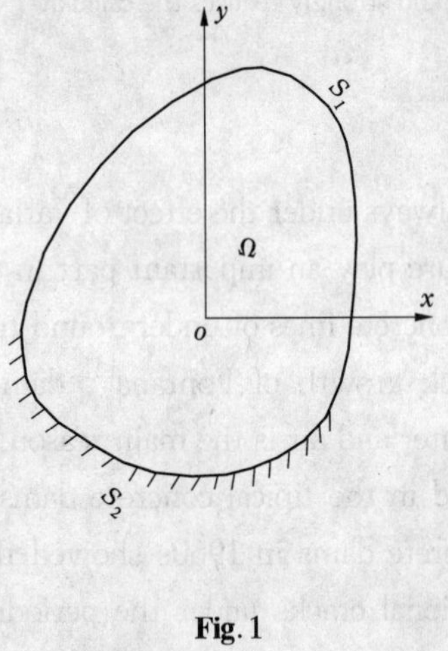

Fig. 1

$$\frac{\partial T}{\partial t} = a\left(\frac{\partial^2 T}{\partial X^2} + \frac{\partial^2 T}{\partial Y^2}\right) \quad \text{in region } \Omega$$

$$T = \overline{T}_0 + \overline{f}\sin\omega t + \overline{g}\cos\omega t \quad \text{on } S_1 \qquad (1)$$

$$-\lambda\frac{\partial T}{\partial n} = \overline{q}_0 + \overline{q}_1\sin\omega t + \overline{q}_2\cos\omega t \quad \text{through } S_2$$

Where: $T = T(x, y)$ is the temperature field; T_0 is the known steady temperature on S_1; f and g are the amplitudes of temperature variation on S_1; q_0 is the known steady heat flow through boundary S_2; q_1 and q_2 are two amplitudes of the known heat flow on boundary S_2; λ is heat conductivity; a is temperature conductivity; n is the exterior normal direction of the boundary.

3 Fundamental Solution

(1) Solution of Steady Temperature Field Caused by Steady Point Thermal Source.

The temperature field in Eq. (1) can be separated into two parts: i. e., the steady temperature field and the harmonic temperature field. The solution for a steady temperature field caused by a point thermal source in an infinite region was given by the wellknown Laplaces equation:

$$T_s^*(r) = \frac{1}{2\Pi\lambda}\ln(r) \qquad (2)$$

where: $T_s^*(r)$ represents the temperature value of a point which has a distance r apart from the source.

(2) The Solution of Temperature Field Caused by a Point Harmonic Thermal Source.

The temperature in the hydraulic structure after long time of operation becomes steadily periodically variating state. The steadily variating temperature field caused by a harmonic point thermal source must satisfy the following equations:

$$\frac{\partial T_H^*}{\partial t} = a\left(\frac{\partial^2 T_H^*}{\partial r^2} + \frac{1}{r}\frac{\partial T_H^*}{\partial r}\right) + (q_1 \sin\omega t + q_2 \cos\omega t)\delta(r) \tag{3}$$

where: $T_H^* = T_H^*(r,t)$ represents the temperature value at point r on time t caused by harmonic thermal source.

The nonuniform power terms represent that there is a unit thermal source having the harmonic variation with time at $r=0$. Let it be in following form:

$$T_H^* = \overline{T}_H(t)G(r)$$

Since the temperature changes with time periodically, the time t must be represented as a triangle function and can be obtained by letting the power of the solution of $T_H(t)$ be an imaginary number. Lets defferentiate the formula(3) and separate variables, then we have:

$$\frac{\overline{T}'_H(t)}{a\overline{T}_H(t)} = \frac{G''(r)}{G(r)} = \pm i\alpha^2 \tag{4}$$

where: α is an arbitrary constant.

Rewrite the above formula, we have:

$$\overline{T}_H{}'(t) - (\pm i\alpha^2)a\overline{T}_H(t) = 0 \tag{4a}$$

$$G''(r) - (\pm i\alpha^2)G(r) = 0 \tag{4b}$$

Solved the Eq. (4a) we obtain:

$$T_H(t) = \exp(\pm \alpha^2 at) \tag{5}$$

The Eq. (4b) is a modified Bessel equation of zero order. The solution is :

$$G(r) = C_1 H_0^{(1)}(r\alpha\sqrt{i}) + C_2 H_0^{(2)}(r\alpha\sqrt{i}) \tag{6}$$

Where: $H_0^{(1)}(Z)$, $H_0^{(1)}(Z)$ are the first and second kind of Bessel function of zero order respectively.

$$H_0^{(1)} = J_0(Z) + iN_0(Z)$$

$$H_0^{(2)} = J_0(Z) - iN_0(Z) \tag{7a}$$

$$N_0(Z) = \frac{2}{\Pi}(\ln\frac{Z}{2} + \gamma)J_0(Z) - \frac{2}{\Pi}\sum_{K=1}^{\infty}\frac{(-1)^K}{(K!)^2}\left(\frac{Z}{2}\right)^{2K}\sum_{m=1}^{K}\frac{1}{m} \tag{7b}$$

$$J_0(Z) = \sum_{K=0}^{\infty}(-1)^K\frac{Z^{2K}}{2^{2K}(K!)^2}$$

Where: γ is Eulers constant.

Considered the physical content of the present problem and the property of Hankal function of zero order, the fundamental solution should be given as:

$$T_H^*(r,t) = \frac{q_1}{4\lambda}[\cos\omega t\,\mathrm{Re}H_0^{(1)}(r\sqrt{\frac{\omega}{a}}i) + \sin\omega t\,\mathrm{Im}H_0^{(1)}(r\sqrt{\frac{\omega}{a}}i)] +$$

$$\frac{q_2}{4\lambda}[\cos\omega t\,\mathrm{Im}H_0^{(1)}(r\sqrt{\frac{\omega}{a}}i) - \sin\omega t\,\mathrm{Re}H_0^{(1)}(r\sqrt{\frac{\omega}{a}}i)]$$

4 The Construction of Boundary integral Equations

Suppose that on the whole boundary of region, there are distributed steady thermal source $h(s)$ and harmonic thermal source $q_1(s)\sin\omega t + q_2(s)\cos\omega t$; the temperature of an arbitrary point z in Ω can be given by the following eqution:

$$T(Z,t) = \int_{\Gamma}\left\{h(s)\frac{1}{2\Pi\lambda}\ln(r_{zs}) + \frac{q_1(s)}{4\lambda}\left[\cos\omega t\,\mathrm{Re}H_0^{(1)}\left(r_{zs}\sqrt{\frac{\omega}{a}i}\right) + \sin\omega t\,\mathrm{Im}H_0^{(1)}\left(r_{zs}\sqrt{\frac{\omega}{a}i}\right)\right] + \frac{q_2(s)}{4\lambda}\left[\cos\omega t\,\mathrm{Im}H_0^{(1)}\left(r_{zs}\sqrt{\frac{\omega}{a}i}\right) - \sin\omega t\,\mathrm{Re}H_0^{(1)}\left(r_{zs}\sqrt{\frac{\omega}{a}i}\right)\right]\right\}\mathrm{d}s \quad (8)$$

where: Γ is the whole exterior boundary of Ω, i. e., $\Gamma = S_1 + S_2$ (See Fig. 1); r_{zs} is the distance between an arbitrary point z in region and point s on the boundary.

Let the point z in region approach to the point Q_0 on the boundary S_1, from formula(9) we have (See Fig. 1):

$$\overline{T}_0(Q_0) + \overline{f}(Q_0)\sin\omega t + \overline{g}(Q_0)\cos\omega t$$

$$= \int_{\Gamma}\left\{h(s)\frac{1}{2\Pi\lambda}\ln(r_{Q_0 s}) + \frac{q_1(s)}{4\lambda}\left[\cos\omega t\,\mathrm{Re}H_0^{(1)}\left(r_{Q_0 s}\sqrt{\frac{\omega}{a}i}\right) + \sin\omega t\,\mathrm{Im}H_0^{(1)}\left(r_{Q_0 s}\sqrt{\frac{\omega}{a}i}\right)\right] + \frac{q_2(s)}{4\lambda}\left[\cos\omega t\,\mathrm{Im}H_0^{(1)}\left(r_{Q_0 s}\sqrt{\frac{\omega}{a}i}\right) - \sin\omega t\,\mathrm{Re}H_0^{(1)}\left(r_{Q_0 s}\sqrt{\frac{\omega}{a}i}\right)\right]\right\}\mathrm{d}s \quad (9)$$

In fact, the above equation can be separated into three equations:

$$\overline{T}_0(Q_0) = \int_{\Gamma}h(s)\frac{1}{2\Pi\lambda}\ln(r_{Q_0 s})\mathrm{d}s$$

$$\overline{f}(Q_0) = \int_{\Gamma}\left[\frac{q_1(s)}{4\lambda}\mathrm{Im}H_0^{(1)}\left(r_{Q_0 s}\sqrt{\frac{\omega}{a}i}\right) - \frac{q_2(s)}{4\lambda}\mathrm{Re}H_0^{(1)}\left(r_{Q_0 s}\sqrt{\frac{\omega}{a}i}\right)\right]\mathrm{d}s \quad (10)$$

$$\overline{g}(Q_0) = \int_{\Gamma}\left[\frac{q_1(s)}{4\lambda}\mathrm{Re}H_0^{(1)}\left(r_{Q_0 s}\sqrt{\frac{\omega}{a}i}\right) + \frac{q_2(s)}{4\lambda}\mathrm{Im}H_0^{(1)}\left(r_{Q_0 s}\sqrt{\frac{\omega}{a}i}\right)\right]\mathrm{d}s$$

Take the derivative of formula (9) along the exterior normal direction of the arbitrary point P_0 on the boundary S_2, and let z approach to point P_0. The another group of the integral equations satisfied the constant heat-flow on S_2 is obtained.

$$\overline{q}_0(P_0) = -\lambda\frac{\partial}{\partial\eta_{P0}}\int_{\Gamma}h(s)\cdot\frac{1}{2\Pi\lambda}\ln(r_{Q_0 s})\mathrm{d}s$$

$$\overline{q}_1(P_0) = -\lambda\frac{\partial}{\partial\eta_{P_0}}\int_{\Gamma}\left[\frac{q_1(s)}{4\lambda}\mathrm{Im}H_0^{(1)}\left(r_{P_0 s}\sqrt{\frac{\omega}{a}i}\right) - \frac{q_2(s)}{4\lambda}\mathrm{Re}H_0^{(1)}\left(r_{P_0 s}\sqrt{\frac{\omega}{a}i}\right)\right]\mathrm{d}s \quad (11)$$

Solve the Eqs. (10) and (11), we obtain thermal source functions distributed on the boundary $h(s)$, $q_1(s)$ and $q_2(s)$. The problem is solved. Numerical method would be satisfy the problem with complicate boundary condition.

5 Example and Comparison

(1)Surpose there is a 10m × 10m plate, the boundary condition of which is shown in Fig. 2. Divide the bounary into 20 sections (boundary elements See Fig. 2), the results given by the present F. T. S method and the analytical solution are shown in Table 1.

(2)Let a harmonic thermal source to be added to the left side of the plate shown in Fig. 2. Its amplitude is 20℃, the period is one year, i.e.:

$T_c = 20\sin\omega(t-4)$ ℃

where: $\omega = 2\pi/12$; Temperature conductivity $a =$ 3.0m/month.

Compared the calculated result with the analytical result given by reference [4], the results are listed in Table 2.

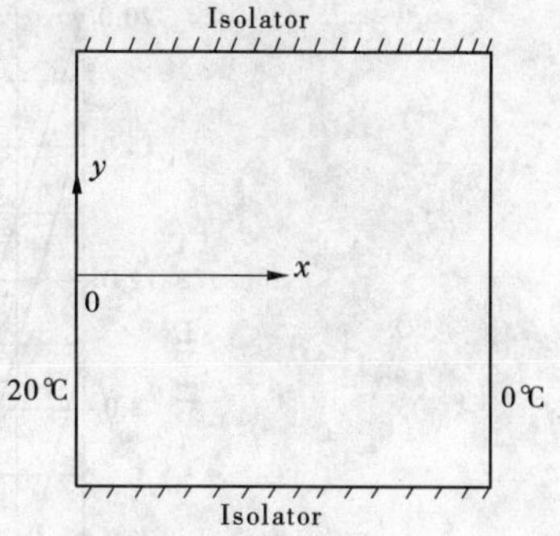

Fig. 2

Table 1 Comparison of the Solutions of the steady Temperature Field

x	0	2.0	4.0	6.0	8.0
F.T.S	20.0	15.999 8	12.001 2	8.003 7	2.001 6
Analytical	20.0	16.0	12.0	8.0	2.0

Table 2 Comparison of the Temperature on Line $y=0$ in June

x	1.0	2.0	4.0	6.0	8.0
Analytic	-14.221	-9.172	-2.337	0.504	0.810
F.T.S	-14.221	-9.170	-2.336	0.503	0.809

The temperature fields in different month on the plate are shown in Fig. 3. It is evidently from Table 1 and Table 2, the F. T. S method is characterised as less boundary elements and high precision. the maximum relative error is only 0.04%, that is precise enough for engineering application. The calculating results of the harmonic temperature field on plate are in good agreement with theoretical soultion (See Fig. 3).

6 Engineering Application

A dam with height of 153.0 m (in China), has its temperature bounbary conditions of the profile as shown in Fig. 4. The temperature distributions of some month are given by the present F. T. S method and shown in Fig. 5～Fig. 8. The comparison of these results with those given by F. E. M with 'thick grid' shown in good agreement. The present F. T. S method has its advantage which would not be influenced by some distorted elements. The calculation of the temperature field of a crown profile requires 40 boundary elements only and a microcomputer.

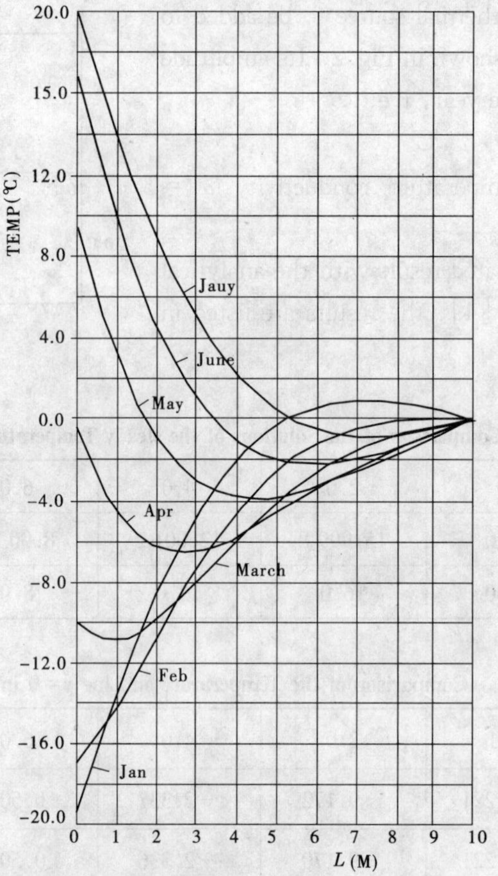

Fig. 3　Temperature distribution in different month

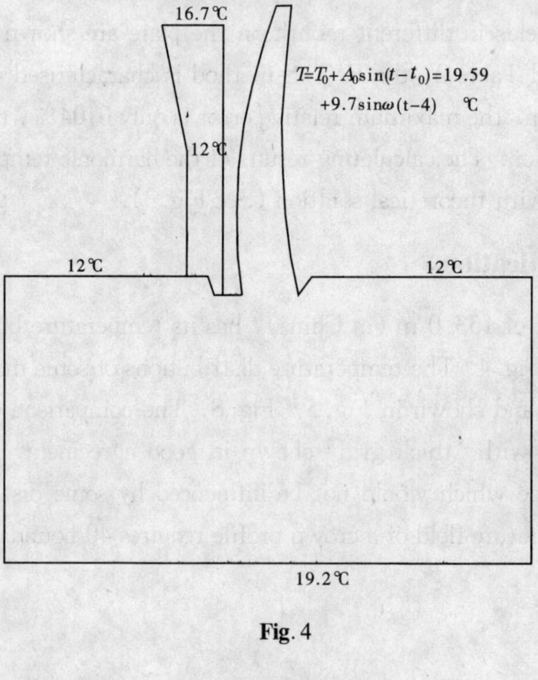

Fig. 4

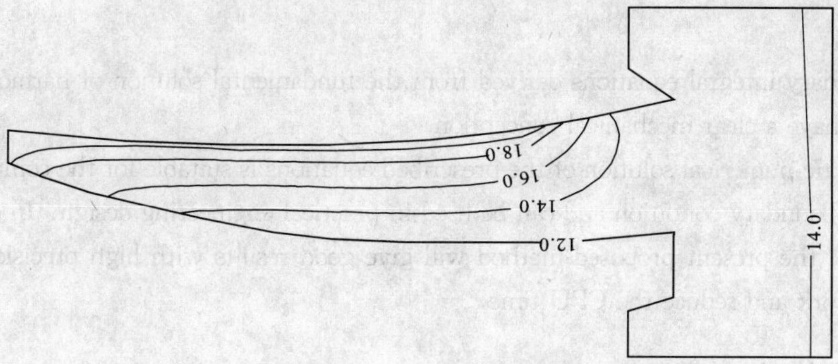

Fig. 8 Steady temperature field

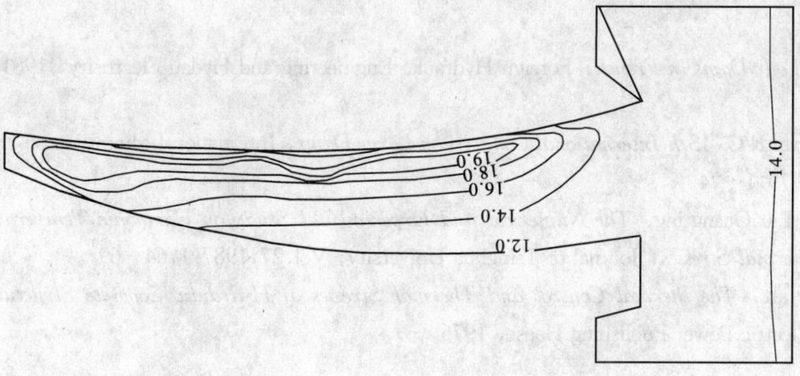

Fig. 7 Temperature distribution in Nov

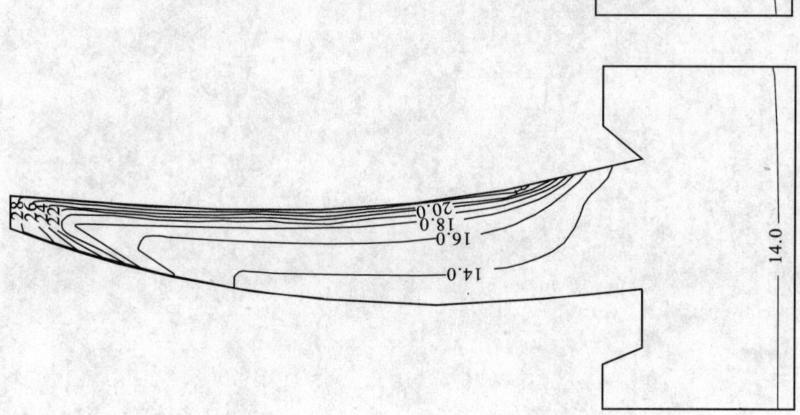

Fig. 6 Temperature distribution in Juny

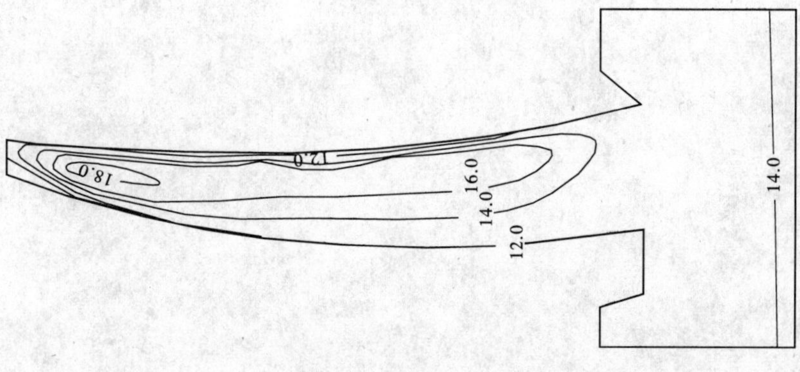

Fig. 5 Temperature distribution in June

7 Conclusions

(1)The boundary integral equations derived from the fundamental solution of harmonic temperature field have a clear mechanical conception.

(2)The analytic-numerical solution of the prescribed equations is suitable for the complicated engineering boundary condition and can be used in practical engineering design. In engineering practice, the present proposed method will give good results with high precision, less preparating work and reduce the CPU time.

References

[1] *The damage of Four Dams in French*. Foreign Hydraulic Engineering and Hydau-Electrisity ,1981.5, 20~27

[2] Abraham I J,Sloan R C. *13th International Congress on Large Dams*. International commision on Large Dams, Vol.1,1979.1~24

[3] Zhang Guoxin, Liu Guangting. *The Numerical and Experimental Study on Harmonic Temperature Field and Its Thermal Stresses*. Journal of Tsinghua University, Vol.27,1987.1,64~69

[4] Zhu Bofang, et al.. *The thermal Control and Thermal Stresses of Hydraulic Concrete Structures*. Hydraulic and Electric Power Publishing House, 1976

SINGULAR INTEGRAL EQUATION GROUPS FOR 3-D CRACK PROBLEMS IN FINITE BODY

Abstract Various shapes of space cracks (not only elliptical) always happen in engineering practice (finite complicated body). It is necessary to determine whether they will propagate and bring danger to the structure. In present paper, the fundamental equations of stress-displacement field in elastic body due to unit concentrated dislocation are given through Hankel transform. Singular integral equation groups caused by fictitious distributed dislocation along the outer boundaries of engineering structure and complicated space crack surface are constructed to satisfy the known boundary conditions. Solutions of these distributed dislocations will directly give the SIF (stress intensity factor) of the crack in various directions, the stress and displacement field of finite body. Simple numerical example of typical elliptical crack is used for precision check, which shows results in good agreement with theoretical result and with less computing time of the present method. The present method has been used for the repairment of the defects in old structure.

Key words singular integral equation; crack; three-dimensional(3-D) fictitious dislocation

The research work made in 3-D problem is less smooth than that made in 2-D problem for its complexity. Dr. N. I. Ioakimidis[1] established a set of singular integral equations for the plane fracture in an infinite elastic region. It can be used for solving the fracture problem with arbitrary shape of the surfaces in plane and with various distributed tensile stress. The similar integral equations are also obtained by Dr. J. Weaver who studied rectangular crack problem in an infinite region as well. But all the work was restricted in mode I condition, in plane crack problems[2] and in infinite region.

For engineering purpose, it is always necessary to solve the problem in space and in finite region. In 1988, through Hankel transform, the fundamental solutions of the integral equation-boundary element methods with discontinuous displacement for 3-D elastic problem were given by the authors of this paper. The discontinuous displacement on the cracking surface and the boundary surface are taken as unknown variables, that will make numerical analytic procedure more easily.

In order to solve 3-D crack problem with arbitrary shape and stress conditions, an improved semianalytic method was proposed in present paper with solution in closed form induced by unit concentrated dislocation and introducing Kutt's[3] numerical processes for the eliminating singularity of r^{-3} order in the integral equations. It offers results of high accuracy for solving complicate 3-D crack with less computing time.

本文选自《清华大学学报(自然科学版)》1996年第1期,作者还有林国裕。

1 Basic Solutions

1.1 Definition of Dislocation

Suppose there is an infinite 3-D elastic body containing an arbitrary crack of tensile type. Local coordinates are x_1, x_2, x_3 with its origin Q on the crack surface. The axis x_3 coincides with the perpendicular line at Q, the dislocation of Q can be defined as: $D_j(Q) = U_j(Q^-) - U_j(Q^+)$, $j = 1,2,3$, in which $U_j(Q^+)$ and $U_j(Q^-)$ represent the displacement components on the upper and lower crack surfaces respectively.

1.2 Elastic Fields of Normal Dislocation

Considering a circular crack with radius of "a" in infinite space, suppose a normal uniform dislocation D_z is distributed on the crack surface and let $D_z \pi a^2$ when $a \to 0$. Dirac function D_z can be defined as

$$D_z = \delta(r) = \lim_{a\to 0}\delta a(r),\ \delta a(r) = \begin{cases} 0 & r > a \\ 1/(\pi a^2) & r \leqslant a \end{cases}$$

Since the considered problem is symmetric with respect to the plane $z = 0$, only the upper half space $z > 0$ will be taken into account. The boundary conditions are

$$\sigma_{ij}\Big|_{\sqrt{r^2+z^2}\to\infty} = 0,\quad \sigma_{rz}\Big|_{z=0} = 0,\quad u_x\Big|_{z=0} = -\frac{1}{2}\delta(r),\ r = \sqrt{x^2+y^2}$$

When the body force is absent, the problem is reduced to solve the double harmonic function:

$$\left(\frac{\partial^2}{\partial r^2} + \frac{\partial}{r\partial r} + \frac{\partial^2}{\partial z^2}\right)^2 \Phi = 0 \tag{1}$$

where Φ is displacement function. By Hankel transform of zero order

$$G(\xi, z) = \int_0^\infty r\Phi(r,z)J_0(\xi r)\mathrm{d}r \tag{2}$$

where $J_0(\xi r)$ denotes zero order of Bessel function. Eq. (1) can be written as

$$\left(\frac{\mathrm{d}}{\mathrm{d}z}(-\xi^2)\right)^2 G(\xi, z) = 0 \tag{3}$$

of which the general solutions are given by

$$G(\xi, z) = (A + Bz)\mathrm{e}^{-\xi z} + (C + Dz)\mathrm{e}^{\xi z} \tag{4}$$

where A, B, C and D are the functions of ξ, which can be determined by the boundary conditions. By means of reverse Hankel transform, through coordinate transformation, displacement and stresses can be written as

$$u_x = -\frac{c}{\mu}\left[-(1-2\nu)\frac{x}{\rho} + 3\frac{xz^2}{\rho^3}\right],\quad u_y = -\frac{c}{\mu}\left[-(1-2\nu)\frac{y}{\rho} + 3\frac{yz^2}{\rho^3}\right]$$

$$u_z = -\frac{c}{\mu}\left[-(1-2\nu)\frac{z}{\rho} + 3\frac{z^3}{\rho^3}\right]$$

$$\sigma_{xx} = -\frac{2c}{\rho}\left[2(1-\nu) - 3(1-2\nu)\frac{y^2}{\rho^2} - 15\frac{x^2z^2}{\rho^4}\right]$$

$$\sigma_{yy} = -\frac{2c}{\rho}\left[2(1-\nu) - 3(1-2\nu)\frac{x^2}{\rho^2} - 15\frac{y^2z^2}{\rho^4}\right] \tag{5}$$

$$\sigma_{zz} = -\frac{2c}{\rho}\left[1 + 6\frac{z^2}{\rho^2} - 15\frac{z^4}{\rho^4}\right], \quad \sigma_{xy} = -\frac{2c}{\rho}\left[3(1-2\nu)\frac{xy}{\rho^2} - 15\frac{xyz^2}{\rho^4}\right]$$

$$\sigma_{zx} = -\frac{2c}{\rho}\left[3\frac{xy}{\rho^2} - 15\frac{xz^3}{\rho^4}\right], \quad \sigma_{yz} = -\frac{2c}{\rho}\left[3\frac{yz}{\rho^2} - 15\frac{yz^3}{\rho^4}\right]$$

where $c = \mu/\{8\pi(1-\nu)\rho^2\}$, $\rho = \sqrt{r^2 + z^2}$.

1.3 Elastic Field of Tangential Dislocation

Considering the same problems as mentioned above, suppose that a tangential uniform dislocation D_x is dispersed over the crack surface and $D_x \pi a^2 = 1$ as $a \to 0$. Similarly, $D_x = \delta(r)$. The problem is antisymmetric and can be solved by using the method recommended by Dr. Muki. According to its antisymmetric character with respect to the plane $z=0$, the upper half space $z>0$ will be taken into consideration. The boundary conditions of cylindrical coordinate system (r, θ, z) can be written as

$$\sigma_{ij}\Big|_{\sqrt{r^2+z^2}\to\infty} = 0, \quad \sigma_{zz}\Big|_{z=0} = 0, \quad u_r\Big|_{z=0} = \frac{1}{2}\delta(r)\cos\theta, \quad u_\theta\Big|_{z=0} = -\frac{1}{2}\delta(r)\sin\theta$$

Dr. Muki gave the displacement and stress fields as

$$u_x = \frac{c}{\mu}\left[(1-2\nu)\frac{z}{\rho} + 3\frac{zx^2}{\rho^3}\right], \quad u_y = -\frac{c}{\mu}\left[3\frac{xyz}{\rho^3}\right],$$

$$u_z = -\frac{c}{\mu}\left[(1-2\nu)\frac{x}{\rho} + 3\frac{xz^2}{\rho^3}\right]$$

$$\sigma_{xx} = -\frac{2c}{\rho}\left[3\frac{xz}{\rho^2} - 15\frac{x^3z}{\rho^4}\right], \quad \sigma_{yy} = -\frac{2c}{\rho}\left[3(1-2\nu)\frac{xz}{\rho^2} - 15\frac{xzy^2}{\rho^4}\right]$$

$$\sigma_{zz} = -\frac{2c}{\rho}\left[3\frac{xz}{\rho^2} - 15\frac{x^3z}{\rho^4}\right], \sigma_{xy} = -\frac{2c}{\rho}\left[3\nu\frac{yz}{\rho^2} - 15\frac{yzx^2}{\rho^4}\right]$$

$$\sigma_{zx} = -\frac{2c}{\rho}\left[2(1+\nu) - 3\nu\frac{y^2}{\rho^2} - 15\frac{x^2y^2}{\rho^4}\right], \sigma_{yz} = -\frac{2c}{\rho}\left[3\nu\frac{xy}{\rho^2} - 15\frac{xyz^2}{\rho^4}\right]$$

2 Singular Integral Equations

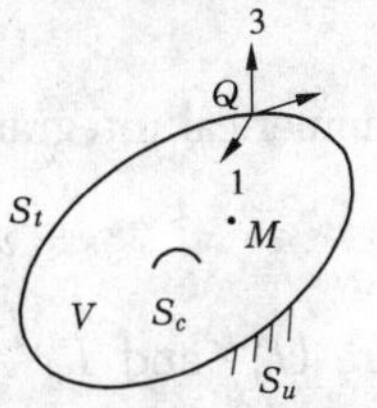

Fig. 1 Symbol

In Fig. 1, an elastic body containing a crack S_c with the boundary $S_b = S_t + S_u$, in which S_t and S_u denote stress and displacement boundary conditions correspondingly. Also take the crack surface S_c as a part of the boundary, and denote $S = S_b + S_c$. Suppose that V is a portion of infinite elastic region with the dislocation $D_j(Q), (j = 1, 2, 3)$ distributed on S, by the superposition principle the displacements and stresses at the point M in V (in the absence of body force) can be written as

$$U_i(M) = \int_S \overline{U}_{ik}(M, Q)D_k(Q)\mathrm{d}S(Q), \quad \sigma_{ij}(M) = \int_S \overline{T}_{ijk}(M, Q)D_k(Q)\mathrm{d}S(Q) \tag{6}$$

where $\overline{U}_{ik}(M,Q)$ denotes the displacements in the direction i at the point M, caused by a unit dislocation emerging in the direction k at the point Q, $\overline{T}_{ijk}(M,Q)$ represents stress components at M, induced by unit dislocation at Q in k direction.

As the point M locates on the boundary S, the point M will be renamed as p to distinguish with the inner points, then we have

$$U_i(p) = \int_S \overline{U}_i(p,Q)D_k(Q)\mathrm{d}S(Q) + C\delta_{ik}D_k(Q), \sigma_{ij}(p) = \int_S \overline{T}_{ijk}(p,Q)D_k(Q)\mathrm{d}S(Q) \tag{7}$$

where C is a coefficient, for the smooth boundary $C=1/2$, δ_{ij} is δ function. The distributive function $D_k(Q)$ of the dislocation can be solved from Eq. (7) by using the boundary conditions on S, and the displacements and stresses at any point in the region can be further obtained from the Eq. (6). It is easy to write out the boundary conditions for the case shown in Fig. 1

$$U_i(p) = \overline{U}_i,\ p \in S_u; \qquad \sigma_{ij}(p)n_j = \overline{t}_i,\quad p \in S_t \text{ or } p \in S_c \tag{8}$$

where n_j denotes cosine of the direction at the boundary, $\overline{u}_i$ and $\overline{t}_i$ denote the known displacement and stress on the boundary respectively.

For crack problem in infinite region, the boundary conditions are

$$\sigma_{ij}(p)n_j + t_i^{\infty} = \overline{t}_i^c,\quad p \in S_c \tag{9}$$

where $t_i^{\infty} = \sigma_{ij}^{\infty}n_j$, σ_{ij}^{∞} are the stress components in the infinity; $\overline{t}_i^c$ is the tensile stress on the crack surface. It is very difficult to give analytical solutions directly according to case Eqs. (8) and (9) except for some special cases. So the numerical methods must be adopted. By discreting the boundary S into M triangular (or quadrilateral) elements, Eq. (8) can be expressed as

$$\begin{aligned}\overline{U}_i &= \sum_{n=1}^{M}\int_{\Delta S_n} \overline{U}_{ik}(p,Q_n)D_k(Q_n)\mathrm{d}S(Q_n) + C\delta_{ik}D_k(Q_n)\\ \overline{t}_i &= \sum_{n=1}^{M}\int_{\Delta S_n} \overline{T}_{ijk}(p,Q_n)D_k(Q_n)\mathrm{d}S(Q_n)n_j(p)\end{aligned} \tag{10}$$

By numerical integrating, following equations can be obtained for every node p

$$u_i^p = \sum_{n=1}^{M} U_{ij}^{n,k}D_j^{n,k} + \frac{1}{2}D_l^p, \qquad t_i^p = \sum_{n=1}^{M} T_{ij}^{n,k}D_j^{n,k} \tag{11}$$

where $U_{ij}^{n,k}$ and $T_{ij}^{n,k}$ are the influence coefficients of displacement and stress of node K in element N to node p respectively, and u_l^p and t_l^p denote the known displacements and tensions of node p in the direction i correspondingly. Similarly, in the case of infinite region, we have Eq. (12), Eqs. (11) and (12), can be written in form of matrix as Eq. (13)

$$t_l^p = t_i^{\infty,p} + \sum_{n=1}^{M} T_{ij}^{n,k}D_j^{n,k} \tag{12}$$

$$K\{D\} = \{R\} \tag{13}$$

in which $\{D\}$ is the dislocation vector of node, $\{R\}$ the load vector and K the coefficient matrix. In the process of numerical integrating the Eq. (10), the higher order singular integral will be encountered with the singularity of $1/r^3$, in the case as node p being in element N, the Kutt's method of finite part integration can be used to this singularity. In general, the triangular element, as shown in Fig. 2, is considered. Assume that the node p coincides with the node i of the triangular element. Then, a polar coordinate (r, θ) with origin i is introduced for convenience. According to the character of Kutt finite part integration, the integral $\int_{\Delta S_n} D/r^3 \mathrm{d}S_n$ is noted as denoting finite part integration, which can be expressed as

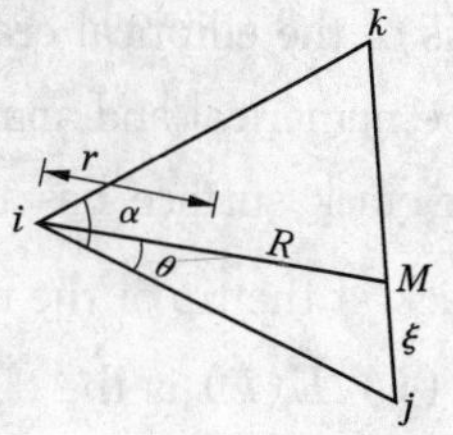

Fig. 2 Triangular element

$$\int_{\Delta S_n} \frac{D(Q_n)}{r^3} \mathrm{d}S(Q_n) = \int_0^\alpha \mathrm{d}\theta \int_0^{R(\theta)} \frac{D(r,\theta)}{r^2} \mathrm{d}r = -\int_0^\alpha \frac{D_i}{R(\theta)} \mathrm{d}\theta \tag{14}$$

$$-\int_0^1 \frac{D_i HL}{RR^2} \mathrm{d}\xi = -D_i HL \int_0^1 \frac{1}{R^3} \mathrm{d}\xi \tag{15}$$

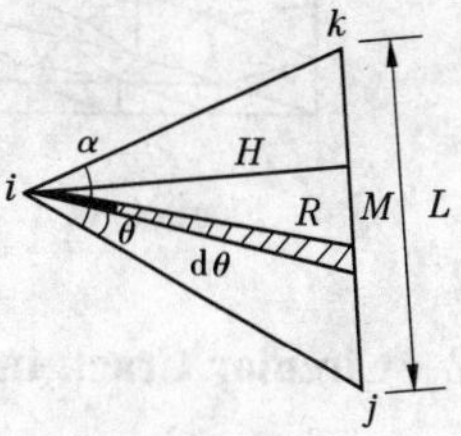

Fig. 3 Symbol

According to Fig. 3 (in which $\mathrm{d}\theta = (HL/R^2)\mathrm{d}\xi$), Eq. (14) can be reduced to Eq. (15), where H denotes the distance between node i and the side kj, L is the length of the side kj, and R is the distance between node i and point M, which is given by

$$R = \{[(1-\xi)x_j + \xi x_k - x_i]^2 + [(1-\xi)y_j + \xi y_k - y_i]^2 + [(1-\xi)z_j + \xi z_k - z_i]^2\}^{\frac{1}{2}}$$

where ξ is one of area coordinates of the triangular element. For quadrilateral element, it can be divided into two triangular elements, and then solved in the same way.

3 Stress Intensity Factor (SIF)

SIF can be calculated by using following formula:

$$-D_3\mu/(1+k) = K_{\mathrm{I}}\sqrt{r/2\pi}, \quad -D_2\mu/(1+k) = K_{\mathrm{II}}\sqrt{r/2\pi}$$
$$-D_1\mu/(1+k) = K_{\mathrm{III}}\sqrt{r/2\pi} \tag{16}$$

where D_1, D_2 and D_3 denote the three dislocations in the directions of x_1, x_2 and x_3 correspondingly; x_1 and x_2 denote two directions, tangential and normal, of the crack frontier, and x_3 denotes the perpendicular direction to the crack surface. $k = 3 - 4\nu$; μ denotes theshear modulus. Therefore, the SIF can be calculated by Eq. (16), if the dislocations near the crack frontier are known.

4 Examples

4.1 Elliptical Crack in An Infinite Region

The elements of elliptical crack is shown in Fig. 4, where $a/b = 2$, is the ratio of major axis of the elliptical crack. The crack is loaded by a uniform tensile stress σ in the infinity. The numerical and analytical results are compared in Fig.5. The opening displacement w of the crack surface has the maximum relative error less than 4%. The SIF of the elliptical crack at the tip of the major axis is obtained to be $K_{\mathrm{I}}/K_{\mathrm{I}}^{*}=1.0206$, where $K_{\mathrm{I}}^{*}=\sigma\sqrt{\pi a}/E(k)$, $E(k)$ is the elliptical integration of the second kind. e is the tip of crack.

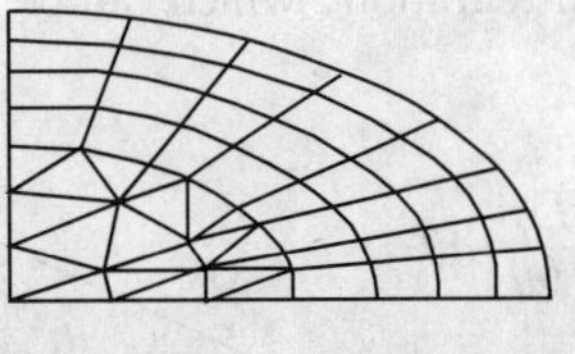

Fig.4 Elements of 1/4 elliptical crack

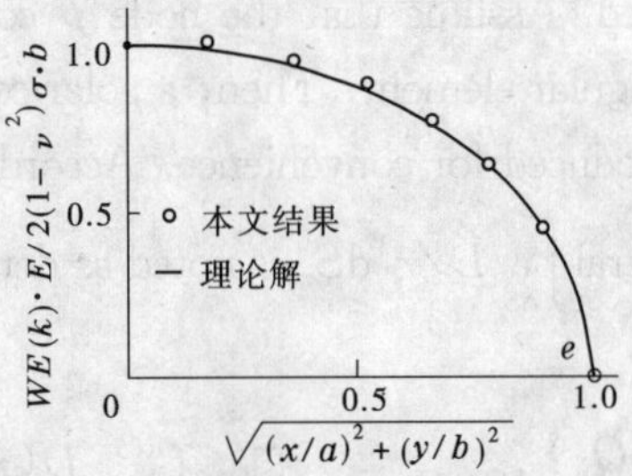

Fig.5 Openning displacement of elliptical crack surface under tension

4.2 Circular Crack in a Cube

A cube with edge length of $10a$ is considered in this example, and in the center of cube there is a circular crack with diameter of $2a$. The place of the crack is parallel to the upper and lower surface of the cube (Fig.6), on which uniform tension σ is applied. According to symmetry character, only one eighth of the cube is analyzed. SIF is given as $K_{\mathrm{I}}/K_{\mathrm{I}}^{\infty}=1.039$, $K_{\mathrm{I}}^{\infty}=2\sigma\sqrt{a/\pi}$ is SIF of a circular crack in a infinity.

5 Discussion

Based on superposition of elastic fields induced by unit concentrated dislocations, a singular integral equation method is proposed for solving 3-D crack problems. Simple elliptical crack in infinity and circular crack in finite body were used for precision check. Results given by proposed method in the present paper are in good agreement with the theoretical. The proposed method can give accurate results of stress, displacement and SIF value for complicated shape of 3-D crack with arbitrary stress and displacement conditions. It is also suitable for solving multi-crack problems in finite body with less computing time.

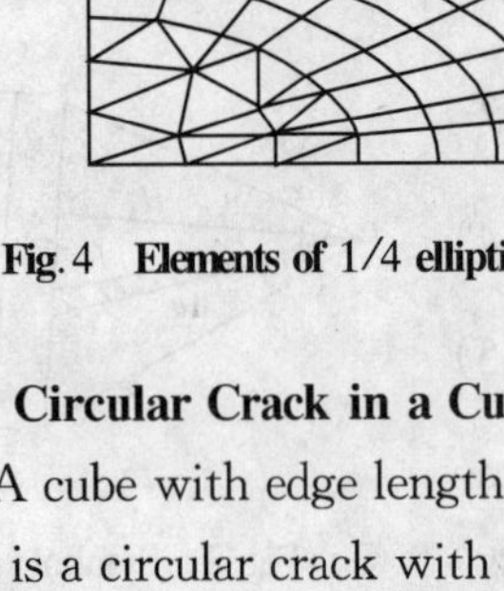

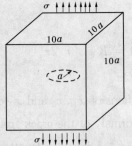

Fig.6 Cube with circular crack

References

[1] Ioakimidis N I. *Application of finite-part integrals for the singular integral equations for crack problems in plane and three dimensional elasticity*. Acta Mechanica, 1982, 45:31～47

[2] 刘光廷,林潮熙. 弹性力学问题的第二类边界积分方程——边界元法及其二维基本解. 清华大学学报,1988,28(2):61～72

[3] Kutt K R. *Quadrature formula for finite-part integrals*. Report WISK-178, The National Research Institute for Mathematical Science, Pretoria, 1975

三维热传导问题的间接边界元法

摘　要　以三维无限域内单位强度点热源作用的温度场为基本解，用二维虚拟热源法求解三维热传导问题的稳态温度场。由于间接边界元方法的数值离散特性，应用二次非协调单元简便可行地解决了数值计算中的角域问题和边界点法向取值不确定问题。对于含 r^{-1} 的奇异积分取其柯西主值积分，含 r^{-2} 的奇异积分由间接方法求得。算例表明此方法有很高的精度。为碾压混凝土拱坝仿真计算提供了有力工具。

关键词　虚拟热源　间接边界元法　二次非协调单元　温度场　角域

1963 年，M. A. Jaswon[1] 用单层位势理论求解拉普拉斯方程，开创了间接边界元法，此法在位势问题上得到了较广泛的应用。它避免了有限单元法对区域内进行离散，只需在域边界上进行离散，大大减小了离散工作量，更便于实际应用。对于稳态热传导问题，用间接边界元法求解温度场可采用无限大域内单位强度点热源作用的温度场作为基本解的虚拟热源法。文献[2]对平面问题的虚拟热源法进行了研究。本文从理论和数值方法上推广应用至三维稳态热传导问题的求解。

1　虚拟热源法的边界积分方程

(1)无限大域内单位强度点热源作用的温度场。设无限大域内点 $Q(a,b,c)$ 处作用有单位强度热源，由稳态热传导基本方程，域内温度 T 必须满足方程

$$\alpha\left(\frac{\partial^2 T}{\partial x^2}+\frac{\partial^2 T}{\partial y^2}+\frac{\partial^2 T}{\partial z^2}\right)+\delta(x-a)\delta(y-b)\delta(z-c)=0 \tag{1}$$

其解为

$$T(x,y,z)=1/(4\pi kr) \tag{2}$$

式中：α 为导温系数；$r=[(x-a)^2+(y-b)^2+(z-c)^2]^{\frac{1}{2}}$ 为场点 (x,y,z) 至源点 $Q(a,b,c)$ 的距离；δ 为 Dirac 函数；k 为导热系数。由此可得热流密度

$$q(x,y,z)=-k\frac{\partial T}{\partial n}=-k\frac{\partial T\partial r}{\partial r\partial n}=\frac{1}{4\pi r^2}[(x-a)n_x+(y-b)n_y+(z-c)n_z] \tag{3}$$

式中：n 为场点 (x,y,z) 处的外法向。

式(2)、式(3)为虚拟热源法的间接边界元法基本解。

(2)设有一各向同性不含内热源的导热体，其域为 Ω，边界为 $\Gamma=\Gamma_T+\Gamma_q$，见图 1。其温度 T 必须满足热传导方程和边界条件：

$$\begin{cases}\dfrac{\partial^2 T}{\partial x^2}+\dfrac{\partial^2 T}{\partial y^2}+\dfrac{\partial^2 T}{\partial z^2}=0 & \Omega\\ T=\overline{T} & \Gamma_T\\ q=\overline{q} & \Gamma_q\end{cases} \tag{4}$$

本文选自《清华大学学报(自然科学版)》1996 年第 1 期，作者还有邱德隆。

将域 Ω 视为无限域的一部分,设域 Ω 边界 Γ 上作用有分布虚拟热源 $\omega(S)$,这域 Ω 内任意点 M 的温度和热流密度分别为

$$T(M) = \int_{\Gamma} T^*(M,S)\omega(S)\mathrm{d}\Gamma(S) \quad (5)$$

$$q(M) = \int_{\Gamma} q^*(M,S)\omega(S)\mathrm{d}\Gamma(S) \quad (6)$$

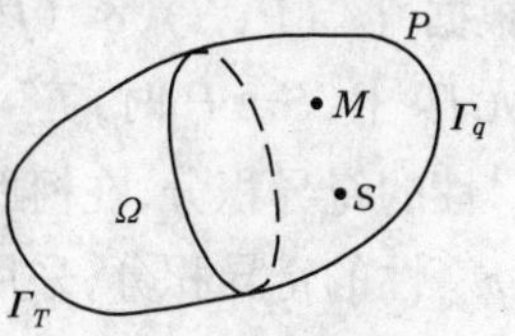

图 1　符号示意图

式中:$T^*(M,S)$为(1)中温度场基本解,即当 S 点作用单位强度热源时 M 点处的温度值;$q^*(M,S)$为(1)中热流密度基本解,即当 S 点作用单位强度热源时 M 点处的热流密度值。

虚拟分布热源 $\omega(S)$为未知数,一旦求得,由式(5)、式(6)即可求得域 Ω 内任一点的温度和热流密度值。

当域内点 M 趋于边界点 P 时,即得到边界积分方程

$$T(P) = \int_{\Gamma} T^*(P,S)\omega(S)\mathrm{d}\Gamma(S) \tag{7}$$

$$(1-\alpha)q(P) = \int_{\Gamma} q^*(P,S)\omega(S)\mathrm{d}\Gamma(S) \tag{8}$$

式中:α 是与边界面在 P 点处的几何特征有关的系数,对于光滑边界条件为 1/2。引入边界条件:$P\in\Gamma_T$ 时,$T(P)=\overline{T}$;$P\in\Gamma_q$ 时,$q(P)=\overline{q}$。便可求得虚拟热源 $\omega(S)$,从而由式(5)、式(6)可求得域内值。

2　边界积分方程的离散及数值处理

显然对于一般问题,不可能求得式(7)、式(8)的解析解。为求式(7)、式(8)的数值解,将整个边界 $\Gamma=\Gamma_T+\Gamma_q$ 划分成 n 个单元:

$$\Gamma=\sum_{i=1}^{n}\Gamma_i \tag{9}$$

其中:$\Gamma_1,\Gamma_2,\cdots,\Gamma_m\in\Gamma_T,\Gamma_{m+1},\Gamma_{m+2},\cdots,\Gamma_n\in\Gamma_q$。

在 i 单元 Γ_i 上设定一定的虚拟热源分布 $\omega^i(\zeta)$,采用一定的插值函数,则 i 单元内的虚拟热源分布值 ω' 可用单元节点处虚拟热源值表示

$$\omega^i(\zeta)=\sum_{j=1}^{l}N_j(\zeta)\omega_j(\zeta_j^i) \tag{10}$$

式中:l 表示单元 i 中的节点数;ζ 为局部坐标矢量;ζ_j 表示单元 i 内节点 j 局部坐标矢量值;$N_j(\zeta)$表示节点 j 的形函数;$\omega_j(\zeta_j^i)$表示节点 j 的虚拟热源值。

将式(10)代入边界积分方程式(7)、式(8),得到离散后的边界积分方程

$$T(P) = \sum_{i=1}^{n}\int_{\Gamma_i}\sum_{j=1}^{l}N_j(\zeta)\omega_j(\zeta_j^i)T^*(P,\zeta)\mathrm{d}\Gamma(\zeta) \tag{11}$$

$$(1-a)q(P) = \sum_{i=1}^{n}\int_{\Gamma_i}\sum_{j=1}^{l}N_j(\zeta)\omega_j(\zeta_j^i)q^*(P,\zeta)\mathrm{d}\Gamma(\zeta) \tag{12}$$

以单元节点处虚拟热源值 ω_j 为未知量,引入边界条件,即可解得 ω_j。

根据 $T^*(P,S)$，$q^*(P,S)$的特性，式(11)、式(12)是两组奇异积分方程。当 P 点位于单元Γ_i 上，$S\to P$ 时，$T^*(P,S)$，$q^*(P,S)$分别具有 r^{-1}、$r^{-2}(r\to0)$性的奇异性。对于 r^{-1}性的奇异积分，在柯西主值意义下是收敛的，取其柯西主值意义下的积分值[3]；而对于 r^{-2}性的奇异积分，采用间接方法求得，即当整个边界上作用均匀势时，边界上的法向异数 q 值之和必须为零。

注意式(12)中 $q^*(P,\zeta)=(4\pi r^2)^{-1}(x_{p_s}n_x+y_{p_x}n_y+z_{p_s}n_z)$，其中法向 n_x、n_y、n_z 为场点P 处的外法向。通常对边界进行离散，采用协调单元，但对任意形状边界上点的法向是不易取得的，而且对于图 2 所示不光滑边界上点和尖角点处其外法向 n 是不确定值，即在 l_1、l_2、l_3 上点 1,2,3,4 考虑不同面 Γ_{12}，Γ_{23}，Γ_{31}时有不同外法向 n 值。为解决这个问题，采用新的非协调单元进行离散处理。

设单元 e 边界上点外法向不能确定，按协调等参单元变换，见图 3 由 $1^e\to2^e$，则单元内变量(含函数值和坐标)可表示成

$$\Phi(\xi_1,\xi_2)=\sum_{i=1}^{8}N_i(\xi_1,\xi_2)\Phi_{i'} \tag{13}$$

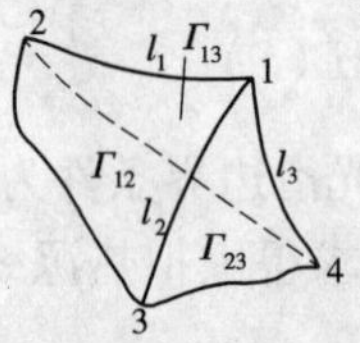

图 2 符号示意图

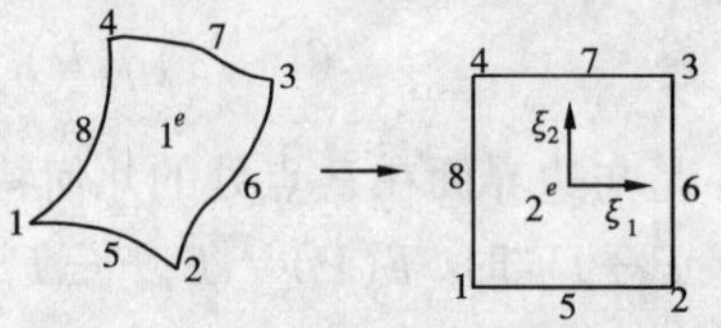

图 3 单元节点号

式中：Φ 为单元内变量；Φ_i 为节点 i 变量值；N_i 为等参变换节点 i 形函数；ξ_1、ξ_2 为局部坐标。

另作如图 4 的 $3^e\to4^e$ 变换，单元等参变换为

$$\Phi'(\xi_1,\xi_2)=\sum_{i=1}^{8}N'_i(\xi_1,\xi_2)\Phi_{i'} \tag{14}$$

式中：Φ'为单元内变量；N'_i 为等参变换节点 i'的形函数；$\Phi_{i'}$ 为节点 i'变量值。令

$$\Phi_{i'}=\sum_{k=1}^{8}N_k(\xi_1^{i'},\xi_2^{i'})\Phi_k \quad (i=1,2,\cdots,8) \tag{15}$$

式中：$\xi_1^{i'}$、$\xi_2^{i'}$ 分别为 $1^e\to2^e$ 变换中 i'点处 ξ_1、ξ_2 坐标值；N_k 为 $1^e\to2^e$ 变换中形函数，Φ_k 为式(13)中 $\Phi_i{}'$。

现证明式(13)和式(14)是一致的，即

$$\Phi'(\xi_1,\xi_2)=\sum_{i=1}^{8}N'_i(\xi_1,\xi_2)\Phi_{i'}=\sum_{i=1}^{8}N'_i(\xi_1,\xi_2)\sum_{k=1}^{8}N_k(\xi_1^{i'},\xi_2^{i'})\Phi_k$$

$$=\sum_{i=1}^{8}N_k(\xi_1,\xi_2)\Phi_k \tag{16}$$

不失一般性，考虑图 5 所示的一维线性单元。则单元上变量可表示为

$$\Phi(\xi)=N_1\Phi_1+N_2\Phi_2 \tag{17}$$

式中：$N_1=0.5(1-\xi)$，$N_2=0.5(1+\xi)$。根据式(15)可得

$$\Phi_{1'} = N_1(\xi^{1'})\Phi_1 + N_2(\xi^{1'})\Phi_2 \tag{18}$$

$$\Phi_{2'} = N_1(\xi^{2'})\Phi_1 + N_2(\xi^{2'})\Phi_2 \tag{19}$$

根据式(14)单元上变量又可表示成

$$\Phi'(\xi) = N'_{1'}(\xi)\Phi_{1'} + N'_{2'}(\xi)\Phi_{2'} \tag{20}$$

$$N'_i(\xi) = (\xi - \xi^{2'})/(\xi^{1'} - \xi^{2'});\qquad N'_2(\xi) = (\xi - \xi^{1'})/(\xi^{2'} - \xi^{1'}) \tag{21}$$

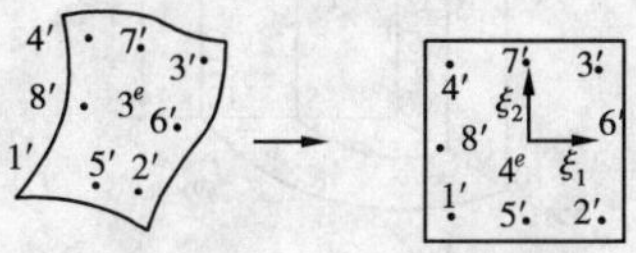

图 4 单元高斯点

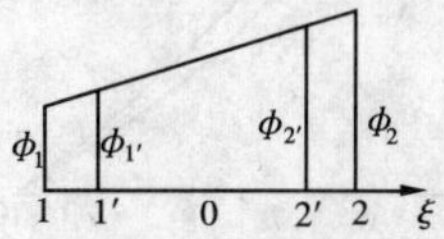

图 5 线性单元

将式(18)、式(19)代入式(20)可得

$$\Phi'(\xi) = [N'_{1'}(\xi)N_1(\xi^{1'}) + N'_{2'}(\xi)N_1(\xi^{2'})]\Phi_1 + [N'_{1'}(\xi)N_2(\xi^{1'}) + N'_{2'}(\xi)N_2(\xi^{2'})]\Phi_2 \tag{22}$$

代入式(15)、式(21)即可推得

$$\Phi'(\xi) = N_1(\xi)\Phi_1 + N_2(\xi)\Phi_2 = \Phi(\xi)$$

既然由式(13)、式(14)决定的 Φ 值是相等的,由此在边界离散时,作如下处理:

(1) 输入单元为 1^e,其对应的等参变换为 $1^e \to 2^e$,即式(13);

(2) 计算单元为 3^e,其对应的等参变换为 $3^e \to 4^e$,$1^e \to 3^e$ 之间满足式(15)。

通过(1)、(2),将协调单元转变成非协调单元,使计算单元的节点不落在单元边界上,即可解决因不光滑边界带来 α 值计算的不易,以及边界处节点不确定法向 n 的处理。由 $1^e \to 3^e$ 所增加的计算机计算量相对很小。

3 计算例证

根据边界积分方程式(7)、式(8)以及积分方程的离散和数值处理,计算厚壁球和厚壁圆筒的稳态热传导问题。

(1)壁厚球。内半径 $r_a = 5\text{m}$,外半径 $r_b = 10\text{m}$,内球面温度为 $T_a = 10℃$,外球面温度为 $T_b = 0℃$,球壳内温度分布数值为

$$T = 100/r - 10$$

根据对称性取球壳 1/8 作计算,沿径向面边界条件为绝热 $q = 0$,见图 6。沿径向划分 5 个单元,沿周向最多 6 个单元。计算值与解析值比较见图 7。可以看出两者吻合很好,其中最大绝对误差不超过0.2℃。

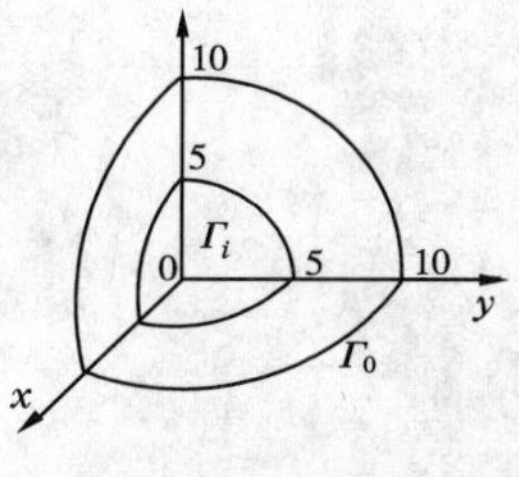

图 6 球壳内温度沿半径分布

(2)厚壁无限长圆筒。内径 $r_a = 5\text{m}$,外径 $r_b = 10\text{m}$,内壁温度为 10℃,外壁温度为 0℃,柱壁内温度分布数值为 $T = 10[1 - (\ln r - \ln 5)/\ln 2]$,由对称性取 1/4 圆筒,轴向取 5 倍

内径长。沿径向划分 5 个单元,沿周向为 9 个单元,见图 8。计算值和解析值比较见图 7。其中最大绝对误差不超过 0.2℃。

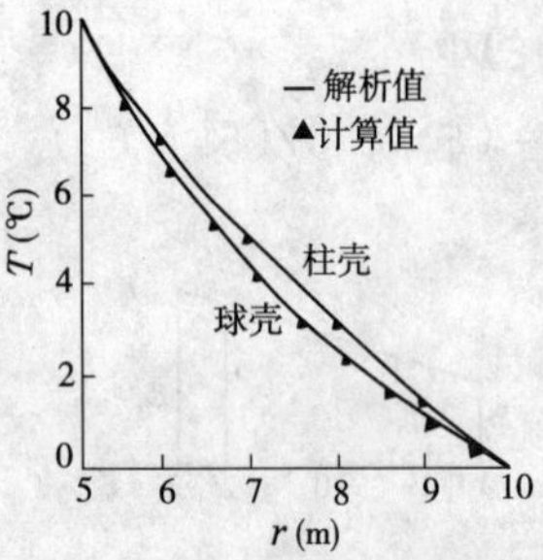

图 7　球、柱壳温度分布解

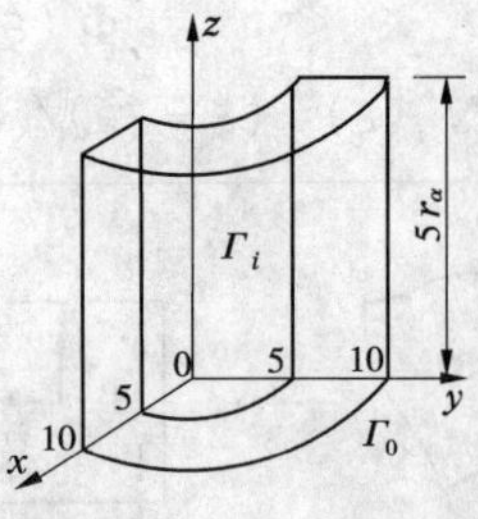

图 8　厚壁圆筒温度分布

参 考 文 献

[1] Jaswon M A, Symm G T. *Integral equation methods in potential theory and elaslostatics*. Academic Press, 1977

[2] Zhang G X, Liu G T. *Thermally stressed multiples system in steady state*. *Theoretical and Applied Fracture Mechanics*. 1992,17: 69～81

[3] Rizzo F J, Shippy D J. *An advanced boundary integral equation method for three-dimensional thermoelasticity*. Int J for Num Meth in Eng, 1977, 11:1231～1247

不连续位移超奇异积分方程法解三维多裂纹问题

摘　要　本文采用 Betti 互等功定理,导出了三维不连续位移基本解的一般形式,然后以该基本解为核函数,建立了求解三维多裂纹问题的超奇异边界积分方程组,并采用三角形单元变换技术和有限部分积分的方法给出了超奇异积分的数值解法,引入非协调单元处理技术解决了法向不确定的角点问题。最后,由裂纹面间断位移可直接求得裂纹前沿任意点的应力强度因子。

关键词　不连续位移　基本解　超奇异积分方程法　有限部分积分　三维多裂纹

实际工程结构中,特别是大型水工建筑物中往往出现复杂的多裂纹问题,如温度裂纹等,其中有些裂纹甚至危及结构的安全,因此迫切需要研究三维多裂纹问题的有效分析方法。分析这类问题的有限元法因工作量巨大,以 Kelvin 基本解[1]为核函数的边界积分方程—直接边界元法因需分域处理,优越性遭到破坏,其应用均受到限制。以点源不连续位移[2]为基本解的不连续位移法及其相应的 Cauchy 型奇异积分方程法[3]能有效地模拟裂纹面和其他软弱面的间断位移,在平面断裂力学问题和岩石力学问题中得到了广泛的应用。但是在三维断裂力学问题中,超奇异边界积分方程的数值计算遇到了困难。自 Iaokimidis[4]将有限部分积分[5]的概念和方法引入断裂力学并成功地求解了超奇异积分方程以后,许多学者[6~9]对这种超奇异积分方程的性质、解法及其在三维单裂纹问题中的应用等作了大量的研究,显示了广阔的应用前景。因此,有必要进一步研究和探讨这类解法。本文将建立可以有效地求解一般三维多裂纹问题的超奇异边界积分方程及其数值解法。

1　三维不连续位移基本解的一般形式

文献[10]、[11]采用 Hankel 积分变换法导出了三维不连续位移基本解的分量形式,由于用到了超几何级数和超越函数,推导过程相当复杂,运算量很大。其实,这种三维不连续位移基本解可由三维弹性力学中著名的 Kelvin 基本解,根据互等功定理能很容易地导出。

考虑同一个三维无限大弹性介质中含有任意两点 Q、P 的两个不同的真实状态。定义 Q 点位移间断时其微元 ΔS 上 k 方向的间断位移或不连续位移为

$$D_k(Q)=u_k(Q^-)-u_k(Q^+)\qquad (k=1\sim 3) \tag{1}$$

式中:± 号表示间断微元面 ΔS 的正负两侧。本文约定英文下标 i、j、k、l 分别取值 1~3,均与物体中所选定的整体坐标 x_1,x_2,x_3 或 x,y,z 相对应。

本文选自《工程力学》1997 年第 2 期,作者还有朱先奎。

状态 1:令 Q 点邻域内存在一微小的位移间断面 ΔS,其法向为 $n_l(Q^{\pm})$。假设在 Q 点沿 k 方向作用一间断位移 $D_k(Q)$,则在 P 点 i 方向产生的位移为 $u_i(P)$,而微元两侧的面力分别为 $t_k(Q^+)$ 和 $t_k(Q^-)$。假如 $D_k(Q)=1$ 时,位移 $u_i(P)$ 用 $\overline{u}_{ik}(P,Q)$ 表示,则当 $D_k(Q)\neq 1$ 时,$u_i(P)$ 可以表示为

$$u_i(P) = \int_{\Delta S} \overline{u}_{ik}(P,Q) D_k(Q) \mathrm{d}S(Q) \tag{2}$$

状态 2:域内无间断点,Q 点处位移连续。用一假想平面将 Q 点切开成法向为 $n_l(Q^{\pm})$ 的一微元 ΔS。假设在 P 点 i 方向作用一集中力 F_i,则在 Q 点微元上 k 方向产生的面力为 $T_k(Q^+)$ 和 $T_k(Q^-)$,位移为 $U_k(Q^+)$ 和 $U_k(Q^-)$。

由 Betti 互等功定理:第一状态的作用力在第二状态的位移上所做的功等于第二状态的作用力在第一状态的位移上所做的功。考虑到第一状态 Q 点微元上的面力为平衡力系,第二状态 Q 点微元上的位移连续,于是有

$$F_i(P)u_i(P) + \int_{\Delta S} T_k(Q^+)u_k(Q^+)\mathrm{d}S(Q) + \int_{\Delta S} T_k(Q^-)u_k(Q^-)\mathrm{d}S(Q) = 0 \tag{3}$$

其中:当 $F_i(P)=1$ 时,面力 $T_k(Q^{\pm})$ 就是三维弹性力学中著名的 Kelvin 基本解[1],本文记为 $\overline{T}_{ki}(Q^{\pm},P)$,其表达式如下:

$$\overline{T}_{ki}(Q^{\pm},P) = -\frac{1}{8\pi(1-\nu)r^2}\{(1-2\nu)[\delta_{ik}r_{,l} + \delta_{il}r_{,k} - \delta_{lk}r_{,i}] + 3r_{,j}r_{,k}r_{,l}\}n_l(Q^{\pm}) \tag{4}$$

式中:$r=r(Q,P)=\|\vec{r}(Q)-\vec{r}(P)\|$;$r_{,i}=r_{,i}(Q,P)=(x_{iQ}-x_{iP})/r$;$\nu$ 为材料的泊松比;δ_{ij} 为 Kronecker delta 符号,重复指标符合常规的求和法则。

在功的平衡方程式(3)中,令 $F_i(P)=1$,注意到第二状态 Q 点微元上的面力大小相等、方向相反,利用间断位移的定义式(1),可得

$$u_i(P) = -\int_{\Delta S} \overline{T}_{ki}(Q^-,P) D_k(Q) \mathrm{d}S(Q) \tag{5}$$

比较式(5)和式(2),即得

$$\overline{u}_{ik}(P,Q) = -\overline{T}_{ki}(Q^-,P) \tag{6}$$

该式表明了三维不连续位移基本解和 Kelvin 基本解之间存在的简单关系,其中负号表示 P、Q 两点的两相对矢径方向相反。式(6)的物理意义是,在 Q 点 k 方向作用一单位不连续位移时,在 P 点 i 方向产生的位移就等于在 P 点 i 方向作用一单位力时在 Q 点微元面 $\Delta S(Q^-)$ 上 k 方向的面力。

由三维弹性力学的几何方程和 Hooke 定理,可以得到由位移分量表示的应力分量如下:

$$\sigma_{ij} = \mu(u_{i,j} + u_{j,i}) + \frac{2\mu\nu}{1-2\nu}u_{k,k}\delta_{ij} \tag{7}$$

式中:μ 为剪切模量。

利用位移基本解式(6),由方程(7)可很容易地求得该问题的应力分量,进而求得面力分量。记在 Q 点沿 k 方向作用单位不连续位移时,在域内点 P 产生的应力分量为

$\bar{\sigma}_{ijk}(P,Q)$,在边界点 p 沿 i 方向产生的面力分量为 $\bar{t}_{ik}(p,Q)$,则三维不连续位移基本解(包括位移、应力和面力分量)的最一般形式如下:

$$\bar{u}_{ik}(P,Q)=-\frac{1}{8\pi(1-\nu)r^2}\{(1-2\nu)[\delta_{ik}r_{,l}+\delta_{il}r_{,k}-\delta_{kl}r_{,i}]+3r_{,i}r_{,k}r_{,l}\}n_l(Q^-) \tag{8}$$

$$\begin{aligned}\bar{\sigma}_{ijk}(P,Q)=-\frac{\mu}{4\pi(1-\nu)r^3}\{&(1-2\nu)[\delta_{ik}\delta_{jl}+\delta_{il}\delta_{jk}]-(1-4\nu)\delta_{ij}\delta_{kl}+3\nu[\delta_{ik}r_{,l}r_{,j}+\\&\delta_{il}r_{,k}r_{,j}+\delta_{jk}r_{,l}r_{,i}+\delta_{jl}r_{,k}r_{,i}]+3(1-2\nu)[\delta_{ij}r_{,k}r_{,l}+\delta_{kl}r_{,i}r_{,j}]-\\&15r_{,i}r_{,j}r_{,k}r_{,l}\}n_l(Q^-)\end{aligned} \tag{9}$$

$$\bar{t}_{ik}(p,Q)=\bar{\sigma}_{ijk}(p,Q)n_j(p) \tag{10}$$

其中:Q 点为作用源点;P 点为任意考察点。

矢径的模和偏导数分别为

$$r=\|\vec{r}(P,Q)\|=[(x_{ip}-x_{iQ})(x_{ip}-x_{iQ})]^{1/2},\qquad r_{,i}=\frac{(x_{ip}-x_{iQ})}{r} \tag{11}$$

如果不连续位移点 Q 就是整体直角坐标的原点,并且 Q 点微元面的法向与 x_3 或 z 轴重合,则由式(8)和式(9)展开后,即可得到分量形式的三维不连续位移基本解的位移场和应力场。例如,Q 点 z 方向作用单位法向不连续位移时,位移基本解为

$$\left.\begin{aligned}\bar{u}_x&=\bar{u}_{13}=\frac{1}{8\pi(1-\nu)}\cdot\frac{x}{r^3}\left[(1-2\nu)-\frac{3z^2}{r^2}\right]\\\bar{u}_y&=\bar{u}_{23}=\frac{1}{8\pi(1-\nu)}\cdot\frac{y}{r^3}\left[(1-2\nu)-\frac{3z^2}{r^2}\right]\\\bar{u}_z&=\bar{u}_{33}=-\frac{1}{8\pi(1-\nu)}\cdot\frac{z}{r^3}\left[(1-2\nu)+\frac{3z^2}{r^2}\right]\end{aligned}\right\} \tag{12}$$

应力基本解为

$$\left.\begin{aligned}\bar{\sigma}_{xx}&=\bar{\sigma}_{113}=-\frac{\mu}{4\pi(1-\nu)}\cdot\frac{1}{r^3}\left[2(1-\nu)-3(1-2\nu)\frac{y^2}{r^2}-\frac{15x^2z^2}{r^4}\right]\\\bar{\sigma}_{yy}&=\bar{\sigma}_{223}=-\frac{\mu}{4\pi(1-\nu)}\cdot\frac{1}{r^3}\left[2(1-\nu)-3(1-2\nu)\frac{x^2}{r^2}-\frac{15y^2z^2}{r^4}\right]\\\bar{\sigma}_{zz}&=\bar{\sigma}_{333}=-\frac{\mu}{4\pi(1-\nu)}\cdot\frac{1}{r^3}\left[1+6\frac{z^2}{r^2}-\frac{15z^4}{r^4}\right]\\\bar{\sigma}_{xy}&=\bar{\sigma}_{123}=-\frac{3\mu}{4\pi(1-\nu)}\cdot\frac{xy}{r^5}\left[(1-2\nu)-\frac{5z^2}{r^2}\right]\\\bar{\sigma}_{yz}&=\bar{\sigma}_{233}=-\frac{3\mu}{4\pi(1-\nu)}\cdot\frac{yz}{r^5}\left[1-\frac{5z^2}{r^2}\right]\\\bar{\sigma}_{zx}&=\bar{\sigma}_{313}=-\frac{3\mu}{4\pi(1-\nu)}\cdot\frac{xz}{r^5}\left[1-\frac{5z^2}{r^2}\right]\end{aligned}\right\} \tag{13}$$

上两式中,(x,y,z)为考察点 P 的坐标,$r=\sqrt{x^2+y^2+z^2}$ 为考察点 P 和源点Q之间的径向距离。通过比较不难发现,以上三维不连续位移基本解的分量形式如式(12)、式(13)和文献[10]、[11]采用 Hankel 积分变换法所导出的结果完全相同,但是本文的推导方法却简单得多,而且可以将这种基本解的一般张量形式和分量形式同时给出。

2 不连续位移超奇异边界积分方程

令三维有限体 Ω 的外边界由应力边界 Γ_t 和位移边界 Γ_u 组成,裂纹边界为 Γ_c,则该问题的边界定义为 $\Gamma=\Gamma_t+\Gamma_u+\Gamma_c$。假设不连续位移源点 q 作用在边界 Γ 上,根据间接边界元法的基本思想和叠加原理,由三维不连续位移基本解式(8)~式(10),域内任意考察点 P 的位移和应力分量可分别表示如下:

$$\begin{aligned} u_i(P) &= \int_\Gamma \bar{u}_{ik}(P,q)D_k(q)\mathrm{d}S(q) \\ \sigma_{ij}(P) &= \int_\Gamma \bar{\sigma}_{ijk}(P,q)D_k(q)\mathrm{d}S(q) \end{aligned} \tag{14}$$

式中:$\bar{u}_{ik}(P,q)$、$\bar{\sigma}_{ijk}(P,q)$分别表示在边界 q 点作用单位不连续位移时在内点 P 产生的位移和应力,其表达式分别为式(8)和式(9);$D_k(q)$为边界上连续分布的虚拟不连续位移函数。不过,对于裂纹边界,$D_k(q)$则为真实的不连续位移。

当域内考察点 P 位于边界 Γ 上的边界 p 点时,式(14)即变为以不连续位移基本解为核函数的奇异边界积分方程

$$\begin{aligned} u_i(p) &= \bar{u}_i = \int_\Gamma \bar{u}_{ik}(p,q)D_k(q)\mathrm{d}S(q) \qquad (p\in\Gamma_u) \\ t_i(p) &= \bar{t}_i = \int_\Gamma \bar{t}_{ik}(p,q)D_k(q)\mathrm{d}S(q) \qquad (p\in\Gamma_t\cup\Gamma_c) \end{aligned} \tag{15}$$

式中:$\bar{u}_{ik}(p,q)$、$\bar{t}_{ik}(p,q)$分别表示位移和面力基本解,其定义式见式(8)和式(10);$u_i(p)$、$t_i(p)$分别为边界 p 点已知的位移和面力;$D_k(q)$为待求的边界不连续位移值。注意,对于无限大三维裂纹体,只有应力边界方程(15)中的第二式。

为了计算边界积分方程(15),采用边界单元法的基本思想,将所考察的物体边界面 Γ 离散成若干个边界单元 Γ_e,然后在每个单元上进行数值积分。假如全部边界面 Γ 离散成 M 个边界单元,共 N 个节点,每个单元用 $\Gamma_e^{(m)}$ 表示,同时令 p 点位于第 n 个节点上,q 点位于第 m 个单元上。则边界离散以后,边界积分方程(15) 变为如下离散方程:

$$\begin{aligned} u_i(p^{(n)}) &= \bar{u}_i^n = \sum_{m=1}^{M}\int_{\Gamma_e^{(m)}} \bar{u}_{ik}(p^{(n)},q^{(m)})D_k(q^{(m)})\mathrm{d}S(q^{(m)}) \qquad (p^{(n)}\in\Gamma_u) \\ t_i(p^{(n)}) &= \bar{t}_i^n = \sum_{m=1}^{M}\int_{\Gamma_e^{(m)}} \bar{t}_{ik}(p^{(n)},q^{(m)})D_k(q^{(m)})\mathrm{d}S(q^{(m)}) \qquad (p^{(n)}\in\Gamma_t\cup\Gamma_c) \end{aligned} \tag{16}$$

式中:$n=1\sim N$。

进一步选用适当的单元,如三角形单元、四边形单元、等参单元等,就可以对离散方程(16)中的单元积分进行数值计算。在方程组(16)的积分计算中,存在两类单元积分:一类是考察点 p 不在积分单元上的普通正常积分,它可以按照常规的数值积分公式计算;另一类是当考察点 p 落在积分单元上的三次超奇异积分,这类积分只有在有限部分积分的意义下才收敛[5],因而需要采用特殊的处理技术。

3 超奇异积分和角点问题的处理技术

关于各类超奇异积分的性质、处理方法和数值积分技术,目前已有众多的文献[4~9]进行了研究。本文将采用三角形单元变换技术和有限部分积分的定义[4,5],将三次超奇异积分化为常规积分。图1所示为一个三角形单元 Γ_e,(r,θ)为其局部坐标。设考察点 p 与节点 i 重合,则该单元上任意一点 q 的不连续位移分布函数可表示为

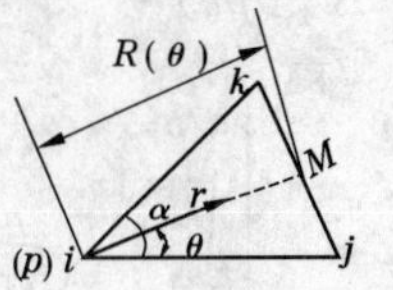

图1 三角形单元

$$D_k(q)=\left[1-\frac{r}{R(\theta)}\right]D_k^{(i)}+(1-L_k)\frac{r}{R(\theta)}D_k^{(j)}+L_k\frac{r}{R(\theta)}D_k^{(k)} \tag{17}$$

式中:$D_k^{(i)}$、$D_k^{(j)}$、$D_k^{(k)}$ 为三角形单元三个节点的不连续位移值,是待求的基本未知变量;$R(\theta)$为节点 i 与点 M 之间的距离;L_k 为与节点 k 相应的点 M 处的单元面积坐标。

于是超奇异单元积分

$$\int_{\Gamma_e}\frac{1}{r^3(p,q)}D_k(q)\mathrm{d}S(q)=\int_0^\alpha \mathrm{d}\theta\int_0^{R(\theta)}\frac{D_k(r)}{r^2}\mathrm{d}r=-2\Delta_e D_k^{(i)}\int_0^1\frac{\mathrm{d}L_k}{R^3(\theta)} \tag{18}$$

式中:$\int$ 表示 Hadmard 主值意义下的超奇异积分;Δ_e 为三角形单元面积,对于四边形单元,可划分为几个三角形单元类似处理。

由式(18)可见,利用三角形单元变换技术和有限部分积分的概念,超奇异积分可转化为正常积分,然后仍可按照常规的数值积分公式进行数值计算。

另外,对于三维有限体的不光滑外部边界和曲折平面裂纹,将会在棱边和角点遇到外法向不确定的现象,即边界单元法中所谓的角点问题[1]。解决这类角点问题的一个简单而有效的办法就是采用位移不连续的非协调单元来解决[1,12]。例如,可采用重心具有一个节点的三角形常量单元和节点在单元内部的四边形8节点等参单元,如图2(a)、(b)所示。对于其他类型的常用非协调单元,可以参照文献[12]的详细介绍。

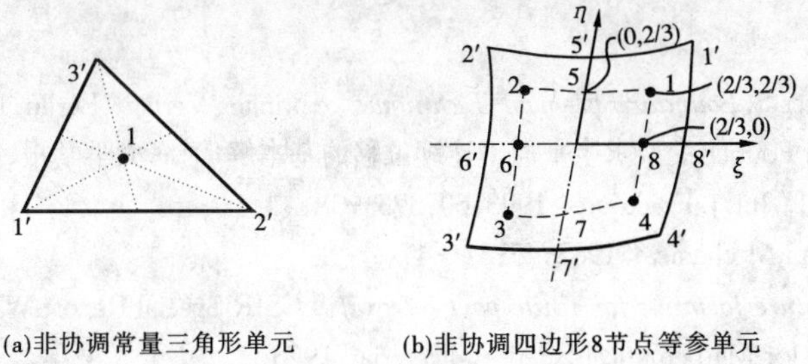

(a)非协调常量三角形单元 (b)非协调四边形8节点等参单元

图2

4 应力强度因子的计算与结论

对于三维裂纹问题,如果采用上述三维不连续位移超奇异积分方程法求得了边界单元各节点的不连续位移值之后,即可容易地计算裂纹前沿的应力强度因子。根据任意三

维裂纹前沿局部位移场,在复合载荷作用下三维裂纹边界上任意一点 p_0 的应力强度因子可直接由该点法平面内邻近点 p 的两裂纹自由面的位移差即不连续位移值确定,即

$$K_{\mathrm{I}}(p_0)=\frac{\mu D_z(p)}{4(1-\nu)}\sqrt{\frac{2\pi}{r}},K_{\mathrm{II}}(p_0)=\frac{\mu D_n(p)}{4(1-\nu)}\sqrt{\frac{2\pi}{r}},\ K_{\mathrm{III}}(p_0)=\frac{\mu D_t(p)}{4(1-\nu)}\sqrt{\frac{2\pi}{r}} \tag{19}$$

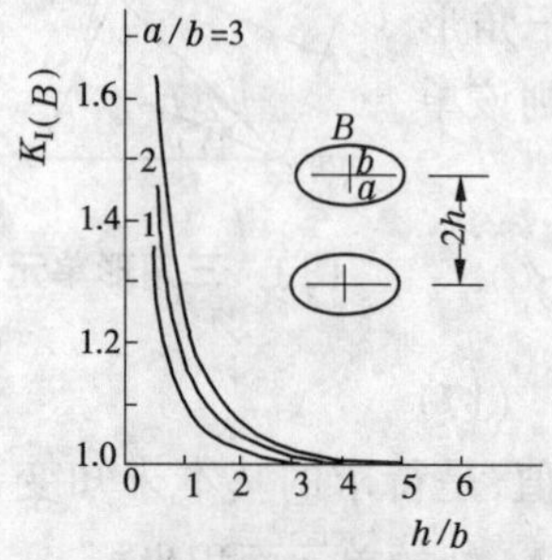

图 3　两平行椭圆裂纹与 $K_{\mathrm{I}}^*(B)$

式中:$r=r(p,p_0)$为两点 p 和 p_0 之间的距离;$D_z(p)$、$D_n(p)$、$D_t(p)$分别为 p 点沿 p_0 点的次法向、主法向和切向的不连续位移值。

例如,利用以上介绍的方法,本文计算了三维无限大弹性体内两者均受法向均匀内部压力 p_0 作用的两平行平片椭圆裂纹,上片裂纹前沿 B 点的相对应力强度因子 $K_{\mathrm{I}}^*(B)=K_{\mathrm{I}}^{(2)}(B)/K_{\mathrm{I}}^{(1)}(B)$(上标 1,2 分别表示体内存在单裂纹、双裂纹)的计算结果如图 3 所示。当两裂纹相距较远时,$K_{\mathrm{I}}^*(B)\approx1$,说明相互干扰较小,这是合理的,并且计算量很小。

以上对求解三维多裂纹问题的不连续位移超奇异积分方程法进行的研究表明:

(1)采用互等功定理,根据 Kelvin 基本解,可以简单方便地导出三维不连续位移基本解的一般形式。由此式展开即可给出现有文献中的分量形式的基本解。

(2)以该基本解为核函数,可以建立求解三维多裂纹问题的不连续位移超奇异边界积分方程组。其中,超奇异积分的数值计算可采用三角形单元变换技术和有限部分积分的定义解决,法向不确定的角点问题可引入位移不连续的非协调单元进行有效处理。最后,由裂纹面间断位移可直接求得裂纹前沿任意点的应力强度因子。

(3)本文方法可以求解任意的三维多裂纹问题,其中所有裂纹均可视为一般的外部边界,不需分域处理,因而具有计算量小的明显优点,值得进一步研究推广。

参 考 文 献

[1] Brebbia C A, Walker S. *Boundary Element Techniques*, Springer-Verlag: Berlin,1984

[2] 朱先奎,姜弘道.用 Fourier 变换求半平面不连续位移的基本解.河海大学学报,1994,22(3):31~36

[3] Qin T Y ,Tang T J. Int.j.Fractuure. 1993,60:373~381

[4] Ioakimidis N I. Acta Mechanica. 1982,45:31~47

[5] Kutt H R. *Quadrature formula for finite-part integrals*. CSIR Special Report WISK-178, The national research institute for Mathematical Science, Pretoria, 1975

[6] Sohn G H, Hong C S. *Boundary Element* 2(edited by A.C.Brebbia and G.Maier), 1985,8:57~67

[7] Martin P A ,Rizzo F J. *On boundary integral equations for crack problems*. Proceedings of the Royal Society London,1989;(A-421):341~355

[8] Ioakomidis N I.Acta Mechanica, 1990,82

[9] Toh K-C ,Mukherjee S.Int.J.Solids Structures, 1994,31:2299~2312

[10] Zhao M,Liu Y ,Cheng C. Engineering Analysis with Boundary Elements. 1994,13

[11] Liu Guangting ,Lin Guoyu, *Singular integral equation groups for 3-D crack problems in Finite Body*.

Journal of TSinghua University, No. 1, 1996: 48～53

[12] Patterson C, EI-Sebai N A S. *A family of partially discontinuous boundary elements for three dimension analysis*. Boundary Elements V: the proceedings of 5th international boundary elements, 1983: 193～206

位移不连续边界元法解多裂纹体的裂缝扩展

摘　要　研究了用位移不连续间接边界元法解多裂纹体的裂纹扩展。由叠加原理可分离出任一单个裂纹面在无限大板中的虚拟应力,从而求出有限或无限域中各条裂纹的应力强度因子值。文中提出一种与裂纹扩展相对应的方程组解法,当裂纹逐步扩展时,该解法不需重新形成和分解整个控制方程组,方程组的全部计算量大致等于一次方程组的求解及 n 次回代(n 为裂纹扩展步数),因而大大减少了计算时间。多裂纹体的裂缝扩展研究为重力式碾压混凝土坝仿真破坏过程研究提供了条件。

关键词　不连续位移边界元　多裂隙体　逐渐破坏过程

大体积混凝土在建造期或者使用期都常出现一些宏观裂纹,了解这些裂纹的相互影响,判断它们的稳定性和危害性,是工程界非常关心的问题。

有限元法计算裂纹问题常常需要在各个裂纹尖端布置密集网格,奇异元在界面附近的变化速率不明确,而且通常要用裂纹尖端附近的位移或者应力场外推得出应力强度因子。当计算多裂纹体特别是不对称应力场,裂纹间间距较近时,使用这种外推法比较困难。裂纹向前扩展延伸,网格密集部位前移,整个网格须作较大的调整。由于网格的调整,每次扩展无疑都需要重新形成和求解支配方程组,因而需耗费大量机时。

第二类边界元法(位移不连续法),对于裂纹边界及常规边界均以不连续位移为基本解。可将这种方法用于域内裂纹、边裂纹以及弯曲裂纹的多裂体分析,方便地求得多裂体裂纹的应力强度因子。当裂纹扩展时,只需在新增加的裂纹面上增加少许单元即可。

与此相配合,本文也提供一种改进方程组解法,不需重新组集和分解整个方程组,对方程组新增的行和列进行处理即可,在计算工程断裂延伸的渐进破坏中大量节省机时。

1　位移不连续法的基本解

图 1 所示的长为 $2a$ 的平面裂纹,无限域内上、下表面作用了均布切向和法向不连续位移 D_x、D_y。Crough 的平面应变解为

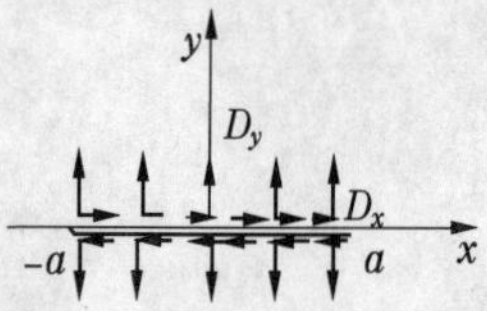

图 1　无限体内裂缝 $2a$

$$
\left.\begin{aligned}
U_x &= [2(1-\nu)F_3 - yF_5]D_x + [-(1-2\nu)F_2 - yF_4]D_y \\
U_y &= [(1-2\nu)F_2 - yF_4]D_x + [2(1-\nu)F_3 - yF_5]D_y \\
\sigma_x &= 2G(2F_4 + yF_3 - yF_6)D_x + 2G(-F_5 + yF_7)D_y \\
\sigma_y &= 2G(-yF_6)D_x + 2G(-F_5 - yF_7)D_y \\
\tau_{xy} &= 2G(-F_5 + yF_7)D_x + 2G(-yF_6)D_y
\end{aligned}\right\} \tag{1}
$$

本文选自《清华大学学报(自然科学版)》,1996 年第 1 期,作者还有涂金良、张镜剑。

式中：

$$F_2=\frac{\partial f(x,y)}{\partial x},F_3=\frac{\partial f(x,y)}{\partial y},\quad F_4=\frac{\partial^2 f(x,y)}{\partial x\partial y},\quad F_5=\frac{\partial^2 f(x,y)}{\partial x^2},$$

$$F_6=\frac{\partial^3 f(x,y)}{\partial x\partial y^2},\quad F_7=\frac{\partial^3 f(x,y)}{\partial y^3},$$

$$f(x,y)=\frac{-1}{4\pi(1-\nu)}\Big\{y(\arctan\frac{y}{x-a}-\arctan\frac{y}{x+a})-(x-a)\ln\sqrt{(x-a)^2+y^2}+(x+a)\ln\sqrt{(x+a)^2+y^2}\Big\}$$

G 为剪切模量；ν 为泊松比；D_x、D_y 分别为切向和法向不连续位移值。

用以上不连续位移基本解可得到第二类间接边界元法的支配方程组

$$\begin{bmatrix}A\\B\end{bmatrix}\begin{Bmatrix}D_1\\D_2\end{Bmatrix}=\begin{Bmatrix}P_1\\U_2\end{Bmatrix}\tag{2}$$

求解上述方程组可得到各单元的不连续位移值$\{D\}$。

域内各点应力和位移由下式求出：

$$\sigma_s^i=\sum_{j=1}^{N}A_{ss}^{ji}D_s^j+\sum_{j=1}^{N}A_{sn}^{ji}D_n^j,\sigma_n^i=\sum_{j=1}^{N}A_{ns}^{ji}D_s^j+\sum_{j=1}^{N}A_{nn}^{ji}D_n^j,\sigma_t^i=\sum_{j=1}^{N}A_{ts}^{ji}D_s^j+\sum_{j=1}^{N}A_{tn}^{ji}D_n^j$$

$$u_s^i=\sum_{j=1}^{N}B_{ss}^{ji}D_s^j+\sum_{j=1}^{N}B_{sn}^{ji}D_n^j,u_n^i=\sum_{j=1}^{N}B_{ns}^{ji}D_s^j+\sum_{j=1}^{N}B_{nn}^{ji}D_n^j\tag{3}$$

式中：

$$A_{ss}^{ji}=2G(-\overline{F}_5+\overline{y}_i\overline{F}_7),A_{sn}^{ji}=2G(-\overline{y}_i\overline{F}_6),A_{ns}^{ji}=2G(-\overline{y}_i\overline{F}_6),A_{nn}^{ji}=2G(-\overline{F}_5-\overline{y}_i\overline{F}_7),$$
$$A_{ts}^{ji}=2G(2\overline{F}_4+\overline{y}_i\overline{F}_7),A_{tn}^{ji}=2G(-\overline{F}_5+\overline{y}_i\overline{F}_7),$$
$$B_{ss}^{ji}=2(1-\nu)\overline{F}_3-\overline{y}_i\overline{F}_5,B_{sn}^{ji}=-(1-2\nu)\overline{F}_2-\overline{y}_i\overline{F}_4,$$
$$B_{ns}^{ji}=(1-2\nu)\overline{F}_2-\overline{y}_i\overline{F}_4,B_{nn}^{ji}=2(1-\nu)\overline{F}_3+\overline{y}_i\overline{F}_5$$

这里$\overline{F}_2,\overline{F}_3,\cdots,\overline{F}_7$见式(1)，它们只是在$j$单元的局部坐标系的相应数值，$\overline{y}_i$是$i$点在$j$单元局部坐标系的$y$坐标。

有限域多裂纹体问题可通过无限域内沿有限边界作用力的基本解和上述无限域断裂缝内作用力的解叠加以及边界条件而解得界面虚拟力(或不连续位移)。

2 多裂纹体的应力强度因子(SIF)计算

只有缝内虚拟力在缝端产生奇异性，外部应力场并不直接影响k值，它只是通过改变缝内虚拟力来影响SIF值，因此可利用解出的裂纹面上的不连续位移值D来求出多裂体的应力强度因子。

由不连续位移值可求出与之对应的裂纹面上的虚拟力值

$$F_s^i=\sum_{j=n_1}^{N}A_{ss}^{ji}D_s^j+\sum_{j=n_1}^{N}A_{sn}^{ji}D_n^j,\ F_n^i=\sum_{j=n_1}^{N}A_{ns}^{ji}D_s^j+\sum_{j=n_1}^{N}A_{nn}^{ji}D_n^j\qquad(j=n_1,n_2,\cdots,N)\tag{4}$$

式中：n_1为此裂纹面上的起始单元号；N为此裂纹面上的末了单元号；F_s^i为第i单元的虚

切向力；F_n^i 为第 i 单元的虚拟法向力。

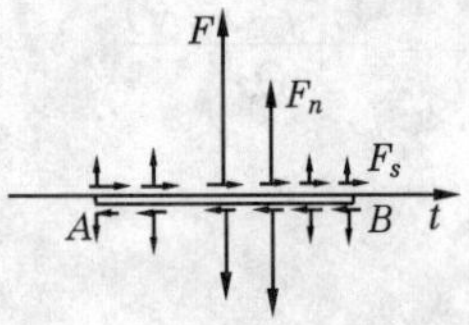

图 2　裂纹虚拟力

用中心裂纹面上受分段集中力的应力强度因子公式可求出裂纹两端的 K_{I}、K_{II} 值，如图 2 所示，B 端的应力强度因子为

$$K_{\mathrm{I}B} = \int_{-a}^{a} F_n \sqrt{\frac{a+t}{a-t}}\mathrm{d}t = \sum_{j=n_1}^{N} F_n^i \sqrt{\frac{a+t_i}{a-t_i}}\Delta t_i$$

$$K_{\mathrm{II}B} = \int_{-a}^{a} F_s \sqrt{\frac{a+t}{a-t}}\mathrm{d}t = \sum_{j=n_1}^{N} F_s^i \sqrt{\frac{a+t_i}{a-t_i}}\Delta t_i \qquad (5)$$

式中：n_i、N、F_s^i、F_n^i 意义见式(4)；$2a$ 为裂纹长度；Δt_i 为第 i 单元的长度。式(5)为带有 $\sqrt{(a+t)/(a-t)}$ 项的积分，采用切比雪夫－高斯数值积分公式可提高其精度。

3　缝端单元位移修正求 K 值

由于常单元不连续位移(平均值)和缝端实际渐变位移变形不一致，文献[1]采用缝端高次奇异单元提高精度，增加了一种单元类型。采用缝端单元位移直接修正法求 K 值的简化方法。

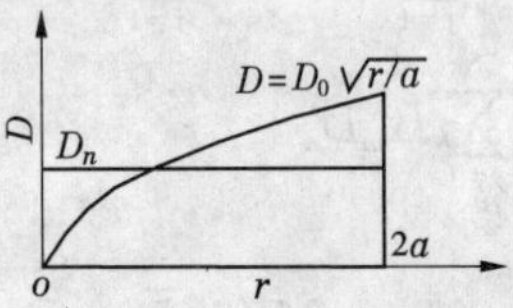

图 3　缝端位移

此法修正系数用 f 表示，由于计算中假定裂纹尖端单元的法向不连续位移 D_n 是均匀分布，实际上它的形式是 $D = D_0\sqrt{r/a}$，见图 3。由 D_n 为 D 的最佳拟合求得 $f = 8/9$ 或 $\sqrt{\pi}/2$，即实际 K_{I} 或 K_{II} 等于 fK_{I}' 或 fK_{II}'。

根据常单元的定义，在常单元中，应力和不连续位移是均匀的，故可根据叠加原理分离出 A 单元的均布虚拟力

$$F_s = \frac{GD_s}{\pi(1-\nu)a} \qquad F_n = \frac{GD_n}{\pi(1-\nu)a}$$

式中：G 为剪切模量；ν 为泊松比；$2a$ 为单元长度；D_s、D_n 为不连续位移。

由裂纹作用均布力的应力强度因子公式，可得到 K_{I}'、K_{II}' 的表达式为

$$K'_{\mathrm{I}} = \sqrt{\pi a}F_n = \frac{D_nG}{(1-\nu)\sqrt{\pi a}} \qquad K'_{\mathrm{II}} = \sqrt{\pi a}F_s = \frac{D_sG}{(1-\nu)\sqrt{\pi a}} \qquad (6)$$

故

$$K_{\mathrm{I}} = fK'_{\mathrm{I}} = \frac{\sqrt{\pi}}{2}\frac{D_nG}{(1-\nu)\sqrt{\pi a}} = \frac{D_nG}{2(1-\nu)\sqrt{a}}$$

$$K_{\mathrm{II}} = fK'_{\mathrm{II}} = \frac{\sqrt{\pi}}{2}\frac{D_sG}{(1-\nu)\sqrt{\pi a}} = \frac{D_sG}{2(1-\nu)\sqrt{a}}$$

本文公式为平面应变情况下的公式，对平面应力问题，只需对 E、ν 做相应的替换即可。

4　裂纹扩展的改进方程求解方法

为表达方便，把式(2)中的方阵写成

$$\begin{bmatrix} a_{11} & a_{12} & \cdots & a_{1n} \\ a_{21} & a_{22} & \cdots & a_{2n} \\ \vdots & & & \vdots \\ a_{n1} & a_{n2} & \cdots & a_{nn} \end{bmatrix} \begin{Bmatrix} D_1 \\ D_2 \\ \vdots \\ D_n \end{Bmatrix} = \begin{Bmatrix} P_1 \\ P_2 \\ \vdots \\ P_n \end{Bmatrix}$$

这里值得着重指出的是，方程组系数 a_{ij}，对于常元只与 i、j 两单元有关；对于高次元也只与 i、j 两结点有关的单元有关。对于上述方阵 $\boldsymbol{A}$，其 LU 分解方法为 $\boldsymbol{A} = \boldsymbol{LU}$，式中：

$$\boldsymbol{A} = \begin{bmatrix} a_{11} & a_{12} & \cdots & a_{1n} \\ a_{21} & a_{22} & \cdots & a_{2n} \\ \vdots & \vdots & & \vdots \\ a_{n1} & a_{n2} & \cdots & a_{nn} \end{bmatrix}, \quad \boldsymbol{L} = \begin{bmatrix} 1 & & & 0 \\ l_{21} & \ddots & & \\ \vdots & & \ddots & \\ l_{nl} & l_{n2} & \cdots & 1 \end{bmatrix}, \quad \boldsymbol{U} = \begin{bmatrix} U_{11} & U_{12} & \cdots & U_{1n} \\ & U_{22} & \cdots & U_{2n} \\ 0 & & & U_{nn} \end{bmatrix}$$

$$U_{ri} = a_{ri} - \sum_{m=1}^{r-1} l_{rm} U_{mi} \qquad (i = r, r+1, \cdots, n)$$

$$l_{ir} = (a_{ri} - \sum_{m=1}^{r-1} l_{im} U_{mr}) / U_{rr} \qquad (i = r+1, \cdots, n;\ r \neq n)$$

很明显，a_{ij} 的分解，即 l_{ij} 及 U_{ij} 只与方程组的前 k 行和前 k 列有关，其中 k 为 i 与 j 中较大者，$k = \max(i, j)$。因而上述 LU 分解与下列分两步进行分解是完全等效的(见图 4)。

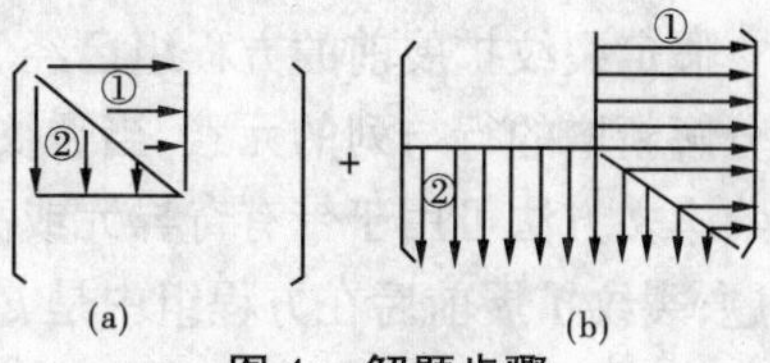

图 4 解题步骤

图 4 中：

$$\text{(a)} \begin{cases} U_{ri} = a_{ri} - \sum_{m=1}^{r-1} l_{rm} U_{mi} & (i = r, r+1, \cdots, k) \\ l_{ir} = (a_{ir} - \sum_{m=1}^{r-1} l_{im} U_{mr}) / U_{rr} & (i = r+1, \cdots, k;\ r \neq k) \end{cases}$$

$$\text{(b)} \begin{cases} U_{ri} = a_{ri} - \sum_{m=1}^{r-1} l_{rm} U_{mi} & (i = \overline{r}_{11}, \cdots, n) \\ l_{ir} = (a_{ir} - \sum_{m=1}^{r-1} l_{im} U_{mr}) / U_{rr} & (i = \overline{r}_{12}, \cdots, n;\ r \neq n), (r = 1, \cdots, n) \end{cases}$$

式中：k 是第一步分解的终了行号，$\overline{r}_{11} \max(r, k)$，$\overline{r}_{12} = \max(r+1, k)$。图 4 的(a)和(b)可统一写成：

$$\begin{cases} U_{ri} = a_{ri} - \sum_{m=1}^{r-1} l_{rm} U_{mi} & (i = \overline{k}_{11}, \cdots, k_2) \\ l_{ir} = (a_{ir} - \sum_{m=1}^{r-1} l_{im} U_{mr}) / U_{rr}, & (i = \overline{k}_{12}, \cdots, k_2;\ r \neq k_2) \end{cases}$$

式中：k_1 为此步分解的起始行、列号；k_2 为此步分解的终止行、列号；$\overline{k}_{11} = \max(k_1, r)$，$\overline{k}_{12} = \max(k_1 + 1, r)$。

当 $k_1 = 1$、$k_2 = n$ 时，上式与通常的 LU 分解相同，这种分步解法不增加任何额外工作量。上述分步求解不但适合于两步，而且适合于分成任意多步求解。

分析裂纹扩展时方程组的变化情况见图 5，结构划分成 $k/2$ 个单元，当裂纹扩展时，裂纹向前延伸，新增裂纹面增加了 $(n-k)/2$ 个单元，总单元数为 $n/2$ 个。总方程组为 n 阶，裂纹扩展前后的方程组方阵分别为

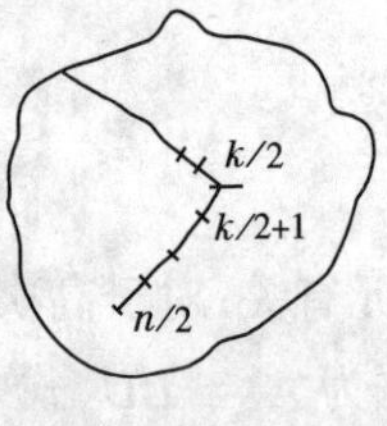

图 5　裂纹扩展增加单元

$$\begin{bmatrix} a_{11} & a_{12} & \cdots & a_{1k} \\ a_{21} & a_{22} & \cdots & a_{2k} \\ \vdots & & & \vdots \\ a_{k1} & a_{k2} & \cdots & a_{kk} \end{bmatrix}, \quad \begin{bmatrix} a_{11} & a_{12} & \cdots & a_{1k} & \cdots & a_{1n} \\ a_{21} & a_{22} & \cdots & a_{2k} & \cdots & \vdots \\ \vdots & & & \vdots & & \\ a_{k1} & \cdots & \cdots & a_{kk} & \cdots & \vdots \\ \vdots & & & & & \\ a_{n1} & \cdots & \cdots & \cdots & \cdots & a_{nn} \end{bmatrix}$$

由上节可知，方程组元素 $a_{ij}(i=1,2,\cdots,k)$ 与裂纹扩展前完全相同，且方程组新增元素与它们无关。故形成和组集方程组时，重新组集和分解的为第 k 至 n 行和列在方程组的元素。也即只需形成新增裂纹面单元的方程数，该子程序只需将循环上下限改为 k_1 和 k_2，k_1 为须形成方程组的起始行、列号，k_2 为终了行、列的号，$k_1=1$、$k_2=n$ 为通常形成的 LU 分解。

假定裂纹扩展前的方程组已经 LU 分解，裂纹扩展后，只需按前进的分步 LU 分解方法分解新增的行与列的元素。当裂纹继续扩展，可重复使用此方法对新增元素进行分解。

本文方法可用于带有奇异元或高次元的边界元程序，不同的是，对于高次元和奇异元问题，裂纹扩展前后在方程组中是 $k/2-1$ 个单元的元素，重新组集和分解的元素为 $k-2$ 行与列到 n 行与列的元素。

5　算例

为对上述方法进行数值验证，编制了 BECRACK 程序进行数值计算。

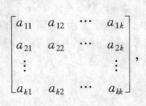

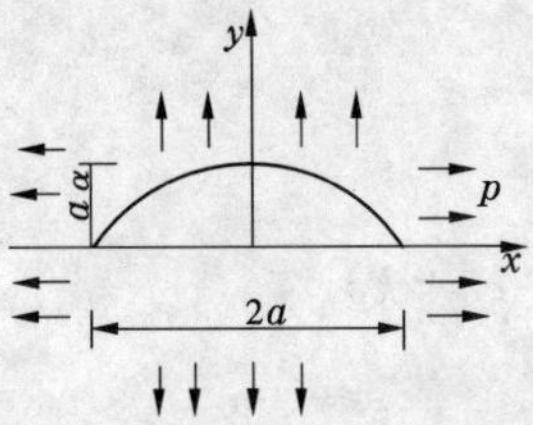

图 6　无限域内抛物线裂纹

(1) 无限大板中的抛物线裂纹(见图 6)。裂纹方程为 $y=\alpha(a^2-x^2)/a$。为了与文献对比，令 $k_{\mathrm{I}}=F_{\mathrm{I}}(\alpha)P\sqrt{\pi a}$，$k_{\mathrm{II}}=F_{\mathrm{II}}(\alpha)P\sqrt{\pi a}$。本文结果与文献[2]的结果比较见表 1。可见本文方法即使对弯曲裂纹计算，精度也良好。

表 1　抛物线裂纹的 k_{I}、k_{II}

α	$F_{\mathrm{I}}(\alpha)$		$F_{\mathrm{II}}(\alpha)$	
	本文	文献[2]	本文	文献[2]
0.2	0.958	0.948	−0.189	−0.182
0.5	0.820	0.816	−0.338	−0.327
1.0	0.740	0.742	−0.393	−0.381

(2) 对于含有 45° 斜裂纹的有限板条，按 $\sigma_{\theta\max}$ 理论判断裂纹扩展方向，其裂纹扩展过程分别由本文方法及重新组集、分解方程组的方法计算，得到的开裂过程一致(见图 7)。本文方法用机时 6.2min，常规方法为 110min。

6 结语

(1)应用第二类边界元法分析多裂体问题时,裂纹边界和常规边界使用同一种基本解,单元模式完全相同,程序通用性强。

(2)求解多裂体时,应用叠加原理,可分离出单个裂纹的应力场,避免了计算应力强度因子时多裂纹的相互干涉影响。并可有效地对域内裂纹和边裂纹进行计算。

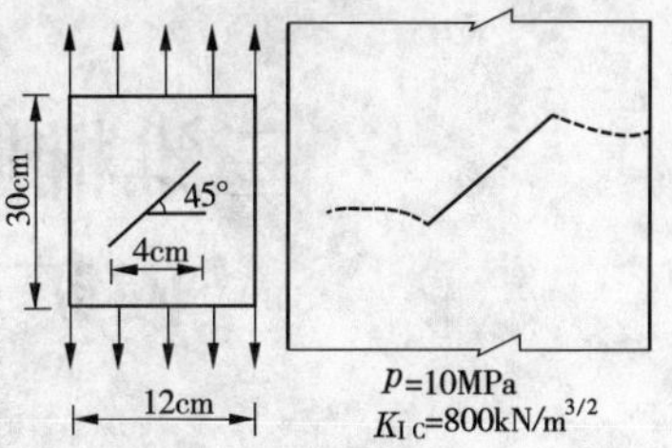

图 7 斜裂缝扩展

(3)采用缝端单元不连续位移和修正系数方法大大简化了计算,并保证了工程计算精度。

(4)本法用于裂纹扩展计算时,能大量节省机时,理论和数值实验均得到满意的验证。

(5)本法只需对已有的边界元程序作微小的修改,不需增加任何特殊措施,经修改后的程序计算其他非裂纹扩展问题时,没有增加任何计算量。

参考文献

[1] 刘光廷,林国裕. 大体积混凝土的弯曲和分叉缝. 见:混凝土坝裂缝国际会议论文集. 美国,柯罗拉多,1991. 275~285

[2] Chen Y Z. *Numerical solution of the curved crack problem by means of polynomial approximation of dislocation distribution*. Engineering Fracture Mechanics, 1991,39(5):791~797

三维椭圆裂纹前沿非法平面内扩展的可能性研究*

摘　要　为了研究三维裂纹在其前沿非法平面内扩展的可能性,本文采用椭球坐标系和一种特殊球坐标系,得到了三维椭圆裂纹前沿任意斜平面内局部应力和位移场。该解形式简单,和椭圆曲率无关。由此局部场,复合断裂准则的分析表明,三维裂纹前沿每一点都将沿其法平面方向扩展。

关键词　三维断裂　椭圆裂纹　应力位移场　扩展方向

许多工程结构,特别是大型水工结构中的裂纹实际上都是三维裂纹问题,因此三维裂纹的起裂和扩展分析的研究具有重要的实际意义。椭圆裂纹因能较好地模拟一般三维平片裂纹而成为人们的研究重点。Kassir 和 Sih[1] 的研究表明,三维椭圆裂纹前沿法平面内的局部应力场为平面应变Ⅰ、Ⅱ、Ⅲ型解的叠加,由此,虽然没有证明,目前三维裂纹的起裂扩展分析都是假设在前沿法平面内进行的[2]。然而最近,Sih[3] 给出的内埋椭圆裂纹前沿斜平面内的局部应力场,形式复杂且与椭圆曲率有关。他用应变能密度因子理论对该应力场描述的三维复合椭圆裂纹的扩展方向进行了分析,结果发现除了椭圆长短轴与裂纹边界的交点外,其余裂纹边界点的扩展将不在法平面内进行(参见文献[3])。这给目前三维断裂力学分析提出了新的难题。因此,有必要进一步探讨这一问题,弄清三维混合裂纹是否会在其前沿非法平面内起裂扩展。

1　基本坐标系与渐近椭球坐标

考虑三维无限大弹性介质中长短半轴分别为 a、b 的一内埋平片椭圆裂纹,如图 1 所示,位于整体坐标系 (x,y,z) 中的 $x \sim y$ 平面内。设裂纹边界上任意点 P 的局部直角坐标系为 (n,t,z),局部球坐标系 (r,θ,φ),其中 n、t 分别为 P 点的外法向和切向,则该球坐标系和整体直角坐标系的关系为

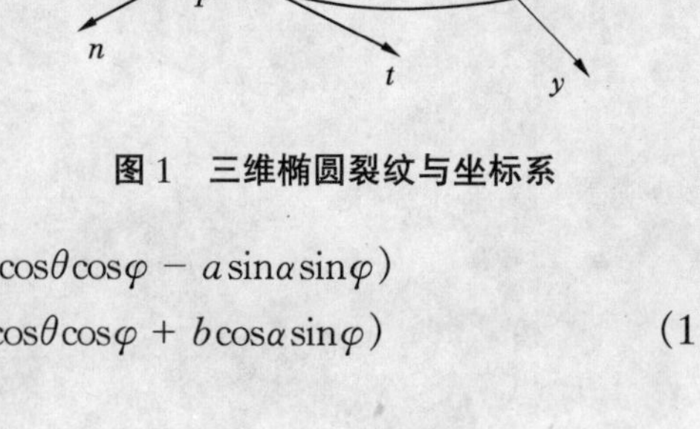

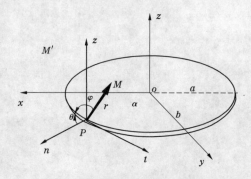

图 1　三维椭圆裂纹与坐标系

$$\begin{cases} x = a\cos\alpha + r\Pi^{-1/2}(b\cos\alpha\cos\theta\cos\varphi - a\sin\alpha\sin\varphi) \\ y = b\sin\alpha + r\Pi^{-1/2}(a\sin\alpha\cos\theta\cos\varphi + b\cos\alpha\sin\varphi) \\ z = r\sin\theta\cos\varphi \end{cases} \tag{1}$$

* 国家自然科学基金和水利部重点科研基金资助项目
本文选自《工程力学》1996 年增刊,作者还有朱先奎。

式中：β 为 P 点外法向与椭圆长轴的夹角，它与椭圆参数方程的参考角 α 的关系为

$$\sin\beta = a\Pi^{-1/2}\sin\alpha \qquad \cos\beta = b\Pi^{-1/2}\cos\alpha \qquad \Pi = a^2\sin^2\alpha + b^2\cos^2\alpha \tag{2}$$

为了便于三维裂纹的渐近分析，本文采用 Whittaker 和 Watson[4] 定义的一种共焦曲线坐标系或简称椭球坐标系(ξ,η,ζ)，它与直角坐标系(x,y,z)的相互对应关系如下：

$$\begin{cases} a^2(a^2-b^2)x^2 = (a^2+\xi)(a^2+\eta)(a^2+\zeta) \\ b^2(b^2-a^2)y^2 = (b^2+\xi)(b^2+\eta)(b^2+\zeta) \\ a^2b^2z^2 = \xi\eta\zeta \end{cases} \quad -a^2 \leqslant \zeta \leqslant -b^2 \leqslant \eta \leqslant 0 \leqslant \xi \leqslant \infty \tag{3}$$

当 $z=0$ 时，$\xi=0$ 对应椭圆面内的点；$\eta=0$ 对应椭圆外平面上的点；$\xi=\eta=0$ 对应椭圆边界上的点。

由式(1)和式(3)可得椭球坐标(ξ,η,ζ)与局部球坐标(r,θ,φ)之间的一种渐近关系

$$\begin{cases} \xi = abr\Pi^{-1/2}(\cos\theta+1)\cos\varphi + o(r) \\ \eta = abr\Pi^{-1/2}(\cos\theta-1)\cos\varphi + o(r) \\ \zeta = -\Pi + 2r(b^2-a^2)\Pi^{-1/2}\sin\alpha\cos\alpha\sin\varphi + o(r) \end{cases} \tag{4}$$

2 椭圆裂纹前沿局部应力位移场

假设上下椭圆裂纹面受大小相等、方向相反的法向均匀拉力 p_0 作用，其边界条件为

$$z=0: \quad \sigma_{zz} = p_0, \xi = 0; \quad u_z = 0, \ \eta = 0 \tag{5}$$

这类关于裂纹平面的空间对称问题的应力和位移场可用一个调和位移势函数表示如下[1]：

$$\begin{aligned} &\sigma_{xx} = 2\mu(f_{,xx} + 2\nu f_{,yy} + zf_{,zxx}) && \sigma_{xy} = 2\mu[(1-2\mu)f_{,xy} + zf_{,xyz}] \\ &\sigma_{xz} = 2\mu(zf_{,xzz}) && \sigma_{yy} = 2\mu(f_{,yy} + 2\nu f_{,xx} + zf_{,zyy}) \\ &\sigma_{zz} = 2\mu(-f_{,zz} + zf_{,zzz}) && \sigma_{yz} = 2\mu(zf_{,yzz}) \\ &u_x = (1-2\nu)f_{,x} + zf_{,xz} && u_y = (1-2\nu)f_{,y} + zf_{,yz} \\ &u_z = -2(1-\nu)f_{,z} + zf_{,zz} \end{aligned} \tag{6}$$

式中：μ 为剪切模量；ν 为泊松比。

Green 和 Sneddon[5] 根据流体力学比拟法发现该问题的调和函数 f 为

$$f(x,y,z) = \frac{A}{2}\int_\xi^\infty \left[\frac{x^2}{a^2+s} + \frac{y^2}{b^2+s} + \frac{z^2}{s} - 1\right]\frac{\mathrm{d}s}{\sqrt{Q(s)}} \qquad A = \frac{ab^2p_0}{4\mu E(k)} \tag{7}$$

式中：$Q(s)=s(a^2+s)(b^2+s)$；$E(k)$ 为第二类完全椭圆积分；模 $k=[1-(b/a)^2]^{1/2}$。将式(7)代入式(6)，通过变换 $\xi = a^2cn^2u/sn^2u$ 引入 Jaoobi 椭圆函数[4] $snu, cnu, \cdots$ 利用其有关性质和椭圆坐标偏导数关系，经过复杂的微积分计算得法向载荷作用下椭圆裂纹前沿局部应力和位移场如下：

$$\sigma_{xx} = \frac{K_{\mathrm{I}}\cos\frac{\theta}{2}}{(2\pi r\cos\varphi)^{1/2}\Pi}\left\{b^2\cos^2\alpha\left[1+\frac{1}{2}(\cos\theta-1)(2\cos\theta+1)\right] + 2\nu a^2\sin^2\alpha\right\} + o(r^{-\frac{1}{2}}) \tag{8a}$$

$$\sigma_{yy} = \frac{K_{\mathrm{I}} \cos\frac{\theta}{2}}{(2\pi r\cos\varphi)^{1/2}\Pi}\left\{a^2\sin^2\alpha\left[1+\frac{1}{2}(\cos\theta-1)(2\cos\theta+1)\right]+2\nu b^2\cos^2\alpha\right\}+o(r^{-\frac{1}{2}}) \tag{8b}$$

$$\sigma_{zz} = \frac{K_{\mathrm{I}}}{(2\pi r\cos\varphi)^{1/2}}\cos\frac{\theta}{2}\left[1-\frac{1}{2}(\cos\theta-1)(2\cos\theta+1)\right]+o(r^{-\frac{1}{2}}) \tag{8c}$$

$$\sigma_{yz} = \frac{aK_{\mathrm{I}}\sin\alpha}{2(2\pi r\cos\varphi)^{1/2}\Pi^{1/2}}\sin\frac{\theta}{2}(\cos\theta+1)(2\cos\theta-1)+o(r^{-\frac{1}{2}}) \tag{8d}$$

$$\sigma_{zx} = \frac{bK_{\mathrm{I}}\cos\alpha}{2(2\pi r\cos\varphi)^{1/2}\Pi^{1/2}}\sin\frac{\theta}{2}(\cos\theta+1)(2\cos\theta-1)+o(r^{-\frac{1}{2}}) \tag{8e}$$

$$\sigma_{xy} = \frac{abK_{\mathrm{I}}\sin\alpha\cos\alpha}{(2\pi r\cos\varphi)^{1/2}\Pi}\cos\frac{\theta}{2}\left[(1-2\nu)+\frac{1}{2}(\cos\theta-1)(2\cos\theta+1)\right]+o(r^{\frac{1}{2}}) \tag{8f}$$

$$u_x = \frac{bK_{\mathrm{I}}\cos\alpha}{2\mu\Pi^{1/2}}\left(\frac{2r\cos\varphi}{\pi}\right)^{1/2}\cos\frac{\theta}{2}\left[(1-2\nu)+\frac{1}{2}(1-\cos\theta)\right]+o(r^{\frac{1}{2}}) \tag{8g}$$

$$u_y = \frac{aK_{\mathrm{I}}\sin\alpha}{2\mu\Pi^{1/2}}\left(\frac{2r\cos\varphi}{\pi}\right)^{1/2}\cos\frac{\theta}{2}\left[(1-2\nu)+\frac{1}{2}(1-\cos\theta)\right]+o(r^{\frac{1}{2}}) \tag{8h}$$

$$u_z = \frac{K_{\mathrm{I}}}{2\mu}\left(\frac{2r\cos\varphi}{\pi}\right)^{1/2}\sin\frac{\theta}{2}\left[2(1-\nu)-\frac{1}{2}(1+\cos\theta)\right]+o(r^{\frac{1}{2}}) \tag{8i}$$

式中：$K_{\mathrm{I}} = \lim_{r\to 0}\sqrt{2\pi r}\sigma_{zz}(r,\theta=0,\varphi=0) = 4\mu A\sqrt{\pi}\Pi^{1/4}/(ab)^{3/2}$ 为 Ⅰ 型椭圆裂纹应力强度因子。

类似式(8)，可得切向载荷作用下椭圆裂纹前沿局部应力和位移场。对于一般载荷，先将其分解为切向载荷和法向载荷，然后由这两种载荷作用下的局部场叠加得混合载荷作用下椭圆裂纹前沿局部场的整体直角坐标分量，通过坐标转换即得裂纹边界局部直角坐标系下场量的最一般解为

$$\begin{aligned}\sigma_{ij} &= \frac{1}{(2\pi r\cos\varphi)^{1/2}}\left[K_{\mathrm{I}}\sigma_{ij}^{\mathrm{I}}(\theta)+K_{\mathrm{II}}\sigma_{ij}^{\mathrm{II}}(\theta)+K_{\mathrm{III}}\sigma_{ij}^{\mathrm{III}}(\theta)\right]\\ u_i &= \left(\frac{2r\cos\varphi}{\pi}\right)^{1/2}\left[K_{\mathrm{I}}u_i^{\mathrm{I}}(\theta)+K_{\mathrm{II}}u_i^{\mathrm{II}}(\theta)+K_{\mathrm{III}}u_i^{\mathrm{III}}(\theta)\right]\end{aligned} \quad (i,j=n,t,z) \tag{9}$$

式中：$\sigma_{ij}^{\mathrm{I}}(\theta)$、$u_i^{\mathrm{I}}(\theta)$ 等分别与平面应变 Ⅰ、Ⅱ、Ⅲ 型裂纹尖端场的应力角函数和位移角函数[2] 相同。

式(9)表明 P 点附近任意斜平面内一点 M(矢径为 r，如图1所示)的应力位移场和它在法平面内投影点 M'(矢径为 $r\cos\varphi$)的应力位移场完全相同，而法平面内的局部应力位移就是平面应变 Ⅰ、Ⅱ、Ⅲ 型结果的叠加，所不同的是三维裂纹的应力强度因子 K_{I}、K_{II}、K_{III} 依赖于裂纹曲率。

3　三维裂纹在其前沿斜平面内扩展的可能性分析

三维裂纹扩展分析可采用基于局部应力场的应变能密度因子准则[3]，它假设裂纹扩展方向是裂纹尖端微小球面上一点应变能密度因子 S 最小的方向，由式(9) 可得应变能密度为

$$\frac{\mathrm{d}W}{\mathrm{d}V} = \frac{S}{r},\ S = \frac{1}{\cos\varphi}[a_{11}K_{\mathrm{I}}^2 + 2a_{12}K_{\mathrm{I}}K_{\mathrm{II}} + a_{22}K_{\mathrm{II}}^2 + a_{33}K_{\mathrm{III}}^2] \tag{10}$$

式中,系数 $a_{11} \sim a_{33}$ 和平面应变问题叠加时的结果[2] 相同。由此式可见,当 $\varphi = 0$ 时 S 最小,即三维混合裂纹前沿每一点都将在法平面内扩展。由于局部应力场(8) 与椭圆曲率无关,因此该结论适用于一般光滑曲线裂纹,这从理论上证实了目前所通用的三维裂纹沿其法平面方向扩展的假设。

参 考 文 献

[1] Kassir M K ,Sih G C. *Three-dimensional stress distribution aroud an elliptical crack under arbitrary loadings*. J. Appl. Mech:1966,(33):601~611

[2] 尹双增.断裂、损伤力学理论及其应用.北京:清华大学出版社,1992

[3] Sih G C. *Mechanics of Fracture Initiation and Propagation*. Kluwer Academic Publishers: Dordrecht, 1991

[4] Whittaker E T ,Watson G N. *A Course of Modern Analysis*. Cambridge University Press, 1927

[5] Green A E, Sneddon I N. *Proceedings of the Cambridge Philosophical Society*. 1950(46):159~164

SOLUTION OF PERIODIC HEAT CONDUCTION BY INDIRECT BOUNDARY ELEMENT METHOD BASED ON FICTITIOUS HEAT SOURCE

Abstract The fundamental solution of the temperature field in an infinite three-dimensional body under the periodic unit thermal source is given in the present paper. According to the indirect boundary element method (IBEM) with fictitious heat sources, the problem of 3-D periodic heat conduction in a finite body is solved. By use of a quadratic inharmonic element, the problem of the corner region and the indetermination of the normal direction at boundary points can be solved in the numerical process. The validity of the present method is checked with two examples of which analytical solutions exist. It offers a useful method for the actual simulated calculation of the 3-D temperature field in engineering.

Key words temperature field; heat source; IBEM

1 Introduction

In many heat conduction problems of practical interest, the temperature or the heat flux at the boundary varies periodically with time, for example, periodic temperature variations in the concrete dam caused by the environmental temperature.

Unfortunately, the analytic solution exists only for very simple cases in the one-dimensional problem. However, most of the practical problems in engineering involve multidimensional configurations and complex geometry.

One of the numerical methods for solving these problems is the finite element method (FEM), given by Seem and Klein[1]. The main problem in the FEM is the treatment of time influence involving the heat conduction. In general, the finite differentiation method is used to solve the influence of time which occurs in the problem of the critical time step. It is not easy in practical engineering problem to choose the suitable time step that ensures the calculation's stability. A new FEM is given by Zheng and Yang[2], using the concept of a complex variable; it reduces the governing unsteady heat conduction equation to two noncoupled Poisson equations that avoid the selection of a time step. However, this method can only give the amplitude of the oscillation of temperature but not the variation of temperature with time.

The boundary element methods: direct (BEM) and indirect (IBEM), are very effective methods for the thermal and thermal fracture problems in the simple region. For the multiple material region, the BEM has to distinguish not only the domain but also the boundary and

本文选自《COMMUNICATIONS IN NUMERICAL METHODS IN ENGINEERING》1996 年第 12 期,作者还有 Qiu Delong。

interface, which greatly reduces the advantage of the BEM, and the influence of time by means of the finite differentiation technique also reduces the precision of the BEM. In order to minimize these disadvantages, the fundamental solution of the temperature field in an infinite 3-D body due to the unit simple harmonic periodic heat source is offered in the present paper to use together with the IBEM and the fictitious heat source method to solve the simple periodic heat conduction problem.

In general, a given problem can have an arbitrary form of periodicity. However, and imposed periodic heat conduction problem can be expressed as a sum of different Fourier components and be solved by the superposition of the solutions for individual frequencies.

2 Fundamental Solution

The equation that governs transient heat conduction in a homogeneous isotropic solid body is,

$$k\nabla^2 T - \rho c\frac{\partial T}{\partial t} + Q(x,y,z,t) = 0 \tag{1}$$

where t is time; ρ is the density; c is the specific heat ; $Q(x,y,z,t)$ is the rate of heat generation per unit volume per unit time at the internal point (x,y,z); k is the thermal conductivity. Let us consider $Q(x,y,z,t)=\delta(r)e^{\omega ti}$ (W/m^3); then we have the equation of the fundamental solution.

Furthermore, consider the symmetric character of the problem; the equation can be written as:

$$k\left(\frac{\partial^2 T}{\partial r^2} + \frac{2}{r}\frac{\partial T}{\partial r}\right) + \delta(r)e^{\omega ti} = \rho c\frac{\partial T}{\partial t} \tag{2}$$

where ω is the frequency of the period heat source and $\delta(r)$ is the Dirac delta function.

For stationary periodic functions, the method of separation of variables is used in the form

$$T(r,t) = F(r)G(t) \tag{3}$$

where function $F(r)$ is the space variable and $G(t)$ is the time variable. Substitute Eq. (3) into Eq. (2) and do not consider the heat source item $\delta(r)e^{\omega it}$ in Eq. (2); we obtain

$$\frac{\rho c}{k}\frac{dG}{dt}\frac{1}{G} = \frac{1}{F}\left(\frac{d^2F}{dr^2} + \frac{2}{r}\frac{dF}{dr}\right) = c^* \tag{4}$$

where c^* is the separation constant expressed as $\pm\lambda^2 i$.

Consider the natural boundary condition, when $r\to\infty$, $T(r,t)\to 0$; then we can write the general solution of Eq. (4),

$$T(r,t) = \frac{1}{r}e^{(-\lambda/\sqrt{2})r}\left[c_1 e^{(\lambda^2(k/\rho c)t-(\lambda/\sqrt{2})r)i} + c_2 e^{-(\lambda^2(k/\rho c)t-(\lambda/\sqrt{2})r)i}\right] \tag{5}$$

Clearly it can be written as

$$T(r,t) = \frac{1}{r}e^{(-\lambda/\sqrt{2})r}\left[A\cos\left(\lambda^2\frac{k}{\rho c}t - \frac{\lambda}{\sqrt{2}}r\right) + B\sin\left(\lambda^2\frac{k}{\rho c}t - \frac{\lambda}{\sqrt{2}}r\right)\right] \tag{6}$$

where c_1, c_2, A, B are arbitrary constants.

Furthermore, by the Fourier law, we can get

$$\int_{\Gamma} - k\frac{\partial T}{\partial n} \cdot n\mathrm{d}\Gamma = \int_{V}\left(\delta(r)\mathrm{e}^{\omega ti} - \rho c\frac{\partial T}{\partial t}\right)\mathrm{d}V \tag{7}$$

where n is the normal direction at the boundary point. Γ is an arbitrary closed surface, and V is the domain of the Γ.

Replacing the arbitrary surface Γ by a sphere Γ_ε of radius r_ε which encloses the heat source $\delta(r)\mathrm{e}^{\omega ti}$ (W/m^3), and taking the limit $r_\varepsilon \to 0$, Eq. (7) can be written as

$$\lim_{r_\varepsilon \to 0}\int_{\Gamma_\varepsilon} - k\frac{\partial T}{\partial n} \cdot n\mathrm{d}\Gamma = \lim_{r_\varepsilon \to 0}\int_{V_\varepsilon}\left(\delta(r)\mathrm{e}^{\omega ti} - \rho c\frac{\partial T}{\partial t}\right)\mathrm{d}V \tag{8}$$

On the sphere,

$$\frac{\partial T}{\partial n} = \frac{\partial T}{\partial r}\frac{\partial r}{\partial n} = \frac{\partial T}{\partial r},$$

so Eq. (8) is

$$4\pi k\left[A\cos\left(\lambda^2\frac{k}{\rho c}t\right) + B\sin\left(\lambda^2\frac{k}{\rho c}t\right)\right] = \cos\omega t + i\sin\omega t \tag{9}$$

Eq. (8) has dimension [W], and we obtain

$$A = \frac{1}{4\pi k} \qquad B = \frac{1}{4\pi k}i \qquad \lambda = \sqrt{\frac{\omega\rho c}{k}} \tag{10}$$

where A, B has dimension [mK].

So the solution of Eq. (2) is

$$T(r,t) = \frac{1}{4\pi k}\frac{1}{r}\mathrm{e}^{(-\sqrt{\omega\rho c/(2k)})r}\left[\cos\left(\omega t - \sqrt{\frac{\omega\rho c}{2k}}r\right) + i\sin\left(\omega t - \sqrt{\frac{\omega\rho c}{2k}}r\right)\right] \tag{11}$$

Furthermore, the temperature solutions corresponding to $\delta(r)\cos\omega t$, $\delta(r)\sin\omega t$ are, respectively,

$$T_c(r,t) = \frac{1}{4\pi k}\frac{1}{r}\mathrm{e}^{(-\sqrt{\omega\rho c/2k})r}\cos\left(\omega t - \sqrt{\frac{\omega\rho c}{2k}}r\right) \tag{12}$$

$$T_s(r,t) = \frac{1}{4\pi k}\frac{1}{r}\mathrm{e}^{(-\sqrt{\omega\rho c/2k})r}\sin\left(\omega t - \sqrt{\frac{\omega\rho c}{2k}}r\right) \tag{13}$$

The solutions (12) and (13) are the fundamental solutions used in the IBEM based on the fictitious heat source in this paper.

3 IEBM Formulation Based on Fictitious Heat Source

The formulations (12), (13) can be written as

$$T_c^*(r,t) = \frac{1}{4\pi k}\frac{1}{r}\mathrm{e}^{(-\sqrt{\omega\rho c/2k})r}\left[\cos\sqrt{\frac{\omega\rho c}{2k}}r\cos\omega t + \sin\sqrt{\frac{\omega\rho c}{2k}}r\sin\omega t\right] \tag{14}$$

$$T_s^*(r,t) = \frac{1}{4\pi k}\frac{1}{r}\mathrm{e}^{(-\sqrt{\omega\rho c/2k})r}\left[-\sin\sqrt{\frac{\omega\rho c}{2k}}r\cos\omega t + \cos\sqrt{\frac{\omega\rho c}{2k}}r\sin\omega t\right] \tag{15}$$

which give heat flux q:

$$q_c^*(r,t)=\frac{1}{4\pi}\frac{\partial r}{\partial n}e^{(-\sqrt{\omega\rho c/2k})r}\left\{\left[\left(\frac{1}{r^2}+\sqrt{\frac{\omega\rho c}{2k}}\frac{1}{r}\right)\cos\sqrt{\frac{\omega\rho c}{2k}}r+\sqrt{\frac{\omega\rho c}{2k}}\frac{1}{r}\sin\sqrt{\frac{\omega\rho c}{2k}}r\right]\right.$$
$$\left.\cos\omega t+\left[\left(\frac{1}{r^2}+\sqrt{\frac{\omega\rho c}{2k}}\frac{1}{r}\right)\sin\sqrt{\frac{\omega\rho c}{2k}}r-\sqrt{\frac{\omega\rho c}{2k}}\frac{1}{r}\cos\sqrt{\frac{\omega\rho c}{2k}}r\right]\sin\omega t\right\} \quad (16)$$

$$q_s^*(r,t)=\frac{1}{4\pi}\frac{\partial r}{\partial n}e^{(-\sqrt{\omega\rho c/2k})r}\left\{\left[-\left(\frac{1}{r^2}+\sqrt{\frac{\omega\rho c}{2k}}\frac{1}{r}\right)\sin\sqrt{\frac{\omega\rho c}{2k}}r+\sqrt{\frac{\omega\rho c}{2k}}\frac{1}{r}\cos\sqrt{\frac{\omega\rho c}{2k}}r\right]\right.$$
$$\left.\cos\omega t+\left[\left(\frac{1}{r^2}+\sqrt{\frac{\omega\rho c}{2k}}\frac{1}{r}\right)\cos\sqrt{\frac{\omega\rho c}{2k}}r+\sqrt{\frac{\omega\rho c}{2k}}\frac{1}{r}\sin\sqrt{\frac{\omega\rho c}{2k}}r\right]\sin\omega t\right\} \quad (17)$$

Assume there is a homogeneous isotropic periodic heat conduction body occupied region Ω without heat source, e.g. Fig. 1. The governing equation is,

$$k\nabla^2 T-\rho c\frac{\partial T}{\partial t}=0 \quad (18)$$

and with the boundary condition,

$$T=\overline{T}_c\cos\omega t+\overline{T}_s\sin\omega t \quad \text{on } \Gamma_T \quad (19)$$

$$q=\overline{q}_c\cos\omega t+\overline{q}_s\sin\omega t \quad \text{on } \Gamma_q \quad (20)$$

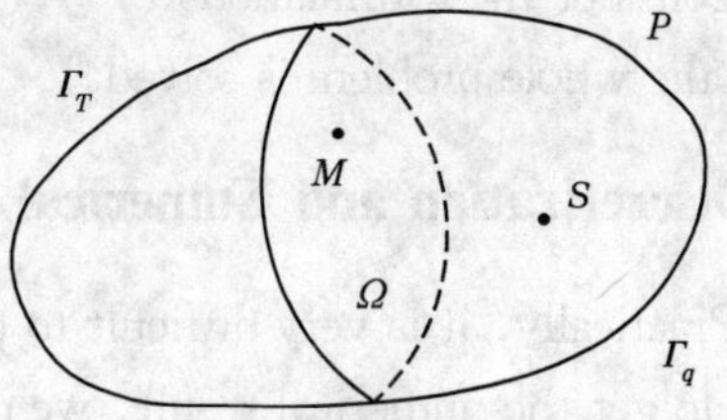

Fig.1

Suppose the region Ω is a part of an infinite body, and there is a fictitious heat source $\Phi(S)=\Phi_c(S)\cos\omega t+\Phi_s(S)\sin\omega t$ on the boundary Γ; by the theorem of superposition, the temperature T and heat flux q of arbitrary point M inside the region can be written as:

$$T(M)=\int_\Gamma[T_{cc}^*(M,S)\Phi_c(S)+T_{sc}^*(M,S)\Phi_s(S)]\cos\omega t\,d\Gamma(S)+$$
$$\int_\Gamma[T_{cs}^*(M,S)\Phi_c(S)+T_{ss}^*(M,S)\Phi_s(S)]\sin\omega t\,d\Gamma(S) \quad (21)$$

$$q(M)=\int_\Gamma[q_{cc}^*(M,S)\Phi_c(S)+q_{sc}^*(M,S)\Phi_s(S)]\cos\omega t\,d\Gamma(S)+$$
$$\int_\Gamma[q_{cs}^*(M,S)\Phi_c(S)+q_{ss}^*(M,S)\Phi_s(S)]\sin\omega t\,d\Gamma(S) \quad (22)$$

where

$$T_{cc}^*=T_{ss}^*=\frac{1}{4\pi k}\frac{1}{r}e^{(-\sqrt{\omega\rho c/2k})r}\cos\sqrt{\frac{\omega\rho c}{2k}}r$$

$$T_{cs}^*=-T_{sc}^*=\frac{1}{4\pi k}\frac{1}{r}e^{(-\sqrt{\omega\rho c/2k})r}\sin\sqrt{\frac{\omega\rho c}{2k}}r$$

$$q_{cc}^*=q_{ss}^*=\frac{1}{4\pi}\frac{\partial r}{\partial n}e^{(-\sqrt{\omega\rho c/2k})r}\left[\left(\frac{1}{r^2}+\sqrt{\frac{\omega\rho c}{2k}}\frac{1}{r}\right)\cos\sqrt{\frac{\omega\rho c}{2k}}r+\sqrt{\frac{\omega\rho c}{2k}}\frac{1}{r}\sin\sqrt{\frac{\omega\rho c}{2k}}r\right]$$

$$q_{cs}^*=-q_{sc}^*=\frac{1}{4\pi}\frac{\partial r}{\partial n}e^{(-\sqrt{\omega\rho c/2k})r}\left[\left(\frac{1}{r^2}+\sqrt{\frac{\omega\rho c}{2k}}\frac{1}{r}\right)\sin\sqrt{\frac{\omega\rho c}{2k}}r-\sqrt{\frac{\omega\rho c}{2k}}\frac{1}{r}\cos\sqrt{\frac{\omega\rho c}{2k}}r\right]$$

where r is the distance between M and S.

These equations are valid for any point inside the domain. In order to formulate the problem as a boundary technique, let the point M be the boundary point P. When M is on the boundary $\Gamma(M=P)$ we have:

$$T(P)=\int_{\Gamma}[T_{cc}^{*}(P,S)\Phi_{c}(S)+T_{sc}^{*}(P,S)\Phi_{s}(S)]\cos\omega t\,d\Gamma(S)+\int_{\Gamma}[T_{cs}^{*}(P,S)\Phi_{c}(S)+T_{ss}^{*}(P,S)\Phi_{s}(S)]\sin\omega t\,d\Gamma(S) \quad (23)$$

$$(1-\alpha)q(P)=\int_{\Gamma}[q_{cc}^{*}(P,S)\Phi_{c}(S)+q_{sc}^{*}(P,S)\Phi_{s}(S)]\cos\omega t\,d\Gamma(S)+\int_{\Gamma}[q_{cs}^{*}(P,S)\Phi_{c}(S)+q_{ss}^{*}(P,S)\Phi_{s}(S)]\sin\omega t\,d\Gamma(S) \quad (24)$$

where α is $1/2$, corresponding to a smooth boundary.

Consider the formulations (19),(20) and (23),(24); once the fictitious heat source is given the whole problem is solved.

4 Discretization and Numerical Method

Practically, it is very difficult to obtain the exact solution of Eqs. (23) and (24). In order to get the numerical result, we divide the boundary $\Gamma=\Gamma_T+\Gamma_q$ into n elements,

$$\Gamma=\sum_{i=1}^{n}\Gamma_i \quad (25)$$

where $\Gamma_1,\Gamma_2,\cdots,\Gamma_m\in\Gamma_T,\Gamma_{m+1},\Gamma_{m+2},\cdots,\Gamma_n\in\Gamma_q$

The fictitious heat source Φ^i on boundary element Γ_i is given by

$$\Phi^{i}(\xi)=\sum_{j=1}^{l_i}N_j(\xi)[\Phi_{cj}(\xi_j^i)+\Phi_{sj}(\xi_j^i)] \quad (26)$$

where l_i is the node number of Γ_i, ξ is the local coordinate variable, ξ_j^i is the local coordinate of the node j in element i, $\Phi_{cj}(\xi_j^i)$ is the fictitious heat source of node j corresponding to $\cos\omega t$, $\Phi_{sj}(\xi_j^i)$ corresponds to $\sin\omega t$ and $N_j(\xi)$ is the shape function.

By putting formulations (25),(26) into (23),(24), Eqs. (23),(24) are discretized as follows:

$$T(P)=\sum_{i=1}^{n}\int_{\Gamma_i}\Big[\sum_{j=1}^{l_i}N_j(\xi)\Phi_{cj}(\xi_j^i)T_{cc}^{*}(P,\xi)+\sum_{j=1}^{l_i}N_j(\xi)\Phi_{sj}(\xi_j^i)T_{sc}^{*}(P,\xi)\Big]\cos\omega t\,d\Gamma(\xi)+\sum_{i=1}^{n}\int_{\Gamma_i}\Big[\sum_{j=1}^{l_i}N_j(\xi)\Phi_{cj}(\xi_j^i)T_{cs}^{*}(P,\xi)+\sum_{j=1}^{l_i}N_j(\xi)\Phi_{sj}(\xi_j^i)T_{ss}^{*}(P,\xi)\Big]\sin\omega t\,d\Gamma(\xi)=[H_c]\cos\omega t+[H_s]\sin\omega t \quad (27)$$

$$(1-\alpha)q(P)=\sum_{i=1}^{n}\int_{\Gamma_i}\Big[\sum_{j=1}^{l_i}N_j(\xi)\Phi_{cj}(\xi_j^i)q_{cc}^{*}(P,\xi)+\sum_{j=1}^{l_i}N_j(\xi)\Phi_{sj}(\xi_j^i)q_{sc}^{*}(P,\xi)\Big]\cos\omega t\,d\Gamma(\xi)+\sum_{i=1}^{n}\int_{\Gamma_i}\Big[\sum_{j=1}^{l_i}N_j(\xi)\Phi_{cj}(\xi_j^i)q_{cs}^{*}(P,\xi)+\sum_{j=1}^{l_i}N_j(\xi)\Phi_{sj}(\xi_j^i)q_{ss}^{*}(P,\xi)\Big]\sin\omega t\,d\Gamma(\xi) \quad (28)$$

Imposing the boundary condition (19),(20),we have

$$[H_c]\cos\omega t + [H_s]\sin\omega t = \overline{T}_c\cos\omega t + \overline{T}_s\sin\omega t \quad \text{on } \Gamma_T \tag{29}$$

$$[Q_c]\cos\omega t + [Q_s]\sin\omega t = \overline{q}_c\cos\omega t + \overline{q}_s\sin\omega t \quad \text{on } \Gamma_q \tag{30}$$

Eqs. (29),(30) is a linear equation of

$$[2\times\sum_{i=1}^{n} l_i]\times[2\times\sum_{i=1}^{n} l_i]$$

order based on variable $\Phi_{cj}(\xi_j^i)$, $\Phi_{sj}(\xi_j^i)$. Solving eq. (29),(30), we obtain the fictitious heat source on the boundary. By using Eq. (21),(22) the periodic temperature of any point inside the domain is obtained.

According to the character of T_{cc}^*, T_{cs}^*, T_{sc}^*, T_{ss}^*, q_{cc}^*, q_{cs}^*, q_{sc}^*, q_{ss}^*, Eqs. (27),(28) are singular integral equations. When P is located in the element Γ_i and $S\to P$, they are terms with the singularity of t^{-1}, $r^{-2}(r\to 0)$, respectively. For the singularity of r^{-1}, the value of the integral is evaluated in the Cauchy principle sense;[3] for the singularity of r^{-2}, the value of the integral has to be obtained by an indirect method, e.g. when a uniform potential function is surrounding the whole boundary, the sum of the differential value in the normal direction around the boundary must be zero.

Note Eq. (28),

$$\frac{\partial r}{\partial n} = \frac{\partial r}{\partial x}n_x + \frac{\partial r}{\partial y}n_y + \frac{\partial r}{\partial z}n_z$$

where n is the normal direction at the point P. In general, the harmonic element is used on the boundary; it is not easy to give the normal direction of the point on the arbitrary boundary directly, and furthermore, the normal directions of those points which are on the unsmooth boundary or on the corner are indeterminate. It is very convenient and efficient to use the nonharmonic element to solve this problem[4].

5 Numerical Results

Consider two simple examples which have exact solutions. One case of heat conduction in a half-infinite body, where the boundary temperature varies periodically with time as $A_T \sin\omega t$, is considered. The problem is shown schematically in Fig.2. The property constants are: $\rho c = 0.5\text{J/m}^3\text{K}$, $k = 1.0\text{W/mK}$, $\omega = 1\text{s}^{-1}$ and $A_T = 100℃$; the analytical solution is

$$T(x,t) = 100e^{-x}\sin(t-x) \quad ℃$$

Let us take a scope of 20m×20m in the boundary of the infinite body as the solution domain. The axis ox is the centre line of the domain. Using a 4-point inharmonic element, the numerical results are compared with analytic solutions as shown in Fig. 3 and Fig.4. It can be seen that the numerical results are in good agreement with the theoretical results.

Another simple case is of a hole with 5m radius located in an infinite body. The temperature of the sphere oscillates with time as $A_T\sin\omega t$. Assuming $\rho c = 0.5\text{J/(m}^3\text{K)}$; $k =$

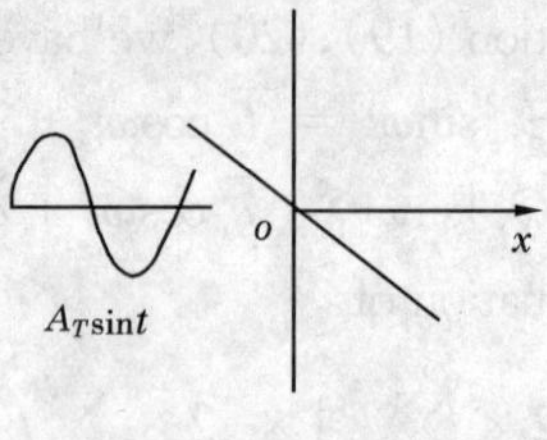

Fig. 2

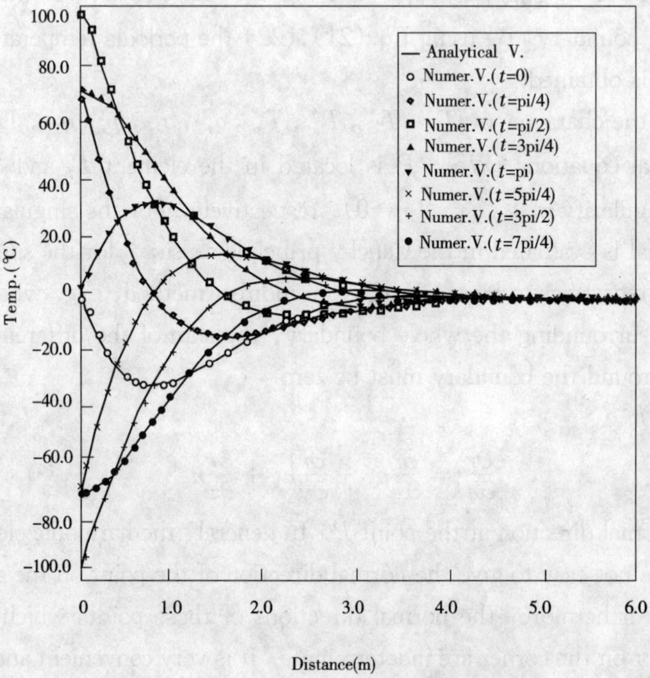

Fig. 3 Temperature distribution along *ox* with *t*

1.0W/(mK) and $\omega = 4\mathrm{s}^{-1}$, $A_T = 100$℃, the analytical solution is

$$T(r,t) = \frac{500}{r}\mathrm{e}^{-2(r-5)}\sin[4t - 2(r-5)]$$

Considering the symmetry, we can take a quarter of the body for the solution domain as shown in Fig. 5. Using a 4~8 point quadratic inharmonic element on the sphere, the maximum element number is 6 in the spherical direction and 5 in the radius direction. Fig. 6 and Fig. 7 show the comparison of the numerical results with the exact solution. It can also be seen that they are in very good agreement.

6 Conclusions

The indirect boundary element method based on a fictitious heat source for solving steady periodic heat conduction problems is presented. The fundamental solution of the temperature field in an infinite three-dimensional body under a periodic unit heat source is given and used in this method. It is convenient and effective to use this method for solving multidimensional problems in the arbitrary domains which may have periodic boundary conditions. The proposed method is proved to have good precision compared with theoretical solutions for two simple cases. The present analytical numerical method has enough precision in calculating complicated engineering problems with errors less than 2%.

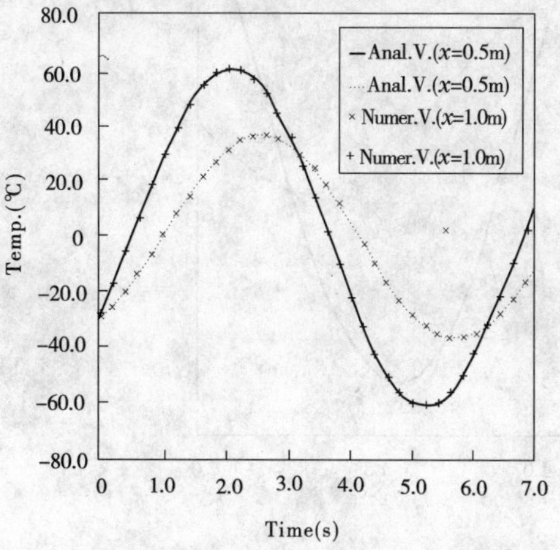

Fig. 4 Temperature variation with *t*

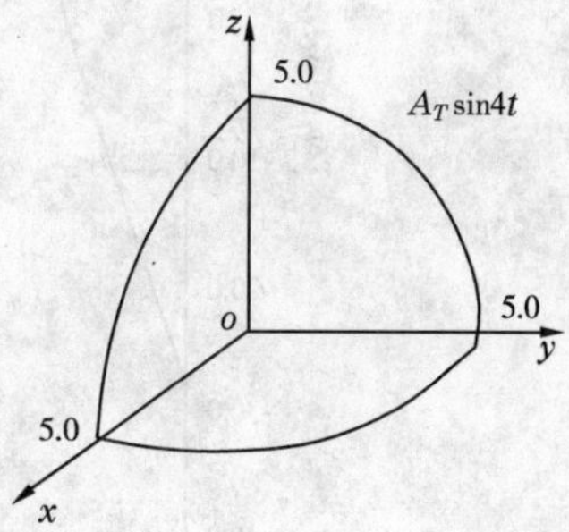

Fig. 5

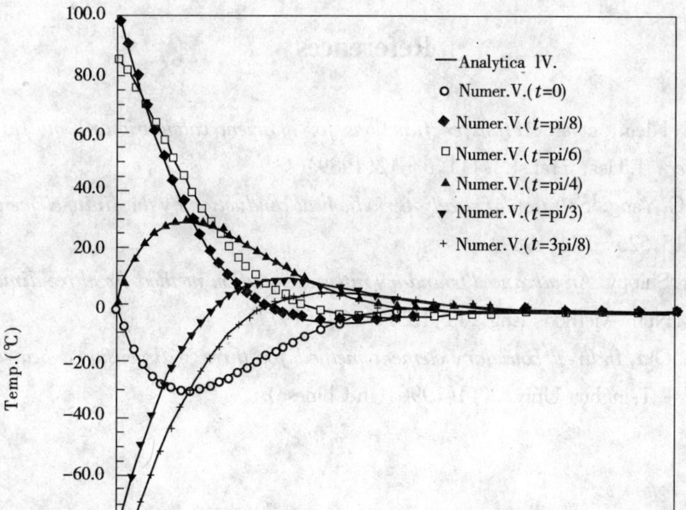

Fig. 6 Temperature distribution along *r* with *t*

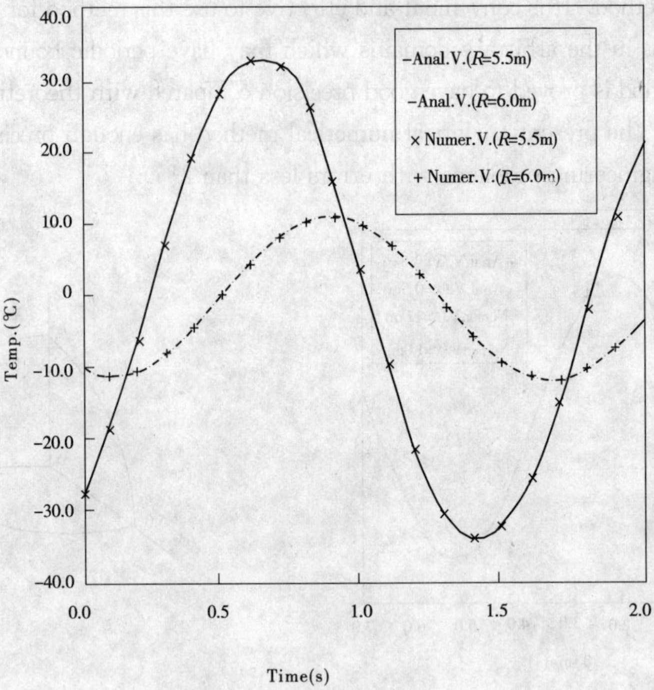

Fig. 7　Temperature variation with *t*

References

[1] J. E. Seem, S. A. Klein, et al.. *Transfer functions for efficient calculation of multidimensional transient heat transfer*. J. Heat Transf.. 111, 5～12(1989)

[2] G. R. Zheng, S. C. Yang. *Solution of steady periodic heat conduction by the finite-element method*. Numer. Heat Transf. 15, 525～534(1989)

[3] F. J. Rizzo, D. J. Shippy. *An advanced boundary integral equation method for three-dimensional thermoelasticity*. Int. J. Num. Methods Eng., 11, 1231～1247(1977)

[4] G. T. Liu, D. L. Qiu, *Indirect boundary element method for three－dimensional heat conductive engineering problem*. J. Tsinghua Univ.. (1)(1996)(in Chinese)

CONTINUOUS NEAR-TIP FIELDS FOR A DYNAMIC CRACK PROPAGATING IN A POWER-LAW ELASTIC-PLASTIC MATERIAL

Abstract By use of the J_2 flow theory and the rectangular components of field quantities, the near-tip asymptotic fields are studied for a dynamic mode -I crack propagating in an incompressible power-law elastic-plastic material under the plane strain conditions. Through assuming that the stress and strain components near a dynamic crack tip are of the same singularity, the present paper constructs with success the fully continuous dominant stress and strain fields. The angular variations of these fields are identical with those corresponding to the dynamic crack propagation in an elastic-perfectly plastic material (Leighton et al., 1987). The dynamic asymptotic field does not reduce to the quasi-static asymptotic field in the limit as the crack speed goes to zero.

Key words power-law hardening material; incompressibility; plane strain, mode - Ⅰ crack; dynamic propagation; asymptotic field

1 Introduction

Research on the asymptotic behavior of the dynamic crack-tip stress and deformation fields is very necessary for the foundation to establish a reasonable fracture criterion, but it is an extremely complicated subject. For elastic-perfectly plastic incompressible and compressible materials, several investigators (Slepyan, 1976; Achenbach and Dunayevsky, 1981; Gao and Nemat-Nasser, 1983a; Gao, 1985; Gao, 1987; Leighton et al., 1987; Zhu, 1995a) have more extensively studied the dynamic crack-tip fields; while for power-law hardening materials, only few examined the near-tip fields. The broad agreement in the available solution to dynamic crack was not found. The attention of this paper is focused on the steadily dynamic mode - Ⅰ crack growth in an incompressible power-law hardening material under the plane strain conditions.

Gao and Nemat-Nasser(1983b) presented the near-tip dynamic fields of a crack advancing in an incompressible power-law elastic-plastic material for all the three modes of cracks, in which the stresses and strains are logarithmically singular and the angular variations of field quantities for every mode are identical with those corresponding to dynamic crack growth in an elastic-perfectly plastic material (Gao and Nemat-Nasser, 1983a). Their solutions to the anti-plane mode-Ⅲ crack are fully continuous, whereas the solutions to the plane strain mode- Ⅰ crack contain strong discontinuities in stresses and strains. However, Leighton et al. (1987), through making an assumption that if the jump in a quantity is zero, then

本文选自《International Jovrnal of Fracture》1997 年刊，作者还有 X. K. ZHU, K. C. HWANG。

that quantity remains constant along any admissible deformation path across the discontinuity, argued that the maximum plastic work inequality prohibits the existence of discontinuities in stresses, strains and particle velocities for a dynamic crack propagating in incompressible elastic-perfectly plastic materials. Moreover, they succeeded in constructing the fully continuous crack-tip fields. By using of the above assumption, although implicitly, Drugan and Shen (1987) came to the same conclusion. Having regarded to the issue that the above assumption on the discontinuities was over-restrictive, Huang et al. (1995) and Zhu (1995b) adopted a thin layer approach that a discontinuity was treated as the limit of an infinitesimal thin layer in which all the field equations are assumed valid and the discontinuities of some quantities occur because of their steep but continuous variation across the thin thickness. As a result of asymptotic analysis, they have confirmed the assumption of Leighton et al. (1987) and shown that the existence of moving strong discontinuity is impossible for both elastic-perfectly plastic materials and power-law hardening materials except in some very special cases. Recently using very fine finite element calculations, Varias and Shih (1994) noticed the non-existence of strong discontinuities for dynamic cracks in the higher power-law hardening materials. On the other hand, from the point of view of continuum mechanics, we require that solution possesses as few discontinuities as possible (minimum dissipation of energy). For these reasons, it is essential and reasonable to further reconsider and construct the fully continuous dynamic crack-tip fields in power hardening materials.

By use of the rectangular components of field quantities and the assumption of the same singularity of stresses and strains, this paper constructs with success the fully continuous asymptotic stress and strain fields for a dynamic mode-Ⅰ crack propagating in an incompressible power-law elastic-plastic material.

2 Basic Equations

Consider a mode-Ⅰ crack growing steadily at speed V in a power-law elastic-plastic material under plane strain conditions. Within the infinitesimal deformation, the material is assumed to be incompressible, to deform plastically according to the J_2 flow theory. Both rectangular coordinates (x_1, x_2) with x_1 aligned in the direction of crack propagation and polar coordinates (r, θ) with $\theta = 0$ corresponding to the line ahead of the crack tip are introduced with their common origin at the tip of the crack and moving with it. Let $\sigma_{\alpha\beta}$ and υ_α be the rectangular components of stress tensor and particle velocity, respectively, then the motion equations are

$$\frac{\partial \sigma_{\alpha\beta}}{\partial x_\beta} = \rho \dot{\upsilon}_\alpha \tag{1}$$

where ρ is the mass density, the superimposed dot denotes a material time derivative. The summation convention to be followed throughout the paper for repeated indices is adopted, Greek indices α, β range over $1 \sim 2$. Let $\varepsilon_{\alpha\beta}$ indicate the rectangular components of strain tensor. In terms of the particle velocity, the components of strain rate tensor are

$$\dot{\varepsilon}_{\alpha\beta} = \frac{1}{2}\left(\frac{\partial v_\alpha}{\partial x_\beta} + \frac{\partial v_\beta}{\partial x_\alpha}\right) \tag{2}$$

For the case of elastic incompressibility and perfect-plasticity, the deformation of material must meet the following incompressibility condition

$$\frac{\partial v_1}{\partial x_1} + \frac{\partial v_2}{\partial x_2} = 0 \tag{3}$$

Under the conditions of plane strain and incompressibility, from the J_2 flow theory, the stress and strain components should meet the Prandtl-Reuss elastic-plastic constitutive equations.

$$\begin{aligned} \dot{\varepsilon}_{11} &= -\dot{\varepsilon}_{22} = \frac{1}{4\mu}(\dot{\sigma}_{11} - \dot{\sigma}_{22}) + \frac{1}{2}\lambda(\sigma_{11} - \sigma_{22}) \\ \dot{\varepsilon}_{12} &= \frac{1}{2\mu}\dot{\sigma}_{12} + \lambda\sigma_{12} \end{aligned} \tag{4}$$

in which μ is the shear modulus, λ is the plastic flow factor. Let σ_0 be initial uniaxial yield stress. The uniaxial elastic-plastic, power-law, stress strain relations considered in the present work are

$$\varepsilon = \begin{cases} \sigma/E, & \text{for elastic range} \\ \sigma/E + c(\sigma - \sigma_0)^n, & \text{for plastic range} \end{cases} \tag{5}$$

where σ and ε are the uniaxial stress and strain respectively, E is Young's modulus, c is a material constant and $n > 1$ is the power hardening exponent.

In terms of the normality rule of plastic deformation in the theory of plasticity, from the power-law hardening relation (5), we can get the plastic flow factor

$$\lambda = \frac{3nc(\sigma_e - \sigma_0)^{n-1}}{2\sigma_e}\dot{\sigma}_e \tag{6}$$

in which σ_e is the effective stress. Under plane strain conditions, it is given by

$$\sigma_e = \sqrt{3}\left[\frac{1}{4}(\sigma_{11} - \sigma_{22})^2 + \sigma_{12}^2\right]^{1/2} \tag{7}$$

3 Asymptotic Field Equations and Fully Continuous Solutions

3.1 Kinematical Quantities

For the elastic-perfectly plastic materials, the stress components near a dynamic crack tip are bounded (cf. Leighton et al., 1987). However for the power-law hardening materials, the stresses should generally be singular with reference to the stationary HRR field and the quasi-static asymptotic solution (c. f. Gao and Hwang, 1981). According to the investigation of Gao and Nemat-Nasser (1983b) for the same problem considered here, it is supposed that the stress components near a dynamic crack tip are of the following logarithmic singularity.

$$\sigma_{\alpha\beta}(r,\theta) = \left(\ln\frac{R}{r}\right)^{\delta}\sum_{m=0}^{\infty}\sigma_{\alpha\beta}^{(m)}(\theta)\left(\ln\frac{R}{r}\right)^{-m} \tag{8}$$

where $\delta > 0$ is an undetermined exponent of stress-singularity, $\sigma_{\alpha\beta}^{(m)}(\theta)$ are the angular functions of the mth order stress field. R is a constant with the physical dimension of length, which may be used as a measure of the plastic zone size. Note that: our experience showed if the stresses with the power singularity is anticipated, there exist no solutions corresponding to the first-order power approximation for the problem considered in this paper.

If we only consider the dominant term (i.e. $m=0$) of the singular stress expansions (8), from the steady-state growth condition $\mathrm{d}(\,)/\mathrm{d}t = -V\partial(\,)/\partial x_1$ (cf. Gao and Nemat-Nasser, 1983a or Leighton et al., 1987) and the motion(1), it appears that the two possibilities leading to the strongest allowable singularity in particle acceleration are

$$v_\alpha \sim A_\alpha\left(\ln\frac{R}{r}\right)^{\delta+1}, \qquad \frac{\mathrm{d}A_\alpha}{\mathrm{d}\theta} = 0 \tag{9a}$$

or

$$v_\alpha \sim B_\alpha(\theta)\left(\ln\frac{R}{r}\right)^{\delta} \tag{9b}$$

that is, the particle velocity near the dynamic crack tip must be taken the asymptotic expansions as

$$v_\alpha(r,\theta) = \left(\ln\frac{R}{r}\right)^{\delta}\left[A_\alpha\ln\frac{R}{r} + B_\alpha(\theta)\right] + o\left[\left(\ln\frac{R}{r}\right)^{\delta}\right] \tag{10}$$

where $A_1 \geqslant 0$ is an unknown constant, $A_2 \equiv 0$ for mode-Ⅰ crack, $B_\alpha(\theta)$ are the angular functions of particle velocity; $o[\,]$ is the infinitesimal order symbol. The further detailed investigation of Zhu and Hwang (1996) (cf. Gao and Nemat-Nasser, 1983b) showed that: when $A_1 \neq 0$, one can only construct the asymptotic crack-tip fields with discontinuous stresses and strains. However, as mentioned earlier in the introduction, both Leighton et al. (1987) with their assumption and Huang et al. (1995) and Zhu (1995b) by using the thin layer approach have showed that the existence of moving strong discontinuities are impossible generally. As an attempt to construct fully continuous asymptotic fields, this paper is motivated by the fully bounded continuous solutions of Leighton et al. (1987) and chooses $A_1 = 0$, that is to assume that the singularities of particle velocity or strain components are the same as those of stress components. Then(10) becomes

$$v_\alpha(r,\theta) = (\ln\frac{R}{r})^{\delta}B_\alpha(\theta) + o\left[\left(\ln\frac{R}{r}\right)^{\delta}\right] \tag{11}$$

Substituting (11) into (3) gets the incompressibility condition which is expressed by the angular functions of particle velocity

$$B'_2(\theta) = B'_1(\theta)\tan\theta \tag{12}$$

where the prime[1] stands for $\partial/\partial\theta$. From (2),(11) and (12), it follows that

$$\begin{aligned}\dot{\varepsilon}_{11} &= -\dot{\varepsilon}_{22} = -\frac{1}{r}\left(\ln\frac{R}{r}\right)^{\delta}\cos\theta B'_2(\theta) + o\left[\frac{1}{r}\left(\ln\frac{R}{r}\right)^{\delta}\right]\\ \dot{\varepsilon}_{12} &= \frac{1}{2r\sin\theta}\left(\ln\frac{R}{r}\right)^{\delta}\cos2\theta B'_2(\theta) + o\left[\frac{1}{r}\left(\ln\frac{R}{r}\right)^{\delta}\right]\end{aligned} \tag{13}$$

The above representations show that the strain components $\varepsilon_{\alpha\beta}$ are of the order of the logarithmic singularity like $(\ln(R/r))^{\delta}$, thus it is as same as the assumed singularity of stress.

3.2 Dynamical Quantities

By virtue of expressions (8), the asymptotic form of the effective stress σ_e is given by

$$\sigma_e(r,\theta) = \left(\ln\frac{R}{r}\right)^{\delta}\sigma_e^{(0)}(\theta) + \left(\ln\frac{R}{r}\right)^{\delta-1}\sigma_e^{(1)}(\theta) + o\left[\left(\ln\frac{R}{r}\right)^{\delta-1}\right] \tag{14}$$

Under the steady-state condition, putting (14) into (6), we have

$$\begin{aligned}\lambda = \frac{3}{2r}ncV\left(\ln\frac{R}{r}\right)^{(n-1)\delta}[\sigma_e^{(0)}(\theta) + \cdots]^{n-2} \times\\ \left[\sin\theta\sigma_e^{(0)\prime}(\theta) + \left(\ln\frac{R}{r}\right)^{-1}(\sin\theta\sigma_e^{(1)\prime}(\theta) + \delta\cos\theta\sigma_e^{(0)}(\theta))\right] + \cdots\end{aligned} \tag{15}$$

where the dots denote the neglected higher terms. On the other hand, (8), (13) and (4) yield $\lambda \sim r^{-1}$. Since $n>1$ is assumed, one can conclude

$$\sigma_e^{(0)\prime}(\theta) = 0 \quad \text{or} \quad \sigma_e^{(0)}(\theta) = \sqrt{3}K, \qquad \delta = \frac{1}{n-1} \tag{16}$$

in which the second equation is the constraint condition of plastic deformation in the power-law hardening material, K is a free constant relating to the power hardening exponent n that can not be determined from the asymptotic solution, but it can be determined by matching the asymptotic solution and the far-field solution such as the finite element numerical solution.

From (8), using the steady-state condition, we have the stress rate components

$$\dot{\sigma}_{\alpha\beta}(r,\theta) = \frac{V}{r}\left(\ln\frac{R}{r}\right)^{\delta}\sin\theta\sigma_{\alpha\beta}^{(0)\prime}(\theta) + o\left[\frac{1}{r}\left(\ln\frac{R}{r}\right)^{\delta}\right] \tag{17}$$

Substitution of (8), (14) and (16) into (7) yields the relationship among the angular functions of first-order stress components in (17) as follows

$$\frac{1}{4}(\sigma_{11}^{(0)}(\theta) - \sigma_{22}^{(0)}(\theta))^2 + (\sigma_{12}^{(0)}(\theta))^2 = K^2 \tag{18}$$

This equation is similar to the Von Mises yield condition of incompressible elastic-perfectly plastic material under the plane strains. Therefore, we may introduce a stress functions $\psi(\theta)$ in such a manner that

$$\begin{aligned}\sigma_{11}^{(0)}(\theta) &= \sigma_h^{(0)}(\theta) - K\cos(\psi(\theta) - 2\theta)\\ \sigma_{22}^{(0)}(\theta) &= \sigma_h^{(0)}(\theta) + K\cos(\psi(\theta) - 2\theta)\\ \sigma_{12}^{(0)}(\theta) &= K\sin(\psi(\theta) - 2\theta)\end{aligned} \tag{19}$$

where $\sigma_h^{(0)}(\theta) = (\sigma_{11}^{(0)}(\theta) + \sigma_{22}^{(0)}(\theta))/2$ is the angular function of mean stress of hydrostatic stress. K is a free constant which is similar to the shear flow stress k (cf. Leighton et al.,

1987).

3.3 The Final Equations

Substituting the representations (8),(11),(19) into the motion(1) and expressions (8),(13),(17),(19) into the constitutive (4), after some manipulation and by noting the relation (12), we obtain the final governing equations of the angular functions of the dominant asymptotic fields for the plastic regions as follows

$$
\begin{aligned}
&(\psi'(\theta)-2)(\cos^2\psi - M^2\sin^2\theta)=0\\
&\overline{\lambda}(\theta)=\frac{1}{2}(\psi'(\theta)-2)\sin\theta\tan\psi\\
&\sigma_h^{(0)\prime}(\theta)=K(\psi'(\theta)-2)\sin\psi\\
&\overline{B}'_1(\theta)=M^{-2}(\psi'(\theta)-2)\cos\psi\cot\theta\\
&\overline{B}'_2(\theta)=M^{-2}(\psi'(\theta)-2)\cos\psi
\end{aligned}
\qquad (20)
$$

where $M=V(\rho/\mu)^{1/2}$ is the Mach number, the dimensionless parameter $\overline{\lambda}(\theta)=\mu r\lambda(r,\theta)/V$, $\overline{B}_\alpha(\theta)=\mu B_\alpha(\theta)/KV$.

From the deformation symmetry of mode - Ⅰ crack and the free traction on the crack faces, the boundary conditions associated with the differential (20) are

$$\psi(0)=0,\qquad \psi(\pi)=\pi,\qquad B_2(0)=0,\qquad \sigma_h^{(0)}(\pi)=K \qquad (21)$$

3.4 Fully Continuous Solutions

It is easy to observe that the above governing (20) and boundary conditions (21) of the dominant asymptotic fields for the dynamic mode - Ⅰ crack in power-law hardening incompressible materials are exactly the same as those of corresponding crack-tip fields in elastic-perfectly plastic incompressible materials (Leighton et al., 1987). Moreover, the further study has shown when $A_1\neq0$ the possible elastic unloading condition for the two kinds of material is also same and when $A_1=0$ the only possible elastic unloading sector is a region of constant stress which must be at yield when the elastic sector is connected with a plastic sector (cf. Leighton et al., 1987; Zhu, 1995b and Zhu and Hwang, 1996). The only difference for the two cases is that K in the stress fields (19) is a free constant relating to the power hardening exponent n in the present work, but it is the shear yielding stress for the perfectly-plastic materials. Therefore, the angular variatons of the field quantities in this paper are identical with those for elastic-perfectly plastic cases which have been considered in great detail by Leighton et al., (1987). The crack tip field consists of a uniform sector in $0\leqslant\theta\leqslant\theta_1^*$, a non-uniform centered fan sector in $\theta_1^*\leqslant\theta\leqslant\theta_2^*$, and another uniform sector in $\theta_2^*\leqslant\theta\leqslant\pi$. For example, the stress function $\psi(\theta)$ and the angular mean stress $\sigma_h^{(0)}(\theta)$ in the angular stress components (19) are given by

$$
\psi(\theta)=\begin{cases}
2\theta, & \text{if } 0\leqslant\theta\leqslant\theta_1^*,\\
\cos^{-1}(-M\sin\theta), & \text{if } \theta_1^*\leqslant\theta\leqslant\theta_2^*,\\
2\theta-\pi, & \text{if } \theta_2^*\leqslant\theta\leqslant\pi
\end{cases}
\qquad (22)
$$

and

$$\sigma_h^{(0)}(\theta) = \begin{cases} K[1 + M\sin\theta_1^* - 2E(\theta_1^*;M) - M\sin\theta_2^* - 2E(\theta_2^*;M)], & \text{if } 0 \leqslant \theta \leqslant \theta_1^* \\ K[1 + M\sin\theta - 2E(\theta;M) - M\sin\theta_2^* - 2E(\theta_2^*;M)], & \text{if } \theta_1^* \leqslant \theta \leqslant \theta_2^* \\ K, & \text{if } \theta_2^* \leqslant \theta \leqslant \pi \end{cases} \tag{23}$$

where $E(\theta;M)$ is the elliptic integral of the second kind, θ_1^* and θ_2^* are the sector transition angles defined by

$$\begin{aligned} \theta_1^* &= \sin^{-1}\left(\frac{M + \sqrt{8 + M^2}}{4}\right) \\ \theta_2^* &= \pi - \sin^{-1}\left(\frac{-M + \sqrt{8 + M^2}}{4}\right) \end{aligned} \tag{24}$$

From(22), (23) and (19), the angular distributions of the stress function ψ and the stress components are shown in Fig. 1 and Fig. 2, respectively. These results are the plastic solution around the entire dynamic crack tip without elastic unloading. K in Fig. 2 is a constant relating to the power hardening exponent n that cannot be determined from the asymptotic solution, but it can be determined by matching the asymptotic solution and the far-field

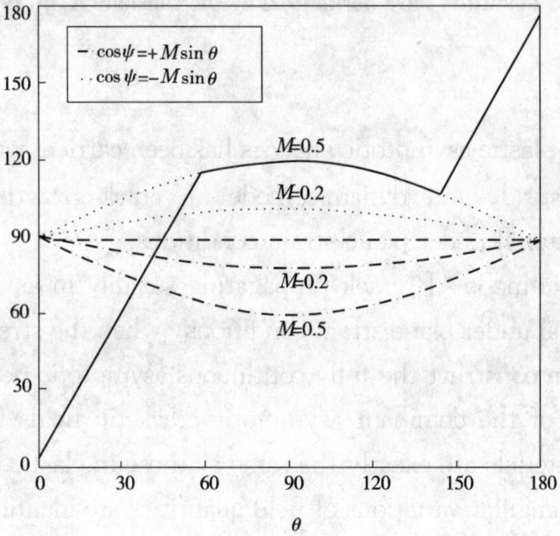

Fig. 1 Solution curves for $\psi(\theta)$ of the type $(\psi)\theta = \pm M\sin\theta$ for $M = 0.2, 0.5$. The solid line represents the angular variations of the stress function over the crack tip for $M = 0.5$

soluti on such as the finite element numerical solution. Fig. 2 shows that the tensile stress on the fracture plane directly ahead of the moving crack tip decreases with the increasing crack speed M. It is similar to the result for elastic-perfectly plastic materials (cf. Leighton et al., 1987), the current dynamic asymptotic solution for power law materials does not reduce to the corresponding quasi-static asymptotic solution (c. f. Gao and Hwang, 1981) because of the absence of elastic unloading behind the crack tip. The possible reason is that the domain of validity of the dynamic asymptotic filed vanishes with vanishing crack tip speed (Leighton et al., 1987).

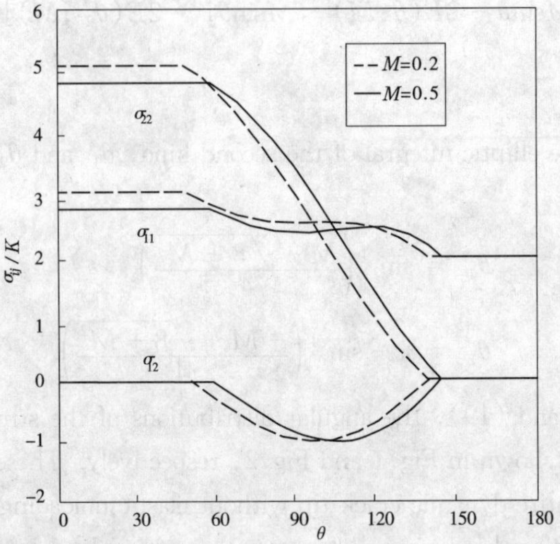

Fig. 2　The angular distributions of the dominant stress components for $0\leqslant\theta\leqslant\pi$. All stress quantities have normalized by the constant K in(19)

4　Conclusions

A first-order elastic-plastic asymptotic analysis has been carried out by using J_2 flow theory for the problem of steady-state dynamic mode - Ⅰ crack growth in an incompressible power-law hardening material under plane strain conditions.

(1) For the dynamic mode - Ⅰ crack propagating steadily in an incompressible power-law elastic-plastic material under plane strain conditions, when the stress and strain-singularity are the same, one can construct the fully continuous asymptotic near-tip fields.

(2) The structures of the dominant asymptotic crack-tip fields for mode - Ⅰ crack in power-law hardening materials are exactly the same as those in elastic-perfectly plastic materials, that is to say, the angular variations of field quantities are identical, the elastic unloading does not appear behind the crack-tip, the crack tip is enclosed entirely by plastic sectors. Therefore, the dynamic asymptotic solution does not reduce to the corresponding quasistatic solution which includes elastic unloading as the crack growth speed goes to zero.

(3) The present asymptotic stress field includes a free constant K relating to the power hardening exponent n which can not be determined from the asymptotic solution, but it can be determined by matching the asymptotic solution and the far-field solution.

(4) For a power-law hardening material, the fully continuous stress and strain fields at a dynamic mode - Ⅰ crack tip possess the same logarithmic singularity

$$\sigma_{\alpha\beta} \sim \left(\ln\frac{R}{r}\right)^{1/n-1},\qquad \varepsilon_{\alpha\beta} \sim \left(\ln\frac{R}{r}\right)^{1/n-1}$$

(5) When $n \rightarrow \infty$, the present solutions will reduce to those given by Leighton et al. (1987) for elastic-perfectly plastic incompressible materials.

Acknowledgments

This work is supported by the National Science Foundation of China and the China Postdoctoral Science Foundation.

References

[1] Achenbach, J.D. ,Dunayevsky, V.(1981). *Fields near a rapidly propagating crack-tip in an elastic perfectly-plastic material*. Journal of the Mechanics and Physics of Solids 29,283～303

[2] Drugan, W.J. ,Shen, Y.(1987). *Restrictions of dynamically propagating surfaces of strong discontinuity in elastic-plastic solids*. Journal of the Mechanics and Physics of Solids 35,771～787

[3] Gao, Y.C.(1985). *Asymptotic dynamic solution to the mode - Ⅰ propagating crack-tip filed*. International Journal of Fracture 29,171～180

[4] Gao,Y.C.(1987). *Plane stress dynamic plastic field near a propagating crack-tip*. International Journal of Fracture 34,111～129

[5] Gao,Y.C., Nemat-Nasser, S.(1983a). *Dynamic fields near a crack tip growing in an elastic perfectly-plastic solids*. Mechanics of Materials 2,47～60

[6] Gao,Y.C. ,Nemat-Nasser, S.(1983b). *Near tip dynamic fields for a crack advancing in a power law elastic-plastic material; Mode Ⅰ, Ⅱ and Ⅲ*. Mechanics of Materials 2,305～317

[7] Gao,Y.C. ,Hwang, K.C.(1981). *Elastic-plastic fields in a steady crack growth in a strain-hardening material*. In Fracture Mechanics (Edited by D. Francois). Proceedings of the 5th International Conference on Fracture. Cannes, France, 669～682

[8] Huang, Y., Zhu,X.K.,Hwang, K.C.(1995). *On the possibility of strong discontinuity for dynamic crack propagating in compressible elastic perfectly-plastic material*. Acta Mechanica Solida Sinica 8, S. Lssuc,188～193

[9] Leighton, J.T., Champion, C.R. ,Freund, L.B.(1987). *Asymptotic analysis of steady dynamic crack growth in an elastic-plastic material*. Journal of the Mechanics and Physics of Solids 35,536～541

[10] Slepyan,L.I.(1976). *Crack dynamics in an elastic-plastic body*. lzv. Akad. SSSR, Mekhanika Tverdogo Tela 11. 144～153

[11] Varias, A.G. ,Shih,C.F.(1994). *Dynamic steady crack growth in elastic-plastic solids-Propagation of strong discontinuities*. Journal of the Mechanics and Physics of Solids 42,1817～1848

[12] Zhu, X.K.(1995a). *Elastic perfectly-plastic near-tip fields of dynamic crack in compressible material*. Modern Mathematics and Mechanics-IV,173～178(in Chinese)

[13] Zhu,X.K.(1995B). *Research on the dynamic near-tip fields in elastic-plastic materials*, Ph.D. dissertation, Tsinghua University, Beijing, China

[14] Zhu,X.K.,Hwang, K.C.(1996). *Dynamic asymptotic fields near a crack tip growing in a power-law hardening compressible material*. Mechanics of Materials 24,213～220

THREE-DIMENSIONAL STRESS AND DISPLACEMENT FIELDS NEAR AN ELLIPTICAL CRACK FRONT

Abstract Local stress and deformation fields for an elliptical crack embedded in an infinite elastic body subjected to normal, shear and mixed loads are considered. Particular emphasis is placed on the direction of propagation of points along the crack border. A confocal curvilinear coordinate system related to a fundamental ellipsoid, and a local spherical coordinate system attached to the crack border are adopted. Using asymptotic analysis, this paper obtains the stress and displacement fields in a plane inclined to the 3-D crack front. Results show that the present solutions are independent of the curvature of the ellipse, and different from those given by Sih (1991). Based on two different fracture criteria, crack growth analysis shows that a 3-D crack would propagate in the direction of the normal plane along the crack front. As a result, the fracture initiation and propagation of a 3-D flat crack can be analyzed in the plane normal to the crack front, and the local fields in the normal plane are the linear superposition of the plane strain mode - Ⅰ, mode - Ⅱ, and mode - Ⅲ crack-tip fields.

Key words Three-dimensional fracture; elliptical crack; stress and displacement fields; stress intensity factor; crack propagation

1 Introduction

Flaws or cracks in engineering structures, especially in pressure vessels and large hydraulic structures, are three-dimensional (3-D) in nature. Such a crack problem should be analyzed using 3-D fracture mechanics theories. In general, a complex state of stresses exists inside the structures, particularly in the neighborhood of cracks, where the stresses undergo a sharp variation. These stresses can often lead to unexpected failure. However, due to the complexity of practical problems and the difficulty of the analysis, the integrity assessment of engineering structures remains mostly using two-dimensional analysis. It appears that 3-D analysis for the crack problems warrants further development.

The 3-D crack problems have received much attention for many years. A number of technical papers presenting analytic and numerical results for the problem are available in the literature. Most concern only the calculation of the stress intensity factors (SIF) for 3-D cracks. Kassir and Sih(1975) systematically introduced the results of 3-D cracks under a variety of loads in early 1970's. The content includes the local stress fields around a circular crack and around an embedded or external elliptical crack, and SIF solutions under various loading conditions. Raju and Newman (1979) summarized the SIF results for 3-D surface cracks. Nishioka and Atluri (1983) and Kuo et al. (1992) reported analytical solutions to

本文选自《International Journal of Fracture》2001年刊，作者还有 X. K. ZHU, Y. J. CHAO。

SIF for embedded and surface elliptical cracks subjected to arbitrary loading. Using asymptotic analysis, Kassir and Sih (1966) showed that the local stress field for a embedded elliptical crack in the plane normal to the crack front is the same as the linear sum of the plane strain mode-Ⅰ, mode-Ⅱ and mode-Ⅲ crack-tip stress fields. The same conclusion was obtained by Qin and Tang (1993) for an embedded flat curvilinear crack, and by Li et al. (1988) for a surface semi-elliptical crack in three dimensions. From these results, although not proved theoretically, one assumes that the propagation of a 3-D crack is in the direction lying in the normal plane (Meguid, 1989). Consequently, the analysis of 3-D crack growth is still simplified as a plane strain crack problem, such as the analysis by Chahrour and Ohtsu (1994).

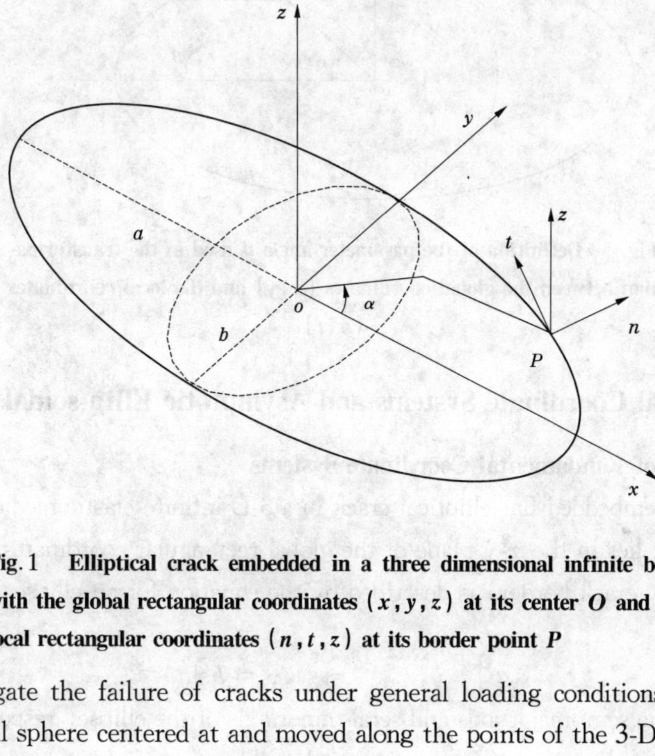

Fig. 1 Elliptical crack embedded in a three dimensional infinite body with the global rectangular coordinates (x, y, z) at its center O and the local rectangular coordinates (n, t, z) at its border point P

To investigate the failure of cracks under general loading conditions, the stresses at points on a small sphere centered at and moved along the points of the 3-D crack front could be used. For this purpose, recently Sih (1991) has given the local stress field of a 3-D elliptical crack in a plane inclined to the crack border. However, this stress field is not only very complex in form, but also depends on the curvature of the ellipse (See Eq. (2.6) in Sih (1991)). Based on this stress field and the strain energy density theory, Sih (1991) analyzed the initial growth direction for a 3-D elliptical crack under an inclined uniform tensile load. Sih concluded that '*It is first found that fracture will not run in the normal plane except at the intersections of the major and minor axes with the crack border*', and then presented the location of the inclined plane in which the crack would extend (See p. 37 and Table 2.1 in Sih, 1991). Obviously, this conclusion contradicts the common practice mentioned above in studying the 3-D crack propagation. Why?

It is the major objective of the present paper to revisit this problem and to theoretically clarify the controversy. By adopting the method of Green and Sneddon (1950), this paper considers the local stress and displacement fields for a 3-D embedded elliptical crack under an inclined tension. Based on two different fracture criteria, the stress field is then applied to investigate the possibility of crack propagation at a point on the crack front in a plane inclined to the front. The comparisons between the present results and Sih (1991) are provided finally.

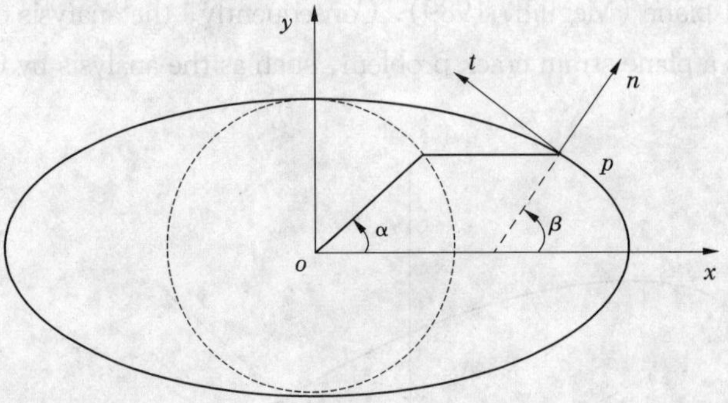

Fig. 2　Definition of the parameter angle β used in the transformation between the global coordinates (x, y) and the local coordinates (n, t)

2　Fundamental Coordinate Systems and Asymptotic Ellip-soidal Coordinates

2.1　Three Sets of Fundamental Coordinate Systems

Consider an embedded flat elliptical crack in a 3-D infinite elastic medium, as shown in Fig. 1. The crack lies in the x-y plane of the global rectangular coordinates (x, y, z). The crack front (i.e., crack border) is described by the equation for an ellipse

$$z = 0: \qquad \frac{x^2}{a^2} + \frac{y^2}{b^2} = 1 \quad \text{or} \quad \begin{matrix} x = a\cos\alpha \\ y = b\sin\alpha \end{matrix} \tag{1}$$

where a, b are the semi-major axis and semi-minor axis of the ellipse, respectively, and α is a reference angle of the parametric equation of the ellipse.

Let a local rectangular coordinates at a point P on the crack border be $(n, t, z,)$, in which $n, t, z,$ are directed along the principal normal, tangential, and binormal of the periphery curve, respectively, as shown in Fig. 2. The transformation between (x, y) and (n, t) is given by

$$x = a\cos\alpha + n\cos\beta - t\sin\beta, \qquad y = b\sin\alpha + n\sin\beta + t\cos\beta \tag{2}$$

where β is the angle between the outward unit normal vector of the elliptic periphery and the x-axis, as shown in Fig. 2. More precisely, β is related to the parametric equations of the ellipse as

$$\sin\beta = a\Pi^{-1/2}\sin\alpha, \qquad \cos\beta = b\Pi^{-1/2}\cos\alpha \tag{3}$$

where $\Pi = a^2\sin^2\alpha + b^2\cos^2\alpha$. For the convenience of asymptotic analysis, a local spherical coordinate system (r, θ, φ) is introduced at the boundary point P, as shown in Fig. 3. Then for a point M in space near point P, the local rectangular coordinates are related to the spherical coordinates as

$$n = r\cos\theta\cos\varphi, \qquad t = r\sin\varphi, \qquad z = r\sin\theta\cos\varphi \tag{4}$$

Substituting of (3) and (4) into (2), one obtains the coordinate components of the space point M in the global rectangular coordinate system as follows

$$\left.\begin{aligned} x &= a\cos\alpha + r\Pi^{-1/2}(b\cos\alpha\cos\theta\cos\varphi - a\sin\alpha\sin\varphi) \\ y &= b\sin\alpha + r\Pi^{-1/2}(a\sin\alpha\cos\theta\cos\varphi + b\cos\alpha\sin\varphi) \\ z &= r\sin\theta\cos\varphi \end{aligned}\right\} \tag{5}$$

in which α determines the position of the boundary point P on the elliptic periphery, and (r, θ, φ) determines the position of the space point M relative to point P.

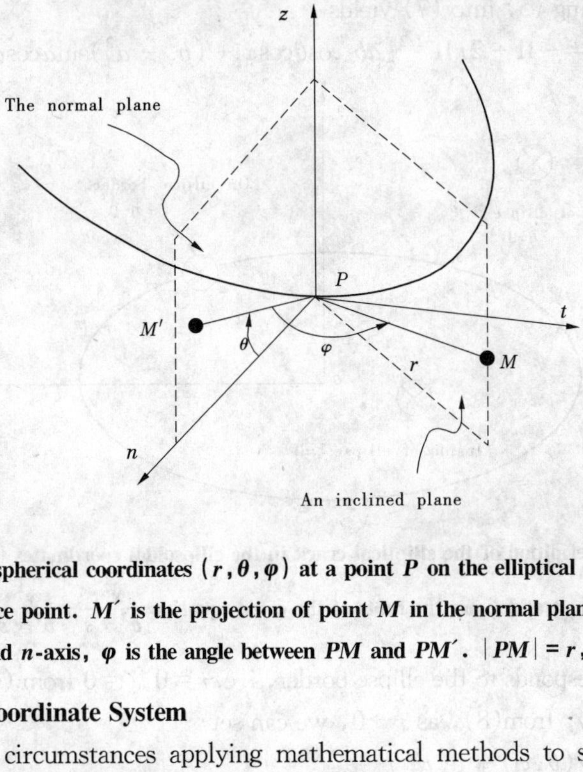

Fig. 3 The local spherical coordinates (r, θ, φ) at a point P on the elliptical crack front. Notice that M is a space point. M' is the projection of point M in the normal plane. θ is the angle between PM' and n-axis, φ is the angle between PM and PM'. $|PM| = r$, $|PM'| = r\cos\varphi$

2.2 Ellipsoidal Coordinate System

Under certain circumstances applying mathematical methods to study physical problems, it is more convenient to use orthogonal curvilinear coordinates than to use rectangular coordinates. Adopting the method of Green and Sneddon (1950), a confocal curvilinear coordinate system is used in this work to investigate the 3-D crack problem. Whittaker and Watson (1927) defined the confocal coordinates relative to the fundamental ellipsoidal Eq. (1) (here the third semi-axis $c = 0$) simply referred to as ellipsoidal coordinates hereafter. The ellipsoidal coordinates (ξ, η, ζ) are related to the rectangular coordinates (x, y, z) in the following form

$$\left.\begin{aligned} a^2(a^2-b^2)x^2 &= (a^2+\xi)(a^2+\eta)(a^2+\zeta) \\ b^2(b^2-a^2)y^2 &= (b^2+\xi)(b^2+\eta)(b^2+\zeta) \\ a^2b^2z^2 &= \xi\eta\zeta \end{aligned}\right\} \tag{6}$$

and

$$\xi+\eta+\zeta = x^2+y^2+z^2-a^2-b^2 \tag{7}$$

where $-a^2 \leqslant \zeta \leqslant -b^2 \leqslant \eta \leqslant 0 \leqslant \xi \leqslant \infty$. One can verify that the three ellipsoidal coordinates (ξ, η, ζ) constitute an orthogonal curvilinear system. In the crack plane $z=0$, $\xi=0$ represents the points (x, y) inside of the ellipse, $\eta=0$ the outside of the ellipse, and $\xi=\eta=0$ the border of the ellipse, as shown in Fig. 4.

2.3 Asymptotic Relation Between Ellipsoidal Coordinates and Spherical Coordinates

For convenience, this section will originally derive an asymptotic relation between the ellipsoidal coordinates (ξ, η, ζ) and the local spherical coordinates (r, θ, φ) of the space point M. Substituting (5) into (7) yields

$$\xi+\eta+\zeta = -\Pi + 2r\Pi^{-1/2}[ab\cos\theta\cos\varphi + (b^2-a^2)\sin\alpha\cos\alpha\sin\varphi] + r^2 \tag{8}$$

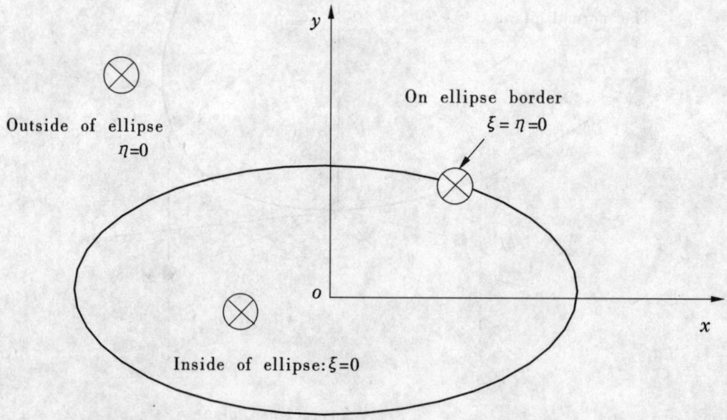

Fig. 4 Definition of the elliptical crack in the ellipsoidal coordinates (ξ, η, ζ). Notice that ξ, η and ζ are the roots of the cubic equation $\frac{x^2}{a^2+s}+\frac{y^2}{b^2+s}+\frac{z^2}{s}-1=0$

Since $\xi=\eta=0$ corresponds to the ellipse border, i. e. $r=0$, $\zeta=0$ from (6). Therefore without loss of generality, from (8), as $r\to 0$, we can set

$$\left.\begin{aligned} \zeta &= -\Pi + r\chi(\theta,\varphi) + o(r) \\ \xi+\eta &= 2r\Pi^{-1/2}[ab\cos\theta\cos\varphi + (b^2-a^2)\sin\alpha\cos\alpha\sin\varphi] - r\chi(\theta,\varphi) + o(r) \end{aligned}\right. \tag{9}$$

where $\chi(\theta, \varphi)$ is an undetermined function, $o(r)$ represents the neglected higher-order terms than r^1.

From the third Eqs. of (5) and (6), and the first Eq. of (9), another equation relating to ξ and ζ is found

$$\xi\eta = -\frac{a^2b^2\sin^2\theta\cos^2\varphi}{\Pi}\left[r^2 + r^3\frac{\chi(\theta,\varphi)}{\Pi}\right] + o(r^3) \tag{10}$$

After substituting the first Eqs. of (5) and (8)~(10) into the first Eq. of (6), the r^0-order terms are automatically the same on both sides of the equation. Then letting the coefficients of r^1-order terms be equal, we have

$$\chi(\theta,\varphi) = 2(b^2 - a^2)\Pi^{-1/2}\sin\alpha\cos\alpha\sin\varphi \tag{11}$$

By inserting (11) into (9) and (10), and noting that $-\pi\leqslant\theta\leqslant\pi$, $-\pi/2<\varphi<\pi/2$, we obtain the asymptotic relationship between the ellipsoidal coordinates and the local spherical coordinates

$$\left.\begin{aligned}\xi &= abr\Pi^{-1/2}(\cos\theta + 1)\cos\varphi + o(r)\\ \eta &= abr\Pi^{-1/2}(\cos\theta - 1)\cos\varphi + o(r)\\ \zeta &= -\Pi + 2r(b^2 - a^2)\Pi^{-1/2}\sin\alpha\cos\alpha\sin\varphi + o(r)\end{aligned}\right\} \tag{12}$$

Notice that the above asymptotic relationship is the basis of the analyses in the present work.

3 Local Stress and Displacement Fields of A 3-D Elliptical crack

3.1 Elliptical Crack Under Normal Tension

A 3-D elliptical crack subjected to normal tension is a symmetric problem with respect to the crack plane $z=0$, where $\sigma_{yz}=\sigma_{zx}=0$ holds true. The stress and displacement fields in this symmetric problem can be described by a single displacement potential function (Green and Sneddon, 1950)

$$\left.\begin{aligned}\frac{\sigma_{xx}}{2\mu} &= \frac{\partial^2 f}{\partial x^2} + 2\nu\frac{\partial^2 f}{\partial y^2} + z\frac{\partial^3 f}{\partial z\partial x^2}\\ \frac{\sigma_{yy}}{2\mu} &= \frac{\partial^2 f}{\partial y^2} + 2\nu\frac{\partial^2 f}{\partial x^2} + z\frac{\partial^3 f}{\partial z\partial y^2}\\ \frac{\sigma_{zz}}{2\mu} &= -\frac{\partial^2 f}{\partial z^2} + z\frac{\partial^3 f}{\partial z^3}\\ \frac{\sigma_{yz}}{2\mu} &= z\frac{\partial^3 f}{\partial y\partial z^2}\\ \frac{\sigma_{zx}}{2\mu} &= z\frac{\partial^3 f}{\partial x\partial z^2}\\ \frac{\sigma_{xy}}{2\mu} &= (1-2\nu)\frac{\partial^2 f}{\partial x\partial y} + z\frac{\partial^3 f}{\partial x\partial y\partial z}\end{aligned}\right\} \tag{13}$$

and

$$\left.\begin{aligned}u_x &= (1-2\nu)\frac{\partial f}{\partial x} + z\frac{\partial^2 f}{\partial x\partial z}\\ u_y &= (1-2\nu)\frac{\partial f}{\partial y} + z\frac{\partial^2 f}{\partial y\partial z}\\ u_z &= -2(1-\nu)\frac{\partial f}{\partial z} + z\frac{\partial^2 f}{\partial z^2}\end{aligned}\right\} \tag{14}$$

where μ is the shear modulus, ν is the Poisson's ratio, and $f(x,y,z)$ is a harmonic function.

For the case of equal and opposite normal uniform traction of magnitude p_0 applied to upper and lower surfaces of the elliptical crack, the boundary conditions are

$$\left.\begin{array}{ll} \sigma_{zz} = p_0, & \text{at } z = 0 \text{ and } \xi = 0 \\ u_z = 0, & \text{at } z = 0 \text{ and } \eta = 0 \end{array}\right\} \tag{15}$$

Based on the analogy method of fluid mechanics, Green and Sneddon (1950) found the potential function $f(x, y, z)$ of the crack problem in the following form

$$f(x,y,z) = \frac{A}{2}\int_{\xi}^{\infty}\left[\frac{x^2}{a^2+s} + \frac{y^2}{b^2+s} + \frac{z^2}{s} - 1\right]\frac{\mathrm{d}s}{\sqrt{Q(s)}} \tag{16}$$

where A is an undetermined constant, ξ is an ellipsoidal coordinate, and $Q(s) = s(a^2+s)(b^2+s)$.

Before performing the differential and integral calculations of (16), it is expedient to introduce the Jacobian elliptical functions snu, cnu, $\cdots$ through the transformation $\xi = a^2cn^2u/sn^2u$. Using the partial derivative of the coordinates (ξ, η, ζ) with respect to (x, y, z) and the properties of the Jacobian elliptical function (Wittaker and Watson, 1927), after complex differential and integral calculations, we obtain the final results of the fundamental partial derivatives as (A1)~(A19) in Appendix A.

It should be noted that for $\xi = 0$ the elliptical integral $E(u)$ in Appendix A becomes the complete elliptical integral of the second kind, $E(k)$, with argument $k = [1-(b/a)^2]^{1/2}$. From the third Eqs. of (13), (15) and (16), by using (A9b), one has

$$A = \frac{ab^2 p_0}{4\mu E(k)} \tag{17}$$

By using the results in Appendix A, substitution of (16) and (17) into (13) and (14) can obtain the stress and displacement fields at any point in the elastic medium. Nevertheless, our attention is focused on the local stress and strain fields and their intensities near the crack border. To this end, the dominant asymptotic results of the partial derivatives of the fundamental integral (16) must be first evaluated. In the limit of $r \to 0$, using (12), we obtain the asymptotic formulae (B1)~(B19) corresponding to (A1)~(A19), and list them in Appendix B.

With(B9) and (B19), substitution of (16) into the third Eq. of (13) yields the asymptotic opening stress

$$\sigma_{zz} = \frac{2\mu A \Pi^{1/4}\cos(\theta/2)}{(2r\cos\varphi)^{1/2}(ab)^{3/2}}[-2 + (2\cos\theta + 1)(\cos\theta - 1)] + o(r^{-1/2}) \tag{18}$$

For 3-D elliptical cracks under normal traction, from (18), the stress intensity factor can be obtained

$$K_{\mathrm{I}} = \lim_{r\to 0}\sqrt{2\pi r}\sigma_{zz}(r, \theta = 0, \varphi = 0) = \frac{4\mu A\sqrt{\pi}}{(ab)^{3/2}}\Pi^{1/4} \tag{19}$$

where the constant A is determined by (17) for normal uniform tension.

By use of (19) and (B1)~(B19) in Appendix B, substituting (16) into (13) and (14) obtains the stress and displacement fields near the 3-D elliptical crack front under normal loads as follows

$$\left.\begin{aligned}
\sigma_{xx} &= \frac{K_{\mathrm{I}}\cos\dfrac{\theta}{2}}{(2\pi r\cos\varphi)^{1/2}\Pi}\{b^2\cos^2\alpha[1+\frac{1}{2}(\cos\theta-1)(2\cos\theta+1)]+2\nu a^2\sin^2\alpha\}+o(r^{-1/2})\\
\sigma_{yy} &= \frac{K_{\mathrm{I}}\cos\dfrac{\theta}{2}}{(2\pi r\cos\varphi)^{1/2}\Pi}\{a^2\sin^2\alpha[1+\frac{1}{2}(\cos\theta-1)(2\cos\theta+1)]+2\nu b^2\cos^2\alpha\}+o(r^{-1/2})\\
\sigma_{zz} &= \frac{K_{\mathrm{I}}}{(2\pi r\cos\varphi)^{1/2}\Pi}\cos\frac{\theta}{2}[1-\frac{1}{2}(\cos\theta-1)(2\cos\theta+1)]+o(r^{-1/2})\\
\sigma_{yz} &= \frac{aK_{\mathrm{I}}\sin\alpha}{2(2\pi r\cos\varphi)^{1/2}\Pi^{1/2}}\sin\frac{\theta}{2}(\cos\theta+1)(2\cos\theta-1)+o(r^{-1/2})\\
\sigma_{zx} &= \frac{bK_{\mathrm{I}}\cos\alpha}{2(2\pi r\cos\varphi)^{1/2}\Pi^{1/2}}\sin\frac{\theta}{2}(\cos\theta+1)(2\cos\theta-1)+o(r^{-1/2})\\
\sigma_{xy} &= \frac{abK_{\mathrm{I}}\sin\alpha\cos\alpha}{(2\pi r\cos\varphi)^{1/2}\Pi}\cos\frac{\theta}{2}[(1-2\nu)+\frac{1}{2}(\cos\theta-1)(2\cos\theta+1)]+o(r^{-1/2})
\end{aligned}\right\}\quad(20a)$$

and

$$\left.\begin{aligned}
u_x &= \frac{bK_{\mathrm{I}}\cos\alpha}{2\mu\Pi^{1/2}}\left(\frac{2r\cos\varphi}{\pi}\right)^{1/2}\cos\frac{\theta}{2}[(1-2\nu)+\frac{1}{2}(1-\cos\theta)]+o(r^{1/2})\\
u_y &= \frac{aK_{\mathrm{I}}\sin\alpha}{2\mu\Pi^{1/2}}\left(\frac{2r\cos\varphi}{\pi}\right)^{1/2}\cos\frac{\theta}{2}[(1-2\nu)+\frac{1}{2}(1-\cos\theta)]+o(r^{1/2})\\
u_z &= \frac{K_{\mathrm{I}}}{2\mu}\left(\frac{2r\cos\varphi}{\pi}\right)^{1/2}\sin\frac{\theta}{2}[2(1-\nu)-\frac{1}{2}(1+\cos\theta)]+o(r^{1/2})
\end{aligned}\right\}\quad(20b)$$

3.2 Elliptical Crack Under Surface Shear

A 3-D elliptical crack subjected to surface shear loads is a skew-symmetric problem with respect to the crack plane $z=0$, where $\sigma_{zz}=0$ holds true. The stress and displacement fields in this skew-symmetric problem can be described by two displacement potential functions (Kassir and Sih, 1966) as follows

$$\left.\begin{aligned}
\frac{\sigma_{xx}}{2\mu} &= -2(1-\nu)\frac{\partial^2 g}{\partial x\partial z}-2\nu\frac{\partial G}{\partial z}+z\frac{\partial^2 G}{\partial x^2}\\
\frac{\sigma_{yy}}{2\mu} &= -2(1-\nu)\frac{\partial^2 h}{\partial y\partial z}-2\nu\frac{\partial G}{\partial z}+z\frac{\partial^2 G}{\partial y^2}\\
\frac{\sigma_{zz}}{2\mu} &= z\frac{\partial^2 G}{\partial z^2}\\
\frac{\sigma_{yz}}{2\mu} &= -(1-\nu)\frac{\partial^2 h}{\partial z^2}+\nu\frac{\partial G}{\partial y}+z\frac{\partial^2 G}{\partial y\partial z}\\
\frac{\sigma_{zx}}{2\mu} &= -(1-\nu)\frac{\partial^2 g}{\partial z^2}+\nu\frac{\partial G}{\partial x}+z\frac{\partial^2 G}{\partial x\partial z}\\
\frac{\sigma_{xy}}{2\mu} &= -(1-\nu)\frac{\partial}{\partial z}\left(\frac{\partial g}{\partial y}+\frac{\partial h}{\partial x}\right)+z\frac{\partial^2 G}{\partial x\partial y}
\end{aligned}\right\}\quad(21)$$

and

$$\left.\begin{aligned} u_x &= -2(1-\nu)\frac{\partial g}{\partial z} + z\frac{\partial G}{\partial x} \\ u_y &= -2(1-\nu)\frac{\partial h}{\partial z} + z\frac{\partial G}{\partial y} \\ u_z &= -(1-2\nu)G + z\frac{\partial G}{\partial z} \end{aligned}\right\} \tag{22}$$

where $G = \partial g/\partial x + \partial h/\partial y$, $g(x,y,z)$ and $h(x,y,z)$ are harmonic functions.

For the case of equal and opposite uniform shear stresses of magnitude q_0 applied to the crack surfaces and directed at an angle ω to the major axis of the ellipse, the boundary conditions are

$$\left.\begin{aligned} &\sigma_{yz} = q_0 \sin\omega, \sigma_{zx} = q_0\cos\omega, \quad \text{at } z = 0 \text{ and } \xi = 0 \\ &u_x = u_y = 0, \qquad\qquad\qquad\quad \text{at } z = 0 \text{ and } \eta = 0 \end{aligned}\right\} \tag{23}$$

For this skew-symmetric problem, Kassir and Sih (1966) provided two displacement potential functions

$$\begin{bmatrix} g(x,y,z) \\ h(x,y,z) \end{bmatrix} = \frac{1}{2}\begin{bmatrix} B \\ C \end{bmatrix}\iint_{\xi}^{\infty}\left[\frac{x^2}{a^2+s} + \frac{y^2}{b^2+s} + \frac{z^2}{s} - 1\right]\frac{\mathrm{d}s}{\sqrt{Q(s)}} \tag{24}$$

where B and C are two undetermined constants, ξ is an ellipsoidal coordinate, and $Q(s) = s(a^2+s)(b^2+s)$.

It should be noted that as $\xi = 0$ the elliptical integral u becomes the complete elliptical integral of the first kind, $K(k)$, with argument $k = [1-(b/a)^2]^{1/2}$. From the fourth and fifth equations of (21), (23) and (24), and using (A4) and (A7)~(A9b), one concludes

$$\left.\begin{aligned} 4\mu B &= \frac{ab^2k^2 q_0\cos\omega}{(k^2-\nu)E(k) + \nu k'^2 K(k)} \\ 4\mu C &= \frac{ab^2k^2 q_0\sin\omega}{(k^2+\nu k'^2)E(k) - \nu k'^2 K(k)} \end{aligned}\right\} \tag{25}$$

where $k' = b/a$ and $k^2 + k'^2 = 1$.

In the local rectangular coordinates, the shear stress components σ_{nz} and σ_{tz} can be expressed by the global shear stress components

$$\left.\begin{aligned} \sigma_{nz} &= \sigma_{xz}\cos\beta + \sigma_{yz}\sin\beta \\ \sigma_{tz} &= -\sigma_{xz}\sin\beta + \sigma_{yz}\cos\beta \end{aligned}\right\} \tag{26}$$

Using the results of Appendix B, substituting (24) and the fourth and fifth equations of (21) into (26) and letting $\theta = \varphi = 0$, the local shear stress components are obtained as

$$\left.\begin{aligned} \sigma_{nz}(r,0,0) &= -\frac{4\mu}{(2r)^{1/2}(ab)^{3/2}\Pi^{1/4}}[Bb\cos\alpha + Ca\sin\alpha] + o(r^{-1/2}) \\ \sigma_{tz}(r,0,0) &= -\frac{4\mu(1-\nu)}{(2r)^{1/2}(ab)^{3/2}\Pi^{1/4}}[Ba\sin\alpha - Cb\cos\alpha] + o(r^{-1/2}) \end{aligned}\right\} \tag{27}$$

Eq. (27) implies that both the edge-sliding and tearing modes of the kinematic movements of the crack surfaces exist in the 3-D crack problems under a skew-symmetric loading.

From (27), one obtains the stress intensity factors for the 3-D elliptical crack under surface shear

$$\left.\begin{aligned} K_{\mathrm{II}} &= \lim_{r\to 0}\sqrt{2\pi r}\sigma_{nz}(r,\theta=0,\varphi=0) = -\frac{4\mu\sqrt{\pi}}{(ab)^{3/2}\Pi^{1/4}}[Bb\cos\alpha + Ca\sin\alpha] \\ K_{\mathrm{III}} &= \lim_{r\to 0}\sqrt{2\pi r}\sigma_{tz}(r,\theta=0,\varphi=0) = \frac{4\mu(1-\nu)\sqrt{\pi}}{(ab)^{3/2}\Pi^{1/4}}[Ba\sin\alpha - Cb\cos\alpha] \end{aligned}\right\} \quad (28)$$

where the constants B and C are determined by (25) for uniform surface shear.

With the relationship (28) and the formulae (B1)~(B19) in Appendix B, by substituting (24) into (21) and (22), one obtains the local stress and displacement fields near the elliptical crack front under surface shear as follows

$$\left.\begin{aligned} \sigma_{xx} &= -\frac{1}{(2\pi r\cos\varphi)^{1/2}\Pi}\sin\frac{\theta}{2}\{K_{\mathrm{II}}[b^2\cos^2\alpha(2+\frac{1}{2}(2\cos\theta-1)(\cos\theta+1)) + \\ &\quad 2\nu a^2\sin^2\alpha] - 2abK_{\mathrm{III}}\sin\alpha\cos\alpha\} + o(r^{-1/2}) \\ \sigma_{yy} &= -\frac{1}{(2\pi r\cos\varphi)^{1/2}\Pi}\sin\frac{\theta}{2}\{K_{\mathrm{II}}[a^2\sin^2\alpha(2+\frac{1}{2}(2\cos\theta-1)(\cos\theta+1)) + \\ &\quad 2\nu b^2\cos^2\alpha] + 2abK_{\mathrm{III}}\sin\alpha\cos\alpha\} + o(r^{-1/2}) \\ \sigma_{zz} &= \frac{K_{\mathrm{II}}}{2(2\pi r\cos\varphi)^{1/2}}\sin\frac{\theta}{2}(2\cos\theta-1)(\cos\theta+1) + o(r^{-1/2}) \\ \sigma_{yz} &= \frac{\cos\frac{\theta}{2}}{(2\pi r\cos\varphi\Pi)^{1/2}}\{aK_{\mathrm{II}}\sin\alpha[1+\frac{1}{2}(2\cos\theta+1)(\cos\theta-1)] + \\ &\quad bK_{\mathrm{III}}\cos\alpha\} + o(r^{-1/2}) \\ \sigma_{zx} &= \frac{\cos\frac{\theta}{2}}{(2\pi r\cos\varphi\Pi)^{1/2}}\{bK_{\mathrm{II}}\cos\alpha[1+\frac{1}{2}(2\cos\theta+1)(\cos\theta-1)] - \\ &\quad aK_{\mathrm{III}}\sin\alpha\} + o(r^{-1/2}) \\ \sigma_{xy} &= -\frac{1}{(2\pi r\cos\varphi)^{1/2}\Pi}\sin\frac{\theta}{2}\{abK_{\mathrm{II}}\sin\alpha\cos\alpha[2(1-\nu) + \\ &\quad \frac{1}{2}(2\cos\theta-1)(\cos\theta+1)] - K_{\mathrm{III}}(a^2\sin^2\alpha - b^2\cos^2\alpha)\} + o(r^{-1/2}) \end{aligned}\right\} \quad (29a)$$

and

$$\left.\begin{aligned} u_x &= \frac{(2r\cos\varphi)^{1/2}}{2\mu\pi^{1/2}\Pi^{1/2}}\sin\frac{\theta}{2}\{bK_{\mathrm{II}}\cos\alpha[2(1-\nu)+\frac{1}{2}(1+\cos\theta)] - 2aK_{\mathrm{III}}\sin\alpha\} + o(r^{1/2}) \\ u_y &= \frac{(2r\cos\varphi)^{1/2}}{2\mu\pi^{1/2}\Pi^{1/2}}\sin\frac{\theta}{2}\{aK_{\mathrm{II}}\sin\alpha[2(1-\nu)+\frac{1}{2}(1+\cos\theta)] + 2bK_{\mathrm{III}}\cos\alpha\} + o(r^{1/2}) \\ u_z &= -\frac{K_{\mathrm{II}}}{2\mu}\left(\frac{2r\cos\varphi}{\pi}\right)^{1/2}\cos\frac{\theta}{2}[(1-2\nu) - \frac{1}{2}(1-\cos\theta)] + o(r^{1/2}) \end{aligned}\right\} \quad (29b)$$

3.3 Elliptical Crack under Mixed Loading

For a 3-D elliptical crack under mixed tensile loads, one can first resolve the loads into the two parts: normal tensile load and shear load to the crack surface. Then through superposition of (20) and (29), the global components of the stress and displacement fields near the 3-D crack front can be obtained. For a more intuitive knowledge of the crack-tip fields, it is necessary to give the local rectangular components of these field quantities. Upon the transformation of coordinate axes from (x, y, z) to (n, t, z), the local shear stress components σ_{nz} and σ_{tz} are determined by (26), and the local normal stress components σ_{nn}, σ_{tt} and σ_{nt} can be determined by

$$\left.\begin{aligned}\sigma_{nn} &= \sigma_{xx}\cos^2\beta + \sigma_{yy}\sin^2\beta + 2\sigma_{xy}\sin\beta\cos\beta \\ \sigma_{tt} &= \sigma_{xx}\sin^2\beta + \sigma_{yy}\cos^2\beta - 2\sigma_{xy}\sin\beta\cos\beta \\ \sigma_{nt} &= -(\sigma_{xx} - \sigma_{yy})\sin\beta\cos\beta + 2\sigma_{xy}\cos2\beta\end{aligned}\right\} \tag{30}$$

The displacement components u_n and u_t in the local rectangular coordinates are determined by

$$\left.\begin{aligned}u_n &= u_x\cos\beta + u_y\sin\beta \\ u_t &= -u_x\sin\beta + u_y\cos\beta\end{aligned}\right\} \tag{31}$$

and the components σ_{zz} and u_z remain invariant.

By substituting (20) and (29) into (26), (30) and (31), respectively, and then by superposing and simplifying the results, we obtain the stress and displacement fields in the close neighborhood of the 3-D elliptical crack front as follows

$$\begin{aligned}\sigma_{nn} &= \frac{K_{\mathrm{I}}}{(2\pi r\cos\varphi)^{1/2}}\cos\frac{\theta}{2}\left(1-\sin\frac{\theta}{2}\sin\frac{3\theta}{2}\right) - \frac{K_{\mathrm{II}}}{(2\pi r\cos\varphi)^{1/2}}\sin\frac{\theta}{2}\left(2+\cos\frac{\theta}{2}\cos\frac{3\theta}{2}\right) \\ \sigma_{zz} &= \frac{K_{\mathrm{I}}}{(2\pi r\cos\varphi)^{1/2}}\cos\frac{\theta}{2}\left(1+\sin\frac{\theta}{2}\sin\frac{3\theta}{2}\right) + \frac{K_{\mathrm{II}}}{(2\pi r\cos\varphi)^{1/2}}\sin\frac{\theta}{2}\cos\frac{\theta}{2}\cos\frac{3\theta}{2} \\ \sigma_{tt} &= \frac{2\nu K_{\mathrm{I}}}{(2\pi r\cos\varphi)^{1/2}}\cos\frac{\theta}{2} - \frac{2\nu K_{\mathrm{II}}}{(2\pi r\cos\varphi)^{1/2}}\sin\frac{\theta}{2} \\ \sigma_{nz} &= \frac{K_{\mathrm{I}}}{(2\pi r\cos\varphi)^{1/2}}\sin\frac{\theta}{2}\cos\frac{\theta}{2}\cos\frac{3\theta}{2} + \frac{K_{\mathrm{II}}}{(2\pi r\cos\varphi)^{1/2}}\cos\frac{\theta}{2}\left(1-\sin\frac{\theta}{2}\sin\frac{3\theta}{2}\right) \\ \sigma_{nt} &= \frac{K_{\mathrm{III}}}{(2\pi r\cos\varphi)^{1/2}}\sin\frac{\theta}{2} \\ \sigma_{tz} &= \frac{K_{\mathrm{III}}}{(2\pi r\cos\varphi)^{1/2}}\cos\frac{\theta}{2}\end{aligned} \tag{32a}$$

and

$$\left.\begin{aligned}u_n = {}& \frac{K_{\mathrm{I}}}{2\mu}\left(\frac{2r\cos\varphi}{\pi}\right)^{1/2}\cos\frac{\theta}{2}\left[(1-2\nu)+\sin^2\frac{\theta}{2}\right] + \\ & \frac{K_{\mathrm{II}}}{2\mu}\left(\frac{2\cos\varphi}{\pi}\right)^{1/2}\sin\frac{\theta}{2}\left[2(1-\nu)+\cos^2\frac{\theta}{2}\right] \\ u_z = {}& \frac{K_{\mathrm{I}}}{2\mu}\left(\frac{2r\cos\varphi}{\pi}\right)^{1/2}\sin\frac{\theta}{2}\left[2(1-\nu)-\cos^2\frac{\theta}{2}\right] - \\ & \frac{K_{\mathrm{II}}}{2\mu}\left(\frac{2\cos\varphi}{\pi}\right)^{1/2}\cos\frac{\theta}{2}\left[(1-2\nu)-\sin^2\frac{\theta}{2}\right]\end{aligned}\right\} \tag{32b}$$

$$u_t = \frac{K_{\mathrm{III}}}{\mu}\left(\frac{2r\cos\varphi}{\pi}\right)^{1/2}\sin\frac{\theta}{2}$$

where the higher-order terms in r have been neglected. Notice that the local solution (32) is independent of the ellipse parameters (a, b, α), the singularity $r^{-1/2}$ of the stresses is preserved and $\sigma_{tt} = \nu(\sigma_{nn} + \sigma_{zz})$ which is the plane strain condition. The strain field can be further obtained from (32b) by using the geometry equations.

In this work, the $n-z$ plane is referred to as the normal plane at the point P, and an inclined plane is the plane with angle φ to the normal plane, as shown in Fig. 3. If the local coordinates (n, z, t) at the point P on the 3-D crack border correspond to the rectangular coordinates (x, y, z) at the tip of a plane crack, then (32) indicates that the stress and displacement fields of a space point M in an inclined plane, located at a distance r from point P, are the same as those of the projection point M' of the point M in the normal plane, located at a distance $r\cos\varphi$ from point P. Moreover, the local stress and displacement fields in the normal plane are precisely the linear sum of the plane strain mode-Ⅰ, mode-Ⅱ and mode-Ⅲ crack-tip fields. The difference from the plane crack problem is only that the stress intensity factors $K_{\mathrm{I}}, K_{\mathrm{II}}, K_{\mathrm{III}}$ for the 3-D crack problem depend on the curvature of crack border or the location of the points along the crack border. These results are the same as those by Kassir and Sih (1966), and are well known in the literature. Further investigation by Zhu (1996) indicates that the local asymptotic fields for an arbitrary curvilinear crack are also the same as (32).

4 Possibility of 3-D Crack Propagation in an Inclined Plane

The analysis of 3-D mixed-mode crack initiation and propagation includes how to determine the direction of crack growth and the condition for a crack initiation, which depends on the fracture criterion. For the present problem we choose two different mixed-mode fracture criteria based on the local stress field near the crack front. One is the strain energy density factor criterion (Sih, 1991), the other is the total strain energy criterion (Zhao, 1987). Notice that these two fracture criteria are sound and have been verified in prediction fracture initiation of brittle materials (Gdoutos, 1990).

The strain energy density factor criterion (Sih, 1991) assumes that the direction of crack propagation at any point along the crack border goes toward the region where the strain energy density factor S is minimum as compared to other regions on the same spherical surface surrounding the point. From the local stress fields given in (32a), the strain energy density of a 3-D crack is obtained as

$$\frac{dW}{dV} = \frac{S}{r}, \quad S = \frac{1}{\cos\varphi}[a_{11}K_{\mathrm{I}}^2 + 2a_{12}K_{\mathrm{I}}K_{\mathrm{II}} + a_{22}K_{\mathrm{II}}^2 + a_{33}K_{\mathrm{III}}^2] \tag{33}$$

where the coefficients $a_{11} \sim a_{33}$ are the same as the superposition of the plane strain mode-Ⅰ, mode-Ⅱ and mode-Ⅲ crack results (Gdoutos, 1990), and are written as

$$
\left.\begin{aligned}
16\mu a_{11} &= (3-4\nu-\cos\theta)(1+\cos\theta)\\
16\mu a_{12} &= 2\sin\theta(\cos\theta-1+2\nu)\\
16\mu a_{22} &= 4(1-\nu)(1-\cos\theta)+(3\cos\theta-1)(1+\cos\theta)\\
16\mu a_{33} &= 4
\end{aligned}\right\}\quad(34)
$$

If the dependence on the angle φ is analyzed, it can be found from (33) that the minimum value of S occurs at $\varphi=0$, i.e., the normal plane. This indicates that the 3-D crack will initially propagate in the plane normal to the crack front.

The total strain energy criterion (Zhao, 1987) assumes that the initial direction of the crack growth takes place along the direction where the distance from the crack tip to the elasticplastic boundary is a minimum. Based on the stress fields given in (32a) and the von Mises yield condition, we can obtain the equation describing the elastic-plastic boundary as

$$
r=\frac{3}{8\pi\sigma_0^2\cos\varphi}\left[b_{11}K_{\mathrm{I}}^2+2b_{12}K_{\mathrm{I}}K_{\mathrm{II}}+b_{22}K_{\mathrm{II}}^2+b_{33}K_{\mathrm{III}}^2\right]\quad(35)
$$

where σ_0 is the yield stress, the coefficients $b_{11}\sim b_{33}$ are the same as the superposition of the plane strain mode-Ⅰ, mode-Ⅱ and mode-Ⅲ crack results (Zhao, 1987), and are written as

$$
\left.\begin{aligned}
b_{11} &= (\eta+1)+\eta\cos\theta-\cos^2\theta\\
b_{12} &= \sin2\theta-\eta\sin\theta\\
b_{22} &= (\eta+4)-\eta\cos\theta-3\sin^2\theta\\
b_{33} &= 4,\ \eta=2(1-2\nu)^2/3
\end{aligned}\right\}\quad(36)
$$

From (35), one easily finds that r assumes the minimum when $\varphi=0$. Again, this indicates that the crack will initially propagate in the plane normal to the crack front.

In the above analyses, the prediction from both fracture criteria shows that a 3-D flat crack under mixed loads will initially propagate in the normal plane at any point along the crack border. In other words, it is impossible for the crack to propagate into an inclined plane with respect to the crack front. This corroborates the common assumption in the 3-D fracture analyses, i.e. the direction of 3-D crack propagation lies in the normal plane. Accordingly, when studying failure of 3-D cracks, one can directly use the conclusion that the crack propagation is in the normal plane, and in which plane the local fields are the superposition of the plane strain mode-Ⅰ, mode-Ⅱ and mode-Ⅲ crack-tip fields.

5　Comparing the Present Results with Those in Sih(1991)

The local stress fields (32a) in the vicinity of the embedded elliptic crack front are different from those given by Sih (1991). Consequently based on these two different local stress fields, the strain energy density factor criterion yields different conclusions. The present analysis indicates that the elliptical crack will propagate in the normal plane at any point along the crack border. But, Sih(1991) concluded that the elliptical crack would not propagate in the normal plane cxcept at the intersections of the major and minor axes with the crack border.

It is well known that a through-thickness 3-D crack with straight crack front propagates in the plane normal to the crack front (Sih, 1971 and Miannay, 1998). Our solution supports this conclusion as a special case, i. e., the limit of the ratio $b/a \to 0$ for an ellipse, which corresponds to a crack with a straight crack front. However, according to the results of Sih (1991), it can be shown that in Table 2.1 of Sih (1991) the ϕ_0-plane, in which the crack extends, can be determined by $\phi_0 = \tan^{-1}((b^2 - a^2)/ab)\sin\alpha\cos\alpha$. From this expression, as $b/a \to 0$, one has $\phi_0 \to -\pi/2$, which means that a 3-D crack with straight crack front will propagate along the tangential plane of the crack front. Apparently, this is impossible.

Sih's stress field near the elliptic crack front is of a very complicated form and uses another spherical coordinates (r, θ, ϕ) (See Fig. 2.5 in Sih, 1991). A direct comparison between Sih's results and our solutions is thus very difficult. If the local spherical coordinates as shown in Fig. 3 is adopted, the stress field (2.6) in Sih (1991) can be expressed by

$$\begin{aligned} \sigma_{nn} &= \frac{K_{\mathrm{I}}}{(2\pi r)^{1/2}}\left(\frac{\kappa+1}{2\lambda}\right)^{1/2}\left(\frac{2-\kappa+\kappa^2}{2\kappa^3}\right) - \frac{K_{\mathrm{II}}}{(2\pi r)^{1/2}}\left(\frac{\kappa-1}{2\lambda}\right)^{1/2}\left(\frac{2+\kappa+3\kappa^2}{2\kappa^3}\right) \\ &\cdots \\ \sigma_{nz} &= \frac{K_{\mathrm{I}}}{(2\pi r)^{1/2}}\left(\frac{\kappa-1}{2\lambda}\right)^{1/2}\left(\frac{2+\kappa-\kappa^2}{2\kappa^3}\right) + \frac{K_{\mathrm{II}}}{(2\pi r)^{1/2}}\left(\frac{\kappa+1}{2\lambda}\right)^{1/2}\left(\frac{2-\kappa+\kappa^2}{2\kappa^3}\right) \end{aligned} \tag{37}$$

where

$$\left.\begin{aligned} \lambda &= \cos\theta\cos\varphi + \frac{b^2-a^2}{ab}\sin\varphi\sin\alpha\cos\alpha \\ \kappa &= \left[1 + \left(\frac{\sin\theta\cos\varphi}{\lambda}\right)^2\right]^{1/2} \end{aligned}\right\} \tag{38}$$

When $\varphi = 0$, Eq. (37) is the same as the stress field given in Eq. (32a), but differs when $\varphi \neq 0$, the parameters λ and κ in Eq. (38) are determined by the asymptotic relationship

$$\xi = abr\Pi^{-1/2}\lambda(1+\kappa), \qquad \eta = abr\Pi^{-1/2}\lambda(1+\kappa), \qquad \zeta = -\Pi \tag{39}$$

Note that Eq. (39) has been transferred from (2.20) of Sih (1991) to the spherical coordinates in Fig. 3.

Comparison shows that the asymptotic relationships (39) given by Sih (1991) are different from the Eqs. (12) obtained in this paper. By substituting (39) and (5) into the first two equations of (6), we found that the coefficients of the r^1-order terms on the two sides of the equations are not equal. This reveals that the r^1-order terms on the two sides of (6) are not compatible for (39). Therefore, some errors are associated with the asymptotic relationships (39) and the parameters in (38). Using the correct asymptotic relationships (12), the parameters in (38) should read

$$\lambda = \cos\theta\cos\varphi, \qquad \kappa = \frac{1}{\cos\theta} \tag{40}$$

One can verify that the stress field (37) with the parameters given by (40) is identical to the stress field of (32a). Therefore, the difference and contradiction between our solutions and the results of Sih (1991) are caused by an error in (39) which is the asymptotic relationship between the ellipsoidal coordinates and the spherical coordinates.

6 Conclusions

Through a rigorous mathematical analysis, this paper reconsiders 3-D flat elliptical cracks under uniform normal, shear and mixed loads, and obtains the local stress and displacement fields near the crack front in an inclined plane. And then this stress field is applied to predict the direction of the crack growth. From present analysis, it can be concluded that:

(1) For a 3-D elliptical crack under arbitrary uniform tensions, the stress and displacement fields at any point near the crack front in an inclined plane are identical to those at the projection point of this point in the plane normal to the crack front. The local stress and displacement fields in the normal plane are the linear superposition of the plane strain mode-Ⅰ, mode-Ⅱ and mode-Ⅲ crack-tip fields, which agrees with the conclusion given by Kassir and Sih (1966).

(2) The local stress and displacement fields derived for an embedded elliptical crack are independent of the curvature of the ellipse; and thus could be applicable to any flat and smooth curvilinear crack. However, the formulae (19) and (28) for the stress intensity factors are only valid for elliptical cracks and not for general curvilinear cracks.

(3) Based on the local stress fields given in (32a), both the strain energy density factor criterion and the total strain energy criterion show that the 3-D crack will propagate in the direction of the normal plane at any point along the crack border. This corroborates the common assumption in the study of 3-D fracture problems. Thus, the fracture initiation and propagation of a 3-D flat crack in an elastic body can be analyzed in the normal plane by using the superposition of the well-known plane strain mode-Ⅰ, mode-Ⅱ and mode-Ⅲ crack-tip fields.

(4) Through a careful analysis and comparison between the present solutions and the results of Sih (1991), it is found that the asymptotic relationships between the ellipsoidal coordinates and the spherical coordinates in Sih (1991) are incorrect. If the correct asymptotic relationships were used, Sih's results are consistent with the results obtained in this paper.

Acknowledgement

The authors gratefully acknowledge the support of this work by the National Natural Science Foundation of China and by NSF through Grand No. 9630167. Special thanks are due to the anonymous reviewers for their useful comments and suggestions to the present paper.

Appendix A

Formulae of the Fundamental Integral and Its Partial Dericatives

The evaluation formulae of the partial derivatives with respect to x, y, z of the fundamental integral

$$I(x,y,z) = \frac{1}{2}\int_{\xi}^{\infty}\left[\frac{x^2}{a^2+s}+\frac{y^2}{b^2+s}+\frac{z^2}{s}-1\right]\frac{ds}{\sqrt{Q(s)}}$$

are listed in this appendix, and used in the previous analysis, where $Q(s)=s(a^2+s)(b^2+s),(s,\xi);\xi=a^2cn^2u/sn^2u, E(u)=\int_0^u dn^2\psi d\psi$.

$$\frac{\partial I}{\partial x} = \frac{2x}{a^3k^2}[u-E(u)] \tag{A1}$$

$$\frac{\partial I}{\partial y} = \frac{2y}{a^3k^2}\left[\left(\frac{a}{b}\right)^2E(u)-u-\left(\frac{a^2-b^2}{b^2}\right)\frac{snucnu}{dnu}\right] \tag{A2}$$

$$\frac{\partial I}{\partial z} = \frac{2z}{ab^2}\left[\frac{snudnu}{cnu}-E(u)\right] \tag{A3}$$

$$\frac{\partial^2 I}{\partial x\partial y} = -\frac{2xy\xi}{(\xi-\eta)(\xi-\zeta)Q^{1/2}(\xi)} \tag{A4}$$

$$\frac{\partial^2 I}{\partial y\partial z} = -\frac{2yz(a^2+\xi)}{(\xi-\eta)(\xi-\zeta)Q^{1/2}(\xi)} \tag{A5}$$

$$\frac{\partial^2 I}{\partial z\partial x} = -\frac{2zx(b^2+\xi)}{(\xi-\eta)(\xi-\zeta)Q^{1/2}(\xi)} \tag{A6}$$

$$\frac{\partial^2 I}{\partial x^2} = \frac{1}{x}\frac{\partial I}{\partial x}-\frac{2x^2Q^{1/2}(\xi)}{(\xi-\eta)(\xi-\zeta)(a^2+\xi)^2} \tag{A7}$$

$$\frac{\partial^2 I}{\partial y^2} = \frac{1}{y}\frac{\partial I}{\partial y}-\frac{2y^2Q^{1/2}(\xi)}{(\xi-\eta)(\xi-\zeta)(b^2+\xi)^2} \tag{A8}$$

$$\frac{\partial^2 I}{\partial z^2} = \frac{1}{z}\frac{\partial I}{\partial z}-\frac{2z^2Q^{1/2}(\xi)}{(\xi-\eta)(\xi-\zeta)\xi^2} \tag{A9a}$$

$$\frac{\partial^2 I}{\partial^2 z} = \frac{2}{ab^2}\left[\frac{snucnu}{dnu}-E(u)\right]+\frac{2\xi^{1/2}[a^2b^2(\xi-\eta-\zeta)-(a^2+b^2)\eta\zeta-\xi\eta\zeta]}{a^2b^2(\xi-\eta)(\xi-\zeta)(a^2+\xi)^{1/2}(b^2+\xi)^{1/2}} \tag{A9b}$$

$$\frac{\partial^3 I}{\partial x\partial y^2} = \frac{2x\xi}{(\xi-\eta)(\xi-\zeta)Q^{1/2}(\xi)}\left\{\frac{2y^2}{\eta-\zeta}\left[\frac{\eta(a^2+\eta)}{(\xi-\eta)^2}-\frac{\zeta(a^2+\zeta)}{(\xi-\zeta)^2}\right]-1+\right.$$
$$\left.\frac{y^2\xi(a^2+\xi)}{(\xi-\eta)(\xi-\zeta)}\left[\frac{2}{\xi-\eta}+\frac{2}{\xi-\zeta}+\frac{1}{a^2+\xi}+\frac{1}{b^2+\xi}-\frac{1}{\xi}\right]\right\} \tag{A10}$$

$$\frac{\partial^3 I}{\partial y\partial x^2} = \frac{2y\xi}{(\xi-\eta)(\xi-\zeta)Q^{1/2}(\xi)}\left\{\frac{2x^2}{\eta-\zeta}\left[\frac{\eta(b^2+\eta)}{(\xi-\eta)^2}-\frac{\zeta(b^2+\zeta)}{(\xi-\zeta)^2}\right]-1+\right.$$
$$\left.\frac{x^2\xi(b^2+\xi)}{(\xi-\eta)(\xi-\zeta)}\left[\frac{2}{\xi-\eta}+\frac{2}{\xi-\zeta}+\frac{1}{a^2+\xi}+\frac{1}{b^2+\xi}-\frac{1}{\xi}\right]\right\} \tag{A11}$$

$$\frac{\partial^3 I}{\partial y\partial z^2} = \frac{2y(a^2+\xi)}{(\xi-\eta)(\xi-\zeta)Q^{1/2}(\xi)}\left\{\frac{2z^2}{\eta-\zeta}\left[\frac{(a^2+\eta)(b^2+\eta)}{(\xi-\eta)^2}-\frac{(a^2+\zeta)(b^2+\zeta)}{(\xi-\zeta)^2}\right]-1+\right.$$

$$\frac{z^2(a^2+\xi)(b^2+\xi)}{(\xi-\eta)(\xi-\zeta)}\left[\frac{2}{\xi-\eta}+\frac{2}{\xi-\zeta}-\frac{1}{a^2+\xi}+\frac{1}{b^2+\xi}+\frac{1}{\xi}\right]\Bigg\} \tag{A12}$$

$$\frac{\partial^3 I}{\partial z\partial y^2}=\frac{2z(a^2+\xi)}{(\xi-\eta)(\xi-\zeta)Q^{1/2}(\xi)}\Bigg\{\frac{2y^2}{\eta-\zeta}\left[\frac{\eta(a^2+\eta)}{(\xi-\eta)^2}-\frac{\zeta(a^2+\zeta)}{(\xi-\zeta)^2}\right]-1+$$
$$\frac{y^2\xi(a^2+\xi)}{(\xi-\eta)(\xi-\zeta)}\left[\frac{2}{\xi-\eta}+\frac{2}{\xi-\zeta}-\frac{1}{a^2+\xi}+\frac{1}{b^2+\xi}+\frac{1}{\xi}\right]\Bigg\} \tag{A13}$$

$$\frac{\partial^3 I}{\partial x\partial z^2}=\frac{2x(b^2+\xi)}{(\xi-\eta)(\xi-\zeta)Q^{1/2}(\xi)}\Bigg\{\frac{2z^2}{\eta-\zeta}\left[\frac{(a^2+\eta)(b^2+\eta)}{(\xi-\eta)^2}-\frac{(a^2+\zeta)(b^2+\zeta)}{(\xi-\zeta)^2}\right]-1+$$
$$\frac{z^2(a^2+\xi)(b^2+\xi)}{(\xi-\eta)(\xi-\zeta)}\left[\frac{2}{\xi-\eta}+\frac{2}{\xi-\zeta}+\frac{1}{a^2+\xi}-\frac{1}{b^2+\xi}+\frac{1}{\xi}\right]\Bigg\} \tag{A14}$$

$$\frac{\partial^3 I}{\partial z\partial x^2}=\frac{2z(b^2+\xi)}{(\xi-\eta)(\xi-\zeta)Q^{1/2}(\xi)}\Bigg\{\frac{2x^2}{\eta-\zeta}\left[\frac{\eta(b^2+\eta)}{(\xi-\eta)^2}-\frac{\zeta(b^2+\zeta)}{(\xi-\zeta)^2}\right]-1+$$
$$\frac{x^2\xi(b^2+\xi)}{(\xi-\eta)(\xi-\zeta)}\left[\frac{2}{\xi-\eta}+\frac{2}{\xi-\zeta}+\frac{1}{a^2+\xi}-\frac{1}{b^2+\xi}+\frac{1}{\xi}\right]\Bigg\} \tag{A15}$$

$$\frac{\partial^3 I}{\partial x\partial y\partial z}=\frac{2xyz\xi}{(\xi-\eta)(\xi-\zeta)Q^{1/2}(\xi)}\Bigg\{\frac{2}{\eta-\zeta}\left[\frac{(a^2+\eta)(b^2+\eta)}{(\xi-\eta)^2}-\frac{(a^2+\zeta)(b^2+\zeta)}{(\xi-\zeta)^2}\right]+$$
$$\frac{(a^2+\xi)(b^2+\xi)}{(\xi-\eta)(\xi-\zeta)}\left[\frac{2}{\xi-\eta}+\frac{2}{\xi-\zeta}+\frac{1}{a^2+\xi}+\frac{1}{b^2+\xi}-\frac{1}{\xi}\right]\Bigg\} \tag{A16}$$

$$\frac{\partial^3 I}{\partial x^3}=\frac{2xQ^{1/2}(\xi)}{(\xi-\eta)(\xi-\zeta)(a^2+\xi)^2}\Bigg\{\frac{2x^2}{\eta-\zeta}\left[\frac{\eta(b^2+\eta)}{(\xi-\eta)^2}-\frac{\zeta(b^2+\zeta)}{(\xi-\zeta)^2}\right]-3+$$
$$\frac{x^2\xi(b^2+\xi)}{(\xi-\eta)(\xi-\zeta)}\left[\frac{2}{\xi-\eta}+\frac{2}{\xi-\zeta}+\frac{3}{a^2+\xi}-\frac{1}{b^2+\xi}-\frac{1}{\xi}\right]\Bigg\} \tag{A17}$$

$$\frac{\partial^3 I}{\partial y^3}=\frac{2yQ^{1/2}(\xi)}{(\xi-\eta)(\xi-\zeta)(b^2+\xi)^2}\Bigg\{\frac{2y^2}{\eta-\zeta}\left[\frac{\eta(a^2+\eta)}{(\xi-\eta)^2}-\frac{\zeta(a^2+\zeta)}{(\xi-\zeta)^2}\right]-3+$$
$$\frac{y^2\xi(b^2+\xi)}{(\xi-\eta)(\xi-\zeta)}\left[\frac{2}{\xi-\eta}+\frac{2}{\xi-\zeta}-\frac{1}{a^2+\xi}+\frac{3}{b^2+\xi}-\frac{1}{\xi}\right]\Bigg\} \tag{A18}$$

$$\frac{\partial^3 I}{\partial z^3}=\frac{2zQ^{1/2}(\xi)}{(\xi-\eta)(\xi-\zeta)\xi^2}\Bigg\{\frac{2z^2}{\eta-\zeta}\left[\frac{(a^2+\eta)(b^2+\eta)}{(\xi-\eta)^2}-\frac{(a^2+\zeta)(b^2+\zeta)}{(\xi-\zeta)^2}\right]-3+$$
$$\frac{z^2(a^2+\xi)(b^2+\xi)}{(\xi-\eta)(\xi-\zeta)}\left[\frac{2}{\xi-\eta}+\frac{2}{\xi-\zeta}-\frac{1}{a^2+\xi}-\frac{1}{b^2+\xi}+\frac{3}{\xi}\right]\Bigg\} \tag{A19}$$

Appendix B

Asymptotic Formulae of Partial Derivatives of the Fundamental Integral

In the limit of $r\to 0$, using the asymptotic relationships (12), we obtain the asymptotic formulae of the partial derivatives (A1)~(A19) of the fundamental integral $I(x,y,z)$ as follows

$$\frac{\partial I}{\partial x}=\frac{2\cos\alpha}{a^2}\left[\frac{\pi}{4}-\frac{(2r\cos\varphi)^{1/2}}{\Pi^{1/4}}\left(\frac{a}{b}\right)^{1/2}\cos\frac{\theta}{2}\right]+o(r^{1/2}) \tag{B1}$$

$$\frac{\partial I}{\partial y}=\frac{2\sin\alpha}{ab}\left[\frac{\pi}{4}-\frac{(2r\cos\varphi)^{1/2}}{\Pi^{1/4}}\left(\frac{a}{b}\right)^{1/2}\cos\frac{\theta}{2}\right]+o(r^{1/2}) \tag{B2}$$

$$\frac{\partial I}{\partial z} = \frac{2(2r\cos\varphi)^{1/2}\Pi^{1/4}}{(ab)^{3/2}}\sin\frac{\theta}{2} + o(r^{1/2}) \tag{B3}$$

$$\frac{\partial^2 I}{\partial x\partial y} = -\frac{2\sin\alpha\cos\alpha}{(2rab\cos\varphi)^{1/2}\Pi^{3/4}}\cos\frac{\theta}{2} + o(r^{-1/2}) \tag{B4}$$

$$\frac{\partial^2 I}{\partial y\partial z} = -\frac{2\sin\alpha}{(2rab\cos\varphi)^{1/2}b\Pi^{1/4}}\sin\frac{\theta}{2} + o(r^{-1/2}) \tag{B5}$$

$$\frac{\partial^2 I}{\partial z\partial x} = -\frac{2\cos\alpha}{(2rab\cos\varphi)^{1/2}a\Pi^{1/4}}\sin\frac{\theta}{2} + o(r^{-1/2}) \tag{B6}$$

$$\frac{\partial^2 I}{\partial x^2} = -\frac{2b\cos^2\alpha}{(2rab\cos\varphi)^{1/2}a\Pi^{3/4}}\cos\frac{\theta}{2} + o(r^{-1/2}) \tag{B7}$$

$$\frac{\partial^2 I}{\partial y^2} = -\frac{2a\sin^2\alpha}{(2rab\cos\varphi)^{1/2}b\Pi^{3/4}}\cos\frac{\theta}{2} + o(r^{-1/2}) \tag{B8}$$

$$\frac{\partial^2 I}{\partial z^2} = \frac{2\Pi^{1/4}}{(2r\cos\varphi)^{1/2}(ab)^{3/2}}\cos\frac{\theta}{2} + o(r^{-1/2}) \tag{B9}$$

$$z\frac{\partial^3 I}{\partial x\partial y^2} = \frac{a\cos\alpha\sin^2\alpha}{(2rab\cos\varphi)^{1/2}\Pi^{5/4}}\sin\frac{\theta}{2}(2\cos\theta - 1)(\cos\theta + 1) + o(r^{-1/2}) \tag{B10}$$

$$z\frac{\partial^3 I}{\partial y\partial x^2} = \frac{b\sin\alpha\cos^2\alpha}{(2rab\cos\varphi)^{1/2}\Pi^{5/4}}\sin\frac{\theta}{2}(2\cos\theta - 1)(\cos\theta + 1) + o(r^{-1/2}) \tag{B11}$$

$$z\frac{\partial^3 I}{\partial y\partial z^2} = \frac{\sin\alpha}{(2rab\cos\varphi)^{1/2}b\Pi^{1/4}}\sin\frac{\theta}{2}(1 - 2\cos\theta)(1 + \cos\theta) + o(r^{-1/2}) \tag{B12}$$

$$z\frac{\partial^3 I}{\partial z\partial y^2} = \frac{a\sin^2\alpha}{(2rab\cos\varphi)^{1/2}b\Pi^{3/4}}\cos\frac{\theta}{2}(1 + 2\cos\theta)(1 - \cos\theta) + o(r^{-1/2}) \tag{B13}$$

$$z\frac{\partial^3 I}{\partial x\partial z^2} = \frac{\cos\alpha}{(2rab\cos\varphi)^{1/2}a\Pi^{1/4}}\sin\frac{\theta}{2}(1 - 2\cos\theta)(1 + \cos\theta) + o(r^{-1/2}) \tag{B14}$$

$$z\frac{\partial^3 I}{\partial z\partial x^2} = \frac{b\cos^2\alpha}{(2rab\cos\varphi)^{1/2}a\Pi^{3/4}}\cos\frac{\theta}{2}(1 + 2\cos\theta)(1 - \cos\theta) + o(r^{-1/2}) \tag{B15}$$

$$z\frac{\partial^3 I}{\partial x\partial y\partial z} = \frac{\sin\alpha\cos\alpha}{(2rab\cos\varphi)^{1/2}\Pi^{3/4}}\cos\frac{\theta}{2}(1 + 2\cos\theta)(1 - \cos\theta) + o(r^{-1/2}) \tag{B16}$$

$$z\frac{\partial^3 I}{\partial x^3} = \frac{b^2\cos^3\alpha}{(2rab\cos\varphi)^{1/2}a\Pi^{5/4}}\sin\frac{\theta}{2}(2\cos\theta - 1)(\cos\theta + 1) + o(r^{-1/2}) \tag{B17}$$

$$z\frac{\partial^3 I}{\partial y^3} = \frac{a^2\sin^3\alpha}{(2rab\cos\varphi)^{1/2}b\Pi^{5/4}}\sin\frac{\theta}{2}(2\cos\theta - 1)(\cos\theta + 1) + o(r^{-1/2}) \tag{B18}$$

$$z\frac{\partial^3 I}{\partial z^3} = \frac{\Pi^{1/4}}{(2r\cos\varphi)^{1/2}(ab)^{3/2}}\cos\frac{\theta}{2}(2\cos\theta + 1)(\cos\theta - 1) + o(r^{-1/2}) \tag{B19}$$

where $\Pi = a^2\sin^2\alpha + b^2\cos^2\alpha$.

References

[1] Chahrour, A. H., Ohtsu, M. (1994). *Crack growth prediction in a scaled down model of a concrete gravity dam*. Theoretical and Applied Fracture Mechanics 21, 29～40

[2] Gdoutos, E. E. (1990). *Fracture Mechanics Criteria and Application*. Kluwer Academic Publishers, Dordrecht

[3] Green, A.E. ,Sneddon,I.N.(1950). *The distribution of stress in the neighborhood of a flat elliptical crack in an elastic solid*. Proceedings of the Cambridge Philosophical Society 46,159～164

[4] Kassir, M.K., Sih,G.C.(1966). *Three-dimensional stress distribution around an elliptical crack under arbitrary loadings*. Journal of Applied Mechanics 33,601～611

[5] Kassir, M.K.,Sih, G.C.(1975). *Mechanics of Fracture 2-Three-Dimensional Crack Problem*. Noordhoff International Publishing, Leiden

[6] Kuo,A.Y., Shvarts. S., Stonesifter, R.B.(1992). *An analytical solution for an elliptical crack in a flat plate subjected to arbitrary loading*. *Fracture Mechanics: Twenty-Second Symposium (Volume* Ⅱ), *ASTM STP* 1131. American Society for Testing and Materials, Philadelphia, 1992,pp.347～367

[7] Li,Y.Z., Li,M.H., Liu,C.T., He,M.Y. (1988). *The near-tip stress and strain fields of a three-dimensional body with a surface crack and the calculation of its stress intensity factor*. Scientia Sinica (Series A) 31,828～842

[8] Meguid.S.A.(1989). *Engineering Fracture Mechanics*. Elsevier Applied Science, London

[9] Miannay.D.P. (1998). *Fracture Mechanics*. Springer-Verlag Inc., New York

[10] Nishioka.T., Atluri, S.N. (1983). *Analytical solution for embedded elliptical cracks and finite element alternating method for elliptical surface cracks subjected to arbitrary loadings*. Engineering Fracture Mechanics 17.247～268

[11] Qin.T.Y.,Tang.R.J.(1993). *Finite-part integral and boundary element method to solve embedded planar crack problems*. International Journal of Fracture 60,373～381

[12] Raju.I.S.,Newman.J.C., Jr.(1979). *Stress intensity factors for a wide range of semi-elliptical surface cracks in finite-thickness plates*. Engineering Fracture Mechanics 11,817～829

[13] Sih.G.C. (1971). *A review of the three-dimensional stress problem for a cracked plate*. International Journal of Fracture 7.39～61

[14] Sih,G.C. (1991). *Mechanics of Fracture Initiation and Propagation-Surface and Volume Energy Density Applied as Failure Criterion*. Kluwer Academic Publishers, Dordrecht

[15] Whittaker.E.T. ,Watson.G.N.(1927). A *Course of Modern Analysis*. Cambridge University Press, Cambridge

[16] Zhao.Y.(1987). *A strain energy criterion for mixed-mode crack propagation*. Engineering Fracture Mechanics 26.533～539

[17] Zhu.X.K. (1996). *Research on stability of 3-D cracks and near-tip fields of cracks propagating in power-law softening materials*. Postdoctoral research report. Tsinghua University. Beijing, China

二、(不确定性问题)随机应力及不均质体强度

大体积混凝土结构温度场的随机有限元算法

摘　要　综合考虑环境因素(如库水温度、气温等)以及混凝土热力学参数的随机性,给出了可以反映材料参数随机性的基于随机场局部平均的温度场随机变分原理和随机有限元列式。为使随机有限元法可以进一步考虑随机过程参数的影响,文中视复频响应函数为随机函数,给出了复频响应函数-随机有限元法。文末算例表明了该方法的正确性和实用性。

关键词　随机温度场　随机变分原理　随机有限元方法

快速施工的碾压混凝土(RCC)拱坝常形成较大的温度应力而成为影响结构安全的主要因素,国外20世纪70年代起就着手研究温度应力的随机性。Heller首先提出了谱密度法,但该法显然不适用于混凝土结构。Tsubaki和Bazant提出了脉冲反应函数法,但系统的脉冲响应函数常不易求得。随后,Bazant等人考虑到环境因素的特殊性,提出了谱分析方法[1]以及与有限元相结合的算法[2]。我国对于混凝土材料随机温度应力的研究很少,学者王同生提出了直接法[3]。综观国内外文献可以看出,目前的研究仍存在以下两点不足:①只研究了稳定变温温度场的随机性,绝热温升的影响未能考虑;②未能考虑结构物理参数的随机性,未能将谱分析方法与随机有限元法相结合。

随机有限元方法经过十余年发展已成为分析结构随机性的强有力的工具[4]。但是,目前几乎所有的随机有限元法都是基于直接刚度矩阵法,随机变分原理对于构造多变量的有限元模型和发展新的数学方法意义重大[5]。为克服以上两点不足,本文提出了随机温度场的随机有限元算法,并给出了随机温度场的计算实例以验证本文理论、方法和程序的正确性。

1　影响温度场的随机因素及其处理方法

1.1　温度场定解方程及其泛函

由热传导理论,温度场 $T(t,x,y,z)$ 为以下定解问题的解:

$$\frac{\partial T}{\partial t}=a\nabla^2 T+\frac{\partial\theta}{\partial t};\quad T\Big|_{t=0}=T_0(x,y,z);\quad \frac{\partial T}{\partial n}\Big|_a=-\frac{b}{\lambda}(T+T_a)\tag{1}$$

式中:a 为导温系数;b 为表面放热系数;λ 为导热系数;T_a 为环境温度,T_0 为初始温度,θ 为绝热温升。

上述热传导定解问题可以归结为求泛函的极值问题。可以看出,影响温度场的随机因素很多,下面对影响温度场的主要随机因素作具体分析。

1.2　边界温度和外部气温

对于重力坝、拱坝等大型水工建筑物,边界温度和外部气温为上游库水温和下游坝面气温,边界温度和外部气温可以统一地表示为

本文选自《清华大学学报(自然科学版)》1996年第1期,作者还有刘宁。

$$T_a(t) = T_m + \sum_{i=1}^{na} T_{ai}(t) \tag{2}$$

式中：T_m 为随机变量；$T_{ai}(t)$ 为周期平稳随机过程。

对于库水温度随机过程，$T_m = T_{wm}(z)$，$na = 2$，$T_{ai}(t) = A_w(z)\cos\omega(t - t_0)\cos[\varepsilon(z)]$，$T_{a2}(t) = -A_w(z)\sin\omega(t - t_0)\sin[\varepsilon(z)]$；对于下游坝面气温随机过程，$T_m = T_B$，$na = 1$，$T_{a1}(t) = T_A\sin\omega(t - t_0)$。其中 $T_{wm}(z)$ 为水深 z 处年平均水温(℃)，$A_m(z)$ 为水温调制函数，$\omega = 2\pi/12$，T_A 和 T_B 为随机变量。

1.3 绝热温升 θ

绝热温升 $\theta = \theta_0(1 - e^{-m_1 t})$，其中 θ_0 和 m_1 为随机变量。式(1)只需用到 $\partial\theta/\partial t = \theta_0 m_1 e^{-m_1 t}$，显然 $\partial\theta/\partial t$ 为一非平稳随机过程。令

$$\partial\theta/\partial t = \partial\bar{\theta}/\partial t + \partial\Delta\theta/\partial t \tag{3}$$

利用 $\partial\theta/\partial t$ 在随机变量 θ_0、m_1 均值处的一阶 Taylor 展式，可得

$$\partial\bar{\theta}/\partial t \approx \overline{\theta}_0\overline{m}_1 e^{-\overline{m}_1 t};\ \partial\Delta\theta/\partial t \approx \overline{m}_1 e^{-\overline{m}_1 t}\Delta\theta_0 + (\overline{\theta}_0 - \overline{\theta}_0\overline{m}_1 t)e^{-\overline{m}_1 t}\Delta m_1 \tag{4}$$

式中：$\overline{\theta}_0$、$\overline{m}_1$ 分别为 θ_0、m_1 的均值，而 $\Delta\theta_0 = \theta_0 - \overline{\theta}_0$，$\Delta m_1 = m_1 - \overline{m}_1$。

关于初始温度 T_0 以及混凝土热学参数 a、λ、b，宜作为三维随机场处理，可以采用三维可部分分离均匀向量随机场模拟[4]，不再多述。

2 随机温度场的求解

2.1 基于随机场局部平均的温度场随机变分原理及随机有限元列式

兼顾精度和效率，本文只给出温度场的一阶随机变分原理及相应的随机有限元列式。

2.1.1 温度场随机变分原理

以 $X(x,y,z)$ 表示随机场，将随机函数 T、T_a 以及随机参数 θ、a、b、λ 在随机场的均值 $\overline{X}$ 和点 (x,y,z) 处一阶 Taylor 展开，根据温度场泛函的一阶变分形式，经推导可得：

(1) 零次变分原理

$$\delta I^{(0)} = \iiint_\Omega \delta T\left[\overline{a}\nabla^2\overline{T} + \left(\frac{\partial\bar{\theta}}{\partial t} - \frac{\partial\overline{T}}{\partial t}\right)\right]d\Omega - \iint_c \delta T\times\overline{a}\left[\frac{\partial\overline{T}}{\partial n} + \frac{\overline{b}}{\overline{\lambda}}(\overline{T} - \overline{T}_a)\right]ds = 0 \tag{5}$$

(2) 一次变分原理

$$\delta I^{(1)} = \iiint_\Omega \delta T[(a'\nabla^2\overline{T} + \overline{a}\nabla^2 T') + \frac{\partial\theta'}{\partial t} - \frac{\partial T'}{\partial t}]d\Omega - \iint_c \delta T\times a'[\frac{\partial\overline{T}}{\partial n} + \frac{\overline{b}}{\overline{\lambda}}(\overline{T} - \overline{T}_a)]ds -$$

$$\iint_a \delta T\times\overline{a}[\frac{\partial T'}{\partial n} + \frac{b'\overline{\lambda} - \overline{b}\lambda'}{\overline{\lambda}^2}(\overline{T} - \overline{T}_a) + \frac{\overline{b}}{\overline{\lambda}}(T' - T'_a)]ds = 0 \tag{6}$$

由于式(5)、(6)中包含时间 t，因此所得变分原理也应称为瞬时变分原理。环境温度以及绝热温升随机过程在时间域上对温度场的影响则可通过后述方法获得。

2.1.2 基于随机场局部平均的温度场随机有限元列式

将随机场离散为 q 个单元，如果随机场离散单元为三维等参元，有

$$X(x,y,z) \approx \sum_{i=1}^{q}[\varphi_i\sum_{k=1}^{ng}X(\xi_k、\eta_k、\delta_k)\mid J\mid_k H_k/(\sum_{k=1}^{ng}\mid J\mid_k H_k)] \tag{7}$$

式中：φ_i 为示性函数，当 $(x,y,z)\in\Omega_i$ 时，$\varphi_i(x,y,z) = 1$；当 $(x,y,z)\notin\Omega_i$ 时，

$\varphi_i(x,y,z)=0$，由此可进一步获得随机场的相关结构[4]。

将温度场离散为 N_e 个单元、N_p 个结点，有 $\overline{\boldsymbol{T}}=\boldsymbol{N}\boldsymbol{T}$；$T'=\boldsymbol{N}\boldsymbol{T}'$，其中 $\boldsymbol{N}$ 为整体位移形函数，$\boldsymbol{T}$ 为整体温度列阵，由此可得随机有限元列式

(1)零次方程

$$\overline{\boldsymbol{K}}_1\overline{\boldsymbol{T}}_1+\overline{\boldsymbol{K}}_2\frac{\partial\overline{\boldsymbol{T}}}{\partial t}+\overline{\boldsymbol{F}}=0 \tag{8}$$

式中：

$$\overline{\boldsymbol{K}}_1=\sum_e\left[\overline{a}\iiint_{\Omega e}\left(\frac{\partial N_i}{\partial x}\frac{\partial N_j}{\partial x}+\frac{\partial N_i}{\partial y}\frac{\partial N_j}{\partial y}+\frac{\partial N_i}{\partial z}\frac{\partial N_j}{\partial z}\right)\mathrm{d}x\mathrm{d}y\mathrm{d}z+\overline{a}\iint_a\frac{\overline{b}}{\overline{\lambda}}N_iN_j\,\mathrm{d}s\right] \tag{9}$$

$$\overline{\boldsymbol{K}}_2=\sum_e\iiint_{\Omega e}N_iN_j\,\mathrm{d}x\mathrm{d}y\mathrm{d}z \tag{10}$$

$$\overline{\boldsymbol{F}}=\sum_e\left(-\iint_e\frac{\partial\overline{\theta}}{\partial t}N_i\,\mathrm{d}s+\overline{a}\iint_{Ce}\frac{\overline{b}}{\overline{\lambda}}\boldsymbol{N}_i\boldsymbol{N}\overline{\boldsymbol{T}}_a\,\mathrm{d}s\right] \tag{11}$$

(2)一次方程

$$\overline{\boldsymbol{K}}_1\boldsymbol{T}'_k+\overline{\boldsymbol{K}}_2\frac{\partial\boldsymbol{T}'_k}{\partial t}+\boldsymbol{F}'_k=0\quad(k=1,2,\cdots,n) \tag{12}$$

式中：

$$\begin{aligned}\boldsymbol{F}'_k=&\iiint_\Omega\left[a'_k\left(\frac{\partial\boldsymbol{N}^{\mathrm{T}}}{\partial x}\frac{\partial\boldsymbol{N}}{\partial x}+\frac{\partial\boldsymbol{N}^{\mathrm{T}}}{\partial y}\frac{\partial\boldsymbol{N}}{\partial y}+\frac{\partial\boldsymbol{N}^{\mathrm{T}}}{\partial z}\frac{\partial\boldsymbol{N}}{\partial z}\right)\overline{\boldsymbol{T}}-\boldsymbol{N}^{\mathrm{T}}\frac{\partial\theta'_k}{\partial t}\right]\mathrm{d}\Omega+\\&\iint_C a'_k\frac{\overline{b}}{\overline{\lambda}}\boldsymbol{N}^{\mathrm{T}}\boldsymbol{N}\overline{\boldsymbol{T}}\mathrm{d}s+\iint_C\overline{a}\frac{b'_k\overline{\lambda}-\lambda'_k\overline{b}}{\overline{\lambda}^2}\boldsymbol{N}^{\mathrm{T}}\boldsymbol{N}\overline{\boldsymbol{T}}\mathrm{d}s-\\&\iint_C\boldsymbol{N}^{\mathrm{T}}\overline{a}\left(\frac{b'_k\overline{\lambda}-\lambda'_k\overline{b}}{\overline{\lambda}^2}\overline{\boldsymbol{T}}_a+\frac{\overline{b}}{\overline{\lambda}}\boldsymbol{T}'_{ak}\right)\mathrm{d}s-\iint_C a'_k\boldsymbol{N}^{\mathrm{T}}\frac{\overline{b}}{\overline{\lambda}}\overline{\boldsymbol{T}}_a\,\mathrm{d}s\end{aligned} \tag{13}$$

式(8)、式(12)即为温度场随机有限元控制方程。由式(8)可求出温度的均值 $\overline{\boldsymbol{T}}$，而由式(12)求出 $\boldsymbol{T}'_k$ 后，温度场的协方差矩阵中的第 i 行第 j 列元素为

$$\mathrm{Cov}(T^{(i)},T^{(j)})=\sum_{k=1}^{q}\sum_{l=1}^{q}T_k^{(i)},T_l^{(j)},\mathrm{Cov}(X_k,X_l)\quad(i,j=1,2,\cdots,NP) \tag{14}$$

2.2 随机温度场定解问题的处理

如果在同一定解问题中同时考虑环境温度和绝热温升随机过程对温度场的影响，问题将十分复杂。本文因此首先将原定解问题式(1)分离为随机环境温度定解问题Ⅰ和随机绝热温升定解问题 Ⅱ，然后再分别对这两类定解问题进行研究。

(1)随机环境温度定解问题Ⅰ

$$\frac{\partial T_1}{\partial t}=a\nabla^2T_1+\frac{\partial\overline{\theta}}{\partial t}\quad T_1\Big|_{t=0}=T_0(x,y,z)\quad\frac{\partial T_1}{\partial n}\Big|_c+\frac{b}{\lambda}T_1\Big|_c=\frac{b}{\lambda}T_a \tag{15}$$

由式(2)、式(15)须进一步分离为以下两部分(定解问题 $\mathrm{I}^{(0)}$ 和定解问题 $\mathrm{I}^{(i)}$)：

(a)定解问题 $\mathrm{I}^{(0)}$

$$\frac{\partial T_1^{(0)}}{\partial t}=a\nabla^2T_1^{(0)}+\frac{\partial\overline{\theta}}{\partial t}\quad T_1^{(0)}\Big|_{t=0}=T_0(x,y,z)\quad\frac{\partial T_1^{(0)}}{\partial n}\Big|_c+\frac{b}{\lambda}T_1^{(0)}\Big|_c=\frac{b}{\lambda}T_m \tag{16}$$

(b)定解问题 $\mathrm{I}^{(i)}(i=1,\cdots,na)$

$$\frac{\partial T_1^{(i)}}{\partial t}=a\nabla^2 T_1^{(i)}+\frac{\overline{\partial\theta}}{\partial t}\quad T_1^{(i)}\Big|_{t=0}=0\quad \frac{\partial T_1^{(i)}}{\partial n}\Big|_c+\frac{b}{\lambda}T_1^{(i)}\Big|_c=\frac{b}{\lambda}T_{ai} \tag{17}$$

(2)随机绝热温升定解问题Ⅱ

$$\frac{\partial \Delta T_2}{\partial t}=a\nabla^2(\Delta T_2)+\frac{\partial\Delta\theta}{\partial t}\quad \Delta T_2\Big|_{t=0}=0\quad \frac{\partial \Delta T_2}{\partial n}\Big|_c+\frac{b}{\lambda}\Delta T_2\Big|_c=0 \tag{18}$$

显然 $\Delta\overline{T}_2=0$,由式(15)~式(18)可知

$$T=T_1+\Delta T_2=T_1^{(0)}+\sum_{i=1}^{na}T_1^{(i)}+\Delta T_2 \tag{19}$$

显然满足原定解问题式(1),式中各量值分别由定解问题Ⅰ和定解问题Ⅱ得出。

2.3　定解问题Ⅰ的求解

2.3.1　定解问题($\mathrm{I}^{(0)}$)的求解

由于式(16)中不包含随机过程影响量,求解较为简单。这里着重说明初始温度 $T_0(x,y,z)$的处理方法。仔细考察温度场随机变分原理的推导,可以看出所建立的瞬时变分原理尚未明确地反映出初始温度 T_0 的随机性。由于:$T_0=\overline{T}_0+\Delta T_0$,$\mathrm{Var}(T_{T0})=\mathrm{Var}(T_{\overline{T}_0+\Delta T_0})=\mathrm{Var}(T_{\Delta T_0})$。式中 T_{T0}表示由初始温度 T_0产生的温度场。由温度场有限元控制方程,可得递推公式

$$\mathrm{Var}(\boldsymbol{T}_i)_{T_0}=-\left\{\left(\boldsymbol{K}_1-\frac{2}{\Delta t_i}\boldsymbol{K}_2\right)/\left(\boldsymbol{K}_1+\frac{2}{\Delta t_i}\boldsymbol{K}_2\right)\right\}^2\mathrm{Var}(\boldsymbol{T}_{i-1})_{T_0} \tag{20}$$

式中,$\mathrm{Var}(\boldsymbol{T}_i)_{T_0}$表示 T_0 的随机性产生的第 i 时刻温度场的方差,由式(20)和式(14)可以断言,只要将初始温度作为基本随机变量,在 $t=0$ 时刻令 $\partial T/\partial T_0=1$,与其余变量一起直接参加式(8)~式(14)的计算,就隐含着式(20),无需分开计算。

2.3.2　定解问题($\mathrm{I}^{(i)}$)的求解:复频响应函数-随机有限元法

根据随机振动有关理论,时不变线性系统在周期平稳随机过程 $A\mathrm{e}^{iw(t-t_0)}$作用下,系统的响应 Y 可由复频响应函数法获得:$Y=Ah(\omega)\mathrm{e}^{iw(t-t_0)}$,式中 $h(\omega)$为复频响应函数。常规的复频响应函数法中复频响应函数为确定性函数,为能反映材料参数随机性的影响,本文首次视复频响应函数为随机材料参数的随机函数,由随机有限元方法获得复频响应函数的统计特性,故本文称之为复频响应函数-随机有限元法。

由于环境温度 T_{ai}为空间随机过程,在有限元离散后应写为:$\boldsymbol{T}_{ai}=\boldsymbol{A}\mathrm{e}^{iw(t-t_0)}$。因此,在 $\boldsymbol{T}_{ai}$作用下,温度场响应列阵可写为一般形式

$$\boldsymbol{T}=\boldsymbol{h}(\omega)\boldsymbol{A}\mathrm{e}^{iw(t-t_0)}=\boldsymbol{H}(\boldsymbol{\omega})\mathrm{e}^{iw(t-t_0)} \tag{21}$$

将上式代入温度场有限元控制方程式,并在两边同时约去 $\mathrm{e}^{iw(t-t_0)}$,可得

$$(\boldsymbol{K}_1+i\omega\boldsymbol{K}_2)\boldsymbol{H}(\boldsymbol{\omega})=\sum_e a\iint_{Ce}\frac{b}{\lambda}\boldsymbol{N}_i\boldsymbol{N}\boldsymbol{A}\,\mathrm{d}s \tag{22}$$

上式即为随机复频响应函数有限元控制方程,其随机有限元列式可用摄动法获得,结果为:

(1)零次方程

$$(\overline{\boldsymbol{K}}_1+i\omega\overline{\boldsymbol{K}}_2)\overline{\boldsymbol{H}}(\boldsymbol{\omega})=\sum_e\overline{a}\iint_{Ce}\frac{\overline{b}}{\lambda}\boldsymbol{N}_i\boldsymbol{N}\overline{\boldsymbol{A}}\,\mathrm{d}s \tag{23}$$

(2)一次方程

$$(\overline{\boldsymbol{K}}_1 + i\omega\overline{\boldsymbol{K}}_2)\boldsymbol{H}'_k(\boldsymbol{\omega}) = \boldsymbol{F}'_k \qquad (k = 1,2,\cdots,n)$$

$$\boldsymbol{F}'_k = -(\boldsymbol{K}'_{1k} + i\omega\boldsymbol{K}'_{2k})\overline{\boldsymbol{H}}(\boldsymbol{\omega}) + \sum_e a'_k\iint_{Ce}\frac{\bar{b}}{\bar{\lambda}}\boldsymbol{N}_i\boldsymbol{N}\overline{\boldsymbol{A}}\mathrm{d}s -$$

$$\sum_e \bar{a}\iint_{Ce}\frac{b'_k\bar{\lambda} - \lambda'_k\bar{b}}{\bar{\lambda}^2}\boldsymbol{N}_i\boldsymbol{N}\overline{\boldsymbol{A}}\mathrm{d}s + \sum_e \bar{a}\iint_{Ce}\frac{\bar{b}}{\bar{\lambda}}\boldsymbol{N}_i\boldsymbol{N}\boldsymbol{A}'_k\mathrm{d}s \tag{24}$$

由式(23)、式(24)可以求出 $\overline{\boldsymbol{H}}(\omega)$、$\boldsymbol{H}'_k(\omega)(k=1,2,\cdots,n)$。根据复数随机过程原理,由式(21)决定的温度列阵 $\boldsymbol{T}$ 的相关函数矩阵为:$\boldsymbol{R}(\omega,t_1,t_2,t_0)=E[\boldsymbol{T}(\omega,t_1,t_0)\boldsymbol{T}^{*\mathrm{T}}(\omega,t_2,t_0)]$,式中 $\boldsymbol{T}^{*\mathrm{T}}(\omega,t_2,t_0)$为 $\boldsymbol{T}$ 的共轭复数列阵的转置,$E[\cdot]$表示求数学期望。将式(21)代入上式,并利用:$\boldsymbol{H}(\omega)\approx\overline{\boldsymbol{H}}(\omega)+\sum_{k=1}^{n}\boldsymbol{H}'_k(\omega)\Delta X_k$,当 $t_1=t_2$ 时,有

$$\boldsymbol{R}(\omega,t,t_0)=\overline{\boldsymbol{H}}(\omega)\overline{\boldsymbol{H}}(\omega)^{*\mathrm{T}}+\sum_{k=1}^{n}\sum_{l=1}^{n}\boldsymbol{H}'_k(\omega)\boldsymbol{H}'_l(\omega)^{*\mathrm{T}}\mathrm{Cov}(X_k,X_l)$$

于是,温度 $\boldsymbol{T}=(T_1,T_2,\cdots,T_{NP})^{\mathrm{T}}$ 的方差为

$$\begin{aligned}\mathrm{Var}(T^{(i)})&=E(T^{(i)2})-E(T^{(i)})E(T^{(i)*})\\&=\sum_{k=1}^{n}|H_k^{(i)'}(\omega)|^2\mathrm{Var}(X_k)\quad(i=1,\cdots,NP)\end{aligned} \tag{25}$$

2.4 随机绝热温升定解问题(Ⅱ)的求解

非平稳随机过程 $\partial\theta/\partial t$ 被简化为式(3)、式(4)的形式,由于 $\Delta\overline{T}_2=0$,所以无需列出随机有限元的零次方程,只需写出一次方程,由式(8)、式(12)可知一次方程为

$$\overline{\boldsymbol{K}}_1\Delta\boldsymbol{T}'_{2k}+\overline{\boldsymbol{K}}_2\frac{\partial\Delta\boldsymbol{T}'_{2k}}{\partial t}+\Delta\boldsymbol{F}'_k=0 \tag{26}$$

$$\Delta\boldsymbol{F}'_k=-\iiint_{\Omega}\boldsymbol{N}^{\mathrm{T}}[\overline{m}_1\mathrm{e}^{-\overline{m}_1t}\Delta\theta'_{0k}+(\bar{\theta}_0-\bar{\theta}_0\overline{m}_1t\mathrm{e}^{-\overline{m}_1t})\Delta m'_{1k}]\mathrm{d}\Omega$$

式(26)中 $\overline{\boldsymbol{K}}_1$、$\overline{\boldsymbol{K}}_2$ 仍如式(9)、式(10)所示。求出 $\Delta\boldsymbol{T}_{2k}$后,自协方差矩阵为

$$\mathrm{Cov}(\Delta T_2^{(i)},\Delta T_2^{(j)})=\sum_{k=1}^{2}\sum_{l=1}^{2}\Delta\overline{T}_{2k}^{(i)\prime}\Delta T_{2l}^{(j)\prime}\mathrm{Cov}(X_k,X_k)$$

式中:随机变量 $X_1=\Delta\theta_0$, $X_2=\Delta m_1$。

3 程序及算例

根据前述理论,编制了"三维混凝土结构随机温度场计算程序 STEM",该程序可考虑各种随机因素(随机入仓温度、随机热力学参数、随机环境温度等)进行施工期、运行期的随机温度场计算。为验证理论及程序的正确性,本文进行了以下三个算例的计算。

(1)算例 1[3],自由板右侧气温 $T=0$,表面放热系数 $b_1=25.2\mathrm{kJ/m^2h℃}$,左侧气温 $T=A\cos\omega(t-t_0)$,$b_2=50.4\mathrm{kJ/m^2h℃}$,见图 1。$\omega=7.169\times10^{-4}\,\mathrm{h^{-1}}$,板厚为 2.6m,导热系数为 $\lambda=5.25\mathrm{kJ/m^2h℃}$,导温系数 $a=21.7\mathrm{cm^2/h}$。只取 A 为随机变量,其均值为8℃,标准差为1.6℃,计算结果见表1。由表1可见,本文视复频响应函数为随机,按式(25)计算温度方差,所得结果与文献[3]结果一致。

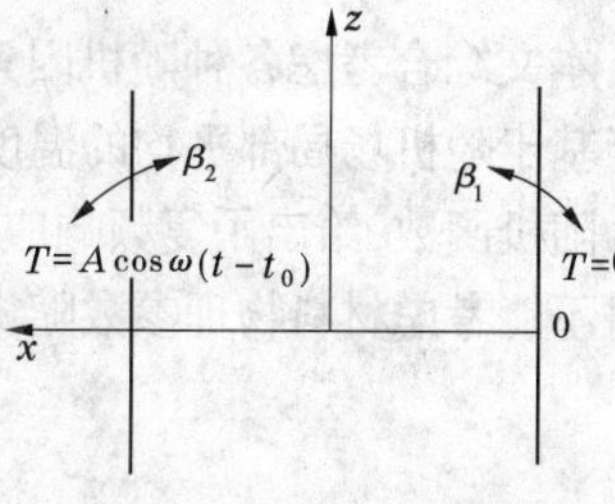

图1 自由板随机温度问题

(2)算例 2,进一步取参数 a、b_1、b_2、λ 为随机变量,变异系数均为 0.2,计算结果见表 2。

表 1　板内温度的标准差

位置 x(m)	0	1.3	2.6
文献[3]结果 σ_T(℃)	0.08	0.80	1.52
本文结果 σ_T(℃)	0.080 9	0.800 1	1.521 2

表 2　板内温度的标准差

位置 x(m)	0	1.3	2.6
随机有限元法 σ_T(℃)	0.199 3	0.993 4	1.539 6
Monte－Carlo 法 σ_T(℃)	0.197 4	0.991 4	1.538 9

(3)算例 3,考虑绝热温升的影响,以上各参数不变,此时温度为非平稳过程(方差随时间变化),取 $\overline{\theta}_0=25.0℃$,$\overline{m_1}=0.397$,变异系数均为 0.2,温度均值结果见图 2,温度标准差见图 3。可以看出,绝热温升对温度均值和方差的影响在 90d 后基本消失,标准差收敛于 0.991 4(同算例 1、2 中结果)。以上算例表明本文理论和程序是正确的。

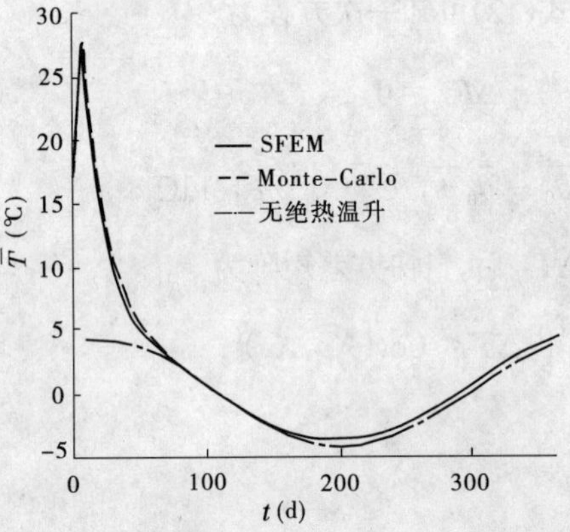

图 2　温度均值($x=1.3$m 处)

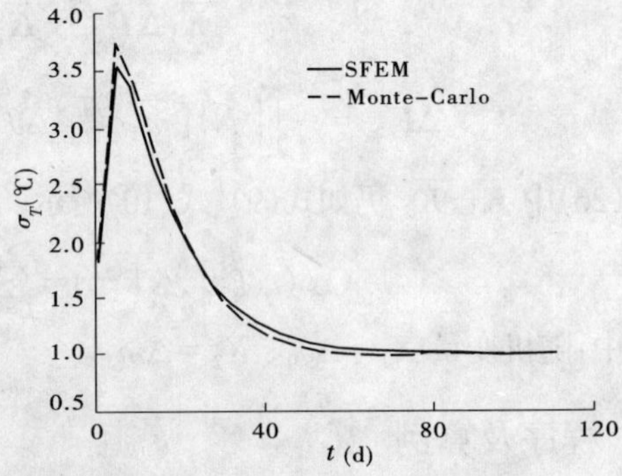

图 3　温度标准差($x=1.3$m 处)

4　结语

本文综合考虑各种随机因素对三维混凝土结构随机温度场的计算方法进行了研究,给出了基于随机场局部平均的温度场随机变分原理和随机有限元列式,并首次视复频响应函数为随机函数,给出了复频响应函数－随机有限元法,有效地克服了谱密度法求解随机温度场时不能考虑材料物理参数随机性的局限性。本文解决了混凝土结构随机温度场的求解问题。

参 考 文 献

[1] Bazant Z P, Wnag T S. *Spectral analysis of random shrinkage in concrete structures*. J of Engng Mech, ASCE, 1984,110(2): 173~186

[2] Bazant Z P, Wnag T S. *Spectral finite element analysis of random shrinkage in concrete*. J of Struct Engng, ASCE, 1984,110(9): 2196~2211

[3] 王同生. 混凝土结构的随机温度应力. 水利学报,1985(1):23~31

[4] 刘宁. 三维可分向量随机场局部平均的三维随机有限元及可靠度计算. 水利学报,1995(7): 75~82

[5] 张汝清,高行山. 随机变量的变分原理及有限元法. 应用数学和力学,1992,13(5):383~388

SPECTRAL STOCHASTIC FINITE ELEMENT ANALYSIS OF PERIODIC RANDOM THERMAL CREEP STRESS IN CONCRETE

Abstract A spectral stochastic finite element method with a numerical step-by-step algorithm for the analysis of thermal creep stresses in concrete structures is presented. The effect of concrete age on creep properties and various kinds of random factors including material parameters and the random temperature process of concrete, etc. is taken into account. In the proposed method, the complex frequency response function is introduced to reflect the influence of the temperature process and is regarded as a random function of the random material parameters of concrete. The algorithm leads to a series of incremental elastic problems in which the stresses and strains, etc. are all complex variables. The suggested method is useful for spectral analysis of the response of concrete structures with random material exposed to random environmental temperature.

Key words stochastic finite element method; mass concrete structures; thermal creep stress

1 Introduction

Thermal stresses can sometimes cause the failure of mass concrete structures. It is very important to calculate the thermal stresses correctly during both the construction and the operation period. However, random variation of the material parameters and the temperature of concrete has a significant effect on the stresses in concrete structures.

A solution to random thermal stress was pioneered by Heller and co-workers[1~5], who applied the spectral method (method of power response spectral). This analytical solution was, however, inapplicable to concrete because of the aging properties of creep. Based on the Bessel and Kelvin functions, Tsubaki and Bazand suggested a method of impulse response functions which could be used for a nonstationary aging system[6]. However, it was computationally inefficient and sometimes the impulse response function could not be obtained, even in a simple structural system. The generalized spectral method recommended by Bazant and his co-workers[7~13] was based on the fact that the environment could be adequately described by only few sinusoidal components. Although the method was used for the random creep shrinkage stress problem, it was suited to the analysis of random thermal stress. However, the influence of a random variation of material parameters was solved by the latin hypercube sampling[11~13] which is within the scope of the statistical method and proved to be inconvenient.

The stochastic finite element method, being a very efficient method (non-statistical method) for analyzing variability of stress in large structures, has been developed for more than 10

本文选自《Engineering Structures》1996年第9期,作者还有 Liu Ning。

years[14~16]. At present, however, the stochastic finite method is constrained in two fields: (a) material parameters being considered as random variables, the load cannot be considered as a random process (random excitation); (b) if the loads are being considered as random processes, material parameters should be constant or at most a definite function of time.

For non-aging concrete structures, creep stress under the influence of periodic temperature can be obtained by the method in References 17 and 18, however, for the analysis of aging concrete, the effect of random varability of temperature and random material parameters is not mentioned at all.

In this paper, the complex frequency response method with a numerical step-by-step algorithm is proposed. The method leads to a series of incremental elastic problems in which the stresses and strains, etc. are all complex variables. Corresponding recursive formulae for the calculation of thermal creep stress in aging concrete structures are derived. In order to reflect the influence of random material parameters, the complex frequency response function is considered as a random function, of which the spacial problem is solved by the suggested spectral stochastic finite element method.

2 Descriptiom of Specific Random Variability

2.1 Creep Compliance

The creep compliance function $C(t,\tau)$ can be expressed as

$$C(t,\tau) = \overline{C}(t,\tau) + \Delta C(t,\tau)$$
$$\approx \overline{C}(t,\tau) + (1 - e^{-\bar{k}(t-\tau)})\Delta\phi + (t-\tau)e^{-\bar{k}(t-\tau)}\overline{\phi}(\tau)\Delta k \quad (1)$$

where $\overline{C}(t,\tau)$ is the expectation of $C(t,\tau)$, k is a random variable, $\phi(\tau)$ can be expressed as

$$\phi(\tau) = p_1 + p_2/\tau^{p_3} \quad (2)$$

in which, p_1, p_2 and p_3 are random variables. Thus

$$\overline{\phi}(\tau) \approx \overline{p}_1 + \overline{p}_2/\tau^{\overline{p}_3}; \Delta\Phi \approx \Delta p_1 + \tau^{-\overline{p}_3}\Delta p_2 - \overline{p}_2 \ln\tau \cdot \tau^{-\overline{p}_3} \cdot \Delta p_3 \quad (3)$$

2.2 Modulus of elasticity

The modulus of elasticity of concrete can be written as

$$E(\tau) = E_0(1 - e^{-m_2\tau}) \approx \overline{E}(\tau) + (1 - e^{-\overline{m}_2\tau})\Delta E_0 + \tau e^{-\overline{m}_2\tau}\overline{E}_0\Delta m_2 \quad (4)$$

where $\overline{E}(\tau)$ is the expectation of $E(\tau)$. E_0 and m_2 are random variables.

2.3 Temperature

Random temperature $T(t,x,y,z)$ (a column matrix in finite element analysis) of concrete can be obtained by the method in Reference [19].

3 Random Thermal Creep Stress

A solution of creep stress caused by periodic load has been given[17,18]. However, the modulus of elasticity in this method should be constant, which is inapplicable for aging concrete. This problem can be solved by the complex frequency response method with a numerical step-by-step algorithm suggested in the following.

3.1 Complex Frequency Response Method

The periodic temperature process $T(t)$ can be written as[17~19]

$$T(t) = \boldsymbol{h}_T(\omega)e^{i\omega t} \tag{5}$$

in which, $\boldsymbol{h}_T(\omega)$ is the frequency response function column matrix of temperature. The displacement, strain and stress can be, respectively, expressed as

$$\left.\begin{aligned} u(t) &= \boldsymbol{h}_u(t,\omega)h_T(\omega)e^{i\omega t} = H_u(t,\omega)e^{i\omega t} \\ \varepsilon(t) &= \boldsymbol{h}_\varepsilon(t,\omega)h_T(\omega)e^{i\omega t} = H_\varepsilon(t,\omega)e^{i\omega t} \\ \sigma(t) &= \boldsymbol{h}_\sigma(t,\omega)h_T(\omega)e^{i\omega t} = H_\sigma(t,\omega)e^{i\omega t} \end{aligned}\right\} \tag{6}$$

where $\boldsymbol{h}_u(t,\omega)$, $\boldsymbol{h}_\varepsilon(t,\omega)$ and $\boldsymbol{h}_u(t,\omega)$ are the frequency response function matrices of displacement, strain and stress, respectively. Similarly, as for the thermal strain and creep strain, we have

$$\varepsilon^{(T)} = H_\varepsilon^{(T)}(t,\omega)e^{i\omega t}, \varepsilon^{(C)} = H_\varepsilon^{(T)}(t,\omega)e^{i\omega t} \tag{7}$$

in which $H_\varepsilon^{(T)}(t,\omega) = \boldsymbol{h}_\varepsilon^{(T)}(t,\omega)h_T(\omega)$, $H_\varepsilon^{(C)}(t,\omega) = \boldsymbol{h}_\varepsilon^{(c)}(t,\omega)h_T(\omega)$. $\boldsymbol{h}_\varepsilon^{(T)}(\omega)$ and $\boldsymbol{h}_\varepsilon^{(C)}(\omega)$ are the frequency response function matrices of thermal strain and creep strain, respectively.

3.2 The Uniaxial Case

Suppose concrete was loaded at the age of t_0. At the age of t, the creep strain can be expressed as[10]

$$\varepsilon^{(C)} = \Delta\sigma_0 C(t,t_0) + \int_{t_0}^{t} C(t,\tau)\frac{\partial\sigma}{\partial\tau}d\tau \tag{8}$$

From Eqs. (6) and (7), the above equation becomes

$$H_\varepsilon^{(C)}(t) = \Delta H_{\sigma 0}C(t,t_0)e^{i\omega t_0} + \sum \phi_i^*(\Delta H_{\sigma i} + i\omega\Delta\tau_i H_{\sigma i})(f_i^{(1)}e^{i\omega t_{i-1}} - f_i^{(2)}e^{(i\omega+k)t_{i-1}-kt}) \tag{9}$$

in which, $\phi_i^* = \phi(t_{i-1} + \Delta\tau_i/2)$, $\Delta\tau_i = t_i - t_{i-1}$. And $f_i^{(1)} = (e^{i\omega\Delta\tau_i} - 1)/(i\omega\Delta\tau_i)$; $f_i^{(2)} = (e^{(i\omega+k)\Delta\tau_i} - 1)/((i\omega+k)\Delta\tau_i)(i=1,2,\cdots)$. Considering three neighbouring times: t_{n-1}, t_n and t_{n+1}, we have

$$H_\varepsilon^{(C)}(t_{n-1})e^{i\omega t_{n-1}} = \Delta H_{\sigma 0}C(t_{n-1},t_0)e^{i\omega t_0} + \sum_{i=1}^{n-1}\phi_i^*(\Delta H_{\sigma i} + i\omega\Delta\tau_i H_{\sigma i})(f_i^{(1)}e^{i\omega t_{i-1}} - f_i^{(2)}e^{(i\omega+k)t_{i-1}-kt_{n-1}}) \tag{10}$$

$$H_\varepsilon^{(C)}(t_n)e^{i\omega t_n} = \Delta H_{\sigma 0}C(t_n,t_0)e^{i\omega t_0} + \sum_{i=1}^{n}\phi_i^*(\Delta H_{\sigma i} + i\omega\Delta\tau_i H_{\sigma i})(f_i^{(1)}e^{i\omega t_{i-1}} - f_i^{(2)}e^{(i\omega+k)t_{i-1}-kt_n}) \tag{11}$$

$$H_\varepsilon^{(C)}(t^{n+1})e^{i\omega t_{n+1}} = \Delta H_{\sigma 0}C(t_{n+1},t_0)e^{i\omega t_0} + \sum_{i=1}^{n+1}\phi_i^*(\Delta H_{\sigma i} + i\omega\Delta\tau_i H_{\sigma i})(f_i^{(1)}e^{i\omega t_{i-1}} - f_i^{(2)}e^{(i\omega+k)t_{i-1}-kt_{n+1}}) \tag{12}$$

Let

$$\left.\begin{aligned} \Delta\Gamma_{\varepsilon n}^{(C)} &= \Delta H_{\varepsilon n}^{(C)} + i\omega\Delta\tau_n H_{\varepsilon n}^{(C)}(n = 1,2,\cdots) \\ \Delta\Gamma_{\sigma n}^{(C)} &= \Delta H_{\sigma n}^{(C)} + i\omega\Delta\tau_n H_{\sigma n}^{(C)}(n = 1,2,\cdots) \\ \Delta\Gamma_{\varepsilon 0}^{(C)} &= \Delta H_{\varepsilon 0}^{(C)} \\ \Delta\Gamma_{\sigma 0}^{(C)} &= \Delta H_{\sigma 0}^{(C)} \end{aligned}\right\} \tag{13}$$

Subtracting equation (10) from equation (11), we obtain

$$\Delta\Gamma^{(C)}_{\varepsilon n} = \Delta\Gamma_{\sigma 0} e^{i\omega(t_0 - t_n)}(C(t_n, t_0) - C(t_{n-1}, t_0)) + (1 - e^{-(i\omega+k)\Delta\tau_n})\omega_n + \phi^*_n \Delta\Gamma_{\sigma n}(f^{(1)}_n e^{-i\omega\Delta}\ \tau_n - f^{(2)}_n e^{-(i\omega+k)\Delta\tau_n}) \tag{14}$$

where

$$\omega_n = \sum_{i=1}^{n-1} \phi^*_i \Delta\Gamma_{\sigma i} f^{(2)}_i e^{-(i\omega+k)(t_n - \Delta\tau_n - t_{i-1})} \qquad (n = 2,3,\cdots) \tag{15}$$

Subtracting Eq. (11) from Eq. (12), we obtain

$$\Delta\Gamma^{(C)}_{\varepsilon(n+1)} = \Delta\Gamma_{\sigma 0} e^{i\omega(t_0 - t_{n+1})}(C(t_{n+1}, t_0) - C(t_n, t_0)) + (1 - e^{-(i\omega+k)\Delta\tau_{n+1}})\omega_{n+1} + \phi^*_{n+1}\Delta\Gamma_{\sigma(n+1)}(f^{(1)}_{n+1} e^{-i\omega\Delta\tau_{n+1}} - f^{(2)}_{n+1} e^{-(i\omega+k)\Delta\tau_{n+1}}) \tag{16}$$

where

$$\omega_{n+1} = \sum_{i=1}^{n} \phi^*_i \Delta\Gamma_{\sigma i} f^{(2)}_i e^{-(i\omega+k)(t_{n+1} - \Delta\tau_{n+1} - t_{i-1})} \tag{17}$$

From Eqs. (15) and (17), a recursive formula can be obtained

$$\omega_{n+1} = \omega_n e^{-(i\omega+k)\Delta\tau_n} + \phi^*_n \Delta\Gamma_{\sigma n} f^{(2)}_n e^{-(i\omega+k)\Delta\tau_n} \qquad (n = 2,3,\cdots) \tag{18}$$

$$\omega_2 = \phi^*_1 \Delta\Gamma_{\sigma 1} f^{(2)}_1 e^{-(i\omega+k)\Delta\tau_1}$$

3.3 The Multi-Axial Stress Case

The above equations can be easily extended into the multi-axial case. The three-dimensional stress recursive formulae can be written as

$$\Delta\Gamma^{(C)}_{\varepsilon n} = \Delta\Gamma_{\sigma 0} e^{i\omega(t_0 - t_n)}(C(t_n, t_0) - C(t_{n-1}, t_0)) + (1 - e^{-(i\omega+k)\Delta\tau_n})\omega_n + \phi^*_n \Delta\Gamma_{\sigma n}(f^{(1)}_n e^{-i\omega\Delta\tau_n} - f^{(2)}_n e^{-(i\omega+k)\Delta\tau_n}) \tag{19}$$

$$\omega_n = \omega_{n-1} e^{-(i\omega+k)\Delta\tau_{n-1}} + \boldsymbol{Q}\phi^*_{n-1}\Delta\Gamma_{\sigma(n-1)} f^{(2)}_{n-1} e^{-i(\omega+k)\Delta\tau_{n-1}}$$

$$\omega_2 = \boldsymbol{Q}\phi^*_1 \Delta\Gamma_{\sigma 1} f^{(2)}_1 e^{-(i\omega+k)\Delta\tau_1}$$

in which

$$\boldsymbol{Q} = \begin{bmatrix} 1 & -\mu & -\mu & 0 & 0 & 0 \\ -\mu & 1 & -\mu & 0 & 0 & 0 \\ -\mu & -\mu & 1 & 0 & 0 & 0 \\ 0 & 0 & 0 & 2(1+\mu) & 0 & 0 \\ 0 & 0 & 0 & 0 & 2(1+\mu) & 0 \\ 0 & 0 & 0 & 0 & 0 & 2(1+\mu) \end{bmatrix} \tag{20}$$

where μ is Poisson's ratio. Note that:

$$\Delta\Gamma\sigma_n = \boldsymbol{D}_n(\Delta\Gamma_{\varepsilon n} - \Delta\Gamma^{(C)}_{\varepsilon n} - \Delta\Gamma^{(T)}_{\varepsilon n}) \tag{21}$$

in which, $\boldsymbol{D}_n$ is the elastic strain-stress matrix when the modulus of elasticity is $E(t_{n-1} + \Delta\tau_n/2)$. The definition of $\Delta\Gamma^{(T)}_{\varepsilon n}$ is similar to Eq. (13). From Eq. (19), we obtain

$$\Delta\Gamma_{\sigma n} = \boldsymbol{D}^*_n(\Delta\Gamma_{\varepsilon n} - \Delta\Gamma^{(C)*}_{\varepsilon n} - \Delta\Gamma^{(T)}_{\varepsilon n}) \tag{22}$$

in which

$$\begin{aligned} \boldsymbol{D}^*_n &= \boldsymbol{D}_n/(1 + \phi^*_n(f^{(1)}_n)e^{-i\omega\Delta\tau_n} - f^{(2)}_n e^{-(i\omega+k)\Delta\tau_n})E(t_{n-1} + \Delta\tau_n/2) \\ \Delta\Gamma^{(C)*}_{\varepsilon n} &= \Delta\Gamma_{\sigma 0} e^{i\omega(t_0 - t_n)}(C(t_n, t_0) - C(t_{n-1}, t_0)) + (1 - e^{-(i\omega+k)\Delta\tau_n})\omega_n \\ \Delta\Gamma^{(T)}_{\varepsilon n} &= \Delta\varepsilon^{(T)}_n e^{-i\omega t_n} = \alpha T[1,1,1,0,0,0]^T e^{-i\omega t_n} \end{aligned} \tag{23}$$

herein, α is the thermal expansion coefficient. According to the theory of fictitious power, the finite element formula can be obtained

$$\boldsymbol{K}_n \Delta \Gamma_{un} = \Delta P_n^{(\mathrm{T})} + \Delta P_n^{(\mathrm{C})} \tag{24}$$

in which

$$\left.\begin{aligned} \boldsymbol{K}_n &= \sum \iiint_{\Omega} \boldsymbol{B}^{\mathrm{T}} \boldsymbol{D}_n^* \boldsymbol{B} \mathrm{d}\nu \\ \Delta P_n^{(\mathrm{T})} &= \sum \iiint_{\Omega} \boldsymbol{B}^{\mathrm{T}} \boldsymbol{D}_n^* \Delta \Gamma_{\varepsilon n}^{(\mathrm{T})} \mathrm{d}\nu \\ \Delta P_n^{(\mathrm{C})} &= \sum \iiint_{\Omega} \boldsymbol{B}^{\mathrm{T}} \boldsymbol{D}_n^* \Delta \Gamma_{\varepsilon n}^{(\mathrm{C})^*} \mathrm{d}\nu \end{aligned}\right\} \tag{25}$$

From equations (19), (24) and (25), $\Delta\Gamma_{\varepsilon n}$ and $\Delta\Gamma_{\sigma n}$ can be calculated step by step. Thus $\Delta H_{\varepsilon n}$, $\Delta H_{\sigma n}$ and $H_{\varepsilon n}$, $H_{\sigma n}$ can be obtained as follows:

$$\left.\begin{aligned} \Delta H_{\varepsilon n} &= (\Delta \Gamma_{\varepsilon n} - i\omega \Delta \tau_n H_{\varepsilon(n-1)})/(1 + i\omega \Delta \tau_n) \\ \Delta H_{\sigma n} &= (\Delta \Gamma_{\sigma n} - i\omega \Delta \tau_n H_{\sigma(n-1)})/(1 + i\omega \Delta \tau_n) \end{aligned}\right\} \tag{26}$$

$$H_{\varepsilon n} = \sum_{i=1}^{n} \Delta H_{\varepsilon i}, H_{\sigma n} = \sum_{i=1}^{n} \Delta H_{\sigma i} \tag{27}$$

3.4 Spectral Stochastic Finite Element Method

According to the above equations and based on the perturbation method, we have:

(1) The zero-order equations

$$\begin{aligned} \Delta \overline{\Gamma}_{\varepsilon n}^{(\mathrm{C})} &= \Delta \overline{\Gamma}_{\sigma 0} \mathrm{e}^{i\omega(t_0 - t_n)} (\overline{C}(t_n, t_0) - \overline{C}(t_{n-1}, t_0)) + \\ &\quad (1 - \mathrm{e}^{-(i\omega + \overline{k})\Delta\tau_n}) \omega_n + \overline{\phi}_n^* \Delta \overline{\Gamma}_{\sigma n} (\overline{f}_n^{(1)} \mathrm{e}^{-i\omega\Delta\tau_n} - \overline{f}_n^{(2)} \mathrm{e}^{-(i\omega + \overline{k})\Delta\tau_n}) \\ \overline{\omega}_n &= \overline{\omega}_{n-1} \mathrm{e}^{-(i\omega + \overline{k})\Delta\tau_{n-1}} + \boldsymbol{Q} \overline{\phi}_{n-1}^* \Delta \overline{\Gamma}_{\sigma(n-1)} \overline{f}_{n-1}^{(2)} \mathrm{e}^{-i(\omega + \overline{k})\Delta\tau_{n-1}} \\ \overline{\omega}_2 &= \boldsymbol{Q} \overline{\phi}_1^* \Delta \overline{\Gamma}_{\sigma 1} \overline{f}_1^{(2)} \mathrm{e}^{-(i\omega + \overline{k})\Delta\tau_1} \\ \Delta \overline{\Gamma}_{\sigma} &= \overline{\boldsymbol{D}}_n (\Delta \overline{\Gamma}_{\varepsilon n} - \Delta \overline{\Gamma}_{\varepsilon n}^{(\mathrm{C})} - \Delta \overline{\Gamma}_{\varepsilon n}^{(T)}) \end{aligned} \tag{28}$$

(2) The first-order equations

$$\begin{aligned} \Delta \Gamma_{\varepsilon n}{}^{(\mathrm{C})\prime} &= \Delta r_0^{(1)} + (1 - \mathrm{e}^{-(i\omega + \overline{k})\Delta\tau_n}) \omega'_n + \Delta\tau_n \overline{\omega}_n \mathrm{e}^{-(i\omega + \overline{k})\Delta\tau_n} k' \\ \omega'_n &= (\omega'_{n-1} - \overline{\omega}_{n-1} \Delta\tau_{n-1} k') \mathrm{e}^{-(i\omega + \overline{k})\Delta\tau_{n-1}} + \\ &\quad \boldsymbol{Q} \mathrm{e}^{-(i\omega + \overline{k})\Delta\tau_{n-1}} (\Delta r_{n-1}^{(2)} - \Delta\tau_{n-1} k' \overline{\phi}_{n-1}^* \Delta \Gamma_{\sigma(n-1)} \overline{f}_{n-1}^{(2)}) \\ \omega'_2 &= \boldsymbol{Q} \mathrm{e}^{-(i\omega + \overline{k})\Delta\tau_1} (\phi_1^* \overline{f}_1^{(2)} + \overline{\phi}_1^* f_1^{(2)} + k' \overline{\phi}_1^* \overline{f}_1^{(2)} \Delta\tau_1) \\ \Delta \Gamma'_{\sigma n} &= \boldsymbol{D}_n^* (\Delta \overline{\Gamma}_{\varepsilon n} - \Delta \overline{\Gamma}_{\varepsilon n}^{(\mathrm{C})^*} - \Delta \overline{\Gamma}_{\varepsilon n}^{(\mathrm{T})}) + \overline{\boldsymbol{D}}_n^* (\Delta \Gamma'_{\varepsilon n} - \Delta \Gamma_{\varepsilon n}^{(\mathrm{C})^*} - \Delta \Gamma_{\varepsilon n}^{(\mathrm{T})'}) \\ \Delta \Gamma'_{\varepsilon n} &= \boldsymbol{B} \Delta \Gamma'_{un} = \boldsymbol{B} \boldsymbol{K}_n^{-1} (\Delta P_n^{(\mathrm{T})'} + \Delta P_n^{(\mathrm{C})'} - \boldsymbol{K}'_n \Delta \overline{\Gamma}_{un}) \end{aligned} \tag{29}$$

herein, the superscript ($'$) denotes differentiation with respect to random variables.

$$\begin{aligned} \Delta r_0^{(1)} &= \Delta \Gamma'_{\sigma 0} \mathrm{e}^{i\omega(t_0 - t_n)} (\overline{C}(t_n, t_0) - \overline{C}(t_{n-1}, t_0)) + \\ &\quad \Delta \overline{\Gamma}_{\sigma 0} \mathrm{e}^{i\omega(t_0 - t_n)} (C'(t_n, t_0) - C'(t_{n-1}, t_0)) \\ \Delta r_{n-1}^{(2)} &= \phi_{n-1}^* \Delta \overline{\Gamma}_{\sigma(n-1)} \overline{f}_{n-1}^{(1)} + \overline{\phi}_{n-1}^* \Delta \Gamma'_{\sigma(n-1)} \overline{f}_{n-1}^{(1)} + \overline{\phi}_{n-1}^* \Delta \overline{\Gamma}_{\sigma(n-1)} f_{n-1}^{(1)'}) \\ \Delta P_n^{(\mathrm{T})'} &= \sum \iiint_{\Omega_e} \boldsymbol{B}^{\mathrm{T}} (\overline{\boldsymbol{D}}_n^* \Delta \Gamma_{\varepsilon n}^{(\mathrm{T})'} + \overline{\boldsymbol{D}}_n^{*'} \Delta \overline{\Gamma}_{\varepsilon n}^{(\mathrm{T})}) \mathrm{d}\nu \\ \Delta P_n^{(\mathrm{C})'} &= \sum \iiint_{\Omega_e} \boldsymbol{B}^{\mathrm{T}} (\overline{\boldsymbol{D}}_n^* \Delta \Gamma_{\varepsilon n}^{(\mathrm{C})'} + \boldsymbol{D}_n^{*'} \Delta \overline{\Gamma}_{\varepsilon n}^{(\mathrm{C})}) \mathrm{d}\nu \end{aligned} \tag{30}$$

in the above equation, we have

$$\boldsymbol{D}_n^{*'} = \frac{\boldsymbol{D}'_n\overline{D}_f - \overline{\boldsymbol{D}}_n D'_f}{\overline{D}_f^2} = \frac{\boldsymbol{D}'_n}{\overline{D}_f} - \overline{\boldsymbol{D}}_n^* \frac{D'_f}{\overline{D}_f^2} \tag{31}$$

in which

$$\boldsymbol{D}'_n = \begin{cases} \boldsymbol{D}_n / E_0 & \text{when } X \text{ is } E_0 \\ \dfrac{(t_{n-1} + \Delta\tau_n/2)\mathrm{e}^{-m_2(t_{n-1}+\Delta\tau_n/2)}}{1 - \mathrm{e}^{-m_2(t_{n-1}+\Delta\tau_n/2)}}\boldsymbol{D}_n & \text{when } X \text{ is } m_2 \\ 0 & \text{otherwise} \end{cases}$$

$$\begin{aligned} \overline{D}_f &= 1 + \overline{\phi}_n^{*'}(\overline{f}_n^{(1)}\mathrm{e}^{-i\omega\Delta\tau_n} - \overline{f}_n^{(2)}\mathrm{e}^{-(i\omega+\overline{k})\Delta\tau_n})\overline{E}(t_{n-1} + \Delta\tau_n/2) \\ D'_f &= \phi_n^{*'}(\overline{f}_n^{(1)}\mathrm{e}^{-i\omega\Delta\tau_n} - \overline{f}_n^{(2)}\mathrm{e}^{-(i\omega+\overline{k})\Delta\tau_n})\overline{E}(t_{n-1} + \Delta\tau_n/2) + \\ &\quad \overline{\phi}_n^*(f_n^{(1)'}\mathrm{e}^{-i\omega\Delta\tau_n} - (f_n^{(2)'} - \Delta\tau_n k'\overline{f}_n^{(2)})\mathrm{e}^{-(i\omega+\overline{k})\Delta\tau_n})\overline{E}(t_{n-1} + \Delta\tau_n/2) + \\ &\quad \overline{\phi}_n^*(\overline{f}_n^{(1)}\mathrm{e}^{-i\omega\Delta\tau_n} - \overline{f}_n^{(2)}\mathrm{e}^{-(i\omega+\overline{k})\Delta\tau_n})E'(t_{n-1} + \Delta\tau_n/2) \end{aligned} \tag{32}$$

After $\Delta\Gamma'_{\sigma n}$ has been calculated, $\Delta H'_{\sigma n}$ can be written as

$$\Delta H'_{\sigma n} = (\Delta\Gamma'_{\sigma n} - i\omega\Delta\tau_n H'_{\sigma(n-1)})/(1 + i\omega\Delta\tau_n) \tag{33}$$

Thus, we have

$$H'_{\sigma n} = \sum_{i=1}^{n} \Delta H'_{\sigma i} \tag{34}$$

According to the theory of complex random process[20], the auto-correlation coefficient function matrix of stress $\boldsymbol{R}_\sigma$ can be written as

$$\boldsymbol{R}_\sigma(\omega, t_i, t_j) = E\{\sigma_i(\omega, t_i) \cdot [\sigma_i(\omega, t_i)]^{*\mathrm{T}}\} \tag{35}$$

here, the superscript (*) denotes the conjugate of complex number, E{·} denotes the expectation of random variable. Substituting Eq. (6) into the above equation, we have

$$\boldsymbol{R}_\sigma(\omega, t_i, t_j) = E\{H_{\sigma i}(\omega, t_i)\mathrm{e}^{i\omega t_i} \cdot [H_{\sigma i}(\omega, t_i)\mathrm{e}^{i\omega t_i}]^{*\mathrm{T}}\} \tag{36}$$

Note that

$$H_{\sigma i}(\omega, t_i) \approx H_{\sigma i}(\omega, t_i) + \sum_{l=1}^{n\nu} H'_{\sigma i, l}(\omega, t_i)\Delta X_l \tag{37}$$

in which, $n\nu$ denotes the total number of random variables. The subscript $(, l)$ denotes differentiation with respect to X_l. Substituting the above equation in Eq. (36) and letting $t = t_1 = t_2$, we have

$$\begin{aligned} \boldsymbol{R}_\sigma(\omega, t) = \overline{H}_\sigma(\omega, t)[\overline{H}_\sigma(\omega, t)]^{*\mathrm{T}} + \sum_{l=1}^{n\nu}\sum_{k=1}^{n\nu} \\ H'_{\sigma, i}(\omega, t)[H'_{\sigma, k}(\omega, t)]^{*\mathrm{T}}\mathrm{Cov}(X_l, X_k), \end{aligned} \tag{38}$$

where Cov(·) denotes covariance. Obviously, the diagonal column of $\boldsymbol{R}_\sigma(\omega, t)$ is the variance-mean square of stress

$$E(\sigma^2) = |\overline{H}_\sigma(\omega, t)|^2 + \sum_{i=1}^{n\nu} |H'_{\sigma, i}(\omega, t)|^2 \mathrm{Var}(X_i) \tag{39}$$

in which, |·| denotes the modulus of the complex number and Var(·) denotes the variance.

Therefore, the variance of stress can be written as

$$\mathrm{Var}(\sigma) \approx \sum_{i=1}^{nv} | H'_{\sigma,i}(\omega, t) |^2 \mathrm{Var}(X_i) \tag{40}$$

4 Applications

4.1 Random Thermal Creep Stress in an Unrestrained Slab

The thickness of the slab is $l = 3.0$m (See Fig. 1). As the size of the slab plan is much larger than the thickness. The distribution of temperature should be uniaxial, i.e. the temperature is changing only along the z-axis. Suppose $T(z,t) = T_0(z^2 + 2.0)\cos\omega t$, $\omega = 2\pi/365$ (1/day). When the modulus of elasticity E does not vary with time, the theoretical solution of thermal stress in the slab is: $\sigma_z = \sigma_y = E(\varepsilon - \alpha T)/1 - \mu, \sigma_z = 0$, in which

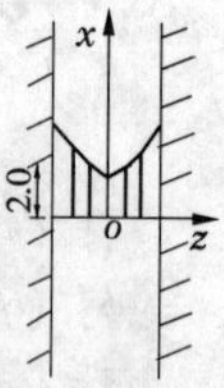

$T(t,x) = T_0(z^2 + 2.0)\cos\omega t$

Fig. 1 Temperature in the cross-section

$$\varepsilon = (A + Bz)\alpha,\ A = \frac{1}{2l}\int_{-l}^{l} T\,\mathrm{d}z = 2.75 T_0 \cos\omega t$$

$$b = \frac{1}{2l^3}\int_{-l}^{l} Tz\,\mathrm{d}z = 0$$

If E varies with time: $E(t) = E_0(1 - \mathrm{e}^{-m_2 t})$, the incremental thermal stress in each time step can be written as:

$$\Delta\sigma_k = \frac{E_k \alpha}{1 - \mu}[(\Delta A_k + \Delta B_k z) - \Delta T_k], \Delta A_k = A_{k+1} - A_k$$

$$\Delta B_k = B_{k+1} - B_k, \Delta T_k = T_{k+1} - T_k$$

Therefore, the stress in a given time is: $\sigma = \sum \Delta\sigma_k$, T_0, E_0 and m_2 are regarded as random variables with normal distribution. $\overline{T_0} = 25.0$℃, $\overline{E_0} = 2.8$MPa, $\overline{m_2} = 0.3$. Variance coefficients $= 0.1$. The Poisson's ratio $\mu = 0.167$. The thermal expansion coefficient $\alpha = 1.2 \times 10^{-5}$(1℃$^{-1}$). The theoretical solution of the expectation of stress at $z = 0$ m is shown in Fig. 2 (curve-1 and curve-3, tensile stress is positive). The quasi-exact solution of variance of thermal stress can be obtained from the following equation:

$$\mathrm{Var}(\sigma) \approx \sum_{i=1}^{nv}\sum_{j=1}^{nv} \frac{\partial\sigma}{\partial X_i}\frac{\partial\sigma}{\partial X_j}\mathrm{Cov}(X_i, X_j) \tag{41}$$

in which, $nv = 3$, X_1, X_2 and X_3 are T_0, E_0 and m_2, respectively. The quasi-exact solution is shown in Fig. 3 (the dotted line). The results calculated by the suggested methods are the real lines shown in Fig. 2 and Fig. 3.

4.2 Random Thermal Creep Stress in a semi-infinite Body

Considering the semi-space $z \geqslant 0$ in Fig. 4. The temperature of the surface ($z = 0$) is $T = A\cos\omega t$. The internal temperature can be obtained by the heat conduction equation: $T(z,t) = A\mathrm{e}^{-pz}\cos(\omega t - pz)$, $p = \sqrt{\omega/2\pi}$. Obviously, the elastic stress is $\sigma_z = \sigma_y = E\alpha T/(1 - \mu)$.

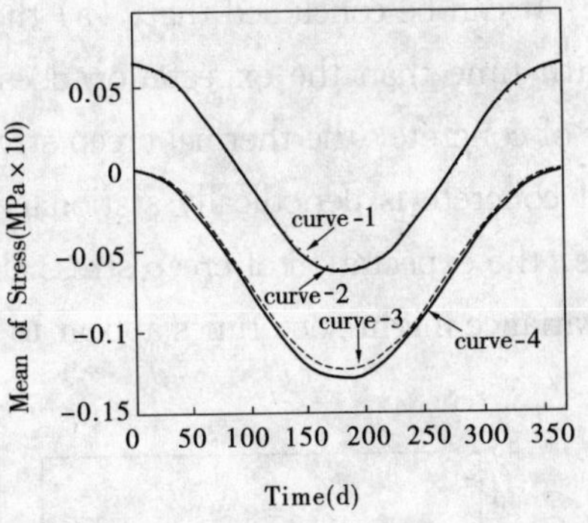

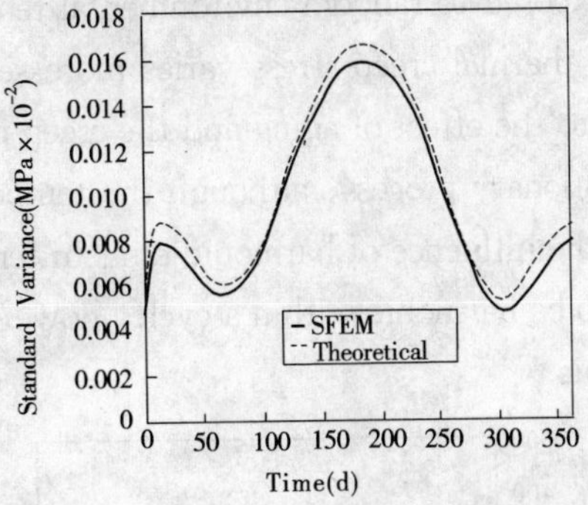

Fig. 2 Expectation of stress
curve-1: theoretical, non-aging system,
curve-3: theoretical, aging system

Fig. 3 Standard variance of stress
curve-2: SFEM, non-aging system,
curve-4: SFEM, aging system

The creep compliance is assumed to be $C(t,\tau)=C(1-e^{-k(t-\tau)})$. The theoretical solution of creep stress can be written as

$$\sigma_x=\sigma_y=-\frac{E\alpha Ae^{-pz}}{1-\mu}\rho\cos(\omega t-pz+\xi) \qquad (42)$$

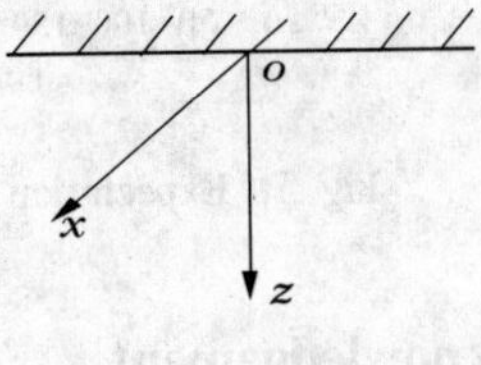

Fig. 4 The semi-infinite body

in which, $\rho=\sqrt{m^2+n^2}$, $\xi=\tan^{-1}(n/m)$, $m=(gk+\omega^2)/(g^2+\omega^2)$, $n=ECk\omega/(g^2+\omega^2)$, $g=(1+EC)k$. Four normally distributed random variables A, E, C and k are taken into account. $\overline{A}=14.5$℃, $\overline{E}=3.0\times10^4$ MPa. $\overline{C}=3.33\times10^{-6}$ cm^2/kg, $\overline{k}=0.03$(1/day). Variance coefficients = 0.1. $\omega=2\pi/365$(1/day). The thermal expansion coefficient $\alpha=1.12\times10^{-5}$ (1℃$^{-1}$). The Poisson's ratio $\mu=0.167$. In Eq. (42), $p=0.293$. The theoretical solutions of the expectation of elastic and creep stress are the dotted lines shown in Fig. 5. The results calculated by the suggested methods are the real line.

Similar to Eq. (41), the quasi-exact solution of the standard variance of creep stress can be obtained and is shown in Fig. 6 (the dotted line). The result calculated by the suggested methods is the real line in Fig. 6.

5 Conclusions

The suggested spectral stochastic finite element method takes advantage of both the complex frequency response method and the stochastic finite element method. Therefore, the influence of both the periodic random temperature process and the random material parameters can be conveniently taken into account. In this paper, random material parameters include the random modulus of elasticity and random creep compliance of concrete. By assuming the creep law to be linear, the effect of the aging properties of concrete is solved by the proposed numerical step-by-step recursive algorithm which is proved to be very efficient. The suggested methods can be used for the stress and reliability analysis of mass concrete structures exposed to random environmental temperature. It can be concluded that: (a) the variance of thermal creep stress varies more severely with time than the expectation does; (b) owing to the effect of aging and the creep properties of concrete, the thermal creep stress is a non-stationary process, although the temperature of concrete is periodically stationary; (c) under the influence of harmonic random temperature, the expectation of creep stress also appears to be harmonic within a cycle, however, the variance might sometimes appear to be inharmonic.

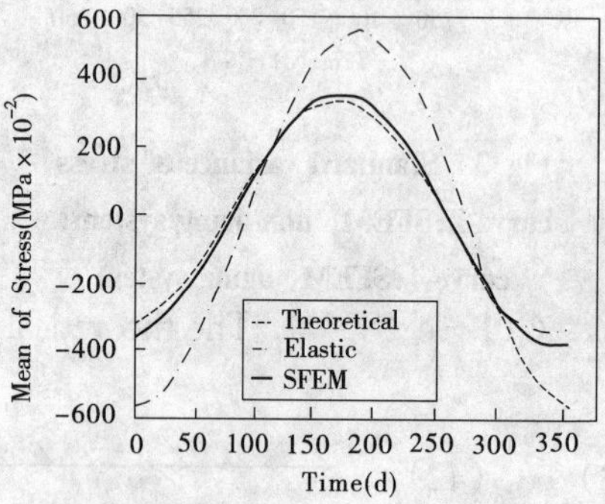

Fig. 5 Expectation of creep stress

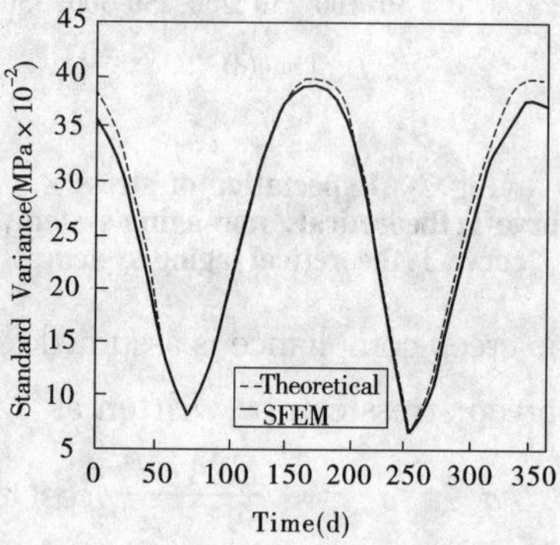

Fig. 6 Standard variance of creep stress

Acknowledgement

This work was supported by the National Natural Science Foundation in China.

References

[1] Heller, R. A. *Temperature response of an infinite thick slab to random surface temperature*. Mech. Res. Commun. 1976, 3. 379～385

[2] Heller, R. A. *Thermal stress as a narrow-band random load*. J. Engng, Mech. ASCE, 1976, 102, 787～805

[3] Heller, R. A. Kamat, M. P. , Singh, M. P. *Probability of solidpropellant motor failure due to environmental temperatures*. J. Spacecrafts Rockets 1979, 16, 140～146

[4] Heller, R. A. , Kamat, M. P. , Singh, M. P. *Probability of solidpropellant motor failure due to environmental temperatures*. J. Spacecrafts Rockets 1983, 20, 144～149

[5] Heller, R. A. , Kamat, M. P. , Singh. M. P. *Probability of solidpropellant motor failure due to environmental temperatures*. J. Spacecrafts Rockets AIAA. 19th Joint Propulsion Conf. , Seattle, 1984, pp. 203～312

[6] Tsubaki, T. , Bazant, Z. P. *Random shrinkage stresses in aging viscoelastic vessel*. J. Engng Mech. ASCE, 1982, 108, 527～545

[7] Bazant, Z. P. , Wang, T. S. *Spectral analysis of random shrinkage in concrete structures*. J. Engng Mech ASCE, 1984, 110, 173～186

[8] Bazant, Z. P. , Wang. T. S. *Spectral finite element analysis of random shrinkage in concrete*. J. Struct.

Engng ASCE, 1984,110,2196~2211

[9] Bazant, Z.P. ,Wang, T.S. *Algorithm for aging viscoelastic structures under periodic load*. J. Engng Mech. ASCE 1984,110,972~985

[10] Bazant, Z.P. *Mathematical models for creep and shrinkage of concrete*. in: Creep and shrinkage in concrete structures (Z.P. Bazant and F.H. Wittmann Eds), Wiley, Chichester, 1982

[11] Bazant, Z.P. ,Xi. Y.P. *Stochastic drying and creep effects in concrete structures*. J. Struct. Engng ASCE 1993. 119,301~322

[12] Bazant, Z.P. *Response of aging linear systems to ergodic random input*. J. Struct. Engng ASCE 1993, 112,322~342

[13] Bazant, Z.P. , Liu, K.L. *Random creep and shrinkage in structures: sampling*. J. Struct. Engng ASCE 1985,111,1113~1134

[14] Vanmarcke, E. , Shinozuka M. , Nakagiri, S. , et al.. *Random fields and stochastic finite element method*. struct. Safety, 1986,3,143~166

[15] Ghanem, R. ,Spanos. P.D. *Stochastic finite elements: a spectral approach*. Springer, New York, 1991

[16] Liu, N. , Lu, T.R. *Stochastic finite element method and its applications in engineering*. Adv. Mech. 1995,25,114~126

[17] Zhu,P.F. , Wang, T.S. ,Ding, B.Y. ,et al.. *Thermal stress and thermal control of hydraulic concrete structures*. Hydraulic-Power Press, Beijing, China,1985

[18] Zhu, P.F. *Collected papers of hydraulic structure and solid mechanics*. Hydraulic-Power Press, Beijing, China, 1985

[19] Liu, N. ,Liu, G.T. *Random temperature field evaluation of mass concrete structures by stochastic finite element method*. J. Tsinghua University,1996,1,41~47(in Chinese)

[20] Papoulis, A. *Probability, random variables and stochastic process*, McGraw-Hill, New York, 1965

RESEARCH ON NONSTATIONARY RANDOM THERMAL CREEP STRESSES IN MASS CONCRETE STRUCTURES

Abstract In this paper, the initial strain-stochastic finite element method is suggested for solving nonstationary random thermal creep stresses in mass concrete structures. By the suggested method, various kinds of random factors such as material parameters can be conveniently taken into account and the random thermal process of concrete can be regarded as a nonstationary process. The double-parametric adjustable functions are also suggested for the simplification of the nonstationary random thermal process. Corresponding stochastic finite element formulas based on the perturbation method are proposed. The suggested method is useful for mass concrete structural design and safety analysis, in which random variabilities should be taken into account.

Key words mass concrete structures; random thermal stress; creep of concrete; stochastic finite element method

1 Introduction

It is well known that the random variation of material parameters and temperature has a significant effect on the stress and deformation in mass concrete structures. The sources of random scatter are basically two: (a) random variation of material parameters including random parameters in creep model; and (b) the influence of the random variation of temperature of concrete which is affected by environmental temperature, hydration heat of concrete and heat conduction parameters.

Studies on the random thermal stress were first undertaken by Heller and co-workers[1~5], who applied the spectral method. This analytical solution is, however, inapplicable to concrete because of the aging properties of concrete creep. A method of impulse response functions which can be used for nonstationary aging system was then suggested by Tsubaki and Bazant[6]; however, for a complicated system, the impulse response function is difficult to obtain. The generalized spectral method recommended by Bazant and co-workers[7~13] is based on the fact that the environment can be adequately described by only a few sinusoidal components. Although the method is used for the random creep shrinkage stress problem, it is suitable for random thermal stress.

The stochastic finite element method, a very efficient method of analyzing the variability of stress or deformation in large structures, and has been under development for more than

本文选自《Finite Elements in Analysis and Design》1997 年刊,作者还有 Liu Ning。

ten years[14~16]. The main purpose of this paper is to develop a numerical procedure for non-stationary random temperature process and to develop the corresponding stochastic finite element method for the evaluation of random creep thermal stress in mass concrete structures.

2 The Initial Strain FEM for the Calculation of Thermal Creep Stress

When FEM is used for the analysis of thermal creep stress in mass concrete structures, the initial strain method is often used[17,18]. If the creep compliance is expressed as

$$C(t,\tau) = \varphi(\tau)(1 - e^{-k(t-\tau)}) \tag{1}$$

The recursive formulas of creep stress and strain can be written as follows:

$$\begin{aligned} \{\Delta\varepsilon_n^C\} &= (1 - e^{-k\Delta\tau_n})\{\omega_n\} + [Q]\{\Delta\sigma_n\}\varphi_n^*(1 - f^{-k\Delta\tau_n}) \\ \{\omega_n\} &= e^{-k\Delta\tau_n}\{\omega_{n-1}\} + [Q]\{\Delta\sigma_{n-1}\}\varphi_{n-1}^* f_{n-1} e^{-k\Delta\tau_{n-1}} \\ \{\omega_1\} &= [Q]\{\Delta\sigma_0\}\varphi_0 \end{aligned} \tag{2}$$

where $\{\Delta\varepsilon_n^C\}$ and $\{\Delta\sigma_n\}$ are the creep strain and stress increment between the time t_{n-1} and t_n, respectively, $\Delta\tau_n = t_n - t_{n-1}$, $\varphi_n^* = \varphi(t_{n-1} + \Delta\tau_n/2)$, and

$$f_n = \frac{e^{-k\Delta\tau_n} - 1}{k\Delta\tau_n} \tag{3}$$

$$[Q] = \begin{bmatrix} 1 & -\mu & -\mu & 0 & 0 & 0 \\ -\mu & 1 & -\mu & 0 & 0 & 0 \\ -\mu & -\mu & 0 & 0 & 0 & 0 \\ 0 & 0 & 0 & 2(1+\mu) & 0 & 0 \\ 0 & 0 & 0 & 0 & 2(1+\mu) & 0 \\ 0 & 0 & 0 & 0 & 0 & 2(1+\mu) \end{bmatrix} \tag{4}$$

The total strain increment $\{\Delta\varepsilon_n\}$ between the time t_{n-1} and t_n is

$$\{\Delta\varepsilon_n\} = \{\Delta\varepsilon_n^e\} + \{\Delta\varepsilon_n^C\} + \{\Delta\varepsilon_n^T\} + \{\Delta\varepsilon_n^0\} \tag{5}$$

where $\{\Delta\varepsilon_n^e\}$, $\{\Delta\varepsilon_n^T\}$ and $\{\Delta\varepsilon_n^0\}$ are the elastic strain, thermal strain and self-volumetric strain increment, respectively. From Eqs. (2) and (5), the stress increment between time t_{n-1} and t_n is

$$\{\Delta\sigma_n\} = [D_n^*]([B]\{\Delta u_n\} - \{\omega_n\}(1 - e^{-k\Delta\tau_n}) - \{\Delta\varepsilon_n^T\} - \{\Delta\varepsilon_n^0\}) \tag{6}$$

where $\{\Delta u_n\}$ is the nodal displacement column matrix increment at the nth time interval. $[B]$ is the deformation matrix, and

$$\begin{aligned} [D_n^*] &= [D_n]/D_{f0} \\ D_{f0} &= 1 + \varphi_n^*(1 - f_n e^{-k\Delta\tau_n}) \cdot E(t_{n-1} + \Delta\tau_n/2) \end{aligned} \tag{7}$$

where $[D_n]$ is the elasticity matrix when the elastic modulus is $E(t_{n-1} + \Delta\tau_n/2)$, with $\Delta\tau_n = t_n - t_{n-1}$. The finite element equation can be written as

$$\begin{aligned} [K_n]\{\Delta u_n\} &= \{\Delta P_n^C\} + \{\Delta P_n^T\} + \{\Delta P_n^0\} + \{F\} \\ [K_n] &= \sum_e \iiint_{v_e} [B][D_n^*][B]\mathrm{d}v \end{aligned} \tag{8}$$

$$\{\Delta P_n^{\mathrm{C}}\} = \sum_e \iiint_{v_e} [B][D_n^*]\{\omega_n\}(1 - e^{-k\Delta\tau_n})\mathrm{d}v \tag{9}$$

$$\{\Delta P_n^{\mathrm{T}}\} = \sum_e \iiint_{v_e} [B][D_n^*]\{\Delta\varepsilon_n^{\mathrm{T}}\}\mathrm{d}v$$

$$\{\Delta P_n^{0}\} = \sum_e \iiint_{v_e} [B][D_n^*]\{\Delta\varepsilon_n^{0}\}\mathrm{d}v$$

where $[K_n]$ is the global stiffness matrix, $\{\Delta P_n^{\mathrm{C}}\}$, $\{\Delta P_n^{\mathrm{T}}\}$ and $\{\Delta P_n^{0}\}$ are the equivalent load increment column matrix caused by the creep strain, the thermal strain and the self-volumetric strain, respectively, $\{F\}$ is the external force, $\{\Delta u_n\}$ can be obtained from Eq. (8) and $\{\Delta\sigma_n\}$ from Eq. (6). Accumulating the strain and stress increments in all time intervals, the total strain and stress are obtained

$$\{\varepsilon_n\} = \sum_{i=1}^{n}\{\Delta\varepsilon_i\},\ \{\sigma_n\} = \sum_{i=1}^{n}\{\Delta\sigma_i\} \tag{10}$$

3 Random Variability the Creep Thermal Stress Evaluation

In practical engineering, there are many random factors in the evaluation of creep stress and specific random variabilities are discussed as follows.

3.1 Creep Compliance $C(t,\tau)$ of Concrete

The creep compliance can be expressed as

$$C(t,\tau) = \overline{C}(t,\tau) + \Delta C(t,\tau) \approx \overline{C}(t,\tau) + (1 - e^{-\overline{k}(t-\tau)})\Delta\varphi + (t-\tau)e^{-\overline{k}(t-\tau)}\overline{\varphi}(\tau)\Delta k \tag{11}$$

where $\overline{C}(t,\tau)$ is the expectation of $C(t,\tau)$. Since $\varphi(\tau)$ usually can be expressed as

$$\varphi(\tau) = p_1 + p_2/\tau^{p_3} \tag{12}$$

where p_1, p_2 and p_3 are random variables. Thus,

$$\overline{\varphi}(\tau) \approx \overline{p}_1 + \overline{p}_2/\tau^{\overline{p}_3},\quad \Delta\varphi(\tau) \approx \Delta p_1 + \tau^{-\overline{p}_3}\Delta p_2 - \overline{p}_2\ln\tau \cdot \tau^{-\overline{p}_3}\cdot\Delta p_3 \tag{13}$$

3.2 The Elastic Modulus $E(\tau)$ of Concrete

The elastic modulus of concrete can be expressed as

$$E(\tau) = E_0(1 - e^{-m_2\tau}) \approx \overline{E}(\tau) + (1 - e^{-m_2\tau})\Delta E_0 + \tau e^{-\overline{m}_2\tau}\overline{E}_0\Delta m_2 \tag{14}$$

where $\overline{E}(\tau)$ is the expectation of $E(\tau)$. E_0 and m_2 are random variables.

3.3 External Force $\{F\}$

For hydraulic concrete structures, the external force is gravity without considering seismic force during the construction. But during the operation, external forces are water pressure and gravity. Unit weight ρ of concrete can be regarded as a constant, however, the water level should be considered as a random variable, for the statistic data can be obtained by the method in reference [19].

3.4 Thermal Field $T(t,x,y,z)$ in Concrete Structures

Random thermal process can be obtained by the method in reference [20]. Under the influence of random environmental temperature, random material parameters and random hydration heat of concrete, the thermal field in concrete is a nonstationary random process.

4 The Double-Parametric Adjustable Functions for the Simplification of Nonstationary Random Thermal Process

For the sake of overcoming the lack of an effective and efficient method for the solution of nonstationary response, especially for the large structures which should be discretized into finite elements, the nonstationary random thermal process $T(t,x,y,z)$ needs to be simplified. In reference [21], two adjustable parameters were introduced and the nonstationary process is equivalently degraded into a stationary process in each time interval. However, the method was based on the hypothesis that the length of each step was not long. Considering the fact that in the creep stress calculation, time intervals sometimes become larger and larger from the beginning to the end. Therefore, a modified method is given, in which the double-parametric adjustable functions are introduced for the simplification of the nonstationary process. The nonstationary random process is simplified as

$$\{T(t)\} \approx \begin{cases} \{a_1^{(1)}(t)T^{(1)}(t_1)+b_1^{(1)}(t),\cdots,a_1^{(NP)}(t)T^{(NP)}(t_1)+b_1^{(NP)}(t)\}^T \\ \quad = \{a_1(t)\}^T[I]\{T(t_1)\}+\{b_1(t)\} \qquad \text{when } t_1 \leqslant t < t_2 \\ \{a_2^{(1)}(t)T^{(1)}(t_2)+b_2^{(1)}(t),\cdots,a_2^{(NP)}(t)T^{(NP)}(t_2)+b_2^{(NP)}(t)\}^T \\ \quad = \{a_2(t)\}^T[I]\{T(t_2)\}+\{b_2(t)\} \qquad \text{when } t_2 \leqslant t < t_3 \\ \cdots\cdots \\ \{a_n^{(1)}(t)T^{(1)}(t_n)+b_n^{(1)}(t),\cdots,a_n^{(NP)}(t)T^{(NP)}(t_n)+b_n^{(NP)}(t)\}^T \\ \quad = \{a_n(t)\}^T[I]\{T(t_n)\}+\{b_n(t)\} \qquad \text{when } t_n \leqslant t < t_{n+1} \end{cases} \tag{15}$$

where NP is the number of total nodes, $[I]$ is the unit matrix. $a_n^{(i)}(t)$ and $b_n^{(i)}(t)$ are all definite and are called double-parametric adjustable functions. The superscript $(i)(i=1, 2,\cdots,NP)$ denotes the ith node. For the fixed time t, $T^{(i)}(t)(i=1,2,\cdots,NP)$ is a random variable. It is obviously that the right-hand side of Eq. (15) is also a nonstationary random process, which is different from reference [21]. $a_n^{(i)}(t)$ and $b_n^{(i)}(t)$ can be determined by the following equations

$$\left.\begin{aligned} \overline{T}^{(i)}(t) &= a_n^{(i)}(t)\overline{T}^{(i)}(t_n)+b_n^{(i)}(t) \\ \mathrm{Var}[T^{(i)}(t)] &= [a_n^{(i)}(t)]^2\mathrm{Var}[T^{(i)}(t_n)] \end{aligned}\right\} \quad (t_n \leqslant t_{n+1}) \tag{16}$$

where, Var (·) denotes variance. From the above equation, we have

$$\begin{aligned} a_n^{(i)}(t) &= \sqrt{\mathrm{Var}[T^{(i)}(t)]/\mathrm{Var}[T^{(i)}(t_n)]} \\ b_n^{(i)}(t) &= \overline{T}^{(i)}(t) - \overline{T}^{(i)}(t_n)\sqrt{\mathrm{Var}[T^{(i)}(t)]/\mathrm{Var}[T^{(i)}(t_n)]} \end{aligned} \tag{17}$$

The autocorrelation coefficient between $\{T(t_k)\}$ and $\{T(t_1)\}$ $(t_i \leqslant t_k < t_{i+1}, t_j \leqslant t_l < t_{j+1})$ on time axis can be approximately calculated as follows:

$$\mathrm{Cov}[T^{(m)}(t_k),T^{(m)}(t_l)] \approx a_i^{(m)}(t_k)a_j^{(m)}(t_l)\mathrm{Cov}[T^{(m)}(t_i),T^{(m)}(t_j)] \tag{18}$$

where the superscript (m) denotes the mth node. Similarly, the autocorrelation coefficient between $T^{(m1)}(t_k)$ and $T^{(m2)}(t_k)(t_i \leqslant t_k < t_{i+1})$ in space can be expressed as

$$\mathrm{Cov}[T^{(m1)}(t_k), T^{(m2)}(t_K)] \approx a_i^{(m1)}(t_k) a_i^{(m2)}(t_k) \mathrm{Cov}[T^{(m1)}(t_i), T^{(m2)}(t_i)] \quad (19)$$

Therefore, by using Eq. (15), it is convenient to represent the correlation structure of the nonstationary random process $\{T(t, x, y, z)\}$.

5 Numerical Procedure for the Random Thermal Creep Stress: the Initial Strain-stochastic Finite Element Method

Let X denote the basic random variable. Random function S (e.g. $\varphi(\tau)$, $\{\sigma\}$, $\{\varepsilon\}$, E_0, m_2, p_1, p_2, p_3 and k, etc.) can be expanded into the first-order Taylor expansion series at the point $\overline{X}$:

$$S = \overline{S} + S'|_{X=\overline{x}dX} \quad (20)$$

where the superscript ($'$) denotes the differentiation with respect to random variables. Let $dX = (X - \overline{X})\alpha$ (α is a very small number). Eq. (20) can be written in the first-order perturbation form as

$$S = \overline{S} + \alpha S' \quad (21)$$

Substituting Eq. (21) into Eqs. (2) and (9) and based on the perturbation method, we obtain:

(a) the zero-order equations

$$\begin{aligned}
\{\Delta\overline{\varepsilon}_n^{\mathrm{C}}\} &= (1 - e^{-\overline{k}\Delta\tau_n})\{\overline{\omega}_n\} + [Q]\{\Delta\overline{\sigma}_n\}\overline{\varphi}_n^*(1 - \overline{f}_n e^{-\overline{k}\Delta\tau_n}) \\
\{\overline{\omega}_n\} &= e^{-\overline{k}\Delta\tau_n}\{\overline{\omega}_{n-1}\} + [Q]\{\Delta\overline{\sigma}_{n-1}\}\overline{\varphi}_{n-1}^*\overline{f}_{n-1}e^{-\overline{k}\Delta\tau_{n-1}} \\
\{\overline{\omega}_1\} &= [Q]\{\Delta\overline{\sigma}_0\}\overline{\varphi}_0
\end{aligned} \quad (22)$$

(b) the first-order equations

$$\begin{aligned}
\{\Delta\varepsilon_n^{\mathrm{C}}\}' &= (1 - e^{-\overline{k}\Delta\tau_n})\{\omega_n\}' + \Delta\tau_n e^{-\overline{k}\Delta\tau_n}\{\overline{\omega}_n\}k' + [Q](\{\sigma_n\}'\overline{\varphi}_n^* - \{\overline{\sigma}_n\}\varphi_n^{*\prime} \times \\
&\quad (1 - \overline{f}_n e^{-\overline{k}\Delta\tau_n}) + [Q]\{\overline{\sigma}_n\}\overline{\varphi}_n^* e^{-\overline{k}\Delta\tau_n}(f'_n + \Delta\tau_n k') \\
\{\omega_n\}' &= (-\Delta\tau_n k'\{\overline{\omega}_{n-1}\} + \{\omega_{n-1}\}')e^{-\overline{k}\Delta\tau_n} + [Q](\{\sigma_{n-1}\}'\overline{\varphi}_{n-1}^* - \{\overline{\sigma}_{n-1}\}\varphi_{n-1}^{*\prime}) \times \\
&\quad \overline{f}_{n-1}e^{-\overline{k}\Delta\tau_{n-1}} + [Q]\{\overline{\sigma}_{n-1}\}\overline{\varphi}_{n-1}^* e^{-\overline{k}\Delta\tau_{n-1}}(f'_{n-1} - \Delta\tau_{n-1}k') \\
\{\omega_1\}' &= [Q](\{\Delta\overline{\sigma}_0\}\varphi'_0 + \{\Delta\sigma_0\}'\overline{\varphi}_0)
\end{aligned} \quad (23)$$

where

$$f'_n = \begin{cases} \dfrac{1}{\Delta\tau_n}\dfrac{(\Delta\tau_n\overline{k} - 1)(e^{-\overline{k}\Delta\tau_n} - 1)}{k^2} & \text{when } X_n = k, \\ 0 & \text{when } X_n \neq k, \end{cases} \quad (24)$$

$$\begin{aligned}
\{\Delta\sigma_n\}' &= [\overline{D}_n^*][\{\Delta\varepsilon_n\}' - \{\omega_n\}'(1 - e^{-\overline{k}\Delta\tau_n}) + \{\overline{\omega}_n\}e^{-\overline{k}\Delta\tau_n}\Delta\tau_n k' - \{\Delta\varepsilon_n^{\mathrm{T}}\}' - \\
&\quad \{\varepsilon_n^0\}') + [D_n^*]'[\{\Delta\overline{\varepsilon}_n\} - \{\overline{\omega}_n\}(1 - e^{-\overline{k}\Delta\tau_n}) - \{\Delta\overline{\varepsilon}_n^T\} - \{\Delta\overline{\varepsilon}_n^0\}]
\end{aligned} \quad (25)$$

$$\begin{aligned}
[\overline{D}_n^*] &= [\overline{D}_n]/\overline{D}_{f1} \\
[\overline{D}_n^*]' &= \frac{[D_n]'\overline{D}_{f1} - [\overline{D}_n]D'_{f1}}{\overline{D}_{f1}^2} = \frac{[D_n]'}{\overline{D}_{f1}} - [D_n^*]\frac{D'_{f1}}{\overline{D}_{f1}}
\end{aligned} \quad (26)$$

with

$$\overline{D}_{f1} = 1 + \overline{\varphi}_n^* (1 - \overline{f}_n e^{-\overline{k}\Delta\tau_n}) \overline{E}(t_{n-1} + \Delta\tau_n/2)$$

$$D'_{f1} = [\varphi_n^{*'} (1 - \overline{f}_n e^{-\overline{k}\Delta\tau_n}) + (\overline{f}_n \Delta\tau_n k' - f_n') \varphi_n^* e^{-\overline{k}\Delta\tau_n}] \overline{E}(t_{n-1} + \Delta\tau_n/2) + \overline{D}_{f0}(1 - e^{-\overline{m}_2(t_{n-1}+\Delta\tau_n/2)}) E'_0 + (t_{n-1} + \Delta\tau_n/2) \overline{D}_{f0} e^{-\overline{m}_2(t_{n-1}+\Delta\tau_n/2)} m'_2$$

$$[D_n]' = \begin{cases} [D_n]/E_0 & \text{when the random variable } X \text{ is } E_0 \\ \dfrac{(t_{n-1} + \Delta\tau_n/2) e^{-m_2(t_{n-1}+\Delta\tau_n/2)}}{1 - e^{-m_2(t_{n-1}+\Delta\tau_n/2)}} [D_n] & \text{where } X \text{ is } m_2, \\ 0 & \text{otherwise.} \end{cases} \tag{27}$$

The expression of D_{f0} has been given in Eq. (7). In Eq. (25)

$$\{\Delta\varepsilon_n\}' = [B]\{\Delta u_n\}' \tag{28}$$

As

$$\{\Delta u_n\} = [K_n]^{-1}\{\Delta P_n\} = [K_n]^{-1}(\{\Delta P_n^C\} + \{\Delta P_n^T\} + \{\Delta P_n^0\} + \{F\}) \tag{29}$$

we have

$$\{\Delta \overline{u}_n\} = [\overline{K}_n]^{-1}\{\Delta \overline{P}_n\}$$

$$\{\Delta \overline{u}_n\}' = [K_n]^{-1}(\{\Delta P_n\}' - [K_n]'\{\Delta \overline{u}_n\}) \tag{30}$$

$$\{\Delta P_n\}' = \{\Delta P_n^C\}' + \{\Delta P_n^T\}' + \{\Delta P_n^0\}' + \{F\}' \tag{31}$$

where

$$[K_n]' = \sum_e \iiint_{v_e} [B]^T [D_n^*]' [B] dv$$

$$\{\Delta P_n^C\}' = \sum_e \iiint_{v_e} [B]^T ([\overline{D}_n^*](\{\omega_n\}'(1 - e^{-\overline{k}\Delta\tau_n}) + \{\overline{\omega}_n\}\Delta\tau_n e^{-\overline{k}\Delta\tau_n}\overline{K}') + [D_n^*]'\{\overline{\omega}_n\}(1 - e^{-\overline{k}\Delta\tau_n})) dv \tag{32}$$

$$\{\Delta P_n^0\}' = \sum_e \iiint_{v_e} ([B]^T [D_n^*]' \{\Delta \overline{\varepsilon}_n^0\} + [B]^T [\overline{D}_n^*] \{\Delta\varepsilon_n^0\}') dv$$

$$\{\Delta P_n^T\}' = \sum_e \iiint_{v_e} ([B]^T [D_n^*]' \alpha \{\overline{T}(t_n)\}[1,1,1,0,0,0]^T + [B]^T [\overline{D}_n^*] \alpha \{T(t_n)\}' [1,1,1,0,0,0]^T) dv$$

When the variability of the self-volumetric strain of concrete is neglected, we have $\Delta \overline{\varepsilon}_n^0 = \Delta\varepsilon_n^0, \Delta\varepsilon_n^{0'} = 0$; therefore, $\{\Delta P_n^0\}' = \int_v [B]^T [D_n^*]' \{\Delta\varepsilon_n^0\} dv$.

From Eqs. (23) and (24), $\{\Delta \overline{\varepsilon}_n\}, \{\Delta\overline{\sigma}_n\}, \{\Delta\varepsilon_n\}'$ and $\{\Delta\sigma_n\}'$ can be calculated step by step. Thus, at time t_n, $\{\overline{\varepsilon}_n\}, \{\overline{\sigma}_n\}, \{\varepsilon_n\}'$ and $\{\sigma_n\}'$ can be obtained:

$$\{\overline{\varepsilon}_n\} = \sum_{i=1}^{n} \{\Delta\overline{\varepsilon}_i\}; \ \{\overline{\sigma}_n\} = \sum_{i=1}^{n} \{\Delta\overline{\sigma}_i\}; \ \{\varepsilon_n\}' = \sum_{i=1}^{n} \{\Delta\varepsilon_i\}'; \ \{\sigma_n\}' = \sum_{i=1}^{n} \{\Delta\sigma_i\}' \tag{33}$$

Therefore, the covariance of strain and stress can be written as follows:

$$\mathrm{Cov}[\varepsilon_i, \varepsilon_j] \approx \sum_{k=1}^{nv} \sum_{l=1}^{nv} \varepsilon'_{i,k} \varepsilon'_{j,l} \mathrm{Cov}(X_k, X_l), \quad \mathrm{Cov}[\sigma_i, \sigma_j] \approx \sum_{k=1}^{nv} \sum_{l=1}^{nv} \sigma'_{i,k} \sigma'_{j,l} \mathrm{Cov}(X_k, X_l) \tag{34}$$

where nv is the number of total number variables. The subscript (i or j) denotes the element of strain or stress.

6 Applications

According to the methods suggested above, a universal code named STAC (FORTRAN language) is developed, with which various kinds of random factors can be taken into account and the random thermal creep stress of mass concrete structures during the construction and operation can be calculated. Two examples are given to verify the suggested method and the code.

6.1 Random Thermal Creep Stress in Semi-infinite Concrete Body

Considering the semi-space $z \geqslant 0$ in Fig. 1, the temperature on the surface ($z=0$) is assumed to be $T = A\cos\omega t$. The internal temperature can be obtained by the theoretical solution of[17]: $T(z,t) = Ae^{-pz}\cos(\omega t - pz)$, $p = \sqrt{\omega/2\pi}$. The elastic stress is $\sigma_z = \sigma_y = -E\alpha T/(1-\mu)$. The creep compliance is assumed to be $C(t,\tau) = C(1 - e^{-k(t-\tau)})$. The theoretical solution of creep stress is

$$
\begin{aligned}
&\sigma_x^* = \sigma_y^* = -\frac{E\alpha A e^{-pz}}{1-\mu}\rho\cos(\omega t - pz + \xi) \\
&\rho = \sqrt{m^2 + n^2}, \xi = \tan^{-1}\left(\frac{n}{m}\right) \\
&m = \frac{gk + \omega^2}{g^2 + \omega^2}, \quad n = \frac{ECk\omega}{g^2 + \omega^2}, \quad g = (1 + EC)k
\end{aligned}
\tag{35}
$$

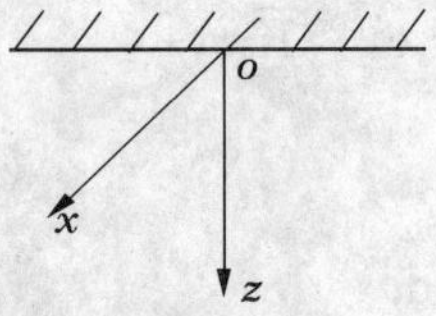

Fig. 1 Semi-infinite body

Considering the 4 normal random variables A, E, C and k with the expectations of: $\overline{A} = 14.5℃$, $\overline{E} = 3.0\times10^4$ MPa, $\overline{C} = 3.33\times10^{-6}\,cm^2/kg$, $\overline{k} = 0.03(1/day)$, respectively. The variance coefficients are all 0.1, $\omega = 2\pi/365(1/d)$, the thermal expansion coefficient $\alpha = 1.12\times10^{-5}(1/℃)$, and the Poisson's ratio $\mu = \frac{1}{6}$. In Eq. (35), $p = \sqrt{\omega/2\pi} = 0.293$. The expectations of elastic stress and creep stress calculated by the suggested methods are given in Fig. 2 (the real line) and the theoretical solution is given as the dotted line.

From Eq. (35), the quasi-theoretical solution of the creep stress variance can be obtained.

$$
\begin{aligned}
&\mathrm{Var}[\sigma_x^*(t)] \approx \sum_{i=1}^{nv}\sum_{j=1}^{nv}\frac{\partial\sigma_x^*(t)}{\partial X_i}\frac{\partial\sigma_x^*(t)}{\partial X_j}\mathrm{Cov}(X_i, X_j) \\
&\mathrm{Var}[\sigma_y^*(t)] = \mathrm{Var}[\sigma_x^*(t)]
\end{aligned}
\tag{36}
$$

where $nv = 4, X_1, X_2, X_3$ and X_4 are A, E, C and k, respectively. The curve of the quasi-theoretical solution (at $z=0$) can be easily obtained from the above equation (See the dotted line in Fig. 3. The standard variance calculated by the suggested methods is drawn in the real line in Fig. 3). Form Fig. 3, we find that when the expectation of creep stress changes in one wave, the standard variance of creep stress appears in two waves. In this example, although the temperature is the periodic stationary random process, the process is still considered as a nonstationary random process and is calculated by the suggested method; satisfactory results can still be obtained.

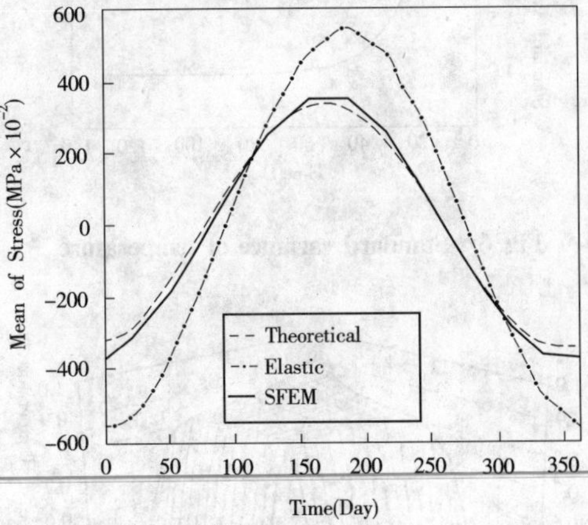

Fig. 2 Expectation of creep stress

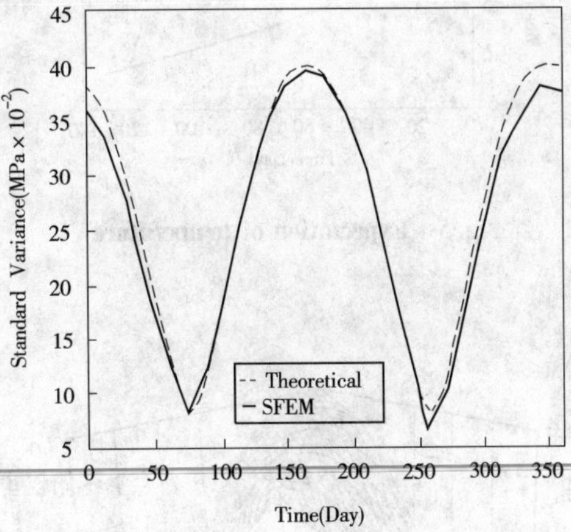

Fig. 3 Standard variance of creep stress

6.2 Random Creep Stress in Unrestrained Concrete Slab

Considering the unrestrained concrete slab in reference [23], in which although the hydration heat of the concrete can not be considered, it is however, taken into account in this paper. The form of the hydration heat is $\theta=\theta_0(1-e^{-m_1 t})$. Obviously, under the influence of the hydration heat, the temperature is nonstationary. The air temperature on the right-hand side of the slab is $T=0$, the surficial heat emission coefficient $b_1=6.0$ kcal/(m^2·h.℃). The air temperature on the left-hand side is $T=A\cos\omega(t-t_0)$, $b_2=12.0$kcal/(m^2·h·℃)(See Fig. 4), $\omega=7.169\times10^{-4}$ 1/h. The thickness of the slab is 2.6m. The coefficient of thermal conductivity is $\lambda=1.25$kcal/(m·h·℃), and the temperature transfer coefficient is $a=0.002\ 17$m^2/h. In the calculation of the temperature, parameters $A, a, b_1, b_2, \lambda, \theta_0$ and m_1 are taken as random variables, $\overline{A}=8.0$℃, $\overline{\theta}_0=25.0$℃, $\overline{m}_1=0.397$. The coefficients of variance are all 0.2. The expectation and standard variance of temperature at $x=1.3$m is shown in Figs. 5 and 6. The autocorrelation coefficient functions on time axis ($x=1.3$m) and on X-axis ($t=20$d) are shown in Figs. 7 and 8.

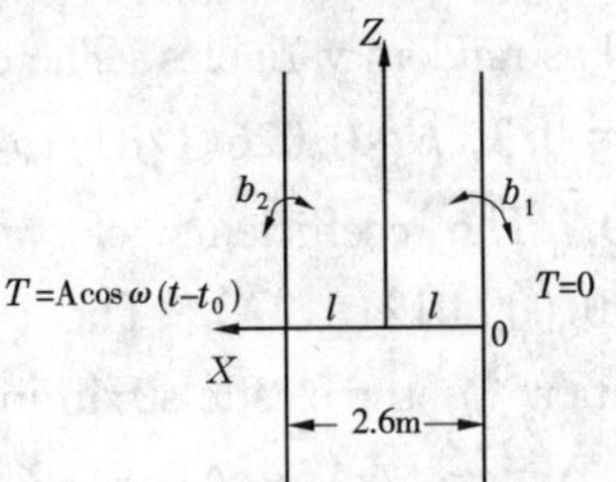

Fig. 4 Unrestrained slab

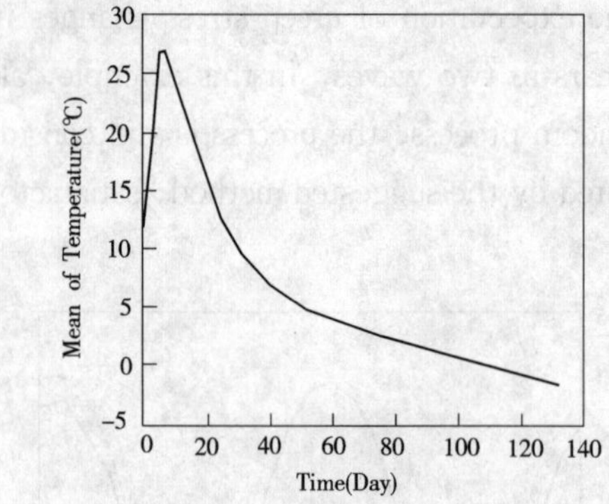

Fig. 5 Expectation of temperature

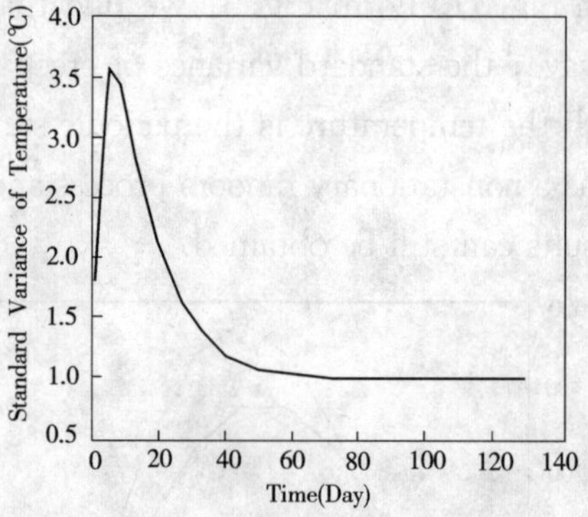

Fig. 6 Standard variance of temperature

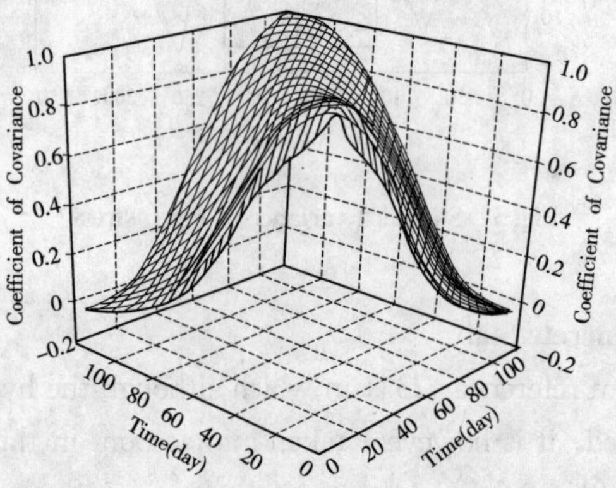

Fig. 7 On time axis($x=1.3$m)

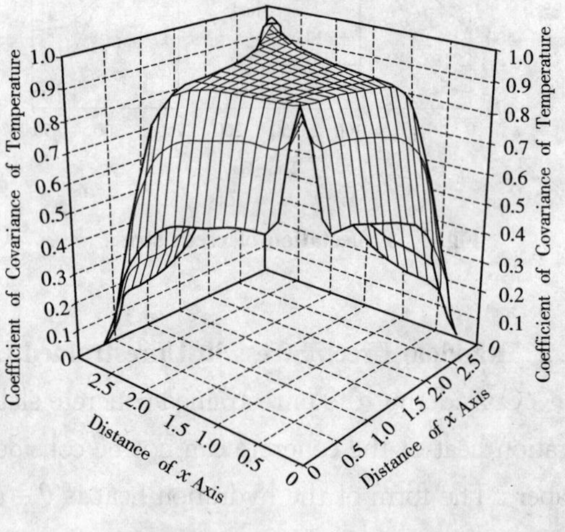

Autocorrelation coefficient function of temperature

Fig. 8 On *X*-axis ($t=20$d)

In the calculation of random creep stress, the creep compliance function is take as $C(t,\tau)=(p_1+p_2/\tau^{p_3})[1-e^{-k(t-\tau)}]$. The parameters E_0, m_2, k, p_1, p_2, and p_3 are considered as random variables. The expectations of the random variables are $\overline{E}_0=2.0\times10^4$ MPa, $\overline{m}_2=0.3$, $\overline{k}=0.026(1/\text{d})$, $\overline{p}_1=0.9\times10^{-5}\,\text{cm}^2/\text{kg}$, $\overline{p}_2=4.82\times10^{-5}\,\text{cm}^2/\text{kg}$, and $\overline{p}_3=1.0$. The coefficients of variance are all 0.1. The thermal expansion coefficient $\alpha=0.000\,012(1/℃)$. The Poisson's ratio μ is 0.167. According to the theoretical solution[18], the elastic strain increment at the kth interval (τ_{k-1},τ_k) is

$$\Delta\varepsilon_k^e=(\Delta A_k+\Delta B_k z)\alpha;\ \Delta A_k=A_{k+1}-A_k;\ \Delta B_k=B_{k+1}-B_k$$

$$A_k=\frac{1}{2l}\int_{-l}^{l}T_k\,\mathrm{d}z;\quad B_k=\frac{1}{2l^3}\int_{-l}^{l}T_k z\,\mathrm{d}z \tag{37}$$

$$A_{k+1}=\frac{1}{2l}\int_{-l}^{l}T_{k+1}\,\mathrm{d}z,\ B_{k+1}=\frac{1}{2l^3}\int_{-l}^{l}T_{k+1}\,z\,\mathrm{d}z$$

The creep strain increment at the kth interval $(\tau_{k+1}\,\tau_k)$ is

$$\Delta\varepsilon_k^C = \sum_{\tau_i=\tau_0}^{\tau_{k-1}} \Delta\sigma_i [C(\tau_k, \tau_i) - C(\tau_{k-1}, \tau_i)] \tag{38}$$

and the creep stress increment at kth interval can be written as

$$\Delta\sigma_k = E_k [\Delta\varepsilon_k^e - \Delta\varepsilon_k^C - \alpha\Delta T_k] \tag{39}$$

The stress at time $t = \tau_k$ can be expressed as $\sigma_k = \sum_i^k \Delta\sigma_i$. Thus, the theoretical expectation of the stress can be obtained (See dotted line in Fig. 9). Similar to Eq. (36), the theoretical solution of the standard variance of stress can be obtained (See dotted line in Fig. 10). The results calculated by the suggested stochastic finite element method are shown as real line in Figs. 9 and 10. The autocorrelation coefficient function of the temperature is not considered in curves-1 and 2 and is considered in curves-3 and 4. The error is caused by three reasons. The first is the error in the calculated temperature; the second is that the selected size of the structure can not be big enough to be same as the ideal size; and the third is the error in finite element mesh. From Fig. 10, it can be found that when the autocorrelation coefficient function of temperature is not considered, the standard variance of stress is much bigger than the actual one. Referring to the expectation of the stress, it can be concluded that it is more reasonable to consider the autocorrelation coefficient function of the temperature in the calculation of random stress.

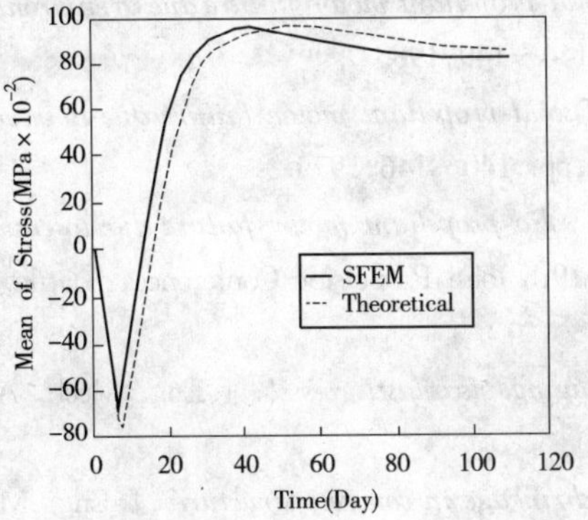

Fig. 9 **Expectation of stress** ($x = 1.3$m)

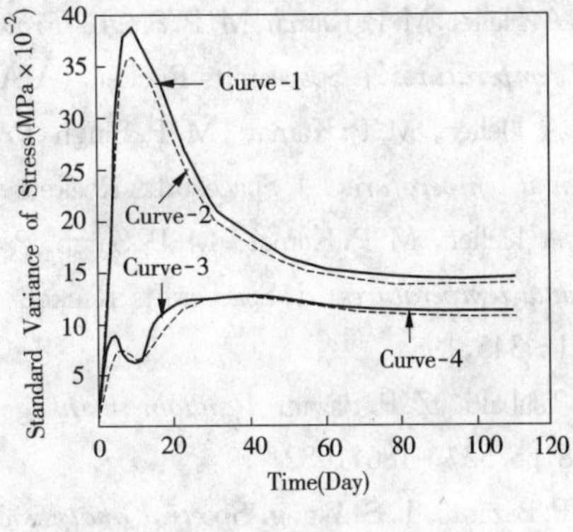

Fig. 10 **Standard variance of stress** ($x = 1.3$m)

Curve 1: Solved by SFEM, not considering autocorrelation coefficient of temperature.

Curve 2: Theoretical solution, not considering autocorrelation coefficient of temperature;

Curve 3: Solved by SFEM, considering autocorrelation coefficient of temperature;

Curve 4: Theoretical solution, considering autocorrelation coefficient of temperature.

7 Conclusions

Under the influence of the random material parameters and nonstationary random thermal process, the thermal creep stresses in mass concrete structures are also nonstationary processes. In this paper, based on the perturbation method, the stochastic finite element method is introduced and combined with the initial strain method for the evaluation of random thermal creep stress. By the suggested method, various kinds of random factors can be conveniently taken into account. As for the simplification of the nonstationary of temperature in concrete, the double-parametric adjustable functions are suggested. It is shown that the autocorrelation in both the time domain and the space of the temperature process can be easily and fully reflected by the simplified nonstationary temperature process with the formulation of time intervals. It can also be concluded that, when the autocorrelation of the temperature is considered, the standard variance of the thermal creep stress appears to be smaller, on the contrary, without considering the autocorrelation, the result will be incorrectly increased.

Acknowledgement

This work was supported by the China Postdoctoral Science Foundation.

References

[1] R. A. Heller. *Temperature response of an infinitely thick slab to random surface temperature*. Mech. Res. Comun. 3. pp. 379～385, 1976

[2] R. A. Heller. *Thermal stress as an narrow-Band random load*. J. Eng. Mech. ASCE 102, pp. 787～805, 1976

[3] R. A. Heller, M. P. Kamat. M. P. Singh. *Probability of solid-propellant motor failure due to environmental temperatures*. J. Spacecrafts Rockets (AIAA)20, pp. 144～149, 1983

[4] R. A. Heller, M. P. Kamat , M. P. Singh. *Probability of solid-propellant motor failure due to environmental temperatures*. J. Spacecrafts Rockets (AIAA) 16, pp. 140～146, 1979

[5] R. A. Heller, M. P. Kamat , M. P. Singh. *Probability of solid-propellant motor failure due to environmental temperatures*. J. Spacecrafts Rockets (AIAA) ; 19th Joint Propulsion Conference, Seattle. pp. 321～345, 1984

[6] T. Tsubaki , Z. P. Bazant. *Random shrinkage stresses in aging viscoelastic vessel*. J. Eng. Mech. ASCE 108. pp. 527～186, 1982

[7] Z. P. Bazant , T. S. Wang. *Spectral analysis of random shrinkage in concrete structures*. J. Eng. Mech. ASCE 110, pp. 173～186, 1984

[8] Z. P. Bazant , T. S. Wang. *Spectral finite element analysis of random shrinkage in concrete*. J. Struct. Eng. ASCE 110, pp. 2196～2211, 1984

[9] Z. P. Bazant , T. S. Wang. *Algorithm for aging viscoelastic structures under periodic load*. J. Eng. Mech. ASCE 110, pp. 972～985, 1984

[10] Z. P. Bazant. *Mathematical models for creep and shrinkage of concrete*/In: Z. P. Bazant and F. H. Wittmann (eds). *Creep and Shrinkage in Concrete Structures*", Willey, London, 1982

[11] Z. P. Bazant , Y. P. Xi. *Stochastic drying and creep effects in concrete structures*. J. Struct. Eng. ASCE 119, pp. 301～332, 1993

[12] Z. P. Bazant. *Response of aging linear systems to ergodic random input*. J. Mech. ASCE 112, pp. 322～342, 1986

[13] Z. P. Bazant , K. L. Liu. *Random creep and shrinkage in structures: sampling*. J. Struct. Engng.

ASCE 111, pp. 1113~1134, 1985

[14] E. Vanmarcke, M. Shinozuka, et al.. *Random fields and stochastic finite element method*. Struct. Safery 3. pp. 143~166, 1986

[15] R. Ghanem, P. D. Spanos. *Stochastic Finite Elements: A Spectral Approach*, Springer. New York, 1991

[16] N. Liu, T. R. Lu. *Stochastic finite element method and its application in engineering*. Adv. Mech. 25, pp. 114~126, 1995

[17] P. F. Zhu, et. al.. *Thermal Stress and Thermal Control of Hydraulic Concrete Structures*. Hydraulic-Power Press. Beijing, China, 1976

[18] P. F. Zhu. *Collected Papers of Hydraulic Structural and Solid Mechanics*. Hydraulic-Power Press, Beijing. China, 1985

[19] S. W. Wu, et. al.. *Statistical values for yearly maximum of head-Water lever of dams*. Proc. 4th IAHR Int. Symp on Stochastic Hydrolics, 31 July-2 August, USA, pp. 129~138, 1984

[20] N. Liu, G. T. Liu. *Random temperature field evaluation of mass concrete structures by stochastic finite element method*. J. Tsinghua Univ. 36(1), pp. 41~48, 1996

[21] N. Liu, Q. S. Meng, S. W. Wu. *Reliability analysis of fatigue crack under nonstationary load*. Eng. Mech. (supplemental div.), pp. 547~552, 1993

[22] N. Liu, G. T. Liu. *Spectral stochastic finite element analysis of periodic random thermal creep stress in concrete*. Eng. Struct. 18(9), pp. 669~674, 1996

[23] T. S. Wang. *Random thermal stress in concrete structures*. J. Water Conservancy 1, pp. 23~31, 1985

大体积混凝土结构随机温度徐变应力计算方法研究

摘　要　首次尝试将随机有限元法引入大体积混凝土结构随机温度徐变应力的计算。综合考虑各种随机因素,对于由材料物理参数随机性引起的随机温度场的影响,本文给出了相应于初应变隐式解法的随机有限元计算方法;对于周期平稳随机温度场对徐变应力场的影响,本文提出了复模量隐式解法,并首次视复频响应函数为材料参数的随机函数,给出了相应的复频响应-随机有限元列式;而对于一般非平稳绝热温升温度场的影响,本文提出了参数调幅逐段简化的方法。本文方法有效地克服了前人不能考虑材料参数随机性或需弹模不随时间变化的局限性。

关键词　随机有限元法　温度应力　徐变应力　混凝土结构

大体积混凝土结构的温度徐变应力受诸多随机因素的影响[1],国外 20 世纪 70 年代起就已着手研究温度应力的随机性。Heller 首先提出了谱密度法[2,3],但该法显然不适用于混凝土材料;Tsubaki 和 Bazant 提出了脉冲反应函数法[4],该法的缺点是系统的脉冲响应函数常不易求得;随后,Bazant 等人考虑到环境因素的周期变化特性,提出了谱分析方法[5~7]。相比之下,我国对于混凝土材料随机温度应力的研究较少[8],目前研究的不足之处在于:①未能考虑混凝土绝热温升引起的非稳定温度场的影响;②未能通过非统计法考虑结构物理参数的随机性;③所采用的 Maxwell 模型中松弛时间 τ_u 无法根据试验确定,而必须事先给定[9],我国通常采用线性叠加模型[10],并采用十分有效的初应变隐式解法计算混凝土徐变变形[10~12]。

随机有限元方法经过十余年发展已成为分析结构随机性的强有力的工具[13,14]。然而,目前的随机有限元方法仍限于以下两个方面:①将荷载视为随机过程(随机激励),而结构物理参数需视为确定;②将结构物理参数视为随机,则荷载不能为随机过程,只能为随机场或随机变量。笔者还未见利用随机有限元法求解混凝土结构随机温度应力的文献,笔者曾在文献[1]中综合考虑各种随机因素,给出了可以反映随机过程因素以及材料参数随机性的温度场随机有限元计算方法。该法最终可获得随机温度场的三个部分,第一部分随机温度场的随机性由随机材料参数产生,非稳定部分由均值绝热温升产生;第二部分为周期平稳随机温度场;第三部分随机温度场由随机绝热温升产生,为一般非平稳随机温度场。由于三部分温度场对徐变应力的影响机制各不相同,本文拟将三部分温度场对徐变应力的影响分开进行研究。本文既为解决前人方法(如谱分析法等)未能解决的问题,进一步完善随机有限元法,也是文献[1]工作的继续,即在获得随机温度场的基础上,进一步计算混凝土结构的随机温度徐变应力。

本文选自《力学学报》1997 年第 2 期,作者还有刘宁。

1 影响徐变应力的随机因素及其处理

1.1 混凝土的徐变度 $C(t,\tau)$

取 $\varphi(\tau)$(对某一固定的 τ)和参数 k 为随机变量,徐变度可表示为

$$C(t,\tau)=\overline{C}(t,\tau)+\Delta C(t,\tau)\approx\overline{C}(t,\tau)+(1-\mathrm{e}^{-\overline{k}(t-\tau)})\Delta\varphi+(t-\tau)\mathrm{e}^{-\overline{k}(t-\tau)}\overline{\varphi}(\tau)\Delta k \tag{1}$$

式中:$\overline{C}(t,\tau)$为徐变度均值过程。

由于徐变参数 $\varphi(\tau)$一般可表示为

$$\varphi(\tau)=p_1+p_2/\tau^{p_3} \tag{2}$$

式中:p_1、p_2、p_3 为随机变量。

于是

$$\overline{\varphi}(\tau)\approx\overline{p}_1+\overline{p}_2/\tau^{\overline{p}_3}\quad\Delta\varphi(\tau)\approx\Delta p_1+\tau^{-\overline{p}_3}\Delta p_2-\overline{p}_2\ln\tau\cdot\tau^{-\overline{p}_3}\Delta p_3 \tag{3}$$

1.2 混凝土的弹性模量 $E(\tau)$

$$E(\tau)=E_0(1-\mathrm{e}^{-m_2\tau})\approx\overline{E}(\tau)+(1-\mathrm{e}^{-m_2\tau})\Delta E_0+\tau\mathrm{e}^{-\overline{m}_2\tau}\overline{E}_0\Delta m_2 \tag{4}$$

式中:$\overline{E}(\tau)$为均值过程;E_0、m_2 为随机变量。

1.3 混凝土温度场 $T(t,x,y,z)$

文献[1]给出了随机温度场统计特性的计算方法,随机温度场可分为以下三部分

$$T(t,x,y,z)=T_1^{(0)}(t,x,y,z)+\sum_{i=1}^{n_a}T_1^{(i)}(t,x,y,z)+\Delta T_2(t,x,y,z) \tag{5}$$

式中:n_a 为周期环境温度种数[1];其余各参变量的含义可参见文献[1]。

本文记

$$T_1=T_1^{(0)},\quad T_2=\sum_{i=1}^{n_a}T_1^{(i)},\quad T_3=\Delta T_2 \tag{6}$$

显然,随机温度场第一部分 T_1 的随机性部分为稳定温度场(材料参数的随机性引起温度场的随机性),而非稳定部分由均值绝热温升产生,因此无需考虑温度场随机过程特性的影响;随机温度场的第二部分 T_2 为周期平稳随机温度场,因此可以针对温度场周期变化的特点加以研究,准确地获得温度场随机过程特性的影响;随机温度场的第三部分 T_3 为一般非平稳随机温度场,考虑到目前对于激励为一般非平稳时结构响应的计算方法还不太完善,因此本文对非平稳随机过程作一定的简化处理加以研究。

2 随机温度徐变应力场的计算方法

由式(5)、式(6),基于线性徐变假定,应变增量可写为

$$\Delta\varepsilon_n=\Delta\varepsilon_n^{(1)}+\Delta\varepsilon_n^{(2)}+\Delta\varepsilon_n^{(3)} \tag{7}$$

$$\left.\begin{aligned}\Delta\varepsilon_n^{(1)}&=\Delta\varepsilon_n^{e}+\Delta\varepsilon_n^{(C_1)}+\Delta\varepsilon_n^{(T_1)}+\Delta\varepsilon_n^{0}\\\Delta\varepsilon_n^{(2)}&=\Delta\varepsilon_n^{(C_2)}+\Delta\varepsilon_n^{(T_2)}\\\Delta\varepsilon_n^{(3)}&=\Delta\varepsilon_n^{(C_3)}+\Delta\varepsilon_n^{(T_3)}\end{aligned}\right\} \tag{8}$$

式中:$\Delta\varepsilon_n^{e}$ 为弹性应变增量;$\Delta\varepsilon_n^{0}$ 为体积应变增量;$\Delta\varepsilon_n^{(C_1)}$ 为外荷载以及 T_1 引起的徐变变

形增量；$\Delta\varepsilon_n^{(C_2)}$ 和 $\Delta\varepsilon_n^{(C_3)}$ 分别为周期平稳温度场 T_2 和非平稳绝热温升温度场 T_3 引起的温度荷载分别作用产生的徐变变形增量；$\Delta\varepsilon_n^{(T_1)}$、$\Delta\varepsilon_n^{(T_2)}$、$\Delta\varepsilon_n^{(T_3)}$ 分别为 T_1、T_2、T_3 产生的温度应变增量。

应力增量相应地成为

$$\Delta\sigma_n = \Delta\sigma_n^{(1)} + \Delta\sigma_n^{(2)} + \Delta\sigma_n^{(3)} \tag{9}$$

$$\left.\begin{aligned} \Delta\sigma_n^{(1)} &= D_n(\Delta\varepsilon_n^{(1)} - \Delta\varepsilon_n^e - \Delta\varepsilon_n^{(C_1)} - \Delta\varepsilon_n^{(T_1)} - \Delta\varepsilon_n^0) \\ \Delta\sigma_n^{(2)} &= D_n(\Delta\varepsilon_n^{(2)} - \Delta\varepsilon_n^{(C_2)} - \Delta\varepsilon_n^{(T_2)}) \\ \Delta\sigma_n^{(3)} &= D_n(\Delta\varepsilon_n^{(3)} - \Delta\varepsilon_n^{(C_3)} - \Delta\varepsilon_n^{(T_3)}) \end{aligned}\right\} \tag{10}$$

式中：D_n 为与弹模 $E(t_{n-1} + \Delta\tau_n/2)$ 对应的应力应变矩阵；$\Delta\tau_n = t_n - t_{n-1}$。

2.1 随机温度场 T_1 影响下的随机温度徐变应力(初应变随机有限元的隐式解法)

统一地以 X 表示基本随机变量，将随机函数 S 在随机变量的均值 $\overline{X}$ 处一阶 Taylor 展开，并写成一次摄动式，有：$S = \overline{S} + \alpha S'$。对于 $\varphi(\tau)$(τ 固定)，应力 σ，应变 ε 以及 k、E_0、m_2 等随机函数，均可按此式展开。将上述展式代入计算徐变应力的初应变隐式解法[11,12]，利用摄动原理，可得

(1)零次式

$$\left.\begin{aligned} \Delta\overline{\varepsilon}_n^{(C_1)} &= (1 - e^{-\overline{k}\Delta\tau_n})\overline{\omega}_n + Q\Delta\overline{\sigma}_n\overline{\varphi}_n^*(1 - \overline{f}_n e^{-\overline{k}\Delta\tau_n}) \\ \overline{\omega}_n &= e^{-\overline{k}\Delta\tau_n}\overline{\omega}_{n-1} + Q\Delta\overline{\sigma}_{n-1}\overline{\varphi}_{n-1}^*\overline{f}_{n-1}e^{-\overline{k}\Delta\tau_{n-1}} \\ \overline{\omega} &= Q\Delta\overline{\sigma}_0\overline{\varphi}_0 \end{aligned}\right\} \tag{11}$$

(2)一次式

$$\left.\begin{aligned} \Delta\varepsilon_n^{(C_1)'} &= (1 - e^{-\overline{k}\Delta\tau_n})\omega'_n + \Delta\tau_n e^{-\overline{k}\Delta\tau_n}\overline{\omega}_n k' + \\ &\quad Q(\sigma'_n\overline{\varphi}_n^* - \overline{\sigma}_n\varphi_n^{*'})(1 - \overline{f}_n e^{-\overline{k}\Delta\tau_n}) + Q\overline{\sigma}_n\overline{\varphi}_n^* e^{-\overline{k}\Delta\tau_n}(f'_n + \Delta\tau_n k') \\ \omega'_n &= (-\Delta\tau_n k'\overline{\omega}_{n-1} + \omega'_{n-1})e^{-\overline{k}\Delta\tau_n} + Q(\sigma'_{n-1}\overline{\varphi}_{n-1}^* - \overline{\sigma}_{n-1}\varphi_{n-1}^{*'})\overline{f}_{n-1}e^{-\overline{k}\Delta\tau_{n-1}} + \\ &\quad Q\overline{\sigma}_{n-1}\overline{\varphi}_{n-1}^* e^{-\overline{k}\Delta\tau_{n-1}}(f'_{n-1} - \Delta\tau_{n-1}k') \\ \omega'_1 &= Q(\Delta\overline{\sigma}_0\varphi'_0 + \Delta\sigma'_0\overline{\varphi}_0) \end{aligned}\right\} \tag{12}$$

式中：

$$f'_n = \begin{cases} \dfrac{1}{\Delta\tau_n}\dfrac{(\Delta\tau_n\overline{k} - 1)(e^{\overline{k}\Delta\tau_n} - 1)}{k^2} & (\text{当 } X_n = k \text{ 时}) \\ 0 & (\text{当 } X_n \neq k \text{ 时}) \end{cases} \tag{13}$$

$$\begin{aligned} \Delta\sigma_n^{(1)'} &= \overline{D}_n^*(\Delta\varepsilon_n^{(1)'} - \omega'_n(1 - e^{-\overline{k}\Delta\tau_n}) + \overline{\omega}_n e^{-\overline{k}\Delta\tau_n}\Delta\tau_n k' - \Delta\varepsilon_n^{(T_1)'} - \Delta\varepsilon_n^{0'}) + \\ &\quad D_n^{*'}(\Delta\overline{\varepsilon}_n^{(1)} - \overline{\omega}_n(1 - e^{-\overline{k}\Delta\tau_n}) - \Delta\overline{\varepsilon}_n^{(T_1)} - \Delta\overline{\varepsilon}_n^0) \end{aligned} \tag{14}$$

$$\left.\begin{aligned} \overline{D}_n^* &= \overline{D}_n/\overline{D}_{f_1} \\ D_n^{*'} &= \frac{D'_n\overline{D}_{f_1} - \overline{D}_n D'_{f_1}}{\overline{D}_{f_1}^2} = \frac{D'_n}{\overline{D}_{f_1}} - D_n^*\frac{D'_{f_1}}{\overline{D}_{f_1}} \end{aligned}\right\} \tag{15}$$

而

$$\left.\begin{aligned}&\overline{D}_{f_1}=1+\overline{\varphi}_n^*(1-\overline{f}_n\mathrm{e}^{-\overline{k}\Delta\tau_n})\overline{E}(t_{n-1}+\Delta\tau_n/2)\\&D'_{f_1}=[\varphi_n^{*'}(1-\overline{f}_n\mathrm{e}^{-\overline{k}\Delta\tau_n})+(\overline{f}_n\Delta\tau_n k'-f'_n)\overline{\varphi}_n^*\mathrm{e}^{-\overline{k}\Delta\tau_n}]\overline{E}(t_{n-1}+\Delta\tau_n/2)+\\&\qquad\overline{D}_{f_0}(1-\mathrm{e}^{-\overline{m}_2(t_{n-1}+\Delta\tau_n/2)})E'_0+(t_{n-1}+\Delta\tau_n/2)\overline{D}_{f_0}\mathrm{e}^{-\overline{m}_2(t_{n-1}+\Delta\tau_n/2)}m'_2\\&D'_n=\begin{cases}\dfrac{D_n}{E_0} & (\text{当随机变量 }X=E_0\text{ 时})\\\dfrac{(t_{n-1}+\Delta\tau_n/2)\mathrm{e}^{-m_2(t_{n-1}+\Delta\tau_n/2)}}{1-\mathrm{e}^{-m_2(t_{n-1}+\Delta\tau_n/2)}}D_n & (\text{当随机变量 }X=m_2\text{ 时})\\0 & (\text{其他})\end{cases}\end{aligned}\right\}\tag{16}$$

$$D_{f_0}=1+\varphi_n^*(1-f_n\mathrm{e}^{-k\Delta\tau_n})\cdot E(t_{n-1}+\Delta\tau_n/2)\tag{17}$$

式(14)中：

$$\Delta\varepsilon_n^{(1)'}=B\Delta u_n^{(1)'}=BK_n^{(1)-1}(\Delta P_n^{(1)'}-K_n^{(1)'}\Delta\overline{u}_n^{(1)})\tag{18}$$

式中，B 为形变矩阵，而

$$\left.\begin{aligned}&K_n^{(1)}=\sum_e\iiint_{v_e}B^{\mathrm{T}}D_n^*B\mathrm{d}v\\&\Delta P_n^{(1)'}=\Delta P_n^{(C_1)'}+\Delta P_n^{(T_1)'}+\Delta P_n^{0'}+F'\\&\Delta P_n^{(C_1)'}=\sum_e\iiint_{v_e}B^{\mathrm{T}}\{\overline{D}_n^*[\omega'_n(1-\mathrm{e}^{-\overline{k}\Delta\tau_n})+\overline{\omega}_n\Delta\tau_n\mathrm{e}^{-\overline{k}\Delta\tau_n}k']+\\&\qquad D_n^{*'}\overline{\omega}_n(1-\mathrm{e}^{-\overline{k}\Delta\tau_n})\}\mathrm{d}v\\&\Delta P_n^{0'}=\sum_e\iiint_{v_e}\{B^{\mathrm{T}}D_n^{*'}\Delta\overline{\varepsilon}_n^0+B^{\mathrm{T}}\overline{D}_n^*\Delta\varepsilon_n^{0'}\}\mathrm{d}v\end{aligned}\right\}\tag{19}$$

当不计混凝土自生体积变形的随机性时，$\Delta\overline{\varepsilon}_n^0=\Delta\varepsilon_n^0$，$\Delta\varepsilon_n^{0'}=0$，有：$\Delta P_n^{0'}=\int_v B^{\mathrm{T}}D_n^{*'}\Delta\varepsilon_n^0\mathrm{d}v$。有水压荷载时，式(19)中 F' 的计算方法可参见文献[16]，无水压荷载时，$F'=0$。

由式(11)、式(12)一步一步地求出 $\Delta\overline{\sigma}_n^{(1)}$ 和 $\Delta\sigma_n^{(1)'}$ 后，可得 t_n 时刻的 $\overline{\sigma}_n^{(1)}$ 和 $\sigma_n^{(1)'}$

$$\overline{\sigma}_n^{(1)}=\sum_{i=1}^n\Delta\overline{\sigma}_i^{(1)}\qquad\sigma_n^{(1)'}=\sum_{i=1}^n\Delta\sigma_i^{(1)'}\tag{20}$$

于是，t_n 时刻应力的协方差为

$$\mathrm{Cov}[\sigma_i^{(1)},\sigma_j^{(1)}]\approx\sum_{k=1}^{n_v}\sum_{l=1}^{n_v}\sigma'_{i,k}\sigma'_{j,l}\mathrm{Cov}(X_k,X_l)\tag{21}$$

式中：n_v 为随机变量总数；下标(i 或 j)表示应变或应力的分量。

2.2 周期平稳随机温度场 T_2 影响下的随机温度徐变应力

下面将给出随机温度场的第 2 部分 $T_2=\sum_{l=1}^{n_a}T_1^{(i)}$ 中任一项 $T_1^{(i)}$(周期平稳随机温度场)对温度徐变应力场影响的计算方法。为简明起见，令：$T_2=T_1^{(i)}$，即取 $n_a=1$。

文献[10]给出了简谐荷载作用下混凝土结构弹性徐变应力的计算方法。然而，该法要求混凝土弹模不随时间变化，因此将首先利用复频响应函数法，考虑混凝土的老化特性，并视复频响应函数为随机函数，给出相应的复频响应－随机有限元列式，使周期平稳随机温度场作用下的随机徐变应力问题得以解决。

2.2.1　简谐温度场作用下徐变应力的复模量隐式解法

由文献[1]、[10]，简谐温度场 T_2 可表示为

$$T_2(t)=h_T(\omega)e^{i\omega t} \tag{22}$$

式中：$h_T(\omega)$为传递函数。

根据随机振动理论[17]，在温度场 T_2 作用下结构的应变、应力可表示为

$$\left.\begin{aligned}\varepsilon^{(2)}(t)=h_\varepsilon(t,\omega)h_T(\omega)e^{i\omega t}=H_\varepsilon(t,\omega)e^{i\omega t}\\ \sigma^{(2)}(t)=h_\sigma(t,\omega)h_T(\omega)e^{i\omega t}=H_\sigma(t,\omega)e^{i\omega t}\end{aligned}\right\} \tag{23}$$

式中：$h_\varepsilon(t,\omega)$、$h_\sigma(t,\omega)$分别为应变、应力传递函数矩阵，对于温差应变和徐变应变，同样有

$$\varepsilon^{(T_2)}=H_\varepsilon^{(T)}(t,\omega)e^{i\omega t}\quad \varepsilon^{(C_2)}=H_\varepsilon^{(C)}(t,\omega)e^{i\omega t} \tag{24}$$

式中：$H_\varepsilon^{(T)}(t,\omega)$、$H_\varepsilon^{(C)}(t,\omega)$分别为对应于温度场 T_2 的温差应变复频响应函数列阵和徐变应变复频响应函数列阵。

为推导公式方便，本文先从单向受力情况入手，然后再转到三维复杂应力情况。根据叠加原理，在龄期 t_0 时刻受力的混凝土，t 时刻徐变变形可写为[10]

$$\varepsilon_{(t)}^C=\Delta\sigma_0 C(t,t_0)+\int_{t_0}^t C(t,\tau)\frac{\partial\sigma}{\partial t}d\tau \tag{25}$$

由式(24)、式(25)，则

$$\begin{aligned}H_\varepsilon^{(C)}(t)e^{i\omega t}\approx{}&\Delta H_{\sigma0}C(t,t_0)e^{i\omega t_0}+\\&\sum\varphi_i^*(\Delta H_{\sigma i}+i\omega\Delta\tau_i H_{\sigma i})[f_i^{(1)}e^{i\omega t_{i-1}}-f_i^{(2)}e^{(i\omega+k)t_{i-1}-kt}]\end{aligned} \tag{26}$$

式中：$\varphi_i^*=\varphi(t_{i-1}+\Delta\tau_i/2)$，$\Delta\tau_i=t_i-t_{i-1}$。而

$$f_i^{(1)}=e^{i\omega\Delta\tau_i}-1/i\omega\Delta\tau_i\quad f_i^{(2)}=(e^{(i\omega+k)\Delta\tau_i}-1)/(i\omega+k)\Delta\tau_i\quad(i=1,2,\cdots) \tag{27}$$

考察在3个相邻时刻 t_{n-1}、t_n、t_{n+1}式(26)的表达式，并令

$$\left.\begin{aligned}\Delta\Gamma_{\varepsilon n}^{(C)}=\Delta H_{\varepsilon n}^{(C)}+i\omega\Delta\tau_n H_{\varepsilon n}^{(C)}\quad(n=1,2,\cdots)\\ \Delta\Gamma_{\sigma n}=\Delta H_{\sigma n}+i\omega\Delta\tau_n H_{\sigma n}\quad(n=1,2,\cdots)\\ \Delta\Gamma_{\varepsilon0}^{(C)}=\Delta H_{\varepsilon0}^{(C)}\quad\Delta\Gamma_{\sigma n}=\Delta H_{\sigma0}\end{aligned}\right\} \tag{28}$$

同时，注意到 $\Delta\varepsilon_n^{(C)}\approx\Delta\Gamma_\varepsilon^{(C)}(t_n)e^{i\omega t_n}$，不难得出以下递推公式

$$\left.\begin{aligned}\Delta\Gamma_{\varepsilon n}^{(C)}={}&\Delta\Gamma_{\sigma0}e^{i\omega(t_0-t_n)}[C(t_n-t_0)-C(t_{n-1}-t_0)]+(1-e^{-(i\omega+k)\Delta\tau_n})\omega_n+\\&\varphi_n^*\Delta\Gamma_{\sigma n}[f_n^{(1)}e^{-i\omega\Delta\tau_n}-f_n^{(2)}e^{-(i\omega+k)\Delta\tau_n}]\\ \omega_{n+1}={}&\omega_n e^{-(i\omega+k)\Delta\tau_n}+\varphi_n^*\Delta\Gamma_{\sigma n}f_n^{(2)}e^{-(i\omega+k)\Delta\tau_n}\\ \omega_2={}&\varphi_1^*\Delta\Gamma_{\sigma1}f_1^{(2)}e^{-(i\omega+k)\Delta\tau_1}\end{aligned}\right\} \tag{29}$$

对于三维复杂应力状态，可以得到以下递推公式

$$\left.\begin{aligned}\Delta\Gamma_{\varepsilon n}^{(C)}={}&\Delta\Gamma_{\sigma0}e^{i\omega(t_0-t_n)}[C(t_n-t_0)-C(t_{n-1}-t_0)]+(1-e^{-(i\omega+k)\Delta\tau_n})\omega_n+\\&\varphi_n^*\Delta\Gamma_{\sigma n}[f_n^{(1)}e^{-i\omega\Delta\tau_n}-f_n^{(2)}e^{-(i\omega+k)\Delta\tau_n}]\\ \omega_n={}&\omega_{n-1}e^{-(i\omega+k)\Delta\tau_{n-1}}+Q\varphi_{n-1}^*\Delta\Gamma_{\sigma(n-1)}f_{n-1}^{(2)}e^{-(i\omega+k)\Delta\tau_{n-1}}\quad(n=3,4,\cdots)\\ \omega_2={}&Q\varphi_1^*\Delta\Gamma_{\sigma1}f_1^{(2)}e^{-(i\omega+k)\Delta\tau_1}\end{aligned}\right\} \tag{30}$$

式中，Q 与文献[12]结果完全一致。由式(10)，不难进一步得到

$$\Delta\Gamma_{\sigma n}=D_n^{**}(\Delta\Gamma_{\varepsilon n}-\Delta\Gamma_{\varepsilon n}^{(C)*}-\Delta\Gamma_{\varepsilon n}^{(T)}) \tag{31}$$

式中：

$$\left.\begin{aligned}
D_n^{**}&=\frac{D_n}{1+\varphi_n^*(f_n^{(1)}\mathrm{e}^{-i\omega\Delta\tau_n}-f_n^{(2)}\mathrm{e}^{-(i\omega+k)\Delta\tau_n})E(t_{n-1}+\Delta\tau_n/2)}\\
\Delta\Gamma_{\varepsilon n}^{(C)*}&=\Delta\Gamma_{\sigma 0}\mathrm{e}^{i\omega(t_0-t_n)}[C(t_n-t_0)-C(t_{n-1}-t_0)]+(1-\mathrm{e}^{-(i\omega+k)\Delta\tau_n})\omega_n\\
\Delta\Gamma_{\varepsilon n}^{(T)*}&=\Delta\varepsilon_n^{(T_2)}\mathrm{e}^{-i\omega t_n}=\alpha T_2[1,1,1,0,0,0]^{\mathrm{T}}\mathrm{e}^{-i\omega t_n}
\end{aligned}\right\} \tag{32}$$

由式(35)，并注意到 $\Delta\Gamma_{\varepsilon n}=B\Delta\Gamma_{un}$，利用虚功原理，可得

$$K_n^{(2)}\Delta\Gamma_{un}=\Delta P_n^{(T_2)}+\Delta P_n^{(C_2)} \tag{33}$$

式中：

$$K_n^{(2)}=\sum_e\iiint_{v_e}B^{\mathrm{T}}D_n^{**}B\mathrm{d}v$$

$$\Delta P_n^{(T_2)}=\sum_e\iiint_{v_e}B^{\mathrm{T}}D_n^{**}\Delta\Gamma_{\varepsilon n}^{(T)}\mathrm{d}v$$

$$\Delta P_n^{(C_2)}=\sum_e\iiint_{v_e}B^{\mathrm{T}}D_n^{**}\Delta\Gamma_{\varepsilon n}^{(C)}\mathrm{d}v$$

由后给出的式(36)、式(37)可以一步一步地求出 $\Delta\Gamma_{\sigma n}$，进而由式(34)可求出 $\Delta H_{\sigma n}$

$$\Delta H_{\sigma n}=(\Delta\Gamma_{\sigma n}-i\omega\Delta\tau_n H_{\sigma(n-1)})/(1+i\omega\Delta\tau_n) \tag{34}$$

最终可得 $H_{\sigma n}=\sum_{i=1}^{n}\Delta H_{\sigma i}$。

2.2.2 周期平稳温度场作用下随机徐变应力的复频响应－随机有限元列式

对式(30)、式(31)引入随机变量的摄动量，由摄动原理，经推导、整理，可得

(1)零次方程

$$\left.\begin{aligned}
\Delta\overline{\Gamma}_{\varepsilon n}^{(C)}&=\Delta\overline{\Gamma}_{\sigma 0}[\overline{C}(t_n,t_0)-\overline{C}(t_{n-1}-t_0)]+(1-\mathrm{e}^{-(i\omega+k)\Delta\tau_n})\overline{\omega}_n+\\
&\quad\overline{\varphi}_n^*\Delta\overline{\Gamma}_{\sigma n}(\overline{f}_n^{(1)}\mathrm{e}^{-i\omega\Delta\tau_n}-\overline{f}_n^{(2)}\mathrm{e}^{-(i\omega+\overline{k}\Delta\tau_n)})\\
\overline{\omega}_n&=\overline{\omega}_{n-1}\mathrm{e}^{-(i\omega+\overline{k})\Delta\tau_n}+\overline{Q}\,\overline{\varphi}_n^*\Delta\overline{\Gamma}_{\sigma n}\overline{f}_n^{(2)}\mathrm{e}^{-(i\omega+\overline{k})\Delta\tau_n}\quad(n=3,4,\cdots)\\
\overline{\omega}_2&=Q\,\overline{\varphi}_1^*\Delta\overline{\Gamma}_{\sigma 1}\overline{f}_1^{(2)}\mathrm{e}^{-(i\omega+\overline{k})\Delta\tau_1}\\
\Delta\overline{\Gamma}_{\sigma n}&=\overline{D}_n(\Delta\overline{\Gamma}_{\varepsilon n}-\Delta\overline{\Gamma}_{\varepsilon n}^{(C)}-\Delta\overline{\Gamma}_{\varepsilon n}^{(T)})
\end{aligned}\right\} \tag{35}$$

(2)一次方程

$$\left.\begin{aligned}
\Delta\Gamma_{\varepsilon n}^{(C)'}&=\Delta r_0^{(1)}+(1-\mathrm{e}^{-(i\omega+\overline{k})\Delta\tau_n})\omega'_n+\Delta\tau_n\overline{\omega}_n^{(2)}\mathrm{e}^{-(i\omega+\overline{k})\Delta\tau_n}k'\\
\omega'_n&=(\omega'_{n-1}-\overline{\omega}_{n-1}\Delta\tau_{n-1}k')\mathrm{e}^{-(i\omega+\overline{k})\Delta\tau_{n-1}}+Q\mathrm{e}^{-(i\omega+\overline{k})\Delta\tau_{n-1}}(\Delta r_{n-1}^{(2)}-\\
&\quad\Delta\tau_{n-1}k'\overline{\varphi}_{n-1}^*\Delta\overline{\Gamma}_{\sigma(n-1)}\overline{f}_{n-1}^{(2)})\\
\omega'_2&=Q\mathrm{e}^{-(i\omega+\overline{k})\Delta\tau_1}[\varphi_1^{*\prime}\overline{f}_1^{(2)}+\overline{\varphi}_1^*f_1^{(2)\prime}-\Delta\tau_1k'\overline{\varphi}_1^*\overline{f}_1^{(2)})\\
\Delta\Gamma'_{\sigma n}&=D_n^{**\prime}(\Delta\overline{\Gamma}_{\varepsilon n}-\Delta\overline{\Gamma}_{\varepsilon n}^{(C)*}-\Delta\overline{\Gamma}_{\varepsilon n}^{(T)})-\\
&\quad\overline{D}_n^{**}(\Delta\Gamma'_{\varepsilon n}-\Delta\Gamma_{\varepsilon n}^{(C)*\prime}-\Delta\Gamma_{\varepsilon n}^{(T)\prime})\\
\Delta\Gamma'_{\varepsilon n}&=B\Delta\Gamma'_{un}=BK_n^{(2)-1}(\Delta P_n^{(T_2)\prime}+\Delta P_n^{(C_2)\prime}-K_n^{(2)\prime}\Delta\overline{\Gamma}_{un})
\end{aligned}\right\} \tag{36}$$

式中：

$$\left.\begin{aligned}&\Delta r_0^{(1)}=\Delta\Gamma'_{\sigma0}[\overline{C}(t_n,t_0)-\overline{C}(t_{n-1},t_0)]+\Delta\overline{\Gamma}_{\sigma0}[C'(t_n,t_0)-C'(t_{n-1},t_0)]\\&\Delta r_{n-1}^{(2)}=\varphi_{n-1}^{*}\Delta\overline{\Gamma}_{\sigma(n-1)}\overline{f}_{n-1}^{(1)}+\overline{\varphi}_{n-1}^{*}\Delta\Gamma'_{\sigma(n-1)}\overline{f}_{n-1}^{(1)}+\overline{\varphi}_{n-1}^{*}\Delta\overline{\Gamma}_{\sigma(n-1)}f_{n-1}^{(1)'}\\&\Delta P_n^{(T_2)'}=\sum_e\iiint_{v_e}B^{\mathrm T}(\overline{D}_n^{**}\Delta\Gamma_{\varepsilon n}^{(T)'}+D_n^{**'}\Delta\overline{\Gamma}_{\varepsilon n}^{(T)})\mathrm{d}v\\&\Delta P_n^{(C_2)'}=\sum_e\iiint_{v_e}B^{\mathrm T}(\overline{D}_n^{**}\Delta\Gamma_{\varepsilon n}^{(C)'}+D_n^{**'}\Delta\overline{\Gamma}_{\varepsilon n}^{(C)})\mathrm{d}v\end{aligned}\right\}\tag{37}$$

其中，$D_n^{**'}$、$f_n^{(1)}$ 以及 $f_n^{(2)}$ 可由直接偏微分法求出，限于篇幅，具体表达式不再列出。

求出 $\Delta\overline{\Gamma}_{\sigma n}$ 和 $\Delta\Gamma'_{\sigma n}$ 后，可按下式获得 $\Delta\overline{H}_{\sigma n}$ 和 $\Delta H'_{\sigma n}$

$$\left.\begin{aligned}\Delta\overline{H}_{\sigma n}&=(\Delta\overline{\Gamma}_{\sigma n}-i\omega\Delta\tau_n\overline{H}_{\sigma(n-1)})/(1+i\omega\Delta\tau_n)\\\Delta H'_{\sigma n}&=(\Delta\Gamma'_{\sigma n}-i\omega\Delta\tau_n H_{\sigma(n-1)})/(1+i\omega\Delta\tau_n)\end{aligned}\right\}\tag{38}$$

最终可得

$$\overline{H}_{\sigma n}=\sum_{i=1}^{n}\Delta\overline{H}_{\sigma i}\qquad H'_{\sigma n}=\sum_{i=1}^{n}\Delta H'_{\sigma i}\tag{39}$$

由式(23)，并根据复数随机过程原理，应力的相关函数矩阵可写为

$$R_\sigma(\omega,t_i,t_j)=E\{H_{\sigma i}(\omega,t_i)\mathrm{e}^{i\omega t_i}\cdot[H_{\sigma i}(\omega,t_j)\mathrm{e}^{i\omega t_j}]^{*\mathrm T}\}\tag{40}$$

式中：上标(*)表示求共轭复数；$E\{\cdot\}$表示求数学期望。

由于：$H_{\sigma i}(\omega,t_i)\approx\overline{H}_{\sigma i}+\sum_{l=1}^{n_v}H'_{\sigma i,l}\Delta X_l(i,j)$，其中，下标 l 表示对随机变量 X_l 求偏导，代入式(40)，当 $t_i=t_j=t$ 时，有

$$R_\sigma(\omega,t)\approx\overline{H}_\sigma(\omega,t)[\overline{H}_\sigma(\omega,t)]^{*\mathrm T}+\sum_{l=1,s=1}^{n_v}H'_{\sigma,l}(\omega,t)[H'_{\sigma,s}(\omega,t)]^{*\mathrm T}\mathrm{Cov}(X_l,X_s)\tag{41}$$

显然，$R_\sigma(\omega,t)$的对角线列阵为应力的均方值。于是，应变和应力的方差为

$$\mathrm{Var}(\sigma)=E(\sigma^2)-E(\sigma)E(\sigma)^{*\mathrm T}\approx\sum_{i=1}^{n_v}|H'_{\sigma,i}(\omega,t)|^2\mathrm{Var}(X_i)\tag{42}$$

2.3 非平稳随机温度场 T_3 作用下的随机徐变应力场

随机绝热温升的均值部分(式(5)中的 $\overline{T}_2(t)$)对应力场的影响已在 2.2.1 中得以完成，而其随机性部分 T_3(式(6)中的 ΔT_2)为非平稳随机过程。前已说明目前对于激励为一般非平稳时响应的计算方法还不太完善，尤其是对于需用有限元离散的大型复杂结构，还未出现成熟的解法，本文因此对非平稳随机过程 ΔT_2 作一定的简化处理。文献[18]中提出了非平稳随机过程逐段平稳叠加的双参数法，由于实际计算时，时段$(t_i,t_{i+1})(i=1,2,\cdots)$不会太长，故本文引入该法参数调幅的思想，对非平稳随机温度场作以下的逐段简化处理

$$\Delta T_2(t)\approx\begin{cases}(x_1^{(1)}(t)\Delta T_2^{(1)}(t_1),\cdots,x_1^{(N_P)}(t)\Delta T_2^{(N_P)}(t_1))^{\mathrm T}=x_1^{\mathrm T}(t)I\Delta T_2(t_1)\quad(t_1\leqslant t<t_2)\\\cdots\cdots\\(x_n^{(1)}(t)\Delta T_2^{(1)}(t_n),\cdots,x_n^{(N_P)}(t)\Delta T_2^{(N_P)}(t_n))^{\mathrm T}=x_n^{\mathrm T}(t)I\Delta T_2(t_n)\quad(t_n\leqslant t<t_{n+1})\end{cases}\tag{43}$$

式中：N_P 为结点总数；I 为单位矩阵；$x_n^{(i)}(t)$为一确定性函数，上标$(i)(i=1,2,\cdots,N_P)$

表示第(i)结点,对给定的时刻t,$\Delta T_2^{(i)}(t)(i=1,2,\cdots,N_P)$为一随机变量。

文献[18]在每一时段内简化为平稳随机过程,而本文则在每一时段内仍为非平稳随机过程,可保证原非平稳随机过程(ΔT_2)逐点方差的准确性,且计算可大为简化。考虑到$\Delta \overline{T}_2=0$,故$x_n^{(i)}(t)$为

$$x_n^{(i)}(t)=\sqrt{\mathrm{Var}[\Delta T_2^{(i)}(t)]/\mathrm{Var}[\Delta T_2^{(i)}(t_n)]} \tag{44}$$

$\Delta T_2(t_k)$、$\Delta T_2(t_l)$间($t_i\leqslant t_k<t_{i+1},t_j\leqslant t_l<t_{j+1}$)在时域上的相关性可以近似地由下式反映

$$\mathrm{Cov}[\Delta T_2^{(m)}(t_k),\Delta T_2^{(m)}(t_l)]\approx x_i^{(m)}(t_k)x_j^{(m)}(t_l)\mathrm{Cov}[\Delta T_2^{(m)}(t_i),\Delta T_2^{(m)}(t_j)] \tag{45}$$

式中:上标(m)表示第m结点;$\Delta T_2^{(m_1)}(t_k)$,$\Delta T_2^{(m_2)}(t_k)(t_i\leqslant t_k<t_{i+1})$在空间上的相关性为

$$\mathrm{Cov}[\Delta T_2^{(m_1)}(t_k),\Delta T_2^{(m_2)}(t_k)]\approx x_i^{(m_1)}(t_k)x_i^{(m_2)}(t_k)\mathrm{Cov}[\Delta T_2^{(m_1)}(t_i),\Delta T_2^{(m_2)}(t_i)] \tag{46}$$

因此,将一般非平稳过程ΔT_2简化为式(43)仍可轻松地反映原非平稳随机过程ΔT_2的相关特性。由式(8)、(11)、(12),并注意此时到$\Delta\overline{\varepsilon}_n^{(3)}=\Delta\overline{\varepsilon}_n^{(C_3)}=\Delta\overline{\varepsilon}_n^{(T_3)}=0$,$\Delta\overline{\sigma}_n^{(3)}=0$,$\overline{\omega}_n=0$,$\Delta\overline{P}^{(C_3)}=\Delta\overline{P}^{(T)}=0$,此时无需列出零次方程,只需列出一次方程

$$\left.\begin{aligned}&\Delta\varepsilon_n^{(C_3)'}=(1-\mathrm{e}^{-\overline{k}\Delta\tau_n})\omega'_n+Q\overline{\varphi}_n^*\Delta\sigma_n^{(3)'}(1-\overline{f}_n\mathrm{e}^{-\overline{k}\Delta\tau_n})\\&\omega'_n=\omega'_{n-1}\mathrm{e}^{-\overline{k}\Delta\tau_n}+Q\Delta\sigma_{n-1}^{(3)'}\overline{\varphi}_{n-1}^*\overline{f}_{n-1}\mathrm{e}^{-\overline{k}\Delta\tau_{n-1}}\\&\omega'_1=Q\Delta\sigma_0^{(3)'}\overline{\varphi}_0\end{aligned}\right\} \tag{47}$$

式中:

$$\left.\begin{aligned}&\Delta\sigma_n^{(3)'}=\overline{D}_n^*[\Delta\varepsilon_n^{(3)'}-\omega'_n(1-\mathrm{e}^{-\overline{k}\Delta\tau_n})-\Delta\varepsilon_n^{(T_3)'}]\\&\Delta\varepsilon_n^{(3)'}=B\Delta u_n^{(3)'}=BK_n^{-1}(\Delta P_n^{(C_3)'}+\Delta P_n^{(T_3)'})\\&\Delta P_n^{(C_3)'}=\sum_{\mathrm{e}}\int_{v_e}B^{\mathrm{T}}\overline{D}_n^*\omega'_n(1-\mathrm{e}^{-\overline{k}\Delta\tau_n})\mathrm{d}v\\&\Delta P_n^{(T_3)'}=\sum_{\mathrm{e}}\int_{v_e}B^{\mathrm{T}}\overline{D}_n^*B\alpha\Delta T'_2(t_n)[1,1,1,0,0,0]^{\mathrm{T}}\mathrm{d}v\end{aligned}\right\} \tag{48}$$

由以上各式一步一步地求出$\sigma_n^{(3)'}$后,可按式(21)方法获得应力的协方差。

3 算例

笔者根据前述理论和方法,编制了“大体积混凝土结构随机温度徐变应力计算大型通用程序STAC”,在486DX2-S/66计算机上调试通过。以下将给出2个算例进行验证。

3.1 算例1 自由板的随机温度应力

取文献[11]中自由板的随机温度应力算例。取板厚度为3.0m,长和宽均为30.0m。由于板的平面尺寸远较其厚度为大,因此温度分布是单向的,只在厚度方向(z方向)变化(见图1)。本文取温度$T(t,z)$在时间和厚度方向上的变化为:$T(z,t)=T_0(z^2+2.0)\cos(\omega t)$,式中,$\omega=\dfrac{2\pi}{365}(1/d)$。根据弹性力学有关公式可知,当弹模$E$为恒定时,自由板内应力为

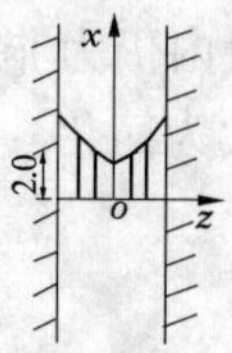

图 1　截面温度分布

$$\left.\begin{aligned}&\sigma_x=\sigma_y=\frac{E(\varepsilon-\alpha T)}{1-\mu},\ \sigma_z=0,\ \varepsilon=(A+Bz)\alpha\\&A=\frac{1}{2l}\int_{-l}^{l}T\mathrm{d}z=2.75T_0\cos(\omega t),\ B=\frac{1}{2l^3}\int_{-l}^{l}Tz\mathrm{d}z=0\end{aligned}\right\}\tag{49}$$

如果弹模 E 取为：$E(t)=E_0(1-\mathrm{e}^{-m_2t})$，则在每一时段内，应力增量为

$$\left.\begin{aligned}&\Delta\sigma_k=\frac{E_k\alpha}{1-\mu}[(\Delta A_k+\Delta B_kz)-\Delta T_k]\\&\Delta A_k=A_{k+1}-A_k,\ \Delta B_k=B_{k+1}-B_k,\ \Delta T_k=T_{k+1}-T_k\end{aligned}\right\}\tag{50}$$

任一时刻的应力为：$\sigma=\sum\Delta\sigma_k$。取随机变量为：温度幅值 T_0，弹模幅值 E_0 以及系数 m_2。随机变量均为正态分布，均值为：$\overline{T}_0=25.0$℃，$\overline{E}_0=2.8$MPa，$\overline{m}_2=0.3$；变异系数都为 0.1。由式(49)可绘出 $z=0.0$m 处应力的均值曲线（见图 2(a)、(b)中的曲线 1 和 3，以拉为正，以下皆同）。本文分别按复频响应－随机有限元法和初应变隐式解法对温度应力的均值进行了计算。复频响应－随机有限元法计算结果见图 2(a)中曲线 2 和 4。初应变隐式解法计算结果见图 2(b)中曲线 2 和 4。可以看出，由于复频响应－随机有限元法直接针对温度场的周期变化特性，所得结果比初应变隐式解法计算结果更为精确。

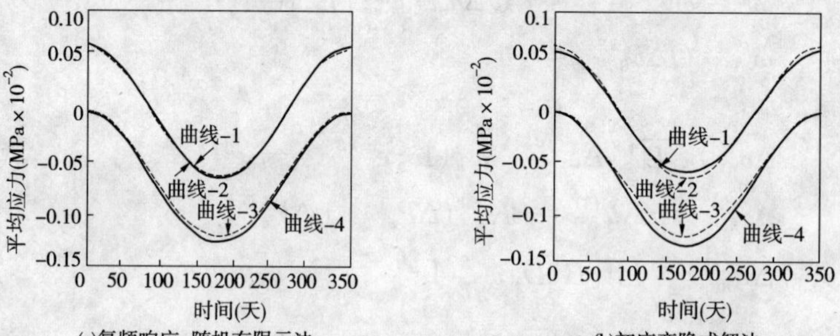

(a)复频响应-随机有限元法　　　　(b)初应变隐式解法

图 2　自由板温度应力的均值(z=0m)

曲线－1　弹模恒定时理论解；　曲线－2　弹模恒定时随机有限元解；

曲线－3　弹模变化时理论解；　曲线－4　弹模变化时随机有限元解。

由式(50)，可以得到任一时刻温度应力方差的准理论解表达式

$$\left.\begin{aligned}&\mathrm{Var}(\sigma)\approx\sum_{i=1}^{n_v}\sum_{j=1}^{n_v}\frac{\partial\sigma}{\partial X_i}\frac{\partial\sigma}{\partial X_j}\mathrm{Cov}(X_i,X_j)\\&\frac{\partial\sigma}{\partial X_i}=\sum\frac{\partial\Delta\sigma_k}{\partial X_i},\quad\frac{\partial\sigma}{\partial X_j}=\sum\frac{\partial\Delta\sigma_k}{\partial X_j}\end{aligned}\right\}\tag{51}$$

上式中，$n_v=3$；X_1、X_2、X_3 分别为 T_0、E_0、m_2；$\partial\Delta\sigma_k/\partial X$ 可对式(50)微分得到。图 3(a)给出了 T_0 为确定而 E_0、m_2 为随机时，应力标准差准理论解的过程曲线（图中虚线）；图 3(b)给出了 T_0、E_0、m_2 均为随机时，应力标准差准理论解的过程曲线（图中虚线）。

图 3(a)、3(b) 中 实线给出了复频响应 - 随机有限元法计算结果。可以看出，按本文方法所得结果与理论解基本一致。造成误差的原因有两点：第一是本算例尺寸与理想尺寸存在误差；第二是有限元网格疏密产生误差。

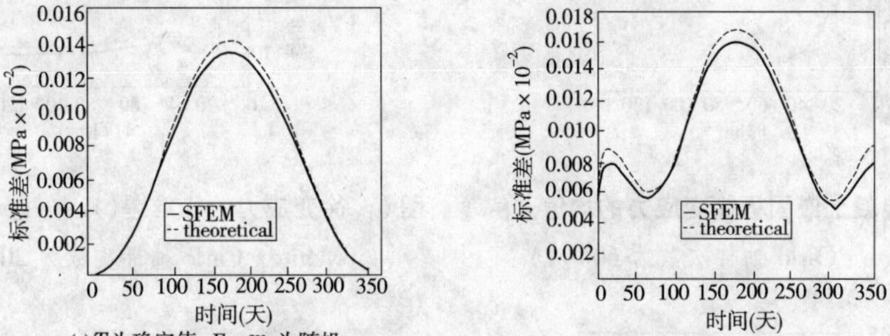

(a) T_0为确定值，E_0、m_2为随机　　(b) T_0、E_0、m_2均为随机

图 3　自由板温度应力的标准差

3.2　算例 2　混凝土嵌固板的随机温度徐变应力

取文献[19] 中矩形混凝土嵌固板，设矩形板长度为 l，宽度为 b，厚度为 h，其端部没有法向位移的可能性。在混凝土龄期 $\tau_0 = 7$ 天时，受到均匀加热，由温度为零度加热到 25℃，取混凝土板的线膨胀系数 $\alpha = 0.000\,012(1/℃)$，泊松比 $\mu = 1/6$，弹性模量的均值为 $\overline{E}_0 = 2.0 \times 10^4$ MPa，混凝土的徐变度均值为

$$\overline{C}(t,\tau) = \left(0.9 + \frac{4.82}{\tau}\right)\left[1 - e^{-0.026(t-\tau)}\right] \times 10^{-5} \tag{52}$$

即式 (1)、(3) 中 $\overline{p}_1 = 0.9 \times 10^{-5}$ cm²/kg，$\overline{p}_2 = 4.82 \times 10^{-5}$ cm²/kg，$\overline{p}_3 = 1.0$，$\overline{k} = 0.026(1/\mathrm{d})$。结构计算简图见图 4，本文取 $l = 30.0$m，$b = 30.0$m，$h = 1.0$m，采用 5×5×3 的有限元网格。随机变量取为 E_0、p_1、p_2、p_3、k，分布均为正态，变异系数均为 0.1。徐变应力均值的计算结果见图 5，图中同时给出了 Monte - Carlo 数值模拟结果(图中虚线与随机有限元计算结果完全吻合）和理论解(圆圈表示）。为考察不同种类随机变量的随机性对徐变应力标准差的影响，本文分别计算了只有弹模 E_0 为随机变量、只有 k 为随机变量以及只有 p_1、p_2、p_3 为随机变量时徐变应力标准差的过程曲线，由于后两者曲线形状基本类同，这里只给出只有弹模 E_0 为随机变量以及 k、p_1、p_2、p_3 为随机变量时徐变应力标准差的过程曲线[图 6 和图 7(a)]，图 7(b) 给出了 E_0、k、p_1、p_2、p_3 均视为随机时徐变应力标准差过程曲线，图中虚线均为 Monte - Carlo 数值模拟结果。从图 5 ~ 图 7 可以看出，徐变应力的均值和标准差在 100 天后都趋于稳定。

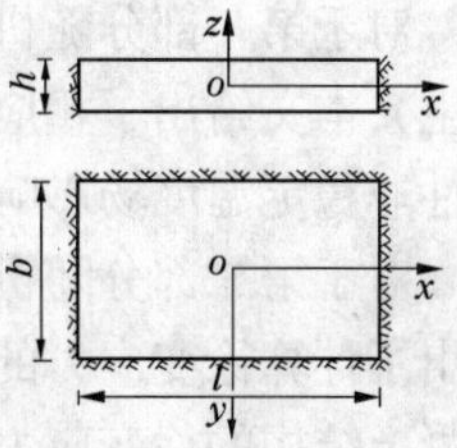

图 4　混凝土嵌固板

4　结语

本文综合考虑混凝土温度徐变应力计算中的各种随机因素(如温度场、弹模、徐变参数等的随机性)，将随机温度场对随机徐变应力场的影响分离为三个部分加以研究。

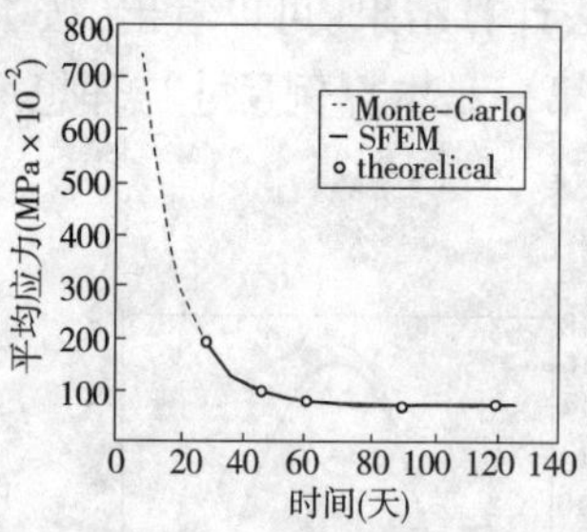

图 5　混凝土嵌固板徐变应力的均值

(Monte - Carlo 抽样次数为 600 次)

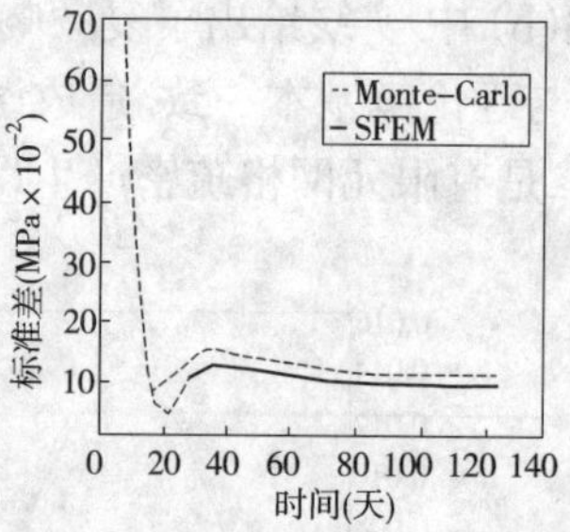

图 6　徐变应力的标准差(只有 E_0 为随机)

(Monte - Carlo 抽样次数为 200 次)

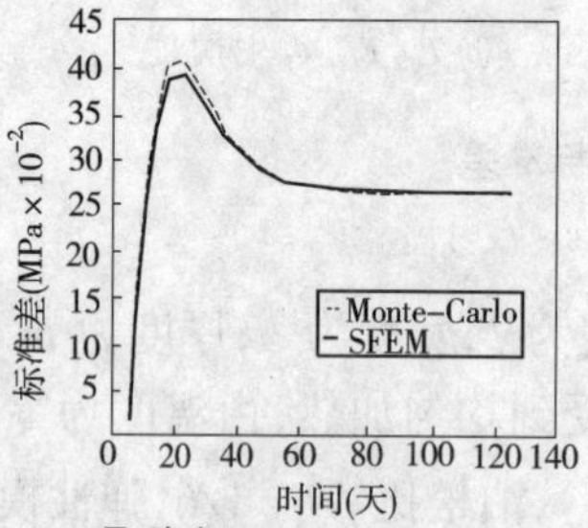

(a) E_0确定,k、p_1、p_2、p_3为随机

Monte-Carlo抽样次数为500次

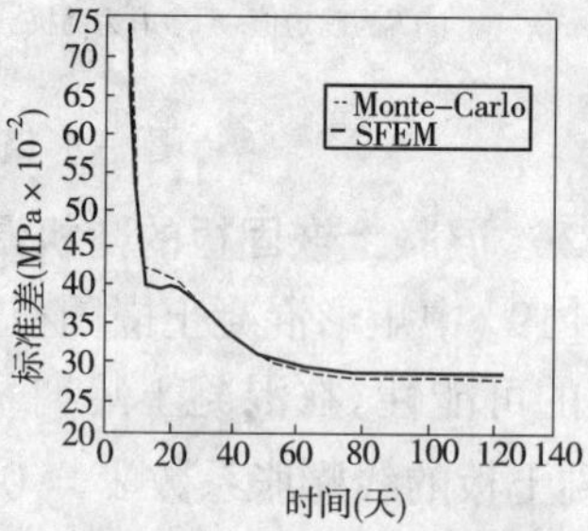

(b) E_0、k、p_1、p_2、p_3均为随机

Monte-Carlo抽样次数为600次

图 7　混凝土嵌固板徐变应力的标准差

对于第一部分随机温度场(随机性部分为稳定温度场,而非稳定部分由均值绝热温升产生),本文给出了相应于初应变隐式解法的随机有限元列式,该列式同时适用于任何确定性非稳定温度场影响下的徐变应力问题。

对于第二部分随机温度场(周期平稳随机温度场),本文针对温度场周期变化的特点,提出了计算徐变应力的复模量隐式解法,该法有效地解决了简谐荷载作用下弹模变化时混凝土结构的徐变应力计算问题。首次视复频响应函数为随机材料参数的随机函数,本文给出了相应于复模量隐式解法的复频响应 - 随机有限元列式,该法既考虑材料参数随机性的影响,又可准确地反映周期平稳温度场随机过程特性的影响,有效地克服了前人方法(谱分析法等)不能考虑材料参数随机性且需弹模为常量的局限性。

对于第三部分随机场温度场(随机绝热温升产生,一般非平稳随机温度场),本文提出了参数调幅逐段简化的方法,与逐段平稳化方法相比,该法在每一时段内将非平稳随机过程仍简化为一非平稳随机过程,原非平稳随机过程无需为缓变过程,既保证了原非平稳随机过程逐点方差的准确性,又可轻松地反映原非平稳随机过程时域和空间相关特性,且计算大为简化。

总之,本文首次成功地将随机有限元法引入混凝土结构随机温度徐变应力的计算。随机有限元法的引入,不仅进一步完善了随机有限元方法本身,而且大大提高了本文方法的实用性,使大体积混凝土结构的随机温度徐变应力计算问题较为圆满地得以解决。

参考文献

[1] 刘宁,刘光廷. 大体积混凝土结构随机温度场的随机有限元算法. 清华大学学报,1996,36(1):41～47

[2] Heller R A. *Temperature response of an infinitely thick slab to random surface temperature*. Mechanics Research Communication, 1976,3(2): 379～385

[3] Heller R A. *Thermal Stress as an Narrow－Band Random Load*. J of Engng Mech, ASCE, 1976,102(5):787～805

[4] Tsubaki T ,Bazant Z P. *Random shrinkage stresses in aging viscoelastic vessel*. J of Engng Mech, ASCE, 1982,108(3): 527～545

[5] Bazant Z P, Wnag T S. *Spectral analysis of random shrinkage in concrete structures*. J of Engng Mech, ASCE, 1984,110(2): 173～186

[6] Bazant Z P, Wnag T S. *Spectral finite element analysis of random shrinkage in concrete*. J of Struct Engng, ASCE, 1984,110(9): 2196～2211

[7] Bazant Z P,Wnag T S. *Algorithm for aging viscoelstic structures under periodic load*. J of Engng Mech, 1984, 110(6): 972～985

[8] 王同生. 混凝土结构的随机温度应力. 水利学报,1985,1:23～31

[9] Bazant Z P. *Methemetical Models for Creep and Shrinkage of Concrete*, *in Creep and Shrinkage in Concrete Structures*. Ed by Bazant Z P and Wittmann F H, New York: John Willey and Sons, 1982,163～258.

[10] 朱伯芳,等. 水工混凝土结构温度应力与温度控制. 北京:水利电力出版社,1976

[11] 朱伯芳. 水工结构与固体力学论文集. 北京:水利电力出版社,1985,182～191

[12] 丁宝瑛. 大体积混凝土结构的温度应力与温度控制论文集. 北京:兵器工业出版社,1991

[13] Zhu W Q,Ren Y J, Wu W Q. *Stochastic FEM Based on Local Averages of Random Vector Fields*. J of Engrg Mech, ASCE,1992,118(3): 496～511

[14] 刘宁,吕泰仁. 随机有限元及其工程应用. 力学进展,1995,25(1): 144～126

[15] Shiweiwu et al. *Statistical values for yearly maximum of head-water lever of dams*. Proc. of 4th IAHR., Int Symp on Stochastic Hydraulics, 31 July～2 August, USA, 1984

[16] 李同春,吴世伟. 基于三维 SFEM 的拱坝可靠度分析. 见:工程结构可靠性全国第二届学术交流会议论文集. 重庆, 1989:114～125

[17] 朱位秋. 随机振动. 北京:科学出版社,1992

[18] 刘宁,孟庆生,吴世伟. 非平稳载荷下疲劳裂纹扩展的可靠度分析. 工程力学,1993,5(增刊):547～552

[19] 阿鲁久涅扬. 蠕变理论中的若干问题. 邬瑞锋等译. 北京: 科学出版社,1962

混凝土结构的随机温度及随机徐变应力

摘　要　大体积混凝土结构随机温度及随机徐变应力的研究已显得越来越重要。本文从随机环境影响因素、混凝土材料的随机热力学参数、随机绝热温升以及混凝土徐变、老化等多种影响方面，对混凝土结构的随机温度以及随机徐变应力目前已有的各种计算方法进行了较为系统的述评，指出了各种方法的适用性以及今后需要解决的问题。

关键词　混凝土结构　温度应力　随机温度场　随机徐变应力　随机有限元

大体积混凝土结构，如重力坝、拱坝等，无论施工期还是运行期，温度的变化对结构的应力状态都有重大影响。对大体积混凝土结构进行仿真计算（包括施工期和运行期），使其温度场、应力场更接近真实状态，是温度应力控制的基础[1~3]。然而，混凝土温度场及温度应力场的仿真计算中存在着诸多的随机性。就温度场的获得而言，首先是边界条件的近似处理；其次是气温、水温和日照影响的随机性，气温往往是按统计资料推算，而水温和日照影响不仅需依据统计资料而且往往需按经验公式进行换算[3]；再次从原材料温度到混凝土出机口温度、浇筑温度的估算，也使混凝土初始温度具有一定的随机性；第四是组成混凝土的材料配合比的随机性引起的混凝土绝热温升的随机性；第五是混凝土热学指标的随机性，包括导热系数 λ，导温系数 α 等，这些参数往往需按半经验半理论的公式换算（如按混凝土各组成成分的重量百分比进行的加权平均法[4]），从而带有统计的色彩。就温度应力场的获得而言，一方面受随机温度场的影响，应力场必然也是随机的；另一方面混凝土材料的力学参数如弹性模量、徐变度等视为随机似乎更为合理。

国外 20 世纪 70 年代起就已着手研究温度应力的随机性。Heller 首先提出了谱密度法[5,6]，并应用于混凝土核反应堆容器[7,8]；随后，在研究了混凝土随机徐变机理的基础上[9~11,33~35]，Tsubaki 和 Bazant 提出了脉冲响应函数法[12,16]；Bazant 等人考虑到环境因素总可描述为正弦分量的线性叠加[12,17]，又进一步提出了计算随机徐变应力的谱分析方法[18,19]，以及与有限元相结合的算法（有限元谱分析法）[20]。为能反映材料参数的随机性，Bazant 等人还利用 Latin 超立方抽样法提出了几种计算方法[21~24]。国外对于非混凝土材料温度场的随机性也进行了一些研究，这些研究主要是针对计算机等精密结构的散热问题，如 Suzuki[25]、Oktay[26] 以及 Shigekazu[27] 的研究，这些研究显然不适用于混凝土材料。文献[27]采用的是随机有限元法，就本文而言尚具有一定的研究价值，文献[25]、[26]的方法则属直接 Monte－Carlo 法，本文不拟多述，我国对于混凝土材料随机温度应力的研究还较少，王同生在美国西北大学访问期间与 Bazant 合作进行过这方面的研究[18~20]，回国后提出了计算混凝土随机温度应力的直接法[28]。笔者则利用随机有限元法进行了混凝土结构随机温度场以及随机徐变应力场的计算[29~32]。但从国内混凝土结构仿真计算的发展趋势可以预言，我国也将日益重视随机温度徐变应力的研究，并出现越

本文选自《力学进展》1998 年第 1 期，作者还有刘宁。

来越多的研究成果。

本文将从随机温度场的计算方法以及随机徐变应力场的计算方法两大方面对现有的各种计算方法进行较为系统的述评,以期既能对感兴趣的学者有所帮助,又能推动国内研究的进一步发展。

1 混凝土结构随机温度场的计算方法

1.1 温度场的定解方法及影响结构温度的随机因素

由热传导理论,温度场 $T(t,x,y,z)$ 为以下定解问题的解

$$\left.\begin{array}{ll}\text{结构内部:} & \partial T/\partial t = a\nabla^2 T + \partial\theta/\partial t \\ \text{初始条件:} & T|_{t=0} = T_0(x,y,z) \\ \text{边界条件:} & \partial T/\partial n|_C = -b(T - T_a)/\lambda\end{array}\right\} \tag{1}$$

式中:a 为导温系数;b 为表面放热系数;λ 为导热系数;T_a 为环境温度;T_0 为初始温度;θ 为 绝热温升。

影响结构温度场的随机因素主要包括:① 边界温度和外部气温(统称环境温度);② 绝热温升 $\theta(t)$;③ 初始温度 T_0 以及混凝土热学参数 a、λ、b。

1.2 谱密度法

如果上述定解方程中不计入混凝土绝热温升,对于一维问题有:$\partial T/\partial t = a\partial^2 T/\partial x^2$。基于环境温度具有周期性的特点,Heller 最先提出了谱密度法[5,6],并用以求解无限厚平板和圆柱结构的随机温度场响应[7,8]。对于无限厚平板,结构的温度场可以表示为

$$T(x,t) = H(\omega,x)T_a(t) \tag{2}$$

式中:$H(\omega,x)$ 为复频响应函数;$T_a(t)$ 为正弦环境温度。

通过分离变量法,可得

$$H(\omega,x) = \exp(-x\sqrt{\omega/2a})(\cos x\sqrt{\omega/2a} - i\sin x\sqrt{\omega/2a}) \tag{3}$$

根据功率谱密度的有关知识,温度场的均方值可以由下式表述[6]

$$E[T^2(x)] = \int_0^\infty |H(\omega,x)|^2 W_0(\omega)\mathrm{d}\omega \tag{4}$$

式中:$W_0(\omega)$ 为 $x = 0$ 处的单边功率谱密度,由此已不难得出温度的方差或标准差。

Heller 的研究为后人提出的有限元谱分析方法和复频响应函数 – 随机有限元法的研究奠定了基础[18~20,29~32]。但从上述可以看出,Heler 的研究还仅局限于周期平稳环境温度影响下结构的一维散热问题,尚未能计及混凝土材料绝热温升和随机材料参数的影响。另外,从数学处理手段来看,对于处于同样条件下的复杂结构,似乎不易得出随机温度场的表达式。

1.3 脉冲响应函数法

针对谱密度法不能考虑结构非平稳温度响应的弱点,Tsubaki 和 Bazant 提出了求解随机温度场的脉冲响应函数法[12,16]。虽然该法最初是用于求解混凝土结构随机湿度场,而湿度场的扩散方程与温度场控制方程是类似的[20,28],该法同样适用于随机温度场的求

解。

仍不计入绝热温升项，对于圆柱结构，温度场控制方程可以写成：$\frac{\partial T}{\partial t} = a\left(\frac{\partial^2 T}{\partial r^2} + \frac{1}{r}\frac{\partial T}{\partial r}\right)$。结构温度场的脉冲响应函数可以写为：$h(r,t) = \frac{1}{2\pi}\int_{-\infty}^{+\infty} H(r,\omega)e^{i\omega t}d\omega$，其中，$H(r,\omega)$ 为复频响应函数，可以由谱密度法得出[5~8]。假设环境温度可以描述为

$$T\mid_C = T_m + \varphi(t) \qquad \varphi(t) = A\exp[i(\omega_0 t + \varphi_0)] \tag{5}$$

式中：T_m 为均值温度；A 为随机变量；$E\{A\} = 0, E\{A^2\} = \sigma_0^2$ （$E\{\cdot\}$ 表示求数学期望）；而 $\varphi(t)$ 的自相关函数可以表示为：$R_{\varphi\varphi} = \sigma_0^2\exp[i\omega_0(t_1 - t_2)]$，当 t_1、$t_2 \geqslant 0$ 时；否则为 0。则温度场的自相关函数可以由下式求出：

$$R_{TT} = \int_{-\infty}^{+\infty} R_{T\varphi}(t_1, t_2 - \tau)h(\tau)d\tau \tag{6}$$

式中：$R_{T\varphi}$ 是 T 与 φ 的互相关函数：$R_{T\varphi} = \int_{-\infty}^{+\infty} R_{\varphi\varphi}(t_1 - \tau, t_2)h(\tau)d\tau$。

从而，结构温度场的标准差已不难得出：$\sigma_T = \sqrt{R_{TT}(t,t)}$。

显然，脉冲响应函数法的优点在于可以考虑环境因素的非平稳效应，该效应由自相关函数反映，并且从后述的随机温度应力的计算方法来看，该法可以考虑混凝土的徐变和老化。但同时我们也不难看出该法仍不能计入混凝土绝热温升的影响，所得温度场仍局限于稳定或准稳定温度场，也无法考虑混凝土材料参数的随机性。另外，对一些实际工程结构，系统的脉冲响应函数往往不易求得[20,28]，这一点极大地限制了脉冲响应函数法的应用。脉冲响应函数法可谓是昙花一现，如何利用数值解法以求出一般结构的离散形式的脉冲响应函数以及进一步将脉冲响应函数法与有限元法相结合，从而可以有效地求解大型复杂结构的随机温度场，还有待于人们进一步研究。

1.4　有限元谱分析法

以上两种方法可以说是针对特殊形式结构的精确求解方法。对于许多实际工程结构，上述方法已不适用，而有限元法早已成为被广泛使用的分析复杂结构的一种数值计算方法。为此，Bazant 和王同生提出了有限元谱分析法，将谱分析法与有限元法有效地结合起来。

由式(1) 表征的温度场控制方程，应用伽辽金变分原理，可以得到结点温度的有限元支配方程

$$\boldsymbol{K}_1\nabla\boldsymbol{T} + \boldsymbol{K}_2\frac{\partial\boldsymbol{T}}{\partial t} + \boldsymbol{F} = 0 \tag{7}$$

式中，$\boldsymbol{K}_1$、$\boldsymbol{K}_2$ 和 $\boldsymbol{F}$ 的表达式可以从许多文献中获得[20,28,36,37]，这里不予列出，仍不计入混凝土绝热温升项，基于环境因素可以描述为若干周期（正弦或余弦）平稳过程叠加的假设，考虑其中任一项的影响，结构经有限元离散后，结点温度列阵可以表示为：$\boldsymbol{T} = \boldsymbol{H}(\omega,t)\exp[i\omega(t - t_0)]$，其中，$\boldsymbol{H}(\omega,t)$ 为结点温度复频响应函数列阵。这里 $\boldsymbol{H}(\omega,t)$ 与时间有关是考虑到用于求解湿度场时，湿度控制方程中水分扩散系数 $a(t)$ 为时间的函数[17~20]。对于温度问题，导温系数 a 一般可以认为是与时间无关的随机变量，$\boldsymbol{H}(\omega,t)$ 可

以退化为 $\boldsymbol{H}(\omega)$,不难得出以下递推公式[20]

$$\left.\begin{aligned}\boldsymbol{K}_a\boldsymbol{H}_{i+1} &= \boldsymbol{K}_b\boldsymbol{H}_i\\ \boldsymbol{K}_a &= (a(t_{i+1/2})\boldsymbol{K}_2 + i\omega\boldsymbol{K}_1)/2 + \boldsymbol{K}_1/\Delta t\\ \boldsymbol{K}_b &= (a(t_{i+1/2})\boldsymbol{K}_2 + i\omega\boldsymbol{K}_1)/2 - \boldsymbol{K}_1/\Delta t\end{aligned}\right\} \tag{8}$$

如果 $a(t)$ 为常量 a,则无需递推公式,有以下的简单计算式

$$(\boldsymbol{K}_1 + i\omega\boldsymbol{K}_2)\boldsymbol{H}(\omega) = \sum_e a\iint_{C_e}\frac{b}{\lambda}\boldsymbol{N}_i\boldsymbol{N}\boldsymbol{A}\,\mathrm{d}s \tag{9}$$

式中:$\boldsymbol{N}$ 为结构整体形函数矩阵;$\boldsymbol{N}_i$ 为单元形函数矩阵;$\boldsymbol{A}$ 的含义同式(5)。

求出各结点的复频响应函数后,各结点温度的方差可由下式求出

$$\mathrm{Var}\{\boldsymbol{T}\} = \mathrm{Var}\{\boldsymbol{A}^{\mathrm{T}}\}\,|\,\boldsymbol{H}(\omega,t)\,|^2 \tag{10}$$

式中:$\mathrm{Var}\{\cdot\}$ 表示求方差;$|\cdot|$ 表示求模。

有限元谱分析法对于求解实际工程中混凝土结构的随机湿度场已较有效,但湿度场控制方程中不存在相应于温度场控制方程中的绝热温升项。因此,该法不适用于混凝土施工前期结构的随机温度场计算,且该法仍未考虑混凝土材料热学参数的随机性。

1.5 随机有限元法

随机有限元法经过近 20 年的发展,目前已成为分析结构随机性的强有力的工具[38~41],该法尤其适用于考虑材料参数的随机性。因此,针对前述方法均不易考虑材料热学参数随机性的特点,人们自然联想到利用随机有限元法求解结构的随机温度场。

1.5.1 不计入环境温度及热源放热的随机过程特性

Shigekazu 等人最先提出估算结构随机温度场的随机有限元法[27]。该法的主要过程如下:根据由 Galerkin 有限元法得出的温度场有限元支配方程,采用偏微分法[41,42],可得以下灵敏度方程

$$\partial\boldsymbol{T}/\partial P_k = \boldsymbol{J}(\boldsymbol{T}_0)\partial\boldsymbol{R}/\partial P_k \tag{11}$$

式中:$\boldsymbol{J}(\boldsymbol{T}_0)$ 为 Jacobi 矩阵;$\boldsymbol{T}_0$ 为参照值温度场;P_k 为温度场控制参数(随机变量),而 $\boldsymbol{R}$ 的任一元素 R_i 可写为

$$\begin{aligned}R_i = {}& a\iiint_\Omega\left(\frac{\partial N_i}{\partial x}\frac{\partial N_j}{\partial x} + \frac{\partial N_i}{\partial y}\frac{\partial N_j}{\partial y} + \frac{\partial N_i}{\partial z}\frac{\partial N_j}{\partial z}\right)T_j\,\mathrm{d}x\mathrm{d}y\mathrm{d}z - {}\\ &\iiint_\Omega QN_i\,\mathrm{d}x\mathrm{d}y\mathrm{d}z + \iint_S qN_i\,\mathrm{d}s\end{aligned} \tag{12}$$

式中:$q = \partial Q/\partial t$,$Q$ 为热源放热量。忽略二阶以至更高项,有:$\boldsymbol{T} \approx \overline{\boldsymbol{T}} + \sum_{k=1}^{n}(\partial\boldsymbol{T}/\partial P_k)\Delta P_k$,其中,$n$ 为随机变量总数。于是 $\boldsymbol{T}$ 的任一元素 T_i 的方差可由下式获得

$$\mathrm{Var}\{T_i\} \approx \sum_{k=1}^{n}(\partial\boldsymbol{T}/\partial P_k)\mathrm{Var}\{P_k\} \tag{13}$$

不难看出,Shigekazu 提出的随机有限元法直观明了,可以考虑材料热学参数的随机性,也计入了热源放热项,可以用于大型复杂结构,有一定的实用价值。但同时也可看出,该法存在两点不足:① 材料参数的随机性往往以随机场的形式出现[40,43,44],该法显然未将材料参数描述为随机场,而只是简单地以随机变量表示;② 该法似乎未能考虑热源放

热的随机性以及随机环境温度的影响,这也正是直接偏微分法的弱点所在。如果说 1.2 ~ 1.4 中所述方法是得了“鱼”而不能得到“熊掌”,那么 Shigekazu 的方法对于混凝土结构而言可谓是得了“熊掌”而舍了“鱼”。当然,对于计算机结构,也许根本没有“鱼”或者“鱼”太小而不值得一取,如果这样,Shigekazu 的方法也应是无可厚非。

1.5.2 考虑环境温度及热源放热的随机过程特性

为试图既能反映材料热学参数的随机性,又能考虑环境温度及热源放热随机过程特性的影响,笔者在文献[29]中给出了可以反映材料参数随机性的基于随机场局部平均的温度场随机变分原理和相应的随机有限元列式,对于环境温度和混凝土绝热温升随机过程特性的影响,文献[29]利用定解问题的叠加原理,将温度场定解问题分离为随机环境温度定解问题 Ⅰ 和随机绝热温升定解问题 Ⅱ,然后再分别进行求解。

(1) 随机环境温度定解问题 Ⅰ

$$\left.\begin{aligned} &\frac{\partial T_1}{\partial t} = a\nabla^2 T_1 + \frac{\partial \theta}{\partial t} \\ &T_1\Big|_{t=0} = T_0(x,y,z) \\ &\frac{\partial T_1}{\partial n}\Big|_C + \frac{b}{\lambda}T_1\Big|_C = \frac{b}{\lambda}T_a(t) \end{aligned}\right\} \tag{14}$$

考虑到环境温度 $T_a(t)$ 总可以近似地表示为:$T_a(t) = T_m + \sum_{i=1}^{na} T_{ai}(t)$,其中 T_m 为随机变量,$T_{ai}(t)(i = 1,\cdots,na)$ 为周期平稳随机过程(余弦过程或正弦过程)[29],na 为环境温度种类数,式(14)可以进一步分为以下两部分。

a) 定解问题 $Ⅰ^{(0)}$

$$\frac{\partial T_1^{(0)}}{\partial t} = a\nabla^2 T_1^{(0)} + \frac{\partial \theta}{\partial t},\quad T_1^{(0)}\Big|_{t=0} = T_0(x,y,z),\quad \frac{\partial T_1^{(0)}}{\partial n}\Big|_C + \frac{b}{\lambda}T_1^{(0)}\Big|_C = \frac{b}{\lambda}T_m \tag{15}$$

可以看出,此定解问题不包含随机过程影响量。根据随机场局部平均的随机有限元法[40,41,44],已不难得出相应的随机温度场。

b) 定解问题 $Ⅰ^{(i)}(i = 1,\cdots,na)$

$$\frac{\partial T_1^{(i)}}{\partial t} = a\nabla^2 T_1^{(i)} + \frac{\partial \theta}{\partial t},\quad T_1^{(i)}\Big|_{t=0} = 0,\quad \frac{\partial T_1^{(i)}}{\partial n}\Big|_C + \frac{b}{\lambda}T_1^{(i)}\Big|_C = \frac{b}{\lambda}T_{ai}(t) \tag{16}$$

由于上式中 $T_{ai}(t)$ 具有周期平稳性,因而有采用复频响应函数法的可能。常规的复频响应函数法中复频响应函数为确定性函数,为能反映材料参数随机性的影响,可视复频响应函数为材料参数的随机函数,由随机有限元方法获得复频响应函数的统计特性,故可称之为复频响应函数 - 随机有限元法(CFRF - SFEM)[29]。其一次方程为

$$(\overline{\boldsymbol{K}}_1 + i\omega\overline{\boldsymbol{K}}_2)\boldsymbol{H}'_k(\omega) = \boldsymbol{F}'_k \quad (k = 1,2,\cdots,n) \tag{17}$$

式中:$\boldsymbol{K}_1$、$\boldsymbol{K}_2$ 以及 $\boldsymbol{F}'_k$ 的表达式可参见文献[29],符号(′)表示求偏导(以下皆同),下标 k 表示对第 k 个随机变量。求出 $\boldsymbol{H}'_k(\omega)(k = 1,2,\cdots,n)$ 后,相应的随机温度场的方差可写为

$$\mathrm{Var}(T^{(i)}) = \sum_{k=1}^{n} |H_k^{(i)'}(\omega)|^2 \mathrm{Var}(X_k) \quad (i = 1,\cdots,NP) \tag{18}$$

式中:NP 为有限元结点总数;上标(i)表示第 i 结点;$|\cdot|$ 表示求模;X_k 表示第k 个随机变量。

可以看出,CFRF－SFEM 有效地克服了谱密度法、有限元谱分析法等不能考虑随机材料热学参数的局限性。需进一步指出的是,对于不考虑材料参数随机性,只需考虑随机环境温度影响的情形,有限元谱分析法最终通过直接法获得结构温度场的方差[20,28],而 CFRF－SFEM 仍视复频响应函数为随机函数(随机环境温度参数的函数,如式(5)中随机幅值 A 的函数),然后由式(18)求出方差。诚然,此时 CFRF－SFEM 与有限元谱分析法得出的是同一结果,有“杀鸡用牛刀”之嫌,但在概念上两者有本质的区别。

(2) 随机绝热温升定解问题 Ⅱ

$$\frac{\partial \Delta T_2}{\partial t} = a\nabla^2(\Delta T_2) + \frac{\partial \Delta\theta}{\partial t},\quad \Delta T_2\Big|_{t=0} = 0,\quad \frac{\partial \Delta T_2}{\partial n}\Big|_C + \frac{b}{\lambda}\nabla T_2\Big|_C = 0 \tag{19}$$

式中:绝热温升 $\theta(t)$ 的形式可取为 $\theta = \theta_0[1 - \exp(-m_1 t)]$,其中 θ_0、m_1 为随机变量。

式(1)中只需用到 $\partial\theta/\partial t = \theta_0 m_1 \exp(-m_1 t)$,显然 $\partial\theta/\partial t$ 为一非平稳随机过程。由于对于激励为非平稳时响应的计算十分复杂,尤其是对于需用有限元离散的大型复杂结构,目前还未出现成熟的解法,因此需对 $\partial\theta/\partial t$ 作一定的简化处理

$$\frac{\partial\theta}{\partial t} = \frac{\partial\bar{\theta}}{\partial t} + \frac{\partial\Delta\theta}{\partial t} \tag{20}$$

而

$$\frac{\partial\bar{\theta}}{\partial t} \approx \bar{\theta}_0\bar{m}_1\exp(-\bar{m}_1 t) \qquad \frac{\partial\Delta\theta}{\partial t} \approx \bar{m}_1\exp(-\bar{m}_1 t)\Delta\theta_0 + (\bar{\theta}_0 - \bar{\theta}_0\bar{m}_1 t)\exp(-\bar{m}_1 t)\Delta m_1 \tag{21}$$

从而式(19)中 $\partial\Delta\theta/\partial t$ 可近似地用式(21)代替,如此不难得出式(19)所对应的随机有限元一次方程[29]

$$\bar{\boldsymbol{K}}_1\Delta\boldsymbol{T}'_{2k} + \bar{\boldsymbol{K}}_2\frac{\partial\Delta\boldsymbol{T}'_{2k}}{\partial t} + \Delta\boldsymbol{F}'_k = 0 \tag{22}$$

于是相应的温度场的方差为

$$\mathrm{Var}\{\Delta T_2^{(i)}\} = \sum_{k=1}^{n}\Delta T_{2k}^{(i)'}\mathrm{Var}(X_i) \tag{23}$$

最终整体温度场的方差可以由以上三部分结果叠加获得。

文献[29]提出的方法已基本上较圆满地解决了混凝土结构随机温度场的计算问题。当然,式(20)、式(21)的处理具有一定的近似性,不易反映出绝热温升过程的自相关特性,不过总体上已能满足实际工程如重力坝、拱坝等的需要。如何直接针对绝热温升的非平稳特性,将结构随机振动分析中脉冲响应函数法[46]有效地与随机有限元法相结合,是笔者将要进一步研究的课题之一。

2 随机温度场影响下混凝土结构随机徐变应力的计算方法

影响混凝土结构徐变应力的随机因素可以分为以下三种:① 随机温度场;② 材料力学参数的随机性,包括随机弹性模量和随机徐变参数;③ 徐变模型的不确定性,由于缺乏

足够的试验资料,目前国际上尚不考虑徐变模型的不确定性[23,24],亦即只针对某一固定形式的徐变模型进行随机徐变应力的研究。

从确定性分析的理论模型来看,徐变应力分析的理论方法主要有[47,48]:① 有效弹模法;② 龄期调整有效弹模法;③ 徐变率法;④ 流动率法;⑤ 叠加法。徐变应力的确定性分析不是本文研究的重点,这里不拟多述。只需指出的是,计算随机徐变应力时,目前采用的方法主要是龄期调整有效弹模法、徐变率法和叠加法。

从确定性分析的数值方法来看,如果直接应用上述几种理论方法进行结构徐变应力的计算,只能得出简单形式结构的理论解,而对于复杂结构则需通过数值计算的方法来解决。到目前为止,比较满意的计算方法主要有三个[48]:① 松弛系数法;② 初应力法;③ 初应变法。目前国外还基本上利用松弛系数法进行随机徐变应力的分析[23],我国则偏重于使用初应变法[36,37],并已应用于许多大型实际工程[3],取得了许多宝贵的经验。笔者也因此在文献[31]、[32] 中利用初应变法结合随机有限元对大体积混凝土结构的随机徐变应力进行了研究。

从随机徐变应力的分析方法来看,目前已有的方法可以归纳为以下几种:① 谱密度法[5~8];② 脉冲响应函数法[12,16];③ 有限元谱分析法[18,20~24,28,49,50],如果从是否考虑结构温度随机过程和随机材料力学参数的影响,该法又可分为直接法[20,28](只考虑结构温度随机过程的影响,不考虑随机材料力学参数的影响)、抽样法(包括点估计法[49,50]、Latin 超立方抽样法[24] 及其改进[21,22],可考虑随机材料力学参数的影响,但结构温度为常量或为与时间无关的随机变量,不能为随机过程[23])以及综合法[23](两者都能考虑);④ 随机有限元法[31,32]。其中谱密度法不能考虑混凝土的徐变和老化特性[5~8],只能计算混凝土的随机弹性温度应力,因此本文不拟对谱密度法作进一步阐述,以下将对其余几种方法进行研究。

2.1 随机温度徐变应力计算的脉冲响应函数法

计算出随机温度场之后,Tsubaki 和 Bazant 进一步提出了随机徐变应力计算的脉冲响应函数法[12,16]。由松弛系数法[4,36,47,48],结构的徐变应力可以写为[12]

$$\left.\begin{aligned} s_{ij} &= \frac{1}{1+\mu}\left[E_C(t)e_{ij} - \int_0^t \frac{\partial E_R(t,\tau)}{\partial \tau} e_{ij}(\tau)\mathrm{d}\tau\right] \\ \sigma_{kk} &= \frac{1}{1-2\mu}\left[E_C(t)\varepsilon_{kk}(t) - \int_0^t \frac{\partial E_R(t,\tau)}{\partial \tau} \varepsilon_{kk}\mathrm{d}\tau\right] \end{aligned}\right\} \tag{24}$$

式中:s_{ij} 为应力偏量;σ_{kk} 为正应力;$E_C(t)$ 为混凝土弹模;$E_R(t,\tau)$ 为混凝土松弛函数;e_{ij} 为应变偏量;ε_{kk} 为正应变。温度对应力的影响通过应变由式(24)反映,将温度脉冲响应函数代入上式;不难得出应力脉冲响应函数 $h_j(\tau)\quad(j=x,y,z)$,于是应力的自相关函数可以写为

$$\left.\begin{aligned} R_{jj}(t_1,t_2) &= \int_{-\infty}^{+\infty} R_{j\varphi}(t_1,t_2-\tau)h_j(\tau)\mathrm{d}\tau \\ R_{j\varphi}(t_1,t_2) &= \int_{-\infty}^{+\infty} R_{\varphi\varphi}(t_1-\tau,t_2)h_j(\tau)\mathrm{d}\tau \end{aligned}\right\} \quad (j=x,y,z) \tag{25}$$

对于中空无限长圆柱结构,上式可进一步简化为以下形式[12]

$$R_{jj}(t_1,t_2) = \sigma_0^2\exp[i\omega(t_1 - t_2)]P_j(r,t_1)P_j^*(r,t_2) \tag{26}$$

式中：σ_0 为环境温度幅值的标准差；符号($*$)表示求共轭。

于是徐变应力的标准差为：$\sigma_j = \sigma_0 | P_j(r,t) |$，只要给出松弛函数 $E_R(t,\tau)$ 的表达式，按上述方法可以获得随机徐变应力的精确解，且可以直接针对结构温度的非平稳特性进行计算，可以方便地考虑混凝土材料的徐变和老化。但是仍需看到，这一方法的实现需基于两个条件：第一，结构的脉冲响应函数可以求出，对于某些简单结构(如中空圆柱)，脉冲响应函数兴许还能求出，但对大多数实际工程结构，这一点却很难做到；第二，该法目前还只能基于徐变应力计算的松弛系数法，对于数值计算来说，松弛系数法需记忆应力历史[4,36]，因而会消耗较大的计算机容量，对于大型结构，松弛系数法几乎难以采用。

2.2 随机温度徐变应力计算的有限元谱分析法

继脉冲响应函数法提出之后，Bazant 等人又进一步提出了有限元谱分析法，有限元的引入，无疑使分析大型复杂结构的随机徐变应力成为可能。

2.2.1 直接法

该法由 Bazant 和王同生提出[17,18,20]，王同生在文献[28]中进一步阐述了该法的思想及其优越性。设系统的复数形式输入为 $I(\omega,t,t_0) = A\bar{I}(\omega,t,t_0)$，相应的复数形式输出为 $O(\omega,x_k,t,t_0) = A\overline{O}(\omega,x_k,t,t_0)$，其中 A 为随机变量(一般为环境温度的随机幅值)，x_k 为位置坐标。根据复数随机过程原理[51]，系统输出的自相关函数则为：$R_0(\omega,x_k,t_1,t_2) = E\{A^2\}\overline{O}(\omega,x_k,t_1,t_0)\overline{O}^*(\omega,x_k,t_2,t_0)$，($*$)表示求共轭。如果随机变量 A 的标准差为σ_I，则输出的标准差为 $\sigma_0 = \sigma_I\left|\overline{O}(\omega,x_k,t,t_0)\right|$。因此，该法只要求得复数输出，即可直接计算出输出的标准差，故称之为直接法[28]。

有限元支配方程为

$$\left.\begin{aligned} &\boldsymbol{K}u = \boldsymbol{F} \\ &\boldsymbol{F} = \sum_e\int_{\Omega_e}\boldsymbol{B}^{\mathrm{T}}\boldsymbol{D}\varepsilon_T\mathrm{d}\Omega, \quad \varepsilon_T = \alpha\boldsymbol{T}[1,1,1,0,0,0]^{\mathrm{T}} \\ &\sigma^e = \boldsymbol{DB}u - \boldsymbol{D}\varepsilon_T \end{aligned}\right\} \tag{27}$$

式中：σ^e 为弹性应力；$\boldsymbol{D}$ 为应变－应力弹性矩阵；$\boldsymbol{B}$ 为形变矩阵；α 为温度线胀系数；$\boldsymbol{T}$ 为结点温度场列阵。

将按 1.4 中方法得出的随机温度(复数)代入上式，可以得到 σ^e 的复数输出。根据松弛系数法，可以写出徐变应力(复数)为

$$\sigma_{(i)} = \sum_{j=1}^{i-1}\frac{1}{E_C(t_{j+1/2})}R(t_j,t_{j+1/2})(\sigma^e_{(j+1)} - \sigma^e_{(i)}) \tag{28}$$

式中：$R(\cdot)$ 为松弛函数；下标(i)表示第 i 时段；下标($j+1/2$)表示时段(t_j,t_{j+1})的中点。由上式再通过直接法，可以得出徐变应力的方差。

由上述可知，Bazant 等人提出的有限元谱分析直接法对随机徐变分析的理论方法有所突破，即有效地考虑了混凝土材料的徐变和老化特性，将谱密度法与有限元法有机地结合在一起。但该法计算徐变应力时仍基于松弛系数法，徐变模型采用的是基于 Maxwell 链的徐变率模型(Rate－type Model)，此模型的关键是松弛时间 τ_u 的确定，τ_u 无法根据试验

确定,只能事先人为给定[10,17]。我国一般采用线性叠加模型[4,36],而不采用徐变率模型。另外,该法还仅局限于周期平稳环境影响因素作用下的随机徐变应力分析。事实上,施工期中的混凝土结构在随机绝热温升的影响下,内部温度已成为一非平稳随机过程。显然,此时该法已不适用。再者,该法仍未考虑材料参数如混凝土弹模和徐变参数的随机性。

2.2.2 Latin 超立方抽样法(Latin Hypercube Sampling Method)

为能反映材料参数的随机性,最易想到的方法自然是 Monte - Carlo 直接抽样法,但该法因工作量太大而难以被人采纳。Madsen 等人于 1983 年提出了计算随机徐变应力的点估计法[50],该法在抽样时对每个随机参数 x_i 用 $\overline{x}_i \pm \Delta x_i$($\Delta x_i$ 为 x_i 的标准差)来表征所有参数的组合,需进行确定性计算的抽样次数显然应为 2^n(n 为随机参数总数)。如果需考虑的随机参数较多,或者每一次确定性计算的工作量较大,点估计法的工作量也是十分可观的[23]。

Latin 超立方抽样法(简称 LHS 法)是对分层抽样法[52]的改进,该法的基本思想是将每一个随机参数的分布函数在概率上 N 等份,即每一等份都具有相同的概率 $1/N$,每一次确定性计算都严格保证在每一等份内抽样一次。如果随机参数有 n 个,对于一般问题只需进行 N 次确定性计算。

Bazant 和 Liu 在文献[24]中将 LHS 法引入随机徐变应力的计算,徐变应力计算采用龄期调整有效弹模法[53],采用此方法可使徐变应力在弹性应力计算出后很快地求出,效率较高。随机徐变应力的计算结果表明,取 $N = 2n$ 时可满足精度要求。

显然,LHS 法比点估计法的效率要高得多,且较易考虑材料的非线性效应[24]。然而,需指出的是,由于 LHS 法只是单纯地对随机参数进行抽样,因而不易反映结构温度随机过程特性的影响,结构内部的温度只能为常量,或至多为与时间无关的随机变量[23],且 LHS 法无法考虑随机参数之间的相关性;第二,LHS 法仍属于统计法的范畴,$2n$ 次确定性计算的工作量对于大型复杂结构(如重力坝、拱坝)仿真计算而言,也是十分庞大的,有时甚至是不可能的;再者,文献[24]采用了龄期调整有效弹模法,当然效率较高。然而,业已证明龄期调整有效弹模法只在三种特殊情况下可以给出较好的结果[27,48]:① 应力为常量(徐变试验);② 应变为常量(松弛试验);③ 应变为 $\varepsilon_1\varphi(t,\tau)$,其中 ε_1 为常量,$\varphi(t,\tau)$ 为徐变系数。而实际情况并不止以上三种。

2.2.3 综合法

为能考虑随机参数间的相关性,Bazant 和 Xi 又提出了联合抽样技术[21,22],该技术可以说是 LHS 法的改进。关于改进的 LHS 法,这里不打算多述,只需指出的是,该法仍无法考虑环境温度随机过程的影响。为此,Bazant 和 Xi 于 1993 年进一步提出了综合法[23],并认为该法已较圆满地解决了混凝土结构随机徐变应力的计算问题。

综合法实际上是有限元谱分析的直接法与改进的 LHS 法的结合,该法将随机环境因素(可以是随机湿度或温度)分成以下几部分:

$$T_a(t) = \overline{T}_a(t) + T_1\cos(\omega_1 t + \varphi_1) + T_2\cos(\omega_2 t + \varphi_2) + A_n W(t,\tau_n) \tag{29}$$

式中:$\overline{T}_a(t)$ 为均值过程;$T_1\cos(\omega_1 t + \varphi_1)$ 为日变化温度;$T_2\cos(\omega_2 t + \varphi_2)$ 为年变化温度;其中 T_1、T_2、φ_1 和 φ_2 均为随机变量,文献[23]称之为随机相位过程;$A_n W(t,\tau_n)$ 为

Poisson 方波过程;A_n 为零均值随机变量,而当 $\tau_n \leqslant t \leqslant \tau_{n+1}$ 时,$W(t,\tau_n) = 1$,否则 $W(t,\tau_n) = 0$,其中 $n = 1,2,\cdots,N(t)$,$N(t)$ 为具有集度为 λ 的 Poisson 过程。

根据线性徐变假定,式(29)各部分的影响可以通过响应的线性叠加获得。

由前所述的有限元谱分析的直接法不难得出 φ_1、φ_2 确定时,$T_1\cos(\omega_1 t + \varphi_1) + T_2\cos(\omega_2 t + \varphi_2)$ 产生的随机响应,随机参数 φ_1、φ_2 和 A_n 的影响可以通过改进的 LHS 法求出。其中,Poisson 方波过程 $A_n W(t,\tau_n)$ 作用下的徐变应力可以写为

$$\sigma(t) = \sum_{n=1}^{N(t)} Y_n^* W(t-\tau) \quad \tau = t_0 + \tau_n \tag{30}$$

式中:$W(t-\tau)$ 为阶梯函数:当 $t-\tau > 0$ 时,$W(t-\tau) = 1$;否则为 0。而

$$Y_n^* = Y_n R(t,\tau)/E_C(\tau) \tag{31}$$

式中:$R(t,\tau)$ 为松弛函数;$E_C(\tau)$ 为 τ 时刻的弹模;Y_n 为温度脉冲响应弹性应力。

式(30)所示的实际上是过滤 Poisson 过程[54],不难得出徐变应力的均值和方差为

$$\left.\begin{aligned} \mu_\sigma(t) &= \int_0^t E\{Y^* W(t-\tau)\}\lambda \mathrm{d}\tau = \lambda\int_0^t E\{Y\}\frac{R(t,\tau)}{E_C(\tau)}W(t-\tau)\mathrm{d}\tau \\ \mathrm{Var}\{\sigma(t)\} &= \int_0^t E\{Y^{*2} W^2(t-\tau)\}\lambda \mathrm{d}\tau = \lambda\int_0^t E\{Y^2\}\frac{R^2(t,\tau)}{E_C^2(\tau)}W^2(t-\tau)\mathrm{d}\tau \end{aligned}\right\} \tag{32}$$

通过将环境影响因素的分离,以及将有限元谱分析的直接法与改进的 LHS 法的有机结合,综合法的确已能较客观地反映出多种随机因素的影响,也能针对一些工程进行较为有效的计算。对于工程量不大,有限元离散后单元或结点不多,运行期或施工后期的混凝土结构,笔者认为该法是首选的方法之一。然而,综合法并非璧玉无瑕,仍存在以下不足之处:① 仍未考虑混凝土绝热温升的影响,当然,对于随机湿度应力问题,不存在相应于温度的绝热温升项;② 该法仍采用松弛系数法进行徐变应力的计算,对于大型工程结构,该法的使用必然受到一定程度的限制;③ 对于部分随机参数仍需由抽样技术反映出结构的随机响应,计算效率必然受到影响,改进的 LHS 法在能反映出随机参数相关性的同时,无形中又增加了工作量。如何进一步减少工作量是综合法需要解决的问题,笔者将拭目以待。

2.3 随机徐变应力计算的随机有限元法

当材料参数可描述为随机变量或随机场时,随机有限元法具有其独特的优越性[40,43,44]。然而,目前利用随机有限元法求解随机激励(往往需描述为随机过程甚至随机场和随机过程的结合[46])作用下随机结构的随机响应尚有一定的困难。朱位秋曾提出随机振动问题中孤立特征值和重特征值的随机有限元法[46],但他指出,该法只适用于时间 $t < 4\pi/\omega_0$ 的情况,此后偏差越来越大,尤其是对方差。对此问题,目前还未找到有效的解决办法。

为此,笔者在文献[30 ~ 32]中,基于线性徐变假定,将随机温度场分为三部分,然后再分别针对这三部分进行研究。以 $\boldsymbol{T}$ 表示有限元离散后结构整体温度场列阵,有 $\boldsymbol{T} = \boldsymbol{T}_1 + \boldsymbol{T}_2 + \boldsymbol{T}_3$,式中 $\boldsymbol{T}_1$、$\boldsymbol{T}_2$ 和 $\boldsymbol{T}_3$ 分别由 1.5.2 中定解问题 Ⅰ$^{(0)}$(式(15))、Ⅰ$^{(i)}$($i = 1,\cdots,na$)(式(16))以及定解问题 Ⅱ(式 19))决定。由 1.5.2 可知,$\boldsymbol{T}_1$ 的随机性部分为稳定

温度场，而不稳定部分由均值绝热温升产生，因而无需考虑温度场随机过程特性的影响；第二部分 $\boldsymbol{T}_2$ 为周期平稳随机温度场，因此可以针对温度场周期变化的特点加以研究；$\boldsymbol{T}_3$ 为一般非平稳随机温度场，文献[31] 对此作了一定的简化处理。

2.3.1 初应变随机有限元的隐式解法

目前，我国对混凝土结构徐变应力的计算通常采用基于叠加模型的初应变隐式解法[3,36,37]。基于这一方法，在每一时段 (t_{n-1},t_n) 内，应变增量应写为

$$\Delta\varepsilon_n = \Delta\varepsilon_n^{(1)} + \Delta\varepsilon_n^{(2)} + \Delta\varepsilon_n^{(3)} \tag{33}$$

式中：$\Delta\varepsilon_n^{(1)} = \Delta\varepsilon_n^e + \Delta\varepsilon_n^{(C1)} + \Delta\varepsilon_n^{(T_1)} + \Delta\varepsilon_n^O$；$\Delta\varepsilon_n^{(2)} = \Delta\varepsilon_n^{(C2)} + \Delta\varepsilon_n^{(T2)}$；$\Delta\varepsilon_n^{(3)} = \Delta\varepsilon_n^{(C3)} + \Delta\varepsilon_n^{(T3)}$；其中，$\Delta\varepsilon_n^3$ 为弹性应变增量；$\Delta\varepsilon_n^O$ 为体积应变增量；$\Delta\varepsilon_n^{(C1)}$ 为外荷载以及 $\boldsymbol{T}_1$ 引起的温度荷载共同作用产生的徐变应变增量；$\Delta\varepsilon_n^{(C2)}$ 和 $\Delta\varepsilon_n^{(C3)}$ 分别为周期平稳温度场 $\boldsymbol{T}_2$ 和非平稳绝热温升温度场 $\boldsymbol{T}_3$ 引起的温度荷载分别作用产生的徐变应变增量；$\Delta\varepsilon_n^{(T1)}$、$\Delta\varepsilon_n^{(T2)}$、$\Delta\varepsilon_n^{(T3)}$ 分别为 $\boldsymbol{T}_1$、$\boldsymbol{T}_2$、$\boldsymbol{T}_3$ 产生的温度应变增量；应力增量也可写成相应的形式。

由初应变隐式解法的有关公式，不难得出相应的一次摄动随机有限元列式。由此列式，可直接计算出 $\boldsymbol{T}_1$ 引起的结构随机温度徐变应力。

2.3.2 复频响应函数 - 随机有限元法

文献[4] 给出了简谐荷载作用下混凝土结构徐变应力的计算方法。然而，该法要求混凝土为晚龄期混凝土。由于施工期混凝土弹模随时间变化，该法已不适用。文献[32] 利用复频响应函数法，考虑混凝土的时变特性，采用类似于文献[4] 的推导方法，给出了简谐温度场作用下混凝土徐变应力的递推计算方法 —— 复模量隐式解法；之后，再考虑各种随机因素，视复频响应函数为随机函数，给出相应的复频响应函数 - 随机有限元列式，使周期平稳随机温度场作用下的随机徐变应力问题得以解决。

2.3.3 非平稳温度场的简化处理及相应的随机有限元法

文献[55] 曾提出了非平稳随机过程逐段平稳叠加的双参数法，对于徐变应力的计算，时段 $(t_i,t_{i+1})(i=1,2,\cdots)$ 不会太长，文献[31] 引入该法参数调幅的思想，对非平稳随机温度场 T_3(温度场的第三部分) 作以下的逐段简化处理：$T_3(t)\approx x_1^{\mathrm{T}}(t)\boldsymbol{IT}_3(t_1)$，当 $t_1\leqslant t<t_2$ 时；…；$\boldsymbol{T}_3(t)\approx x_n^{\mathrm{T}}(t)\boldsymbol{IT}_3(t_n)$，当 $t_n\leqslant t<t_{n+1}$ 时。其中，NP 为结点总数，$\boldsymbol{I}$ 为单位矩阵，$x_n^{(i)}(t)$ 为一确定性函数，上标 $(i)(i=1,2,\cdots,NP)$ 表示第 (i) 结点，对给定的时刻 t，$\boldsymbol{T}_3^{(i)}(t)(i=1,2,\cdots,NP)$ 为一随机变量。$x_n^{(i)}(t)$ 可通过 $\boldsymbol{T}_3^{(i)}(t)$ 的一阶和二阶矩获得[31]。上述简化方法使 $\boldsymbol{T}_3(t)$ 在每一时段内仍为非平稳随机过程，可保证原非平稳随机过程逐点方差的准确性，且可轻松地反映 $\boldsymbol{T}_3$ 在时间和空间上的相关性[31]。如此已不难得出相应的随机有限元列式。

从总体来看，文献[30～32]提出的随机有限元法已基本上解决了实际工程的需要，可用以计算随机环境温度、随机绝热温升以及随机材料参数影响下大型复杂结构的随机温度徐变应力，计算效率较高，且可方便地考虑各参数间的相关性。不过该法是通过对非平稳过程的简化处理，回避了直接针对随机激励作用下采用随机有限元法可能遇到的困难，不可否认具有一定的近似性。另外，在考虑随机温度场时，未计入除周期平稳项外还可能出现的“随机噪声”项[23]（这一项因目前缺乏足够的实测资料尚不能考虑）。以上这两点

问题包括随机有限元法在随机振动问题中的进一步应用,都是笔者十分感兴趣的问题,今后将进一步研究。

3 结语

混凝土结构随机温度以及随机徐变应力的研究,因其重要性日益为越来越多的人所重视。笔者对一典型重力坝的计算结果表明,结构内部温度标准差的最大值可达4℃,徐变应力标准差的最大值约为0.25MPa。从本文所讨论的方法来看,计算随机温度场时,如果是在混凝土后期,无需考虑混凝土水化热影响,环境温度可以分离为若干周期平稳随机过程的叠加,且无需考虑材料参数的随机性时,有限元谱分析法中的直接法是值得推荐的方法,当然这种情况下,复频响应函数-随机有限元法也是有效的方法,但有“杀鸡用牛刀”之嫌。如果假设环境影响因素还包括噪声项,且需考虑材料参数的随机性时,对于工程量不大的结构,综合法是首选的方法。考虑混凝土水化热的影响,且需考虑材料参数的随机性时,经对绝热温升过程简化处理的随机有限元法是惟一可以选用的方法。

今后需要解决的课题是:①进一步提高综合法的效率,使之能适用于大型结构工程;②采集足够的实测数据,研究出可以反映环境因素中噪声项影响的随机有限元法;③直接针对混凝土绝热温升的随机过程特性,研究出相应的随机有限元法。

参考文献

[1] 王国秉,孙计平. 水工混凝土结构温度场与温度徐变应力的三维有限元分析. 水力发电,1988(7):6~12

[2] 李广远,赵代深,柏承新. 碾压混凝土坝温度场与应力场全过程的仿真计算和研究. 水利学报,1991(10):60~69

[3] 刘志辉. 碾压混凝土拱坝累计温度场和仿真应力场的研究. 清华大学硕士学位论文,1994

[4] 朱伯芳,等. 水工混凝土结构温度应力与温度控制. 北京:水利电力出版社,1976

[5] Heller R A. *Temperature response of an infinitely thick slab to random surface temperature*. Mech. Research Communication, 1976 3(2): 379~385

[6] Heller R A. *Thermal stress as an narrow-band random load*. ASCE, J. of Engrg., 1976 102(5):787~805

[7] Heller R A, Kamat M P, Singh M P. *Probability of solid-propellant motor failure due to environmental temperatures*. J. of Spacecrafts and Rockets (AIAA), 1979, 16: 140~146

[8] Singh M P, Heller R A. *Random thermal stress in nuclear containents*. In: Proc. ASCE Special Conf. on Probabilistic Mech. and Structure Reliability, Ed. by Ang and Shinozuka, Tucson, Ariz, Jan, 10~12, 1978. 16~19

[9] Bazant Z P, Wu S T. *Creep and shrinkage law for concrete at variable humidity*. J. of Engng. Mech., ASCE, 1974, 100(3): 1183~1209

[10] Bazant Z P, Wu S T. *Rate-type creep law of aging concrete based on Maxwell chain*. Mat. and Struct., 1974, 37(7):45~60

[11] Reinhardt H W, Pat M G M, Wittmann F H. *Variability of creep and shrinkage of concrete*. Int. Sym. on Fundamental Research on Creep and Shrinkage of Concretes, Lausanne: 1980. 79~93

[12] Tsubaki T , Bazant Z P. *Random shrinkage stresses in aging viscoelastic vessel*. ASCE, J. of Engng. Mech. ,1982,108(3):527～545
[13] Bazant Z P. *Mathematical models for creep and shrinkage of concrete*. In: Bazant Z P and Wittmann F H eds. Creep and Shrinkage in Concrete Structures. New York: John Willey and Sons, 1982. 163～258
[14] Bazant Z P. *Probabilistic problems in prediction of creep and shrinkage effects in structures*. In: Proc. of 4th Int. Conf. on Application of Statistics and Probability in Soil and Structural Engng. ,Florence, Italy, 1983. 325～356
[15] Cornelissen H. *Creep on concrete—a stochastic quantity*. Int. Sym. on Fundamental Research on Creep and Shrinkage of Concrets, Lausanne, 1980. 95～110
[16] Tsubaki T, et al.. *Probabilistic models*. IN: Bazant, John Willey and Sons, eds. Mathematical Modeling of Creep and Shrinkage of Concrete. London, England, 1988
[17] Bazant Z P , Wang T S. *Algorithm for aging viscoelastic structures under periodic load*. J. of Engrg. Mech. , ASCE, 1984,110(6): 972～985
[18] Bazant Z P , Wang T S. *Spectral analysis of random shrinkage in concrete structures*. J of Engrg. Mech. , ASCE, 1984, 110(2): 173～186
[19] Bazant Z P. Response of aging linear systems to ergodic random input. J. of Engrg. Mech. , ASCE, 1986, 112(3): 322～342
[20] Bazant Z P , Wang T S. *Spectral finite element analysis of random shrinkage in concrete*. J. of Struct. Engrg, ASCE, 1984, 110(9): 2196～2211
[21] Bazant Z P , Xi Y P. *Prediction of concrete creep and shrinkage by sampling on the basis of correlated random parameters*. Probabilistic Engrg. Mech. , 1989,4(4): 174～186
[22] Bazant Z P , Xi Y P. *Probabilistic prediction of creep and shrinkage in concrete structures: combined sampling and spectral approach*. 5th Int. Conf. on Struct. Safety, and Reliability. 1989. 803～808
[23] Bazant Z P ,Xi Y P. *Stochastic drying and creep effects in Concrete structures*. J. of Struct. Engrg. , ASCE, 1993, 119(1): 301～322
[24] Bazant Z P ,Liu K L. *Random creep and shrinkage in structures: sampling*. J. of Struct. Engrg. , ASCE, 1985, 111(5): 1113～1134
[25] Suzuki K, Szmyd J, Kolenda Z, et al.. *An approach to practical heat transfer problems with uncertain specification utilizing supplementary data*. In: Proc. of the First KSME - JSME Thermal and Fluids Engrg. Conf. 1988, 2. 443～448
[26] Oktay S, Kammerer H C. *A conduction - cooled module for high performance LSI devices*. IBM J. Res. Development, 1982, 26(1): 55～66
[27] Shigekazu K, Noriyuki A, Takahiro D, et al.. *Application of SFEM to thermal analysis for computer cooling*. J. of Electronic Packaging, Transactions of the ASME, 1993, 115(9): 270～275
[28] 王同生. 混凝土结构的随机温度应力. 水利学报, 1985(1):23～31
[29] 刘宁,刘光廷. 大体积混凝土结构温度场的随机有限元算法. 清华大学学报, 1996,36(1):41～47
[30] 刘宁,刘光廷. 大体积混凝土结构随机温度徐变应力计算方法研究. 力学学报, 1997, 29(2): 189～202
[31] Liu N, Liu G T. *Nonstationary random thermal creep stress in mass concrete structures*. Finite Elements in Analysis and Design, 1997,(26): 83～95
[32] Liu N, Liu G T. *Spectral stochastic finite element analysis of periodic random thermal creep stress in concrete*. Engrg. Struct. 1996,18(9): 669～674

[33] Bazant Z P ,Chern J C. *Bayesian statistical prediction of concrete creep and shrinkage*. J. ACI, 1984,81(6): 319～330
[34] Cinlar E. *Stochastic process for extrapolating concrete creep*. J. of Engrg. Mech., ASCE, 1997,103(4): 1069～1088
[35] Bazant Z P ,Chern J C. *Concrete creep at variable humidity: constitutive law and mechanism*. Mat. and Struct., 1985, 103(18): 1～20
[36] 朱伯芳. 水工结构与固体力学论文集. 北京:水利电力出版社,1985
[37] 丁宝瑛. 大体积混凝土结构的温度应力与温度控制论文集.北京:兵器工业出版社,1991
[38] Ghanem R , Spanos P D. *Stochastic Finite Elements: A Spectral Approach*. New York: Springer-Verlag 1991
[39] Kleiber M ,Hien T D. *The stochastic Finite Element Method——Basic Perturbation Technique and Computer Implementation*. New York: John Willey and Sons, 1992
[40] Zhu W Q, Ren Y J, Wu W Q. *Stochastic FEM based on local averages of random vector fields*. J. of Engrg. Mech., ASCE, 1992,118(3): 496～511
[41] 刘宁,吕泰仁. 随机有限元及其工程应用. 力学进展,1995,25(1):114～126
[42] Ryu Y S, Haririan M, Wu C C, et al.. *Structural design sensitivity analysis of nonlinear response*. Computers and Structures, 1985, 21(1/2): 245～255
[43] Vanmacke E, Shinozuka M. *Random fields and stochastic finite element method*. Struct. Safety. 1986,3: 143～166
[44] 刘宁. 三维可分向量随机场局部平均的三维随机有限元及可靠度计算. 水利学报,1995(6):75～82
[45] Wittmann F H. *Creep and shrinkage mechanisms*. In: Bazant ed. Creep and Shrinkage in Concrete Structures. London: John Willey and Sons, 1982. 129～161
[46] 朱位秋. 随机振动. 北京:科学出版社,1992
[47] 阿鲁久涅扬. 蠕变理论中的若干问题. 邬瑞锋等译. 北京:科学出版社,1962
[48] 舒学全. 大体积混凝土结构温度徐变应力分析的初应力法. 见:河海大学硕士学位论文. 1991
[49] Diamentidis D, Madsen H O ,Rachwitz R. *On the variability of the creep coefficient of structural concrete*. Mat. and Struct., 1983, 100(17): 321～238
[50] Madsen H O ,Bazant Z P. *Uncertainty analysis of creep and shrinkage effects in concrete structures*. J. ACI, 1983, 80(3): 116～121
[51] Papoulis A. Probability. *Random Variabvles and Stochastic Process*. New York: McGraw-Hill, 1965
[52] Raj D. *Sampling Theory*. New York: McGraw Hill, Inc. 1973
[53] Bazant Z P. *Prediction of concrete creep effects using age-adjusted effective modulus method*. J. of ACI, 1972, 69: 271～282
[54] Paren E. *Stochastic Processes*. New York: Holden Day, Inc., 1962
[55] 刘宁,孟庆生,吴世伟. 非平稳载荷下疲劳裂纹扩展的可靠度分析. 工程力学, 1993(5)(增刊): 547～552

非平稳温度场影响下混凝土结构的随机徐变应力

摘　要　大体积混凝土结构的徐变应力受多种随机因素的影响。文中视混凝土结构内部温度场为非平稳随机过程,对此非平稳温度场采用了时域上简化处理的方法。同时,为进一步考虑材料参数(如徐变度、弹模等)随机性的影响,文中将随机有限元法引入到混凝土结构随机徐变应力的计算中,提出了求解随机徐变应力的初应变随机有限元隐式解法。

关键词　混凝土结构　随机温度场　徐变应力　随机有限元法

大体积混凝土结构温度徐变应力的仿真计算中存在着诸多的随机性,研究随机徐变应力的计算方法具有很重要的意义。Heller 首先提出了计算随机温度应力的谱密度法,并计算了一个半无限体的随机温度问题(准稳定温度场)[1]和一个圆柱的随机弹性温度应力(准稳定温度场、常量弹模,不考虑徐变)[2],该法显然不适用于混凝土材料。Tsubaki 和 Bazant 提出了脉冲反应函数法[3],该法的优点是可求解非平稳过程,缺点是系统的脉冲响应函数常不易求得。随后 Bazant 等人考虑到周期变化特性,提出了谱分析方法[4~6]。我国对于混凝土材料的随机温度应力问题研究得较少,王同生与 Bazant 合作进行过这方面的研究,之后又提出了直接法[7]。可以看出以上方法均未采用随机有限元法,因而不易考虑材料参数随机性以及混凝土绝热温升的影响。目前的随机有限元法仍局限于以下两方面[8]:①将荷载视为随机过程(随机激励),而结构物理参数需视为确定;②结构物理参数视为随机,则荷载不能为随机过程。笔者曾在文献[9]中综合考虑各种随机因素,给出了可以反映随机过程因素以及材料参数随机性的温度场随机有限元计算方法,并在文献[10]中针对周期环境温度作用下混凝土结构温度场的周期变化特性,提出了计算徐变应力的复频响应——随机有限元法,该法显然仍未考虑混凝土绝热温升引起的非平稳温度场的影响。本文既为解决前人方法(如谱分析法等)未能解决的问题,也是文献[9]、[10]工作的继续,即考虑混凝土结构温度场为非平稳随机过程,计算非平稳温度场影响下混凝土结构的随机徐变应力。

1　确定性徐变应力的计算方法

在利用有限元进行确定性徐变应力计算时,目前通常采用初应变隐式解法[11,12]。在线性徐变条件下,设混凝土的徐变度为:$C(t,\tau)=\varphi(\tau)(1-\mathrm{e}^{-k(t-\tau)})$。对于三维复杂应力状态,有以下递推计算格式:

$$\left.\begin{aligned}\{\Delta\varepsilon_n^c\}&=(1-\mathrm{e}^{-k\Delta\tau_n})\{\omega_n\}+[Q]\{\Delta\sigma_n\}\varphi_n^*(1-f_n\mathrm{e}^{-k\Delta\tau_n})\\\{\omega_n\}&=\mathrm{e}^{-k\Delta\tau_n}\{\omega_{n-1}\}+[Q]\{\Delta\sigma_{n-1}\}\varphi_{n-1}^*f_{n-1}\mathrm{e}^{-k\Delta\tau_{n-1}}\\\{\omega_1\}&=[Q]\{\Delta\sigma_0\}\varphi_0\end{aligned}\right\}\tag{1}$$

本文选自《应用力学学报》1998 年第 2 期,作者还有刘宁。

式中:f_n 和$[Q]$的表达式可参见文献[9]、[10];$\{\Delta\varepsilon_n^c\}$ 为 t_{n-1} 时刻到 t_n 时刻的徐变变形增量;$\{\Delta\sigma_n\}$ 为 t_{n-1} 到 t_n 时刻的应力增量;$\Delta\tau_n = t_n - t_{n-1}$;$\varphi_n^* = \varphi(t_{n-1} + \Delta\tau_n/2)$。

第 n 时段总应变增量为:$\{\Delta\varepsilon_n\} = \{\Delta\varepsilon_n^e\} + \{\Delta\varepsilon_n^C\} + \{\Delta\varepsilon_n^T\} + \{\Delta\varepsilon_n^0\}$,其中$\{\Delta\varepsilon_n^e\}$、$\{\Delta\varepsilon_n^T\}$ 和$\{\Delta\varepsilon_n^0\}$ 分别为弹性、温差和自生体积变形增量。第 n 时段的应力增量则为

$$\{\Delta\sigma_n\} = [D_n^*]([B]\{\Delta u_n\} - \{\omega_n\}(1 - e^{-k\Delta\tau_n}) - \Delta\varepsilon_n^T - \Delta\varepsilon_n^0) \tag{2}$$

式中:$\{\Delta u_n\}$ 为第 n 时段节点位移增量列阵,而:

$$[D_n^*] = [D_n]/D_{f0},\ D_{f0} = 1 + \varphi_n^*(1 - f_n e^{-k\Delta\tau_n})E(t_{n-1} + \Delta\tau_n/2) \tag{3}$$

式中:$[D_n]$ 为 t_n 时刻的弹性矩阵。

由虚功原理,可以得到有限元支配方程:

$$[K_n]\{\Delta u_n\} = \{\Delta P_a^C\} + \{\Delta P_n^T\} + \{\Delta P_n^0\} + \{F\} \tag{4}$$

$$\left.\begin{aligned}\{\Delta P_n^T\} &= \sum_e \iiint_{V_e} [B][D_n^*]\{\omega_n\}(1 - e^{-k\Delta\tau_n})dv \\ \{\Delta P_n^C\} &= \sum_e \iiint_{V_e} [B][D_n^*]\{\Delta\varepsilon_n^T\}dv \\ \{\Delta P_n^0\} &= \sum_e \iiint_{V_e} [B][D_n^*]\{\Delta\varepsilon_n^0\}dN\end{aligned}\right\} \tag{5}$$

式中:$\{\Delta P_n^C\}$、$\{\Delta P_n^T\}$ 和$\{\Delta P_n^0\}$ 分别为徐变变形、温差荷载和自生体积变形产生的当量荷载增量;$\{F\}$ 为外荷载。

由式(4) 求出$\{\Delta u_n\}$ 后,可由式(2) 得出$\{\Delta\sigma_n\}$。将各时段的位移增量和应力增量累加,即可求得任意时刻的应变和应力

$$\{\varepsilon_n\} = \sum_{i=1}^{n}\{\Delta\varepsilon_i\} \qquad \{\sigma_n\} = \sum_{i=1}^{n}\{\Delta\sigma_i\} \tag{6}$$

2 影响徐变应力的随机因素

影响徐变应力的随机因素很多,主要包括徐变度 $C(t,\tau)$、弹模 $E(\tau)$、外荷载$\{F\}$ 以及混凝土结构内部的温度场。文献[9] 给出了随机温度场统计特性的计算方法,在随机环境温度和随机绝热温升的作用下,混凝土温度场为非平稳随机过程。随机徐变度可表示为

$$C(t,\tau) \approx \overline{C}(t,\tau) + (1 - e^{-k(t-\tau)})\Delta\varphi + (t-\tau)e^{-k(t-\tau)}\overline{\varphi}(\tau)\Delta k \tag{7}$$

式中:$\overline{C}(t,\tau)$ 为徐变度均值过程。

由于徐变参数 $\varphi(\tau)$ 一般可表示为:$\varphi(\tau) = p_1 + p_2/\tau^{p_3}$,其中 p_1、p_2 和 p_3 为随机变量,于是

$$\left.\begin{aligned}\overline{\varphi}(\tau) &\approx \overline{p}_1 + \overline{p}_2/\tau^{\overline{p}_3} \\ \Delta\varphi(\tau) &\approx \Delta p_1 + \tau^{-\overline{p}_3}\Delta p_2 - \overline{p}_2\ln\tau\cdot\tau^{-\overline{p}_3}\Delta p_3\end{aligned}\right\} \tag{8}$$

与之类似,混凝土的弹模可以表示为

$$E(\tau) \approx \overline{E}(\tau) + (1 - e^{-m_2\tau})\Delta E_0 + \tau e^{-\overline{m}_2\tau}\overline{E}_0\Delta m_2 \tag{9}$$

式中:$\overline{E}(\tau)$ 为 $E(\tau)$ 的均值过程;E_0、m_2 为随机变量。

3　随机温度场的处理

目前对于激励为一般非平稳时响应的计算方法还不太完善，尤其是对于需用有限元离散的大型复杂结构，还未出现成熟的解法，因此文中对非平稳随机温度场作一定的简化处理。文献[13]中提出了非平稳随机过程逐段平稳叠加的方法，文中引入该法参数调幅的思想，对随机温度场作以下的逐段简化处理：

$$\{T(t)\}=\begin{cases}\{a_1^{(1)}(t)T^{(1)}(t_1)+b_1^{(1)}(t),\cdots,a_1^{(NP)}(t)T^{(NP)}_{(t_1)}+b_1^{(NP)}(t)\}^{\mathrm T}\\ \quad=\{a_1(t)\}^T[I]\{T(t_1)\}+\{b_1(t)\}\quad 当\ t_1\leqslant t<t_2\ 时\\ \{a_2^{(1)}(t)T^{(1)}(t_2)+b_2^{(1)}(t),\cdots,a_2^{(NP)}(t)T^{(NP)}(t_2)+b_2^{(NP)}(t)\}^{\mathrm T}\\ \quad=\{a_2(t)\}^T[I]\{T(t_2)\}+\{b_2(t)\}\quad 当\ t_2\leqslant t<t_3\ 时\\ \quad\cdots\cdots\\ \{a_n^{(1)}(t)T^{(1)}(t_n)+b_n^{(1)}(t),\cdots,a_n^{(NP)}(t)T^{(NP)}(t_n)+b_n^{(NP)}(t)\}^{\mathrm T}\\ \quad=\{a_n(t)\}^T[I]\{T(t_n)\}+\{b_n(t)\}\quad 当\ t_n\leqslant t<t_{n+1}\ 时\end{cases}\tag{10}$$

式中：NP 为结点总数；$[I]$ 为单位矩阵；$a_n^{(i)}(t)$ 和 $b_n^{(i)}(t)$ 均为确定性函数；上标 $(i)(i=1,2\cdots,NP)$ 表示第 (i) 结点，对给定的时刻 t，$T^{(i)}(t)(i=1,2,\cdots,NP)$ 为一随机变量。与文献[13]不同的是，文献[13]在每一时段内将 $\{T(t)\}$ 简化为平稳随机过程，而文中则在每一时段内乃简化为非平稳随机过程，可保证原非平稳随机过程 $\{T(t)\}$ 逐点均值和方差的准确性，且可使计算大为简化。$a_n^{(i)}(t)$ 和 $b_n^{(i)}(t)$ 可由下式确定：

$$\left.\begin{aligned}\overline{T}^{(i)}(t)&=a_n^{(i)}(t)\overline{T}^{(i)}(t_n)+b_n^{(i)}(t)\\ \mathrm{Var}[T^{(i)}(t)]&=[a_n^{(i)}(t)]^2\mathrm{Var}[T^{(i)}(t_n)]\end{aligned}\right\}\quad(t_n\leqslant t<t_{n+1})\tag{11}$$

式中：Var(·)表示求方差。

由上式可得出：

$$\left.\begin{aligned}a_n^{(i)}(t)&=\sqrt{\mathrm{Var}[T^{(i)}(t)]/\mathrm{Var}[T^{(i)}(t_n)]}\\ b_n^{(i)}(t)&=\overline{T}^{(i)}(t)-\overline{T}^{(i)}(t_n)\sqrt{\mathrm{Var}[T^{(i)}(t)]/\mathrm{Var}[T^{(i)}(t_n)]}\end{aligned}\right\}\tag{12}$$

$\{T(t_k)\}$ 和 $\{T(t_l)\}$ 间 $(t_i\leqslant t_k<t_{i+1},t_j\leqslant t_l<t_{j+1})$ 在时域上的相关性可以近似地由下式反映：

$$\mathrm{Cov}[T^{(m)}(t_k),T^{(m)}(t_l)]\approx a_i^{(m)}(t_k)a_j^{(m)}(t_l)\mathrm{Cov}[T^{(m)}(t_i),T^{(m)}(t_j)]\tag{13}$$

式中：上标 (m) 表示第 m 结点。

而 $T^{(m1)}(t_k)$、$T^{(m2)}(t_k)(t_i\leqslant t_k<t_{i+1})$ 在空间上的相关性可表示为：

$$\mathrm{Cov}[T^{(m1)}(t_k),T^{(m2)}(t_k)]\approx a_i^{(m1)}(t_k)a_i^{(m2)}(t_k)\mathrm{Cov}[T^{(m1)}(t_i),T^{(m2)}(t_i)]\tag{14}$$

由此可见，将非平稳过程 $\{T(t)\}$ 简化为式(10)仍可较准确地反映 $\{T(t)\}$ 的相关结构。

4　初应变随机有限元的隐式解法

统一地以 X 表示基本随机变量，将随机函数 S（如 $\varphi(\tau)$，应力 σ、应变 ε 以及 k、E_0、m_2 等随机函数）在 $\overline{X}$ 处一阶 Taylor 展开，有：$S=\overline{S}+S|_{X=X}\mathrm{d}X$。其中上标(′)表示对随

机变量 X 求偏导,令 $\mathrm{d}X=(X-\overline{X})\alpha$($\alpha$ 为很小的数),有:$S=\overline{S}+\alpha S'$。将此式代入计算徐变应力的初应变隐式解法计算式(式(1)、(5)),利用摄动原理,经整理可得:

(1) 零次式

$$\left.\begin{aligned}&\{\Delta\overline{\varepsilon}_n^{c'}\}=(1-\mathrm{e}^{-k\Delta\tau_n})\{\overline{\omega}_n\}+[Q]\{\Delta\overline{\sigma}_n\}\overline{\varphi}_n^*(1-\overline{f}_n\mathrm{e}^{-k\Delta\tau_n})\\&\{\overline{\omega}_n\}=\mathrm{e}^{-k\Delta\tau_n}\{\overline{\omega}_{n-1}\}+[Q]\{\Delta\overline{\sigma}_{n-1}\}\overline{\varphi}_{n-1}^*\overline{f}_{n-1}\mathrm{e}^{-k\Delta\tau_{n-1}}\\&\{\overline{\omega}_1\}=[Q]\{\Delta\overline{\sigma}_0\}\overline{\varphi}_0\end{aligned}\right\}\tag{15}$$

(2) 一次式

$$\left.\begin{aligned}&\{\Delta\varepsilon_n^{c'}\}=(1-\mathrm{e}^{-k\Delta\tau_n})\{\omega_n\}'+\Delta\tau_n\mathrm{e}^{-k\Delta\tau_n}\{\overline{\omega}_n\}k'+[Q](\{\sigma_n\}'\overline{\varphi}_n^*-\\&\qquad\{\overline{\sigma}_n\}\varphi_n^{*'})(1-\overline{f}_n\mathrm{e}^{-k\Delta\tau_n})+[Q]\overline{\sigma}_n\overline{\varphi}_n^*\mathrm{e}^{-k\Delta\tau_n}(f'_n+\Delta\tau_nk')\\&\{\omega_n\}'=(-\Delta\tau_nk'\{\overline{\omega}_{n-1}\}+\{\omega_{n-1}\}')\mathrm{e}^{-k\Delta\tau_n}+[Q](\{\sigma\}'_{n-1}\overline{\varphi}_{n-1}^*-\\&\qquad\{\overline{\sigma}_{n-1}\}\varphi_{n-1}^{*'})\overline{f}_{n-1}\mathrm{e}^{-k\Delta\tau_{n-1}}+[Q]\{\overline{\sigma}_{n-1}\}\overline{\varphi}_{n-1}^*\mathrm{e}^{-k\Delta\tau_{n-1}}(f'_{n-1}-\Delta\tau_{n-1}k')\\&\{\omega_1\}'=[Q](\{\Delta\overline{\sigma}_0\}\varphi'_0+\{\Delta\sigma_0\}'\overline{\varphi}_0)\end{aligned}\right\}\tag{16}$$

式中:

$$f'_n=\begin{cases}\dfrac{1}{\Delta\tau_n}\dfrac{(\Delta\tau_n\overline{k}-1)(\mathrm{e}^{k\Delta\tau_n}-1)}{k^2} & \text{当 } X_n=k \text{ 时}\\0 & \text{当 } X_n\neq k \text{ 时}\end{cases}\tag{17}$$

$$\begin{aligned}\{\Delta\sigma_n\}'=&[\overline{D}_n^*][B][\{\Delta\varepsilon_n\}'-\{\omega_n\}'(1-\mathrm{e}^{-k\Delta\tau_n})+\{\overline{\omega}_n\}\mathrm{e}^{-k\Delta\tau_n}\Delta\tau_nk'-\{\varepsilon_n^T\}'-\\&\{\Delta\varepsilon_n^0\}']+[D_n^*]'[B][\{\Delta\overline{\varepsilon}_n\}-\{\overline{\omega}_n\}(1-\mathrm{e}^{-k\Delta\tau_n})-\{\Delta\overline{\varepsilon}_n^T\}-\{\Delta\overline{\varepsilon}_n^0\}]\end{aligned}\tag{18}$$

$$\left.\begin{aligned}&[\overline{D}_n^*]=[\overline{D}_n]/\overline{D}_{f1}\\&[D_n^*]'=\frac{[D_n]'\overline{D}_{f1}-[\overline{D}_n]D'_{f1}}{\overline{D}_{f1}^2}=\frac{[D_n]'}{\overline{D}_{f1}}-[\overline{D}_n^*]\frac{D'_{f1}}{\overline{D}_{f1}}\end{aligned}\right\}\tag{19}$$

其中:

$$\left.\begin{aligned}&\overline{D}_{f1}=1+\overline{\varphi}_n^*(1-\overline{f}_n\mathrm{e}^{-k\Delta\tau_k})\overline{E}(t_{n-1}+\Delta\tau_n/2)\\&D'_{f1}=[\varphi_n^{*'}(1-\overline{f}_n\mathrm{e}^{-k\Delta\tau_n})+(\overline{f}_n\Delta\tau_nk'-f'_n)\overline{\varphi}_n^*\mathrm{e}^{-k\Delta\tau_n}]\overline{E}(t_{n-1}+\Delta\tau_n/2)+\\&\qquad\overline{D}_{f0}(1-\mathrm{e}^{-\overline{m}_2(t_{n-1}+\Delta\tau_n/2)})E'_0+(t_{n-1}+\Delta\tau_n/2)\overline{D}_{f0}\mathrm{e}^{-\overline{m}_2(t_{n-1}+\Delta\tau_n/2)}m'_2\\&[D_n]'=\begin{cases}\dfrac{[D_n]}{E_0} & \text{当随机变量 } X=E_0 \text{ 时}\\\dfrac{(t_{n-1}+\Delta\tau_n/2)\mathrm{e}^{-m_2(t_{n-1}+\Delta\tau_n/2)}}{1-\mathrm{e}^{-m_2(t_{n-1}+\Delta\tau_n/2)}}[D_n] & \text{当 } X=m_2 \text{ 时}\\0 & \text{其他}\end{cases}\end{aligned}\right\}\tag{20}$$

而 D_{f0} 的表达式如式(3)所示。式(18)中:$\{\Delta\varepsilon_n\}'[B]\{\Delta u_n\}'$,由于 $\{\Delta u_n\}=[K_n]^{-1}\{\Delta P_n\}$,有:

$$\left.\begin{aligned}&\{\Delta\overline{u}_n\}=[\overline{K}_n]^{-1}\{\Delta\overline{P}_n\}\\&\{\Delta u_n\}'=[\overline{K}_n]^{-1}(\{\Delta P_n\}'-[K_n]'\{\Delta\overline{u}_n\})\end{aligned}\right\}\tag{21}$$

而： $$\{\Delta P_n\}' = \{\Delta P_n^C\}' + \{\Delta P_n^{\mathrm{T}}\}' + \{\Delta P_n^0\}' + \{F\}' \tag{22}$$

$$\left.\begin{aligned}
[K_n]' &= \sum_e \iiint_{v_e} [B]^{\mathrm{T}}[D_n^*]'[B]\mathrm{d}v \\
\{\Delta P_n^C\}' &= \sum_e \iiint_{v_e} [B]^{\mathrm{T}}([\overline{D}_n^*][\{\omega_n\}'(1-\mathrm{e}^{-k\Delta\tau_n}) + \{\overline{\omega}_n\}\Delta\tau_n \mathrm{e}^{-k\Delta\tau_k}k'] + \\
&\quad [D_n^*]'\{\overline{\omega}_n\}(1-e^{-k\Delta\tau_n})\mathrm{d}v \\
\{\Delta P_n^0\}' &= \sum_e \iiint_{v_e} ([B]^{\mathrm{T}}[D_n^*]'\{\Delta\varepsilon_n^0\} + [B]^{\mathrm{T}}[\overline{D}_n^*]\{\Delta\varepsilon_n^0\}')\mathrm{d}v \\
\{\Delta P_n^{\mathrm{T}}\}' &= \sum_e \iiint_{v_e} ([B]^{\mathrm{T}}[D_n^*]'\alpha\{\overline{T}(t_n)\}[1,1,1,0,0,0]^{\mathrm{T}} + \\
&\quad [B]^{\mathrm{T}}[\overline{D}_n^*]\alpha[T'(t_n)\}[1,1,1,0,0,0]^{\mathrm{T}}\mathrm{d}v
\end{aligned}\right\} \tag{23}$$

当不计混凝土自生体积变形的随机性时，$\{\Delta\overline{\varepsilon}_n^0\} = \{\Delta\varepsilon_n^0\}$，$\{\Delta\varepsilon_n^0\}' = 0$，有：

$$\{\Delta P_n^0\}' = \sum_e \iiint_{v_e} [B]^T[D_n^*]'\{\Delta\varepsilon_n^0\}\mathrm{d}v$$

由式(16)、式(17)一步一步地求出$\{\Delta\overline{\sigma}_n\}$、$\{\Delta\overline{\sigma}_n\}'$后，可得 t_n 时刻的$\{\overline{\sigma}_n\}$、$\{\sigma_n\}'$：

$$\{\overline{\sigma}_n\} = \sum_{i=1}^{n}\{\Delta\overline{\sigma}_i\} \qquad \{\sigma_n\}' = \sum_{i=1}^{n}\{\Delta\sigma_i\}' \tag{24}$$

于是，t_n 时刻徐变应力的协方差为

$$\mathrm{Cov}[\sigma_i,\sigma_j] \approx \sum_{i=1}^{nv}\sum_{j=1}^{nv}\sigma'_{i,k}\sigma'_{j,l}\mathrm{Cov}(X_k,X_l) \tag{25}$$

式中：nv 为随机变量总数；下标(i 或 j)表示应力的分量。

5 算例

5.1 算例1——自由板的随机徐变应力

取文献[7]中自由板算例。文献[7]未考虑混凝土的绝热温升，文中则进一步考虑混凝土绝热温升的影响。绝热温升形式取为 $\theta = \theta_0(1-\mathrm{e}^{-m_1 t})$。此时温度场为非平稳随机温度场，可按文献[9]方法获得温度场的统计特性。自由板右侧气温 $T = 0$，表面放热系数 $b_1 = 7\times10^{-3}\mathrm{W/(m^2\cdot K)}$；左侧气温 $T = A\cos\omega(t-t_0)$，$b_2 = 14\times10^{-3}\mathrm{W/(m^2\cdot K)}$。板厚为2.6m，$\omega = 7.169\times10^{-4}\mathrm{1/h}$，导热系数 $\lambda = 1.45\times10^{-3}\mathrm{W/(m^2\cdot K)}$，导温系数 $a = 0.002\ 17\mathrm{m^2/h}$。计算温度场时，取参数 A、a、b_1、b_2、λ、θ_0、m_1 为随机变量，$\overline{A} = 8℃$，$\overline{\theta}_0 = 25.0℃$，$\overline{m}_1 = 0.397$。变异系数均为0.2。徐变度形式为：$C(t,\tau) = (p_1 + \frac{p_2}{\tau^{p_3}})(1-\mathrm{e}^{-k(t-\tau)})$。取混凝土弹模参数 E_0、m_2 以及徐变参数 k、p_1、p_2、p_3 为随机变量，均值为 $\overline{E}_0 = 2.0\times10^4\mathrm{MPa}$，$\overline{m}_2 = 0.3$，$\overline{k} = 0.026\mathrm{d^{-1}}$，$\overline{p}_1 = 0.9\times10^{-5}\mathrm{MPa^{-1}}$，$\overline{p}_2 = 4.82\times10^{-5}\mathrm{MPa^{-1}}$，$\overline{p}_3 = 1.0$，变异系数均为0.1。混凝土线胀系数为 $\alpha = 12\times10^{-6}\mathrm{MPa^{-1}}(1/℃)$，泊松比 $\mu = 0.167$。根据弹性力学有关公式可知，在第 k 时段(τ_{k-1},τ_k)内，弹性应变增量为

$$\left.\begin{aligned}
&\Delta\varepsilon_k^c = (\Delta A_k + \Delta B_k Z)\alpha \quad \Delta A_k = A_{k+1} - A_k \quad \Delta B_k = B_{k+1} - B_k \\
&A_k = \frac{1}{2l}\int_{-l}^{l} T_k\mathrm{d}z \quad B_k = \frac{1}{2l^3}\int_{-l}^{l} T_k z\mathrm{d}z
\end{aligned}\right\} \tag{26}$$

在第 k 时段内产生的徐变应变为

$$\{\Delta\varepsilon_k^c\} = \sum_{\tau_i=\tau_0}^{\tau_{k-1}} \Delta\sigma_i [C(\tau_k, \tau_i) - C(\tau_{k-1}, \tau_i)] \tag{27}$$

在第 k 时段内产生的徐变应力增量为：$\Delta\sigma_k = E_k[\Delta\varepsilon_k^e - \Delta\varepsilon_k^c - \alpha\Delta T_k]$。于是，$t = \tau_k$ 时的应力为 $\sigma_k = \sum_{i=1}^{k}\Delta\sigma_i$。由此可得应力均值理论解的过程曲线（见图 1 中虚线）。徐变应力标准差的准理论解可按下式计算：$\mathrm{Var}(\sigma_k) = \sum_{i=1}^{nv}\sum_{j=1}^{nv}\frac{\partial\sigma_k}{\partial X_i}\frac{\partial\sigma_k}{\partial X_j}\mathrm{Cov}(X_i, X_j)$，计算结果见图 2 中虚线。文中按随机有限元法分别计算了不考虑温度场的相关结构和考虑温度场的相关结构两种情况下徐变应力场的均值和方差（图 1 和图 2 中实线）。图 2 中曲线 curve－1 为不考虑温度场相关结构时的 SFEM 解；curve－2 为不考虑相关结构的理论解；curve－3 为考虑相关结构时的 SFEM 解；curve－4 为考虑相关结构时的理论解。可以看出，不考虑温度场的相关结构时，所得应力标准差结果偏大。

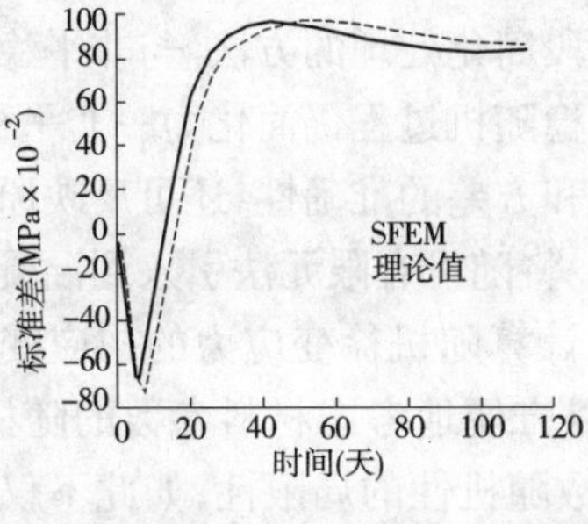

图 1　自由板中点处徐变应力的均值

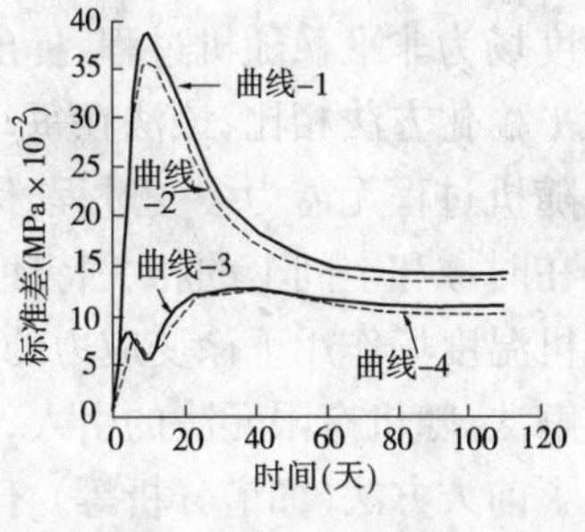

图 2　自由板中点处徐变应力的标准差

5.2　算例 2——混凝土浇筑块的随机徐变应力

考虑一 6m×4m×4m 的混凝土浇筑块（如图 3 所示），除底面外，其余各面均暴露于大气之中，气温为 $T_a = A\cos\omega t$，$\overline{A} = 10℃$，$\omega = 2\pi/365(1/\mathrm{d})$，浇筑块下部基岩假定一直恒温在 10℃。混凝土表面放热系数 $\overline{b} = 14\times10^{-3}\mathrm{W/(m^2\cdot K)}$，导热系数 $\overline{\lambda} = 1.45\times10^{-3}\mathrm{W/(m^2\cdot K)}$，导温系数 $\overline{a} = 0.002\ 17\mathrm{m^2/h}$，绝热温升参数为 $\overline{\theta}_0 = 25.0(℃)$，$\overline{m}_1 = -0.397$。随机变量的变异系数均为 0.1。基岩考虑为刚性，混凝土弹模参数为：$\overline{E}_0 = 2.0\times10^4\mathrm{MPa}$，$\overline{m}_2 = 0.3$，徐变参数同算例 1，随机力学参数的变异系数也均为 0.1，取 4 个考察点（见图 3）。考察点处徐变应力的均值和标准差的计算结果分别见图 4 和图 5。由图 4 可知，由于受到基岩的刚性约束，混凝土浇筑块的第 2、3、4 点除最初的时段外，均受较大的拉应力作用，且越往下部拉应力越大。同时，从图 5 可以看出，即使在周期平稳环境温度作用下（混凝土浇筑后期，绝热温升的影响完全消失），由于混凝土的徐变和老化，徐变应力仍为非平稳随机过程，这一点与文献[7] 结论一致。

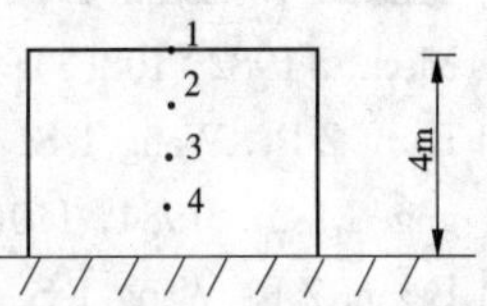

图 3　混凝土浇筑块

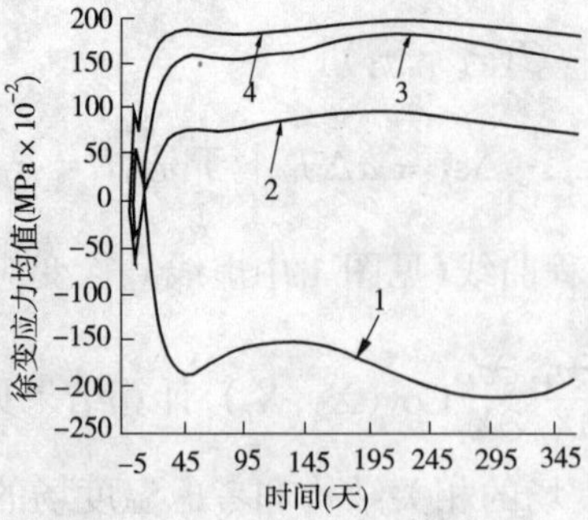

图4　考察点处徐变应力的均值

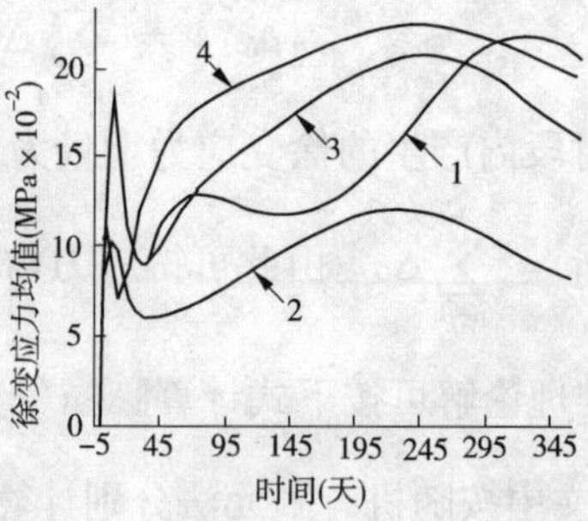

图5　考察点处徐变应力的标准差

6　结语

综合考虑混凝土徐变应力计算中的各种随机因素(如温度场、弹模、徐变参数等),视混凝土温度场为非平稳随机过程,提出了在时域上逐段简化处理的方法。与非平稳随机过程的逐段平稳化方法相比,该法在每一时段内将非平稳随机过程仍简化为一非平稳过程,原非平稳随机过程无需为缓变过程,保证了逐点均值和方差的准确性,还可反映原非平稳随机过程在时域和空间上的相关特性,且使计算简化。将随机有限元法引入到混凝土结构非平稳随机温度场作用下徐变应力的计算中,提出了计算随机徐变应力的初应变随机有限元隐式解法。随机有限元法的引入,使本文方法可以方便地考虑材料参数的随机性,有效地克服了前人方法(如谱分析等)不能考虑材料参数随机性的局限性,如此不仅进一步完善了随机有限元方法本身,而且提高了本方法的实用性,使大体积混凝土结构的随机徐变应力问题得以较为圆满地解决。

参 考 文 献

[1] Heller R A. *Temperature Response of an Infinitely Thick Slab to Random Surface Temperature*. Mech. Research Communication, 1976, 3: 379～385

[2] Heller R A. *Thermal Stress as an Narrow-Band Random Load*. ASCE, J. of Enfng., 1976, 2(3): 787～805

[3] Tsubaki T ,Bazant Z P. *Random Shrinkage Stresses in Aging Viscoelastic Vessel*. ASCE, J. of Engng. Mech., 1982, 108(3): 527～545

[4] Baznt Z P , Wang T S. *Spectral Analysis of Random Shrinkage in Concrete Structures*. ASCE J. of Engng. Mech.,1984, 110(2): 173～186

[5] Bazant Z P ,Wang T S. *Spectral Finite Element Analysis of Random Shrinkage in Concrete*. ASCE J. of Struct. Engng., 1984, 110(9): 2196～2211

[6] Bazant Z P ,Wang T S. *Algorithm for Aging Viscoelstic Structures under Periodic Load*. J. of Engng. Mech., 1984,110(6): 972～985

[7] 王同生. 混凝土结构的随机温度应力. 水利学报,1985(1):23～31

[8] 刘宁,吕泰仁. 随机有限元及其工程应用. 力学进展,1995,25(1):114～126
[9] 刘宁,刘光廷. 大体积混凝土结构随机温度场的随机有限元算法. 清华大学学报, 1996,36(1):41～47
[10] Liu N, Liu G. T. *Spectral Finite Element Analysis of Periodic Thermal Creep Stress in Concrete*. Engrg. Struct. 1996, 18(9): 669～674
[11] 朱伯芳,等. 水工混凝土结构温度应力与温度控制. 北京:水利电力出版社,1976
[12] 朱伯芳,等. 水工结构与固体力学论文集. 北京:水利电力出版社, 1985
[13] 刘宁,孟庆生,吴世伟. 非平稳载荷下疲劳裂纹扩展的可靠度分析. 工程力学,1993,5(增刊):547～552

混凝土结构温度徐变应力的首次超越可靠度

摘　要　基于随机有限元法，充分考虑大体积混凝土结构徐变温度应力计算中的各种随机因素，视混凝土温度场、弹模、徐变度以及抗力等为非平稳随机过程，针对非线性功能函数情况，首次提出了大体积混凝土结构随机温度徐变应力首次超越可靠度的计算方法。该方法可以方便地退化为求解任一时刻混凝土结构的静态可靠度。

关键词　大体积混凝土结构　温度徐变应力　首次超越可靠度　动态可靠度　随机有限元法

混凝土温度场及温度应力场的计算中存在着诸多的随机因素。国外20世纪70年代起就已着手研究温度应力的随机性[1,2]，而我国目前在这一领域基本上还是空白。笔者曾分别针对大体积混凝土结构的随机温度场和随机徐变应力场提出了随机有限元方法[3]，正是由于混凝土结构徐变温度应力场的仿真计算中存在的诸多随机性，使常规设计所依赖的安全系数法显得不够科学合理。国内外对于结构可靠度理论已进行了大量研究[4]，但现今用于结构设计校核的可靠度计算往往不考虑时间因素，所得可靠度实际上是时不变可靠度(Time-invariant Reliability)，目前尚无随机温度徐变应力场作用下结构时变可靠度(Time-dependent Reliability，也称动态可靠度)的计算方法。

混凝土材料强度准则所决定的功能函数可能为基本随机变量(随机过程)的非线性函数，由于一般很难直接获得非线性功能函数的分布类型和一阶二阶矩，将非线性功能函数线性化的方法自然地为人们所接受。对于以平稳随机过程为自变量的非线性功能函数的期望穿阈率问题，已有一些学者进行了研究[5]，然而，大体积混凝土结构的随机温度场以及随机徐变应力场均为非平稳随机过程[3]。对于非平稳向量随机过程非线性组合的时变可靠度问题，尚未见有关研究结果。为此，本文充分考虑大体积混凝土结构温度徐变应力计算中的各种随机因素，视混凝土温度场、弹模、徐变度以及抗力等为非平稳随机过程，基于随机有限元法，首次提出了大体积混凝土结构徐变温度应力首次超越可靠度的计算方法。

1　大体积混凝土结构温度徐变应力计算中的随机因素

本文考虑以下几种随机因素：

(1) 混凝土的徐变率 $C(t,\tau)$，可表示为 $C(t,\tau) \approx \overline{C}(t,\tau) + (1 - e^{-k(t-\tau)})\Delta\varphi + (t-\tau)e^{-k(t-\tau)}\overline{\varphi}(\tau)\Delta k$，其中，$\overline{C}(t,\tau)$ 为徐变度均值过程，k 为随机变量。$\varphi(t)$ 为非平稳随机过程：$\varphi(t) = p_1 + p_2/t^{p_3} \approx \overline{p}_1 + \overline{p}_2/t^{p_2} + \Delta p_1 + t^{-\overline{p}_2}\Delta p_2 - \overline{p}_2 \ln t \cdot t^{-\overline{p}_2} \cdot \Delta p_3$，$p_1$、$p_2$、$p_3$ 为随机变量。

(2) 混凝土的弹性模量 $E(t)$，亦为非平稳随机过程，可表示为：$E(t) = E_0(1 -$

本文选自《固体力学学报》1998年第1期，作者还有刘宁。

$e^{-m_2 t}$)，其中 E_0、m_2 为随机变量，$\overline{E}(t)$ 为 $E(t)$ 的均值过程。

(3) 混凝土温度场 $T(t)$：在随机环境温度、随机绝热温升随机热学参数的共同作用下为非平稳随机过程。

(4) 混凝土的抗力 $R(t)$，类似混凝土的弹模，为非平稳随机过程，可表示为：$R(t) = R_0(1-e^{-m_3 t})$，其中 R_0、m_3 为随机变量。

2 首次超越可靠度的计算方法

设非线性功能函数为 $G[\boldsymbol{X}(t)]$，$\boldsymbol{X}(t) = \{\boldsymbol{X}_1(t),\cdots,\boldsymbol{X}_n(t)\}^{\mathrm{T}}$ 为非平稳向量随机过程，如果 $G[\boldsymbol{X}(t)]$ 是高斯过程，并假设 $G[\boldsymbol{X}(t)]$ 与阈值 $x=0$ 的穿阈次数服从泊松分布(对于工程问题一般可作此假定)，则在时间 $[0,T]$ 内失效概率可以表示为：$P_F = 1-P_S = 1-\exp[-\int_0^T v_0^-(t)\mathrm{d}t]$，其中，$v_0^-(t)$ 表示以 $x=0$ 为阈值的负向期望穿阈率

$$v_0^-(t) = \frac{\sigma\dot{G}(t)}{2\pi\sigma_0(t)}\left\{\sqrt{1-\rho^2}\exp\left[-\frac{1}{1-\rho^2}\frac{\overline{G}^2(t)}{2\sigma_G^2(t)}\right]+\sqrt{2\pi}\frac{\rho\overline{G}(t)}{\sigma_G}\exp\left(-\frac{\overline{G}^2}{2\sigma_G^2}\right)\Phi\left(\frac{\rho}{\sqrt{1-\rho}}\frac{\overline{G}}{\sigma_G}\right)\right\} \tag{1}$$

式中：$\rho(t)$ 为 G 与 G 之间的相关系数；$\Phi(\cdot)$ 为正态累计分布函数。

由于 $G[\boldsymbol{X}(t)]$ 是 $\boldsymbol{X}(t)$ 的非线性函数，$G[\boldsymbol{X}(t)]$ 的分布类型以及一阶二阶矩一般很难直接得出。

Hohenbichler[4] 和 Grigoriu[5] 已给出了非高斯随机变量及随机过程当量正态化的方法。由于当量正态处理不影响本文以下的推导，本文以下将认为 $\boldsymbol{X}(t)$ 是已经过当量正态处理的高斯向量过程。在任一时刻 t 作如下变换：$\boldsymbol{Y}(t) = \boldsymbol{T}(t)[\boldsymbol{X}(t)-\overline{\boldsymbol{X}}(t)]$，其中 $\boldsymbol{T}^{-1}(t)$ 为 $\boldsymbol{C}_X(t)$ 经 Cholesky 分解产生的下三角矩阵的逆矩阵，$\boldsymbol{C}_X(t)$ 为 t 时刻 $\boldsymbol{X}(t)$ 的互协方差矩阵。对任一时刻 t，显然有

$$\begin{cases} \boldsymbol{C}_Y = \boldsymbol{I} \\ \boldsymbol{C}_{\dot{Y}} = \boldsymbol{T}\boldsymbol{C}_{\dot{X}}\boldsymbol{T}^{\mathrm{T}}\dot{\boldsymbol{T}}\boldsymbol{C}_X\dot{\boldsymbol{T}}^T + 2\dot{\boldsymbol{T}}\boldsymbol{C}_{X\dot{X}}\boldsymbol{T}^T \\ \boldsymbol{C}_{Y\dot{Y}} = \boldsymbol{T}\boldsymbol{C}_{X\dot{X}}\boldsymbol{T}^T + \boldsymbol{T}\boldsymbol{C}_X\dot{\boldsymbol{T}}^T \end{cases} \tag{2}$$

相应的功能函数应转变为 $G[\boldsymbol{X}(t)] = G\{\boldsymbol{T}^{-1}(t)\boldsymbol{Y}(t)+\overline{\boldsymbol{X}}(t)\} = g[\boldsymbol{Y}(t)]$。

将基本随机过程向量 $\boldsymbol{X}(t)$ 分为两部分：$\{\boldsymbol{X}(t)\} = \{\boldsymbol{X}_1\}+\{\boldsymbol{X}_2(t)\}$，其中 $\{\cdot\}$ 表示集合，$\boldsymbol{X}_1$ 为随机变量向量，$\boldsymbol{X}_2(t)$ 为随机过程向量。相应地，对于 $\boldsymbol{Y}(t)$ 有：$\{\boldsymbol{Y}(t)\} = \{\boldsymbol{Y}_1\}+\{\boldsymbol{Y}_2(t)\}$。从而，失效概率可以写为：$P_F = 1-[1-P_{FO}(\boldsymbol{Y}_1)](1-P_F[\boldsymbol{Y}_2(t)])$，其中，$P_{FO}(\boldsymbol{Y}_1) = P\{g[\boldsymbol{Y}_1,\boldsymbol{Y}_2(0)]<0\}$，$P_F[\boldsymbol{Y}_2(t)] = P\{g[\boldsymbol{Y}_1,\boldsymbol{Y}_2(t)]<0 \mid g[\boldsymbol{Y}_1,\boldsymbol{Y}_2(0)]\geqslant 0\}$。$P_{FO}(\boldsymbol{Y}_1)$ 的计算属于静态可靠度理论的范畴，本文不再多述。将 $g[\boldsymbol{Y}_1^*,\boldsymbol{Y}_2(t)]$ 对 $x=0$ 的期望穿阈率记为 $v_0^-(t,\boldsymbol{Y}_1^*)$，显然有以下关系式：$v_0^-(t) = v_0^-(t,\boldsymbol{Y}_1^*)/[1-P_{FO}(\boldsymbol{Y}_1)]$，式中，$\boldsymbol{Y}_1^*$ 为求解 $P_{FO}(\boldsymbol{Y}_1)$ 时获得的设计验算点。将时段 $(0,T)$ 分割为 N_T 个子时段(N_T 足够大以保证精度)，失效概率可写为

$$P_F = 1 - [1 - P_{FO}(Y_1)]\exp\left[-\sum_{i=1}^{N_T}\frac{v_0^-(t_i,\boldsymbol{Y}_1^*)}{1-P_{FO}(\boldsymbol{Y}_1)}\Delta\tau_i\right] \tag{3}$$

式中:$\Delta\tau_i = t_i - t_{i-1}$。至此问题转化为求解 $v_0^-(t_i,\boldsymbol{Y}_1^*)$。

$g(\boldsymbol{Y}_1^*,\boldsymbol{Y}_2(t))$ 简记为 $g[\boldsymbol{Y}_2(t)]$。过 $g[\boldsymbol{Y}_2(t)]$ 面上最佳线性化点 $\boldsymbol{Y}_2^*(t)$(可选为 Hasofer - Lind 点[9],为确定值)作一切平面,原点与切平面之间的距离就是瞬时可靠指标 $\beta(t)$:$\beta(t) = \alpha^{\mathrm{T}}(t)\boldsymbol{Y}_2^*(t)$,$\alpha(t) = -\nabla g[\boldsymbol{Y}_2^*(t)]/\|\nabla g[\boldsymbol{Y}_2^*(t)]\|$, 而:$\nabla g[\boldsymbol{Y}_2^*(t)] = [\boldsymbol{T}_2^{-1}(t)]^{\mathrm{T}}\nabla G[\boldsymbol{X}_2^*(t)]$,$\boldsymbol{T}_2$ 为 $\boldsymbol{T}$ 的子矩阵,令:$\boldsymbol{Z}(t) = \alpha^{\mathrm{T}}(t)\boldsymbol{Y}_2(t)$,$\boldsymbol{Z}(t)$ 一般是非平稳随机过程。显然,求解 $v_0^-(t,\boldsymbol{Y}_1^*)$ 可以转化为求解 $Z(t)$ 以 $x = \beta(t)$ 为阈值的正向期望穿阈率 $v_\beta^+(t)$。$\boldsymbol{Z}(t)$ 的期望和方差以及 $\dot{\boldsymbol{Z}}(t)$ 的方差可以按下式求出

$$E[Z(t)] = \overline{Z}(t) = \alpha^{\mathrm{T}}(t)E[\boldsymbol{Y}_2(t)] = 0 \tag{4}$$

$$\mathrm{Var}[Z(t)] = \sigma_Z^2(t) = \alpha^{\mathrm{T}}(t)\boldsymbol{C}_{Y_2}\alpha(t) = \alpha^{\mathrm{T}}(t)\alpha(t) \tag{5}$$

$$\mathrm{Var}[\dot{Z}(t)] = \sigma_{\dot{Z}}^2(t) = \dot{\alpha}^{\mathrm{T}}(t)\dot{\alpha}(t) + \alpha^{\mathrm{T}}(t)\boldsymbol{C}_{\dot{Y}_2}\alpha(t) + 2\dot{\alpha}^{\mathrm{T}}(t)\boldsymbol{C}_{Y_2\dot{Y}_2}\alpha(t) \tag{6}$$

式中:$\boldsymbol{C}_{Y_2\dot{Y}_2}$ 和 $\boldsymbol{C}_{\dot{Y}_2}$ 可以由式(2)得出;Z 与 $\dot{Z}$ 之间的相关系数 $\rho_{Z\dot{Z}}(t)$ 可以写为:$\rho_{Z\dot{Z}}(t) = [\alpha^{\mathrm{T}}(t)\dot{\alpha}(t) + \alpha^{\mathrm{T}}(t)\boldsymbol{C}_{Y_2\dot{Y}_2}\alpha(t)]/[\sigma_Z(t)\sigma_{\dot{Z}}(t)]$。

由式(1)可得 $Z(t)$ 对 $x = \beta(t)$ 的期望穿阈率 $v_\beta^+(t)$。求出 $v_\beta^+(t)$ 后,可按式(3)求出 P_F。对于离散时刻 $t_i(i = 0,1,\cdots,N_T)$,上述各式以离散形式出现,具体公式这里不再一一列出。其中 $\dot{T}(t_i)$ 以及 $\dot{\alpha}(t_i)(i = 0,1,\cdots,N_T)$ 可以由差分公式近似求得。Y^* 可由以下的叠代格式获得

$$\boldsymbol{Y}_2^{(m+1)}(t) = (\boldsymbol{Y}_2^{(m)\mathrm{T}}(t)\alpha^{(m)}(t) + g[\boldsymbol{Y}_2^{(m)}(t)]/\|\nabla g[\boldsymbol{Y}_2^{(m)}(t)]\|)\alpha^{(m)}(t) \tag{7}$$

3 大体积混凝土结构温度徐变应力的首次超越可靠度

从上述可知,大体积混凝土结构温度徐变应力首次超越可靠度的计算关键在于求解 $\partial G/\partial\boldsymbol{X}$、$\dot{\boldsymbol{X}}(t)$ 的方差 $\mathrm{Var}[\dot{\boldsymbol{X}}(t)]$ 以及 $\boldsymbol{X}(t)$ 和 $\dot{\boldsymbol{X}}(t)$ 之间的协方差 $\mathrm{Cov}[\boldsymbol{X}(t),\dot{\boldsymbol{X}}(t)]$。

3.1 基于随机有限元求解 $\partial G/\partial\boldsymbol{X}$

若 $X_i(t)$ 为抗力项(如抗拉强度等),则 $\partial G/\partial\boldsymbol{X}$ 可由功能函数式直接微分得出[6],其中所用应力值由有限元计算得出。如果 $X_i(t)$ 不是抗力项(如弹模等),由 $\partial G/\partial X_i = (\partial G/\partial\sigma)^{\mathrm{T}}(\partial\sigma/\partial X_i)$ 式中,$\partial G/\partial\sigma$ 可由功能函数形式直接计算出,而 $\partial\sigma/\partial X_i$ 则需通过随机有限元法获得。

3.1.1 温度徐变应力分析的初应变解法简述

在利用有限元进行温度徐变应力分析时,目前通常采用初应变隐式解法。对于三维复杂应力状态,有以下递推计算格式

$$\begin{cases}\Delta\varepsilon_n^C = (1 - \mathrm{e}^{-k\Delta\tau_n})\omega_n + Q\Delta\sigma_n\varphi_n^*(1 - f_n\mathrm{e}^{-k\Delta\tau_n}) \\ \omega_n = \mathrm{e}^{-k\Delta\tau_n}\omega_{n-1}Q\Delta\sigma_{n-1}\varphi_{n-1}^*f_{n-1}\mathrm{e}^{-k\Delta\tau_{n-1}} \\ \omega_1 = Q\Delta\sigma_0\varphi_0\end{cases} \tag{8}$$

式中：$f_n = (e^{k\Delta\tau_n} - 1)/(k\Delta\tau_n)$；$Q$ 的表达式可参见有关文献；$\Delta\varepsilon_n^C$ 和 $\Delta\sigma_n$ 分别为 t_{n-1} 时刻到 t_n 时刻的徐变变形增量和应力增量；$\Delta\tau_n = t_n - t_{n-1}, \varphi_n^* = \varphi(t_{n-1} + \Delta\tau_n/2)$。

第 n 时段总应变增量 $\Delta\varepsilon_n$ 为：$\Delta\varepsilon_n = \Delta\varepsilon_n^e + \Delta\varepsilon_n^C + \Delta\varepsilon_n^T + \Delta\varepsilon_n^0$，其中：$\Delta\varepsilon_n^e$ 为弹性应变增量，$\Delta\varepsilon_n^T$ 为温差应变增量，$\Delta\varepsilon_n^0$ 为自生体积变形增量。

第 n 时段应力增量为：$\Delta\sigma_n = D_n^* \{B\Delta u_n - \omega_n(1 - e^{-k\Delta\tau_n}) - \Delta\varepsilon_n^T - \Delta\varepsilon_n^0\}$，其中：$\Delta u_n$ 为第 n 时段位移增量，而：$D_n^* = D_n/[1 + \varphi_n^*(1 - f_n e^{-k\Delta\tau_n}) \cdot E(t_{n-1} + \Delta\tau_n/2)]$，其中 D_n 为弹性矩阵。由虚功原理，可以得到有限元支配方程

$$K_n\Delta u_n = \Delta P_n^C + \Delta P_n^T + \Delta P_n^0 + F \tag{9}$$

式中：F 为外荷载；K_n、ΔP_n^C、ΔP_n^T、ΔP_n^0 的含义及表达式可参阅有关文献。

任意时刻的应变和应力可以写为：$\varepsilon_n = \sum_{i=1}^{n}\Delta\varepsilon_i, \sigma_n = \sum_{i=1}^{n}\Delta\sigma_i$。

3.1.2 初应变隐式解法的随机有限元列式

对式(8)、(9)引入随机变量的摄动量，利用摄动原理，经整理可得随机有限元列式的零次式和一次式，零次式与式(8)类同，这里只给出一次式

$$\begin{cases}\Delta\varepsilon_n^C f = (1 - e^{-k\Delta\tau_n})\omega'_n + \Delta\tau_n e^{-k\Delta\tau_n}\overline{\omega}_n k' + Q(\sigma'_n\overline{\varphi}_n^* - \overline{\sigma}_n\varphi_n^{*\prime})(1 - \overline{f}_n e^{-k\Delta\tau_n}) + \\ \quad Q\overline{\sigma}_n\overline{\varphi}_n^* e^{-k\Delta\tau_n}(f'_n + \Delta\tau_n k') \\ \omega'_n = (-\Delta\tau_n k'\overline{\omega}_{n-1} + \omega_{n-1}')e^{-k\Delta\tau_n} + Q(\sigma_{n-1}'\overline{\varphi}_{n-1}^* - \overline{\sigma}_{n-1}\varphi_{n-1}^{*\prime})\overline{f}_{n-1}e^{-k\Delta\tau_{n-1}} + \\ \quad Q\overline{\sigma}_{n-1}\overline{\varphi}_{n-1}^* e^{-k\Delta\tau_{n-1}}(f_{n-1}' - \Delta\tau_{n-1}k') \\ \omega'_1 = Q(\Delta\overline{\sigma}_0\varphi'_0 + \Delta\sigma'_0\overline{\varphi}_0)\end{cases} \tag{10}$$

$$\begin{aligned}\Delta\sigma'_n = {} & \overline{D}_n^*[\Delta\varepsilon'_n - \omega'_n(1 - e^{-k\Delta\tau_n}) + \overline{\omega}_n e^{-k\Delta\tau_n}\Delta\tau_n k' - \Delta\varepsilon_n^{T'} - \Delta\varepsilon_n^{0'}] + \\ & D_n^{*\prime}[\Delta\overline{\varepsilon}_n - \overline{\omega}_n(1 - e^{-k\Delta\tau_n}) - \Delta\overline{\varepsilon}_n^T\Delta\overline{\varepsilon}_n^0]\end{aligned} \tag{11}$$

$$\Delta u'_n = \overline{K}_n^{-1}(\Delta P'_n - K'_n\Delta\overline{u}_n) \tag{12}$$

式(10)、(11)中 f'_n、$D_n^{*\prime}$ 可直接微分得出，这里不再列出。由式(10)～(12)一步一步地求出 $\Delta\varepsilon'_n$、$\Delta\sigma'_n$ 后，可得 t_n 时刻的 ε'_n、σ'_n

$$\varepsilon'_n = \sum_{i=1}^{n}\Delta\varepsilon'_i \qquad \sigma'_n = \sum_{i=1}^{n}\Delta\sigma'_i \tag{13}$$

3.2 $\mathrm{Var}[\dot{X}(t)]$ 及 $\mathrm{Cov}[X(t), \dot{X}(t)]$ 的计算

3.2.1 当 $X(t)$ 为 $E(t)$、$\varphi(t)$ 和 $R(t)$ 时

$X(t)$ 总可以近似地表示为：$X(t) = \overline{X}(t) + \sum_k X'_k(t)\Delta B_k$。其中，$B_k$ 为对应于 $X(t)$ 的基本随机变量，$X'_k(t)$ 为 $X(t)$ 对 B_k 的偏导数。如果 $X(t)$ 为 $\varphi(t)$，则 $B_1 = p_1$，$B_2 = p_2, B_3 = p_3$；如果 $X(t)$ 为 $E(t)$，则 $B_1 = E_0, B_2 = m_2$；如果 $X(t)$ 为 $R(t)$，则 $B_1 = R_0, B_2 = m_2$。于是：$\dot{X}(t) = \dot{\overline{X}}(t) + \sum_k \dot{X}_k'(t)\Delta B_k$。从而，$\mathrm{Var}[X(t)]$ 及 $\mathrm{Cov}[X(t), \dot{X}(t)]$ 可以近似地按下式计算

$$\begin{cases}\text{Var}[\dot{X}(t)] \approx \sum_{k1}\sum_{k2} X'_{k1}(t)X'_{k2}(t)\text{Cov}(B_{k1},B_{k2}) \\ \text{Cov}[X(t),\dot{X}(t)] \approx \sum_{k1}\sum_{k2} X'_{k1}(t)X'_{k2}(t)\text{Cov}(B_{k1},B_{k2})\end{cases} \tag{14}$$

3.2.2　当 $X(t)$ 为温度随机过程 $T(t)$ 时

影响温度场的随机因素考虑为[3]:① 边界温度,对于重力坝、拱坝等大型水工建筑物,边界温度总可以表示为:$T_n(t) = T_m + \sum_{i=1}^{na} T_{ai}(t)$($na$ 为环境温度种类数);② 绝热温升 θ:$\theta = \theta_0(1 - e^{-m_1 t})$,其中 θ_0、m_1 为随机变量;③ 初始温度 T_0 以及混凝土热学参数:导温系数 a、表面放热系数 λ 和导热系数 b。如果在同一定解问题中同时考虑环境温度和绝热温升随机过程对温度场的影响,问题将十分复杂。文献[3]因此利用定解问题的叠加原理,将原定解问题分离为随机环境温度定解问题 Ⅰ 和随机绝热温升定解问题 Ⅱ,其中定解问题 Ⅰ 可进一步分离为定解问题 $\text{Ⅰ}^{(0)}$ 和定解问题 $\text{Ⅰ}^{(i)}$($i = 1,\cdots,na$)。

定解问题 $\text{Ⅰ}^{(0)}$ 中不包含随机过程影响量,文献[3]基于摄动法随机有限元给出了随机温度场的一阶摄动方程

$$\overline{\boldsymbol{K}}_1 \boldsymbol{T}'_k + \overline{\boldsymbol{K}}_2 \dot{\boldsymbol{T}}'_k + \boldsymbol{Q}'_n = 0, \quad (k = 1,2,\cdots) \tag{15}$$

式中:$\overline{\boldsymbol{K}}_1$、$\overline{\boldsymbol{K}}_2$ 以及 $\boldsymbol{Q}'_k$ 的表达式可参见文献[3]。

由上式可得

$$\dot{\boldsymbol{T}}'_k = \overline{\boldsymbol{K}}_2^{-1}(-\boldsymbol{Q}'_k - \overline{\boldsymbol{K}}_1 \boldsymbol{T}'_k) \tag{16}$$

从而,$\text{Var}[\dot{\boldsymbol{T}}(t)]$ 和 $\text{Cov}[\boldsymbol{T}(t),\dot{\boldsymbol{T}}(t)]$ 可以近似按下式计算

$$\begin{cases}\text{Var}[\dot{T}^{(i)}(t)] \approx \sum_{k1}\sum_{k2} \dot{T}_{k1}^{(i)}\dot{T}_{k2}^{(i)}\text{Cov}(B_{k1},B_{k2}) \\ \text{Cov}[T^{(i)}(t),\dot{T}^{(i)}(t)] \approx \sum_{k1}\sum_{k2} T_{k1}^{(i)}\dot{T}_{k2}^{(i)'}\text{Cov}(B_{k1},B_{k2})\end{cases} \quad (i = 1,\cdots,NP) \tag{17}$$

式中:B_{k1}、B_{k2} 为影响温度场的基本随机变量;i 表示第 i 结点;NP 为结点总数。

定解问题 $\text{Ⅰ}^{(i)}$($i = 1,\cdots,na$)为周期平稳温度场问题,温度场可写为

$$\boldsymbol{T} = \boldsymbol{H}(\omega)e^{i\omega(t-t_0)} \tag{18}$$

式中:$H(\omega)$ 温度场复频响应函数列阵,文献[3]将 $\boldsymbol{H}(\omega)$ 视为随机材料参数的随机函数,提出了复频响应 - 随机有限元法,可得 $\boldsymbol{H}(\omega)$ 的均值 $\overline{\boldsymbol{H}}(\omega)$ 和对温度场基本随机变量的偏导数 $\boldsymbol{H}'_k(\omega)$($k = 1,2,\cdots$)。将 $\boldsymbol{H}(\omega) \approx \overline{\boldsymbol{H}}(\omega) + \sum_{i=1}^{n} \boldsymbol{H}'_k(\omega)\Delta B_k$ 代入式(18),可得

$$\boldsymbol{T}(t) \approx \overline{\boldsymbol{H}}(\omega)e^{i\omega(t-t_0)} + \sum_k \boldsymbol{H}'_k(\omega)e^{i\omega(t-t_0)}\Delta B_k \tag{19}$$

于是,$\dot{\boldsymbol{T}}(t)$ 可表示为

$$\dot{\boldsymbol{T}}(t) \approx i\omega[\overline{\boldsymbol{H}}(\omega)e^{i\omega(t-t_0)} + \sum_k \boldsymbol{H}'_k(\omega)e^{i\omega(t-t_0)}\Delta B_k] \tag{20}$$

根据复数随机过程原理,可得

$$\text{Var}[\dot{T}^{(i)}(t)] \approx \sum_{k1}\sum_{k2} \omega^2 \mid H_{k1}^{(i)'}(\omega) \mid \mid H_{k2}^{(i)'}(\omega) \mid \text{Cov}(B_{k1}B_{k2}) \quad (i = 1,\cdots,NP) \tag{21}$$

$$\mathrm{Cov}[T^{(i)}(t),\dot{T}^{(j)}(t)] \approx \sum_{k1}\sum_{k2}\omega \mid H_{k1}^{(i)'}(\omega) \mid \mid H_{k2}^{(j)'}(\omega) \mid \mathrm{Cov}(B_{k1},B_{k2})$$
$$(i,j=1,\cdots,NP) \tag{22}$$

式中：$|\cdot|$ 表示求模。

对于随机绝热温升定解问题 Ⅱ，有以下的随机有限元一次方程式

$$\overline{\boldsymbol{K}}_1\Delta\boldsymbol{T}'_{2k}+\overline{\boldsymbol{K}}_2\Delta\dot{\boldsymbol{T}}'_{2k}+\Delta\boldsymbol{Q}'_k=0 \tag{23}$$

式中：$\Delta\boldsymbol{Q}'_k$ 的表达式参见文献[3]。与式(16)、式(17)类似，由上式可以方便地求出 $\mathrm{Var}[\Delta\dot{\boldsymbol{T}}]$ 和 $\mathrm{Cov}[\Delta\boldsymbol{T},\Delta\dot{\boldsymbol{T}}]$。

总的随机温度场的 $\mathrm{Var}[\dot{\boldsymbol{T}}(t)]$ 和 $\mathrm{Cov}[\boldsymbol{T}(t),\dot{\boldsymbol{T}}(t)]$ 由上述三部分计算结果累加而得到。实际计算时，以上公式的计算与随机温度场的计算同步进行，所增加的计算量不大。

4 算例

自由板右侧气温 $T=0$，表面放热系数 $b_1=6.0\mathrm{kal/(m^2\cdot h\cdot ℃)}$；左侧气温 $T=A\cos\omega(t-t_0)$，$b_2=12.0\mathrm{kal/(m^2\cdot h\cdot ℃)}$，见图1。$\omega=7.169\times10^{-4}\mathrm{1/h}$，板厚2.6m，导热系数 $\lambda=1.25\mathrm{kal/(m^2\cdot h\cdot ℃)}$，导温系数 $\alpha=0.002\,17\mathrm{m^2/h}$。计算温度场时，取参数 A、a、b_1、b_2、λ、θ_0、m_1 为随机变量，$\overline{A}=30℃$，$\overline{\theta}_0=25.0℃$，$\overline{m_1}=0.397$，变异系数均为0.2。由于此时已不易得出温度的精确解，本文按在文献[3]中提出的方法计算出随机场温度场的均值和方差。由计算出的随机场温度场可进一步计算随机温度徐变应力，所得结果称之为准精确解(quasi－exact)。徐变度形式为 $\overline{C}(t,\tau)=p_1+\dfrac{p_2}{\tau^{p_3}}[1-\mathrm{e}^{-k(t-\tau)}]$。取混凝土弹模参数 E_0、m_2 以及徐变参数 k、p_1、p_2、p_3 为随机变量，均值为 $\overline{E}_0=2.0\times10^4\mathrm{MPa}$，$\overline{m}_2=0.3$，$\overline{k}=0.026(1/\mathrm{d})$，$\overline{p}_1=0.9\times10^{-5}\mathrm{cm^2/kg}$，$\overline{p}_2=4.82\times10^{-5}\mathrm{cm^2/kg}$，$\overline{p}_3=1.0(\mathrm{cm^2/kg})$，变异系数均为0.1。混凝土线胀系数为 $\alpha=0.000\,012(1/℃)$，泊松比 $\mu=0.167$。混凝土的抗拉强度参数 R_0 和 m_3 的均值为：$\overline{R}_0=150\mathrm{MPa}$，$\overline{m}_3=0.3$，变异系数分别为0.2和0.1，强度准则采用最大拉应力准则。图2～图5中分别给出了温度徐变应力、瞬时可靠指标、期望穿阈率和首次超越可靠指标的准精确解以及本文计算结果(分别为实线和虚线)。从图2～图5可知，约前18d自由板中心点处基本处于受压状态(最初约2d受较小的拉应力)，故瞬时可靠指标较大而期望穿阈率则几乎为0，首次超越可靠指标则出现一小段平台，18d之后，自由板中心点受迅速增大的拉应力作用，瞬时可靠指标很快降低，期望穿阈率大幅度增加，使首次超越可靠指标迅速减少。中后期拉应力值的波动使瞬时可靠指标和期望穿阈率也出现波动，由于中后期 $\mathrm{Var}[\dot{X}(t)]$ 较小，反使期望穿阈率不如前期大。可以看]出，与不考虑混凝土绝热温升情况相比，虽然初始时刻首次超越可靠指标基本相同，但考虑混凝土绝热温升后自由板中心点基本处于拉应力状态，首次超越可靠

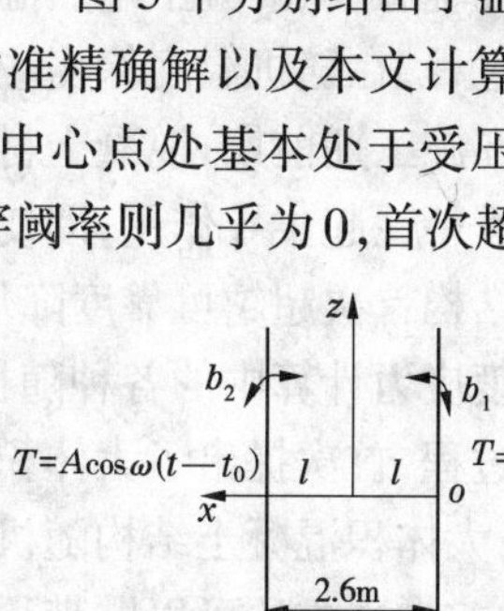

图1 混凝土自由板

指标减小较大。

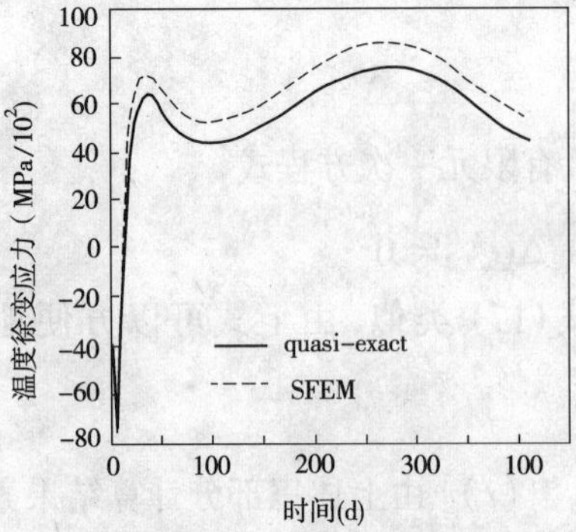

图 2　自由板中心点处的温度徐变应力

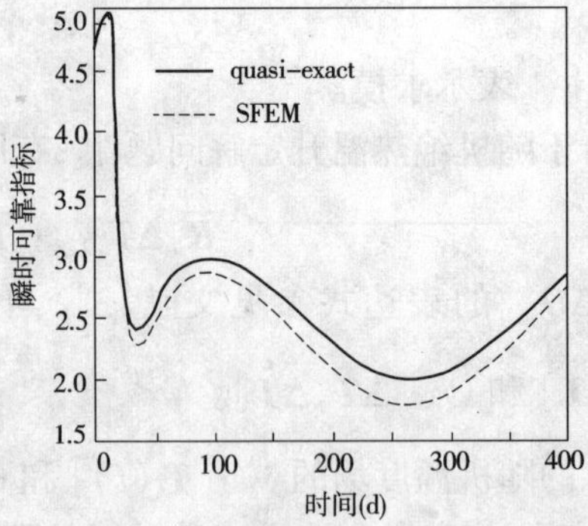

图 3　自由板中心点处的瞬时可靠指标

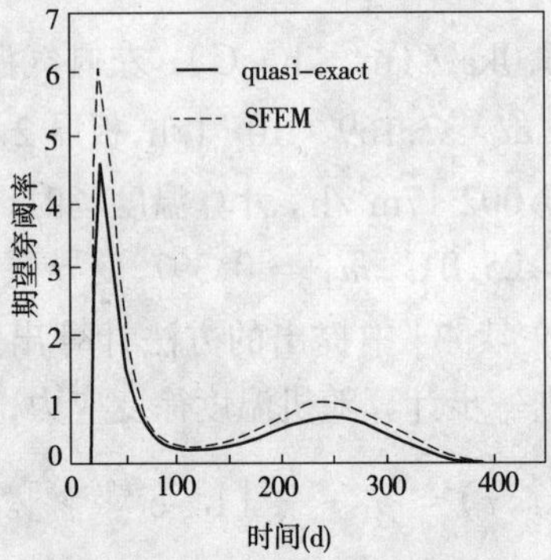

图 4　期望穿阈率过程曲线

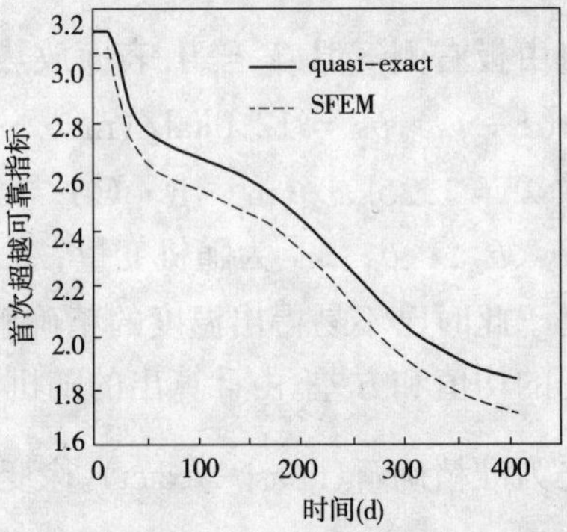

图 5　自由板中心点处的首次超越可靠指标

5　结语

环境温度、混凝土绝热温升以及热学参数的随机性使混凝土结构内部温度为非平稳随机过程，在随机温度徐变应力场作用下混凝土结构的失效概率随时间的增长逐渐增大，尤其在施工期前期，混凝土材料参数以及温度场的非平稳特性较为强烈，后期温度场的随机过程特性起主导作用，即使混凝土温度为平稳随机过程，但可能存在的长时间的作用仍会使结构首次超越可靠度降低。本文基于随机有限元法，充分考虑大体积混凝土结构徐变温度应力计算中的各种随机因素，视混凝土温度场、弹模、徐变度以及抗力等为非平稳随机过程，首次提出了大体积混凝土结构随机温度徐变应力首次超越可靠度的计算方法。至此，大体积混凝土结构随机温度徐变应力首次超越可靠度问题已较为有效地得以解决。同时，按本文方法可以顺带得出任一时刻的静态可靠指标（瞬时可靠指标），本文方法无疑具有一定的实用价值。

参考文献

[1] Heller R A. *Temperature response of an infinitely thick slab to random surface temperature*. Mech Research Communication, 1976, 3:379～385

[2] Bazant Z P, Wang T S. *Spectral analysis of random shrinkage in concrete structures*. J of Engng Mech, ASCE,1984, 110(2): 173～186

[3] 刘宁,刘光廷. 大体积混凝土结构随机温度场的随机有限元算法. 清华大学学报,1996,36(1):41～47

[4] Madsen H O, et al. . *Methods of structural safty*. Prentice-Hall, Englewood Cliffs, N J, 1986

[5] Grigoriu M. *Crossing non-gaussian translation processes*. J of Engng Mech, ASCE, 1984, 110(4): 610～620

[6] 刘宁,吕泰仁. 随机有限元及其工程应用. 力学进展, 1995,25(1): 114～126

TIME-DEPENDENT RELIABILITY ASSESSMENT FOR MASS CONCRETE STRUCTURES

Abstract Under the influences of random thermal creep stresses, the safety of mass concrete structures could be described by time-dependent reliability. In this paper, based on probabilistic finite element method (PFEM), numerical methods for the time-dependent reliability assessment are presented. By using the presented methods, various kinds of random variability including non-stationary temperature of concrete, modulus of elasticity, creep compliance and strength parameters of concrete can be conveniently taken into account. The suggested method is useful for the mass concrete structural design and safety evaluation when random factors should be taken into account.

Key words structural reliability; probabilistic finite element method; thermal creep stress; mass concrete structure

1 Introduction

It has been the subject of worldwide attention for many years that structural failures of mass concrete structures such as concrete gravity dams and arch dams could be caused by thermal cracks which usually come from thermal stresses. It is very important, therefore, to calculate the thermal stresses correctly during both the construction period and operation period. For deterministic research, in the early studies, Bazant and his coworkers proposed a Dirichlet series creep function for aging concrete[1] and suggested an exponential algorithm for concrete creep[2] which is now in prevalent use. After then, a similar algorithm termed as the initial strain method was presented by Zhu[3]. The paper was, however, written in Chinese and therefore has not aroused much international attention. The method was successfully used by Du and Liu[4] for thermal creep stress analysis and developed for random creep stress analysis by Liu[5].

It is known that inherent random variations of both thermal and mechanical parameters of concrete have significant effects on structural temperature field, thermal stresses, and hence, the structural reliability. The solution of random thermal creep stress of concrete was initiated in the middle 1970s[6]. Since then, many valuable studies have been performed, among which the work done by Tsubaki and Bazant[30] Bazant and Wang[7~9], Liu[5,10], are notable.

So far, many methods have been developed for the evaluation of time-invariant reliability (see, for example, the work of Madsen[11] and Melchers)[12]. Because of the time-

本文选自《Structural Safety》1999 年刊,作者还有 Liu Ning。

dependent effects of thermal creep stresses, it is not easy (if not impossible) for a time-invariant reliability theory to handle the safety of mass concrete structure. Comparatively, assessment of time-dependent reliability is much more difficult than that of the time-invariant one. From the viewpoint of structural damage mechanism, the first crossing problem is the most important one among those time-dependent reliability theories. Many efforts have been made on this problem since the 1940s. However, up to now, the available analytical solution is still the solution of inclusion and exclusion series suggested by Rice. For many practical engineering problems, exact analytical solutions can not be obtained. Therefore, approximate numerical methods are used instead of the analytical one. One of the most widely used numerical models is the Poisson's model, which is, to the knowledge of the authors, precise enough for many practical engineering problems, and thus, is readily adopted in this paper for the analysis of time-dependent (the first crossing) reliability of mass concrete structures influenced by thermal creep stresses.

Usually, the performance function of mass concrete structures could be modeled as a nonlinear function of random processes or random variables. In order to handle the problem, the nonlinear performance function is often linearized, for which the work done by Hohenbichler and Rackwitz[14] and Dolinsky[15], among many others can be referred to. Moreover, when the method of linearization is used, the best point for the linearization should be determined. Breitung[16] suggested that the point, which is closest to the origin, could be used for linearization. It was shown by his work that an approximation of this point leads to an asympototically correct result when reliability index $\beta \rightarrow \infty$. Alternatively, Pearce and Wen[17] suggested a linearization method at the point of the maximum local mean out-crossing rate. Additionally, some other choices could also be made according to different situations. Ditlevsen[18] proved that, however, for simplicity, the point closest to the origin could be used for the linearization without sacrificing much precision. Therefore, in this paper, this point is used for the linearization when calculating the time-dependent reliability.

When nonlinear performance function is described as a function of stationary processes (or say a combination of stationary processes), some methods have already been suggested. The work done by Pearce and Wen[17], Breitung and Rackwitz[19], Grigoriu[20], Wen and Chen[21], Ditlevsen[22], Madsen and Tvedt[23], among many others should be mentioned. However, many natural phenomena can not be sufficiently described by stationary random processes. Actually, for the time-dependent reliability of mass concrete structures, it is much more reasonable to model the thermal creep stress in concrete mentioned above as a nonstationary process rather than a stationary one. For this reason, an efficient numerical method was suggested by Liu[24].

The main purpose of this paper is to develop numerical methods for evaluating the reliability of mass concrete structures, which is influenced by the non-stationary random thermal creep stresses. For this purpose, a numerical method for the time-dependent reliability (the first crossing reliability) is presented. By using this method, and based on the first order perturbation technique and the initial strain method, a probabilistic finite element method is suggested to deal with the problem.

2 Description of Random Variability

2.1 Creep Compliance C(t,τ)

Under the assumption of linear creep, the creep compliance of concrete is usually expressed as follows[3,5]

$$C(t,\tau) = \varphi(\tau)(1 - e^{-k(t-\tau)}) \tag{1}$$

in which t and τ denote time and time interval, respectively. k is a coefficient obtained from test data, and

$$\varphi(\tau) = p_1 + p_2/\tau^{p_3} \tag{2}$$

in which p_1, p_2, p_3 are parameters determined by concrete creep test. Therefore, in the expression of creep compliance, there are in total four parameters. It is necessary to model them as random variables. By using the first order Taylor expansion, the creep compliance could be approximated expressed as

$$C(t,\tau) \approx \overline{C}(t,\tau) + (1 - e^{-\overline{k}(t-\tau)})\Delta\varphi + (t-\tau)e^{-\overline{k}(t-\tau)}\overline{\varphi}\Delta k \tag{3}$$

in which, $\overline{C}(t,\tau)$ is the expectation of $C(t,\tau)\cdot\Delta p_1, \Delta p_2, \Delta p_3$, and Δk are the small fluctuation parts of p_1, p_2, p_3 and k respectively; and $\Delta\varphi \approx \Delta p_1 + \tau^{-\overline{p}_3}\Delta p_2 - \overline{p}_2 \ln\tau \cdot \tau^{-\overline{p}_3}\Delta p_3$.

2.2 Elastic Modulus $E(\tau)$

The elastic modulus of concrete could be expressed as[5,10]

$$E(\tau) = E_0(1 - e^{-m_1\tau}) \tag{4}$$

in which, E_0 is the ultimate modulus of elasticity of concrete; m_1 is a coefficient obtained from test data. And therefore, when $\tau = 0$ we have $E = 0$, which denotes the beginning state of concrete; and when $\tau \to \infty$, we have $E = E_0$, which denotes the ultimate state of concrete. When describe the two parameters E_0 and m_1 as random variables, we have

$$E(\tau) \approx \overline{E}(\tau) + (1 - e^{-\overline{m}_1\tau})\Delta E_0 + \tau e^{-\overline{m}_1\tau}\overline{E}_0\Delta m_1 \tag{5}$$

2.3 Temperature of Concrete $T(x,y,z,t)$

Under the influence of random environmental temperature and random hydration heat of concrete, the random temperature of mass concrete structure could be obtained by using the probabilistic finite element method suggested by Liu[25].

2.4 Strength $R(\tau)$

For concrete structures, the strength of concrete could be described by the limit tensile strength. Similar to the expression of modulus of elasticity, $R(\tau)$ can be expressed as follows

$$R(\tau) = R_0(1 - e^{-m_2\tau}) \tag{6}$$

in which, R_0 and m_2 are random variables obtained from test data. And thus, we have

$$R(\tau) \approx \overline{R}(\tau) + (1 - e^{-\overline{m}_2 \tau})\Delta R_0 + \tau e^{-\overline{m}_2 \tau}\overline{R}_0 \Delta m_2 \tag{7}$$

3 Numerical Method for the First Crossing Reliability

Let the performance function be denoted as $G[\boldsymbol{X}(t)]$, where $X(t) = \{X_1(t), X_1(t), \cdots X_n(t)\}$ is a non-stationary stochastic process vector. During the time interval $[0, T]$, the failure probability can be expressed as[13,26]

$$P_f = 1 - P_s = 1 - \exp\left[-\int_0^T \nu_0^-(t)\mathrm{d}t\right] \tag{8}$$

in which, ν_0^- denotes the out-crossing rate from the negative direction with respect to the boundary $x = 0$. According to the study of Lin[27], we have

$$\nu_0^- = \frac{\sigma_{\dot{G}}(t)}{2\pi\sigma_G(t)}\left\{\sqrt{1-\rho^2}\exp\left[-\frac{1}{1-\rho^2}\frac{\overline{G}^2(t)}{2\sigma_G^2(t)}\right] + \sqrt{2\pi}\frac{\rho\overline{G}(t)}{\sigma_G}\exp\left(-\frac{\overline{G}^2}{2\sigma_G^2}\right)\Phi\left(\frac{\rho}{\sqrt{1-\rho}}\frac{\overline{G}(t)}{\sigma G}\right)\right\} \tag{9}$$

in which $\dot{G}$ is the differentiation of performance function with respect to time; ρ is the coefficient of covariance between G and $\dot{G}$. $\Phi(\cdot)$ is the Gaussian cumulative distribution function; σ_G and $\sigma_{\dot{G}}$ are the standard deviations of G and $\dot{G}$, respectively. At any time t, $\boldsymbol{X}(t)$ can be transformed to $\boldsymbol{Y}(t)$ by the following equation

$$\boldsymbol{Y}(t) = \boldsymbol{L}(t)[\boldsymbol{X}(t) - \overline{\boldsymbol{X}}(t)] \tag{10}$$

in which, $\boldsymbol{L}(t)$ is the lower triangular Cholesky factorization matrix with respect to the covariance matrix $\boldsymbol{C}_X(t)$ of $\boldsymbol{X}(t)$ at any time t. Accordingly, the original performance function $G[\boldsymbol{X}(t)]$ can be rewritten as follows

$$G[\boldsymbol{X}(t)] = G[\boldsymbol{L}^{-1}(t)\boldsymbol{Y}(t) + \overline{\boldsymbol{X}}(t)] = g[\boldsymbol{Y}(t)] \tag{11}$$

The random vector $\boldsymbol{X}(t)$ could be separated into two parts: the random variable part $\boldsymbol{X}_1$ and the random process part $\boldsymbol{X}_2(t)$. Correspondingly, $\boldsymbol{Y}(t)$ could also be separated into two parts: $\boldsymbol{Y}_1$ and $\boldsymbol{Y}_2(t)$, respectively. Therefore, the failure probability can be written as follows

$$P_f = 1 - [1 - P_{f0}(\boldsymbol{Y}_1)](1 - P_f[\boldsymbol{Y}_2(t)]) \tag{12}$$

in which

$$P_{f0}(\boldsymbol{Y}_1) = P\{g[\boldsymbol{Y}_1, \boldsymbol{Y}_2(0)] < 0\},$$
$$P_f[\boldsymbol{Y}_2(t)] = P\{g[\boldsymbol{Y}_1, \boldsymbol{Y}_2(t)] < 0 \mid g[\boldsymbol{Y}_1, \boldsymbol{Y}_2(0)] \geqslant 0\}$$

The calculation of $P_{f0}(\boldsymbol{Y}_1)$ is within the scope of time-invariant reliability problem and therefore need not be discussed any more. Let $\nu_0^-(t)$ and $\nu_0^-(t, \boldsymbol{Y}_1^*)$ denote the mean out-crossing rate of $g[\boldsymbol{Y}_1, \boldsymbol{Y}_2(t)]$ *and* $g[\boldsymbol{Y}_1^*, \boldsymbol{Y}_2(t)]$ respectively, in which $\boldsymbol{Y}_1^*$ is the design point coming from the computation of $P_{f0}(\boldsymbol{Y}_1)$. Obviously, we have[23]: $\nu_0^-(t) = \nu_0^-(t, \boldsymbol{Y}_1^*)/[1 - P_{f0}(\boldsymbol{Y})]$. Thus, the key problem is to obtain $\nu_0^-(t, \boldsymbol{Y}_1^*)$. Generally, it is difficult, if not impossible, to obtain an analytical expression of $\nu_0^-(t, \boldsymbol{Y}_1^*)$. A numerical method could be used instead. By dividing the time interval $(0,t)$ into N_T sub-intervals, $\nu_0^-(t, \boldsymbol{Y}_1^*)$ is discretized into $\nu_0^-(t_i, \boldsymbol{Y}_1^*)(i=1,2,\cdots,N_T)$. And then, Eq.(8) should be rewritten as

$$P_f = 1 - P_s = 1 - \exp\left[-\sum_{i=1}^{N_T}\frac{\nu_0^-(t_i, \boldsymbol{Y}_1^*)}{1-P_{f0}(\boldsymbol{Y}_1)}\Delta\tau_i\right] \tag{13}$$

in which, $\Delta\tau_i = t_i - t_{i-1}$. Let $g[\boldsymbol{Y}_1^*, \boldsymbol{Y}_2(t)]$ be simply denoted as $g[\boldsymbol{Y}_2(t)]$. The distance between the origin and the hyper-plane which is tangent to $g[\boldsymbol{Y}_2(t)]$ and passes through the best linearization point $\boldsymbol{Y}_2^*(t)$ (the design point), Hasofer and Lind[28] is the instantaneous reliability index

$$\beta(t) = [\boldsymbol{Y}_2^{*\mathrm{T}}\boldsymbol{Y}_2^*]^{1/2} = \alpha^{\mathrm{T}}(t)\boldsymbol{Y}_2^*(t) \tag{14}$$

in which $\alpha(t) = -\nabla g[\boldsymbol{Y}_2^*(t)]/\|\nabla g[\boldsymbol{Y}_2^*(t)]\|$, $\nabla g[\boldsymbol{Y}_2^*(t)] = \boldsymbol{L}_2^{-1}(t)\nabla G[\boldsymbol{X}_2^*(t)]$, where $\boldsymbol{L}_2(t)$ is the sub-matrix of $\boldsymbol{L}(t)$. Usually, an iterative scheme is needed for the determination of the design point $\boldsymbol{Y}_2^*(t)$[11].

$$\boldsymbol{Y}^{(m+1)}(t) = \left[\boldsymbol{Y}^{(m)\mathrm{T}}(t)\alpha^{(m)}(t) + \frac{g(\boldsymbol{Y}^{(m)})}{\|\nabla g(\boldsymbol{Y}^{(m)})\|}\right]\alpha^{(m)}(t) \tag{15}$$

Let $\boldsymbol{Z}(t) = \alpha^{\mathrm{T}}(t)\boldsymbol{Y}_2(t)$. $\boldsymbol{Z}(t)$ is a non-stationary process. It has been proved[23] that the calculation of mean out-crossing rate $\nu_0^-(t, \boldsymbol{Y}_1^*)$ of $g[\boldsymbol{Y}_1^*, \boldsymbol{Y}_2(t)]$ can be equivalently replaced by that of the mean out-crossing rate $\nu_\beta^+(t)$ of $\boldsymbol{Z}(t)$ from the positive direction with respect to the boundary of $x = \beta(t)$. The expectation and the variance $\boldsymbol{Z}(t)$ as well as the variance of $\dot{\boldsymbol{Z}}(t)$ can be calculated as follows

$$\begin{aligned} &E[\boldsymbol{Z}(t)] = 0 \\ &\mathrm{Var}[\boldsymbol{Z}(t)] = \alpha^{\mathrm{T}}(t)\alpha(t) \\ &\mathrm{Var}[\dot{\boldsymbol{Z}}(t)] = \dot{\alpha}^{\mathrm{T}}(t)\dot{\alpha}(t) + \alpha^{\mathrm{T}}(t)\boldsymbol{C}_{\dot{Y}_2}\alpha^{T}(t) + 2\dot{\alpha}^{\mathrm{T}}(t)\boldsymbol{C}_{Y_2,\dot{Y}_2}\alpha^{\mathrm{T}}(t) \end{aligned} \tag{16}$$

in which, $\boldsymbol{E}(\cdot)$ and $\mathrm{Var}(\cdot)$ denote expectation and variance, respectively. The correlation between $Z(t)$ and $\dot{Z}(t)$ can be expressed as

$$\rho_{Z\dot{Z}}(t) = \frac{\mathrm{Cov}[Z(t), \dot{Z}(t)]}{\sigma_Z(t)\sigma_{\dot{z}}(t)} = \frac{\alpha^{\mathrm{T}}(t)\dot{\alpha}(t) + \dot{\alpha}^{\mathrm{T}}(t)C_{Y_2\dot{Y}_2}\alpha^{T}(t)}{\sigma_Z(t)\sigma_{\dot{Z}}(t)} \tag{17}$$

in which σ_Z and $\sigma_{\dot{Z}}$ are the standard deviation of $Z(t)$ and $\dot{Z}(t)$, respectively, From Eqs.(9),(16) and (17), we can easily obtain the expression of $\nu_\beta^+(t)$.

Because of the discretization in time domain, Eqs.(9) and (14~17) all appear in discrete forms in time-domain. And therefore, $\dot{\boldsymbol{L}}(t_i)$ and $\dot{\alpha}(t_i)(i=1,2,\cdots,N_T)$ could be approximated by using the finite difference scheme:

$$\dot{\boldsymbol{L}}(t_i) = [\boldsymbol{L}(t_i) - \boldsymbol{L}(t_{i-1})]/\Delta\tau_i \tag{18a}$$

$$\dot{\alpha}(t_i) \approx [\alpha(t_i) - \alpha(t_{i-1})]/\Delta\tau_i \tag{18b}$$

Therefore, by step by step calculations, $\nu_\beta^+(t_i)(i=1,2,\cdots,N_T)$ can be obtained. And then, from Eq.(13), the failure probability can be calculated.

4 The First Crossing Reliability of Concrete Structures

According to the above discussion, the key to the first crossing reliability assessment is the calculation of $\partial G/\partial \boldsymbol{X}$, Var $[\dot{\boldsymbol{X}}(t)]$ and cov $[\boldsymbol{X}(t),\dot{\boldsymbol{X}}(t)]$. For mass concrete structure, as mentioned in the Section 2, $X_i(t)(i=1,2,\cdots,n)$ could be the random variable k, and random processes $\varphi(t), E(t), R(t)$ and $T(t)$, respectively. The performance function $G(\boldsymbol{X})$ in terms of the maximum tensile strength criterion is written as

$$G(\boldsymbol{X}(t),t) = R(t) - \sigma_1(t) \tag{19}$$

in which $\sigma_1(t)$ is the maximum tensile strength at time t, which is a function of $\sigma_x, \sigma_y, \sigma_z, \tau_{xy}, \tau_{yz}, \tau_{zx}$. Therefore, σ_1 is a nonlinear and implicit function of random variables and random processes, which implies that $G(\boldsymbol{X})$ is also a nonlinear implicit function of random variations.

4.1 Calculation of $\partial G/\partial X_i$ (i=1,2,…,n)

When X_i is strength parameter, the expression of $\partial G/\partial X_i$ can be easily obtained. When X_i is not the strength parameter, we have $\partial G/\partial X_i = (\partial G/\partial \sigma)^{\mathrm{T}}(\partial \sigma/\partial X_i)$, in which $\partial G/\partial \sigma$ can be conveniently obtained. While $\partial \sigma/\partial X_i$ can be obtained by using the PFEM discussed in the following.

For creep stress analysis, creep strain can be obtained by the following recursive formulas

$$\left.\begin{aligned} \Delta\varepsilon_i^c &= (1-\mathrm{e}^{-k\Delta\tau_i})\omega_i + \boldsymbol{Q}\Delta\sigma_i\varphi_i^*(1-f_i\mathrm{e}^{-k\Delta\tau_i}) \\ \omega_i &= \mathrm{e}^{-k\Delta\tau_i}\omega_{i-1} + \boldsymbol{Q}\Delta\sigma_{i-1}\varphi_{i-1}^* f_{i-1}\mathrm{e}^{-k\Delta\tau_{i-1}} \\ \omega_1 &= \boldsymbol{Q}\Delta\sigma_0\varphi_0 \end{aligned}\right\} \tag{20}$$

where the subscript (i) denotes the ith step for the time interval $(t_{i-1}), t_i, \Delta\tau_i = t_i - t_{i-1}$. $\Delta\varepsilon_i^C$ and $\Delta\sigma_i$ denote creep strain and stress increment tensor respectively, $f_i = (\mathrm{e}^{-k\Delta\tau_i}-1)/(k\Delta\tau_i)$. The expression of $\boldsymbol{Q}$ can be found in a lot of literature[3,4], for instance. $\varphi_i^* = \varphi(t_{i-1}+\Delta\tau_i/2)$. The total strain increment tensor can be written as

$$\Delta\varepsilon_i = \Delta\varepsilon_i^e + \Delta\varepsilon_i^C + \Delta\varepsilon_i^{(T)} + \Delta\varepsilon_i^\nu \tag{21}$$

in which $\Delta\varepsilon_i^e, \Delta\varepsilon_i^C, \Delta\varepsilon_i^{(\mathrm{T})}$ and $\Delta\varepsilon_i^\nu$ are elastic, creep, thermal and self-volumetric strain increment, respectively. Therefore, when regarding the $\Delta\varepsilon_i^C, \Delta\varepsilon_i^T$ and $\Delta\varepsilon_i^\nu$ as initial strain, stress increment can be written as

$$\Delta\sigma_{\mathrm{i}} = \boldsymbol{D}_i^*[\Delta\varepsilon_i - \omega_i(1-\mathrm{e}^{-k\Delta\tau_i}) - \Delta\varepsilon_i^{(T)} - \Delta\varepsilon_i^\nu] \tag{22}$$

in which $\boldsymbol{D}_i^* = \boldsymbol{D}_i/[1+\varphi_i^*(1-f_i\mathrm{e}^{-k\Delta\tau_i})E(t_{i-1}+\Delta\tau_i/2)]$ and $\boldsymbol{D}_i$ is the strain-stress matrix of elasticity at the time $(t_{i-1}+\Delta\tau_i/2)$. From the above equation, a finite element governing equation can be easily obtained

$$\boldsymbol{K}_i\Delta\boldsymbol{u}_i = \Delta\boldsymbol{F}_i + \Delta\boldsymbol{P}_i^C + \Delta\boldsymbol{P}_i^{(T)} + \Delta\boldsymbol{P}_i^\nu \tag{23}$$

in which, $\boldsymbol{K}_i$ is the global stiffness matrix at the time $t_{i-1}+\Delta\tau_i/2$; $\Delta\boldsymbol{F}_i, \Delta\boldsymbol{P}_i^C, \Delta\boldsymbol{P}_i^{(T)}$ and

$\Delta \boldsymbol{P}_i^{\nu}$ are the external load increment and the equivalent creep, thermal and volumetric load, respectively[4,5]. From Eqs. (22) and (23), the stress and strain increment tensor can be calculated. Consequently, the total stress and strain can be obtained by accumulating the stress and strain increment respectively: $\varepsilon = \sum \Delta \varepsilon_i, \sigma = \sum \Delta \sigma_i$.

By applying the first order perturbation technique, the first order equations in correspondence with the above initial strain method can be written as follows

$$\overline{\boldsymbol{K}}_i \Delta \boldsymbol{u}'_i = \Delta \boldsymbol{F}_i + \Delta \boldsymbol{P}_i^{C'} + \Delta \boldsymbol{P}_i^{(T)'} + \Delta \boldsymbol{P}_i^{\nu'} - \boldsymbol{K}_i \Delta \overline{\boldsymbol{u}}_i \tag{24}$$

in which, $\Delta \overline{\boldsymbol{u}}_i$ can be obtained from Eq. (23). The superscript (′) denotes differentiation with respect to random variable $X_i(t)$ with any fixed t. And

$$\begin{aligned}
\boldsymbol{K}'_i &= \sum_e \iiint_{\Omega_e} \boldsymbol{B}^{\mathrm{T}} \boldsymbol{D}_i^{*'} \boldsymbol{B} \mathrm{d}\nu \\
\Delta \boldsymbol{P}_i^{C'} &= \sum_e \iiint_{\Omega_e} \boldsymbol{B}^{\mathrm{T}} \{ \overline{\boldsymbol{D}}_i^{*'} [\omega'_i (1 - \mathrm{e}^{-\bar{k}\Delta\tau_i}) + \overline{\omega}_i \Delta\tau_i \mathrm{e}^{-\bar{k}\Delta\tau_i} k'] + \boldsymbol{D}_i^{*'} \overline{\omega}_i (1 - \mathrm{e}^{-\bar{k}\Delta\tau_i}) \} \mathrm{d}\nu \\
\Delta \boldsymbol{P}_i^{(\mathrm{T})'} &= \sum_e \iiint_{\Omega_e} \boldsymbol{B}^{\mathrm{T}} (\boldsymbol{D}_i^{*'} \overline{\boldsymbol{T}} + \overline{\boldsymbol{D}}_i^{*} \boldsymbol{T}') \alpha [1,1,1,0,0,0]^{\mathrm{T}} \mathrm{d}\nu \\
\Delta \boldsymbol{P}_i^{\nu'} &= \sum_e \iiint_{\Omega_e} \boldsymbol{B}^{\mathrm{T}} (\boldsymbol{D}_i^{*'} \Delta \overline{\varepsilon}_i^{\nu} + \overline{\boldsymbol{D}}_i^{*} \boldsymbol{T}' \Delta \varepsilon_i^{\nu'}) \mathrm{d}\nu
\end{aligned} \tag{25}$$

in which, α is the coefficient of thermal expansion (a deterministic constant). When the random variation of self-volumetric strain is neglected, in above equations, we have $\Delta \varepsilon_i^{\nu'} = 0$. After $\Delta \boldsymbol{u}'_i$ obtained from Eq. (24), we obtain the first order differentiation of stress increment tensor

$$\begin{aligned}
\Delta \sigma'_i = \overline{\boldsymbol{D}}_i^{*} [\boldsymbol{B} \Delta \boldsymbol{u}'_i - \omega'_i (1 - \mathrm{e}^{-\bar{k}\Delta\tau_i}) + \overline{\omega}_i \mathrm{e}^{-\bar{k}\Delta\tau_i} \Delta\tau_i k' - \Delta \varepsilon_i^{(T)'}] + \\
\boldsymbol{D}_i^{*'} [\Delta \overline{\varepsilon}_i - \overline{\omega}_i (1 - \mathrm{e}^{-\bar{k}\Delta\tau_i}) - \Delta \overline{\varepsilon}_i^{(T)} - \Delta \overline{\varepsilon}_i^{\nu}]
\end{aligned} \tag{26}$$

Therefore, $\partial\sigma / \partial X_i$ can be obtained as follows

$$\frac{\partial \sigma}{\partial X_i} = \sum \frac{\partial \Delta \sigma}{\partial X_i} \tag{27}$$

4.2 Calculation of Var $[\dot{X}(t)]$ and Cov$[X(t), \dot{X}(t)]$

4.2.1 When $X_i(t)$ is $E(t), \varphi(t)$ or $R(t)$

According to Eqs. (3), (5) and (7), it is known that $X(t)$ can be expressed in the form of $X(t) = \overline{X}(t) + \sum_i^{n_b} X'_i \Delta B_i$, in which $B_i (i = 1, 2, \cdots, n_b)$ are the basic random variables with respect to $X(t)$. When $X(t)$ is $E(t)$, we have $n_b = 2, B_1 = E_0, B_2 = m_1$; when $X(t)$ is $R(t)$, we have $n_b = 2, B_1 = R_0, B_2 = m_2$; and when $X(t)$ is $\varphi(t)$, we obtain $n_b = 3$, $B_1 = p_1, B_2 = p_2, B_3 = p_3$. Then, we have

$$\dot{X}(t) \approx \dot{\overline{X}}(t) + \sum_i^{n_b} \dot{X}'_i \Delta B_i \tag{28}$$

Therefore, Var$[\dot{X}(t)]$ and Cov$[x(t), \dot{\overline{X}}(t)]$ can be approximated as follows

$$\left.\begin{aligned}\operatorname{Var}[\dot{X}(t)] &\approx \sum_{k_1}\sum_{k_2}\dot{X}'_{k_1}(t)\dot{X}'_{k_2}(t)\operatorname{Cov}(B_{k_1},B_{k_2}) \\ \operatorname{Cov}[X(t),\dot{X}(t)] &\approx \sum_{k_1}\sum_{k_2}X'_{k_1}(t)\dot{X}'_{k_2}(t)\operatorname{Cov}(B_{k_1},B_{k_2})\end{aligned}\right\} \tag{29}$$

4.2.2 When $X_i(t)$ is the thermal process $\boldsymbol{T}(x,y,z,t)$

Based on random variational principle of heat conductivity and corresponding probabilistic finite element method, a method for the assessment of $\boldsymbol{T}(x,y,z,t)$ was given by Liu[25]. By using the method, calculations of $\operatorname{Var}[\dot{\boldsymbol{T}}(t)]$ and $\operatorname{Cov}[\boldsymbol{T}(t),\dot{\boldsymbol{T}}(t)]$ are further discussed in the following.

It is known that the temperature field of mass concrete structure is mainly influenced by the random variabilities including environmental temperature $T_a(t)$, hydration heat of concrete $\theta(t)$ and initial temperature of concrete $T_0(x,y,z)$ as well as the random parameters such as temperature transfer coefficient a, coefficient of heat conductivity λ and coefficient of surface heat emission b. The environmental temperature could be simulated as $T_a(t) = T_m + \sum_{k=1}^{n_a} T_{ak}(t)$, in which T_m is a random variable and $T_{ak}(t)(k=1,2,\cdots n_a)$ are periodic (sine or cosine) stochastic processes. The hydration heat of concrete could be simulated as $\theta(t)=\theta_0(1-\mathrm{e}^{-m_3 t})$, in which θ_0 and m_3 are random variables, a, λ and b are also modeled as random variables.

In order to calculate the influences of both the environmental temperature and the hydration heat of concrete, the temperature of concrete structure is separated into three parts $\boldsymbol{T}_{1(0)}$, $\boldsymbol{T}_{1(k)}(k=1,2,\cdots,n_a)$, and $\Delta\boldsymbol{T}_2$.

(1) Temperature field $\boldsymbol{T}_{1(0)}$ comes from the following equations

$$\begin{aligned}\dot{\boldsymbol{T}}_{1(0)}(t) &= a\nabla^2\boldsymbol{T}_{1(0)}(t)+\dot{\bar{\theta}}(t),\ \boldsymbol{T}_{1(0)}\Big|_{t=0} \\ &= \boldsymbol{T}_0(x,y,z),\ \frac{\partial\boldsymbol{T}_{1(0)}}{\partial n}\Big|_C+\frac{b}{\lambda}\boldsymbol{T}_{1(0)}\Big|_C=\frac{b}{\lambda}\boldsymbol{T}_m\end{aligned} \tag{30}$$

(2) Temperature field $\boldsymbol{T}_{1(k)}(k=1,2,\cdots,n_a)$ is determined by

$$\dot{\boldsymbol{T}}_{1(k)}(t)=a\nabla^2\boldsymbol{T}_{1(k)}(t),\ \boldsymbol{T}_{1(k)}\Big|_{t=0}=0,\frac{\partial\boldsymbol{T}_{1(k)}}{\partial n}\Big|_C+\frac{b}{\lambda}\boldsymbol{T}_{1(k)}\Big|_C=\frac{b}{\lambda}\boldsymbol{T}_{ak} \tag{31}$$

And (3) temperature field $\Delta\boldsymbol{T}_2$ yields

$$\Delta\dot{\boldsymbol{T}}_2(t)=a\nabla^2[\Delta\boldsymbol{T}_2(t)]+\Delta\dot{\theta},\Delta\boldsymbol{T}_2\Big|_{t=0}=0\ \frac{\partial\Delta\boldsymbol{T}_2}{\partial n}\Big|_C+\frac{b}{\lambda}\Delta\boldsymbol{T}_2\Big|_C=0 \tag{32}$$

As for $T_{1(0)}$, we have the first order perturbation equation as in the following

$$\overline{\boldsymbol{T}}'_{1(0)}=\overline{\boldsymbol{K}}_2^{-1}(-\boldsymbol{q}'_1-\overline{\boldsymbol{K}}_1\boldsymbol{T}'_{1(0)}) \tag{33}$$

in which

$$\begin{aligned}\overline{\boldsymbol{K}}_1 &= \sum_e[K_1^{(ij)}] \\ &= \sum_e\left[\bar{a}\iiint_{\Omega_e}\left(\frac{\partial N_i}{\partial x}\frac{\partial N_j}{\partial x}+\frac{\partial N_i}{\partial y}\frac{\partial N_j}{\partial y}+\frac{\partial N_i}{\partial z}\frac{\partial N_j}{\partial z}\right)\mathrm{d}x\mathrm{d}y\mathrm{d}z+\bar{a}\iint_C\frac{\bar{b}}{\bar{\lambda}}N_iN_j\mathrm{d}s\right]\end{aligned}$$

$$\overline{\boldsymbol{K}}_2 = \sum_e [K_2^{(ij)}] = \sum_e \left[\iiint_{\Omega_e} N_i N_j \, \mathrm{d}x\mathrm{d}y\mathrm{d}z \right]$$

$$\boldsymbol{q}'_1 = \iiint_{\Omega} \left[a' \left(\frac{\partial \boldsymbol{N}^{\mathrm{T}}}{\partial x}\frac{\partial \boldsymbol{N}}{\partial x} + \frac{\partial \boldsymbol{N}^{\mathrm{T}}}{\partial y}\frac{\partial \boldsymbol{N}}{\partial y} + \frac{\partial \boldsymbol{N}^{\mathrm{T}}}{\partial z}\frac{\partial \boldsymbol{N}}{\partial z} \right) \boldsymbol{T} - \frac{\partial \theta'}{\partial t} \right] \mathrm{d}\Omega +$$

$$\iint_{C_e} \left(a' \frac{\overline{b}}{\overline{\lambda}} + \overline{a} \frac{b'\overline{\lambda} - \overline{b}\lambda'}{\overline{\lambda}^2} \right) \boldsymbol{N}^{\mathrm{T}} \boldsymbol{N} \overline{T} \mathrm{d}s -$$

$$\iint_{C_e} \boldsymbol{N}^{\mathrm{T}} \left[\left(a' \frac{\overline{b}}{\overline{\lambda}} + \overline{a} \frac{b'\overline{\lambda} - \overline{b}\lambda'}{\overline{\lambda}^2} \right) \overline{\boldsymbol{T}}_a + \overline{a} \frac{\overline{b}}{\overline{\lambda}} \boldsymbol{T}'_a \right] \mathrm{d}s$$

where $\boldsymbol{N}$ is global shape function matrix, and N_i is the value of $\boldsymbol{N}$ at the ith node. From Eq. (33), we obtain

$$\left.\begin{aligned} \mathrm{Var}[\dot{T}^{(l)}(t)] &\approx \sum_{k_1}\sum_{k_2} \dot{T}_{k_1}^{(l)} \dot{T}_{k_3}^{(l)} \mathrm{Cov}(B_{k_1}, B_{k_2}) \\ \mathrm{Cov}[T^{(l)}(t), \dot{T}^{(l)}(t)] &\approx \sum_{k_1}\sum_{k_2} T_{k_1}^{(l)} \dot{T}_{k_2}^{(l)} \mathrm{Cov}(B_{k_1}, B_{k_2}) \end{aligned}\right\} (l = 1, 2, \cdots, N_P) \tag{34}$$

where B_{k_1} and B_{k_2} are the basic random variables for the thermal conduction problem. The superscript (l) denotes the ith node. N_P is the total number of nodes.

Because the environmental temperature could be modeled as $\boldsymbol{T}_a = \boldsymbol{A}\mathrm{e}^{i\omega(t-t_0)}$, the temperature $\boldsymbol{T}_{l(k)}$ $(k = 1, 2, \cdots n_a)$ can be expressed as

$$\boldsymbol{T}_{l(k)} = \boldsymbol{H}(\omega)\mathrm{e}^{i\omega(t-t_0)} \tag{35}$$

in which $\boldsymbol{H}(\omega)$ is a column matrix of the complex frequency response function. Because of the random properties of material thermal parameters, $\overline{\boldsymbol{H}}(\omega)$ is a random function of those random parameters. Therefore, $\boldsymbol{H}(\omega)$ can be approximately expressed as

$$\boldsymbol{H}(\omega) \approx \overline{\boldsymbol{H}}(\omega) + \sum_k H'_k(\omega)\Delta B_k \tag{36}$$

in which

$$\overline{\boldsymbol{H}}(\omega) = (\overline{\boldsymbol{K}}_1 + i\omega \overline{K}_2)^{-1} \sum_e \overline{a} \iint_{C_e} \frac{\overline{b}}{\overline{\lambda}} N_i \boldsymbol{N} \overline{\boldsymbol{A}} \mathrm{d}s$$

$$\boldsymbol{H}'(\omega) = (\overline{\boldsymbol{K}}_1 + i\omega \overline{\boldsymbol{K}}_2)^{-1} \boldsymbol{q}'_2$$

$$\boldsymbol{q}'_2 = -(\boldsymbol{K}'_1 + i\omega \boldsymbol{K}'_2)\overline{\boldsymbol{H}}(\omega) + \sum_e a' \iint_{C_e} \frac{b'\overline{\lambda} - \overline{b}\lambda' + \overline{b}\,\overline{\lambda}}{\lambda^{-2}} N_i \boldsymbol{N} \overline{\boldsymbol{A}} \mathrm{d}s +$$

$$\sum_e \overline{a} \iint_{C_e} \frac{\overline{b}}{\overline{\lambda}} N_i \boldsymbol{N} \boldsymbol{A}' \mathrm{d}s$$

From Eqs. (35) and (36), we have

$$\boldsymbol{T}_{lk}(t) \approx \overline{\boldsymbol{H}}(\omega)\mathrm{e}^{i\omega(t-t_0)} + \sum_j \boldsymbol{H}'_j(\omega)\mathrm{e}^{i\omega(t-t_0)}\Delta B_j \tag{37a}$$

$$\dot{\boldsymbol{T}}_{lk}(t) \approx i\omega[\overline{\boldsymbol{H}}(\omega)\mathrm{e}^{i\omega(t-t_0)} + \sum_j \boldsymbol{H}'_j(\omega) e^{i\omega(t-t_0)}\Delta B_j] \tag{37b}$$

According to theory of complex stochastic processes[29], we obtain

$$\left.\begin{aligned} \mathrm{Var}[\dot{T}^{(l)}(t)] &\approx \sum_{k_1}\sum_{k_2} \omega^2 \mid H_{k_1}^{(l)'}(\omega) \parallel H_{k_2}^{(l)'}(\omega) \mid \mathrm{Cov}(B_{k_1}, B_{k_2}) \\ \mathrm{Cov}[T^{(l)}(t), \dot{T}^{(l)}(t)] &\approx \sum_{k_1}\sum_{k_2} \omega \mid H_{k_1}^{(l)'}(\omega) \parallel H_{k_2}^{(l)'}(\omega) \mid \mathrm{Cov}(B_{k_1}, B_{k_2}) \end{aligned}\right\} \tag{38}$$

As for the third part $\Delta \boldsymbol{T}_2$, we have $\Delta \overline{\boldsymbol{T}}_2 = 0$ and

$$\overline{\boldsymbol{K}}_1 \Delta \overline{\boldsymbol{T}}'_2 + \overline{\boldsymbol{K}}_2 \Delta \dot{\overline{\boldsymbol{T}}}'_2 + \boldsymbol{q}'_3 = 0 \tag{39}$$

in which

$$\boldsymbol{q}'_3 = -\iiint_{\Omega} \boldsymbol{N}^{\mathrm{T}} [\overline{m}_3 \mathrm{e}^{-\overline{m}_3 t} \Delta\theta'_0 + (1 - \overline{m}_3 t \mathrm{e}^{-\overline{m}_3 t}) \Delta m'_3 \overline{\theta}_0] \mathrm{d}\Omega$$

from Eq. (39), and similar to Eq. (34), Var $[\Delta \dot{\boldsymbol{T}}_2]$ and Cov$[\Delta \boldsymbol{T}_2, \Delta \dot{\boldsymbol{T}}_2]$ can be conveniently obtained.

Therefore, by accumulating the above three parts of temperature filed, Var $[\dot{\boldsymbol{T}}]$ and Cov $[\boldsymbol{T}, \dot{\boldsymbol{T}}]$ of the total temperature filed can be approximately obtained.

5 Numerical Examples

5.1 Example 1——Time-dependent Reliability of an Unconstrained Concrete Slab

The time-dependent reliability of an unconstrained concrete slab under the influence of random thermal creep stress is considered. The thickness of the slab is assumed to be 2.6m (See Fig. 1). The temperature transfer coefficient and the coefficient of thermal conductivity of the concrete are assumed to be $a = 0.002\ 17\mathrm{m}^2/\mathrm{h}$ and $\lambda = 1.25$ kcal/(m·h·℃) respectively. Two different cases are taken into account. The first one is that hydration heat of concrete is not taken into account, while the second one is that hydration heat is taken into account. On the left side of the slab, the air temperature and the coefficient of surface heat emission are assumed to be $T_{a1} = 0$℃ and $b_1 = 6.0$kcal/(m^2·h·℃), respectively. While, on the right side, it is assumed that $T_{a2} = A\cos\omega t$ and $b_2 = 12.0$kcal/(m^2·h·℃), respectively, in which $\omega = \dfrac{2\pi}{365}(1/d)$. The hydration heat of concrete is assumed to be $\theta = \theta_0(1 - \mathrm{e}^{-m_3 t})$. When calculating the temperature field of slab, the parameters $A, a, b_1, b_2, \lambda, \theta_0$ and m_3 are taken as random variables. $\overline{A} = 30$℃, $\overline{\theta}_0 = 25.0$℃, $\overline{m}_3 = 0.397$. The coefficients of variation are all assumed to be 0.2. The creep compliance is assumed to be $C(t, \tau) = \left(p_1 + \dfrac{p_2}{\tau^{p_3}}\right)[1 - \mathrm{e}^{-k(t-\tau)}]$, in which the parameters k, p_1, p_2 and p_3 are regarded as random variables. $\overline{k} = 0.026(1/d)$, $\overline{p}_1 = 0.9\times10^{-5}\mathrm{cm}^2/\mathrm{kg}$, $\overline{p}_2 = 4.82\times10^{-5}\mathrm{cm}^2/\mathrm{kg}$ and $\overline{p}_3 = 1.0$. As for the modulus of elasticity, the parameters E_0 and m_1 are random variables. $E_0 = 2.0\times10^4$MPa, $\overline{m}_1 = 0.03$. The coefficients of variation of k, p_1, p_2 and p_3 as well as E_0 and m_1 are all

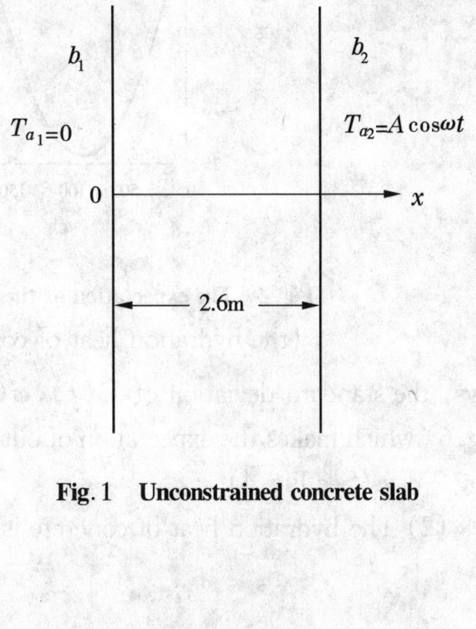

Fig. 1 Unconstrained concrete slab

assumed to 0.1. $\alpha = 1.2\times10^{-5}(1/℃)$. The Poisson's ratio $\mu = 0.167$. As for the strength parameters, R_0 and m_2 the tensile strength parameters, are taken as random variables. $\overline{R}_0 = 1.5\text{MPa}$, $\overline{m}_2 = 0.3$. And the coefficients of variation are 0.2 and 0.1, respectively.

(1) The hydration heat of concrete is not taken into account.

In this case, because the hydration heat of concrete is not taken into account, it is not difficult to obtain the theoretical solution of the temperature of the slab. Correspondingly, according to the theory of elastic mechanics, the thermal creep stress could be obtained (Fig.2). And therefore, the theoretical solution of instantaneous reliability index and the expectation of out-crossing rate as well as the first crossing reliability can be conveniently calculated (Figs 3~5). The results calculated by the suggested methods in this paper are also given in Figs 2~5. It is shown by Figs 2~5 that during the first 180 days (except for the 2 days at the beginning), the central point of the concrete ($x = 1.3$m) slab is basically under compression (Fig.2), therefore, the instantaneous reliability index appears to be a large positive number (Fig.3). Because the maximum tensile strength criterion is used, the expectation of out-crossing rate is about zero (Fig.4). Between 180 days and 350 days, the central point is under tension. Because of the periodic property of the temperature, the standard deviation of temperature is invariant with time ($\sigma_T(t) \approx 0.04626℃/\text{d}$), however, after 180

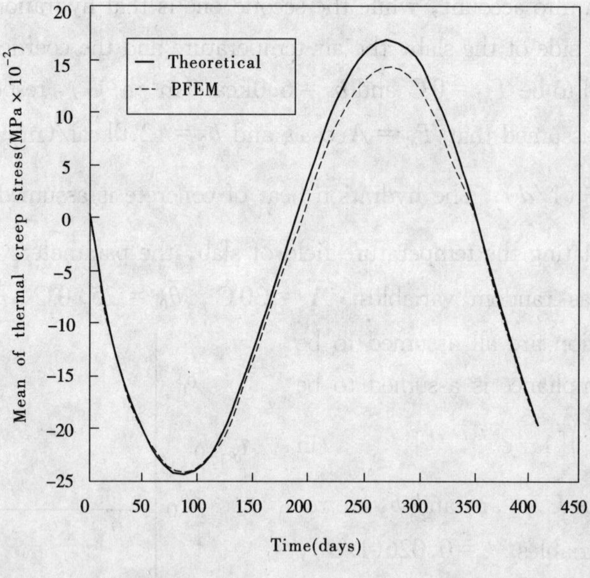

Fig.2 The expectation of thermal creep stress at the point $x = 1.3$m

(the hydration heat of concrete is not taken into account)

days, the standard deviation of $\dot{E}(t)$, $\dot{\varphi}(t)$ and $\dot{R}(t)$ have been largely decreased (See Fig.6) which makes the expectation of out-crossing rate much smaller than that of the beginning 2 days(See Fig.4).

(2) The hydration heat of concrete is taken into account.

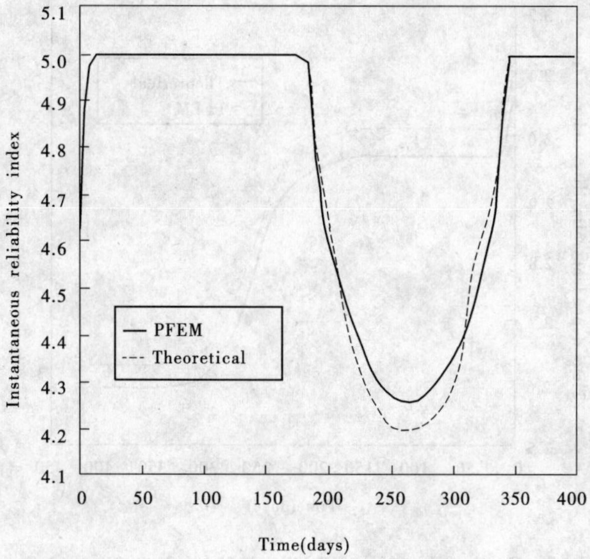

Fig. 3 Instantaneous reliability index at the point $x = 1.3$m
(the hydration heat of concrete is not taken into account)

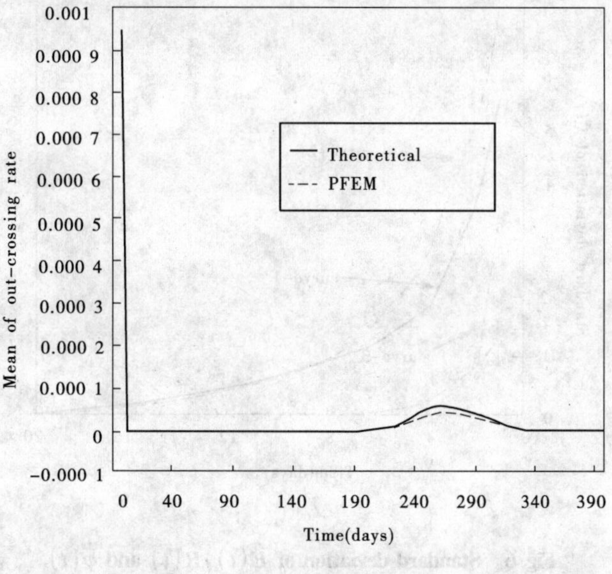

Fig. 4 Expectation of out-crossing rate at the point $x = 1.3$m
(the hydration heat of concrete is not taken into account)

Under this circumstance, theoretical solution is not available. Quasi-exact solutions, however, could be used instead[5,25]. The quasi-exact solutions and the computational results obtained by using the suggested methods are given in Figs 7~10. Since the hydration heat is taken into account, thereafter about 18 days, the central point of the slab is under tension, which makes the first reliability decrease more rapidly than that of the case (1).

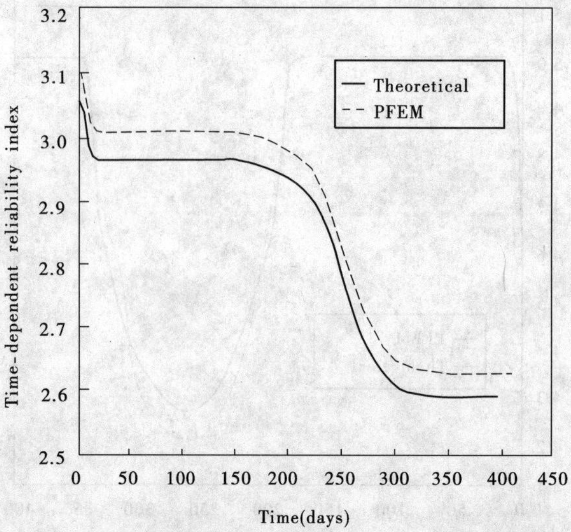

Fig. 5 The time-dependent reliability index at the point $x = 1.3$m

the hydration heat of concrete is not taken into account)

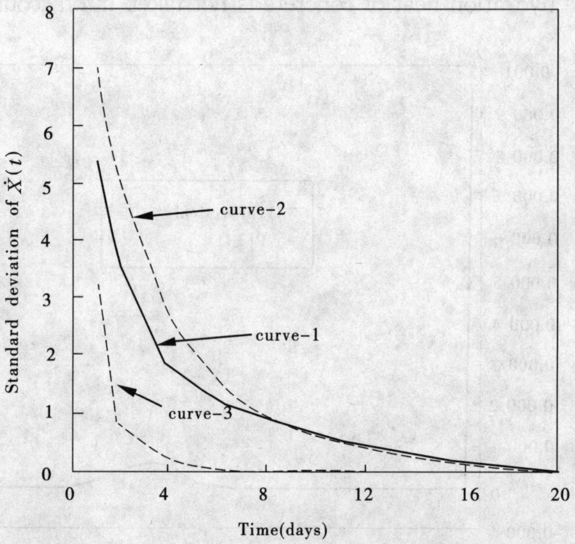

Fig. 6 Standard deviation of $\dot{E}(t)$, $\dot{R}(t)$ and $\dot{\varphi}(t)$

curve 1—$\dot{E}(t)$, curve 2—$\dot{R}(t)$, curve 3—$\dot{\varphi}(t)$

(the hydration heat of concrete is not taken into account)

5.2 Example 2——Time-Dependent Reliability of a Typical Concrete Mass

Considering a typical concrete mass (6m in length, 4m in height and 4m in width) on a rock foundation. A cross section of the concrete mass is shown in Fig. 11. Except for the bottom of the concrete mass, all sides are exposed in the air, of which the temperature is assumed to be $T_a = A\cos\omega t$, $\overline{A} = 10℃$, $\omega = \frac{2\pi}{365}(1/d)$. The temperature of the rock foundation is assumed to be a deterministic constant (10℃). The thermal parameters of the concrete are

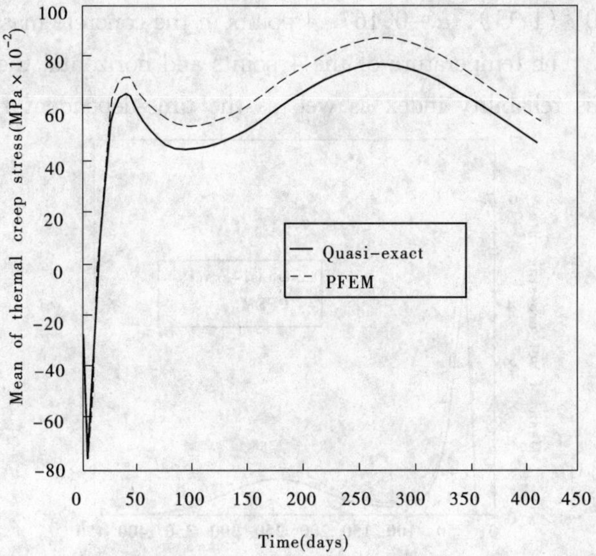

Fig. 7 The expectation of thermal creep stress at the point $x = 1.3$m

(the hydration heat of concrete is taken into account)

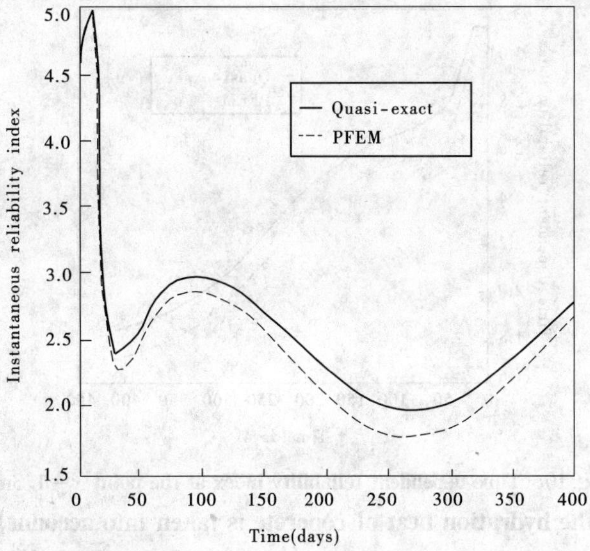

Fig. 8 Instantaneous reliability index at the point $x = 1.3$m

(the hydration heat of concrete is taken into account)

assumed to be $\overline{a} = 0.002\,17 m^2/h$, $\overline{b} = 12.0 kcal/(m^2 \cdot h \cdot ℃)$, $\overline{\lambda} = 1.25 kcal/(m \cdot h \cdot ℃)$. And the parameters of the hydration heat of concrete are $\overline{\theta}_0 = 25.0℃$, $\overline{m}_3 = 0.397$. The parameters for the modulus of elasticity and creep compliance as well as the tensile strength are assumed to be $\overline{E}_0 = 2.0\times10^4$MPa, $\overline{m}_1 = 0.3$, $\overline{p}_1 = 0.9\times10^{-5}\text{cm}^2/\text{kg}$, $\overline{p}_2 = 4.82\times10^{-5}\text{cm}^2/\text{kg}$, $\overline{p}_3 = 1.0\text{cm}^2/\text{kg}$, $\overline{R}_0 = 2.0$MPa and $\overline{m}_2 = 0.3$. The coefficients of variation are all assumed to be 0.1. $\alpha = 1.2\times10^{-5}(1/℃)$, $\mu = 0.167$. 4 points in the concrete mass are taken into account (See Fig. 11). The temperature of the 4 points and horizontal thermal creep stresses and the instantaneous reliability index as well as the time-dependent reliability index are

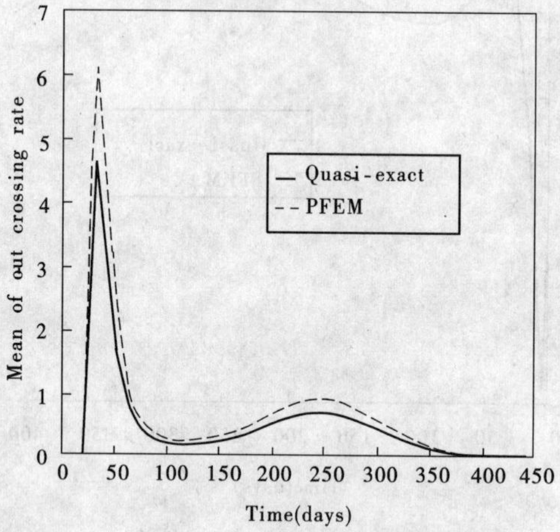

Fig. 9　Expectation of out-crossing rate at the point $x = 1.3$m
(the hydration heat of concrete is taken into account)

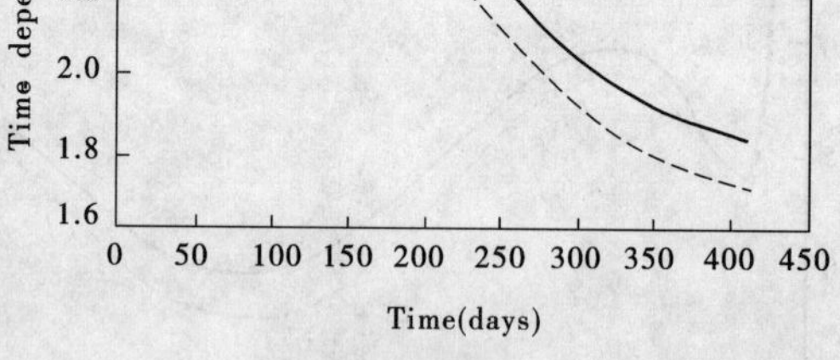

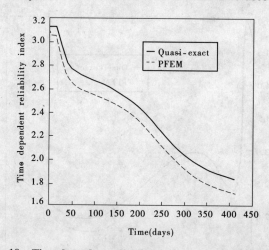

Fig. 10　Time-dependent reliability index at the point $x = 1.3$m
(the hydration heat of concrete is taken into account)

given in Fig. 12～15. From Fig. 13, it is known that the point 1 is basically under compression, therefore, the instantaneous reliability index and time-dependent reliability index are quite large (Figs 14 and 15). Other points, however, are under the influences of tensile stresses. Therefore, comparatively, the reliability indices are much smaller (Figs 14 and 15). And in Fig. 15, it is known that the time-dependent reliability indices of point 3 and point 4 are so small that they are almost definitely unsafe. This conclusion, however, could not be obtained by the calculation of ordinary time-invariant reliability index (the aforementioned instantaneous reliability index in Fig. 14).

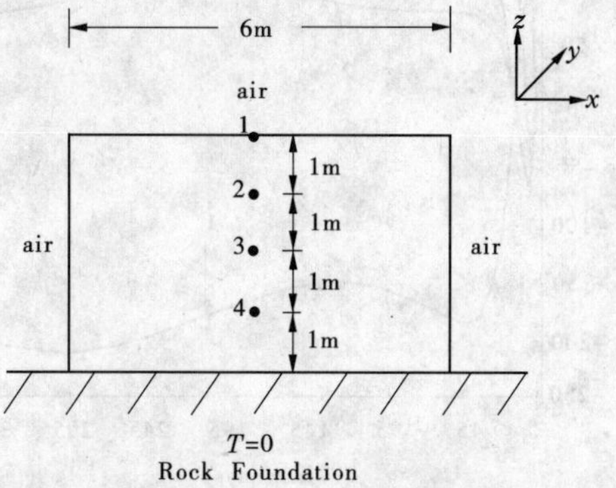

Fig. 11 A cross-section of the concrete mass

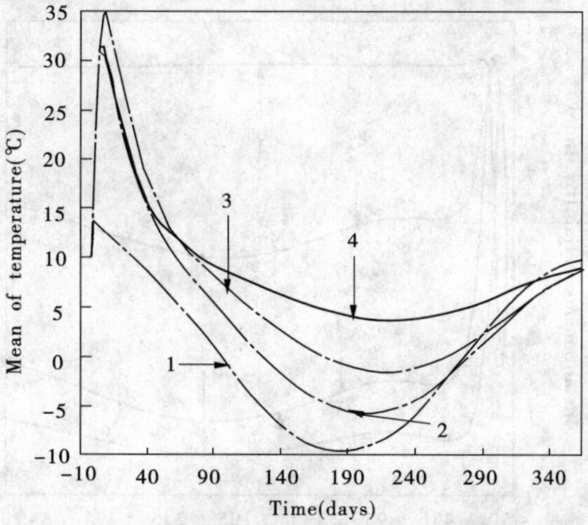

Fig. 12 Expectation of temperature

6 Conclusions

Under the influences of the environmental random temperature and the random hydration heat as well as the random material parameters of concrete, the temperature and stresses in concrete structures could be non-stationary processes. Because of the properties of the stochastic processes, it is insufficient to use the time-invariant reliability to describe the safety of mass concrete structures. Actually, for any fixed time t, the instantaneous reliability index suggested in this paper is within the scope of time-invariant reliability, which might over-estimate the safety of concrete structures. The effect of stochastic processes of temperature, modulus of elasticity, strength and creep compliance as well as stresses would gradually reduce the time-dependent reliability of concrete structures. At the beginning of construction period, both the temperature and the stress of concrete vary severely with time due to the

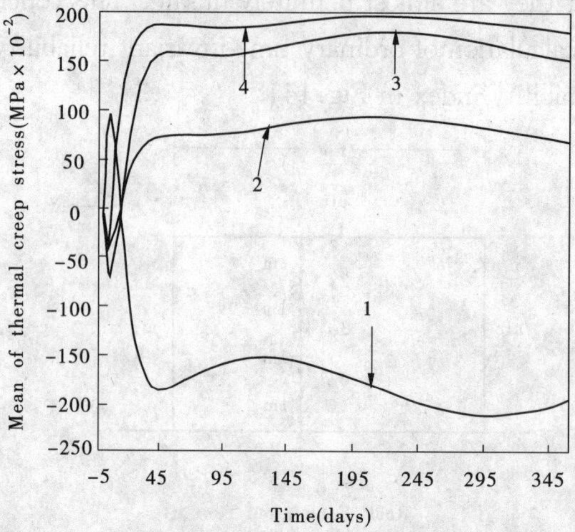

Fig. 13　Expectation of thermal creep stresses (σ_x)

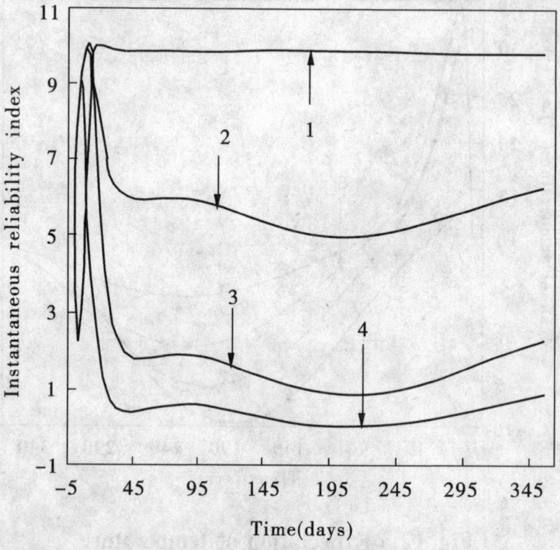

Fig. 14　Instantaneous reliability indices

release of hydration heat of concrete. Although the expectation of tensile stress would not be large, differentiation of modulus of elasticity, creep compliance function and the strength with respect to time appear to be very large, which might cause a large out-crossing rate. During the later construction period, the effect of stochastic material parameters such as the modulus of elasticity and creep compliance function etc. become weaker and weaker. Meanwhile, the temperature in the concrete gradually becomes a periodic stationary process. Therefore, the expectation of out-crossing rate would not be large in comparison with the previous stage. However, a long time influence resulting from those stochastic processes could cause a large decrease in time-dependent reliability of the concrete structure. It can be concluded that besides the variation of the random parameters, both the variation ofdifferen

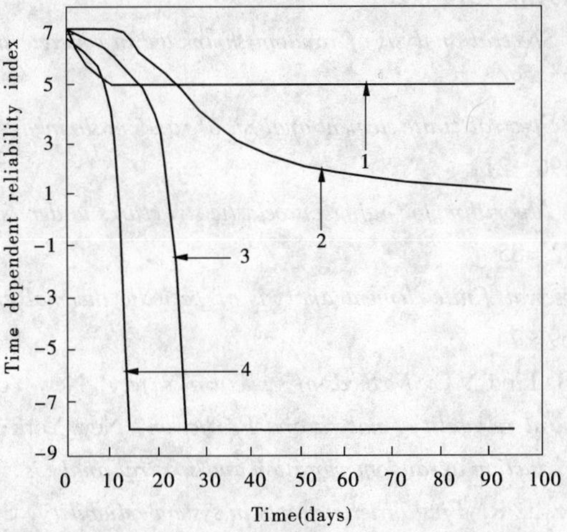

Fig. 15 Time-dependent reliability indices

tiation of the stochastic processes with respect to time and the loading period also have significant influences on the time-dependent reliability of the structure. As for a practical engineering project, for example a concrete gravity dam, the construction period could cover quite a few years. Therefore, it is very important to evaluate the time-dependent reliability caused by the random thermal creep stresses rather than a time-invariant one. The methods presented in this paper could be useful for the engineering design and reliability evaluation for mass concrete structures.

Acknowledgement

The authors would like to acknowledge the support of the National Science Foundation of China.

References

[1] Bazant Z P, Wu S T. *Dirichlet series creep function for aging concrete*. J of Eng Mech ASCE 1974; 100 (3): 575~97

[2] Bazant Z P. *Numerical stable algorithm with increasing time steps for integral-type aging creep*. Proc. of the lst Int. Conf. on Struct. Mech. In Reactor Technology. West Berlin, 4, 1971. H2/2

[3] Zhu P F. *An implicit algorithm for thermal creep stress in concrete*. Chinese J of Water Resource (in Chinese) 1983; 5: 32~40

[4] Du C J, Liu G T. *Numerical procedure for thermal creep stress in mass concrete structures*. Communications in Num Methods in Eng 1994; 10: 545~54

[5] Liu N, Liu G T, *Research on non-stationary random thermal creep stresses in mass concrete structures*. Finite Elements in Analysis and Design 1997; 26: 83~95

[6] Heller R A. *Temperature response of an infinitely thick slab to random surface temperature*. Mech Re-

search Communication 1976;3:379～85

[7] Bazant Z P, Wag T S. *Spectral analysis of random shrinkage in concrete structures*. J of Engng Mech ASCE 1984;110(2):173～86

[8] Bazant Z P, Wang T S. *Spectral finite element analysis of random shrinkage in concrete*. J of Struct Eng ASCE 1984;110(9):2196～211

[9] Bazant Z P,Wang T S. *Algorithm for aging viscoelastic structures under periodic load*. J of Eng Mech ASCE 1984;110(6):972～85

[10] Liu N, Liu G T. *Spectral finite element analysis of periodic thermal creep stress in concrete*. Eng Struct 1996;18(9):669～74

[11] Madsen H O, Krenk S, Lind N C. *Methods of structural safety*. New York: Springer Verlag, 1986

[12] Melchers R E. *Structural reliability Analysis and Prediction*. New York: John wiley and Sons, 1987

[13] Newland D E. *An introduction to random vibration and spectral analysis*. New York: Longman, 1975

[14] Hohenbichler M, Rackwitz R. *First order concepts in system reliability*. Struct Safety 1983;1(3):177～88

[15] Dolinsky K. *First order second moment approximation in reliability of structural system*. Struct Safety 1983;1(3):221～31

[16] Breitung K. *Asymptotic approximation for the cross rates of stationary gaussian vector processes*. *Research Report*: Deptartment of Mathmatical Statistics, University of Lund, Sweden, 1984

[17] Pearce H T. Wen Y K. *On linearization points for nonlinear combination of stochastic load processes*. Struct Safety 1985;2(2):169～76

[18] Ditlevsen O. *On the choice of expansion point in FORM or SORM*. Struct Safety 1987;4(4):243～5

[19] Breitung K, Rackwitz R. *Nonlinear combination of load processes*. J of Struct Eng ASCE 1982,10(2):145～66

[20] Grigoriu M. *Crossing non-gaussian translation porcesses*. J of Eng Mech ASCE 1984,110(4):610～20

[21] Ditlevsen O. *Gaussian out-crossing from safe convex polyhedrons*. J of Eng Mech ASCE 1983,109(1):127～48

[22] Madsen H O, Tvedt L. *Method for time-dependent reliability and sensitivity analysis*. J of Eng Mech ASCE 1990;116(10):2118～35

[23] Liu N. *A computational method for first excursion reliability*. Acta Mechanica Sinica 1996,12(4):377～86

[24] Lin Y K, *Probability theory of tructural dynamics*. New York: McGraw－Hill,1967

[25] Liu N, Liu G T. *Random temperature field of mass concrete structures by using stochastic finite element method*. J of Tsinghua University 1996,36(1):41～7

[26] Lin Y K. Methods of stochastic structural dynamics. *Struct Safety* 1986,3:167～94

[27] Hasofer A M, Lind N C. *Exact and invariant second moment code format*. J of Eng Mech. (ASCE) 1994,100(1):111～21

[28] Papoulis A. *Probability, random variables and stochastic process*. New York: McGraw-Hill,1965

[29] Wen Y K, Chen H C. *On fast integration for time variant structural reliability*. Prob Eng Mech 1987;2(3):156～62

[30] Tsubaki T, Bazant Z P. *Random shrinkage stresses in aging viscoelastic vessel*. ASCE J of Eng Mech 1982,108(3):527～45

EXPERIMENTS AND SIMULATION ON THE PROPAGATION OF THE JUNCTURE CRACK BETWEEN GRAVEL AND MORTAR

Abstract The analytical-numerical method is used for determining quantitative relationship between outer load and inner crack propagation of complex material to the stage of damage. In order to determine the propagation of cracks in complex material, it is necessary to compare the stress intensity factor in every direction with its corresponding fracture toughness and find out the weakest face. Since experimental parameters of crack propagation keep stable (in engineering precision), the numerical predictions are in good agreement with experimental results. Study on quantitative rule between inner crack and macro-mechanical properties of concrete offers a new way for the strength evaluation of the mixtrue and for the improvement of mechanical properties of concrete. The present numerical method is suitable for the analysis of the juncture crack running through mortar.

Key words crack propagation; gravel and mortar; experiment; simulation

Propagation of cracks in concrete under loading and global damage (evident decrease of bearing capacity) is a complicate process. Depending on toughness of fracture between various materials, the propagation may be due to the damage in cement-mortar, between the aggregates and cement-mortar or in aggregates themselves. The differences between elastic modulus of aggregates and cement-mortar, coherent force on the inner-surface, etc give important effects on the strength of specimen. Observations in field show that there are primary weakness and cracks on the lower surface of aggregates during construction and the variation of temperature. In this paper, the quantitative relationship between the development of inner flaw and the macro-mechanical properties of specimen is discussed for the development on the strength computation of concrete and improvement of the mechanical properties of concrete.

1 Boundary Fictitious Force Subregion Method

Boundary fictitious force subregion method is used for the solution of interface crack in composite material and outer surface cracks. The solution of multi-crack problem in the homogeneous elastic bodies given in Ref. [1] can be concluded as follows:

(1) By Kelvin solutions the relationships between stress, displacement and unknown boundary fictitious force $\{P\}$ are given with influence coefficient matrix $\boldsymbol{A}$, $\boldsymbol{B}$: $\{\boldsymbol{\sigma}\} = \boldsymbol{A}\{\boldsymbol{P}\}$, $\{\boldsymbol{u}\} = \boldsymbol{B}\{\boldsymbol{P}\}$, and A, B are the functions of coordinates.

本文选自《清华大学学报(自然科学版)》1996 年第 1 期,作者还有 Chi Yuan。

(2) Using analytical solution of the single crack surface with concentrated load, the relationships between stress, displacement and $\{F\}$, the fictitious force on the crack surface, are given with influence coefficient matrix $\boldsymbol{C}, \boldsymbol{D}$: $\{\boldsymbol{\sigma}\} = \boldsymbol{C}\{\boldsymbol{F}\}, \{\boldsymbol{u}\} = \boldsymbol{D}\{\boldsymbol{F}\}$, and $\boldsymbol{C}$, $\boldsymbol{D}$ are also the functions of the coordinates.

(3) The superposed stress and displacement caused by fictitious forces on the boundary and surface of crack can be simply written as: $\{L\} = H\{R\}$, where $\{L\}$ is the vector of boundary conditions, $\{R\}$ is the vector of fictitious forces, and H is influence column matrix.

Suppose the studied object is divided into Ω_1, Ω_2 or more zones composited with different kind of materials, the boundary can be divided into two kinds, as shown in Fig. 1, in which: ①The outer boundaries of Ω_1, Ω_2 including crack boundary are represented as L_1, L_4, which have definitely known boundary conditions. ②The common boundaries are L_2 and L_3, on which the stress and displacement are unknown, but can be defined by continuity of displacement and equilibrium of forces: $u(L_2) = u(L_3) = u_2$, $T(L_2) = P(L_3) = T_3$. Just the same as in homogeneous material, we can apply the fictitious forces R_1 and R_2 to the L_1 and L_2, the boundary of Ω_1, and R_3 and R_4 to the L_3 and L_4, the boundary of Ω_2. From Ω_1, Ω_2, we have Eq. (1). Eliminating u_2 and T_3, Eq. (1) can be reduced to Eq. (2).

$$\begin{Bmatrix} L_1 \\ U_2 \\ T_3 \end{Bmatrix} = \begin{bmatrix} H_{11} H_{12} \\ H_{21} H_{22} \\ H_{31} H_{32} \end{bmatrix} \begin{Bmatrix} R_1 \\ R_2 \end{Bmatrix}, \begin{Bmatrix} U_2 \\ T_3 \\ L_4 \end{Bmatrix} = \begin{bmatrix} H_{23} H_{24} \\ H_{33} H_{34} \\ H_{43} H_{44} \end{bmatrix} \begin{Bmatrix} R_3 \\ R_4 \end{Bmatrix} \tag{1}$$

$$\begin{Bmatrix} L_2 \\ 0 \\ 0 \\ L_4 \end{Bmatrix} = \begin{bmatrix} H_{11} & H_{12} & 0 & 0 \\ H_{21} & H_{22} & -H_{23} & -H_{24} \\ H_{31} & H_{32} & -H_{33} & -H_{34} \\ 0 & 0 & H_{43} & H_{44} \end{bmatrix} \begin{Bmatrix} R_1 \\ R_2 \\ R_3 \\ R_4 \end{Bmatrix} \tag{2}$$

Substituting the known boundary conditions L_1 and L_4 into Eq. (2), we have the solutions of R_1, R_2, R_3 and R_4 directly, and by dividing the structure into subregions we can further obtain the stress and displacement field of each subregion and the K values of all cracks (except for the crack on interface) from corresponding fictitious forces. K value of interface crack is determined by contact stress near the tip of the crack, the stress field is of $r^{-1/2}$ singularity approximately. A modified equation with an additional item was developed in Ref. [2], but its effect was small. Computing results show that it is sufficiently accurate to take the results of 5 micro elements (Fig. 2) on each tip of the crack for computing K value.

Let the size of the 10 tip elements be one tenth of the other elements at both sides. The stress points defined in Fig. 3 are also proved to be accurate enough for curve crack by the computational results. Experiments show that propagation of the inner crack in homogeneous mortar has the direction which is approximately perpendicular to the maximum surrounding tension stress $\sigma_{\theta\max}$. Around the crack tip, σ_θ can be calculated with Eq. (3) and the fracture angle θ_0 which satisfies the condition Eq. (4) is given by Eq. (5).

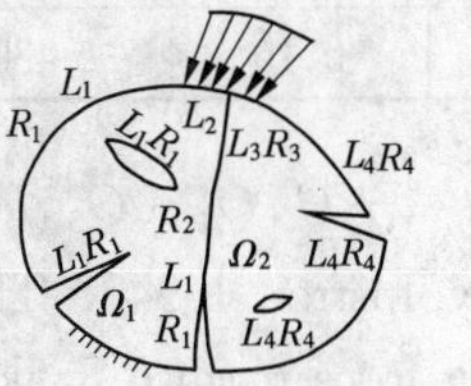

Fig. 1 Multi-crack problem in composite material

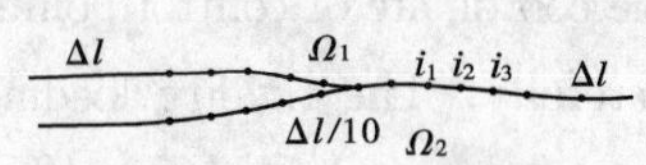

Fig. 2 Elements beyond the tip

$$\sigma_\theta = \frac{1}{2\sqrt{2\pi r}}\cos\frac{\theta}{2}[K_I(1+\cos\theta) - 3K_{\mathrm{II}}\sin\theta] \tag{3}$$

$$\left.\frac{\partial\sigma_\theta}{\partial\theta}\right|_{\theta=\theta_0} = 0, \quad \left.\frac{\partial^2\sigma_\theta}{\partial\theta^2}\right|_{\theta=\theta_0} < 0 \tag{4}$$

$$K_{\mathrm{I}}\sin\theta_0 + K_{\mathrm{II}}(3\cos\theta_0 - 1) = 0 \tag{5}$$

$$K_\theta = \frac{1}{2}\cos\frac{\theta}{2}[K_{\mathrm{I}}(1+\cos\theta) - 3K_{\mathrm{II}}\sin\theta] \tag{6}$$

The stress intensity factor in θ direction K_θ can be given by Eq. (6). If the tip of the crack is located in the homogeneous zone and the direction of fracture is not defined, it is feasible to apply various composite criteria of K_{I} and K_{II}. Nevertheless, if the direction of crack is limited, for example, the fracture direction is known or the different K_0 values of the material in the various direction are known (K_{IC} of the interface is relatively small), it is necessary to use $K_\theta = K_{IC}$ as the criterion, where θ is the real fracture angle. The method of computing stress intensity factor of non-interface crack can be found in Ref[1].

2 Computation and Experiment

The specimen consists of three kinds of materials as shown in Fig. 3. In order to make the specimen, we embedded the stone cylinders of different elastic modulus in the specimen of the size 20cm × 20cm × 20cm and cut it into 3cm thick slices after hardening of specimen. The loading surfaces BE and AF are finished to parallel the plan.

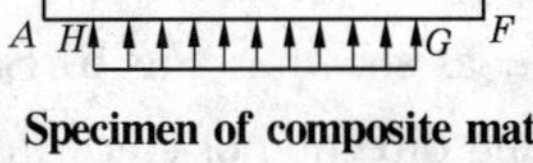

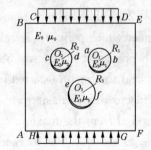

Fig. 3 Specimen of composite material

We made the interface crack with one fourth of peripheral by painting the aggregate before concreting. It was found after cutting that the surface of crack extended to places of a, b, c, d, e and f in Fig. 3, the middle point of crack on the bottom surface had the maximum opening of about 1.5mm, and the bleeding had a distinct effect on lower part of aggregate.

Table 1　The elastic parameters of mortar and aggregate　(unit: kN/cm^2)

E_0	μ_0	E_1	μ_1	E_2	μ_2	E_3	μ_3
2 724	0.2	6 700	0.16	6 700	0.16	5 430	0.16

The coordinate of control points of sliced specimen $A \sim H, O_1 \sim O_3, a \sim f$ were measured carefully. The rigidity loading was controlled by Instron 1 342. The displacement loading rate was set to 4.167×10^{-3} mm/s after loading force reached 8.5kN. The typical loading curve is shown in Fig. 4. The first yielding point was corresponding to load 12.4kN. It is found that at this loading point the crack extended along the aggregate interface firstly from d, and then the other tips of the cracks, and finally the two upper aggregates departed from mortar completely. The fracture went into mortar in the second stage. It is difficult to observe where the fracture began. Nevertheless, it is found that when the load reached 16.7kN, the cracks in the mortar extended quickly and the strength of the specimen descended. The typical fracture is shown in Fig. 5.

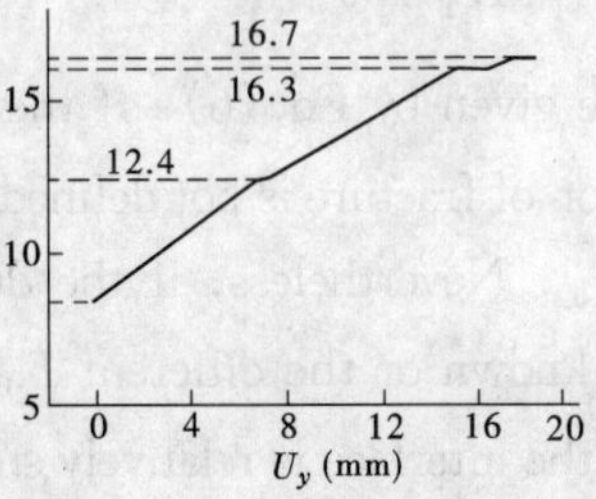

Fig. 4　Loading curve

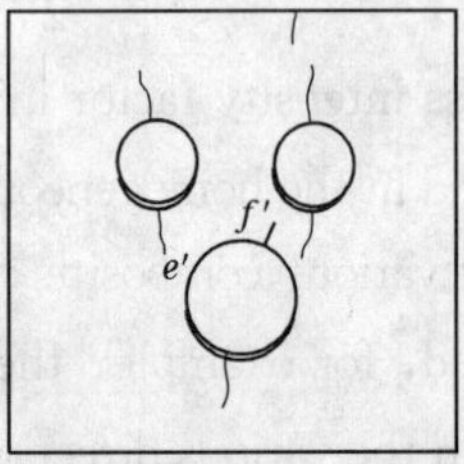

Fig. 5　Typical fracture in specimen

The structure shown in Fig. 3 was used for numerical analysis and the results are given in Table 2. Table 3 shows that when computational load comforted with the experimental load under which peripheral crack lost the stability (12.4kN) the maximum stress intensity factor happened at tip d, was 888.5kN/cm$^{3/2}$ and coincided with the observation in experiments, and the fracture started from tip firstly. As the crack appeared in the inner part, observed macro displacement rose sharply (Fig. 4). The angle of the maximum surrounding stress solved from the maximum surrounding stress theory always direct to the body of aggregate, as shown in Fig. 6. Since toughness of aggregate is larger than that of interface, the extending direction of crack in the composite material is different from the perpendicular direction of the maximum surrounding stress. The direction of crack propagation should be that by which K_θ defined in Eq. (3) reaches K_{IC} value of θ direction. The experimental results show that the crack extends along the interface and the K_{IC} of interface is smaller than that of aggregate. The fracture condition of the interface is: $K_\theta|_{\theta=0} = K_I = K_{IC}^0$. It is confirmed by the experiment and computation that the peripheral K_{IC}^0 of upper aggregate (two smaller columns) is about 880kN/cm$^{3/2}$, the K_{IC} of aggregate itself is larger than 959 N/cm$^{3/2}$ and the peripheral (interface) K_{IC} of lower aggregate is larger than 610N/cm$^{3/2}$.

Table 2 The crack situations under force 12.4kN (around tip)

Tip of crack	Distance of stressed point γ_i (cm)	σ_N (N/cm^2)	σ_n (N/cm^2)	$K'_{\rm I}$ (N/cm$^{3/2}$)	$K'_{\rm II}$ (N/cm$^{3/2}$)
a	0.169	250.1	66.5	257.7	68.5
	0.255	201.6	22.7	255.2	28.7
	0.341	166.2	8.3	243.3	−12.1
b	0.169	580.3	−297.7	598.0	−306.8
	0.255	459.8	−233.3	582.0	−295.3
	0.341	377.8	−195.9	553.0	−286.7
c	0.169	284.7	377.2	293.4	388.7
	0.255	239.0	291.4	302.5	368.8
	0.341	212.3	237.5	310.8	347.6
d	0.169	816.2	−184.2	841.1	−189.8
	0.255	646.7	−132.9	818.6	−168.2
	0.341	530.2	−103.6	776.1	−151.6
e	0.169	600.7	108.8	619.0	112.1
	0.255	496.8	67.0	628.8	84.8
	0.341	421.9	39.5	617.6	5.78
f	0.169	242.3	−530.6	249.7	−546.8
	0.255	205.3	−431.3	259.9	−545.9
	0.341	179.9	−367.7	263.3	−538.2

Table 3 The crack situations under force 12.4kN(at tip)

Tip of crack	$K_{\rm I}$ (N/cm$^{\frac{3}{2}}$) ($r=0$)	$K_{\rm II}$ (N/cm$^{\frac{3}{2}}$) ($r=0$)	θ_0 (°)of max. surrounding stress	K value in θ direction K_θ (N/cm$^{\frac{3}{2}}$)
a	266.2	128.8	−39.50	337.6
b	628.5	−322.5	40.76	813.8
c	280.1	419.1	−58.50	653.8
d	884.8	−219.7	25.20	959.3
e	614.8	152.9	−25.23	666.8
f	237.8	−551.5	62.56	775.8

The second stage is the fracture propagation in mortar. From loading curve shown in Fig.4 the critical load of failure is 16.3kN, and all the common surfaces of aggregate and mortar except in $e'f'$ zones are out of contact. The boundary stress around the mortar is shown in Fig.7. At the crack tip f', $K_1=306.8$N/cm$^{3/2}$, smaller than $K_{\rm IC}=880$N/cm$^{3/2}$. The angle between perpendicular direction of the maximum surrounding stress and tangential direction of interface is 62.38°, and K_θ in that direction is 982.8N/cm$^{3/2}$, as shown in Fig.7, therefore the fracture will not go along interface, but direct into the mortar body at point f', which agreed with the experiment as shown in Fig.5.

The further analysis of failure procedure was made by leaving two sort of cracks on the peripheral surface of mortar as shown in Fig.7. The cracks are located at the maximum tension points g and h. The length of the cracks is 0.5mm. Considering the interaction among the cracks and boundary, the systematic computation results were given as follows.

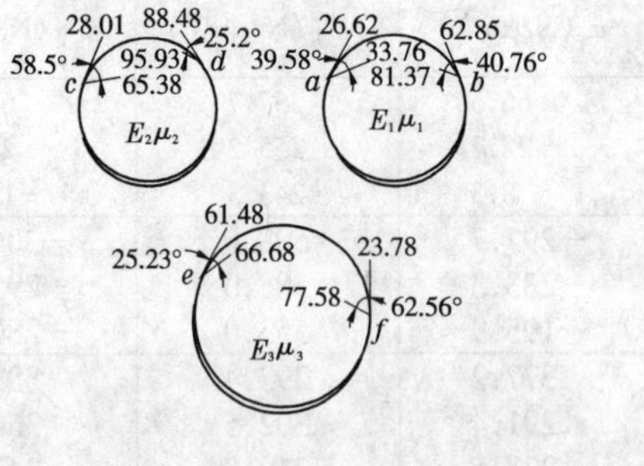

Fig. 6 K_θ value in tangential direction of crack tip ($\theta = 0$) and direction of max surrounding stress

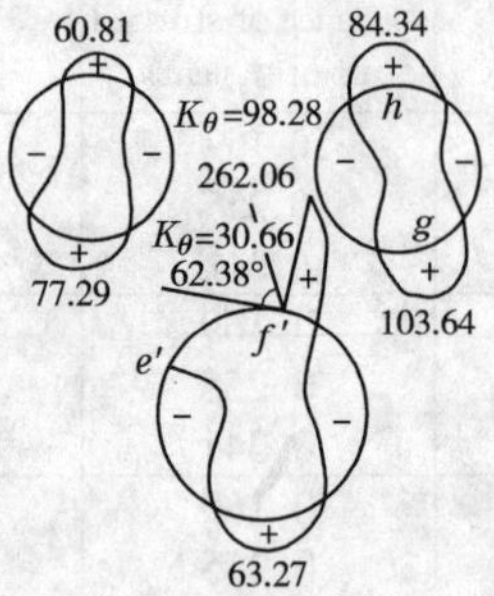

Fig. 7 The boundary stress of mortar during load 16.3**kN**(10N/cm^2)

If the critical load $P = 16.3$kN, then:

at point g: $K_{\mathrm{I}} = 948.3\mathrm{N/cm}^{3/2}$, $K_{\mathrm{II}} = 68.9\mathrm{N/cm}^{3/2}$

at point h: $K_{\mathrm{I}} = 439.4\mathrm{N/cm}^{3/2}$, $K_{\mathrm{II}} = -114.7\mathrm{N/cm}^{3/2}$

It is interesting that if the crack started at point f' with K_θ taken as the toughness of the mortar (K_{IC}982.8N/cm$^{3/2}$), the external load under which the cracks of mortar lost its stability was about 16.8kN, which was not far from the maximum load of the experiment, when the maximum load reached 16.3kN, the fracture in mortar propagated from point f' to g quickly and lost part of its bearing capacity.

3 Discussions

The numerical analytical method for studying propagation of inner cracks in composite materials is discussed in this paper. The computing results show a good agreement with experiments. The numerical analytical method which describes the quantitative relationship between extending of inner crack and loading will be an effective tool for developing concrete computing strength. It is not sufficient to adapt the crack criteria of homogeneous materials for composite materials. To find out the weakest surface by comparing K_θ and K_C in the direction θ (for different material and interface) is necessary for crack detection.

References

[1] Liu G T, Chi Y. *An analytical-fictitious boundary forces method for calculating multi-crack problem in arbitrary region with mixed mode boundaries*. In: S. P. Shah, et al. Fracture of Concrete and Rock Recent Development, USA, 1989. 91～102

[2] Zhou R Z, Liu G T. *Fracture analysis for curved cracks on the juncture-surface between aggregate and cement-mortar*. In: S. P. Shah, et al. Micromechanics of Failure of Quasi-Brittle Materials, USA, 1990. 444～452

用随机骨料模型数值模拟混凝土材料的断裂

摘　要　将混凝土看做由水泥砂浆、骨料及二者间的黏结带构成的三相复合材料，根据混凝土骨料的级配随机产生了混凝土骨料结构，将有限元网格投影到该结构上，并根据单元的位置确定单元的材料特性，用以代表混凝土的三个相结构。提出了断裂韧性与强度综合破坏准则，采用非线性有限元技术模拟了单边裂缝受拉试件从损伤到断裂破坏的全过程，为混凝土破坏机理的研究和发展、混凝土计算强度提供了新的技术路径。

关键词　复合材料　随机骨料模型　断裂　破坏准则

近代混凝土试验表明，混凝土的宏观力学性能和内部裂缝发展相关。目前混凝土类材料力学行为的研究，大都是建立在试验的研究基础上，需要花费大量的人力、物力，所得到的试验成果又往往囿于试验条件、环境条件等的变化及材料本身的复杂性，试验成果的离散性较大偏离原型。科学工作者正在试图寻求一种近似计算法，结合理论和试验数值模拟去研究混凝土的结构与性能之间的关系，企图在细观裂缝发展和宏观力学性能之间架起一座桥梁。

宏微观相结合研究，在20世纪90年代已发展成为主要学科方向之一。本文从细观层次上分析了混凝土的内部结构，认为混凝土是由骨料、水泥砂浆和二者间的黏结带组成的三相材料，借助于蒙特卡罗方法，在空间上随机确定骨料的位置、形状和尺寸，产生出随机骨料结构，然后再将有限元网格投影到该结构上。分配不同的材料特性给相应的单元，用以代表不同的三个相结构——水泥砂浆、骨料和黏结带，进行拉伸条件下单边裂纹扩展破坏全过程的数值模拟，并和试验宏观变形过程进行对比。

1　计算模型

1.1　随机骨料结构

为定性研究取已知级配骨料，假定骨料颗料为球状，其横断面颗粒直径可借助于Fuller曲线[2]确定，由该级配曲线浇筑的混凝土可产生优化的结构密度和强度。下面的累计分布函数代表在混凝土中位于一个内截面平面上任一点具有直径 $D<D_0$ 的概率

$$P_c(D<D_0)=P_k[1.455(D_0/D_{max})^{0.5}-0.50(D_0/D_{max})^2+0.036(D_0/D_{max})^4+0.006(D_0/D_{max})^6+0.002(D_0/D_{max})^8+0.001(D_0/D_{max})^{10}] \quad (1)$$

使用这个函数，对于一个特定的混凝土拌和物，即可产生结构横截面上骨料的分布。图1为一个由蒙特卡罗方法产生的均匀分布的随机骨料结构。试件中最大骨料尺寸 $D_{max}=16$mm，骨料体积与混凝土的体积比 $P_k=0.75$，由于本文采用的三角单元的尺寸是1.25mm，所以结构中小于4mm的骨料计入砂浆均质体。

本文选自《清华大学学报(自然科学版)》1996年第1期，作者还有王宗敏。

1.2　材料性能分配

将三角形网格投影到所产生的骨料结构上,不同的强度和刚度等材料性质分配给相应的三角形单元,见图2。当单元位于骨料内部时,将骨料的材料性能分配给该单元;当单元位于骨料和水泥砂浆之间时,将粘结带的材料性能分配给该粘结带单元;当单元位于水泥砂浆中时,将水泥砂浆的性能分配给该水泥砂浆单元。本文借助于计算几何实现了计算机自动识别与分配。

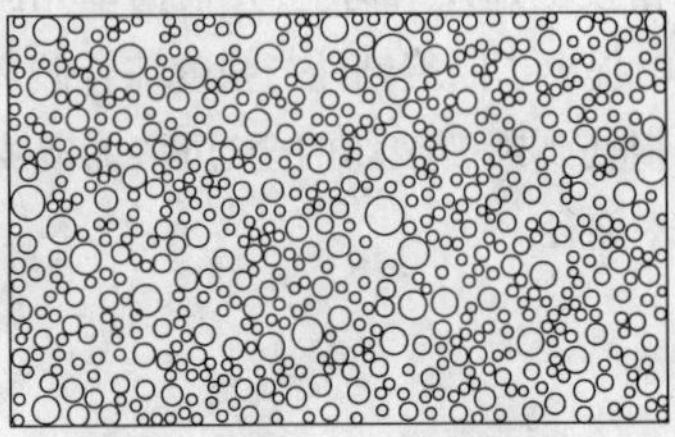

图1　随机骨料结构

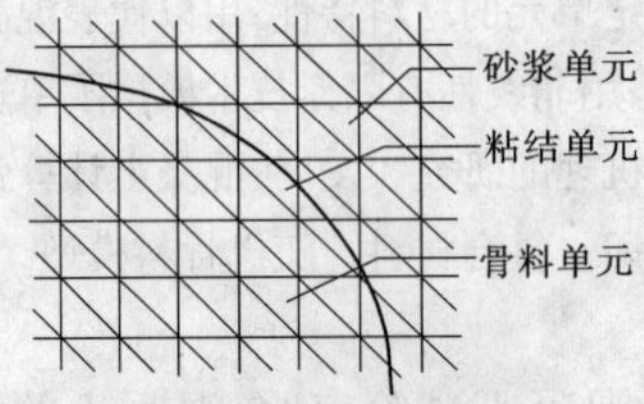

图2　单元性能分配

1.3　本构关系

用混凝土拌和物的两个主要构元——骨料和水化了的水泥砂浆分别进行试验,都会出现弹性破坏,而混凝土本身在破坏前却表现出非弹性性质。因此,本文采用混凝土的各相在破坏前符合弹脆性材料假设,应力应变关系为线弹性关系;在破坏后,采用片状裂缝模型,其优点是裂缝发生在单元体内部,一旦单元体主拉应力大于混凝土抗拉强度,就按计算得出的主拉应力角度开裂,仅需要修改单元的刚度矩阵,而不需要重新划分网格,能自动连续计算,裂缝也能自动形成,而且裂缝方向也是完全自由的,不受单元形状和相邻单元边界的限制。

当裂缝出现后,增量的应力应变关系为

$$\begin{Bmatrix} d\sigma_1 \\ d\sigma_2 \\ d\sigma_{12} \end{Bmatrix} = \begin{bmatrix} E_1 & 0 & 0 \\ 0 & E_2 & 0 \\ 0 & 0 & \beta G \end{bmatrix} \begin{Bmatrix} d\varepsilon_1 \\ d\varepsilon_2 \\ d\gamma_{12} \end{Bmatrix} \tag{2}$$

式中:β 取一较小的值,本文取 $\beta=0$;当单向开裂时 $E_1=0, E_2=E$,当双向开裂时 $E_1=E_2=0$。式(2)是按缝的局部坐标系表示的,而在应用单元刚度矩阵建立平衡方程时,需要的是按整体坐标系表示的弹性矩阵,因此式(2)应通过转轴关系变换至整体坐标系中。

1.4　破坏准则

由于混凝土微裂缝发展过程既有强度破坏问题,在缝端又存在韧性破坏,因此本文提出了综合断裂与强度的破坏准则

$$\begin{cases} (\sigma_\theta)_{\max} \geqslant (\sigma_\theta)_c & \text{当 } r < r_0 \text{ 时} \\ \sigma_1 \geqslant f_t & \text{当 } r \geqslant r_0 \text{ 时} \end{cases} \tag{3}$$

式中:r 为缝端周围单元距缝尖端的距离,$r_0 = \frac{1}{2\pi}(K_{IC}/f_t)^2$;$\sigma_1$ 为主拉应力;f_t 为材料的抗拉强度;σ_θ 为裂缝尖端的周向应力分量:$\sigma_\theta = \frac{\sigma_x+\sigma_y}{2} - \frac{\sigma_x-\sigma_y}{2}\cos2\theta - \tau_{xy}\sin2\theta$;最大周

向应力的临界值可通过 I 型的断裂韧性 K_{IC}来确定,即$(\sigma_\theta)_c = K_{IC}/\sqrt{2\pi r}$;裂缝的开裂方向根据式(3)假定为最大周向应力方向或者为最大主拉应力方向。

2　单边裂缝板拉伸试件的计算机模拟

试件的尺寸为 100mm×200mm,在中部有一宽为 5mm,深为 15mm 的预裂缝。考虑到微机容量的限制,仅裂缝附近 100mm×50mm 范围内采用细观单元来模拟骨料结构,其余部分采用较大的单元,共划分了 6 980 个单元,3 555 个节点,细观单元尺寸为 1.25mm 量级,见图 3。试件的一端约束,另一端采用位移控制加载,骨料、砂浆及黏结带的材料性能见表 1。

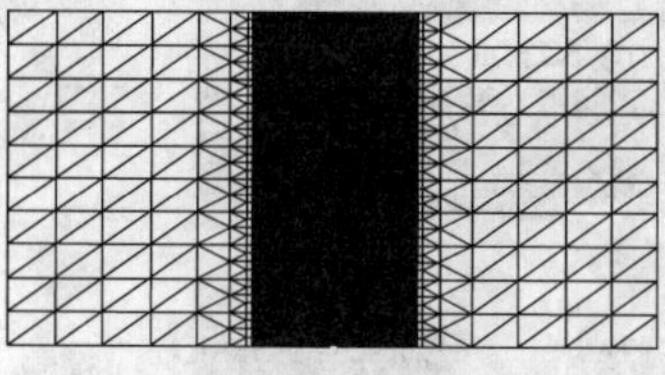

图 3　具有随机骨料结构的有限元网格

表 1　材料性能

参数	砂浆(M)	骨料(A)	粘结带(B)		
f_t(MPa)	4.25	14.01	1.5	2.0	2.5
E(GPa)	27.8	55.3	25.0	25.0	25.0
G_{IC}(J/m^2)	10.3	17.5	1.5	2.0	2.5
υ	0.22	0.16	0.16	0.16	0.16

为了考察骨料结构对混凝土宏观性能的影响,本文随机产生了两种不同的骨料结构。在其他参数不变的前提下,对试件的开裂过程进行了模拟,图 4 和图 5 为不同的黏结强度和不同的骨料结构对构件宏观性能的影响,图 6~图 8 和图 9、图 10 分别为骨料结构 1、骨料结构 2 在不同黏结强度的裂缝扩展全过程。

从图 4 和图 5 可以看到,不同骨料分布结构的宏观力学性能是相近的,因此采用随机骨料结构模型模拟混凝土的开裂过程具有客观性,比较图 5 中的无量纲化 $p\sim V$ 曲线,可见计算和试验曲线相似。

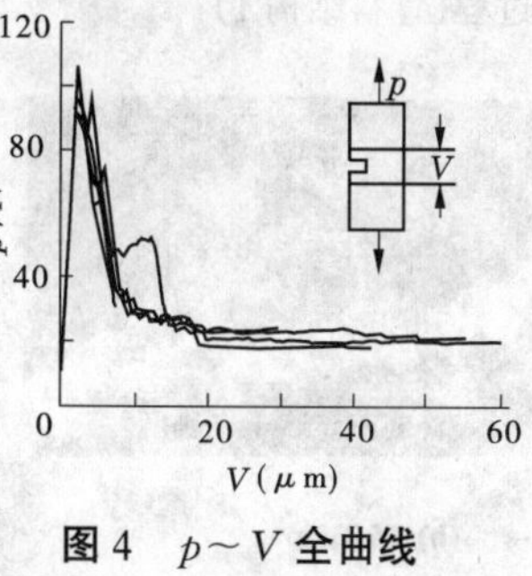

图 4　$p\sim V$ 全曲线

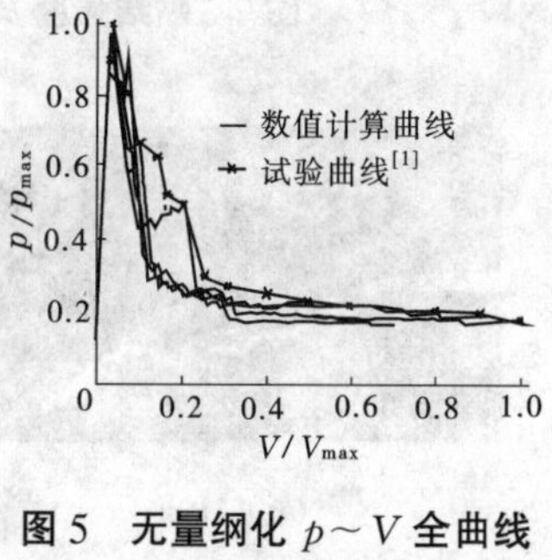

图 5　无量纲化 $p\sim V$ 全曲线

假定 σ_B/σ_A 和 σ_B/σ_M 为材料的非均质因子,即当 σ_B/σ_A 和 σ_B/σ_M 趋近于 1 时,材料愈接近于均质;当 σ_B/σ_A 和 σ_B/σ_M 趋近于 0 时,材料愈接近于不均质。对比图 6 和图 8、图 9 和图 10,可以看出,对于较均质的材料(图 8 和图 10),裂缝的扩展较为连续和单一;而对于较不均质的材料(图 6 和图 9),裂缝的扩展是极不连续的,且是分叉的,表现出较强的"裂缝面桥现象"和"骨料拔出现象",从而使得裂缝的韧带增长,这时混凝土受拉表现出较长的软化段(下降段)。

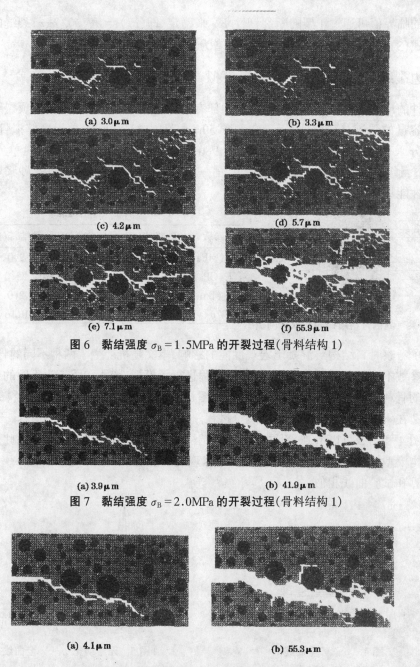

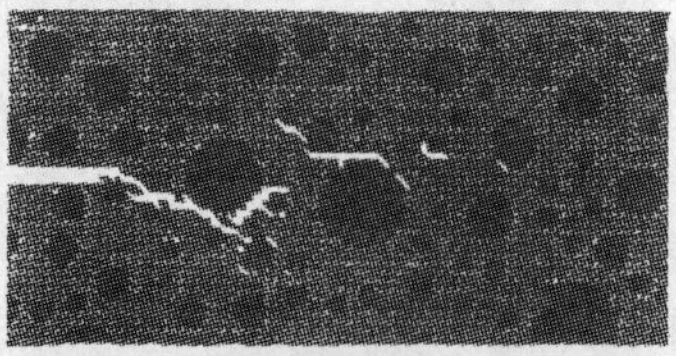

(a) 3.0μm

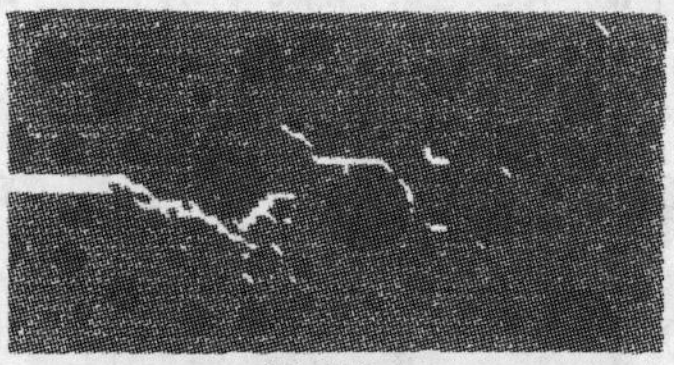

(b) 3.3μm

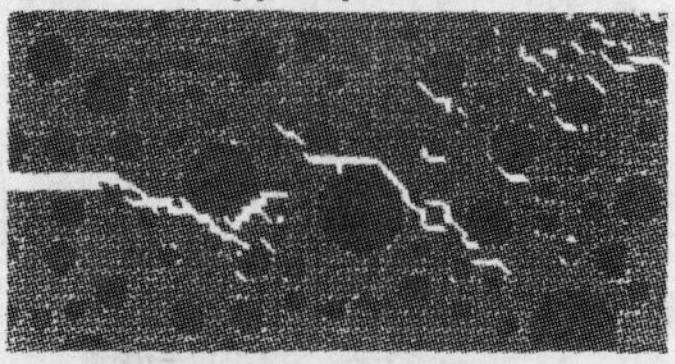

(c) 4.2μm

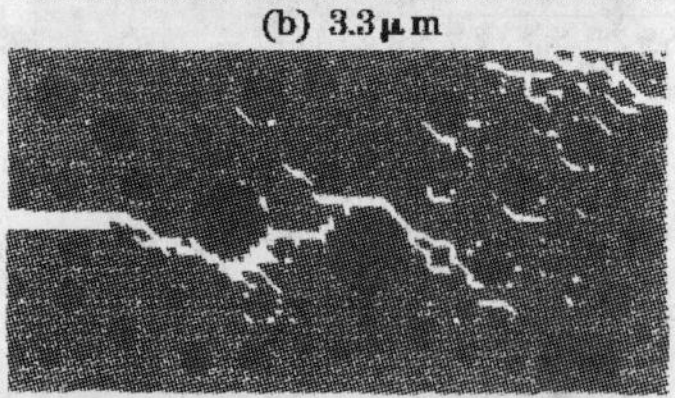

(d) 5.7μm

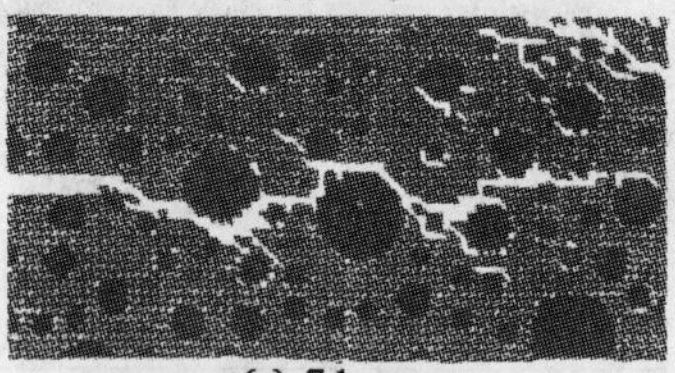

(e) 7.1μm

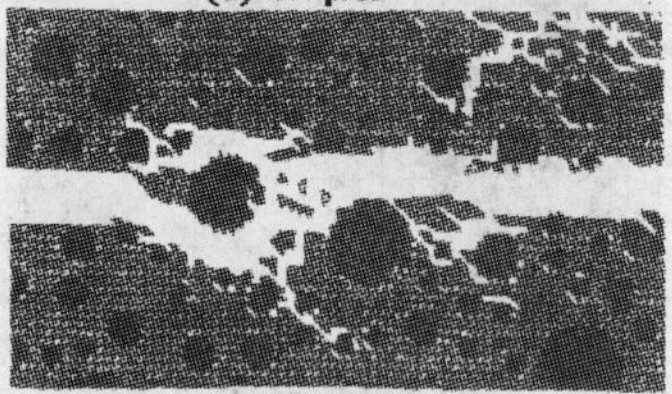

(f) 55.9μm

图 6　黏结强度 $\sigma_B = 1.5$MPa 的开裂过程(骨料结构 1)

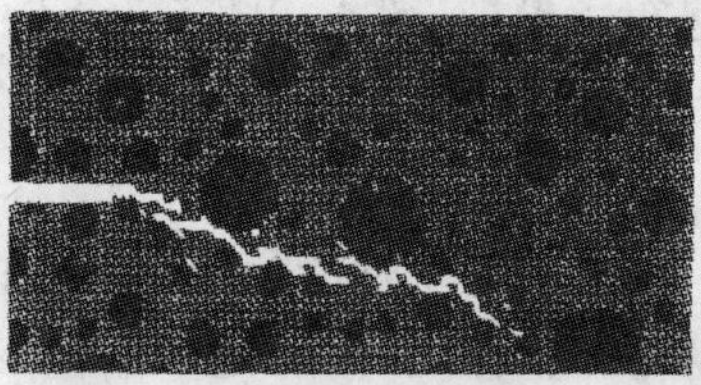

(a) 3.9μm

(b) 41.9μm

图 7　黏结强度 $\sigma_B = 2.0$MPa 的开裂过程(骨料结构 1)

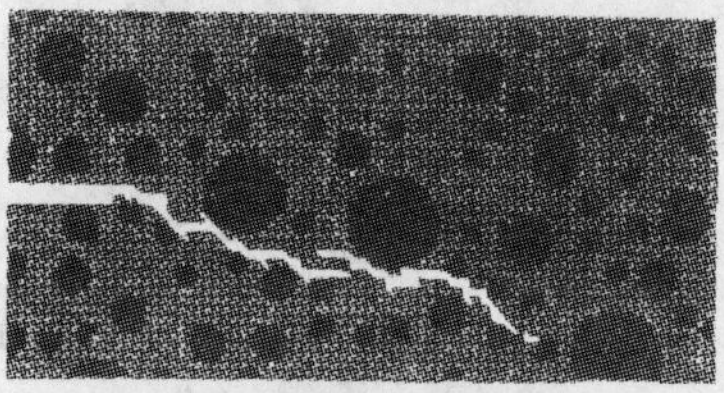

(a) 4.1μm

(b) 55.3μm

图 8　黏结强度 $\sigma_B = 2.5$MPa 的开裂过程(骨料结构 1)

从图 6～图 10 可以看出,拉伸时混凝土的破坏不是由众多的裂缝所引起,而是由少数几条裂缝所致,表现出较强的拉应变软化现象和局部化现象。从图 6～图 8 中(a)到(b)的变化可以看到,保持同样的外部边界条件和变形速率(两端控制位移从 5.5μm 到 6.0μm),裂缝附近的局部变形速率却不同。说明了非均质因子愈小,应变局部化出现得愈晚;非均质因子愈大,应变局部化出现得愈早,但裂缝一开始扩展,就出现应变局部化现象。

(a) 3.1μm　　(b) 7.5μm

图 9　黏结强度 $\sigma_B = 1.5$MPa 的开裂过程(骨料结构 2)

(a) 3.5μm　　(b) 7.4μm

图 10　黏结强度 $\sigma_B = 2.5$MPa 的开裂过程(骨料结构 2)

图 6～图 10 现象表明当黏结强度大时混凝土宏观断裂近似断裂带模型,但断裂带的宽度仅为 1～2 倍的最大骨料直径,骨料与水泥砂浆的黏结强度是一个重要的力学参数,不同的黏结强度可能会导致不同的裂缝开裂方式与形态。

3　结语

(1)本文提出内部裂缝延伸的强度和韧性综合判别式,采用混凝土随机骨料模型及非线性有限元模拟了混凝土从损伤至断裂破坏的全过程,模拟的宏观结果和试验的破坏软化曲线近似,说明了本文模型及方法的有效性。

(2)"裂缝面桥现象"是混凝土宏观拉应变软化现象的主要原因,其内因是由于混凝土的高度不均质性,裂缝面桥的尺寸依赖于混凝土的不均质性。

(3)骨料与水泥砂浆的黏结强度是一个重要的力学参数,黏结较差的材料破坏前会导致较多的裂缝分叉和面桥。

研究混凝土破坏机理及发展混凝土计算强度在我国尚处于初始阶段,还有许多工作有待进一步努力。

参 考 文 献

[1] Schlangen E, Van Mier J G M. *Experimental and numerical analysis of micromechanisms of fracture of cement-based composites*. Cement & Concrete Composites, 1992,14:105～118

[2] Schlangen E, Van Mier J G M. *Simple lattice model for numerical simulation of fracture of concrete materials and structures*. Materials and Structures, 1992,25:534～542

[3] Buyukozturk Oral, Lee K M. *Assessment of interfacial fracture toughness in concrete composites*. Cement & Concrete Composites, 1993,15:143～151

地震动随机场变界展开法*

摘　要　针对地震动随机场特性进行解析展开，提出一种有效的变界展开方法，同时将频率相关的非线性方程精确线性化，且只须一次分解给定频率相应空间随机场即可直接进行整个频域随机场分析的效果。计算结果表明，该方法不但计算简单，而且具有截断误差小的特点，通常取解析展开的前五项即可满足工程需要。该方法非常适应大型结构多点地震动随机输入分析。

关键词　时－空随机场　地震动　解析展开

结构地震分析的基础是合理而有效地确定地震动输入。由于地震动受多种不确定因素的影响，应用随机场来描述是适合的。因此，进行随机场分析是有效地确定工程结构地震作用的关键。

对随机场进行离散或分解近年来得到了广泛的研究，并提出了许多有效的方法[1~9]。然而，所有这些方法都是针对空间随机场的，即与时间无关的随机场分析。地震动随机场是与时间有关的，应该用时－空随机场来表示。地震台网数据记录表明：地震动的相关性随空间距离和频率的加大而减小；随视波速的增大而加大。地震动随机场可由频率相关的自功率谱与相关函数表示[6]，应用现有的空间随机场分析方法需要针对离散的频率点进行分析，这样大型结构多频点随机分析计算量是很大的。

本文针对常用的线性指数衰减地震动随机场，提出一种变界展开法，只需一次分解空间随机场即可对所感兴趣的所有频点进行分析，而且是精确的展开法。

1　地震动随机场表示

由于地震的强不确定性，下面假设地震随机场关于时间是平稳的，而空间是非均匀的。地震波沿随机场 y 轴方向与水平面夹角 θ 传播，并且地震动随机场由自功率谱 $S_g(\omega)$与两点 r_1 与 r_2 相关函数 $C(r_1, r_2, \omega)$确定。这样，随机场中任意两点的互功率谱函数为

$$S(r_1, r_2, \omega) = C(r_1, r_2, \omega)\exp\left[-i\omega\left(\frac{y_1 - y_2}{c_y}\right)\right]S_g(\omega) \tag{1}$$

式中：$i=\sqrt{-1}$；y_1 和 y_2 是 r_1 与 r_2 在 y 轴上的坐标；c_y 是地震波水平传播视波速，是随机场波速 v_s 与入射角 θ 的函数

$$c_y = \frac{v_s}{\sin\theta} \tag{2}$$

*　基金项目：国家教委博士后重点科研基金(980506)。

本文选自《清华大学学报(自然科学版)》1999 年第 11 期，作者还有刘天云。

关于地震运动的相关函数，目前已有多种根据地震台网确定的经验公式，都能反映地震随机场的基本特征。本文针对下面一类常用线性指数衰减型相关函数[6]进行研究

$$C(r_1,r_2,\omega)=\exp\left(-\frac{\gamma_x\omega}{v_s}\mid x_1-x_2\mid-\frac{\gamma_y\omega}{v_s}\mid y_1-y_2\mid\right) \tag{3}$$

式中：x_1、y_1 和 x_2、y_2 分别是点 r_1 和 r_2 的坐标；γ_x 和 γ_y 分别是两个方向的相关因子。如果 $\gamma_x=\gamma_y$，随机场是各向同性的。

行波效应可以单独分解为 e^{-iy_1} 和 e^{-iy_2}，因此下面仅对相关函数的随机场进行分解。

2　随机场解析展开法

由于随机场的相关函数是对称正定的函数，基于 K—L 展开理论[5]，可由下式表达

$$C(x_1,x_2)=\exp(-c\mid x_1-x_2\mid)=\sum_{n=1}^{\infty}\lambda_n f_n(x_1)f_n(x_2) \tag{4}$$

式中，$f_n(x)$ 和 λ_n 是下面积分方程的特征值与特征函数。

$$\int_D C(x_1,x_2)f_n(x_1)\mathrm{d}x_1=\lambda_n f_n(x_2) \tag{5}$$

式中：D 是随机场的定义域。

$f_n(x)\quad(n=1,2,3,\cdots)$形成一组完备的正交基，随机场可应用此组基展开为

$$u(x,\xi)=\sum_{n=1}^{\infty}\sqrt{\lambda_n}f_n(x)\xi_n \tag{6}$$

式中：ξ 与 ξ_n 分别是标准的连续随机变量和离散随机变量。理论已经证明展开式在 2－范数意义上是最优的。

对于式(3)所示相关函数的一维随机场，可以展开为[5]

$$u(x,\xi)=\sum_{n=1}^{\infty}\left[\sqrt{\lambda_n}f_n(x)\xi_n+\sqrt{\lambda_n^*}f_n^*(x)\xi_n^*\right] \tag{7}$$

$$f_x(x)=\frac{\cos(\beta_n x)}{\sqrt{a+\dfrac{\sin(2\beta_n a)}{2\beta_n}}} \tag{8}$$

$$f_x^*(x)=\frac{\sin(\beta_n^* x)}{\sqrt{a-\dfrac{\sin(2\beta_n^* a)}{2\beta_n^*}}} \tag{9}$$

式(8)、式(9)中：a 是一维随机场的半长；β_n 与 β_n^* 分别由以下两式确定

$$c-\beta\tan(\beta a)=0 \tag{10}$$

$$\beta^*+c\tan(\beta^* a)=0 \tag{11}$$

式(7)中：特征值 λ_n 和 λ_n^* 分别由下式确定

$$\lambda_n=\frac{2c}{\beta_n^2+c^2} \tag{12}$$

$$\lambda_n^*=\frac{2c}{\beta_n^{*2}+c^2} \tag{13}$$

由于 c 是地震动随机场频率的函数,特征值 λ_n 和 λ_n^* 也是频率的函数。考虑式(10)和式(11)是超越函数方程,对于不同的频率点值,都得重新计算 β_n 和 β_n^*,这对于地震动随机场分析很不方便,下节提出一种高效精确的线性化方法。

3　随机场变界法

考虑到式(10)和式(11)的特点,将方程两边同乘 a 为

$$ca - \beta a\tan(\beta a) = 0 \tag{14}$$

$$\beta^* a + ca\tan(\beta^* a) = 0 \tag{15}$$

式中,ca 是量纲 1 的频率 $a_0 = \frac{\omega a}{\gamma v_s}$。对于给定的 a_0 值,式(14)和式(15)的解是确定的。当频率值 ω 由小到大增长时,随机场边界 a 应该同比例缩小,相应地 β_n 和 β_n^* 同比例增大。这样通过变化地震动随机场的边界将非线性问题精确线性化(见算例 4.1),使时-空随机场的分析工作量降低到最小。量纲 1 的频率 a_0 由感兴趣的随机场定义域和最高频率来确定。

4　算例

4.1　地震动随机场变界分析

为了说明变界展开法,研究一维地震动随机场:$a = 250.0, c = 0.001, \omega = 0 \sim 10.0$,且具有如下的相关函数

$$C(x_1, x_2, \omega) = \exp\left(-\frac{\omega}{1\ 000}\mid x_1 - x_2 \mid\right) \tag{16}$$

下面只列出部分结果:

图 1(a)是按一般方法确定的 $\beta_n \propto \omega$ 曲线,而图 1(b)则是变界法的 $\beta_n \propto \omega$ 直线关系。应注意两者的区别:(a)图对于任意 ω 值,都对于边界 a;而(b)图则为不同的 ω 值,对于不同的边界 a。

图 1(c)是特征值 λ_n 与频率 ω 的关系。对于较小的 ω 值,特征值 λ_n 差值很大;而对于较大的 ω 值,特征值 λ_n 差值较小。只有特征值 λ_n 大的前几阶对随机场展开有贡献。

图 1(d)是前五阶特征函数曲线。曲线明显受 β_n 的强烈影响。

4.2　一维地震动随机场展开截断误差

图 2(a)是当 $a_0 = 2.5$,式(7)取 $n = 5$ 的随机场展开方差误差结果。由图可见误差很小,然而明显受频率 ω 值影响。另一方面,误差关于频率 ω 与坐标 x 有对称的关系。图 2(b)是随机场与原点相关函数的误差结果。很明显,与方差一样,误差关于频率 ω 与坐标 x 亦有对称的关系。这是由于量纲 1 的 a_0 关于频率与坐标对称的结果。

4.3　二维地震动随机场

对于具有式(3)的相关函数的地震动随机场,两个方向是可分离的,即单独研究两个方向的一维随机场,然后合并形成二维问题。只对随机场截断误差最大的对角线元素(即 $x = y$)进行分析,如图 3 所示。由图可见,自动率谱与相关函数误差要比一维情况的大,但仍然有关于频率和坐标的对称性。这是此类地震动随机场的共性。

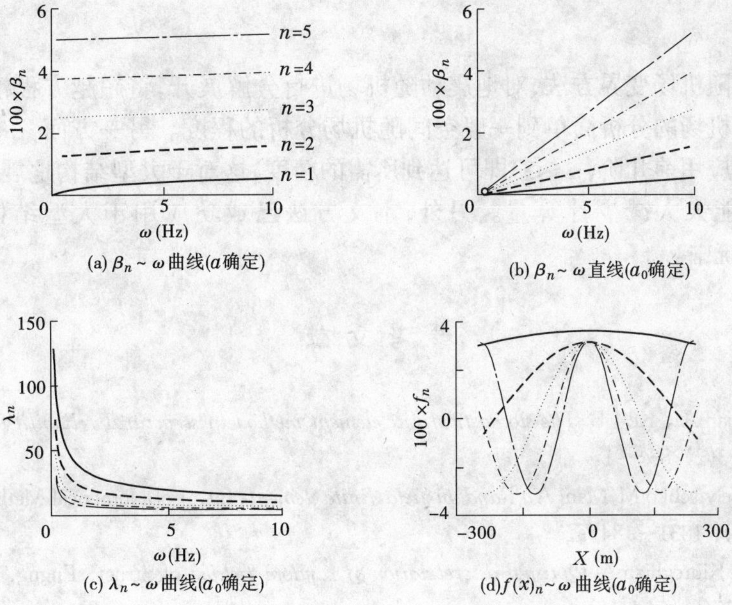

(a) $\beta_n \sim \omega$曲线(a确定)　(b) $\beta_n \sim \omega$直线(a_0确定)

(c) $\lambda_n \sim \omega$曲线(a_0确定)　(d) $f(x)_n \sim \omega$曲线(a_0确定)

图 1　地震动随机场特征曲线

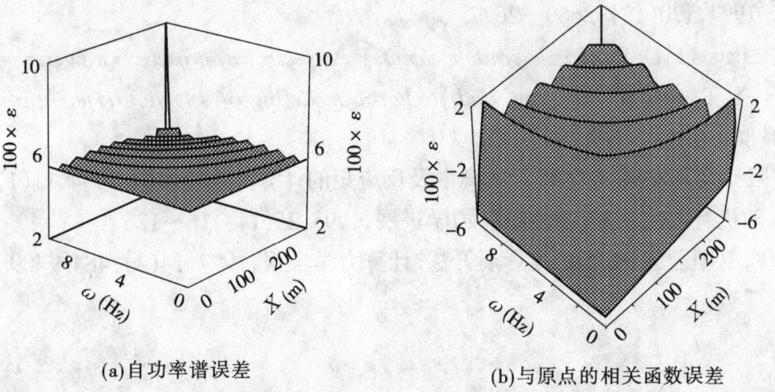

(a)自功率谱误差　(b)与原点的相关函数误差

图 2　一维地震动随机场展开误差

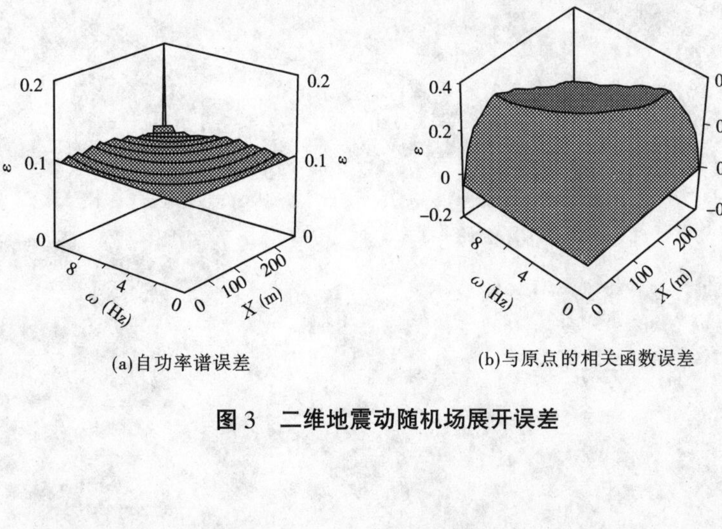

(a)自功率谱误差　(b)与原点的相关函数误差

图 3　二维地震动随机场展开误差

5 结论

本文提出随机场变界方法,对地震动随机场进行分解展开,将超越方程精确线性化,使得时-空随机场的分析简单到一般空间随机场分析的程度。另一方面,一维地震动随机场展开只须应用前几阶($n\leqslant5$)即可达到所需的精度,这对于大型结构地震随机反应是十分重要的,能大大减少计算量。另外,本文方法已成功应用于大型结构随机分析ASAS-99系统中。

参考文献

[1] Der Kiureghian A , Ke J B. *The stochastic finite element method in structural reliability*. Prob. Engng, Mech. 1988,3(2):83~91

[2] Liu W K, Belytschko M, Mani A. *Random field finite element*. Int. J of Numerical Methods in Engng. 1986,23(10): 1831~1845

[3] Li C C, Der Kiureghian A. *Optimal discretization of random field*. J of Struct. Engng. ASCE, 1993, 119(6): 1136~1154

[4] Zhang J, Ellingwood B. *Orthogonal series expansion of random fields in reliability analysis*. J of Engng Mech. ASCE, 1994,120(12):2660~2677

[5] Ghanem R G, Spanos P D. *Stochastic finite elements: A spectral approach*. Springer-verlag,1991

[6] Loh C H, Yeh Y T. *Spatial variation and stochastic modeling of seismic differential ground movement*. EESD,1988,16(4):583~596

[7] 秦权. 随机有限元及其发展,I:随机场的离散及反应矩的计算. 工程力学,1994,11(1):1~10

[8] 刘宁,吕泰仁.随机有限元及其工程应用.力学进展,1995,25(1):116~126

[9] 刘天云,伍朝晖,赵国藩.随机场的投影展开法.计算力学学报,1997,14(4):484~489

地震动随机场投影展开法

摘　要　本文发展了随机场投影展开方法,对地震动随机场进行变界近似解析展开。地震动采用自功率谱与具有高斯指数衰减的相关函数模型。本文方法只须求解一次随机场特征值问题,具有简单和展开误差小的特点,非常适应结构多点随机输入分析。

关键词　时-空随机场　地震动　投影展开

结构地震分析的基础是合理和有效地确定地震动输入。由于地震动受多种不确定因素的影响,应用随机场来描述是适合的。因此,进行随机场分析是有效地确定工程结构地震作用的关键。

近年来,对随机场进行离散或分解得到了广泛的研究,并提出了许多有效的方法[1~9]。然而,所有这些方法都是针对空间随机场的,即与时间无关的随机场分析。地震动随机场是与时间有关的,应该用时-空随机场来表示。由于地震动随机场的自功率谱与相关函数都是地震波频率的函数[5,6],应用现有的空间随机场分析方法需要对离散的频率点进行分析,因而大型结构多频点随机分析计算量是很大的。

对于具有线性指数衰减相关函数的地震动随机场[6],变界展开法十分有效[10]。本文则针对更一般的具有高斯指数衰减相关函数地震动随机场[5],发展了投影展开法[9],使其也只需一次分解空间随机场即可对所感兴趣的所有频点进行分析,极大地简化了结构随机分析输入,特别是拱坝地震随机分析[11]。最后针对一维和二维地震动随机场展开截断误差进行了分析。

1　地震动随机场表示

假设地震波沿随机场 y 轴方向与水平面夹角 θ 传播,并且地震动随机场由功率谱 $S_g(\omega)$与两点 r_1 与 r_2 相关函数 $C(r_1,r_2,\omega)$确定。这样,随机场中任意两点的互功率谱函数为

$$S(r_1,r_2,\omega) = C(r_1,r_2,\omega)\exp\left[-i\omega\left(\frac{y_1-y_2}{c_y}\right)\right]S_g(\omega)$$

式中:$i=\sqrt{-1}$;y_1 和 y_2 是 r_1 与 r_2 在 y 轴上的坐标;c_y 是地震波水平传播视波速,是随机场波速 v_s 与入射角 θ 的函数

$$c_y = \frac{v_s}{\sin\theta}$$

关于地震运动的相关函数,目前已有多种经验公式。本文针对下面一般的高斯指数衰减型相关函数[5]进行研究。

$$C(r_1,r_2,\omega) = \exp\left\{-\left[\frac{\gamma_x\omega}{v_s}(x_1-x_2)\right]^2-\left[\frac{\gamma_x\omega}{v_s}(y_1-y_2)\right]^2\right\} \tag{1}$$

本文选自《计算力学学报》2000 年第 4 期,作者还有刘天云。

式中：(x_1,y_1)和(x_2,y_2)分别是点 r_1 和 r_2 的坐标；γ_x 和 γ_y 分别是两个方向的相关因子。

如果 $\gamma_x=\gamma_y$，随机场是各向同性的。具有线性指数衰减型的相关函数[6]是式(1)的特例，因为相关函数都是两点相对距离的函数。

由于随机场功率谱值和行波效应不影响随机场的展开，不妨取单位值。因此，下面仅对一维的地震动随机场进行分解，然后推广到二维情况。

2 随机场解析展开法

由于随机场的相关函数是对称正定的函数，基于 K—L 展开理论[5]，可由下式表达：

$$C(x_1,x_2)=\sum_{n=1}^{\infty}\lambda_n f_n(x_1)f_n(x_2) \tag{2}$$

式中：$f_n(x)$和 λ_n 是下面积分方程的特征函数与特征值

$$\int_D C(x_1,x_2)f_n(x_1)\mathrm{d}x_1=\lambda_n f_n(x_2) \tag{3}$$

式中：D 是随机场的定义域。$f_n(x)\quad(n=1,2,3,\cdots)$形成一组完备的正交基。理论已经证明展开式在 2－范数意义上是最优的。

对于式(1)所示相关函数的一维随机场，不能解析求解式(3)的特征值与特征函数。而随机场投影展开法[9]则能近似显式求得特征函数为

$$f_n(x)=\frac{1}{\lambda_n}p(x)^{\mathrm{T}}\phi_n \qquad (n=1,2,\cdots,N) \tag{4}$$

式中：$p(x)^{\mathrm{T}}=(p_1(x),p_2(x),\cdots,p_N(x))$，且 $p_i(x)=E[u(x),u(x_i)]\quad(i=1,2,\cdots,N)$；$E(\cdot)$是随机变量的数学期望；$N$ 是随机场的离散点数；λ_n 和 ϕ_n 是随机场的相关矩阵 $R=[C(x_i,x_j,\omega)]_{N\times N}$的特征值与特征向量

$$R\phi_i=\lambda_i\phi_i \qquad (i=1,2,\cdots,N) \tag{5}$$

通常只须前 r 个特征值大的特征对就可反映随机场的特征[9]。由于相关矩阵 R 是地震动频率的函数，特征值与特征函数也是频率的函数。因此，对于不同的频率点值，都得重新计算 λ_n 和 ϕ_n。这对于地震动随机场分析很不方便，下面提出一种有效的解决方法。

3 随机场变界法

考虑到式(1)的频率与坐标关系的特点，将地震动随机场 A：$[-a,a]$扩张成随机场 B：$[-\omega_m a,\omega_m a]$，其中，a 和 ω_m 分别是地震随机场所感兴趣边界和最高频率。对随机场 B 进行投影展开，式(2)可写为

$$\tilde{C}(\tilde{x}_1,\tilde{x}_2,\omega_m)=\sum_{n=1}^{r}\lambda_n f_n(\tilde{x}_1)f_n(\tilde{x}_2) \tag{6}$$

式中：$\tilde{x}\in[-\omega_m a,\omega_m a]$。

当频率值 ω 由小到大增大时，随机场点按 $\tilde{x}=\omega x$ 同比例增大，相应的随机场边界扩

张为 $\tilde{a}=\omega a$；进一步虚拟将边界扩成随机场 B 的边界$[-\omega_m a,\omega_m a]$。这样，可以统一应用随机场 B 建立的随机场的特征函数基。通过变化地震动随机场的边界将多次求特征值问题简化为只需一次，使时－空随机场的分析工作量降低到最小。

由于式(1)相关函数关于 x 和 y 方向等同，y 方向随机场也可以按上述步骤分解。最后，二维地震动随机场可由 x 和 y 方向分别近似解析展开合成为

$$\tilde{C}(x_1,x_2,y_1,y_2,\omega)=\left(\sum_{l=1}^{r_1}\frac{1}{\lambda_l}f_l(x_1)f_l(x_2)\right)\left(\sum_{m=1}^{r_2}\frac{1}{\lambda_m}f_m(y_1)f_m(y_2)\right) \tag{7}$$

式中：r_1、r_2 分别是随机场 x 和 y 方向展开的项数。

4 算例

例1 为了说明变界展开法，研究一维地震动随机场：$a=250.0$，$\omega=0\sim100.0$，且相关函数如下

$$C(x_1,x_2,\omega)=\exp\left\{-\left[\frac{\omega}{10\,000}(x_1-x_2)\right]^2\right\} \tag{8}$$

展开结果如下：

(1)图1(a)按展开式(6)取 $r=5$ 的随机场自功率谱的误差结果；而图1(b)则是 $r=10$ 的误差结果。两者的误差分布很相似，都具有波动现象且关于频率与坐标具有对称的

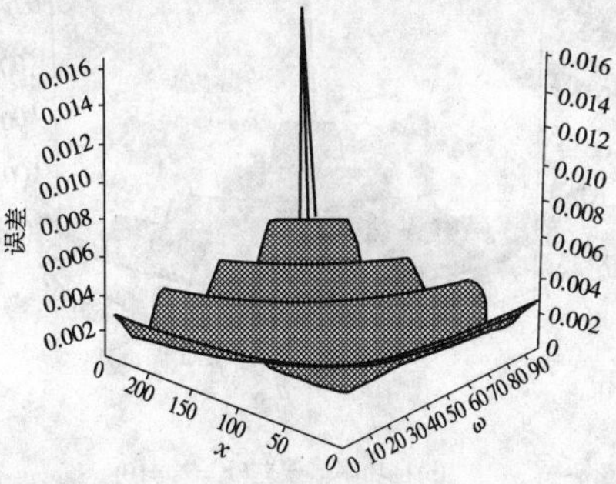

(a)自功率谱误差($r=5$)

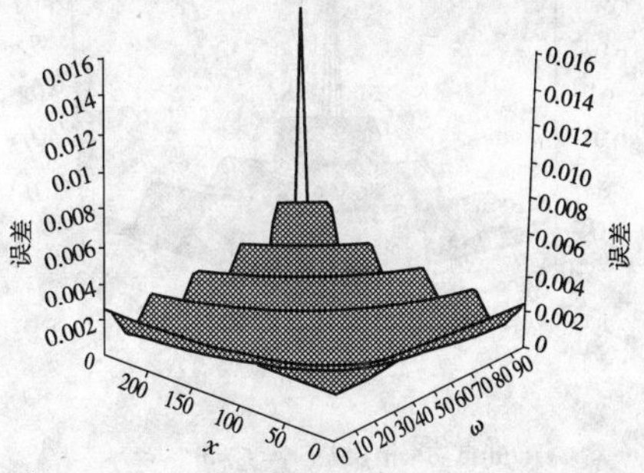

(b)自功率谱误差($r=10$)

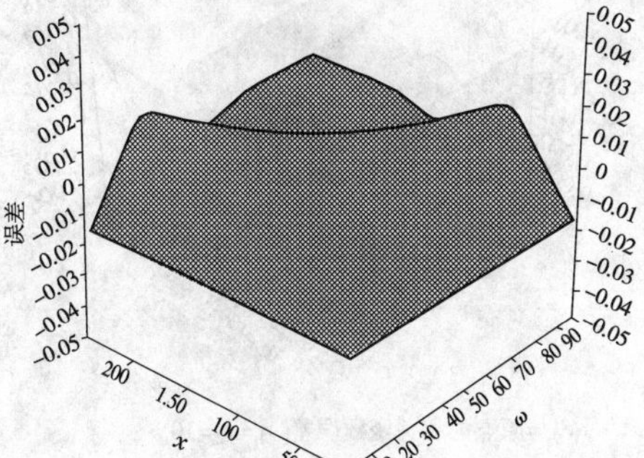

(c)与原点的相关函数误差($r=5$)

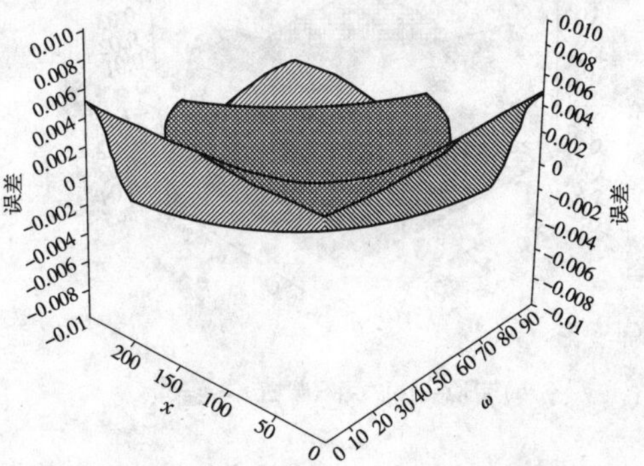

(d)与原点的相关函数误差($r=10$)

图1 一维地震动随机场展开误差

关系;在高频段随机场边缘区域误差高于其他区域。另一方面,两图的误差值表明随机场的展开误差明显随展开项数增加而降低,且式(6)展开值不会大于精确解。

(2)图1(c)和图1(d)分别是随机场展开式(6)中 $r=5$ 和 $r=10$ 的与原点相关函数的误差。由图可见,相关函数的展开误差与自功率谱一样,具有关于坐标与频率对称的特性,但误差值要大于自功率谱误差。另一方面相关函数展开误差有正有负,但随展开项的增多误差绝对值减小。

例2　二维地震动随机场展开误差

考虑具有式(1)的相关函数的二维地震动随机场。为了便于比较,取例1的参数。由于沿随机场对角线的方向展开误差最大,因此下面只列出这方向的结果,$r=r_1=r_2$,且以 x 方向坐标标出。

图2(a)与图2(b)是当式(7)取 $r=5$ 和 $r=10$ 的随机场展开自功率谱误差结果。由图可见,虽然误差大于一维的情况,但误差仍然很小,且仍具有关于频率和坐标对称的特性。图2(c)和图2(d)分别是与原点相关函数的误差结果。很明显,与自功率谱误差一样,关于频率 ω 与坐标 x 对称的关系。另一方面,误差要大于一维的情况,且误差绝对值随展开项的增多而减小。

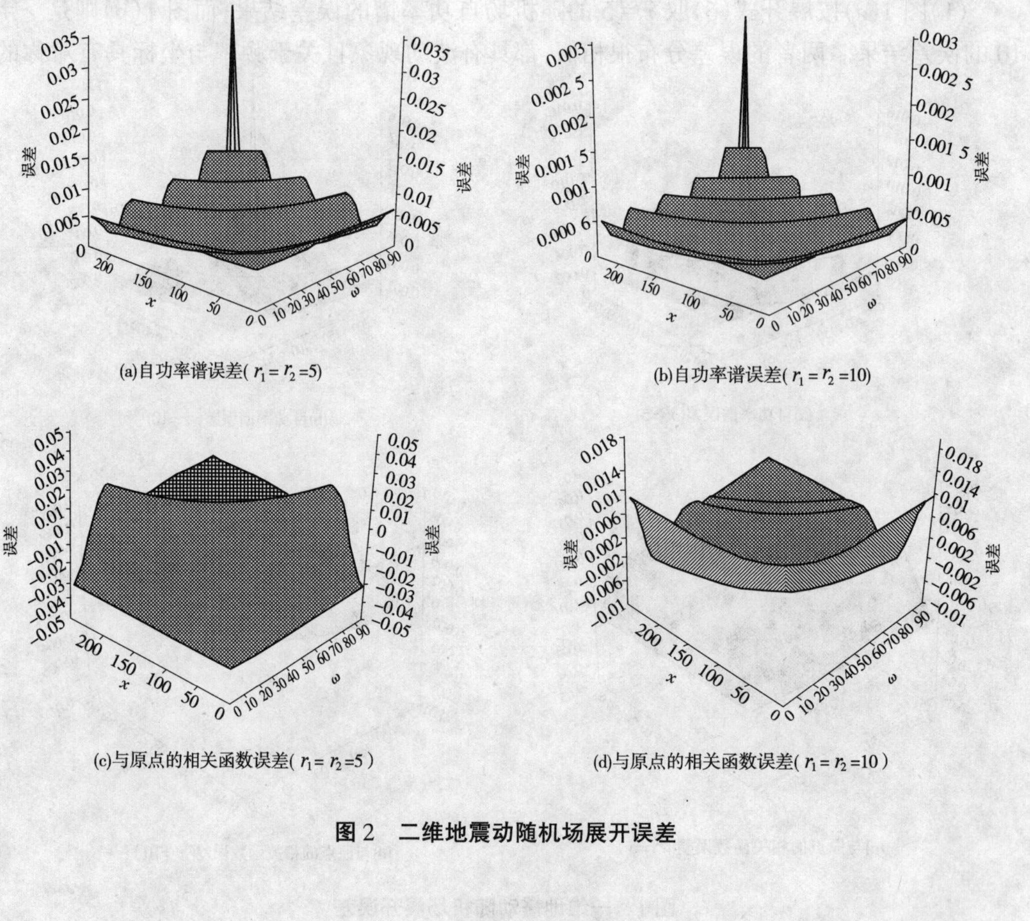

(a)自功率谱误差($r_1=r_2=5$)　　(b)自功率谱误差($r_1=r_2=10$)

(c)与原点的相关函数误差($r_1=r_2=5$)　　(d)与原点的相关函数误差($r_1=r_2=10$)

图2　二维地震动随机场展开误差

5 结论

本文提出随机场变界方法,对地震动随机场进行投影展开,将频率相关的问题转化为只须求解一次随机场的特征值问题,将时-空随机场的分析简化到一般空间随机场分析的程度。另一方面,地震动随机场展开只须应用前几阶($n\leqslant5$)即可达到所需的精度,这对于大型混凝土拱坝结构地震随机反应是十分重要的,能大大减少计算量。根据本文地震随机场展开法编制的随机激励子程序已成功应用于拱坝动力分析系统(ASAS-98)[11]中,使计算效率显著提高,有效地解决了拱坝地震随机的计算关键问题。

参考文献

[1] Der Kiureghian A , Ke J-B. *The stochastic finite element method in structural reliability*. Prob. Engng, Mech. 1988,3(2):83~91
[2] Liu W K, Belytschko M, Mani A. *Random field finite element*. Int. J. of Numerical Methods in Engng. 1986,23(10): 1831~1845
[3] Li C C, Der Kiureghian A. *Optimal discretization of random field*. J. of Struct. Engng. ASCE, 1993, 119(6): 1136~1154
[4] Zhang J, Ellingwood B. *Orthogonal series expansion of random fields in reliability analysis*. J. of Engng. Mech. ASCE., 1994,120(12):2660~2677
[5] Ghanem R G, Spanos P D. *Stochastic finite elements: A spectral approach*. Springer-verlag, 1991
[6] Loh C H, Yeh Y T. *Spatial variation and stochastic modeling of seismic differential ground movement*. EESD, 1988,16(4):583~596
[7] 秦权. 随机有限元及其发展,I:随机场的离散及反应矩的计算. 工程力学,1994,11(1):1~10
[8] 刘宁,吕泰仁.随机有限元及其工程应用.力学进展,1995,25(1):116~126
[9] 刘天云,伍朝晖,赵国藩.随机场的投影展开法.计算力学学报,1997,14(4):484~489
[10] 刘天云,刘光廷.地震动随机场变界展开法.清华大学学报,1999,39(11):18~20
[11] 刘天云.拱坝地震分析系统 ASAS-98(Arch dam Seismic Analysis System-98).清华大学水利系研究报告,No.9801,1998

拱坝地震动随机响应分析

摘　要　将河谷地震动随机场半解析展开为正交函数随机过程及采用简化的地基模型,应用振型分解法可直接求得拱坝－地基－库水系统的各种随机响应及功率谱密度。本文方法不仅考虑地震动的空间随机性,山体放大作用及行波效应,而且考虑非比例阻尼的拱坝振型之间的相关性;地震动随机场只须分解一次,计算过程简单,是大型拱坝结构随机分析的一种有效方法。

关键词　地震动随机场　拱坝　随机振动　动力相互作用

在结构随机震动分析中,功率谱方法是计算结构随机响应的主要方法,然而这种方法在工程应用时由于计算困难而未被广泛采用。在大型结构如高拱坝与大跨桥等设计中,仍采用反应谱法。虚拟激励法通过分解输入功率谱矩阵来构造确定性的激励荷载,直接计算结构响应,是一种有效的计算方法[1,2]。

拱坝结构与地基有较大的接触面,地震激励功率谱矩阵阶数很高,且是激励频率的函数[3,4],多次矩阵分解计算量很大。本文采用随机场分解方法一次性确定正交的函数随机过程,根据坝基节点直接形成激励向量,求得拱坝结构随机响应;进一步通过响应自乘计算结构的自功率谱与互功率谱密度。最后通过拱坝实例说明本文方法。

1　地震动随机场分解

地震动随机场模型应体现地震动空间随机变化,行进地震波及河谷山体放大效应,空间变化的功率谱密度为[1,2]

$$S(x,\omega)=(1+\alpha\frac{h(x)}{H})^2\frac{1+4\xi_g^2\frac{\omega^2}{\omega_g^2}}{(1-\frac{\omega^2}{\omega_g^2})^2+4\xi_g^2\frac{\omega^2}{\omega_g^2}}(\frac{\omega^6}{\omega^6+\omega_c^6})[\frac{1}{1+(D\omega)^2}S_0]\qquad(1)$$

式中变量说明见文献[1]、[2]。

地震动相干随机模型[6]一般可表示为

$$C(d_{jk},c_0,\omega)=\exp[-(\frac{\gamma\omega d_{jk}}{2\pi c_0})^2]\exp[-i(\frac{\omega d_{jk}}{c_0})]\qquad(2)$$

式中:$i=\sqrt{-1}$;c_0 是地震波水平传播视波速;d_{jk} 是 jk 两点间的距离。给定频率,式(2)中第二项行波相位很容易分解,而第一项相干函数一般不能用解析法求特征值与特征向量。采用随机场投影展开法[7]能得近似显式而求得特征函数为

$$f_k(x)=\frac{1}{\sqrt{\lambda_k}}p(x)^{\mathrm{T}}\phi_k\qquad(k=1,2,\cdots,N)\qquad(3)$$

本文选自《工程力学》2000 年第 6 期,作者还有刘天云。

式中:$p(x)^{\mathrm{T}}=(p_1(x),p_2(x),\cdots,p_N(x))$, 且 $p_i(x)=E[u(x),u(x_i)]$;$E(\cdot)$是随机变量的数学期望;N 是坝基接触面离散点数;λ_k 和 ϕ_k 是随机场的相关矩阵的特征值与特征向量。

由于相关矩阵是地震动频率的函数,对于不同的频率点值,都得重新计算 λ_k 和 ϕ_k。考虑到相关函数频率与坐标的关系,将地震动随机场边界$[-a,a]$扩张成虚拟边界$[-\omega_m a,\omega_m a]$,其中 a 和ω_m 分别是地震随机场所感兴趣的边界和最高频率。首先对高频随机场进行投影展开,当频率由小到大增加时,坝基离散点位置按 $\tilde{x}=\omega x$ 变化。这样可以应用已确定的特征函数基,通过变化地震动随机场的离散点位置将多次求特征值问题简化为只需一次,使时-空随机场的分析工作量降低到最小。

地震动随机场加速度可以半解析展开为

$$\ddot{u}_f(x,t)=\sum_{k=1}^{r}\sum_{j=1}^{m}\sqrt{S(x,\omega_j)\Delta\omega}f_k(\tilde{x})\exp(-\frac{i\tilde{x}}{c_s})\mathrm{e}^{i\omega_j t}\xi_{jk} \tag{4}$$

式中:$\Delta\omega$ 是频率间距;ξ_{jk}是独立的标准随机变量;下标 f 表示随机场。

对于给定的频率与坝基离散点坐标,可简单地由上式确定地震动激励向量。在地震有效频段内,式(4)精度完全能满足工程要求[7]。

2 拱坝系统动力相互作用

采用不可压缩性假设,库水动压力应用 Westergaard 公式确定附加质量,半无限地基采用简化的具有辐射阻尼的无质量地基模型[8]。因此,拱坝系统动力方程为

$$\begin{bmatrix} M_{ss} & 0 \\ 0 & M_{bb} \end{bmatrix}\begin{Bmatrix} \ddot{u}_s^t \\ \ddot{u}_b^t \end{Bmatrix}+\begin{bmatrix} C_{ss} & C_{sb} \\ C_{bs} & C_{bb}+C_0 \end{bmatrix}\begin{Bmatrix} \dot{u}_s^i \\ \dot{u}_b^i \end{Bmatrix}+\begin{bmatrix} K_{ss} & K_{sb} \\ K_{bs} & K_{bb}+K_0 \end{bmatrix}\begin{Bmatrix} u_s^t \\ u_b^t \end{Bmatrix}=\begin{Bmatrix} 0 \\ C_0\dot{u}_f+K_0u_f \end{Bmatrix} \tag{5}$$

式中:$[M]$、$[C]$、$[K]$分别代表拱坝的质量(包括动水附加质量)、相对运动阻尼和刚度矩阵;C_0、K_0 分别为半无限地基的辐射阻尼与静力刚度,且 $C_0=\dfrac{r}{(2\pi)^2c_s}K_0$, r 与 c_s 分别是拱坝地基的平均半径与剪切波速,相对运动阻尼与简化辐射阻尼详见文献[8];u^t 代表拱坝的总动力位移;下标 b 指拱坝与地基面相接触节点的自由度;下标 s 指其余的节点自由度;右端激励作用在拱坝与地基相接触面上;u_f 代表随机场的地震位移。

由于阻尼矩阵采用相对粘滞阻尼,因此拱坝节点的总位移 u^t 可由拟静力位移 u^k 和惯性位移 u^i 组成

$$u^t=u^k+u^i \tag{6}$$

拟静力位移 u^k 按下式计算

$$\begin{bmatrix} K_{ss} & K_{sb} \\ K_{bs} & K_{bb}+K_0 \end{bmatrix}\begin{Bmatrix} u_s^k \\ u_b^k \end{Bmatrix}=\begin{Bmatrix} 0 \\ C_0\dot{u}_f+K_0u_f \end{Bmatrix} \tag{7}$$

将上式代入式(5)可得惯性相互作用位移 u^i 为

$$\begin{bmatrix} M_{ss} & \\ & M_{bb} \end{bmatrix}\begin{Bmatrix} \ddot{u}_s^i \\ \ddot{u}_b^i \end{Bmatrix}+\begin{bmatrix} C_{ss} & C_{sb} \\ C_{bs} & C_{bb}+C_0 \end{bmatrix}\begin{Bmatrix} \dot{u}_s^i \\ \dot{u}_b^i \end{Bmatrix}+\begin{bmatrix} K_{ss} & K_{sb} \\ K_{bs} & K_{bb}+K_0 \end{bmatrix}\begin{Bmatrix} u_s^i \\ u_b^i \end{Bmatrix}=-\begin{bmatrix} M_{ss} & \\ & M_{bb} \end{bmatrix}\begin{Bmatrix} \ddot{u}_s^k \\ \ddot{u}_b^k \end{Bmatrix} \tag{8}$$

因此,可分别采用静力和动力方法求解式(7)和式(8)。

状态空间不但能处理系统非比例阻尼特性,而且对求解系统的特征值与特征向量十分有效[9]。引用状态向量 $x=[u^i,\dot{u}^i]^{\mathrm{T}}$,式(8)可改写为

$$D\dot{x} = x + Dx_s \tag{9}$$

式中:

$$D = \begin{bmatrix} -K^{-1}C & -K^{-1}M \\ 1 & 0 \end{bmatrix} \tag{10}$$

$$x_s = [0, \ddot{u}_s^{kt}, \ddot{u}_b^{kt}]^{\mathrm{T}} \tag{11}$$

由于线性系统不改变系统的输入随机特性,因此位移响应仍具有类似式(4)的表达式

$$u^t(t) = \sum_{k=1}^{r}\sum_{j=1}^{m}[u_k^k(\omega_j) + u_k^i(\omega_j)]\sqrt{\Delta\omega}\mathrm{e}^{i\omega_j t}\xi_{jk} \tag{12}$$

式中:$u_k^k(\omega_j)$与 $u_k^i(\omega_j)$分别是由式(7)和式(9)确定的拟静力位移与惯性力位移幅值。

利用独立随机变量的特性,可以求得离散点处拱坝位移响应的功率谱矩阵

$$S_{uu}(\omega_j) = \sum_{k=1}^{r}[u_k^i(\omega_j) + u_k^s(\omega_j)][u_k^i(\omega_j) + u_k^s(\omega_j)]^* \tag{13}$$

式中:上标 * 表示复共轭转置。

上式表明:结构响应功率谱密度为 r 项之和,这是地震动随机场正交分解的结果;当随机场完全相关时 $r=1$。

同理,根据位移响应随机向量,可计算结构应力功率谱密度

$$S_{\sigma\sigma}(\omega_j) = \sum_{k=1}^{r}[\sigma_k^i(\omega_j) + \sigma_k^s(\omega_j)][\sigma_k^i(\omega_j) + \sigma_k^s(\omega_j)]^* \tag{14}$$

式中:$\sigma_k^s(\omega_j)$和 $\sigma_k^i(\omega_j)$分别是拟静力位移应力与惯性位移应力。

3　工程实例

石门子主坝为碾压混凝土双曲拱坝,最大中心角 110°,最大坝高 110m,坝顶宽 5m,底宽 30m(见图 1)。坝址区域稳定性差,多次发生中强地震,是重点的抗震设防地区。地震基本烈度按 8 度设计。

本文采用整体拱坝计算模型,剖分结构节点分别为 4 616,单元 3 207 个(8 节点与 6 节点块元)。混凝土动弹性模量 $E_d=32\mathrm{GPa}$,泊松比 $\mu=0.16$。坝基是非均匀的砂砾岩,主要分三层,动弹性模量分别为 $E_{d1}=15\mathrm{GPa}$,$E_{d2}=9\mathrm{GPa}$ 和 $E_{d3}=6\mathrm{GPa}$,泊松比为 $\mu=0.26$。应用子结构叠代法很容易计算坝基的静力刚度。

地震动输入参数[1,2]分别为:$\alpha=0.5$,$S_0=107.73$,$\xi_g=0.64$,$\omega_g=31.42$,$\omega_c=1.63$,$D=0.03\mathrm{s}$ 及相干系数 $\gamma=0.125$。

应用 ASAS－99 系统对石门子拱坝进行了地震动随机响应分析。由于梁向应力很小,仅列出拱向应力结果。图 2 是视波速 $c_0=1\ 000.0\mathrm{m/s}$ 时坝高 94m 处各点拱向应力功率谱曲线及坝下游面应力方差;图 3 是视波速 $c_0=2\ 500.0\mathrm{m/s}$ 时相应的结果。

由图可见:①应力功率谱低频段幅值相对很大,这是由于应力与位移直接相关而非加

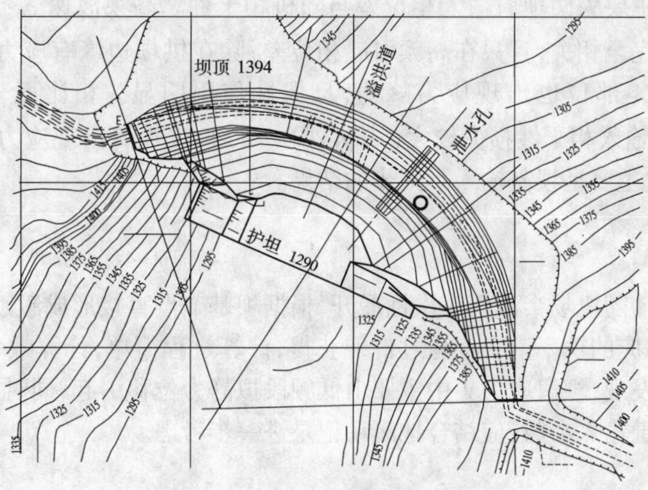

图 1 石门子拱坝平面布置图

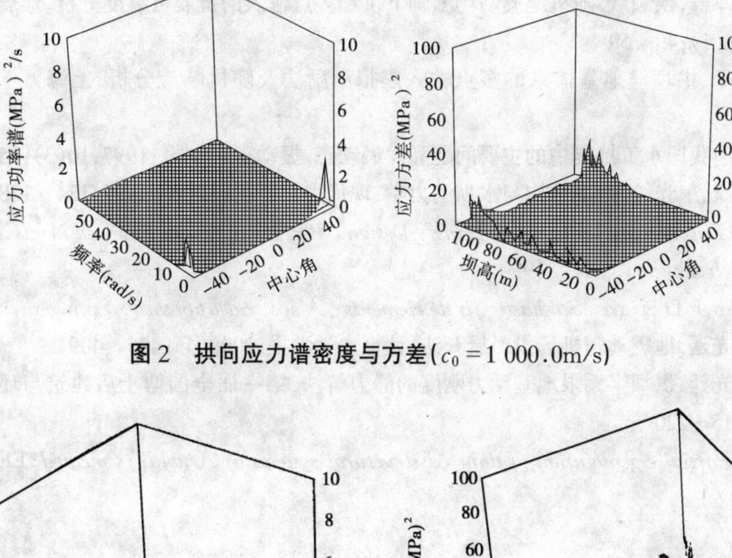

图 2 拱向应力谱密度与方差($c_0 = 1\ 000.0$m/s)

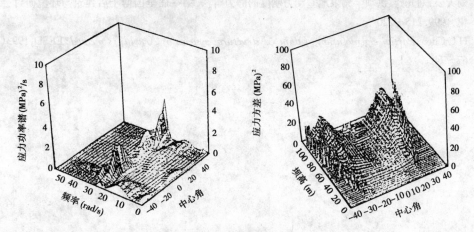

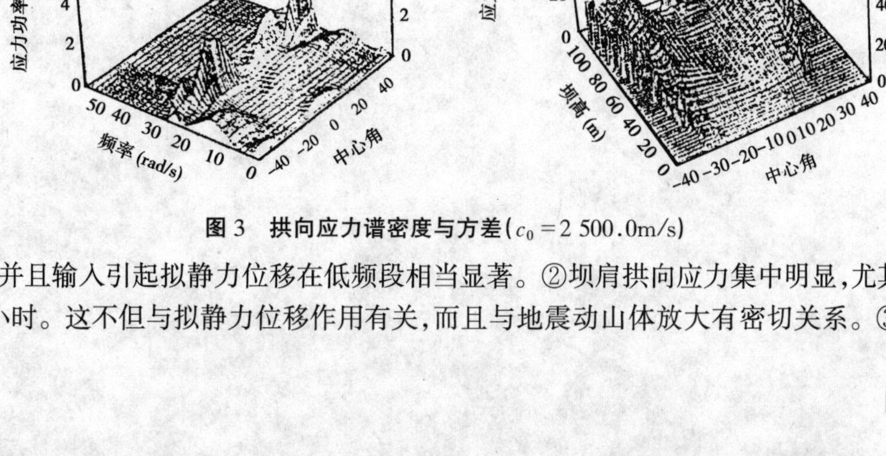

图 3 拱向应力谱密度与方差($c_0 = 2\ 500.0$m/s)

速度,并且输入引起拟静力位移在低频段相当显著。②坝肩拱向应力集中明显,尤其视波速较小时。这不但与拟静力位移作用有关,而且与地震动山体放大有密切关系。③视波速对拱坝的影响主要为两坝肩输入相位差与随机相干性。高视波速 $c_0 = 2\ 500.0$m/s 几乎坝基随机输入完全相关,且只在高频引起相位差;除在拱坝边缘有应力集中现象外,拱坝中上部左右 1/4 部位也出现应力峰值,且惯性作用明显。相比而言,视波速 $c_0 = 1\ 000.0$m/s 则使输入相干性损失较大(式(4)中 $r=3$);仅坝肩出现应力集中,而在坝内未有应力峰值,这主要是坝基输入不同步的结果。

4 结语

本文将地震动随机场半解析一次性展开,根据坝基节点直接形成激励向量,计算结构的随机响应,而响应的功率谱密度通过自乘获得,计算过程简单,计算效率较高。通过对石门子拱坝分析发现,坝肩应力集中主要由低频段拟静力位移引起;同时视波速是影响拱坝地震响应的关键输入参数,应结合地震动记录进一步考虑。

参 考 文 献

[1] 梁爱虎,陈厚群,侯顺载.随机地震动场激励下拱坝多点输入的抗震可靠度分析.地震工程与工程振动,1996,16(1):49~59

[2] 陈健云,林皋.拱坝－地基体系的多点输入虚拟激励法及随机响应分析.上海力学,1999,20(1):76~81

[3] 陈厚群.当前我国水工抗震中的主要问题和发展动态.振动工程学报,1997,10(3):253~257

[4] 林皋,张楚汉,王光纶.地下结构与水坝动力学.现代力学与科技进步,1997.124~128

[5] *Earthquake Engineering for Concrete Dams: Design, Performance and Research Needs*. National Academy Press, Washington, D.C. 1990

[6] R G Ghanem, P D Spanos. *Stochastic finite elements: A spectral approach*. Springer－verlag, 1991

[7] 刘天云,刘光廷.地震动随机场投影展开法.计算力学学报,2000(4):405~409

[8] 刘天云,刘光廷.拱坝半无限地基动力刚度的静力解法.第一届全国博士后建筑与环境研讨会论文集,1999.215~220

[9] H C Chen. *Partial eigensolution of damped structural systems by Arnoldi's method*. EESD, 1993(22):67~74

子费用模糊估算的水电工程总造价概率估计

摘　要　根据工程系统的可分解性，将水电工程总体造价分解成若干个子工程造价。用模糊数学贴近度原理，建立子工程造价的模糊估算模型；运用主观估计法，估计出各个子工程造价随机变化的期望值和方差。然后依据概率论多元随机变量理论，推出水电工程总体造价概率分布的期望值和方差，并确定了造价随机变化的概率分布关系曲线。该估计方法客观、全面地反映了工程造价的实际随机变化特性。

关键词　工程造价　模糊贴近度　概率估计　造价估算

大中型水电工程，在投资前必须进行经济评价，评价的主要内容之一是预估工程造价。尤其目前在社会主义市场机制下的水电工程建设，工程造价估算是国家立项决策的重要依据，其造价估计得准确与否，是工程技术经济分析评价结果是否可靠、合理的关键所在。

以往由于工程造价估算不尽合理，加上投资控制不力，经常发生大幅度概算超估算、预算超概算、决算超预算的"三超"现象，致使国家的建设投资计划被打乱，按计划投资，不能按计划建成项目；或如要按计划建成建设项目，又发生资金短缺，不得不延长工期，有的还要停建。从这些教训中可以看到工程造价合理估算是十分重要的。

目前国内外在水电项目的规划和设计阶段，其造价估算一般是参照概算、预算编制方法和扩大指标估算法，估算的工程造价值是确定的数值。实际上，工程竣工后决算值往往超过开工前预算值，在建设水电工程的过程中，工程的费用总是不断地变化，工程费用受到许多不确定性因素的影响，诸如建筑材料价格、工人工资等费用要素变化；水文、气象、地形、地质等客观条件的变化引起费用发生变化，即由于建筑工地暴雨、洪水、冰冻等水文气候条件变化，或对地形、地质等环境条件的了解不够而造成费用的变化，由工期延误而造成造价大幅度增加等。因此，工程造价的变化是客观存在的，并具有一定程度的随机波动性。同时，这种不确定性变化是可以用模糊理论和概率理论来测度的。

考虑到水电工程造价的复杂性及多变性，本文依据系统分析的观点，即依据系统的层次性和可分解性，将总体工程造价分解成若干个子费用。然后利用模糊数学贴近度原理，在同类型水电工程项目体系下，通过研究和对比拟建子工程和已建子工程的相似程度来估算拟待建子工程造价。运用模糊数学方法，使已建子工程和待建子工程的相似程度定量化，从而得到欲估子工程的造价。在此基础上运用专家主观估计方法求各子工程造价值随机变化的统计特征参数期望值与方差；最后利用多元随机变量有关理论推导求得总体工程造价变化的期望值和方差，该概率估计方法为决策部门提供总体工程造价变化的幅动范围、分布中心等信息，从而把握了总造价不确定变化的分布规律。

本文选自《清华大学学报(自然科学版)》1996 年第 1 期，作者还有唐晓阳、吴之明。

1 子工程造价值的模糊估算

1.1 子工程造价的模糊估算可行性

子工程造价的模糊估算方法，是利用模糊数学的基本原理，依据贴近度概念和择近原则，在同一条件下，研究和对比待建子工程项目与已建子工程项目的相似程度，根据类似的已建子工程造价资料估算待建子工程项目造价的过程。它的最大特点是，既不需计算工程数量，也不用查概预算定额。

待建子工程虽然不可能与已建子工程完全一致，但在大量的已建子工程中，总有一些已建子工程和拟建子工程相似。所以专家根据已建成的许许多多各种类型的工程项目预算，由待建工程和某些已建工程的相似程度，择取最相似于待建工程的一个或几个已建工程的造价资料，根据以往的经验，引入一个系数加以调整，从而估算出待建工程的造价。但是这种估算过程是含糊的。因为这只能定性地判断所择取的已建与待建工程相似，却不能用精确的数学语言来定量描述它们究竟相似到什么程度，所以引入的调整系数也难以做到准确，往往使估算出的待建工程的造价有相当的误差。本文运用模糊数学的基本原理，使这种含糊的估算方法成为科学的估算方法，使得已建工程和待建工程的相似程度定量化。

1.2 模糊相似程度的定量化

判断一事物和其他事物相似，是基于一事物和其他事物的诸方面相同或相似而言的。研究上述待建子工程和多个已建子工程的相似程度，可以选取 m 个特征因素，从 m 个方面考虑，如果用 $Z_1, Z_2, Z_3, \cdots, Z_m$ 分别表示特征因素，用数学语言来表达，该问题的论域是

$$Z = \{Z_1, Z_2, Z_3, \cdots, Z_m\} \tag{1}$$

针对上式中 m 个特征因素，那么待建子工程与已建子工程分别具有多少这些特征；待建子工程与已建子工程的相似程度如何，可以用隶属函数值和贴近度来表征。

1.2.1 隶属函数值的确定

表示某些元素隶属于某种特性的函数称为隶属函数，用[0,1]间的一个数值来表示，其值越接近1，意味着隶属程度越高；反之就越低。设选取 k 个已建子工程，对应于 m 个特征因素，通过 k 个已建子工程的造价资料，并结合子工程方案的繁简程度由以下步骤来确定隶属函数值。

(1)分别计算 k 个已建子工程对应于 m 个特征因素的单方造价。将二元对比排序推广到多元对比排序，k 个已建子工程针对某一特征因素找出比较基准，将单方造价费用较高、较复杂的子工程，取其优先关系值为1，反之取为0。其他子工程对应于这一特征因素，再根据单方造价的高低在[0,1]之间内插求得。同理，可求得 k 个已建子工程对应于其他特征因素的优先关系值。

(2)优先关系值体现了具有某种特征因素的诸子工程之间的优先次序，用文献[1]、[2]二元对比排序方法步骤，可得 k 个已建子工程对应于某个特征因素的隶属函数值，同理可求出 k 个已建子工程对应于其他特征因素的隶属函数值。

1.2.2 贴近度的计算

相似程度的定量化问题就是贴近度的计算问题,贴近度越大相似程度越高,贴近度越小相似程度就越低。第 i 个($i=1,2,\cdots,k$)已建子工程对于 m 个特征因素的隶属函数值设为 $a_{i1},a_{i2},a_{i3},\cdots,a_{im}$;待建子工程对应于 m 个特征因素的隶属函数值设为 $b_1,b_2,\cdots,b_m$;根据模糊数学运算法则,贴近度的计算由下列公式导出

内积: $$B\otimes A_i=(b_1\wedge a_{i1})\vee(b_2\wedge a_{i2})\vee\cdots\vee(b_m\wedge a_{im}) \tag{2}$$

外积: $$B\odot A_i=(b_1\vee a_{i1})\wedge(b_2\vee a_{i2})\wedge\cdots\wedge(b_m\vee a_{im}) \tag{3}$$

所谓贴近度一般定义[2]是 $F(U)$上的一个模糊关系 $\alpha(\in F(U)\times F(U))$,它具有性质:

①$\alpha(\underset{\sim}{A},\underset{\sim}{A})=1$;②$\alpha(\underset{\sim}{A},\underset{\sim}{B})=\alpha(\underset{\sim}{B},\underset{\sim}{A})\geqslant0$;③若对任意 $u\in U$,有 $\mu_{\underset{\sim}{A}}(u)\leqslant\mu_{\underset{\sim}{B}}(u)\leqslant\mu_{\underset{\sim}{C}}(u)$或 $\mu_{\underset{\sim}{A}}(u)\geqslant\mu_{\underset{\sim}{B}}(u)\geqslant\mu_{\underset{\sim}{C}}(u)$,则有

$$\alpha(\underset{\sim}{A},\underset{\sim}{C})\leqslant\alpha(\underset{\sim}{B},\underset{\sim}{C}) \tag{4}$$

由式(2)和式(3)其贴近度计算为

$$\alpha_i=\alpha(B,A_i)=\frac{1}{2}[B\otimes A_i+(1-B\odot A_i)] \tag{5}$$

式(2)、(3)中,"∨"表示取最大值,"∧"表示取最小值。可根据已建和待建子工程的隶属函数值,通过上述公式,求出待建子工程与每一个已建子工程的贴近度,从而将待建子工程与已建子工程的相似程度定量化。

1.3 子工程造价估算数学模型的建立

在预测技术中,被广泛应用的预测方法叫指数平滑法。子工程造价的估算公式,就以指数平滑法为理论依据。按照指数平滑预测法的原理,由上述确定的贴近度,就可建立子工程造价的估算模型。

选取近期的 k 个已建子工程,并将它们按物价指数折算到基准日期。则 k 个已建子工程与待建欲估子工程的贴近度(即相似程度)$\alpha_i(i=1,2,3,\cdots,k)$,从大到小排列成一个有序数列令为 $\alpha_1,\alpha_2,\alpha_3,\cdots,\alpha_k$,相对应的已建子工程的造价值为 $E_1,E_2,E_3,\cdots,E_k$。也就是说,与待建欲估子工程最相似(贴近度最大)的已建子工程造价为 E_1,次相似为 E_2,依次类推,最不相似的为 E_k。

设第 i 个相似子工程的造价预测值为E_i^*,其预测误差为 $E_i-E_i^*$,则第 $i-1$ 个相似子工程的造价预测值为

$$E_{i-1}^*=E_i^*+\alpha_i(E_i-E_i^*) \tag{6}$$

上式意义是:对第 i 个相似子工程的造价预测值进行修正,方法是加上其预测误差 $E_i-E_i^*$ 和该子工程与待建子工程的贴近度 α_i 的乘积,然后把修正后的造价值作为与待建子工程第 $i-1$ 个相似子工程的造价预测值。式(6)可改写为

$$E_{i-1}^*=\alpha_iE_i+(1-\alpha_i)E_i^* \tag{7}$$

依次类推并展开,则可得待建子工程的造价预测值

$$\begin{aligned}E_g&=\alpha_1E_1+(1-\alpha_1)E_i^*=\alpha_1E_1+(1-\alpha_1)[\alpha_2E_2+(1-\alpha_2)E_2^*]\\&=\alpha_1E_1+\alpha_2(1-\alpha_1)E_2+\alpha_3(1-\alpha_1)(1-\alpha_2)E_3+\cdots\end{aligned}$$

$$+ \alpha_k(1-\alpha_1)(1-\alpha_2)\cdots(1-\alpha_{k-1})E_k + (1-\alpha_1)(1-\alpha_2)\cdots(1-\alpha_k)E_k^* \quad (8)$$

一般只要取与待建欲估子工程最相似的3个已建子工程就完全可以满足待建子工程的造价估算精度要求；则待建欲估子工程的造价估算公式为

$$E_g = \alpha_1 E_1 + \alpha_2 E_2(1-\alpha_1) + \alpha_3 E_3(1-\alpha_1)(1-\alpha_2) + (1-\alpha_1)(1-\alpha_2)(1-\alpha_3)(E_1+E_2+E_3)/3 \quad (9)$$

此式即为子工程造价的模糊估算模型；E_g 值就是子工程造价的模糊估算值。

2　子工程造价的概率估计

由于各个相似子工程与待建子工程只是相似而不是相同，即存在着差异；再者，由于所处水电工程条件的复杂性及主客观条件的限制，某些未来影响因素不可能全面考虑到，这些不确定因素就影响了待建子工程造价的准确性。所以通过模糊相似理论得到的子工程造价值只能是最可能值，需要对子工程造价进行概率估计。

子工程造价的概率估计就是用概率分布来定量描述子工程造价值的变化规律，给出子工程造价出现的大小及其可能性。此时，在子工程造价的概率估计过程中，采用主观估计方法，充分发挥专家们的主观能动性，依据专家们工程经验和现状调查收集到的资料和信息，在由模糊贴近度概念确定子工程造价最可能值 x_2（即 E_g）的基础上，作上下浮动估计，浮动的极限值作为子工程造价的最大值和最小值。从而构成子工程造价的3个特征估计值，即最小值 x_1（在最有利条件下的乐观估计），最可能值 x_2 即 E_g（由子工程造价模糊估算模型确定），最大值 x_3（在最不利条件下的悲观估计）。这也就是所谓的“三值估计法”。

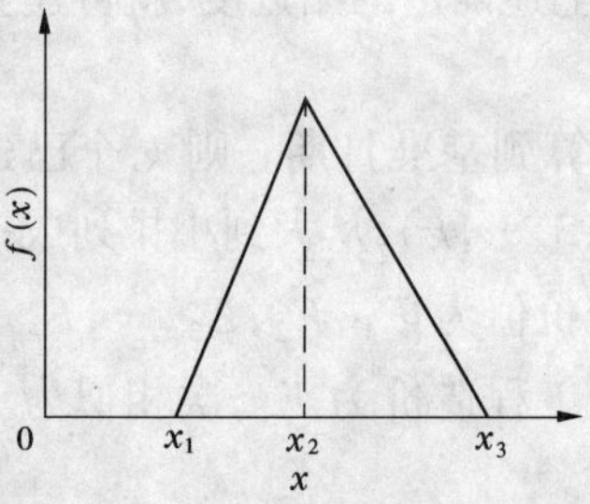

图1　特征估计值图

采用概率论方法来推求三个估计值的期望值 $E(x)$ 及方差 $D(x)$，可采用两种方法：

(1)三角形分布法。由三个特征估计值概化成三角形分布，见图1，其概率密度公式为

$$f(x) = \begin{cases} \dfrac{2(x-x_1)}{(x_3-x_1)(x_2-x_1)}; & x_1 \leqslant x < x_2 \\ \dfrac{2(x_3-x)}{(x_3-x_1)(x_3-x_2)}; & x_2 \leqslant x < x_3 \\ 0 & \text{其他} \end{cases} \quad (10)$$

由此概率密度可推求

$$E(x) = (x_1 + x_2 + x_3)/3 \quad (11)$$

$$D(x) = \sigma^2 = [(x_3-x_1)^2 + (x_2-x_1)(x_2-x_3)]/18 \quad (12)$$

式中：σ 为均方差。

(2) β 分布法[3]。在计划评审技术(PERT)中，推出 β 分布的均值 $E(x)$ 和方差 $D(x)$ 为

$$E(x) = (x_1 + 4x_2 + x_3)/6 \quad (13)$$

$$D(x) = (x_3 - x_1)^2/36 \tag{14}$$

将三个特征估计值视为随机样本值，则由概率统计知识，可求得统计特征均值和方差为

$$\overline{x} = \frac{1}{3}\sum_{i=1}^{3} x_i = \frac{1}{3}(x_1 + x_2 + x_3) \tag{15}$$

$$S^2 = \sigma_2 = \frac{1}{2}\sum_{i=1}^{3}(x_i - \overline{x})^2 \tag{16}$$

事实上，式(15)与按三角形分布计算得到的期望值公式(11)是相同的。将各个子工程造价均按上述方法推求各自的概率分布特征参数期望值 $E(x)$和方差 $D(x)$。

3 总体工程造价的概率估计

概率估计是指依据上述各个子工程造价的概率分布特征参数来推求总体工程造价的概率分布。很显然，总体工程造价可以通过各个子工程造价相叠加而获得，但如何根据各个子工程造价的不确定性来推求总体工程造价不确定性的量值呢？可采用蒙特卡洛(Monte－Carlo)模拟的方法，也可采用统计参数解析法，本文主要研究解析法的计算原理。

设水电工程的总体造价 C 由 n 个子工程造价叠加组成，其表达式为

$$C = g_1 + g_2 + \cdots + g_n \tag{17}$$

子工程造价 $g_i(i=1,2,\cdots,n)$是随机变量，上面子工程造价的概率估计方法已确定了它们的期望值及方差，则总体工程造价 C 是多元随机变量的函数。根据概率论多元随机变量有关理论，可得到总体工程造价的期望值和方差

$$E(c) = E(g_1) + E(g_2) + \cdots + E(g_n) \tag{18}$$

$$D(c) = \sigma_c^2 = \sigma_1^2 + \sigma_2^2 + \cdots + \sigma_n^2 + 2\sum_{i<j}(\nu_{ij}\sigma_i\sigma_j) \tag{19}$$

式中：σ_c 是总体工程造价 C 的均方差；σ_i 为子工程造价 g_i 的均方差；ν_{ij} 为 g_i 与 g_j 的相关系数。

相关系数的确定可采用主观分析判断的方法，当认为各个子工程造价之间是相互独立的，则其相关系数等于零；当认为某些子工程造价值之间存在着较密切的关系，其相关系数可在 0.6～1.0 之间选取。

4 总体工程造价与概率的关系

前面得到总体工程造价的数学期望 $E(c)$及方差 $D(c)$(均方差 σ_c)，$E(c)$反映了总体工程造价随机变化的分布中心，方差反映了总体工程造价变化的均不均匀程度。然而总体工程造价—概率曲线可在一定程度上更好地反映造价值的不确定性，也就可以把握总体工程造价值随机变化的分布规律。在推求总体造价的大小 C—概率 p 的关系曲线时，需要借助理论分布函数来揭示总体造价的变化规律。依据影响因素的多少及变化特性，通常可用正态、P－Ⅲ型理论分布函数来描述。因总体工程造价往往受许多不确定因素的影响，而每个因素影响的大小往往难以确定，故在大多数情况下，C 的随机变化服从

正态分布。

将上面求得的总体工程造价估计值作为平均值，它实现的概率为50%，那么按照正态分布计算，总体造价估计值加上1σ_c所实现的概率则就为84.1%，这是因为总体造价服从正态分布的密度函数为

$$f(c) = \frac{1}{\sqrt{2\pi}\sigma_c}\exp\left\{-\frac{1}{2\sigma_c^2}[c - E(c)]^2\right\} \tag{20}$$

则小于任一造价值C的概率为

$$p(c \leqslant C) = \int_{-\infty}^{C}\frac{1}{\sqrt{2\pi}\sigma_c}\exp\left\{-\frac{1}{2\sigma_c^2}[c - E(c)]^2\right\}\mathrm{d}c \tag{21}$$

令 $y = \dfrac{c - E(c)}{\sigma_c}$，$\mathrm{d}c = \sigma_c \mathrm{d}y$ 代入式(2)化为标准正态分布

$$p(c \leqslant C) = \int_{-\infty}^{\frac{c-E(c)}{\sigma_c}}\frac{1}{\sqrt{2\pi}}\exp - \frac{y^2}{2}\mathrm{d}y = \Phi(y) \tag{22}$$

于是当总体工程造价估计值加上1σ_c，即$E(c)+\sigma$，则得

$$P = \frac{1}{\sqrt{2\pi}}\int_{-\infty}^{1}\exp\frac{y^2}{2}\mathrm{d}y \tag{23}$$

查表$P = 0.841\ 3$。

同理，造价估计值加上2σ_c所实现的概率为0.977 2。通过这样一组对应的造价—概率数据可推求得到造价值—概率的关系曲线。该关系曲线较全面地描述了总体工程造价的随机变化情况，它所提供的信息比现今仅给造价某个确定值所提供的信息要客观、全面得多。

5　结语

本文提出的基于子工程费用模糊估算的工程总体造价的概率估计方法，将总体造价分解成若干个子工程造价，可使复杂问题简单化、明朗化，更容易把握工程造价的估算，同时考虑了工程造价的随机变化特性。与确定型估算方法相比，更为客观、真实地反映了工程造价的随机变化特性，为水电工程技术经济评价提供了可靠的科学依据。此外应认识到，人们不可能超越客观条件，把工程造价估算得与实际最终造价(结算价)完全一致，但可以肯定，如果能掌握工程建设的各种情况，全面分析各种不确定因素，那么造价估算的准确性也必然能够提高。

参 考 文 献

[1] Dubos D, Prade H. *Fuzzg sets and system: Theory and application*. Academic press, New York, 1980
[2] 王琦.实用模糊数学.北京:科学技术文献出版社,1992
[3] 林延江.水利土木工程系统分析.北京:水利电力出版社,1985
[4] 唐晓阳.工程造价估算方法及准确性浅析.水利水电工程造价,1994(3):29~31

工程项目投资费用的随机—模糊估算方法研究

摘　要　由于工程造价受到许多不确定性因素影响,既有随机性,又有模糊性,为了对其进行经济论证,根据系统的可分解性,将总体工程费用分解成若干个子工程费用;运用模糊数学贴近度概念估算出子工程费用;由子工程费用叠加构成总体工程费用的最可能造价值。依据专家经验和工程实际,在最可能造价值基础上上下波动组成最小值、最可能值、最大值三个特征估计值。考虑到随机性和模糊性,根据概率论和模糊数学原理,确立随机—模糊数学特征的统计方法,提出了工程造价的随机—模糊估算方法,客观地反映了工程造价的实际变化特性。

关键词　工程造价　贴近度　随机—模糊估算方法

工程造价估算是利用某种方法,对工程投资费用所作的一个预先估计或预测。

目前,在工程项目规划及设计阶段,造价估算一般是参照概算、预算编制方法和扩大指标估算法[2,3],估算值是确定的数值。

然而,如果对任何一个工程项目作一简单费用分析,会发现在工程建设过程中,其费用总是不断地变化着,工程竣工之后的决算值与开工前的预算值往往是不吻合的,造成差异的原因是多方面的:①由于建筑材料的价格,工人工资等构成费用要素的变化而使造价变化;②因建筑工地暴雨、洪水、冰冻等水文气候条件变化而引起造价的变化;③对建设工地地形、地质等环境条件的了解不够而造成费用的变化。这里工程造价的变化是客观的,且具有一定程度的随机波动性。造价估算中还存在另一类不确定性,就是大量的不精确性,界限的不清晰性,统称为模糊性。由于工程条件的复杂性,未来的一些关键因素不可能都预计到,由此某些估计值往往是采用"大概"、"估计是"、"可能"、"多或少"等带有模糊性的语言值或判断,这就导致了造价估算的模糊性。如"三值估计法"中的"最可能值"本身就是个模糊概念,具有强烈的模糊性。此外,人为的因素在造价估算尤其是主观估计中的影响是至关重要的,它有双重因素,既可能产生随机性,又可能产生模糊性。如统计、观测等产生差错(误差)是随机性的例子;而人的工程经验丰富与否、技术能力的高低、反应灵敏程度和偏好等人为主观能动性的因素将对造价估算带来大量的模糊结果,故而,人为因素在造价估算中的影响作用也是具有模糊性的。

因此,工程造价受到许多不确定性因素的影响,既具有一定程度的随机性,又具有明显的模糊性。本文将综合考虑随机性和模糊性,研究确定工程造价的随机—模糊估算方法。

本文所研究的工程投资费用随机—模糊估算的原理逻辑步骤如下:

(1)根据系统的层次性和可分解性,将总体工程费用分解成若干个子工程费用;

(2)由某些已建子工程和待估子工程的相似程度,运用模糊数学原理中贴近度概念,估算出子工程费用;

(3)由子工程估算费用叠加构成总体工程费用的最可能造价值;

本文选自《清华大学学报(自然科学版)》1996年第4期,作者还有唐晓阳、吴之明。

(4)利用专家工程经验及当时信息资料，以最可能造价值作上下浮动，组成最小值、最可能值、最大值三个造价估计值；

(5)考虑三个特征估计值的随机性和模糊性，结合概率论和模糊数学，建立工程造价的随机—模糊估算方法。

1 分解子工程费用的模糊相似估算

子工程费用的模糊相似估算方法，是运用模糊数学的基本原理，在同一可比条件下，通过分析和对比待建子工程项目与已建子工程项目的相似程度，依据贴近度概念和择近原则，选择类似的已建子工程造价资料来估算待建分解的子工程项目的造价。具体的子工程模糊相似估算过程参见文献[7]。

2 总体工程造价的随机—模糊估算方法

显然，总体工程造价可通过各个子工程造价相叠加而获得，由 n 个子工程造价 E_{Q_1}，E_{Q_2}，…，E_{Q_n} 组成总造价设为 $E_{总}$，其表达式为

$$E_{总} = E_{Q_1} + E_{Q_2} + E_{Q_3} + \cdots + E_{Q_n} \tag{1}$$

但还存在某些问题：① 待建子工程根据相似程度择取若干个相似已建子工程进行造价估算，只是相似而非相同，总存在某些差异；② 由于所处工程条件的复杂性及主客观条件的限制，某些未来影响因素不可能全面考虑到，这就影响了待建子工程造价的准确性，那么总造价 $E_{总}$ 与真实总体工程造价总是存在或多或少的差异，$E_{总}$ 只能是总体工程总造价的最可能值。为研究方便，令 $x_2 = E_{总}$。

此时在造价估算过程中，就要采用主观估计，充分发挥专家们的主观能动性；依据专家们丰富的工程经验和现状调查收集到的资料和信息，在总体工程造价最可能值 x_2 的基础上，作上下浮动估计，浮动极限值作为总体工程造价的最小值和最大值，构成总造价的三个特征估计值，即最小值 x_1(在最有利条件下的乐观估计)，最可能值 x_2 即 $E_{总}$(由子工程造价叠加构成)，最大值 x_3(在最不利条件下的悲观估计)。

文献[6] 运用概率论方法推求估计值 x_1, x_2, x_3 的期望值 $E(x)$ 及方差 $D(x)$，一般有两种方法。一是三角形分布法，将三个估计值概化成三角形分布，可推求 $E(x)$ 及 $D(x)$ 分别为

$$E(x) = \frac{1}{3}(x_1 + x_2 + x_3) \tag{2}$$

$$D(x) = \sigma^2 = \frac{1}{18}[(x_3 - x_1)^2 + (x_2 - x_1)(x_2 - x_3)] \tag{3}$$

σ 为均方差。二是 β 分布法，在计划协调技术中，推出 β 分布的 $E(x)$ 及 $D(x)$ 为

$$E(x) = \frac{1}{6}(x_1 + 4x_2 + x_3) \tag{4}$$

$$D(x) = \frac{1}{36}(x_3 - x_1)^2 \tag{5}$$

将三个估计值视为随机样本值，由概率统计知识可得随机统计特征均值和方差为

$$\overline{x} = \frac{1}{3}\sum_{i=1}^{3} x_i = \frac{1}{3}(x_1 + x_2 + x_3) \tag{6}$$

$$S^2 = \sigma^2 = \frac{1}{2}\sum_{i=1}^{3}(x_i - \overline{x})^2 \tag{7}$$

事实上,式(6)与按三角形分布计算得到期望值公式(2)是相同的。

由引言知,三个特征估计值具有明显模糊性,它们同时包含了随机性和模糊性,需将概率统计与模糊数学结合起来,对三个估计值进行随机—模糊数学处理,以合理确定总体工程造价不确定性变化的均值和方差。

2.1 三个特征估计值的均值 $\overline{x}$

取论域 $U = \{x_1, x_2, x_3\}$,设 $\underset{\sim}{A}$ 为 U 上的一个模糊子集,论域 U 中的元素 $x_i (i = 1, 2, 3)$ 对于 $\underset{\sim}{A}$ 的隶属度为 $\mu_A(x_i)$,本文所研究问题目的是要寻找 $\underset{\sim}{A}$ 的清晰估计:$\underset{\sim}{A} = \{\overline{x} \mid \mu_{\underset{\sim}{A}(\overline{x})} = 1\}$。

由问题性质和特征,根据模糊数学中以适中的隶属度为最大的隶属函数 $\mu(x) = \exp(-k(x-a)^2)(k > 0, a$ 为一常数)的构造特征,取隶属函数 $\mu_{\underset{\sim}{A}}(\overline{x}_i)$ 采用以下形式

$$\mu_{\underset{\sim}{A}}(\overline{x_i}) = \exp[-D(x_i, \overline{x})] \tag{8}$$

x_i 关于模糊集合 $\underset{\sim}{A}$ 中均值 $\overline{x}$ 的马氏距离

$$D(x_i, \overline{x}) = \omega_{c1}(x_i - \overline{x})^2 \quad (\omega_{c1} \text{ 为权重}) \tag{9}$$

隶属函数 $\mu_{\underset{\sim}{A}(x_i)}$ 具有这样的规律:x_i 距均值 $\overline{x}$ 的马氏距离 $D(x_i, \overline{x})$ 越大,则它对 $\underset{\sim}{A}$ 的隶属度越小;x_i 距均值 $\overline{x}$ 的马氏距离越小,则它对 $\underset{\sim}{A}$ 的隶属度越大;在均值 $\overline{x}$ 处,隶属度最大为1,因而所取隶属函数 $\mu_{\underset{\sim}{A}(x_i)}$ 的形式是合理的。同时 $\mu_{\underset{\sim}{A}(x_i)}$ 可写成

$$\mu_{\underset{\sim}{A}(x_i)} = \overline{\mu}_{\underset{\sim}{A}}[D(x_i, \overline{x})] \tag{10}$$

确定隶属函数后,文中所求均值 $\overline{x}$ 应当在最大程度上反映客观真实的总造价,故可按照使三个特征样本估计值整体上隶属于模糊子集 $\underset{\sim}{A}$ 的程度最大这一原则来求解 $\overline{x}$ 所具有的统计特征,为此,构造组成目标函数为

$$\max I = \sum_{i=1}^{3} \overline{\mu}_{\underset{\sim}{A}}[D(x_i, \overline{x})] \tag{11}$$

对上式求导得

$$\frac{\mathrm{d}I}{\mathrm{d}\overline{x}} = \frac{\partial I}{\partial D(x_i, \overline{x})} \cdot \frac{\mathrm{d}D(x_i, \overline{x})}{\mathrm{d}\overline{x}} = \sum_{i=1}^{3} \overline{\mu}'_{\underset{\sim}{A}}[D(x_i, \overline{x})][-2\omega_{c1}(x_i - \overline{x})] = 0$$

即得

$$\overline{x} = \sum_{i=1}^{3} \overline{\mu}'_{\underset{\sim}{A}}[D(x_i, \overline{x})]x_i \Big/ \sum_{i=1}^{3} \overline{\mu}'_{\underset{\sim}{A}}[D(x_i, \overline{x})] \tag{12}$$

又

$$\overline{\mu}'_{\underset{\sim}{A}}[D(x_i, \overline{x})] = -\exp[-D(x_i, \overline{x})] = -\overline{\mu}_{\underset{\sim}{A}}[D(x_i, \overline{x})]$$

整理得

$$\overline{x} = \frac{\sum_{i=1}^{3} \overline{\mu}_{\underset{\sim}{A}}[D(x_i, \overline{x})] x_i}{\sum_{i=1}^{3} \overline{\mu}_{\underset{\sim}{A}}[D(x_i, \overline{x})]} \tag{13}$$

2.2　三个样本估计值的方差 σ^2

设 ζ 是基于论域 $U = \{x_1, x_2, x_3\}$ 的随机 — 模糊变量[5]，令

$$\zeta_i = (x_i - \overline{x})^2 \tag{14}$$

ζ_i 取值构成另一论域 $R = \{\zeta_1, \zeta_2, \zeta_3\} = \{(x_1 - \overline{x})^2, (x_2 - \overline{x})^2, (x_3 - \overline{x})^2\}$，$\underset{\sim}{B}$ 为论域 R 上模糊子集，$\underset{\sim}{B}$ 为对应普通集合，所研究问题实质就是寻求 $\underset{\sim}{B}$ 的清晰估计

$$\underset{\sim}{B} = \{\zeta \mid \mu_{\underset{\sim}{B}}(S^2) = 1\} \tag{15}$$

类似于 2.1，取 ζ_i 对应于模糊集合 $\underset{\sim}{B}$ 的隶属函数

$$\mu_{\underset{\sim}{B}}(\zeta_i) = \exp[-D(\zeta_i, S^2)] \tag{16}$$

式中：$D(\zeta_i, S^2)$ 是 ζ_i 关于模糊集合 $\underset{\sim}{B}$ 的方差 S^2 的马氏距离，其表达式为

$$D(\zeta_i, S^2) = \omega_{c2}(\zeta_i - S^2)^2$$

式中：ω_{c2} 取常数。

与 2.1 类似，可将 $\mu_{\underset{\sim}{B}}(\zeta_i)$ 记为：$\mu_{\underset{\sim}{B}}(\zeta_i) = \overline{\mu}_{\underset{\sim}{B}}[D(\zeta_i, S^2)]$。所求方差应当在最大程度上反映客观现实，故可按照使 ζ_i 整体上隶属于模糊集合 $\underset{\sim}{B}$ 的程度最大这一原则来寻求方差 S^2 所具有的统计特征，据此，组成目标函数为

$$\max J = \sum_{i=1}^{3} \overline{\mu}_{\underset{\sim}{B}}[D(\zeta_i, S^2)] \tag{17}$$

对上式求导，有

$$\frac{dJ}{dS^2} = \frac{\partial J}{\partial D(\zeta_i, S^2)} \frac{dD(\zeta_i, S^2)}{dS^2} = \sum_{i=1}^{3} \overline{\mu}'_{\underset{\sim}{B}}[D(\zeta_i, S^2)] \cdot [-2\omega_{c2} \cdot (\zeta_i - S^2)] = 0$$

考虑到 ζ_i 表达式，又

$$\overline{\mu}'_{\underset{\sim}{B}}[D(\zeta_i, \sigma^2)] = -\exp[-D(\zeta_i, S^2)] = -\overline{\mu}_{\underset{\sim}{B}}[D(\zeta_i, S^2)]$$

得方差

$$S^2 = \sum_{i=1}^{3} \overline{\mu}_{\underset{\sim}{B}}[D(\zeta_i, S^2)](x_i - \overline{x})^2 / \sum_{i=1}^{3} \overline{\mu}_{\underset{\sim}{B}}[D(\zeta_i, S^2)] \tag{18}$$

上式即为总体方差所服从的随机 — 模糊统计特征公式，而三个特征样本估计值方差所服从的随机 — 模糊统计特征关系由 $\sigma^2 = \frac{n}{n-1} S^2$ 得三个特征样本估计值方差为

$$\sigma^2 = \frac{3}{2} \times \frac{\sum_{i=1}^{3} \overline{\mu}_{\underset{\sim}{B}}[D(\zeta_i, S^2)](x_i - \overline{x})^2}{\sum_{i=1}^{3} \overline{\mu}_{\underset{\sim}{B}}[D(\zeta_i, S^2)]} \tag{19}$$

2.3　随机 — 模糊处理方法的合理性

由上面经过随机 — 模糊数学处理获得的三个特征估计值的均值、方差，实际上其物理意义是以基于三个特征样本估计值的随机 — 模糊变量 x，ζ 关于相应模糊集合 $\underset{\sim}{A}$，$\underset{\sim}{B}$ 的

隶属函数 $\mu_{\underset{\sim}{A}}(x_i)$,$\mu_{\underset{\sim}{B}}(\zeta_i)$ 的导数为权重对随机 — 模糊变量 x,ζ 的加权平均值,即随机 — 模 糊数学处理的实质是一种加权平均。而三个估计值是由专家们依据工程经验、资料和信息提供的,三个特征估计值对工程造价估计的可能性程度是不相同的,因而要进行加权平均;可见这种随机 — 模糊数学处理方法是合乎数学逻辑与实际情况的。

当三个特征样本估计值不包含模糊性时,随机 — 模糊样本蜕变成随机样本估计值,模糊子集变成普通集合,依据模糊集合及普通集合定义,一致有

$$\begin{cases} D(x_i,\overline{x}) = D(\zeta_i,S^2) = 0 \\ \mu_{\underset{\sim}{A}}(x_i) = \overline{\mu}_{\underset{\sim}{A}}[D(x_i,\overline{x})] = e^{\circ} = 1 \qquad i = 1,2,3 \\ M_{\underset{\sim}{B}}(\zeta_i) = \overline{\mu}_{\underset{\sim}{B}}[D(\zeta_i,S^2)] = e^{\circ} = 1 \end{cases} \tag{20}$$

分别代入均值及方差公式,则它们蜕变成

$$\overline{x} = \frac{1}{3}\sum_{i=1}^{3} x_i \quad \sigma^2 = \frac{3}{2}\left[\sum_{i=1}^{3}(x_i - \overline{x})^2/3\right] = \frac{1}{2}\sum_{i=1}^{3}(x_i - \overline{x})^2$$

上两式即为随机变量的均值与方差计算公式,事实上,相同于前述式(6) 与式(7)。由此可见,传统经典的随机统计处理方法是随机 — 模糊数学统计处理方法的一种特例。

2.4 计算方法与步骤

$$\omega_{c1} = \frac{1}{(L_{1\max} - L_{1\min})/2},\ L_{1i} = (x_i - \overline{x})^2, \quad i = 1,2,3$$

取

$$\omega_{c2} = \frac{1}{(L_{2\max} - L_{2\min})/2},\ L_{2i} = [(x_i - \overline{x})^2 - \sigma^2]^2, \quad i = 1,2,3$$

式中:$L_{j\max}$、$L_{j\min}$ 分别是 L_{ji} 中最大值、最小值($j = 1,2;\ i = 1,2,3$)。

将 ω_{c1}、ω_{c2} 表达式代入均值和方差公式,整理后得

$$\overline{x} = \frac{\sum_{i=1}^{3}\exp[-2(x_i - \overline{x})^2/(L_{1\max} - L_{1\min})]x_i}{\sum_{i=1}^{3}\exp[-2(x_i - \overline{x})^2/(L_{1\max} - L_{1\min})]} \tag{21}$$

$$\sigma^2 = \frac{3}{2} \times \frac{\sum_{i=1}^{3}\exp\{-2[(x_i - \overline{x})^2 - \sigma^2]^2/(L_{2\max} - L_{2\min})\}(x_i - \overline{x})^2}{\sum_{i=1}^{3}\exp\{-2[(x_i - \overline{x})^2 - \sigma^2]^2/(L_{2\max} - L_{2\min})\}} \tag{22}$$

上两式就是经随机 — 模糊数学统计处理的三个特征估计值的均值和方差计算公式。它们都是具有隐函数式,在实际计算工作中,采用叠代法求解。其计算步骤如下:

(1) 取初值 $\overline{x}_0$、σ_0 分别为三个特征样本估计值的随机统计均值与方差。按照式(6) 与式(7) 分别计算得到。

(2) 由式(21) 与式(22) 计算随机 — 模糊统计均值 $\overline{x}_1$,方差 σ_1。

(3) 检验判断,若 $|\overline{x}_1 - \overline{x}_0| < \varepsilon_1$,$|\sigma_1 - \sigma_0| < \varepsilon_2$($\varepsilon_1$、$\varepsilon_2$ 为指定精度),则 $\overline{x}_1$、σ_1 即为所求;反之,则令 $\overline{x}_0 = \overline{x}_1$,再返回到(2) 步,直到满足精度要求为止。

由上面方面和步骤可推求得到总体工程造价的均值和方差,均值 $\overline{x}$ 反映了总体工程

造价随机—模糊不确定性变化的分布中心;方差 σ^2 反映了总体工程造价随机—模糊变化的不均匀程度。有了这两个特征参数,也就把握了总造价不确定性变化的分布中心、大致范围等信息,从而掌握了总造价不确定性变化的分布规律。

参考文献

[1] 卢谦,张琰.建筑工程招投标工作手册.北京:中国建筑工业出版社,1987

[2] 吕发钦.实用建筑工程估价手册.北京:北京科学技术出版社,1991

[3] 任玉峰,董玉学,刘金昌.建筑工程概预算与投标报价.北京:中国建筑工业出版社,1992

[4] Dubois D, Prode H. *Fuzzy sets and systems: Theory and Application*. Academic press, New York, 1980

[5] Kwakernaak H. *Fuzzy random variables I*. Information Science, 1978, 15(1):1~28

[6] 林延江.水利土木工程系统分析.北京:水利电力出版社,1985

[7] 唐晓阳,刘光廷.基于子工程费用模糊估算的大中型水电工程总体造价的概率估计方法.清华大学学报,1996,36(1): 113~118

二维混凝土随机骨料模型研究*

摘　要　本文的主要目的是研究二维混凝土随机骨料的投放算法，建立二维混凝土不均质模型，为混凝土宏观强度分析研究提供基础。文中将混凝土考虑为由粗骨料和水泥砂浆胶体构成的复合材料，采用计算机模拟方法建立混凝土材料的非均质数值模型。本文建立了以面积为标度的骨料侵入判断准则、凸多边形骨料生成方式，以及在此基础上形成的二维混凝土随机骨料投放算法。同其他方法相比，本文建立的“凸型”骨料随机投放算法简单，更易于推广到三维空间。文章最后给出了骨料随机投放的二维数值混凝土模型和一个简单的混凝土不均质特性分析实例，以说明本文算法实现的有效性。

关键词　混凝土　二维模型　随机骨料模型　计算机模拟

混凝土是一种复杂的多相非均质材料。混凝土随机骨料投放技术是混凝土材料强度计算研究的重要内容。混凝土计算模型要求粗骨料的形状、尺寸以及分布都要求同真实的混凝土在统计意义上一致。国内外学者在这方面进行了许多研究。Wittmann 等[1]建立了角度和边数都随机选择的多棱角无规则骨料模型，并用 Beddow 和 Meloy[2]的方法自动生成圆形骨料模型。其他研究者都仅仅将骨料假定为圆形或球形[3~5]。在二维数值混凝土研究领域，最为成熟方法是王宗敏[6~7]建立的二维混凝土任意形状骨料随机投放的算法。在骨料尺寸和空间分布仿真研究中，众多研究者均用骨料投放方式[1,3,5]，只有 De Schutter 与 Taerwe[8]使用了空间分割填充方法。

对于卵石骨料混凝土，骨料假定为圆形或球形是合适的，而且算法简单。但对于一般的碎石骨料混凝土，需要建立不规则多边形或多面体模拟骨料。碎石骨料因其破碎加工工艺，骨料形状基本上呈“凸型”。因此，本文主要研究二维凸多边形骨料的随机投放算法。首先利用面积为参数给出相应的骨料侵入判断准则，再按照多边形随机生长方式建立随机骨料的投放算法。同已有的任意多边形骨料投放算法相比，这种采用凸型骨料假定的算法简单，投放效率高。而且算法思想容易推广到三维空间，建立统一的随机骨料投放算法。本文最后给出任意形状的凸多边形骨料的投放实例和实用实例。

1　面积判别准则(凸多边形侵入判别准则)

如图 1，任一凸多边形 $a_1\_a_n$，P 为内部任一点，多边形顶点 a_i 的坐标为(x_i, y_i, z_i)并按逆时针顺序编号。

P 点坐标为(x_P, y_P, z_P)，则三角形 ΔPa_ia_{i+1}的面积 S_i 为

$$S_i=\frac{1}{2}\begin{vmatrix} x_P & y_P & 1 \\ x_i & y_i & 1 \\ x_{i+1} & y_{i+1} & 1 \end{vmatrix} \tag{1}$$

* 基金项目：清华大学 985 基金资助项目(资助号 201010－004)；中国博士后科研基金资助项目。
本文选自《清华大学学报(自然科学版)》2003 年第 6 期，作者还有高政国。

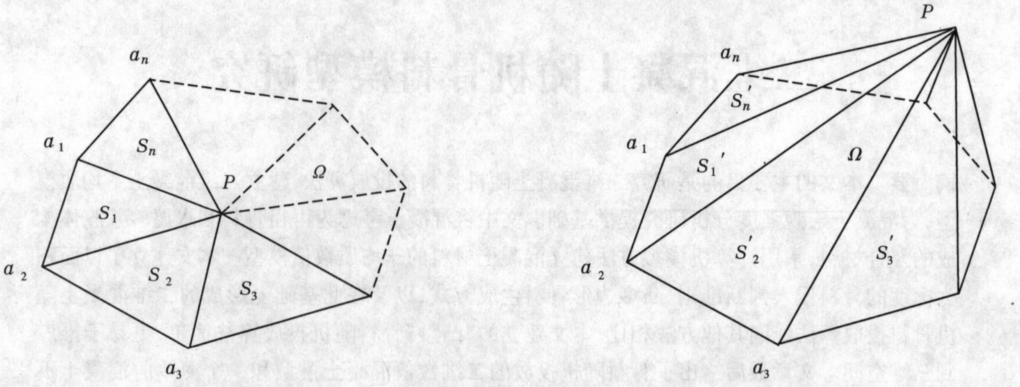

(a) P点在多边形内部　　　　　　(b) P点在多边形外部

图 1　凸多边形

(p,i,j)为逆时针顺序。

多边形 a_1—a_n 围成内部区域为Ω,则有

$$\begin{cases} P\in\Omega,\ S_i>0 \quad (i=0,1,\cdots,n) \\ P\ \text{在}\ \Omega\ \text{边界上,至少有一个}\ S_i=0 \\ P\notin\Omega\ \text{点,至少有一个}\ S_i<0 \end{cases} \tag{2}$$

P 在凸多边形内部或边上时,其面积 S 可表示为 $S=S_1+S_2+S_3+\cdots+S_N$;当 P 在凸多边形外时,则 P 与各顶点围成的区域面积(阴影部分)为 $S'=|S'_1|+|S'_2|+|S'_3|+\cdots+|S'_N|$,此时很容易证明凸多边形的面积也可以表示为 $S=S'_1+S'_2+S'_3+\cdots+S'_N$;从几何关系可知,当 P 在凸多边形外时有 $S'>S$。所以定义一坐标点在一凸多边形外部的条件也可以表示为

$$|S'_1|+|S'_2|+|S'_3|+\cdots+|S'_N|>S'_1+S'_2+S'_3+\cdots+S'_N \tag{3}$$

为防止出现图 2 所示特殊情况,还需进行边检查[6]。面积侵入准则针对凸多边形骨料。允许凹多边形骨料的侵入算法可采用文献[6]的方法。

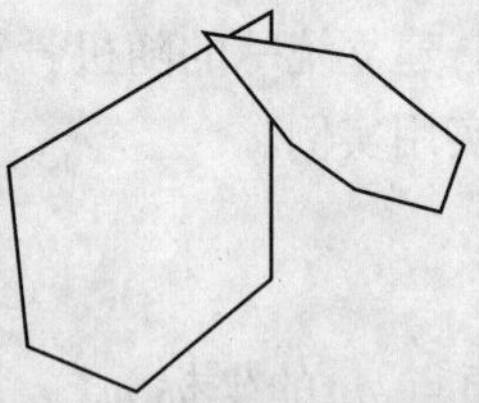

图 2　特殊的骨料侵入情况

2　凸多边形生成算法

凸多边形骨料的自由生成是混凝土骨料投放的第一步。首先随机生成"三角形或四边形骨料基"。生成的任意凸多边形是由三角形或四边形变化而来的(见图 3)。"三角形或四边形基"决定骨料的粒径尺度和骨料的基本几何构型。

2.1　"凸性"限定条件

在凸多面体随机形成中,保证多边形为凸多边形是关键控制条件。因此,要求算法给出"凸性"限定条件。

点 P 为边 La_ia_{i+1} 插入的顶点,形成多边形新的边 La_iP、LPa_{i+1}(图 4)。保证为凸多边形的条件为:点 P 与边 La_ia_{i+1} 以外各边围成的三角形面积(按公式(1)计算)都为正。

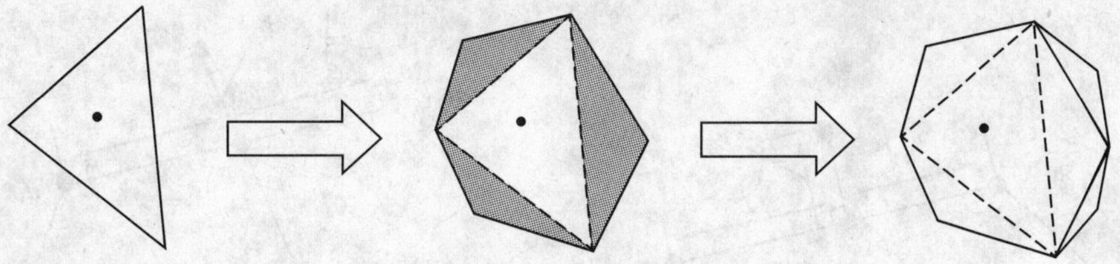

(a)三角形骨料基生成凸多面体

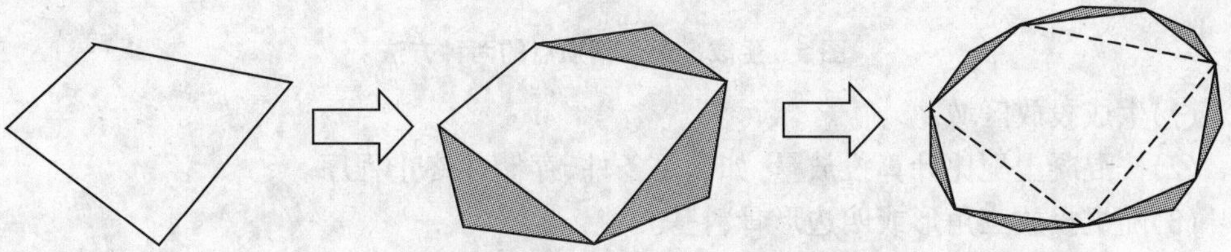

(b)四边形骨料基生成凸多面体

图 3　凸多边形随机骨料生成

因为原多边形为凸多边形。这一条件可简化为:点 P 与边 La_ia_{i+1} 邻边 $La_{i-1}a_i$、$La_{i+1}a_{i+2}$ 围成的三角形 $\Delta Pa_{i-1}a_i$、$\Delta Pa_{i+1}a_{i+2}$ 按公式(1)计算的面积 $S_{i-1}>0$、$S_{i+1}>0$;因此算法中限定生成顶点满足以上条件。

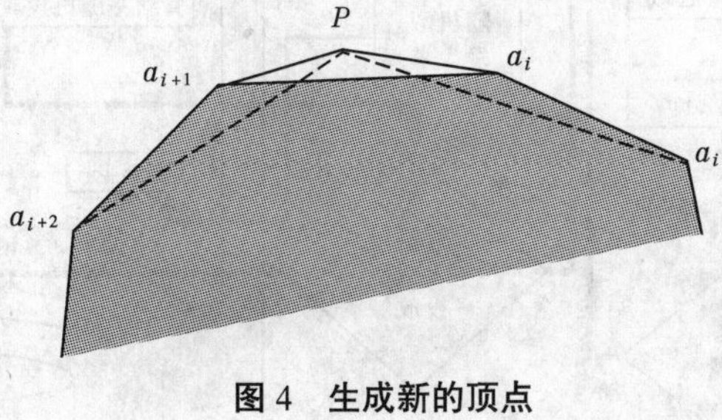

图 4　生成新的顶点

2.2　凸多边形生长条件和生长方式

凸多边形生长条件是:多边形至少有一边长大于限定边长 L_{max}。在生成凸多边形新的顶点时按最小限定边长 L_{min} 限制新生成边长。

生成方式可按如下两种方法进行:

(1)沿边 La_ia_{i+1} 外法线方向生成(见图 5(a));

(2)沿骨架三角形和四边形形心引出向量方向生成(见图 5(b))。

两种方式中,L_1 与 L_2 在满足 $L_1>L_{min}$,$L_2>L_{min}$ 条件下随机生成;L_3 在满足"凸性"限定条件下随机选取。

3　二维混凝土随机凸多边形骨料生成算法实现

随机骨料的生成分为以下几个步骤:

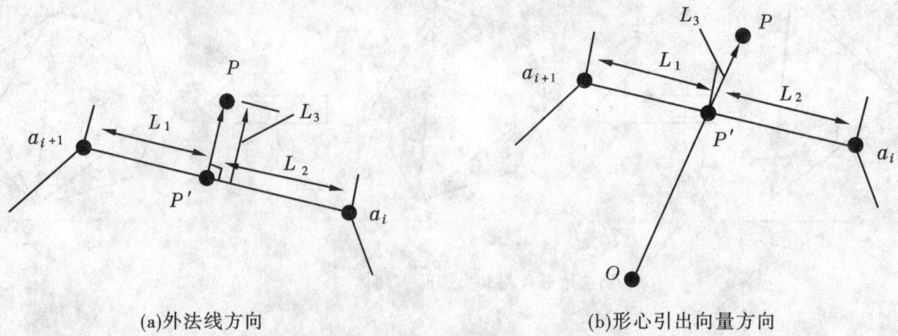

(a)外法线方向　　(b)形心引出向量方向

图 5　生成多边形新顶点的两种方法

(1)生成投放区域。

(2)按混凝土配比计算投放量,如满足条件,存储并终止程序。

(3)随机投放三角形或四边形骨料基。

(4)进行骨料侵入判断,如发生侵入执行(3)。

(5)判断多边形至少有一个边长满足生长条件。如否则生长完成,执行(2);满足条件则按边循环对满足生长条件的边按一定生长条件和生长方式进行生长,执行(2)。

程序实现如图 6 所示。

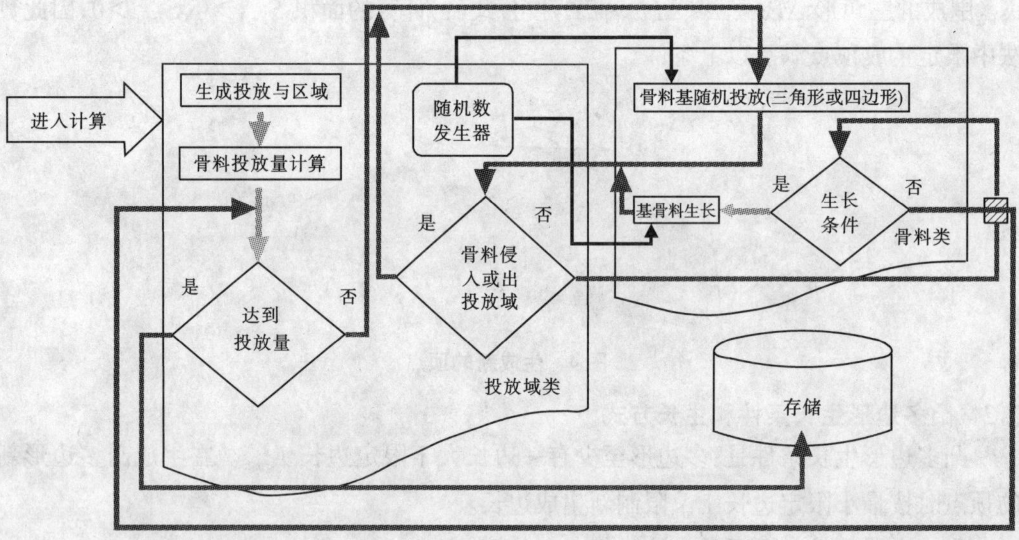

图 6　二维混凝土随机骨料投放程序基本流程

4　计算实例

4.1　随机骨料模型

按照上述算法生成的二维随机骨料模型见图 6。随机骨料模型生成的控制参数有 6 个:矩形投放域尺寸、骨料面积与投放域面积比、骨料最大控制半径、骨料最小控制半径、骨料最大控制边长和骨料最小控制边长。当不限定最小骨料半径参数时,最小尺寸骨料由最小控制边长控制。图 7(a)和图 7(b)是由不同控制参数计算的随机骨料投放分布。

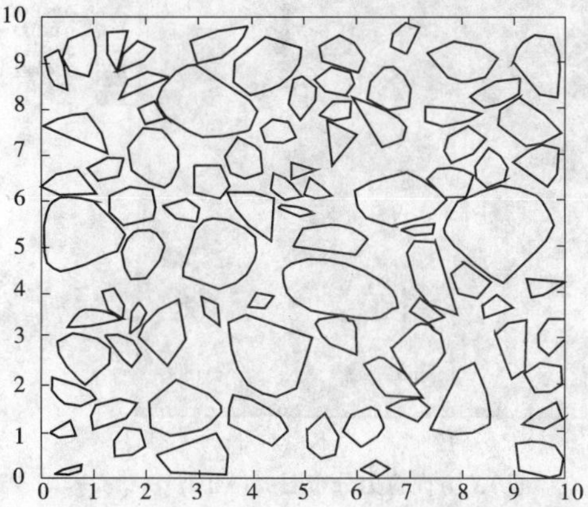

(a) 投放域10×10,骨料颗粒最大控制半径1.2,面积比45.02%,骨料最大控制边长0.6,最小控制边长0.3

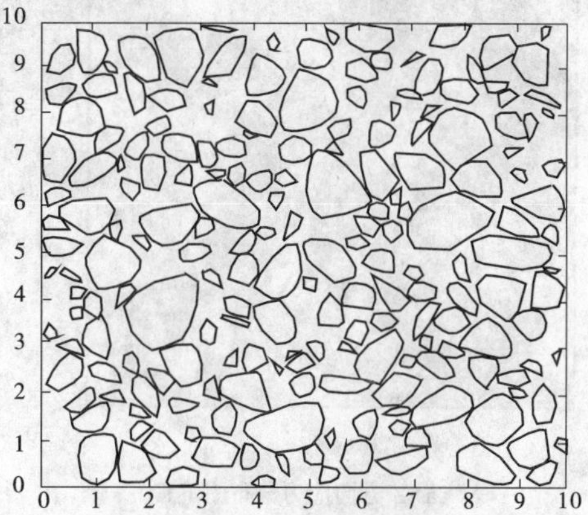

(b) 投放域10×10,骨料颗粒最大控制半径1.0,面积比50.0%,骨料最大控制边长0.5,最小控制边长0.25

图 7 计算随机骨料投放实例 (单位:cm)

4.2 模拟混凝土计算分析

以一个简单的算例说明混凝土骨料对结构应力分布的影响。按本文方法给出随机骨料模型,再剖分平面应变有限元网格。如图 8 所示(混凝土试件尺寸 10cm×10cm,骨料颗粒最大控制半径 2.0cm,面积比 40.01%,骨料最大边长 0.8 最小边长 0.4)。

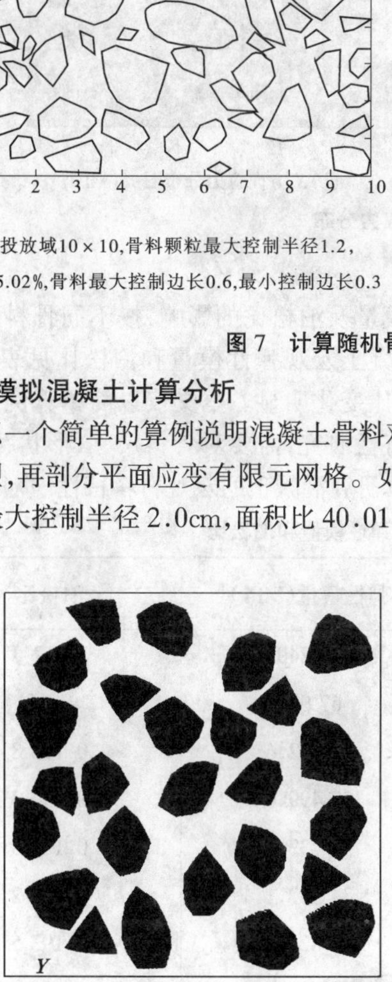

(a)骨料随机分布模型

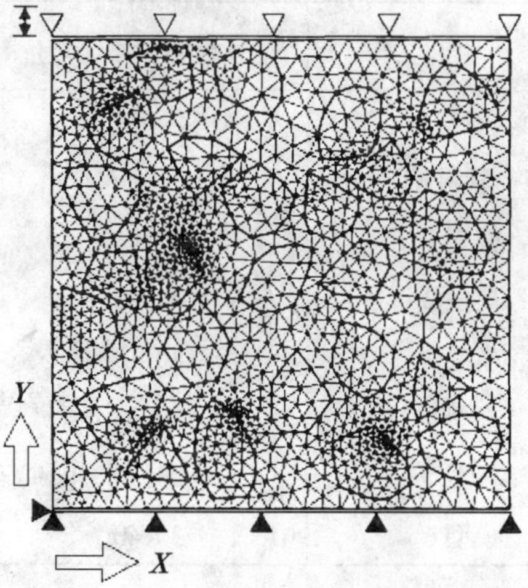

(b)有限元网格

图 8 计算试件模型

混凝土视为二相材料:粗骨料和水泥砂浆。骨料材料弹性模量 $E=67\ 000$MPa,泊松比 $\mu=0.16$;水泥砂浆弹性模量 $E=27\ 240$MPa,泊松比 $\mu=0.2$;混凝土承受竖向变形为 0.001cm;计算混凝土内部应力分布如图 9 所示。

从图 9 结果来看,骨料造成的混凝土不均质性使结构局部产生最大的拉压应力分别为1.11MPa 和 −7.6MPa。计算得数值混凝土宏观弹性模量为 37 622.6MPa,宏观泊松比

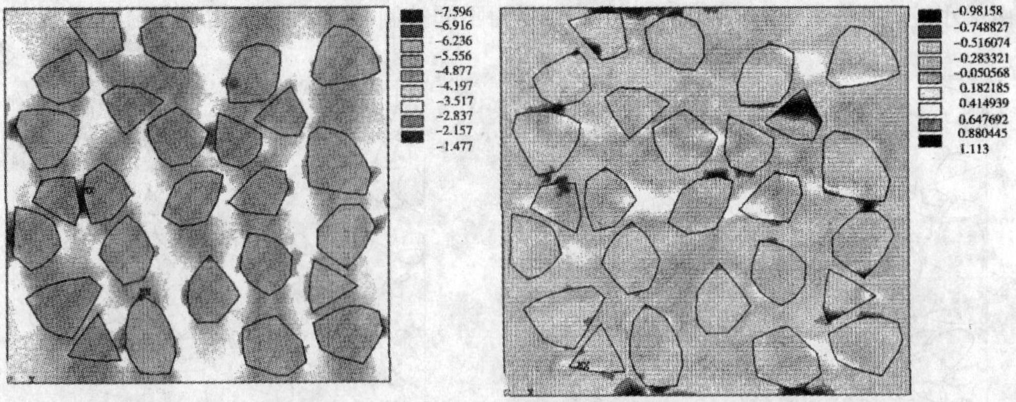

(a) Y 方向应力分布图 σ_y(MPa)　　(b) X 方向应力分布图 σ_x(MPa)

图 9　计算试件应力分布

为 0.190 8。

为了说明骨料投放对数值混凝土宏观弹性模量及泊松比的影响，按不同骨料面积比投放骨料共生成 6 个数值混凝土模型。数值混凝土宏观弹性模量和泊松比见表 1。从表 1 可以看出，数值混凝土宏观弹性模量随骨料比变化明显。本文仅以简单算例说明数值混凝土模型建立的意义。数值混凝土不均质特性研究，需要对骨料尺寸、形状、分布密度、分布形式等随机特性进行详尽的计算分析，以研究混凝土的宏观材料特性。

表 1　数值混凝土模型宏观弹性模量和泊松比

项目	骨料面积比(%)	弹性模量(MPa)	泊松比
砂浆	0	27 240	0.2
骨料	100	67 000	0.16
模型 1	40.01	37 622.6	0.190 8
模型 2	40.02	37 499.0	0.193 3
模型 3	40.13	37 733.8	0.189 3
模型 4	30.38	34 562.1	0.193 2
模型 5	30.30	34 821.8	0.193 5
模型 6	30.40	34 698.1	0.193 5

5　结论

本文以面积判别准则和凸多边形生长方式建立了二维混凝土骨料随机投放的算法。同已有的二维随机骨料投放算法相比，本文采用“凸型”骨料假定建立的算法，能获得更高的计算效率。算法思想容易推广到三维混凝土的随机骨料投放，本研究下一步的主要工作内容便是建立三维随机骨料模型。本文最后给出了二维随机骨料模型的投放实例和简单的混凝土不均质分析计算算例,说明随机骨料模型研究对混凝土计算强度理论研究的重要意义。

参 考 文 献

[1] Wittmann F H, Roelfstra P E, Sadouki H. *Simulation and analysis of composite structures*. Mater Sci Engng 1984,68:239～248

[2] Beddow J K, Meloy T. *Testing and characterization of powders and fine particles*. London: Heyden, 1980

[3] Bazant Z P, Tabbara M R, Kazemi M T. *Pijaudier－Cabot G.Random particle model for fracture of aggregate or fiber composites*. J Engrg Mech, ASCE 1990, 116

[4] Schorn H, Rode U.*Numerical simulation of crack propagation from microcracking to fracture*. Cem Concr Compos, 1991,13:87～94

[5] Schlangen E, van Mier JGM. *Simple lattice model for numerical simulation of fracture of concrete materials and structures*. Mater Struct, 1992,25: 534～542

[6] 王宗敏.不均质材料(混凝土)裂隙扩展及宏观计算强度与变形．清华大学水利水电工程系,1996

[7] WANG Z M, Kwan A K H,Chan H C. *Mesoscopic study of concrete I: generation of random aggregate structure and finite element mesh*. Computers and Structures, 1999,70:533～544

[8] De Schutter G, Taerwe L. *Random particle model for concrete based on Delaunay triangulation*. Mater Struct,1993,26:67～73

三维混凝土骨料随机投放算法研究*

摘 要 本文的主要目的是研究三维混凝土随机骨料的投放算法,建立三维数值混凝土模型。本文以体积为标度建立了一般多面体和凸型多面体两种形状骨料的侵入判别准则。并以凸多面体为目标建立了凸型骨料的生长模式和骨料"凸性"条件,给出相应的随机投放的算法。与球形骨料假定建立的数值混凝土模型相比,本文建立的凸多面体随机骨料模型能够更广泛地模拟混凝土材料结构。文章最后给出了空间骨料投放的示例和简单的应用实例。

关键词 三维模型 混凝土 随机骨料 计算机模型 凸多面体

在混凝土细观力学研究中,骨料的尺寸、形状和分布直接影响着混凝土强度特性。由于混凝土内部细观结构难以观测,通过常规试验方法进行不均质材料(混凝土)强度特性的研究很难进行。由于数值技术和计算机技术的不断发展,在目前已经取得的混凝土材料试验研究成果基础上,应用数值方法进行三维混凝土强度研究是值得关注的一个方向。目前在三维混凝土计算强度分析中,三维随机骨料模型仍然以球形骨料假定为主[1~5]。由于一般的混凝土骨料大多采用"破碎"工艺加工而成,因此将混凝土骨料分布模拟成空间多面体随机分布,在统计特性上最能模拟实际混凝土构成。目前这方面的研究还很少,其主要原因是三维多面体骨料的投放算法比二维多边形骨料投放算法难度要大很多,许多成功的二维骨料投放算法并不能有效地在三维空间推广。另外,三维多面体骨料随机投放模型计算规模要比二维模型大很多。由于计算机技术的进步,数值计算规模已经不再是研究的主要困难。因此,本文在建立空间骨料侵入准则、骨料生成模式方式基础上研究了混凝土三维随机骨料投放的算法。

一般混凝土骨料因其加工生产工艺基本上呈"凸型"。本文选取"凸型"多面体骨料随机投放为主要研究对象,旨在更大限度地模拟混凝土实际结构,并且建立相应的算法以获得较高的计算效率。同时文中给出了任意多面体骨料的侵入准则,由此可以很方便地生成相应的任意多面体骨料投放的算法。文章最后给出了三维随机骨料的投放模拟结果和一个简单的应用算例。

1 空间多面体侵入准则

1.1 凸型多面体

判断空间任一点是否在空间凸体内常用的计算方法是利用矢量进行判断。本节以空间体积为标度建立一点是否侵入空间凸型多面体的判断准则。

如图 1,假定 P 点和 a_1、a_2 和 a_3 顶点坐标分别为 (x, y, z)、(x_1, y_1, z_1)、(x_2, y_2, z_2) 和 (x_3, y_3, z_3),空间四面体体积为[6]

* 基金项目:清华大学 985 基金资助项目(资助号 201010-004);中国博士后科研基金资助项目。

本文选自《清华大学学报(自然科学版)》2003 年第 8 期,作者还有高政国。

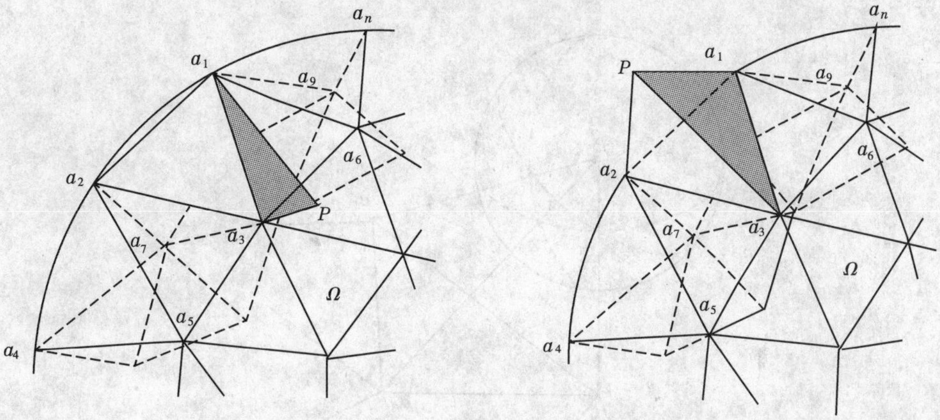

(a) P点在凸体内部与面单元围成四面体　　(b) P点在凸体外部与面单元围成四面体

图 1　P 点在凸空间体位置关系

$$V=\frac{1}{6}\begin{vmatrix} x & y & z & 1 \\ x_1 & y_1 & z_1 & 1 \\ x_2 & y_2 & z_2 & 1 \\ x_3 & y_3 & z_3 & 1 \end{vmatrix} \tag{1}$$

图中点 P 在凸体内部与面三角单元围成四面体体积为负值,在外部与面单元围成体积为正值。同二维情况类似,定义点 P 在凸体内部的判断准则为

$$\begin{cases} P\notin\Omega & \text{当存在 } V_P>0 \\ P \text{ 在 } \Omega \text{ 边界} & \text{当存在 } V_P=0 \\ P\in\Omega & \text{当所有 } V_P<0 \end{cases} \tag{2}$$

式中:Ω 为凸体围成空间区域;凸体三角形面单元顶点顺序为由外向内视方向逆时针顺序;V_P 为点P 与面单元按公式(1)计算的面积。

另一种定义准则为:

$$\begin{cases} P\notin\Omega & \text{当有} \sum V_P< V_\Omega \text{ 或} \sum|V_P|>|V_\Omega| \\ P\in\Omega \text{ 或} P \text{ 在} \Omega \text{ 边界} & \text{当有} \sum V_P = V_\Omega \end{cases} \tag{3}$$

式中:V_Ω 为凸体体积;$\sum V_P$ 为与凸体面单元围成的体积之和。

对于图 2 所示特殊的侵入情况可补充判定条件,检验边线与其他凸体各面单元是否相交。

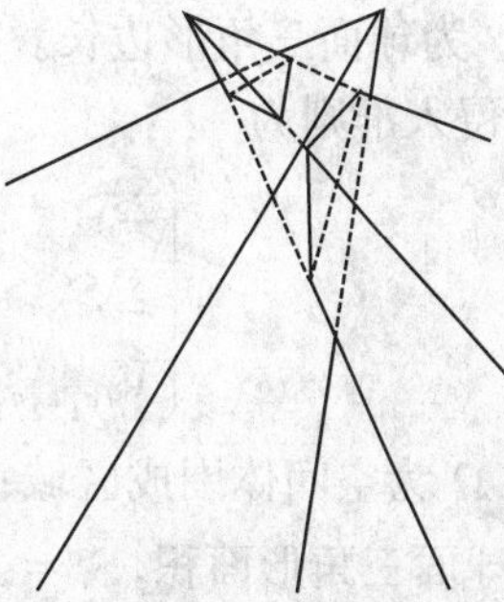

图 2　空间侵入的特殊情况

1.2　任意多面体

当骨料不限定为凸型体时,可建立以下侵入准则。具体实施步骤为:

(1)以被检测点 P 为圆心建立一半径为单位长度的辅助球(见图 3);

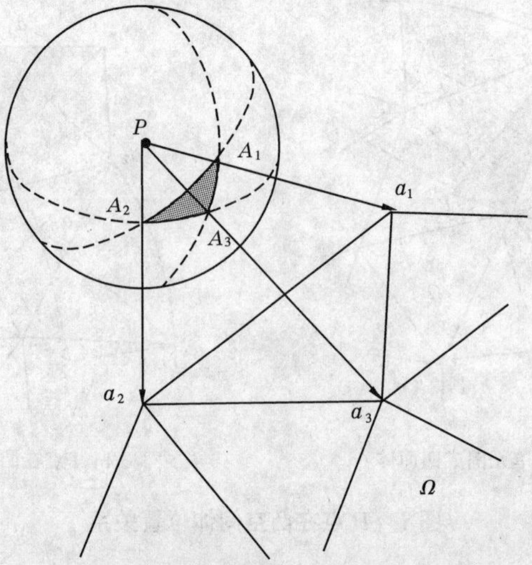

图 3　空间体面单元在 P 点辅助圆上的投影

(2)计算从 P 点引向空间体单元三角形顶点三个空间向量；

(3)利用三个空间向量计算凸体单元三角形在辅助球上投影的球面三角形面积；

(4)计算空间体所有单元三角形在辅助球上的投影的球面三角形面积,并计算辅助球球面面积；

(5)按公式(1)计算 P 点和空间体各单元三角形围成体积；

(6)按侵入准则判断。

如图 3 所示球面三角形面积 $S_{\triangle}$(阴影部分面积)定义如下[6]

$$S_{\triangle} = \mathrm{sign}(V_{Pa_1a_2a_3})R^2\delta \tag{4}$$

式中:R 为球半径;δ 是球面三角形 $A_1A_2A_3$ 的球面超角,定义为

$$\sin\left(\frac{\delta}{2}\right) = \frac{\sqrt{\sin p \sin(p-\alpha)\sin(p-\beta)\sin(p-\gamma)}}{2\cos\left(\frac{\alpha}{2}\right)\cos\left(\frac{\beta}{2}\right)\cos\left(\frac{\gamma}{2}\right)}$$

其中 $p = \frac{1}{2}(\alpha+\beta+\gamma)$; $V_{Pa_1a_2a_3}$ 是 P 点与空间体面单元三角形围成体积,按公式(1)计算;α、β、γ 为球面三角形边长。

定义侵入准则为

$$\begin{cases} \sum S_i^a = -S' & V_{Pa_1a_2a_3} \neq 0 \text{ 则 } P \in \Omega \\ \sum S_i^a > -S' & V_{Pa_1a_2a_3} \neq 0 \text{ 则 } P \notin \Omega \\ V_{Pa_1a_2a_3} = 0 & \text{则 } P \text{ 在空间体面上} \end{cases} \tag{5}$$

其中 Ω 为空间体围成区域;辅助球半径 $R=1$,辅助球表面积 $S'=4\pi$,S_i^a 为辅助球上第 i 个球面三角形面积,$S_i^a = \mathrm{sign}(V_{Pa_1a_2a_3})\delta$。

2 骨料的随机生成

同平面骨料一样,空间骨料也是由骨料基随机生成。以随机形状和位置的八面体为骨料基生成空间骨料实施过程如图 4 所示。

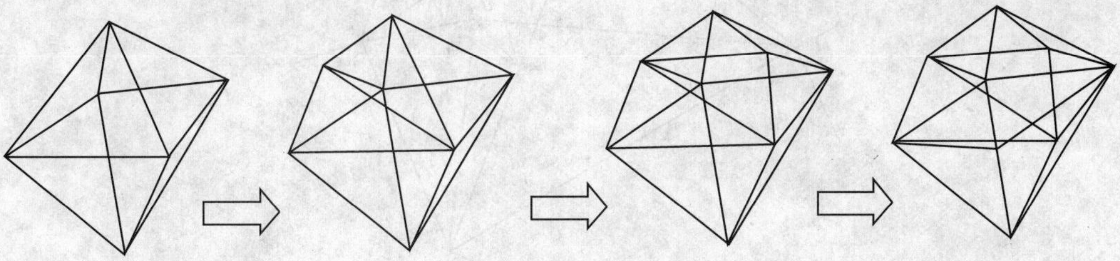

图 4 骨料生长示意图

空间骨料的生成方式与平面骨料生成方式略有不同。骨料表面单元钝角三角形过多时,不利于后续数值计算工作中有限单元模型的建立,所以骨料新顶点的生成始终选择在最大边长上进行。

3 骨料凸性判别条件

一般混凝土骨料是由石料经破碎获得,其加工方式使得骨料形状基本保持为凸型。限定骨料为凸型,既能保证最大限度地模拟实际骨料构成,也能简化算法,提高计算机仿真效率。在本文中重点研究凸型骨料的随机投放。

假定新顶点为 a,由三角形面单元 m 和 n 的公共边 L 上随机生成,则 a 与三角形面单元 k 围成的体积,按公式(1)计算为 V_k^a。则骨料形成过程中为"凸型"约束条件为

$$V_i^a < 0 \qquad (i \neq m, i \neq n) \tag{6}$$

因为骨料始终保持凸性,故约束条件可降低为只检验与 m 和 n 相邻单元满足式(6)。

4 顶点随机生长方式

新顶点 a 在三角形面单元 m 和 n 公共边界 bd 上随机生成如图 5 所示。首先随机生成新顶点 a 的在边 bd 上的投影点 A,A 的生成方式与二维新顶点投影点相同。然后确定空间方向向量 V_a,a 是由 A 点上沿 V_a 方向随机选取长度确定。这里单位向量 V_a 是由平面 m 和 n 的外法线向量 V_m 和 V_n 向量和的基向量。

5 算法描述

空间随机骨料自动生成的算法与二维骨料生成过程基本相同。

(1)首先生成投放空间。

(2)检验空间骨料投放量,如果达到要求,存储并退出。否则执行下一步。

(3)生成空间骨料基,检验是否在投放域内并未侵入已投放骨料。如果否,执行(2);如果是,执行下一步。

(4)判断骨料是否生长完成。如完成执行(2);如未完成执行下一步。

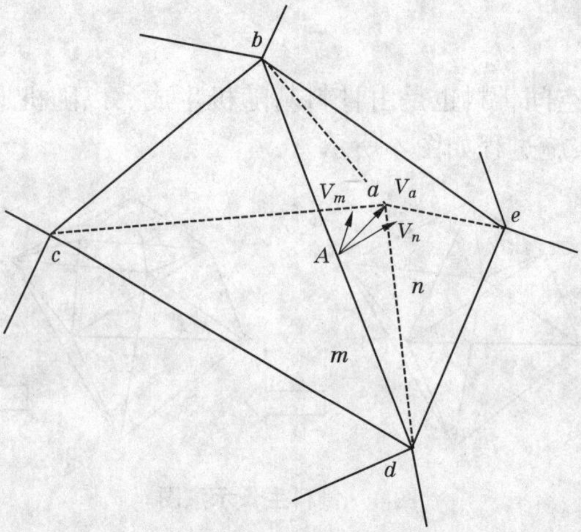

图 5　新顶点生成方式

(5)预选骨料最大边长成新顶点。判断新顶点是否与其他骨料发生侵入。如侵入不接受新顶点,执行(4);如满足执行下一步。

(6)判断骨料是否满足“凸型”,如满足接受新顶点并存储记录,执行(4);如不满足不接受新顶点,执行(4)。

6　计算实例

6.1　随机骨料投放

按照本文算法计算的随机骨料投放实例见图 6。控制随机骨料投放模型的基本参数有投放域尺寸、骨料体积与投放域骨体积比、料颗粒最大控制半径和最小控制半径、骨料最大控制边长和最小边长。图 7 是一个模拟骨料的空间形状;图 6 是选择不同控制参数计算的数值混凝土骨料模型。从图 6 可以看出,不同控制参数可以模拟不同骨料形式的混凝土构成。

6.2　数值混凝土模型的材料不均质性计算

三维混凝土随机骨料模型可以为混凝土细观力学分析提供数值模型。本节给出一个简单的混凝土空间应力计算实例,说明混凝土三维随机模型研究的意义。

首先按照上述方法生成混凝土随机骨料试件模型,见图 8(a)。然后将模型剖分有限元网格,根据骨料空间分布定义模型参数,见图 8(b)。最后定义荷载进行计算分析。

这里模拟混凝土试件尺寸为1cm×1cm×1cm,投放的骨料体积比为28.49%;骨料材料弹性模量 $E=67\ 000$MPa,泊松比 $\mu=0.2$;水泥砂浆弹性模量 $E=27\ 240$MPa,泊松比 $\mu=0.16$;混凝土承受竖向变形为 0.001cm(忽略混凝土自重)。混凝土内部应力分布计算结果见图 9。

图 9(b)、(c)、(d)为整体模型局部剖开的表面应力分布示意图,剖开部分见图 9(a)。从计算结果来看,整体模型中出现的最大拉压应力为 0.633MPa 和 −7.74MPa。从计算结果可以看出,骨料空间随机分布造成的不均质性使得混凝土承受荷载时局部产生较大拉应力。

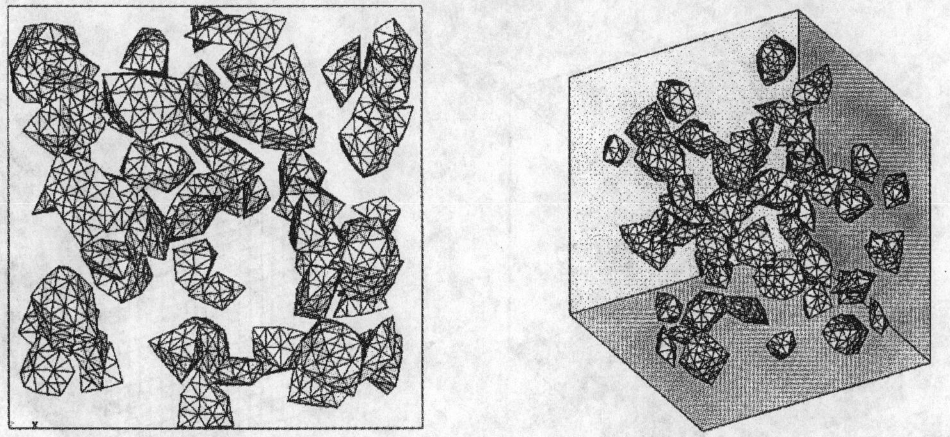

体积率 5.01%　　　　空间分布

(a)(投放域 10×10×10;控制骨料粒半径最大 2.0,最小 0;控制边长最大 0.8,最小 0.4)

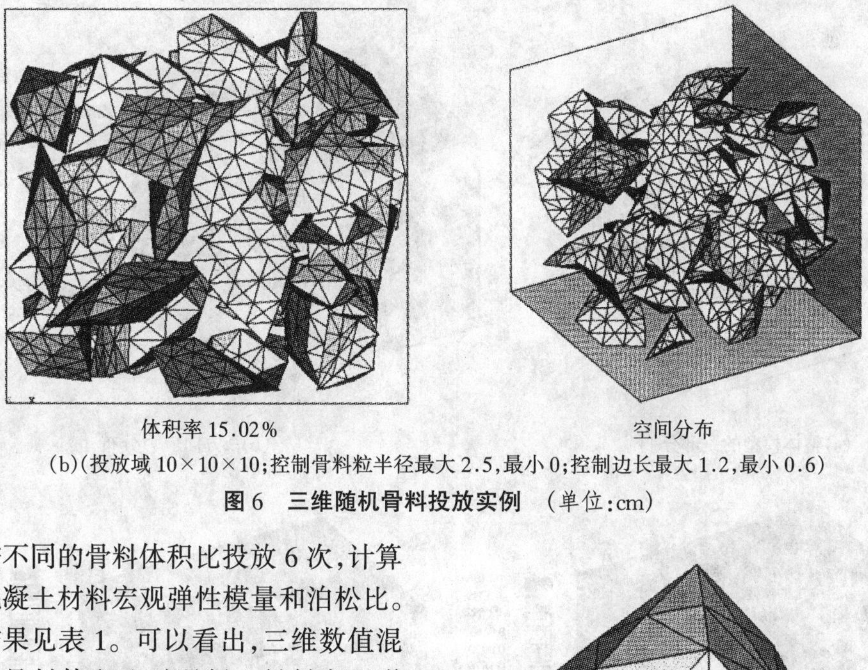

体积率 15.02%　　　　空间分布

(b)(投放域 10×10×10;控制骨料粒半径最大 2.5,最小 0;控制边长最大 1.2,最小 0.6)

图 6　三维随机骨料投放实例　(单位:cm)

按不同的骨料体积比投放 6 次,计算数值混凝土材料宏观弹性模量和泊松比。计算结果见表 1。可以看出,三维数值混凝土的骨料体积比对混凝土材料宏观弹性模量和泊松比有直接影响。因此,依靠本文建立的三维数值混凝土模型可以研究混凝土的不均质特性对材料攻关宏观特性的影响。

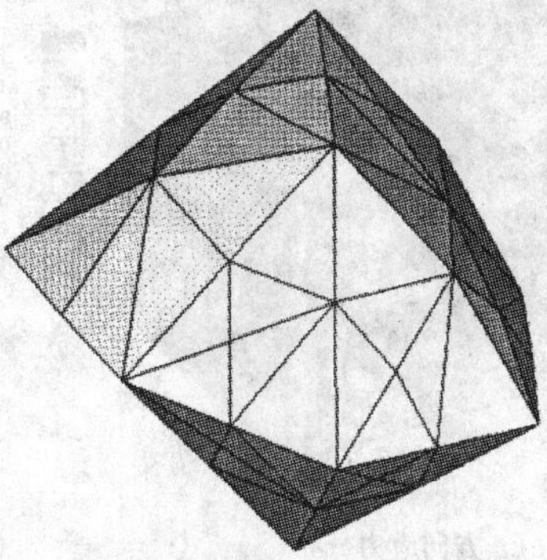

图 7　计算骨料典型形状

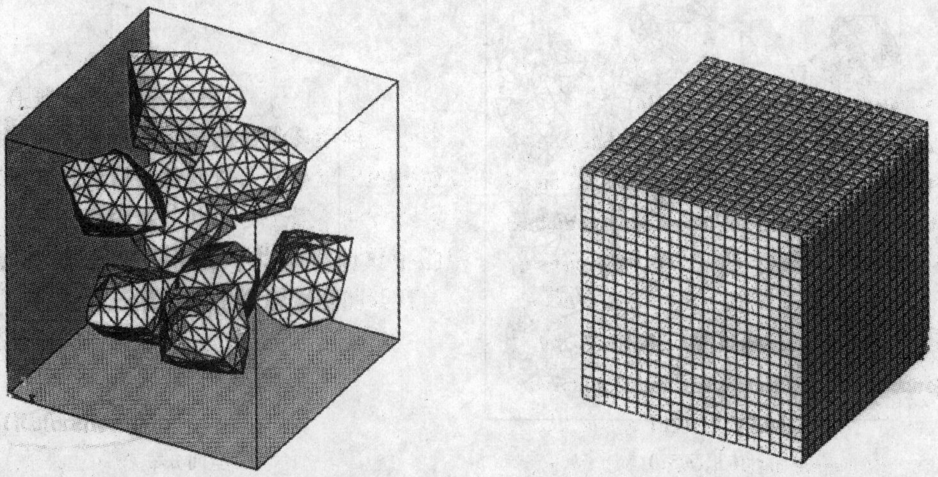

(a)混凝土骨料分布(投放域 1×1×1;控制最大骨料粒半径最大 0.25,最小 0.15;控制边长最大 0.1,最小 0.05　　(b)按模型剖分的有限元网格

图 8　计算模型　(单位:cm)

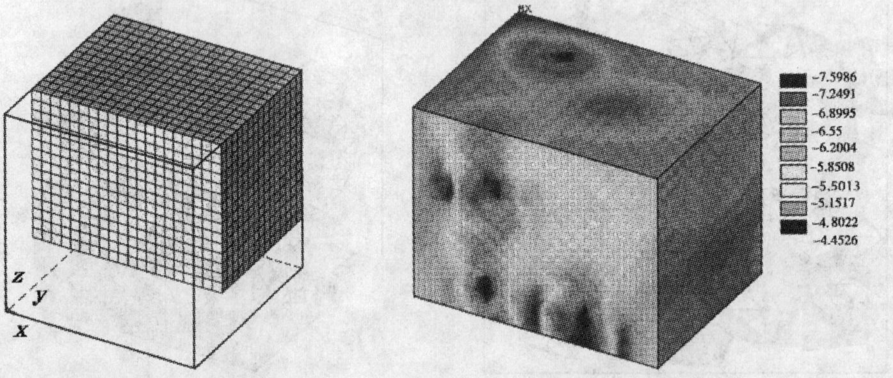

(a)整体模型的一部分　　(b)z 方向应力分布

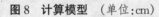

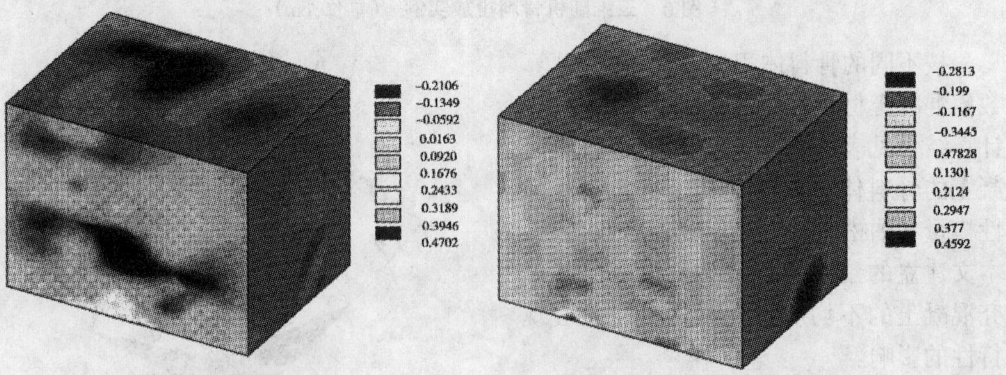

(c)x 方向应力分布　　(d)y 方向应力分布

图 9　模型局部剖面应力计算结果　(单位:MPa)

表 1 数值混凝土模型宏观弹性模量和泊松比

项目	骨料体积比 (%)	弹性模量 (MPa)	泊松比
砂浆	0	27 240	0.2
骨料	100	67 000	0.16
模型 1	28.49	35 818.7	0.189 2
模型 2	28.88	35 523.4	0.190 6
模型 3	25.05	34 329.3	0.191 7
模型 4	35.4	37 465.1	0.186 5
模型 5	40.06	39 952.3	0.184 5
模型 6	38.3	39 024.0	0.185 5

7 结论

本文在建立以体积为标度的空间多面体骨料侵入判别准则的基础上,对凸型骨料给出了相应的生成方式和随机骨料投放算法。文章给出的投放算例说明了算法的有效性,并以一个简单的算例说明三维随机骨料模型在混凝土不均质性研究中的应用。本文目的是为三维混凝土细观强度的研究提供数值模型基础。

参考文献

[1] Wittmann F H, Roelfstra P E, Sadouki H. *Simulation and analysis of composite structures*. Mater Sci Engng, 1984,68:239～248

[2] Beddow J K, Meloy T. *Testing and characterization of powders and fine particles*. London: Heyden, 1980

[3] Bazant Z P, Tabbara M R, Kazemi M T, Pijaudier－Cabot G. *Random particle model for fracture of aggregate or fiber composites*. J Engrg Mech, ASCE 1990,116:1686～1705

[4] Schom H, Rode U. *Numerical simulation of crack propagation from microcracking to fracture*. Cem Concr Compos, 1991,13:87～94

[5] Schlangen E, Van Mier JGM. *Simple lattice model for mumerical simulation of fracture of concrete materials and structures*. Mater Struct, 1992.25:534～542

[6] 数学手册编写组．数学手册．北京:高等教育出版社,1979

数值计算中的一种无网格方法研究*

摘 要 本文的主要工作是推导了一种基于新的形函数形式的无网格方法。由于目前的无网格方法中,紧支域的大小和形状不同直接影响整体场函数的分布,有时会造成计算结果的严重失真。为了弱化紧支域尺寸的选取对计算结果的影响,本文以节点约束的形式构造一种形函数对位移场进行近似。一维位移场的计算实例表明本文方法能有效地弱化覆盖尺寸对计算结果的影响。一个简单的三维数值算例也表明利用该形函数构造的应变场进行无网格方法计算是可行的。本文方法的缺点是弱化核函数覆盖尺寸的影响是以增大计算量为代价的,需进一步改进。

关键词 无网格方法 形函数 核函数 覆盖尺寸

在计算力学领域,许多几何非线性和材料非线性问题应用有限元方法已经得到了很好的解决。但是常规有限元方法在处理材料裂缝或大变形问题时,局部可能出现计算网格扭曲造成的计算结果严重失真。虽然提出了一些改进的有限元方法能够在计算过程中不断重构单元网格,但普遍存在着前处理工作计算量增大、计算结果震荡等问题。特别涉及到三维结构分析,网格重构与细化成倍地消耗计算资源,使大型结构断裂或大变形计算分析以及细观结构裂纹损伤计算分析等工作难以进行。无网格方法的出现为这些问题的解决提供了一个崭新的思路。这些方法有 SPH(Smooth Particle Hydrodynamics Method)[1~3]、PIC(Particle in Cell Method)[4]、DEM(Diffuse Element Method)[5]、EFG(Element Free Galerkin Method)[6~8]、RKPM(Reproducing Kernel Particle Method)[10~17]及 HP-Cloud 方法[18]和单位分解法(PU)[19]等。文献[9]较为详尽地介绍了这些方法。它们的共同特点是整个求解域由一系列点离散而成,无须生成网格。从而大大减少计算的前处理工作。在无网格方法中,EFG 和 RKPM 方法被证明最适合结构计算[14]。

虽然无网格方法的实现避免了数值计算中繁琐和复杂的网格重构工作,但仍存在着许多不足使无网格方法难以像有限元方法那样广泛的应用。主要表现在:虽然无网格方法中不需构造网格,但在计算过程中需要不断构造离散节点的局部紧支域以建立节点之间的联系,描述局部位移场。紧支域的大小和形状的选取直接影响整体位移场的分布,尤其在边界、裂缝等区域选取不同紧支域尺寸可能造成计算较大结果差异;另外无网格方法求解变形能的积分问题和边界处理问题等需要进一步研究。

本文研究的目的是寻找一种新的形函数构造形式,弱化紧支域尺寸的选取对计算结果的影响。在本文第 1 节对比分析了有限元方法、EFGM 和 RKPM 场函数近似形式,并以 RKPM 为例计算了在一维情况下紧支子域尺寸对计算结果影响问题。本文第 2 节尝试了一种新的场函数近似形式,并作了几个简单的一维算例与第 1 节的算例进行了对比

* 清华大学 985 基金资助项目;中国博士后科研基金资助项目。
本文选自《工程力学》2003 年第 6 期,作者还有高政国。

分析。本文最后以一个简单的三维算题说明了新方法的特点。

1 无网格方法的位移场函数近似

1.1 有限元方法、EFGM 方法和 RKPM 方法

同有限元方法一样,EFGM 方法和 RKPM 方法都是利用最小势能原理的一类变分方程求解近似位移。这些方法的不同之处主要在于场函数的近似方式。

有限元方法位移场函数近似为

$$u(x) = \sum_I N_I(x) u_I \tag{1}$$

式中:$N_I(x)$ 为节点 I 的形函数;u_I 为节点 I 位移值。

这样单元内任一点位移通常以单元节点位移插值形式描述。

EFGM 方法的位移场函数近似为[9]

$$u(x) = \sum_j p_j(x) a_j(x) = p^T a \tag{2}$$

p^T 为基函数向量,根据对问题的分析选取。如三维分析中选用二阶基函数向量为

$$p^T = \{1, x, y, z, x^2, xy, y^2, yz, z^2, zx\}$$

a 为待定系数函数向量。在局部意义下位移场函数近似为

$$u(x,\bar{x}) = \sum_j p_j(\bar{x}) a_j(x) \tag{3}$$

采用计算子域内离散点权函数意义下最小二乘解的方法确定 a,从而定义一个局部意义的位移场函数。

RKPM 方法的位移场函数描述为[14]

$$u(x) = \sum_I c(x : x - x_I)\psi(x - x_I) u_I \tag{4}$$

式中:$\psi(x - x_I)$ 为核函数,也可称为权函数;$c(x : x - x_I)$ 为修正函数,一般取为

$$c(x : x - x_I) = H^T(x - x_I) b(x)$$

$H^T(x - x_I) = \{1, x - x_I, \cdots, (x - x_I)^N\}$ 为 N 阶基函数向量;$b(x)$ 为待定系数函数。RKPM 方法是通过严格满足位移场函数的 N 阶 TayLor 级数展开式确定修正函数。

以 EFGM 方法和 RKPM 方法为代表的无网格方法与有限元方法主要不同点在于:① 有限元 方法以事先离散的单元定义求解子域,无网格方法是通过定义核函数在计算过程中确定求解子域。② 在位移场近似方式描述上,有限元单元中任一节点的形函数在该节点处值为 1,在其他节点处值为 0,在节点处位移场函数值等于节点位移,即 $u(x_I) = u_I$。这样,计算单元内任一插值点的位移时,各节点位移变量可看成独立贡献插值点位移值;在无网格方法中,一般节点处位移场函数值不等于节点位移。求解域内各离散点位移对任一点的位移贡献不是独立的,而是通过直接影响和在核函数覆盖范围内通过其他离散点间接影响进行贡献的。

虽然 EFGM 方法和 RKPM 方法在位移场近似方式上不同,但同样是采用离散点核函数覆盖意义下局部位移场近似。所以在应用同样的核函数并选取同阶的基函数时,采用 EFGM 方法和 RKPM 方法的计算结果是一致的。图 1 和图 2 分别以 EFGM 方法和 RKPM 方

法计算的近似位移场(核函数采用 $\Phi(x)=\dfrac{2}{a}\varphi(\dfrac{x}{a})$,$\varphi(z)$ 为立方 B 样条函数,$a=5.2$)。

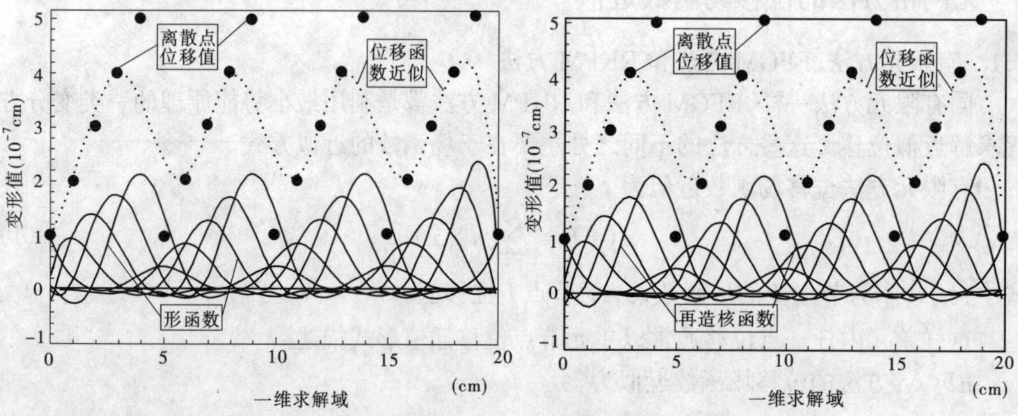

(a)EFGM方法（Element Free Galerkin Method）　(b)RKPM方法（Reproducing Kernel Particle Method）

图 1　无网格方法对位移场的近似

1.2　核函数覆盖尺寸的选取对位移场近似的影响

核函数覆盖尺寸是确定无网格方法中求解子域大小的重要参数。覆盖尺寸的选取直接影响计算结果精确程度,尤其对非线性变化较大的位移核函数场影响更大。本节以一维位移场为例采用 RKPM 方法说明无网格方法的核函数覆盖尺寸选择对位移场近似的影响。RKPM 基函数选取 2 阶,核函数采用 $\Phi(x)=2/a\varphi(x/a)$,$\varphi(z)$ 为立方 B 样条函数,a 为覆盖半径。应用 RKPM 方法选取不同的 a 值计算整个求解域位移场见图 2、图 3。

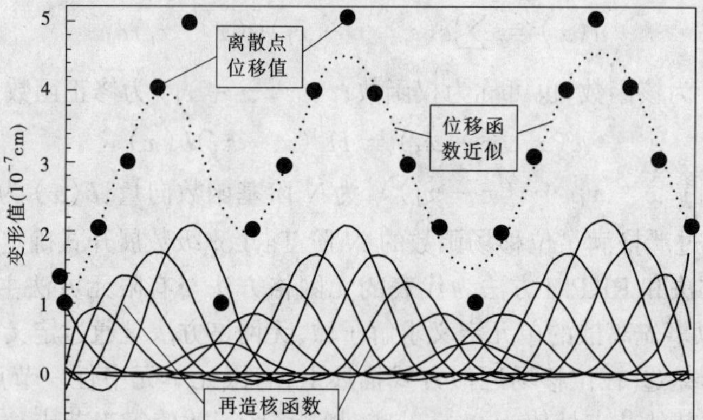

图 2　$a=5.2$ 时 RKPM 位移场函数近似

核函数覆盖半径直接影响计算位移场对实际位移场的近似程序。核函数覆盖半径值的选取要求:① 整体方程有解;② 求解域覆盖充分;③ 较高的计算精度和计算效率。较大的覆盖半径易于满足方程有解和充分覆盖的条件,对于均匀变化的位移场,选用稍大的覆盖半径也能满足对位移场的近似精度,但对于变化剧烈的位移场,选取较大的覆盖半径将

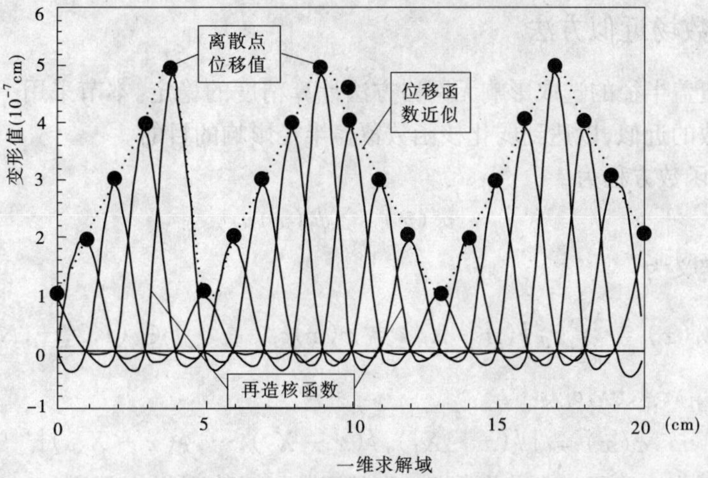

图3 $a = 2.1$ 时 RKPM 位移场函数近似

造成局部位移值的失真(见图2),这种局部失真的原因在于该求解域内离散点位移在核函数多重覆盖下的位移“均化”。而选取较小的覆盖半径近似程度明显提高(见图3)。这说明在满足整体方程有解及求解子域覆盖充分的前提下尽可能选取较小的覆盖半径是提高无网格方法计算精度的有效手段。选取较小的覆盖半径的另一个好处是减少求解域的覆盖“厚度”,减少计算子域内离散点数量,提高计算效率。核函数覆盖半径的选取是无网格方法中的一个关键性工作,这一参数的选取跟节点离散形式有关。对于节点均匀离散形式,可根据方程组解存在和求解域覆盖充分的条件确定一个固定的最小覆盖半径值。对于局部需要节点加密的情况,覆盖半径需要根据求局部节点疏密情况较小的选取以提高计算精度。但即使如此,对于节点稀疏极度不均的地方也会发生局部失真(如图4所示,在 $x = 4.0$ 附近节点密集处位移失真严重)。如何选取合理的覆盖尺寸是 EFGM 方法和 RKPM 方法保证稳定计算精度和计算效率面临的一个问题。

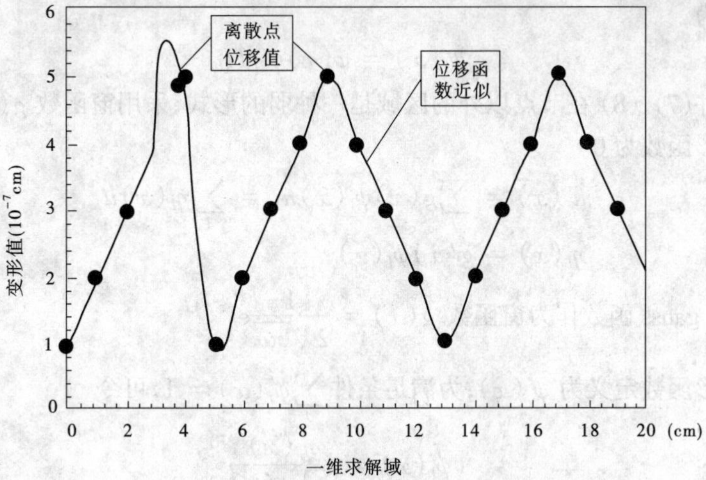

图4 $a = 2.1$ 节点分布极度不均时 RKPM 位移场函数近似

2　位移函数场近似方法

核函数覆盖半径的选取影响无网格方法计算精度的稳定。本节采用一种新的形式建立位移场函数的近似，以达到弱化核函数覆盖半径影响的目的。

这里，位移场函数方程为

$$u^c(x)=\sum_I \psi_I(x)u_I \tag{5}$$

其中形函数定义为

$$\psi_I(x)=\sum_{K=1}^{NP} c_{IK}\phi(x-X_K)=\varphi(x)c_I \qquad I\in(1,2,\cdots,NP) \tag{6}$$

这里 $c_I=\{c_{I1},c_{I2},\cdots,c_{I,NP}\}^T$ (7)

$$\varphi(x)=\{\phi(x-X_1),\phi(x-X_2),\cdots,\phi(x-X_{NP})\} \tag{8}$$

式中：NP 是 I 点决定子域内节点数；c_{ij} 为基函数权系数；ϕ 为基函数；X_I 为节点 I 坐标。

这样形函数表述为各节点基函数的多项式。

由上一节的分析可知，求解子域尺寸不宜取得过大。并且为减少节点变量之间的相关性，这里定义形函数满足如下约束条件

$$\psi_I(X_I)=\varphi(X_I)c_I=\varphi_I c_I=1 \qquad I\in(1,2,\cdots,NP) \tag{9}$$

$$\psi_I(X_J)=\varphi(X_J)c_I=\varphi_J c_I=0 \qquad J\neq I \quad I,J\in(1,2,\cdots,NP) \tag{10}$$

公式(7)、(8) 可表示如下

$$\varphi_{IJ}c_I=H_I \tag{11}$$

这里　$\varphi_{IJ}=\{\varphi_1^T,\varphi_2^T,\cdots,\varphi_{NP}^T\}^T=[\phi_{IJ}]_{NP\times NP},H_I=\{0,0,\cdots,\underset{No.I}{1},\cdots,0\}$

$$\phi_{IJ}=\phi(X_I-X_J)$$

由公式(9) 求解 c_I

$$c_I=\phi_{IJ}^{-1}H_I$$

得到形函数为

$$\psi_I(x)=\varphi(x)\varphi_{IJ}^{-1}H_I \tag{12}$$

由于约束条件(7)、(8) 在节点以外的区域是一种弱的形式，采用窗函数 $g(x)$ 限定节点 I 影响域远处形函数为 0

$$u^c(x)=\sum_I g(x)\psi_I(x)u_I=\sum_I \eta_I(x)u_I$$

$$\eta_I(x)=g(x)\psi_I(x)$$

这里，可选用 gauss 函数作为窗函数 $g(x)=\dfrac{1}{2\sqrt{\pi a}}\mathrm{e}^{-t^2/4a}$

将修正后的形函数定义为 $\psi^c(x)$，为满足条件 $\sum\limits_I \psi_I^c(x)=1$，可令

$$\psi_I^c(x)=\frac{\eta_I(x)}{\sum\limits_J \eta_J(x)}$$

用上一节的例子说明本文方法对场函数近似的特点，见图 5。

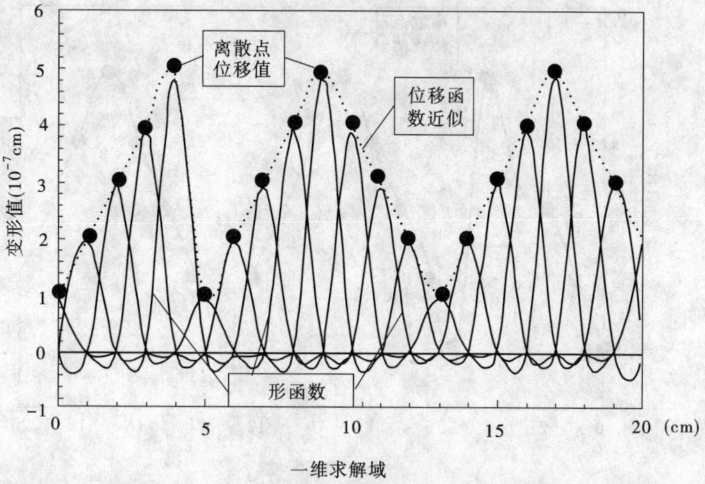

图 5　$a=5.2$ 时本文方法计算的位移场函数

从图 5 与图 2、图 6 与图 3、图 7 与图 4 对比来看,本文提出方法能有效弱化覆盖半径选择对计算精度的影响,并且在一定程度上减小畸变网格的影响。但是,因为基函数矩阵的维数与覆盖域内节点数有关,因此在覆盖半径选取较大时,按公式(10) 进行基函数矩阵求逆的计算量会增大。因此,本文方法弱化覆盖半径对计算精度的影响是以增大计算量为代价的,这也是本文方法的不足之处。

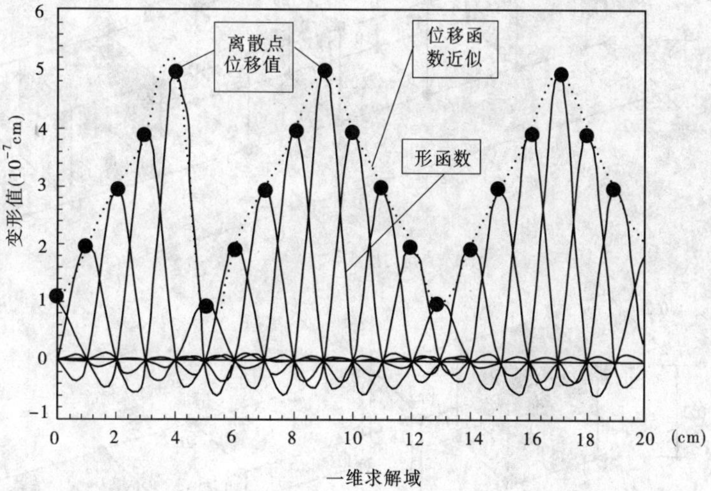

图 6　$a=2.1$ 时本文方法计算的位移场函数

3　算例

本节以一个简单的三维受拉杆结构算例说明本文位移场近似方法在数值计算中的可行性。结构材料为各向同性均质材料,杨氏弹性模量 $E=2\times10^4$ MPa,泊松比为 0.3。结构尺寸和约束条件见图 8,杆端 4 个节点拉力 $P=2$N。

以有限元方法同 RKPM 方法和本文方法分别选用均布节点和极度不均匀两种模型

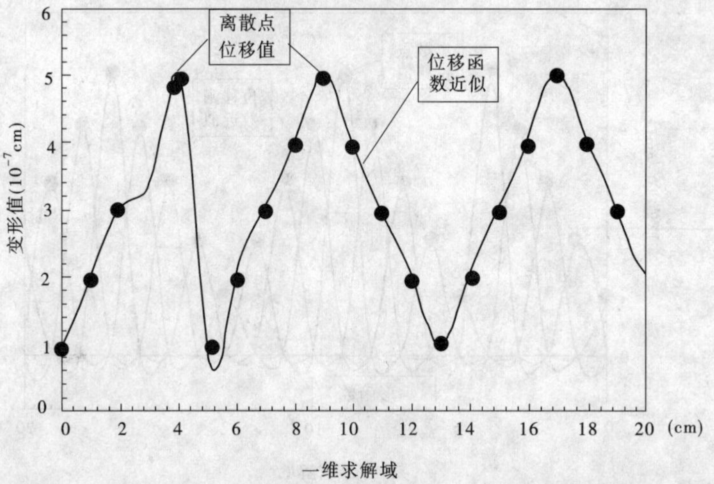

图 7 $a=2.1$ 节点分布极度不均时本文方法计算的位移场函数

图 8(a)、图 8(b)进行计算。核函数(基函数)覆盖半径根据局部节点疏密选取。部分计算结果见表 1、表 2。

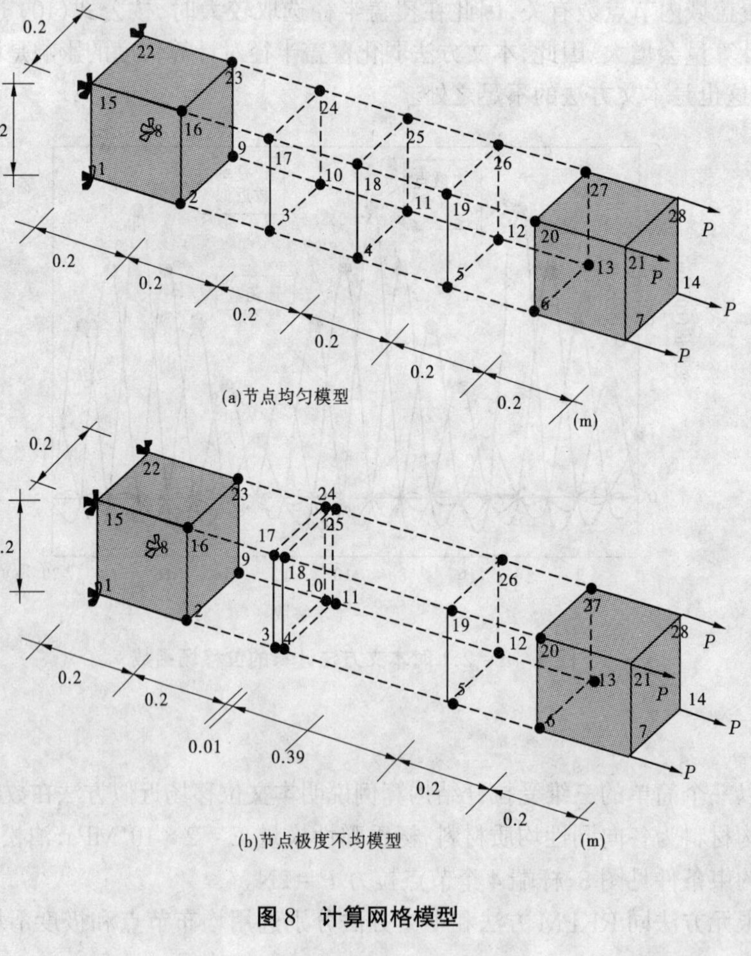

图 8 计算网格模型

表1 按模型(a)计算典型节点位移 (×10⁻⁷cm)

节 点	方 向	节点位移(FEM)	节点位移(RKPM)	节点位移(本文方法)
1	X	0.0	0.0	0.0
	Y	0.0	0.0	0.0
	Z	0.0	0.0	0.0
2	X	1.782	1.613	1.771
	Y	0.346	0.350	0.326
	Z	0.346	0.350	0.326
3	X	3.815	3.990	3.825
	Y	0.293	0.328	0.304
	Z	0.293	0.328	0.304
4	X	5.810	5.916	5.816
	Y	0.301	0.269	0.307
	Z	0.301	0.269	0.307
5	X	7.811	7.869	7.824
	Y	0.300	0.340	0.309
	Z	0.300	0.340	0.309
6	X	9.811	10.192	9.834
	Y	0.300	0.300	0.303
	Z	0.300	0.300	0.303
7	X	11.811	11.978	11.832
	Y	0.300	0.255	0.298
	Z	0.300	0.255	0.298

从计算结果可以看出,在均匀模型中本文方法计算结果同有限元方法和RKPM方法都有较高的计算精度,但对于不均模型,本文方法在计算精度上比RKPM方法较高一些。

4 结论

本文通过对有限元方法、EFGM方法和RKPM方法的位移场函数分析,以无网格理论为基础建立了一种位移场函数形式。其目的是弱化在无网格方法中覆盖半径的选取对计算结果的影响。计算实例证明本文方法的有效性。本文最后给出一个简单的算例说明本文建立的位移场函数在数值变分法中是可行的。本文作为一种探讨性的研究存在许多不足之处,主要表现为选取较大覆盖函数时需要较高的计算消耗。另外位移场函数近似的理论方法还需进一步完善,以减小节点分布不均对计算精度的影响。

表 2　按模型(b)计算典型节点位移　　($\times 10^{-7}$cm)

节　点	方　向	节点位移(FEM)	节点位移(RKPM)	节点位移(本文方法)
1	X	0.0	0.0	0.0
	Y	0.0	0.0	0.0
	Z	0.0	0.0	0.0
2	X	1.782	1.538	1.773
	Y	0.346	0.371	0.258
	Z	0.346	0.371	0.258
3	X	3.815	5.418	3.794
	Y	0.292	0.935	0.303
	Z	0.292	0.935	0.303
4	X	3.915	3.513	3.906
	Y	0.297	−0.304	0.296
	Z	0.297	−0.304	0.296
5	X	7.805	8.307	7.805
	Y	0.301	0.316	0.326
	Z	0.301	0.316	0.326
6	X	9.811	10.540	9.299
	Y	0.300	0.299	0.241
	Z	0.300	0.299	0.241
7	X	11.811	12.332	11.199
	Y	0.300	0.257	0.305
	Z	0.300	0.257	0.305

参 考 文 献

[1] L Lucy. *A numerical approach to testing the fission hypothesis*. Astron. J. 82(1977)1013～1024

[2] J J Monaghan. *An introduction to SPH*. Comput. Phys. Commun. 1988, 48: 89～96

[3] P W Randles, L D Libersky. *Smoothed particle hydrodynamics: some recent improvements and applications*. Comput. Meth. Appl. Mech. Engng. 1996, 139: 375～408

[4] F H Harlow. *The particle-in-cell computing method for fluid dynamics*. in B. Adler, S. Fernbach and M. Rorengerb, eds., Methods for Comput. Phys. 1964, 3: 319～343

[5] B Nayroles, G Touzot, P Villon. *Generalizing the finite elment method: diffuse approximation and diffuse elements*. Comput. Mech. 1992, 10: 307～318

[6] T Belytschko, Y Y Lu, L Gu. *Element free Galerkin methods*. Int. J. Numer. Meth. Engng. 1994, 37: 229～256

[7] Y Y Lu, T Belytschko, L Gu. *A new implementation of the element free Galerkin method*, Comput. Meth. Appl. Mech. Engng. 1994, 113: 397～414

[8] T Belytschko, M Tabarra. *Dynamic fracture using Element-Free Galerkin methods*. Int. J. Numer. Meth. Engng. 1996, 39: 923～938.

[9] T Belytschko, Y Krongauz, D Organ, et al.. *Meshless methods: an overview and recent development*.

Comput. Meth. Appl. Mech. Engng. 1996, 139: 3~49

[10] W K Liu, S Jun, Y F Zhang. *Reproducing Kernel particle methods*. Int. J. Numer. Meth. Fluids 1995, 20: 1081~1106

[11] W K Liu, S Jun, S Li, et al.. *Reproducing Kernel particle methods for structural dynamics*. Int. J. Numer. Mech. Engng. 1995, 38: 1655~1679

[12] W K Liu, Y Chen, C T Chang, et al.. *Advances in multiple scale kernel particle methods*. Comput. Mech. 1996, 18(2): 31~111

[13] W K Liu, Y Chen, R A, Uras. et al.. *Generalized multiple scale reproducing Kernel particle methods*. Comput. Meth. Appl. Mech. Engng. 1996, 139: 91~158

[14] J S Chen, C Pan, C T Wu, et al.. *Reproducing Kernel Particle Methods for large deformation analysis of non-linear structures*. Comput. Meth. Appl. Mech. Engng. 1996, 139: 195~227

[15] W K Liu, S Li, T Belytschko. *Moving least square kernel Galerkin method methodology and convergence Trans I*. Comput. Meth. Appl. Mech. Engng. 1997, 143: 113~154

[16] J S Chen, C Pan, C T Wu. *Large deformation analysis of rubber based on a Reproducing Kernel Particle Method*. Comput. Mech. 1997, 19: 211~227

[17] J S Chen, C Pan, C T Wu. *Applications of reproduction Kernel particle method to large deformation and contact analysis of elastomers*. Rubber Chem. Technol. 1997: 191~213

[18] C A M Duarte, J T Oden. *A $h-p$ adaptive method using clouds*. Comput. Meth. Appl. Mech. Engng. 1996, 139: 237~262

[19] J M Melenk, I Babuska. *The partition of unity finite element method: basic theory and applications*. Comput. Meth. Appl. Mech. Engng. 1996, 139: 289~314

三、碾压混凝土拱坝新结构、仿真计算及参数测定

FINITE ELEMENT ANALYSIS OF ACCUMULATED STRESSES DUE TO DEAD WEIGHT IN RCC DAMS

Abstract To understand more about the stress distribution due to dead weight in RCC dams, the 3-dimensional finite element analysis and the model experiment for a RCC dam have been performed, yielding new knowledge in this field. This paper describes mainly the computational aspect of this work.

The Accumulated Approach and the Conventional Approach are used in the analysis. The difference between these two approaches resides in whether the aging effect of concrete and the construction procedure for RCC dams are taken into account. The results obtained through these two approaches are compared and discussed in detail. It is pointed out that the stress distribution due to dead weight in RCC dams is related closely to the construction procedure. The results obtained prove to be realistic and are useful for the design and construction of RCC dams.

1 Introduction

Most of the roller compacted concrete (RCC) dams built or planned in the world are gravity dams[1]. A concrete gravity dam is a structure which relies upon its own weight to resist the forces exerted upon it, and for stability against sliding and overturning. For a given rock foundation, the safety of a concrete dam and the cost of the project depend on the quantity and distribution of the weight of the dam.

Although portland cement concrete has been used for many years, it is still a material about which the practicing engineer knows little. For design purposes he assumes that it is isotropic, homogeneous, time-independent and linearly elastic. Strictly speaking, none of these assumptions is true. In fact, this concrete is a kind of material whose properties vary with age, curing conditions and the rate of loading. For a mass concrete structure, the construction procedure thus has influence on the stress distribution. RCC is a relatively new material. It provides the engineer with new possibilities for concrete dam designs, schedules and budgets. In the RCC dam construction, a rapid, entire-area and thinlift concreting construction method is adopted. With increase of time, on one hand, the age of concrete increases, resulting in an increase of the modulus of elasticity of the concrete in each lift, so that the stiffness of the structure increases. On the other hand, the height of the dam body increases with dam construction, resulting in accumulation of dead weight stresses. Different stiffnesses in different parts of a structure may result in different stress distribution.

In the design of RCC dams, the finite element method has proved to be a powerful tool

本文选自由 CIVIL-COMP PRESS 1993 年出版的《Developmens in Structural Engineering Computing》一书，作者还有 C. Du。

for the solution of stress distribution due to dead weight. In the conventional calculation the modulus of elasticity of concrete is taken as a constant; the dam is simply regarded as a whole structure on which the dead weight is exerted at one time. For convenience of discussion, we call this approach the Conventional Approach. Obviously this approach is simple, but the construction procedure and the variety of the properties of material are not included in this approach; this is not reasonable and cannot lead to a reliable conclusion. To avoid this shortcoming, we have used the so-called Accumulated Stress Calculation Approach (abbr. Accumulated Approach), in which the properties of concrete are taken as a function of its age, and the dead weight acts on each lift according to the construction procedure.

By the above-mentioned two approaches we have carried out the 3-dimensional finite element analysis for a RCC overflow dam block in the Tongjiezi Hydropower Plant in China. The results are useful for the design and construction of RCC dams.

2 Numerical Procedure

The implementation of the finite element method for the solution of stress accumulation problems is particularly useful. In the following work, we will emphasize the application of the stress analysis towards the comprehension of the accumulation of stresses in RCC dams. In the Accumulated Approach, the modulus of elasticity of concrete is taken as a function of age: $E = E(t)$. The solution of accumulated stresses is based on the numerical step-by-step algorithms. According to the construction procedure, the construction period T is subdivided by discrete times $t_0, t_1, \cdots t_n$ into time steps $\Delta t_n = t_n - t_{n-1}$. Time t_0 coincides with the instant of first loading (or concreting). The modulus of elasticity in the step Δt_n can be approximated as

$$E_n = \frac{1}{2}[E(t_{n-1}) + E(t_n)] \tag{1}$$

Then the elasticity matrix in this step has the form

$$[D_n] = C\begin{bmatrix} 1 & a & a & 0 & 0 & 0 \\ a & 1 & a & 0 & 0 & 0 \\ a & a & 1 & 0 & 0 & 0 \\ 0 & 0 & 0 & b & 0 & 0 \\ 0 & 0 & 0 & 0 & b & 0 \\ 0 & 0 & 0 & 0 & 0 & b \end{bmatrix} \tag{2}$$

where $C = \dfrac{E_n(1-\mu)}{(1+\mu)(1-2\mu)}$; $a = \dfrac{\mu}{1-\mu}$; $b = \dfrac{1-2\mu}{2(1-\mu)}$; μ is the Poisson' ratio of concrete.

The dam and its foundation are discretized using finite elements resulting in a system of equations given as

$$[K_n]\{\Delta\delta_n\} = \sum_k \{\Delta P_n^k\} \tag{3}$$

where $[K_n]$ is the structural stiffness matrix; $\{\Delta\delta_n\}$ the displacement increment vector, and

$\{\Delta P_n\}$ the load vector. It is necessary to note that the height of the dam body increases with the dam construction, so that the calculation domain is enlarged with the time steps.

Solving Eq. (3), we obtain $\{\Delta\delta_n\}$; then the stress increment vector in time step t_n can be obtained

$$\{\Delta\sigma_n\} = [D_n][B]\{\Delta\delta_n\} \tag{4}$$

where $[B]$ is the strain shape function matrix. Therefore the stresses at the time t_n are

$$\{\sigma_n\} = \{\sigma_{n-1}\} + \{\Delta\sigma_n\} \tag{5}$$

A finite element program was developed by the authors at Tsinghua University, Beijing. It has the capacity of applying specific boundary conditions, thin-layer elements and stage construction. It can also be used to yield for temperature, thermal and creep stresses in mass concrete structures and concrete dams. The experience with the program has been satisfactory in the sense that the program gives realistic results which can be used for design.

3 Calculation of Accumulated Stresses

The Tongjiezi Hydropower Plant is located in mid-China on Daduhe River, a tributary of the Yangtze River. The dam was a composite structure with mass concrete gravity dam and earth embankment. It has a dam height above the lowest foundation of 88.0m and a crest length of 1 028.6m. The elevation of the dam crest is 479.0m. The concrete dam has a volume of $750 \times 10^3 m^3$, in which RCC volume is 430×10^3. The dam was completed in 1990. Fig. 1 is the layout plan of the project.

The RCC was used in the overflow dam blocks and a part of the non-overflow dam blocks in the river bed. The vertical transverse joints were set between the dam blocks. Fig. 2 shows the section of the overflow dam. Conventional concrete was used in the zone of contact between the dam and bedrock, in the 2.0 mthick upstream and downstream facing, the overflow facing, the piers and the diversion outlet. The RCC was placed 0.6~1.0m/lift (interval 3~5 days). The conventional concrete of the piers and the diversion outlet was placed 1.5m/lift. Fig. 3 shows the construction procedure.

In this paper an overflow dam block with a width of 21m is analyzed with 3-dimensional finite element method. To study the general stress distribution in the dam body, the gallaries are not included in the simplified model. And to reduce the number of elements, the conventional concrete of the downstream facing is not taken into account. The stress distribution in this zone can be inferred from the upstream facing. The simplifications above have no appreciable influence on the universal stress distribution of the dam. The simplified sketch is shown in Fig. 4. The extent of the dam foundation in the calculation is taken as $0.6H$, $1.0H$ and $0.8H$ in the upstream and downstream directions and in depth, respectively, where $H = 79.0$m is the dam height of this block, to accommodate the one in the corresponding experiment.

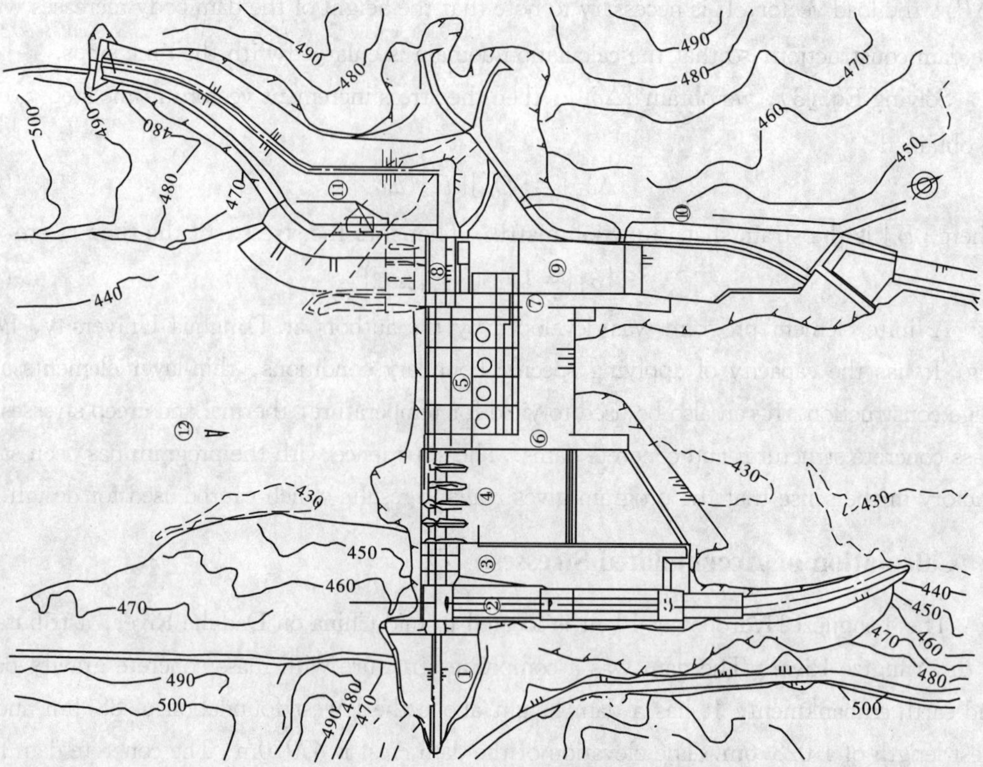

Fig. 1　Layout of the Tongjiezi project

where: ①Right bank embankment, ②Raft lock, ③Right non-overflow dam, ④Spillway, ⑤Powerhouse, ⑥Right deep outlet, ⑦Left deep outlet, ⑧Diversion channel, ⑨Switchyard, ⑩Highway, ⑪Left bank embankment, ⑫Daduhe River

The mathematical model of the modulus of elasticity of concrete has the form

$$E(t) = E_0(1 - e^{-\alpha t^{\beta}}) \tag{6}$$

where E_0 stands for the ultimate modulus of elasticity; t is the age of the concrete; and α and β are constants which can be determined from experimental data. Some properties of the concrete are tabulated below.

The mesh is made according to the materials in the dam and foundation and the construction procedure. In the above-mentioned program we developed the thin-layer elements to accommodate RCC. The calculation was performed on an ELXSI computer. The results are as follows.

4　Results and Discussions

The calculation was carried out by both the conventional Approach and Accumulated Approach with the same mesh and the 3-dimensional finite element program. The typical sections of stress distribution are shown in Figs. 5 and 6. We obtain:

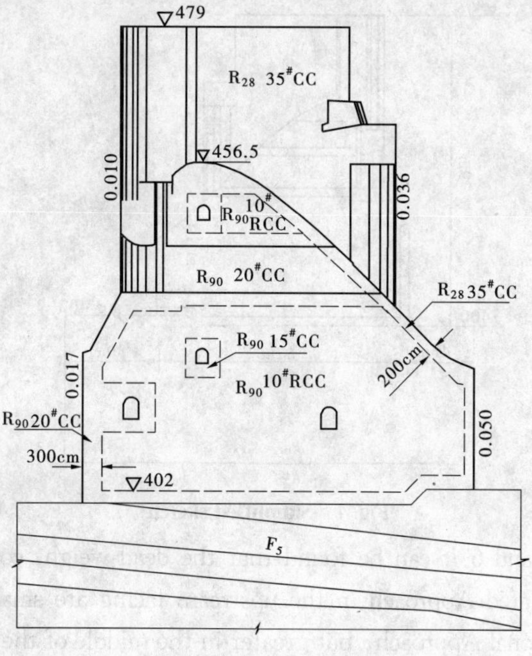

Fig. 2 Cross section through the overflow dam

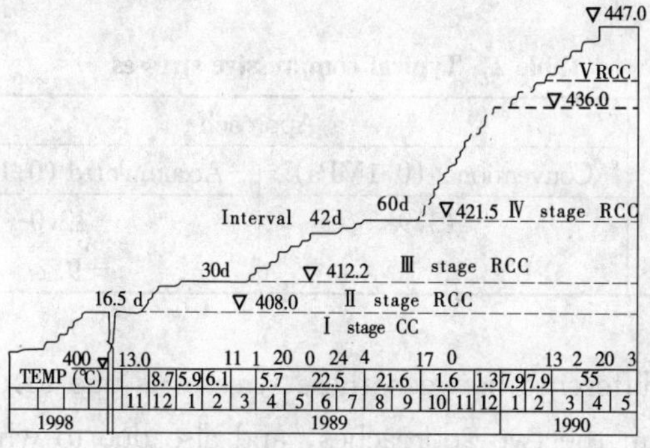

Fig. 3 Construction procedure of the dam

Table 1 Some parameters of concrete

Concrete mark	Ultimate modulus of elasticity E_0 (GMPa)	α	β
RCC R_{90} 10#	29.20	0.400	0.333
CC R_{90} 15#	31.71	0.419	0.327
CC R_{90} 20#	36.02	0.472	0.308
CC R_{28} 35#	47.04	0.595	0.266

Note: RCC = roller compacted concrete;
CC = conventional concrete.

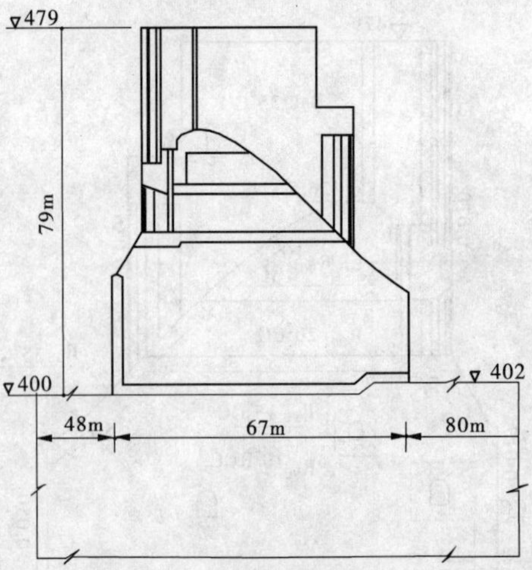

Fig.4　Simplified sketch

1) From Figs. 5 and 6 it can be found that the dead-weight compressive stresses obtained by the Accumulated Approach in the upstream facing are smaller than the ones obtained by the Conventional Approach, but greater in the middle of the dam body; the differences are about ±(10～15)%. For example, at EL.412.0m, the dead-weight compressive stresses are listed in Table 2.

Table 2　Typical compressive stresses

Position	Approach		Error (%)
	Conventional (0.1MPa)	Accumulated (0.1MPa)	
Upstream face	-13.9	-12.0	+16
Middle	-8.1	-9.2	-12

We think that the difference between these stresses is due to the different moduli of elasticity of the concrete in the two approaches, and also due to whether the construction procedure is taken into account. In the Conventional Approach, the modulus of elasticity is taken as a constant (normally at the age of 90 or 180 days) which can reach the 80%～90% ultimate modulus of elasticity. For this reason, the dam body is relatively rigid. Because the dead weight is applied at one time, a false impression is given that the deformations and stresses of the dam body at horizontal sections vary uniformly from the upstream to the downstream face. In fact, the modulus of elasticity of concrete varies with its age. In the Accumulated Approach, the aging effect of the modulus of elasticity of concrete [Eq. (6)] and the placement procedure of the dam are taken into consideration, hence the stiffness of each part of the dam increases with the age of the concrete and the dead weight is applied lift by lift. Because the modulus of elasticity of concrete at the early age is relatively small, the stiffness of the structure is correspondingly small, and the stresses and deformations depend on the amount(thickness) of the concrete over the point. Fig.2 shows that the concrete is

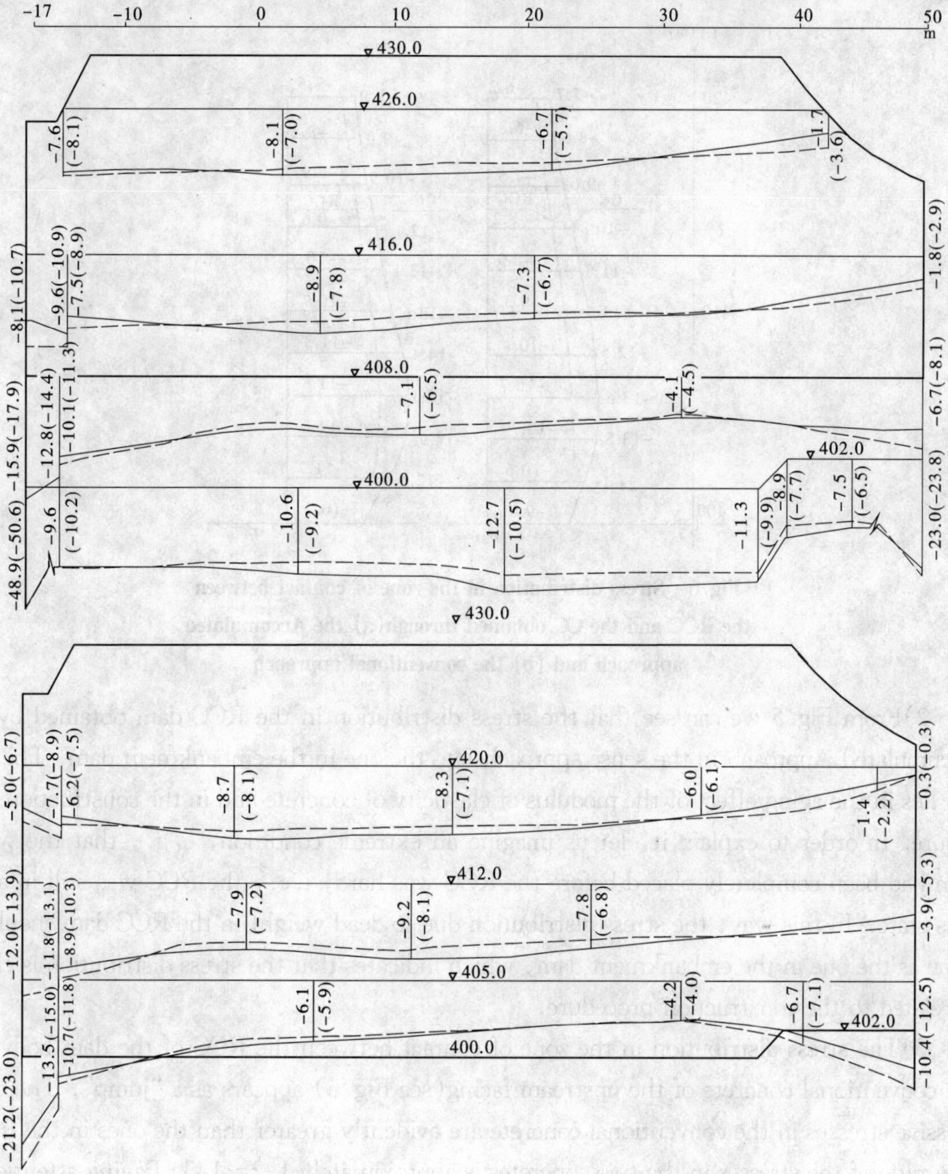

Fig. 5 Vertical stresses due to dead weight obtained through the Accumulated Approach (solid lines) and the Conventional Approach (dashed lines): 0.1MPa

thickest in the middle of the dam body; therefore, the stresses and deformations are also great, but exactly the reverse holds true in the upstream and downstream zone. It is thus evident that the results obtained by the Accumulated Approach conform to reality. Therefore we can predict that great errors may result from calculating the stress distribution due to dead weight in RCC dams by the Conventional Approach, and we suggest that the Accumulated Approach be used if possible for the analysis of accumulated stresses due to dead weight in the design of RCC dams.

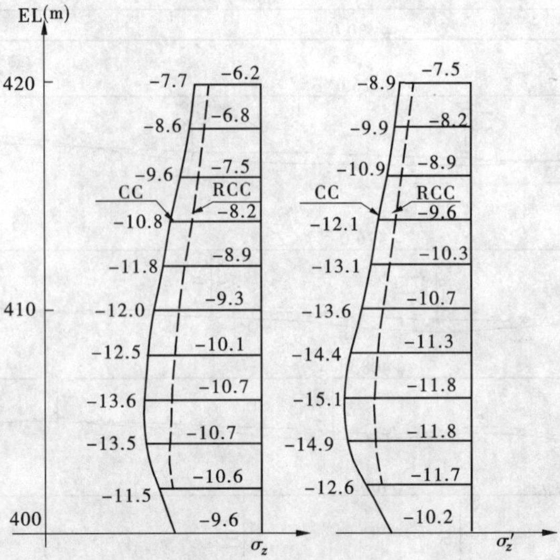

Fig. 6 Stress distribution in the zone of contact between the RCC and the CC obtained through (a) the Accumulated approach and (b) the conventional approach

2) From Fig. 5 we can see that the stress distribution in the RCC dam obtained by the Accumulated Approach in the sense approaches to the one in the embankment dam. The reason lies in the aging effect of the modulus of elasticity of concrete and in the construction procedure. In order to explain it, let us imagine an extreme condition, e. g., that the whole dam had been completely placed before the RCC was hard, i. e., the RCC was still in a porous state. In this way, the stress distribution due to dead weight in the RCC dam should be same as the one in the embankment dam, which indicates that the stress distribution is closely related to the construction procedure.

3) The stress distribution in the zone of contact between the RCC of the dam body and the conventional concrete of the upstream facing (see Fig. 6) appears as a "jump". The compressive stresses in the conventional concrete are evidently greater than the ones in the RCC. The ratio of the stresses in the two concretes is approximately 1.2～1.3. Paying attention to the ratio of the ultimate moduli of elasticity of the two concretes, we have $E_{CC}/E_{RCC} = 36.06/29.20 = 1.23$; thus it can be found that the ratio of the compressive stresses in this zone is equal approximately to the ratio of the moduli of elasticity of the concretes.

The "jump" of the stresses may cause complicated stress conditions in this zone, therefore we suggest that the ratio of the moduli of elasticity of the conventional concrete and the RCC should not be too great in dams with the conventional concrete facing.

Acknowledgement

The authors are thankful to Senior Engineer B. J. Wang of the Chengdu Hydroelectric

Investigation and Design Institute and Senior Engineer C. S. Lin of the Seventh Hydroelectric Construction Bureau, Energy Ministry, P. R. China for their kind support in supplying data.

References

[1] Serafim, L.. *Ge neral Report Q62: New Developments in the Construction of Concrete Dams*. ICOLD, San Francisco, 1988, Vol. 3

[2] Zienkiewicz, O. C. (Ed.). *The Finite Element Method (3rd. Ed.)*. MCGRAW-HILL Bock Company (UK) Limited.

[3] Lin, C. S.. *Temperature control of RCC dam of Tongjiezi Hydropower station* (in Chinese), Water Power, No. 11, 1992, pp. 50～55

[4] Su, J. F.. Construction of RCC dam of Tongjiezi Hydropower station (in Chinese), Water Power, No. 11,1992, pp. 46～49

NUMERICAL PROCEDURE FOR THERMAL CREEP STRESS IN MASS CONCRETE STRUCTURES

Abstract In this paper the experimental results considering the effects of temperature on the elastic modulus and creep of concrete are introduced into the mathematical models of the three-dimensional finite-element method to improve the calculation of creep stresses in mass concrete structures. The finite-element implementation of the exponential algorithm for concrete creep at variable temperatures is studied. The numerical solution procedure for thermal creep stresses in mass concrete structures with temperature effects is presented and a three-dimensional finite-element program is developed.

1 Introduction

For evaluating the thermal creep stress in a mass concrete structure, the elastic modulus and creep compliance under standard temperature (20℃) are usually used. In fact, they are not only functions of the actual age of the concrete. Several experiments show that they are remarkably affected by the variation of temperature[1]. The temperature increase accelerates the initial elastic modulus of concrete (Fig. 1), but the ultimate elastic modulus is not significantly affected[2,3]. The creep rate also grows with higher temperature and the creep strain is enlarged. A higher elastic modulus in the initial stage reduces the creep rate, but the creep increase always prevails. For example, as the temperature rises from 20℃ to 50℃, the creep increases about 100%[1] (see Fig. 2). Therefore, the elastic modulus and creep variation at different points of the mass concrete structure are also functions of temperature.

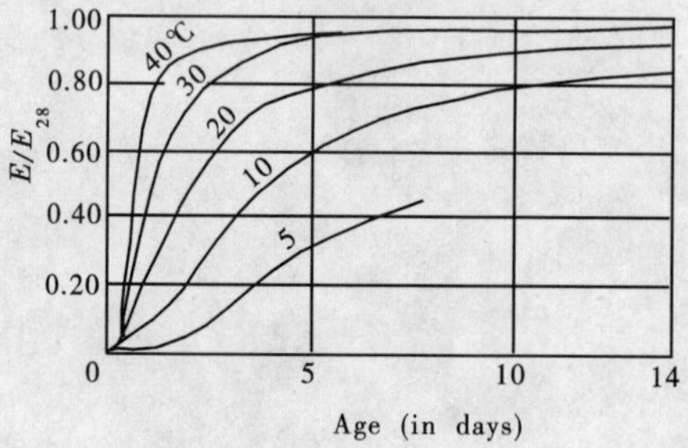

Fig. 1

In the early investigations, Bazant and Wu[4] proposed a Dirichlet series creep function for aging concrete. Glasstone et al.[1] studied the temperature effects in concrete structures and described the effect of temperature on the rate of aging by replacing concrete age with a certain equivalent age. Bazant[5] presented an exponential algorithm for concrete creep, which is now in prevalent use. Later a similar algorithm was presented by Zhu[7]. However, the

本文选自《Communications in Numerical Methods in Engineerine》1994 年第 10 期，作者还有 Du Chongjiang。

effects of temperature on the elastic modulus and creep of concrete were not included in the algorithms. Thus it has become an objective of this research to modify and extend Bazant's algorithm to take into account the effects of temperature on the elastic modulus and creep of concrete. By means of numerical methods, a new formulation of the problem is led to and a three-dimensional finite-element program for thermal creep stresses in mass concrete structures which takes into account the temperature effects is developed. A numerical example is included to demonstrate the efficiency of the procedure.

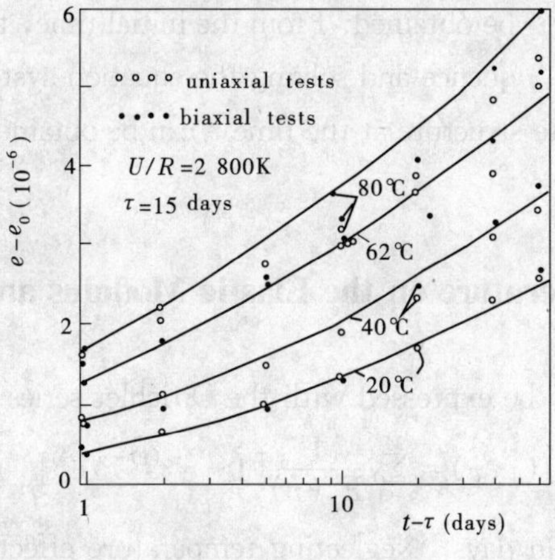

Fig. 2

2 Computation of Unsteady Thermal Field

Consider a domain Ω with the internal heat generation and various boundary conditions; let Γ_1 stand for the surface of a given boundary temperature T_c; Γ_2 the adiabatic surface and Γ_3 the convective heat exchange surface with ambient temperature T_a; then the three-dimensional unsteady thermal field of a mass concrete structure satisfies the governing equation and its boundary conditions:[2]

$$\frac{\partial T}{\partial t}=\alpha\left(\frac{\partial^2 T}{\partial x^2}+\frac{\partial^2 T}{\partial y^2}+\frac{\partial^2 T}{\partial z^2}\right)+\frac{\partial \theta}{\partial t} \qquad (1)$$

$$\left.\begin{array}{ll} T(x,y,z,0)=T_0(x,y,z) & (x,y,z)\in\Omega \\ T(x,y,z,t)=T_c(x,y,z,t) & (x,y,z)\in\Gamma_1 \\ \dfrac{\partial T(x,y,z,t)}{\partial n}=0 & (x,y,z)\in\Gamma_2 \\ \lambda\dfrac{\partial T(x,y,z,t)}{\partial n}=-\beta[T(x,y,z,t)-T_a] & (x,y,z)\in\Gamma_3 \end{array}\right\} \qquad (2)$$

where $T=T(x,y,z,t)$ is the transient temperature, θ is the adiabatic temperature rise of concrete, t is time, T_0 is the known initial temperature, n is the outer unit normal of Γ; α is the temperature coefficient of conductivity, λ is the thermal coefficient of conductivity and β is the heat release coefficient of the surface (see Fig. 3).

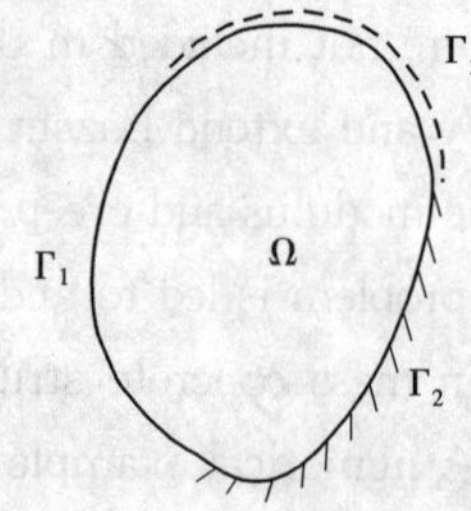

$\Gamma = \Gamma_1 + \Gamma_2 + \Gamma_3$

Fig. 3

We can solve the equations to obtain the temperature distribution in a mass concrete structure by the finite-element method which appears to be the practical solution to this type of problem. After the spatial discretization with the finite elements, the time is subdivided by discrete times $t_0, t_1 \cdots, t_n$ into time steps. Assuming that $\partial T/\partial t$ has a linear change within a typical step $[t_{i-1}, t_i]$, a linear equation system can be obtained. From the initial time, taking the time step in sequence and solving the equation system, the temperature distribution in the mass concrete structure at the time t can be obtained. The numerical formulation can be found elsewhere[8,9].

3 The Effects of Temperature on the Elastic Modulus and Creep of Concrete

The creep function may be expressed with the Dirichlet series as[4]

$$J(t,\tau)=\sum_{\gamma=1}^{M}\frac{1}{E_\gamma(\tau)}\left[1-e^{y_\gamma(\tau)-y_\gamma(t)}\right] \tag{3}$$

where τ is the loading age in days. Neglecting temperature effects, a specific form of the compliance function is often used,[2]

$$J(t,\tau)=\frac{1}{E(\tau)}+C(t,\tau) \tag{4}$$

where

$$E(\tau)=E_0(1-e^{-\alpha\tau^\beta})$$

$$C(t,\tau)=\sum_{\gamma=1}^{3}\varphi_\gamma(\tau)\left[1-e^{-s_\gamma(t-\tau)}\right]$$

$$\varphi_1=A_1+B_1\tau^{-G_1},\ \varphi_2=A_2+B_2\tau^{-G_2},\ \varphi_3=De^{-s_3\tau}$$

where $A_\gamma, B_\gamma, G_\gamma, D$, S_γ, α, β are all constants and may be determined from experimental data; $E(\tau)$, E_0 are transient and ultimate elastic moduli, respectively; $C(t,\tau)$ is the creep compliance.

Considering temperature effects and neglecting the effects of moisture diffusion caused by temperature gradients, the effect of temperature on the rate of aging may be described by replacing the concrete age with a certain equivalent age τ_e representing the hydration period for which the same degree of hydration is reached at temperature T as that reached during the actual time period t at reference temperature T_r. The rate of hydration depends only on the current temperature and not on the past temperatures[1]. Then for variable temperature we have

$$\tau_e=\int_0^\tau \beta_T(t')\mathrm{d}t' \tag{5}$$

where $\beta_T(t')$ is a function of current temperature

$$\beta_T(t') = \exp\left[\frac{U_h}{R}\left(\frac{1}{T_r} - \frac{1}{T(t')}\right)\right]$$

in which T is the current temperature (K); T_r is the reference temperature (K) and may be taken as the temperature in the laboratory; U_h is the activation energy of hydration and R is the gas constant; $U_h/R = 2\,700\text{K}$[1].

To describe the change of creep compliance with temperature, a function $y_\gamma(t)$ is introduced and s_γ in equation (4) will increase as the temperature rises. This may be expressed as

$$y_\gamma(t) = s_\gamma \int_0^t \Psi_T(t')\,dt' \tag{6}$$

where $\Psi_T(t')$ is a function of current temperature,

$$\Psi_T(t') = \exp\left[\frac{U_\alpha}{R}\left(\frac{1}{T_r} - \frac{1}{T(t')}\right)\right]$$

in which U_α is the activation energy of creep; $U_\alpha/R = 5\,000\text{K}$[1].

Introducing the ideas mentioned above, Eq. (4) may be rewritten as

$$\left.\begin{aligned} &J(t,\tau) = \frac{1}{E(\tau)} + C(t,\tau) \\ &E(\tau) = E_0(1 - e^{-\alpha\tau_e^\beta}) \\ &C(t,\tau) = \sum_{\gamma=1}^{3} \varphi_\gamma(\tau_e)\{1 - e^{-[y_\gamma(t) - y_\gamma(\tau)]}\} \\ &\varphi_1 = A_1 + B_1\tau_e^{-G_1}, \quad \varphi_2 = A_2 + B_2\tau_e^{-G_2}, \quad \varphi_3 = De^{-y_3(\tau)} \end{aligned}\right\} \tag{7}$$

if $\beta_T = \Psi_T = 1$ (or $T_r = T$), then $\tau_e = \tau$, $y_\gamma(t) = s_\gamma t$, and Eq. (7) degenerates into Eq. (4).

4 The Formulation of Concrete Creep with Temperature Effects

4.1 Computation of Creep Strain Increment for Uniaxial Stress

The creep strain may be expressed as[2]

$$\varepsilon^c(t) = \sigma_0 C(t, t_0) + \int_{t_0}^{t} C(t,\tau)\frac{\partial\sigma}{\partial\tau}d\tau \tag{8}$$

where σ, σ_0 are the transient and initial stresses, respectively.

Let the time interval $[t_0, t]$ be subdivided into N steps; for a typical step $[t_{i-1}, t_i]$ $(i = 1, 2, \cdots, N)$, assuming $\partial\sigma/\partial\tau = $ constant, i.e. assuming the stress varies linearly, substituting equation (7) into equation (8) and integrating the equation, we obtain

$$\varepsilon^c(t) = \sum_{\gamma=1}^{3}\left\{\sigma_0\varphi_\gamma(t_{e0})[1 - e^{-y_s(t)}] + \sum_{i=1}^{N}\frac{\Delta\sigma_i}{\Delta\tau_i}\int_{t_{i-1}}^{t_i}\varphi_\gamma(\tau_e)[1 - e^{-(y_s(t) - y_s(\tau))}]d\tau\right\}$$

Using the integral mean-value theorem, the above-mentioned equation may be further brought to the form

$$\varepsilon^c(t) = \sum_{\gamma=1}^{3}\left[\sigma_0\varphi_{\gamma0}^*(1-e^{-y_s(t)}) + \sum_{i=1}^{N}\Delta\sigma_i\varphi_{\gamma i}^*(1-f_{\gamma i}^*e^{-y_s(t)})\right] \tag{9}$$

where

$$\varphi_{\gamma0}^* = \varphi_\gamma(t_{e0}); \qquad \varphi_{\gamma i}^* = \varphi_\gamma(\tau_{ei-1/2}); \qquad f_{\gamma i}^* = \frac{1}{\Delta\tau_i}\int_{t_{i-1}}^{t_i} e^{y_s(\tau)}d\tau$$

$$y_s(t) = s_\gamma\int_{t_0}^{t}\Psi_T dt'; \qquad t_{t_0} = \int_0^{t_0}\beta_T dt'; \quad \tau_e = \int_0^{\tau}\beta_T dt'$$

Considering three discrete times t_{n-1}, t_n, t_{n+1}, the steps are $\Delta\tau_n = t_n - t_{n-1}$, $\Delta\tau_{n+1} = t_{n+1} - t_n$.

From Eq. (9) we obtain

$$\varepsilon^c(t_{n-1}) = \sum_{\gamma=1}^{3}\left[\sigma_0\varphi_{\gamma0}^*(1-e^{-y_s(t_{n-1})}) + \sum_{i=1}^{N-1}\Delta\sigma_i\varphi_{\gamma i}^*(1-f_{\gamma i}^*e^{-y_s(t_{n-1})})\right] \tag{9a}$$

$$\varepsilon^c(t_n) = \sum_{\gamma=1}^{3}\left[\sigma_0\varphi_{\gamma0}^*(1-e^{-y_s(t_n)}) + \sum_{i=1}^{N}\Delta\sigma_i\varphi_{\gamma i}^*(1-f_{\gamma i}^*e^{-y_s(t_n)})\right] \tag{9b}$$

$$\varepsilon^c(t_{n+1}) = \sum_{\gamma=1}^{3}\left[\sigma_0\varphi_{\gamma0}^*(1-e^{-y_s(t_{n+1})}) + \sum_{i=1}^{N+1}\Delta\sigma_i\varphi_{\gamma i}^*(1-f_{\gamma i}^*e^{-y_s(t_{n+1})})\right] \tag{9c}$$

Subtracting (a) from (b), the creep strain increment can be obtained within the nth step

$$\begin{aligned}\Delta\varepsilon_n^c &= \varepsilon^c(t_n) - \varepsilon^c(t_{n-1})\\ &= \sum_{\gamma=1}^{3}\Big\{\Big[\sigma_0\varphi_{\gamma0}^*e^{-y_s(t_{n-1})} + \sum_{i=1}^{n-1}\Delta\sigma_i\varphi_{\gamma i}^*f_{\gamma i}^*e^{-y_s(t_{n-1})}\Big]\Big[1-e^{-(y_s(t_n)-y_s(t_{n-1}))}\Big] +\\ &\quad \Delta\sigma_n\varphi_{\gamma n}^*(1-f_{\gamma n}^*e^{-y_s(t_n)})\Big\}\end{aligned} \tag{9d}$$

In the form of numerical integration we have

$$\begin{aligned}\Delta\varepsilon_n^c = \sum_{\gamma=1}^{3}\Big[&(1-e^{-s_\gamma\Delta\tau_n\Psi_{Tn}})\Big(\sigma_0\varphi_{\gamma0}^*e^{-Y_{n-1}} + \sum_{i=1}^{n-1}\Delta\sigma_i\varphi_{\gamma i}^*f_{ri}^*e^{-Y_{n-1}}\Big) +\\ &\Delta\sigma_n\varphi_{\gamma n}^*(1-f_{\gamma n}^*e^{-Y_n})\Big]\end{aligned} \tag{9e}$$

Similarly,

$$\begin{aligned}\Delta\varepsilon_{n+1}^c &= \varepsilon^c(t_{n+1}) - \varepsilon^c(t_n)\\ &= \sum_{\gamma=1}^{3}\Big[(1-e^{-s_\gamma\Delta\tau_{n+1}\Psi_{Tn+1}})\Big(\sigma_0\varphi_{\gamma0}^*e^{-Y_n} + \sum_{i=1}^{n}\Delta\sigma_i\varphi_{\gamma i}^*f_{\gamma i}^*e^{-Y_n}\Big) +\\ &\quad \Delta\sigma_{n+1}\varphi_{\gamma n+1}^*(1-f_{\gamma n+1}^*e^{-Y_{n+1}})\Big]\end{aligned} \tag{9f}$$

let

$$\omega_{\gamma n} = \sigma_0\varphi_{\gamma0}^*e^{-Y_{n-1}} + \sum_{i=1}^{n-1}\Delta\sigma_i\varphi_{\gamma i}^*f_{\gamma i}^*e^{-Y_{n-1}}$$

$$\omega_{\gamma n+1} = \sigma_0\varphi_{\gamma0}^*e^{-Y_n} + \sum_{i=1}^{n}\Delta\sigma_i\varphi_{\gamma i}^*f_{\gamma i}^*e^{-Y_n}$$

$$h_{\gamma n}^* = 1 - f_{\gamma n}^*e^{-Y_n}$$

$$Y_n = s_\gamma\sum_{j=1}^{n}\Psi_{Tj}\Delta\tau_j$$

hence

$$\omega_{\gamma n+1} = \omega_{\gamma n} e^{-s_\gamma \Delta\tau_n \Psi_{Tn}} + \Delta\sigma_n \varphi^*_{\gamma n} f^*_{\gamma n} e^{-Y_n}$$

Reassembling the above-mentioned formulas of creep strain increment,

$$\begin{aligned}
\Delta\varepsilon^c_n &= \sum_{\gamma=1}^{3} [\omega_{\gamma n}(1 - e^{-s_\gamma \Psi_{Tn} \Delta\tau_n}) + \Delta\sigma_n \varphi^*_{\gamma n} h^*_{\gamma n}] \\
\omega_{\gamma n+1} &= \omega_{\gamma n} e^{-s_\gamma \Psi_{Tn} \Delta\tau_n} + \Delta\sigma_n \varphi^*_{\gamma n} f^*_{\gamma n} e^{-Y_n} \\
\omega_{\gamma 1} &= \sigma_0 \varphi_{\gamma 0} = \sigma_0 \varphi_\gamma(t_{e0}) \\
h^*_{\gamma n} &= 1 - f^*_{\gamma n} e^{-Y_n} \\
f^*_{\gamma n} &= \frac{1}{\Delta\tau_n} \int_{t_{n-1}}^{t_n} e^{y_s(\tau)} d\tau \\
y_s(t) &= s_\gamma \int_{t_0}^{t} \Psi_T dt' \\
Y_n &= S_\gamma \sum_{j=1}^{n} \Psi_{Tj} \Delta\tau_j \\
\varphi^*_{\gamma n} &= \varphi_\gamma(\tau_{en-1/2}) \qquad (n = 1,2,3\cdots,N)
\end{aligned} \tag{10}$$

where $f^*_{\gamma n}$ can be evaluated with the numerical integration method.

4.2 Computation of Creep Strain Increment for Multiaxial Stress

In the case of a multiaxis, the total strain column vector within the nth interval may be generalized as

$$\{\Delta\varepsilon_n\} = \{\Delta\varepsilon^e_n\} + \{\Delta\varepsilon^c_n\} + \{\Delta\varepsilon^T_n\} + \{\Delta\varepsilon^0_n\} \tag{11}$$

where $\{\Delta\varepsilon^e_n\}$, $\{\Delta\varepsilon^c_n\}$, $\{\Delta\varepsilon^T_n\}$, $\{\Delta\varepsilon^0_n\}$ refer to elastic, creep, temperature and initial strain increment column vectors, respectively.

From t_0 to t, the creep strain column vector is[6]

$$\{\varepsilon^c(t)\} = [\boldsymbol{Q}]\{\boldsymbol{\sigma}_0\}C(t,t_0) + [\boldsymbol{Q}]\int_{t_0}^{t} C(t,\tau)\left\{\frac{\partial\sigma}{\partial\tau}\right\} d\tau \tag{12}$$

$$[\boldsymbol{Q}] = \begin{bmatrix} 1 & -\mu & -\mu & 0 & 0 & 0 \\ & 1 & -\mu & 0 & 0 & 0 \\ & & 1 & 0 & 0 & 0 \\ & & & 2(1+\mu) & 0 & 0 \\ & \text{symmetry} & & & 2(1+\mu) & 0 \\ & & & & & 2(1+\mu) \end{bmatrix} \tag{13}$$

The creep strain increment column vector within step $[t_{n-1}, t_n]$ may be generalized as

$$\{\Delta\varepsilon^c\} = [\boldsymbol{Q}]\sum_{\gamma=1}^{3}[(1 - e^{-s_\gamma \Psi_{Tn} \Delta\tau_n})\{\boldsymbol{\omega}_{\gamma n}\} + \{\Delta\boldsymbol{\sigma}_n\}\varphi^*_{\gamma n} h^*_{\gamma n}] = \{\boldsymbol{\eta}_n\} + q_n[\boldsymbol{Q}]\{\Delta\boldsymbol{\sigma}_n\} \tag{14}$$

where $\{\boldsymbol{\eta}_n\} = \sum_{\gamma=1}^{3}(1 - e^{-s_\gamma \Psi_{Tn} \Delta\tau n})\{\boldsymbol{\omega}_{\gamma n}\}$

$$\{\boldsymbol{\omega}_{\gamma n}\} = \{\boldsymbol{\omega}_{\gamma n-1}\}e^{s_\gamma \Psi_{Tn-1}\Delta\tau_{n-1}} + [\boldsymbol{Q}]\{\Delta\boldsymbol{\sigma}_n\}\varphi^*_{\gamma n-1}f^*_{\gamma n-1}e^{-Y_{n-1}} \tag{15}$$

$$q_n = \sum_{\gamma=1}^{3}\varphi^*_{\gamma n}h^*_{\gamma n}$$

$$\{\Delta\boldsymbol{\sigma}_n\} = [\overline{\boldsymbol{D}}_n](\{\Delta\boldsymbol{\varepsilon}_n\} - \{\boldsymbol{\eta}_n\} - \{\Delta\boldsymbol{\varepsilon}^{\mathrm{T}}_n\} - \{\Delta\boldsymbol{\varepsilon}^0_n\}) \tag{16}$$

where $[\overline{\boldsymbol{D}}_{\mathrm{n}}]=[\boldsymbol{D}_n]/(1+q_nE_n)$; $[\boldsymbol{D}_n]$ is the elastic matrix of the nth time interval[6]

$$[\boldsymbol{D}_n] = \frac{E_n(1-\mu)}{(1+\mu)(1-2\mu)}\begin{bmatrix} 1 & \frac{\mu}{1-\mu} & \frac{\mu}{1-\mu} & 0 & 0 & 0 \\ & 1 & \frac{\mu}{1-\mu} & 0 & 0 & 0 \\ & & 1 & 0 & 0 & 0 \\ & & & \frac{1-2\mu}{2(1-\mu)} & 0 & 0 \\ & \text{symmetry} & & & \frac{1-2\mu}{2(1-\mu)} & 0 \\ & & & & & \frac{1-2\mu}{2(1-\mu)} \end{bmatrix} \tag{17}$$

where μ is Poisson's ratio; E_n is the elastic modulus within the nth step.

By the equilibrium equation of the finite-element method, we obtain

$$[\boldsymbol{K}_n]\{\Delta\boldsymbol{\delta}_n\} = \{\Delta\boldsymbol{P}^{\mathrm{e}}_n\} + \{\Delta\boldsymbol{P}^{\mathrm{c}}_n\} + \{\Delta\boldsymbol{P}^{\mathrm{T}}_n\} + \{\Delta\boldsymbol{P}^0_n\} \tag{18}$$

where $[\boldsymbol{K}_n]$ is the global stiffness matrix; $\{\Delta\boldsymbol{\delta}_n\}$ is the column matrix of nodal displacement; $\{\Delta\boldsymbol{P}^{\mathrm{c}}_n\}$ is the equivalent load column matrix of nodal creep:

$$\{\Delta\boldsymbol{P}^{\mathrm{c}}_n\} = \sum_e \{\Delta\boldsymbol{P}^{\mathrm{c}}_n\}^e$$

$$\{\Delta\boldsymbol{P}^{\mathrm{c}}_n\}^e = \iiint_{\Omega^e}[\boldsymbol{B}]^{\mathrm{T}}[\overline{\boldsymbol{D}}_n]\{\eta_n\}\mathrm{d}\Omega \tag{19}$$

$\{\Delta\boldsymbol{P}^e_n\}^e$, $\{\Delta\boldsymbol{P}^{\mathrm{T}}_n\}^e$ and $\{\Delta\boldsymbol{P}^0_n\}^e$ are the equivalent load column matrices of nodal elastic, temperature and initial stress, respectively.

Given all constants in equations (1), (2), (5), (6), (7) and initial temperature T_0 and stress σ_0, from the initial time t_0, taking the time step Δt in sequence, the temperature T at time t can be calculated from the procedure described in Section 2 of this paper. Substituting them into equations (5) and (6), β_T and Ψ_T can be evaluated. According to the placing sequence of concrete layer or block, the loading age τ is determined. From equations (7) and (10) the creep strain increment $\Delta\varepsilon^{\mathrm{c}}$ is obtained.

Solve equation (18) to obtain the column matrix of nodal displacement increment $\{\Delta\boldsymbol{\delta}_n\}$, and thus to obtain the column matrix of nodal strain increment and stress increment within the nth step. Therefore, the column matrix of nodal stresses at the moment of the nth step is

$$\{\boldsymbol{\sigma}_n\} = \{\boldsymbol{\sigma}_{n-1}\} + \{\Delta\boldsymbol{\sigma}_n\} \tag{20}$$

5 The Computer Program and Example

With the method proposed above and according to the accumulated stress requirements, a three-dimensional finite-element program is developed.

The triangular and hexahedral prism elements in which the number of nodes is variable are included in the program for stress computation on complex structural shapes in order to meet the accuracy requirement of the thin-layer element and to increase the flexibility of the nodal arrangement. The program includes the calculation of stresses and deformations during construction caused by dead load, concentrated load and water pressure, the continuously changing behaviour of material, and the three-dimensional unsteady thermal field with its thermal stresses and deformations (with the effects of temperature on elastic modulus and creep of concrete). It can be used for design, construction and scientific research.

Example. Consider a concrete slab 3m thick on the rockbed, with plane dimensions much greater than its thickness (as shown in Fig. 4). The upper surface of the slab is exposed to the air, and the ambient temperature is 10℃. For concrete, suppose $\alpha = 0.004\text{m}^2/\text{h}$, $\lambda = 2.16\text{cal}/(\text{m}\cdot\text{h}\cdot℃)$, $\beta = 20\text{cal}/(\text{m}^2\cdot\text{h}\cdot℃)$, Poisson's ratio $\mu = 1/6$, linear thermal dilatation coefficient $\alpha = 10^{-5}1/℃$, adiabatic temperature rise $\theta = 30(1 - e^{-0.30\tau})(℃)$, and the elastic modulus and creep compliance of concrete (without the temperature effects) as follows:

$$E(\tau) = 2 \times 10^4(1 - e^{-0.14\tau}) +$$

$$C(t,\tau) = \{(0.115 + 1.058\tau^{-0.45})[1 - e^{-0.30(t-\tau)}] + (0.26 + 0.44\tau^{-0.45})[1 - e^{-0.005(t-\tau)}]\} \times 10^{-6}$$

The reference temperature is $T_r = 20℃$ (293K). The expression of elastic modulus and creep compliance with the temperature effects refers to Eq. (7). Assume that the rockbed under the slab is stiff and its thermal behaviour is the same as concrete. The initial temperatures of concrete and rockbed are 10℃. As a result, the temperature and stress curves at the central point of the slab are shown in Figs. 5 and 6, respectively.

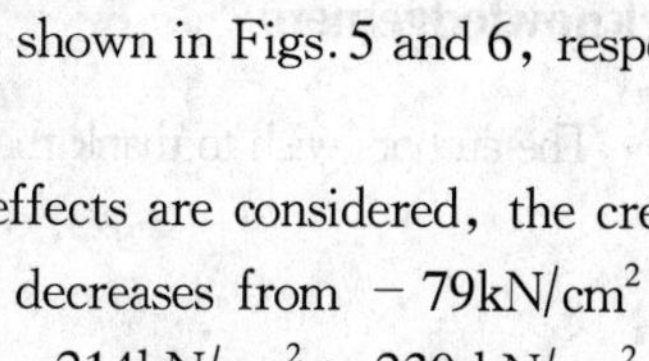

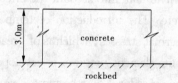

Fig. 4

From Figs. 5 and 6 we conclude that, if temperature effects are considered, the creep stress at the central point of this single-layer concrete slab decreases from -79kN/cm^2 to -75kN/cm^2 by 5.3% in the initial stage and it increases from 214kN/cm^2 to 230 kN/cm^2 by 7% in the later stage. Since the peak value of temperature does not appear on the rockbed surface, the maximum tensile stress moves to the middle of the slab.

6 Conclusions

This paper modifies and extends the exponential algorithm for concrete developed by Ba-

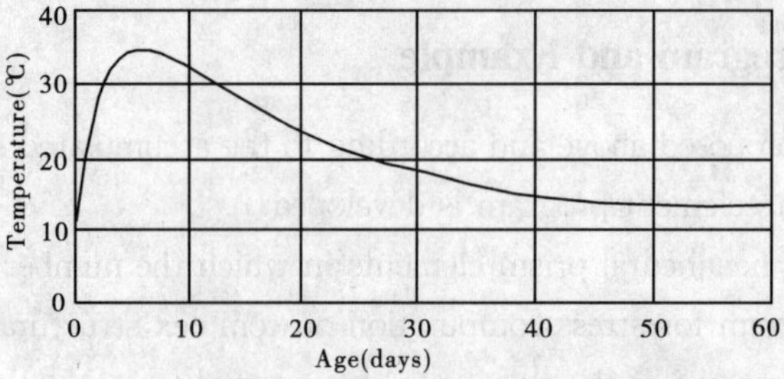

Fig. 5　Temperature curve at central point of slab

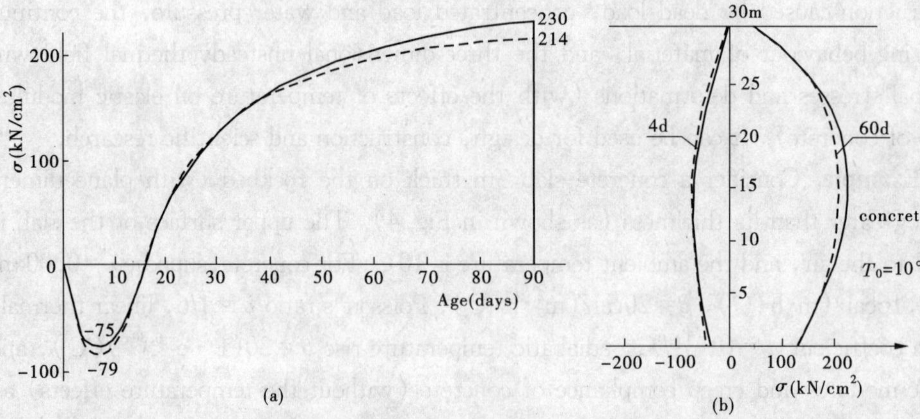

Fig. 6　(a) Creep stress curves at central point of slab ; (b) Creep stress distribution along the height

—— with and······without temperature effects

zant to take into account the effects of temperature on the elastic modulus and creep of concrete. The introduction of temperature effects improves the accuracy in evaluation of the thermal stresses, which is of great significance in practice. An appropriate three-dimensional finite element program is developed. The numerical example demonstrates the efficiency of the procedure. Furthermore, we think that the formulation in this paper is not limited to mass concrete structures but that it can be extended to the other concrete structures.

Acknowledgement

The authors wish to thank the referees for the valuable comments on an earlier draft of this paper.

References

[1] Z. P. Bazant. *Mathematical models for creep and shrinkage of concrete*, in Creep and Shrinkage in Concrete Structure. Z. P. Bazant and F. H. Wittman (Eds), Wiley, 1982

[2] B. F. Zhu, T. S. Wang, B. Y. Ding. *Thermal Stresses and Temperature Control in Hydraulic Concrete Structures* (in Chinese) Water Power Press, Beijing, 1976

[3] A. M. Neville, W. H. Dilger, J. J. Brooks. *Creep of Plain and Structural Concrete*. Construction Press,

Longman, London and New York, 1983

[4] Z.P.Bazant, S.T.Wu. *Dirichlet series creep function for aging concrete*. J.Eng.Mech.Div., ASCE, 100,(EM3),1974

[5] Z.P.Bazant. *Numerically stable algorithm with increasing time steps for integral-type aging creep* in: Proceedings of the First International Conference on Structural Mechanics in Reactor Technology, West Berlin, 4, 1971, p.H2/2

[6] RILEM Committee TC-69(chaired by Z.P.Bazant). *Material models for structural creep analysis*. Chapter 2 in Mathematical Modeling of Creep and Shrinkage of Concrete. Z.P.Bazant, (Ed.), Wiley, 1988, pp.99~200

[7] *B.F.Zhu. An implicit algorithm for thermal creep stress in concrete structures (in Chinese)*. J. Hydraulic Eng., (5), 1983

[8] K.H.Huebner, E.A.Thornton. *The Finite Element Method for Engineers*. *Wiley*, 1982

[9] O.C.Zienkievicz. *The Finite Element Method*. 4 *Edn*. McGraw-Hill,UK,1989

NUMERICAL-EXPERIMENTAL ANALYSIS OF THE CRACKS IN MASSIVE CONCRETE UNDER COMPRESSION-SHEAR CONDITIONS

Abstract　In present paper the massive concrete structure with multiple cracks under tension-shear and compression-shear conditions is studied. Since the friction on the cracked surfaces give a resistance to the growth of cracks under compression, the propagating energy beyond the tip of crack is reduced. Four possible phases of compression-shear condition were discussed respectively. The experimental methods were also used for checking with the numerical results under mixed condition (stress and displacement field). They show in good agreement.

1　Introduction

The general solutions for the stress, displacement and SIF of a finite body with multiple cracks can be obtained after solving the fictitious forces on the cracks and outer boundaries form the following equation-systems[1]:

(1) At the points on the crack surface:

$$P_n(S_n)+\sum_{k=1}^{M}{}'\int_{-l_k}^{l_k}P_k(S_k)f_{nn,nk}(S_k,S_n)\mathrm{d}S_k+\sum_{k=1}^{N}{}'\int_{-l_k}^{l_k}Q_k(S_k)f_{nt,nk}(S_k,S_n)\mathrm{d}S_k+\sum_{j=1}^{L}{}'\int_{a_j}^{b_j}N_j(\xi)H_{nn,n\xi}(\xi,S_n)\mathrm{d}\xi_j+\sum_{j=1}^{L}\int_{a_j}^{b_j}T_j(\xi)H_{nt,n\xi}(\xi,S_n)\mathrm{d}\xi_j=p_n(S_n) \tag{1}$$

$$Q_n(S_n)+\sum_{k=1}^{N}{}'\int_{-l_k}^{l_k}P_k(S_k)f_{tn,nk}(S_k,S_n)\mathrm{d}S_k+\sum_{k=1}^{N}{}'\int_{-l_k}^{l_k}Q_k(S_k)f_{tt,nk}(S_k,S_n)\mathrm{d}S_k+\sum_{j=1}^{L}\int_{a_j}^{b_j}N_j(\xi)H_{tn,n\xi}(\xi,S_n)\mathrm{d}\xi_j+\sum_{j=1}^{L}\int_{a_j}^{b_j}T_j(\xi)H_{tt,n\xi}(\xi,S_n)\mathrm{d}\xi_j=q_n(S_n) \tag{2}$$

$$k=1,2,\cdots,N\qquad \xi\in S,\ |S_n|<l_n,\ |S_k|<l_k$$

(2) At the points on the boundary:

$$C_{nj}T_n(\xi)+\sum_{j\neq n}^{L}{}'\int_{a_j}^{b_j}N_j(\eta)H_{tn,\xi n}(\eta,\xi)\mathrm{d}\eta_j+\sum_{j\neq n}^{L}{}'\int_{a_j}^{b_j}T_j(\eta)H_{tt,\xi\eta}(\eta,\xi)\mathrm{d}\eta_j+\sum_{k=1}^{N}\int_{-l_k}^{l_k}P_k(S_k)f_{tn,S_k}(S_k,\xi)\mathrm{d}S_k+\sum_{k=1}^{N}\int_{-l_k}^{l_k}Q_k(S_k)f_{tt,S_k}(S_k,\xi)\mathrm{d}S_k=t_n(\xi) \tag{3}$$

$$C_{nj}N_n(\xi)+\sum_{j\neq n}^{L}{}'\int_{a_j}^{b_j}N_j(\eta)H_{nn,\xi\eta}(\eta,\xi)\mathrm{d}\eta_j+\sum_{j\neq n}^{L}{}'\int_{a_j}^{b_j}T_j(\eta)H_{nt,\xi\eta}(\eta,\xi)\mathrm{d}\xi_j+\sum_{k=1}^{N}\int_{-l_k}^{l_k}P_k(S_k)f_{nn,\xi S_k}(S_k,\xi)\mathrm{d}S_k+\sum_{k=1}^{n}\int_{-l_k}^{l_k}Q_k(S_k)f_{nn,\xi S_k}(S_k,\xi)\mathrm{d}S_k=\eta_n(\xi) \tag{4}$$

本文选自《International Symposium on Pumd-Storage Engineering》,1990 年 10 月,作者还有 Zhou Ruizhong。

where the prime in $\sum_{k=1}^{N}{}'$ represents the influence come from all other cracks(except itself), f_{nn}, f_{nt}, f_{tn}, f_{tt} are corresponding to normal and shear stresses caused by the unit force acting at the given point of crack surface, i.e. Green's function in fracture mechanics. H_{nn}, H_{nt}, H_{tn}, H_{tt} are corresponding to normal and shear stresses caused by the unit force acting at the boundary point. They can be represented by the solutions of Kelvin's problem. For the cracks under tension-shear conditions $P_n(S_n)$, $q_n(S_n)$, $n_n(\xi)$, $t_n(\xi)$ are the known resultant components acting on the surface of the cracks and boundaries of the structure, the unknowns $P_k(S_k)$, $Q_k(S_k)$, $P_n(S_n)$, $Q_n(S_n)$, $N_j(\xi)$, $T_j(\xi)$ at each inter-polate point of cracks and boundaries are the fictitious intensity function (to be solved).

$$C_{nj} = \begin{cases} 1/2 & \text{on the smooth boundary} \\ \theta/2 & \text{on the corner of boundary with the internal angle } \theta \end{cases}$$

If all the cracks are under tension-shear conditions only(i.e. Griffith crack), the resultant components on crack surfaces are equal to zero. $P_n(S_n) = q_n(S_n) = 0$. Therefore the unknowns are easily solved from the upper mentioned equation systems with the aid of computer. When some of the cracks are under compression-shear conditions, $P_n(S_n)$, $q_n(S_n)$ are unknowns and could not be determined at once, the following method is advised to a simple effective determination.

2 The Experimental Analysis of Transmitting Compression-Shear Force Through the Crack

In fact the change of stress distribution on a compression-shear crack surfaces is much complicate than the crack of open type (which is usually taken as zero or with known forces). But for engineering purpose a simple general mechanical rule is needed only which can be constructed directly from the experimental results. Suppose there is a crack in concrete with initial small width C_0(theoretical ideal cracks $C_0 = 0$ when $\sigma_n = 0$, do not always happen in fact). The opposite faces of the crack do not tightly contact with each other at the beginning of compression, since the surfaces of concrete are not absolutely smooth. Experimental results (Fig.1) show two linear relationships at different compression stages between normal pressure σ_n and crack width Δ after loading, which may be considered as if there is a elastic material of low modulus E_2, μ_2 full filling the crack of width Δ(Fig.2). (when $\sigma_n > \sigma_0$, E_2 change to E'_2).

For the opposite points i, j of a crack we have:
(when the original strain $\varepsilon \approx 0$)

$$V_{tj} - V_{ti} = \frac{2(1+\nu_2)}{E_2 bh} P_{tj} C_0 F(\sigma_n)$$

$$U_{nj} - U_{ni} = \frac{C_0(1-\nu_2^2)}{E_2 bh} P_{nj} \tag{5}$$

where V_{tj}, V_{ti}, U_{nj}, U_{ni} represent the displacement in the co-ordinate n, t direction, h is thickness (third direction), $P_{nj}=P_{ni}$, $P_{tj}=P_{ti}$ are forces in the local co-ordinate system. $F(\sigma_n)$ is the coefficient of Normal-pressure influence.

The experimental relationship between shear stress τ and tangential displacement δ_t on the surface of concrete under pressure-sheared state is shown in Fig. 3 (σ_n is the normal pressure stress) and can be expressed as:

$$\tau=\frac{1}{b}\left(1-\frac{a}{a+b\delta}\right)\ \text{when}\ \sigma_n\leqslant 0 \tag{6}$$

The physical meanings of the constant a, b are mentioned in Fig. 4, we have:

$$a=\frac{C_0(1-\nu_2)^2}{E_2bh},\quad b=\frac{2(1+\nu_2)}{E_2bh}C_0F(\sigma_n) \tag{7}$$

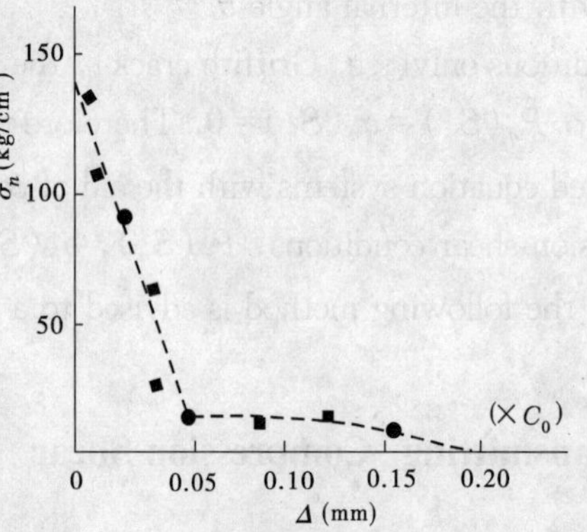

Fig. 1 The normal pressure σ_n verses crack width
Δ(C_0 – original width, unit: cm)

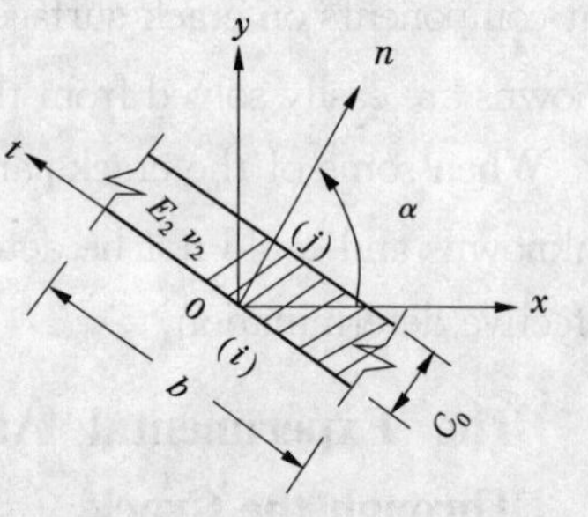

Fig. 2 Geometrical measurement of a crack segment

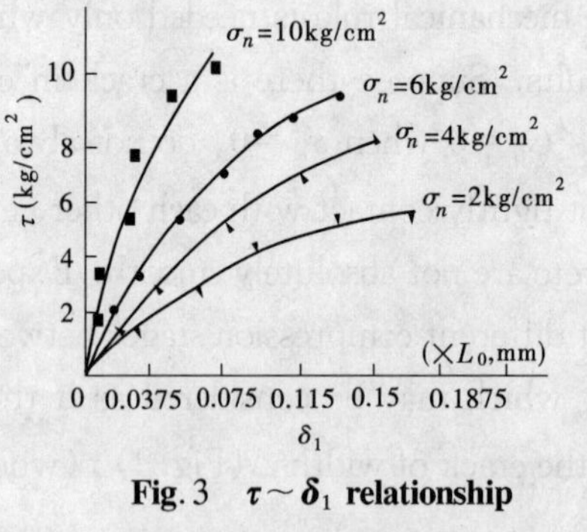

Fig. 3 $\tau\sim\delta_1$ relationship
(L_0 – original length, unit: cm)

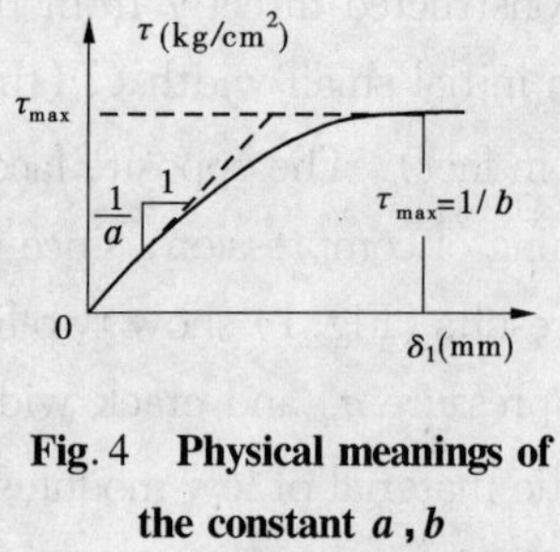

Fig. 4 Physical meanings of the constant a, b

Since τ-δ curves are given by experimental method for the different normal stresses σ_n, coefficients $F(\sigma_n)$ are solved. The ultimate failure criterion for compression-sheared crack in concrete follows Mohr-Columb principle and can also be determined by experimental method. Take the effect of normal pressure σ_n into account, we can easily calculated the rigidity corresponding to the displacements of points i and j in four phases:

A. Crack in concrete with small width or joint in rock mass filled with thin layer of the material of low modulus.

(1) In the elastic state, the rigidity is symmetric.

$$\begin{bmatrix} \frac{1}{A}\cos^2\alpha+\frac{1}{B}\sin^2\alpha & (\frac{1}{A}-\frac{1}{B})\cos\alpha\sin\alpha & -(\frac{1}{A}\cos^2\alpha+\frac{1}{B}\sin^2\alpha) & -(\frac{1}{A}-\frac{1}{B})\cos\alpha\sin\alpha \\ (\frac{1}{A}-\frac{1}{B})\sin\alpha\cos\alpha & \frac{1}{A}\sin^2\alpha+\frac{1}{B}\cos^2\alpha & -(\frac{1}{A}-\frac{1}{B})\cos\alpha\sin\alpha & -(\frac{1}{A}\sin^2\alpha+\frac{1}{B}\cos^2\alpha) \\ -(\frac{1}{A}\cos^2\alpha+\frac{1}{B}\sin^2\alpha) & -(\frac{1}{A}-\frac{1}{B})\cos\alpha\sin\alpha & \frac{1}{A}\cos^2\alpha+\frac{1}{B}\sin^2\alpha & (\frac{1}{A}-\frac{1}{B})\sin\alpha\cos\alpha \\ -(\frac{1}{A}-\frac{1}{B})\cos\alpha\sin\alpha & -(\frac{1}{A}\sin^2\alpha+\frac{1}{B}\cos^2\alpha) & (\frac{1}{A}-\frac{1}{B})\cos\alpha\sin\alpha & \frac{1}{A}\sin^2\alpha+\frac{1}{B}\cos^2\alpha \end{bmatrix} \tag{8}$$

(2) In the positive sliding state (j slides relatively to i in the t direction), according to Mohr-columb principle we have:

$$-P_{xj}\sin\alpha+P_{yj}\cos\alpha=2K-f(P_{xj}\cos\alpha+P_{yj}\sin\alpha)$$

$$(u_j-U_i)\cos\alpha+(V_j-V_i)\sin\alpha=A(P_{xj}\cos\alpha+P_{yj}\sin\alpha)$$

The rigidity of elements can be represented as follows:

$$\begin{bmatrix} \frac{1}{A}J_1\cos\alpha+J_3 & \frac{1}{A}J_1\sin\alpha+J_3 & -\frac{1}{A}J_1\cos\alpha+J_3 & -\frac{1}{A}J_1\sin\alpha+J_3 \\ \frac{1}{A}J_2\cos\alpha-2K\cos\alpha & \frac{1}{A}J_2\sin\alpha-2K\cos\alpha & -\frac{1}{A}J_2\cos\alpha-2K\cos\alpha & -\frac{1}{A}J_2\sin\alpha-2K\cos\alpha \\ -\frac{1}{A}J_1\cos\alpha-J_3 & -\frac{1}{A}J_1\sin\alpha-J_3 & \frac{1}{A}J_1\cos\alpha-J_3 & \frac{1}{A}J_1\sin\alpha-J_3 \\ -\frac{1}{A}J_2\cos\alpha+2K\cos\alpha & -\frac{1}{A}J_2\sin\alpha+2K\cos\alpha & \frac{1}{A}J_2\cos\alpha+2K\cos\alpha & \frac{1}{A}J_2\sin\alpha+2K\cos\alpha \end{bmatrix} \tag{9}$$

in which $J_1=\cos\alpha+f\sin\alpha$, $J_2=\sin\alpha-f\cos\alpha$, $J_3=2K(1-J_1\cos\alpha)/J_2$

(3) In the negative sliding state (j slides relatively to i in the $-t$ direction), now we need only to replace the f,k of (9) by $(-f),(-k)$.

(4) In the disengaging state $\sigma_n>0$ such that the node forces: $P_{xj}=P_{yj}=P_{xi}=P_{yi}=0$.

B. Fissure (i.e. the crack width is zero), the critical value $\tau^*=|2K-\sigma_n,f|$, so that:

$\tau<\tau^*$,	$\sigma_n\leqslant 0$	in the clastic phase
$\tau>\tau^*$,	$\sigma_n\leqslant 0$	in the positive sliding phase
$-\tau<-\tau^*$,	$\sigma_n\leqslant 0$	in the negative sliding phase
	$\sigma_n>0$	in the disengaging phase (opening)

In the pratical procedure of solving this problem, we expand the value of rigidity between i and j (weighted function) to avoid the relative "in trusion" each other in the normal direction, such that the normal displacements of i and j are consistent, but the node forces are different from what a phase can be judged.

For the compression-sheared crack the decreasing part of rigidity induces the released shear stress in the elastic phase, in the sliding phase the additional part of excess shear stress

$\tau - \tau^*$ is also released.

3 The Computed Example and Its Experiment

The concrete specimen(24cm × 15cm × 3cm) with three cracks was loaded under compression on the boundaries (Fig. 5) from the initial load 13kg/cm^2 to final load 53.5kg/cm^2. The digital strain gage with the automatic recorder and speckle method was used for the increasing strain and displacement measurement.

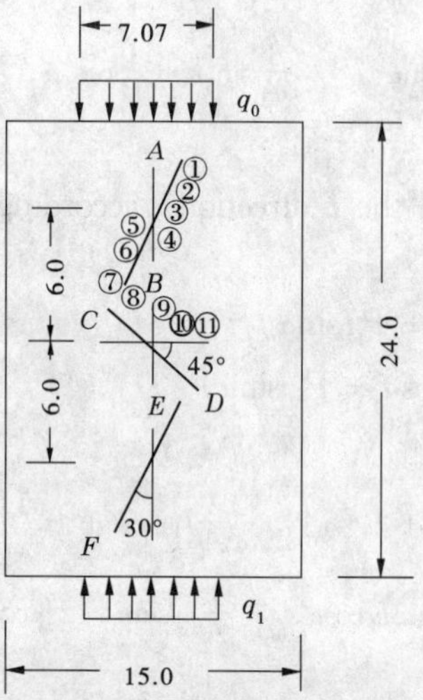

Fig. 5 The computed example and concrete specimen size

The actual compression strength of the concrete material $R_{28} = 124.7$kg/cm^2, $E = 1.942 \times 10^5$kg/cm^2, $\mu = 0.171$, the crack length is $2a = 6$cm. The same numerical model was used for calculating the mixed mode crack problem by the method discribed in present paper. The results of experimental and analytic-numerical method are given in Table 1. In spite of the heterogeneous character of concrete specimen(the maximm. size of gravel is less than 1 cm), the stable values of measurement were obtained, the stresses (strains) obtained from the both experimental and numerical are in good agreement. Increased again the load to maximum capacity of the specimen, the observation of the failure phenomena showed there is a similarity in the expanding order of the cracks for both pressure-sheared crack and Griffith crack (uncontacted crack surface) having the same primary direction with compression field. The ultimate bearing capacity of the presure-sheared crack is higher than that of Griffith crack about 17.4% (from 58.9kg/cm^2 goes up to 69.2kg/cm^2).

4 Discussions

The analytic-numerical solution based on the concept of "the released stress" is more effective to solve the multiple-crack problem when the interaction between the cracks, interaction between the crack and boundary is considered. The released stress at the every point of Griffith (tensionsheared) crack always equals to the fictitious forces on the crack faces. Since the relationship of $\tau - \delta_t$ for the different σ_n is curved, the mechanical character of the pressure-sheared crack is non-linear in essence. At the point of the compression-sheared crack, the final real existed stresses in cracks not only satisfy the mechanical equilibrium condition (Mohr-Columb principle), but also satisfy consistent condition with stress and deformation (th non-linear relationship between force and displacement, etc.) The released coefficent of the compression-sheared crack is always less than 1.0.

For the structure of complicate boundaries with both the press-sheared cracks and Griffith's cracks, the proposed method in this paper can be used for the stress, displacement field and SIF studies, which make very much reduction in computer time with necessary engineering precision.

Table 1 The Comparison between stresses by eletric determination and by computer calculation

Point	Position	Electric determination value(loading 1－3)			Computer calculation value (loading 1－3)		
		σ_t	σ_n	τ_{nt}	σ_t	σ_n	τ_{nt}
2	Left	－20.71	－8.54	－15.87	－20.05	－8.38	－15.39
	Right	－20.03	－7.49	－15.03			
4	Left	－18.31	－4.12	－14.41	－18.50	－3.78	－13.73
	Right	－18.80	－3.49	－1.53			
6	Left	－18.01	－1.93	－11.73	－17.83	－1.67	－11.44
	Right	－18.20	－1.65	－11.50			
9	Left	－9.05	－8.84	－12.44	－8.22	－8.74	－13.32
	Right	－8.38	－10.40	12.42			
11	Left	－8.95	－8.77	－12.31	－8.96	－9.20	－12.61
	Right	－8.95	－8.83	－12.38			

References

[1] Guanting Liu, Ruizhong Zhou. *The strength of finite body with multiple cracks*. Int. Con. on Fracture and Damage, Vinna, Austria, July 4－6, 1988

[2] V. V. Panasyak etc., *Engineering Fracture*. Mech. Vol. 9, 1977, pp. 481～497

[3] Yizhou Chen. *Engineering Fracture*. Mech. Vol. 20, No. 4(1984)

[4] Ruizhong Zhou, Guangting Liu. *The synthetic deformation modulus and the synthetic poisson's ratio of a multiple crack bodies*. Int. Confer., Vienng, Austria, July 4－6, 1988

[5] F. A. McClintock, J. B. Walsh. *Proceedings of 4th U. S. N. C of applied mech*. Vol. 2, 1962, pp. 1015～1021.

混凝土、砂浆早期温度断裂韧性实验研究

摘　要　用直接加温度应力的含裂缝圆环试件,对混凝土、砂浆早期温度断裂韧性进行了实验研究。根据实验测得的裂缝扩展时的温度边界条件,结合边界元数值计算,可获得混凝土、砂浆的温度断裂韧性。提出了应变强度因子的概念。实验结果给出了砂浆的 K_{IC} 以及混凝土不同龄期的应力 K_{IC} 及应变 K^{ε}_{IC}。实验表明,作者提出的应变强度因子及应变断裂韧性的概念对反映混凝土材料的断裂特性更稳定更具实际意义。研制了混凝土温度断裂研究专用的温度加载及自动采集、控制系统,编写了专用软件。

关键词　温度断裂韧性　混凝土　砂浆　应变强度因子　应变断裂韧性

大体积混凝土结构内部出现宏观裂缝,一直都是影响水工建筑物质量和安全的重要问题,20 世纪 60 年代初混凝土裂缝曾引起我国大部分大型混凝土坝停工处理。"七·五"期间曾进行攻关,在裂缝防治方面取得了一些进展,但对混凝土裂缝的出现、扩展等定量研究尚有待进一步努力。工程统计表明,混凝土宏观裂缝中绝大部分是由温度引起的。因此,混凝土温度断裂的研究是水工混凝土建筑物强度问题的重要研究课题。近年来,国内外在温度应力及温度断裂理论和数值计算方面做了一些工作[1,2],但在混凝土温度断裂韧性实验方面研究很少。国外仅见到少数几篇研究混凝土低温断裂特性的文章[3,4],研究表明,混凝土在低温下的断裂韧性和强度与常温下结果有明显的差异。国内尚未见到这方面的成果发表。本实验采用圆环直接加温度荷载方法可准确提供温度场和约束条件(温度应力),用实验和虚拟力边界元数值计算相结合的杂交法获得砂浆、混凝土早期和后期的温度断裂韧性。

1　实验方法

1.1　实验方案

混凝土温度断裂实际包括两部分内容:一是引起混凝土结构破坏的温度应力场;二是环境温度对混凝土材料强度的影响,即对混凝土断裂韧性的影响。因此,对混凝土温度断裂韧性的研究也可有两种不同的方案:

(1)实验将温度应力用外荷载代替,而温度只作为一种环境条件,它对混凝土断裂韧性的影响则通过在不同环境温度下加外载荷测定。但外载荷作用下混凝土的断裂韧性是否与温度应力引起的断裂真正等效,是未搞清的问题。根据文献[5],混凝土在外载荷作用下发生破坏时在断裂部位出现非均匀温度场。因此,这一非均匀温度场将会产生温度应力,使得原应力场发生变化,它对温度断裂韧性影响多大尚不清楚。

(2)直接在温度应力作用下研究混凝土断裂特性。这样既包括了温度应力因素对断裂韧性的影响,又包括了环境温度因素的影响。本文采用了这种方案。

本文选自《清华大学学报(自然科学版)》1996 年第 1 期,作者还有薛慧、陈凤岐、张国新。

1.2 试件

试件形状为圆环,温度应力通过在圆环内外边界加不同温度产生。试件有两种形式:外热内冷和外冷内热。预制裂缝开在冷边(如图 1)。对砂浆试件考虑到加热、制冷的条件限制(功率),取外径 $D_1 = 200$mm,在此基础上对试件的内径及裂缝长度通过数值计算进行了正交优化设计。最终选定内径 $D_0 = 60$mm,缝长 $a = 9$mm。对混凝土试件,考虑到 20mm 的集料,取试件尺寸 $D_1 = 300$mm,$D_0 = 80$mm。裂缝长取为 20mm。裂缝采用成型时预埋薄刀片的方法获得。

砂浆试件配比　　　　水泥:砂:水为 1:3:0.56(水泥 325#)

混凝土试件配比　　　水泥:砂:石:水为 1:1.87:3.36:0.57

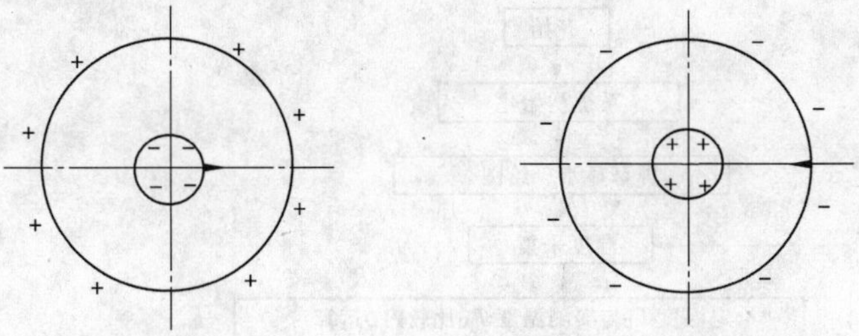

(a)砂浆内裂缝试件　　　　(b)砂浆、混凝土外裂缝试件

图 1　两种类型试件

1.3 试件的加热、制冷

实验中使用两种加热制冷装置:

(1)对外边界加热、内边界制冷的内裂缝试件。加热器用电阻丝绕成,加热温度的高低通过调节加在加热器两端的电压实现。调节是在系统自动控制下完成的。制冷采用半导体制冷堆实现。制冷温度也由系统自动控制。实验表明,使用的半导体制冷堆功率应加大,才能有利于控制效果并防止沿铜柱轴线方向上的温度变化。

(2)对内边界加热、外边界冷却的外裂缝试件。加热同样使用电阻丝加热器,系统自动控制。冷却采用自来水自然冷却。虽然冷却不能自动调节,但实验表明在不长的实验时间内冷却温度很稳定,效果不错。实验中多采用内边界加热装置。

为了模拟试件轴向两端面的绝热条件,以上两种试件形式均采用了同场保温技术,即在试件上、下两面各加温度场和试件相近的保温板。

2 混凝土温度断裂实验自动采集、控制系统

2.1 实验装置

混凝土温度断裂实验自动采集、控制系统的原理图见图 2。该实验系统硬件分为 5 部分,即 PC 电脑、采集子系统、控制子系统、试件以及终端,共同组成一个稳定的闭环自动控制系统。

2.2 软件

软件分两部分,一是用编译 BASIC 编制的主体程序,二是用汇编语言编写的应用子程序。软件框图见图 3。

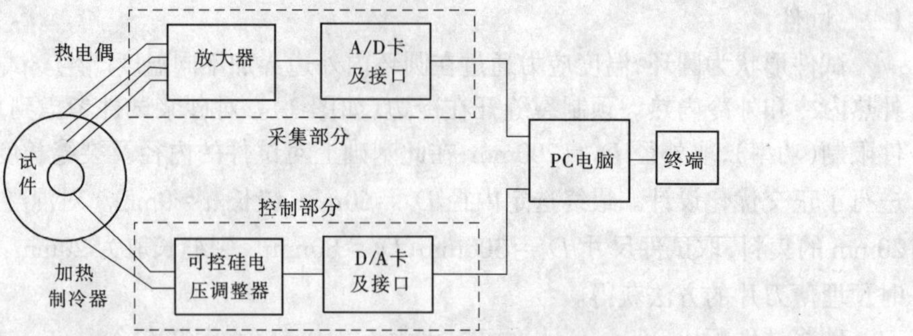

图2　混凝土温度断裂实验自动采集、控制系统原理图

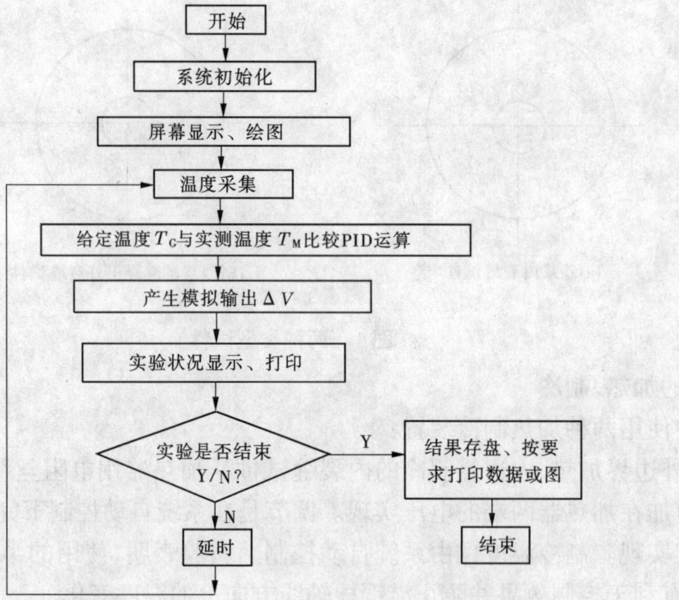

图3　软件框图

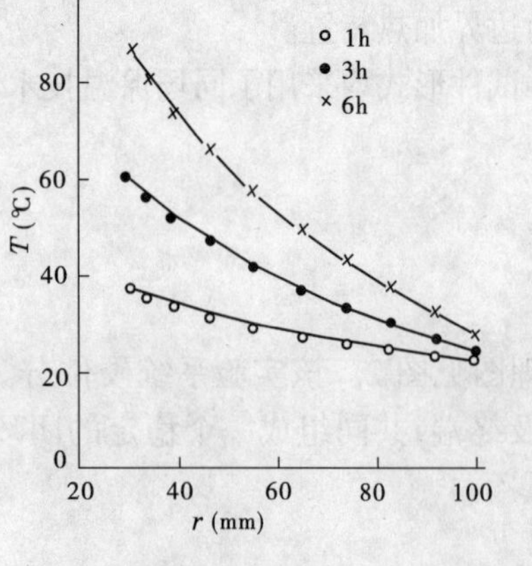

图4　温度场沿试件径向分布实测和计算比较

3　实验结果及讨论

3.1　应力强度因子与应变强度因子

实验过程中冷却边界温度保持不变，加热温度逐渐升高。在两边温差小于30℃以前，每小时约升高10℃(可改变)；在温差大于30℃以后每小时升高6℃左右(可改变)。在如此缓慢的温度变化下，可近似认为试件处于稳定温度场。图4为试件在不同时刻实测的温度场分布与根据边界温度算出的理论温度分布规律，两者吻合良好，特别是温升速率越小两者越接近。

温度应力实验难以直接测得应力分布及应力

强度因子，本研究采用混合法。将实测的裂缝扩展时的圆环温度边界条件和相应的裂缝长度代入以下的解析表达式中，用边界元数值解算出 K_{I} 值，即为试件的 K_{IC}。由文献[6]知，用奇异积分方程解出虚拟力，进而给出应力和位移的边界积分方程为

$$\begin{cases}\sigma_n^e(P_0)-i\sigma_t^e(P_0)+\sigma_n^T(P_0)-i\sigma_t^T(P_0)+\sigma_n^c(P_0)-i\sigma_t^c(P_0)=\overline{N}(P_0)-\overline{iT}(P_0)\\ U^e(Q_0)+iV^e(Q_0)+U^T(Q_0)+iV^T(Q_0)+U^c(Q_0)+iV^c(Q_0)=\overline{U}(Q_0)+\overline{iV}(Q_0)\\ \sigma_{yk}^e(C_0)-i\tau_{xyk}^e(C_0)+\sigma_{yk}^T(C_0)-i\tau_{xyk}^T(C_0)+\sigma_{yk}^c(C_0)-i\tau_{xyk}^c(C_0)=0\end{cases}$$

式中：上标 e、T、c 为由虚拟边界力、温度荷载及裂面虚拟力引起的应力和位移；下标 n、t 为法向和切向；x、y 分别为裂缝面的切向和法向；k 为第 k 条裂缝；P_0、Q_0 为边界 S_1、S_2 上的点；C_0 为裂缝面的点。各缝端应力强度因子为

$$K_{\mathrm{I}}^n-iK_{\mathrm{II}}^n=-\frac{1}{\sqrt{\pi a_n}}\int_{-a_n}^{a_n}[F_y(S_n)-iF_x(S_n)]\sqrt{\frac{a_n\pm S_n}{a_n\mp S_n}}\mathrm{d}S_n$$

根据线弹性断裂力学，在裂缝尖端附近（$r\ll a$）应力、应变场分量 σ_y、ε_y，近似为

$$\sigma_y=\frac{K_{\mathrm{I}}}{\sqrt{2\pi r}}\cos\frac{\theta}{2}\left[1+\sin\frac{\theta}{2}\sin\frac{3\theta}{2}\right]$$

$$\varepsilon_y=\frac{1-\nu'}{2G(1+\nu')}\cdot\frac{K_{\mathrm{I}}}{\sqrt{2\pi r}}\cos\frac{\theta}{2}\left[1+\frac{1+\nu'}{1-\nu'}\sin\frac{\theta}{2}\sin\frac{3\theta}{2}\right]$$

可见应力、应变都具有 $r^{1/2}$ 的奇异性，若令 $K_{\mathrm{I}}^{\varepsilon}=[(1-\nu')/2G(1+\nu')]\cdot K_{\mathrm{I}}$，考虑应力、应变沿裂缝方向（$\theta=0$）的变化：

$$\sigma_y=K_{\mathrm{I}}/\sqrt{2\pi r}\qquad\qquad \varepsilon_y=K_{\mathrm{I}}^{\varepsilon}/\sqrt{2\pi r}$$

比较两式，不妨将 $K_{\mathrm{I}}^{\varepsilon}$ 叫做应变强度因子，它是反映应变分量 ε_y 的 $r^{1/2}$ 奇异性的常数。对于平面应力状态 $K_{\mathrm{I}}^{\varepsilon}=[(1-\nu')/E]\cdot K_{\mathrm{I}}$，其中 E、ν' 为材料的弹性模量和泊松比。

3.2 结果讨论

要想得到温度对混凝土、砂浆断裂韧性的影响规律，需做大量的实验研究。本文做了初步的工作，目的是探索出一种解决混凝土、砂浆温度断裂的实验方法和技术，为以后的研究打下基础。本文测定了砂浆 8d 龄期的 K_{IC}，一级配混凝土 8d 和 28d 龄期的 K_{IC}。

砂浆、混凝土试件的实验数据及计算结果（包括裂缝开裂过程中不同缝长时的结果）见表 1、表 2，砂浆、混凝土试件的断裂韧性 K_{IC}、$K_{\mathrm{IC}}^{\varepsilon}$ 与缝端温度的关系见图 5、图 6。由表 1、表 2 可见：

(1)饱和（湿）砂浆 K_{IC} 远大于干燥试件的 K_{IC}。

(2)低强混凝土试件 8d 龄期（$E=7.96$GPa，$a=7.10$）$K_{\mathrm{IC}}=147.8\sim236.5\mathrm{kN/m^{3/2}}$，$K_{\mathrm{IC}}^{\varepsilon}=13.92\times10^{-6}\sim22.27\times10^{-6}\mathrm{m^{1/2}}$；28d 龄期（$E=18.73$GPa，$a=7.10mm$）$K_{\mathrm{IC}}=321.0\sim485.3\mathrm{kN/m^{3/2}}$，$K_{\mathrm{IC}}^{\varepsilon}=12.85\times10^{-6}\sim19.43\times10^{-6}\mathrm{m^{1/2}}$。

(3)缝端温度对 K_{IC} 的影响在常温（20～60℃）下不明显。对砂浆试件缝端在 30℃ 附近的 K_{IC} 比在 45～60℃ 之间的 K_{IC} 略低。

(4)混凝土实验 8d 与 28d 结果比较，（应力）断裂韧性 $K_{\mathrm{IC}}^{28}>K_{\mathrm{IC}}^{8}$。但在断裂时内外边界的温差无太大差别，也即 8d 与 28d 龄期的应变断裂韧性 $K_{\mathrm{IC}}^{\varepsilon}$ 基本相同。可见混凝

土材料随龄期的增加其强度或承载能力(极限应力或 K_{IC})增加是由于其弹模增加所致，其极限应变或应变断裂韧性并未发生明显变化。对于温度断裂这种破坏形式,混凝土材料或结构不会因为龄期的增大而提高其承受温度变形的能力。

(5)提出的实验方法对研究混凝土(砂浆)温度断裂韧性是可行的。研制的专用温度加载,自动采集、控制系统为实验提供了保证。

表1　砂浆试件前期温度 K_{IC}

实验参数	实验号									
	1	2		3	4				5	6
内环温度 T(℃)	14.0	73.9	80.1	74.2	80.1	85.4	86.8	88.4	81.6	88.0	78.0
外环温度 T(℃)	95.0	25.5	27.4	22.9	27.2	27.8	28.2	28.6	24.5	27.2	21.1
a(mm)	7.0	10	49	10	10	29	39	45	10	44	10
K_{IC}(kN/$m^{\frac{3}{2}}$)	273.4	100.9	108.8	108.8	110.7	167.6	161.7	146.0	121.5	153.9	122.5
备　注	内裂缝饱和面干	外裂缝干燥									

表2　混凝土试件不同龄期的温度 K_{IC}和 K^{ε}_{IC}

参　数	实验号											
	C8－1[#]		C8－2[#]		C8－3[#]		C8－4[#]		C28－1[#]		C28－2[#]	
外环温度 T(℃)	19.7	20.6	20.4	20.6	21.7	22.3	22.3	21.5	22.6	24.1	19.8	20.3
内环温度 T(℃)	63.8	69.1	56.9	66.6	60.7	64.3	56.5	63.1	61.4	63.7	48.9	53.3
a(mm)	25	43	49	76	40	56	32	47	65	75	42	46
K_{IC}(kN/$m^{\frac{3}{2}}$)	175.4	236.5	179.5	197.1	183.9	208.0	147.8	204.4	430.5	390.4	321.0	373.9
K^{ε}_{IC}($10^{-6}m^{\frac{1}{2}}$)	16.52	22.27	16.90	18.56	17.32	19.59	13.92	19.25	17.24	15.63	12.85	14.47

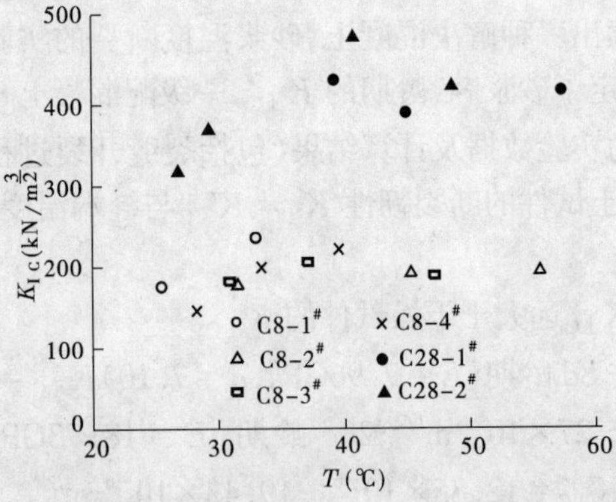

图5　混凝土不同龄期 K_{IC}(应力)与缝端温度的关系

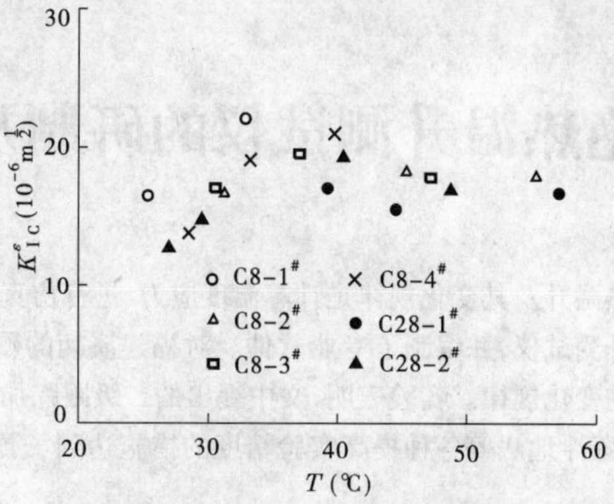

图 6　混凝土不同龄期应变断裂韧性 K^{ε}_{IC} 与缝端温度的关系

参 考 文 献

[1] Liu Guangting, Zhang Guoxin. *Study on steady-thermal fracture with different conductive material filled in crack*. Proc Int Conf on Fracture of Concrete and Rock, 1989,737～746

[2] Kang Yong Lee. *Determination of thermal stress intensity factors for traction free cusp cracks under uniform heat flow*. Engineering Fracture Mechanics, 1988, 31(4):661～672

[3] Elices M. *Cryogenic prestressed concrete*: *Fracture aspects*. Theoretical and Applied Fracture Mechanics, 1987,7:51～63

[4] Ohlsson U, Daerga P. *Fracture energy and fatige strength of unreinforced concrete beams at normal and low temperatures*. Proc Int Conf on Fracture and Damage of Concrete and Rock,1988

[5] Luong M M. *Infrared thermography of fracture concrete and rock*. SEM/RILEM International Conference on Fracture of Concrete and Rock, Houston Texas, June,1987,343～353

[6] Liu Guangting, Zhang Guoxin. *The analytic-numerical solution for thermal crack problems and crack prevention of RCAD*. Dam Fracture Proceedings from the International Conference, September 11～13, 1991,Boulder, Colorado, USA,1991,605～622

混凝土绝热温升测试仪的研制及其应用

摘　要　混凝土的绝热温升及其变化规律是计算温度应力、进行仿真计算的重要参数。研制了一套混凝土绝热温升测试仪,并编制了专业软件。对福建溪柄的碾压混凝土做了测试,给出了绝热温升随时间的变化规律。实验表明,文中提出的二级跟踪加热法以及采用的模拟滤波、数字滤波和双层屏蔽浮地法等各种提高实验精度的措施达到了预期目的。软件功能强,使用方便。

关键词　碾压混凝土　绝热温升　数值仿真　碾压混凝土薄拱坝

1　测试原理及装置

混凝土的绝热温升是指在绝热条件下,由于水泥水化热所生热量使混凝土升高的温度。所谓绝热条件是指在整个实验过程中混凝土试件不与外界发生热交换。由于水泥的水化过程进行得很缓慢,因此本实验所花时间长,一般至少需 28d。本实验装置的主要技术难题也就是在这么长的时间里如何实现绝热条件。这对系统的温度测试、温度控制精度以及系统的抗干扰能力和稳定性都有很高的要求。研制者从软、硬件两方面都采取了一些措施,达到了预期目的。

图 1 为装置原理图。主要有两大部分,即绝热箱和仪器柜。绝热箱由大保温箱、模具筒及两级跟踪加热器组成。测温系统(热电偶、放大器及采集卡)同时测取试件中心温度、边界温度及两级加热器温度,根据试件边界与中心的温度差,通过温度控制部分调节加热器电压,使边界温度与中心温度始终保持一致,从而达到绝热的目的。

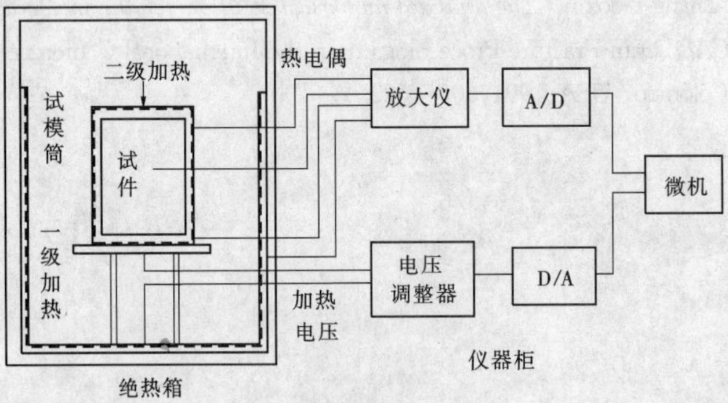

图 1　装置原理图

为了提高边界温度跟踪的质量,采用二级加热跟踪法。一级加热器做在大保温箱内壁,为克服外界气温变化的影响,使大保温箱内的温度与试件温度基本保持一致。但由于空气的导热性能较差,时间滞后大,试件边界温度很难迅速、准确地跟踪内部温度,为此又

本文选自《清华大学学报(自然科学版)》1996 年第 1 期,作者还有薛慧、陈凤岐。

增加了第二级加热跟踪器,它由电阻丝和电阻带绕成,表面包一层 0.2mm 厚的铜箔,直接裹在试模的外边界。这样跟踪系统的时间滞后就可以很小。在计算机控制下试件边界温度就能迅速、准确地跟踪内部温度。目前国内所了解的绝热温升仪都为一级加热跟踪[1]。

2 提高实验精度的措施

如前所述,混凝土的绝热温升变化缓慢,实验持续时间长。要保持绝热条件,对仪器的测试精度、稳定性及可靠性要求很高。在系统的各部分仪器指标一定的情况下,笔者在软、硬件两方面均采取了一些提高测试精度及可靠性的措施。

2.1 过程通道的抗干扰措施

在微机控制系统的现场或附近,往往有许多强电设备,它们的启动和工作过程将对测控系统产生强烈的干扰。例如,大功率马达和其他电气设备产生的磁场,高压电气设备产生的电场以及各种电磁波辐射等。实验中所用热电偶产生的被测信号在放大前是微弱的。如果不采取抗干扰措施,实验将无法正常进行。

按干扰的作用方式不同,可分为串模和共模干扰两种。

串模干扰是指叠加在被测信号上的干扰噪声。在本实验中,由于温度变化很缓慢,串模干扰相对被测信号为高频噪声干扰。因此,在电路中加入了π型滤波网络,有效地消除了高频干扰,见图 2。改变不同的阻容值,可改变滤波电路的通过频率。但对于低频的干扰,需增加时间常数,也即增大阻容值,这会使漏电电流增大,且对系统的阻抗匹配带来问题。为此,作者在软件中增加了数字滤波法。由于它无硬件设备,故具有稳定可靠、参数灵活可调,不存在阻抗匹配问题等优点。数字滤波法有多种,各有特点。针对本实验选择了算术平均值法。其表达式为

$$Y = \frac{1}{N}\sum_{k=1}^{N} X_k \qquad (1)$$

算术平均法对信号的平滑程度取决于 N。本实验 N 为 200。

共模干扰是指模/数转换器两个输入端上共有的干扰电压。通常被测信号与 A/D 转换器存在一定的距离,因此在被测信号 U_s 的参考接地点和 A/D 转换器的参考接地点之间存在一定的电压差 U_{cm},这就是共模干扰电压。在单端对地输入时共模干扰完全转化为串模干扰。在双端对地输入时,如果阻抗不匹配也会转化成相应的串模干扰。共模干扰可以是交流或直流,因此即使转化成串模干扰,上述滤波法也不能将其影响去掉。实验中采用了浮地输入双层屏蔽法(见图 3),同时采用公共接地点将各仪器的参考地接在一起,提高了抗共模干扰的能力。

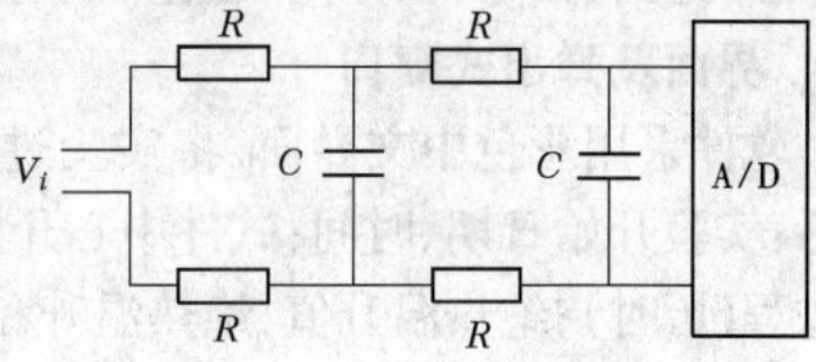

图 2 π 型滤波网络

2.2 热电偶的 $T \sim V$ 曲线

热电偶是常见的测温传感元件,但其热电势与温度呈弱非线性关系。对于本实验的低温测试范围,选用铜和康铜热电偶。实验前进行了率定。本实验不是对热电偶的温度——热电势进行率定,而是直接率定温度与经放大器放大后 A/D 转换器采集到的电压

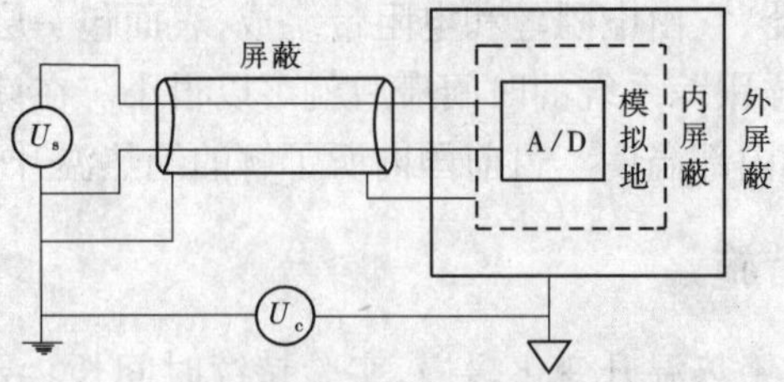

图3 浮地输入双层屏蔽法

关系,然后用最小二乘法进行非线性拟合,分别给出各通道不同参数的拟合公式。这样既考虑了热电偶本身的非线性,同时又克服了放大器的非线性误差及各通道放大倍数不同的影响。$T \sim V$ 曲线的实测值与拟和曲线吻合良好。

2.3 多通道超差剔除平均法

由于实验时间长,对系统的精度和可靠性要求高,因此实验中的各个数据(如试件中心温度、二级加热器的温度)均采用多通道测试。如,试件中心温度利用7个热电偶共同测得。对于多通道测量值用超差剔除平均法进行处理,如果多通道中的最大值与最小值之差小于某一给定值(实验中为0.3℃),则所有通道取平均,否则剔除最大值与最小值,其余通道取平均。这样就减小了系统的随机误差和个别通道出现意外故障所造成的不良影响。

3 软件简介

3.1 实验流程

软件用 Quick BASIC 和汇编语言混合编程,见图4,经编译联接后形成可执行软件。可运行于配有 VGA 显示卡的任何 286 以上的 PC－AT 机。它采用中文图形界面,使用方便。系统每隔 10s 进行一次采集、控制循环,直到实验结束。实验中温度控制部分采用 PID 法(比例、微分、积分)。通过合理选择各控制参数,使系统控制精度满足实验要求。

3.2 界面及弹出式窗口

软件采用彩色中文界面,将实验过程中的多种信息用中文和图形的方式显示出来。包括:实验开始日期、时间;试件中心开始温度;试件中心当前温度;试件边界当前温度;实验进程(历时);绝热温升值;绝热温升和时间曲线;部分热键功能说明。另外,还可通过特定热键打开(关闭)弹出式窗口,显示各个通道热电偶的测定值和控制输出等信息,以便随时发现实验中的异常现象。

3.3 热键

实验过程中常需要进行短暂的人机对话而又不中断实验进程。为了增加实验的灵活性,本软件增加了热键功能。主要热键有:F1 为打开/关闭数据窗口;F2 为输入基准温度(冰筒温度);F3 为显示/关闭控制输出等;F10 为将实验中的结果文件随时拷贝到软盘,以便对正在进行中的实验结果加以处理;F11 为拷贝硬盘中的任意文件到软盘;Print Screen 为硬拷贝屏幕;ESC 为结束实验。

3.4 其他

实验中采用不同的方式进行记录,有屏幕显示、打印机输出和硬盘存储。另外还有重

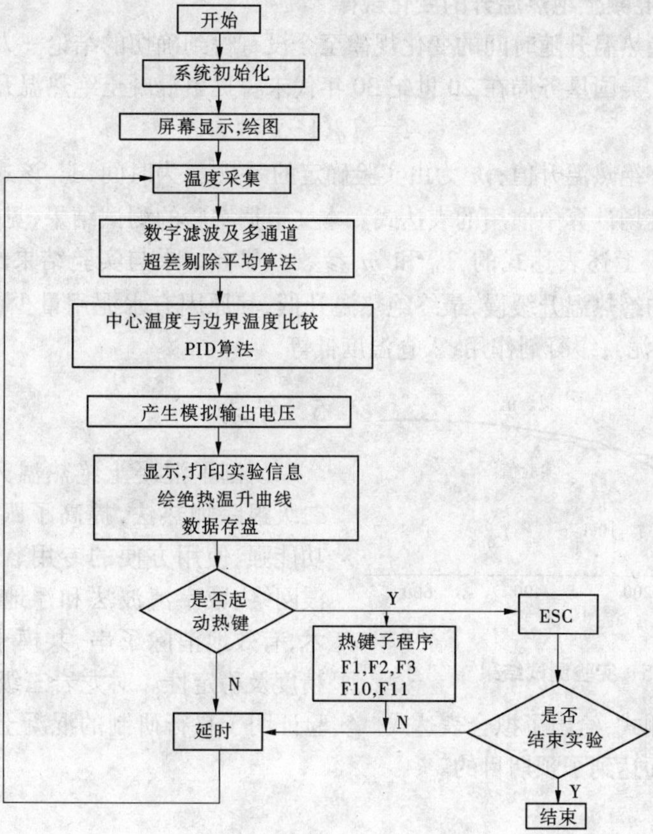

图4 软件框图

启动功能。如果发生意外情况(如突然断电等)使程序中断,则用软件再启动功能可将原数据调入内存继续进行实验。

4 福建龙岩三级配碾压混凝土绝热温升实验研究

4.1 实验过程

龙岩三级配碾压混凝土的配合比如下(kg/m^3):

水	水泥	粉煤灰	砂	小石	中石	大石	木钙(固)
93.75	75	112.5	705	600	600	300	0.469

碾压混凝土拌和后,立即装入容器,分三层用振动台振实,同时用砝码捣实。注意在成型过程中的混凝土内部测温部位放入热电偶;两级跟踪加热器的测温热电偶已预先贴在相应位置。混凝土装入量离试模口 2cm 为宜。密封成型后立即放入绝热室内,开机实验,进行跟踪控制。为了使混凝土试件各部位的温度均匀以及使试件温度与试模温度保持一致,选取实验开始后 0.5h 的中心温度为混凝土试件的初始温度。实验中混凝土的初始温度为 16.45℃,共进行了 28d。

4.2 龙岩碾压混凝土绝热温升的变化规律

混凝土的绝热温升随时间的变化规律至今没有得到确切的结论。人们曾提出过不同形式的表达式。美国垦务局在20世纪30年代末曾提出混凝土绝热温升—历时表达式为

$$T = T_0(1 - e^{-mt}) \tag{2}$$

式中：T_0 为最终绝热温升值；m 为由实验确定的系数；t 为时间，d。该式已成为各国在大体积混凝土温度场计算中惯用的表达式。本文根据实验的测试结果（见图5）用非线性最小二乘法给出了上述表达式的 T_0 和 m 参数。拟合结果与实验结果比较，两者吻合较好。本实验中的绝热温升缓慢，最终绝热温升低，其原因有水泥用量少、水泥为低标号水泥（425# 普通水泥）；缓凝剂作用；入仓温度低等。

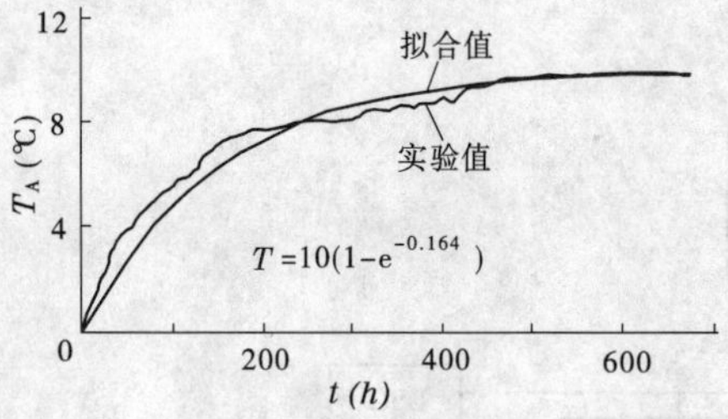

图5 实验测试结果

5 结语

研制了混凝土绝热温升测试仪，提出了二级跟踪加热法，提高了跟踪精度。编制了功能强、使用方便的专用软件。采用π型滤波网络、数字滤波法和浮地输入双层屏蔽技术，有效地消除了串、共模干扰，提高了测试精度及稳定性。对龙岩三级配碾压混凝土的绝热温升做了测式，给出了拟合表达式。实验证明了自行研制的混凝土绝热温升测试仪在工程应用方面达到了预期目的。

参 考 文 献

[1] 姜福田．碾压混凝土．北京：中国铁道出版社，1991
[2] 水工混凝土试验规程．SD105—82．北京：水利电力出版社，1983
[3] 谢剑英．微型计算机控制系统．北京：国际工业出版社，1985

碾压混凝土拱坝坝体应力的简化计算

摘　要　碾压混凝土坝受施工条件影响常在混凝土碾压层间出现结合面夹层(缺陷),影响坝体变形及内应力分布。混凝土夹层强度较低,形成结构破坏控制面。为了了解层状体的内应力分布,用位移等效原则把层状体结构转换为横观各向同性体进行位移和应力计算,根据计算的宏观位移场再进一步进行局部夹层应力计算,由此得到精度高、方法简单、工作量大大减少的碾压混凝土(成层)结构应力简化计算方法。研究还发现,碾压混凝土结构(成层材料)存在边界局部应力集中效应,需另行采取结构改进措施。

关键词　碾压混凝土坝　成层结构　有限元法

在碾压混凝土坝中,由于施工期条件变化,混凝土碾压层与层之间的结合缺陷至今难以消除。由于层间软弱带的存在,使得结构易于在层间发生破坏。只有了解含水平缺陷坝体结构的真实应力状态以及碾压混凝土材料(特别是层间结合部位)真实的强度特性,才能建立合理的坝体结构设计标准。

层状结构的数值分析可以用有限元方法把结构按层划分成许多本体和夹层单元来进行。我国碾压混凝土坝的层状体厚度常为20～40cm。当进行尤其是三维坝体结构分析时,为得到可用的结果,需按层采用大量的单元,实际上由于工作量太大而难以实现。本文研究采用等效单元,即把层状体结构按照位移等效原则变换成一个均质体,通过对该均质体进行分析,可以了解层状体结构的宏观结构变形,根据这一变形再具体计算层状体结构各部位的真实应力状态。可减少计算工作量,便于工程应用。

1　碾压混凝土含水平层缺陷结构的应力分析方法

首先把碾压混凝土层状体结构简化为两部分,一部分是碾压混凝土本体,另一部分是层间软弱体。这两部分介质均假定是各向同性弹性体。在应用等效模量理论时,本文采用单元角点位移作为等效宗量来建立等效原则,即在单元角点处,层状体的位移值与均质横向各向同性体的位移值相等。对实际碾压混凝土芯的观察表明,层间软弱带的厚度不断变化,一般为0.5～2.0cm。当层间胶结较好时,软弱带厚度就较小,反之就较大。实际结构中层间软弱带与混凝土本体的界限是不明确的,但借助试验结果可以建立实际结构与简化层状体结构的联系。

例如,对国内某工程碾压混凝土的变形特性曾进行过试验。对高14cm的混凝土芯测定其弹性模量,发现当混凝土芯不包括层间软弱带时,$E = 32\text{GPa}$,而包括层间软弱带时,$E = 20\text{GPa}$。根据这一试验结果,就可以建立简化层状体结构,对这一结构的软弱带厚度及其与弹性模量的关系进行估算。

设碾压混凝土本体的弹性模量和泊松比分别为 E_b、μ_b,相应的层间软弱带的弹性参

本文选自《清华大学学报(自然科学版)》1996年第1期,作者还有郝巨涛。

数为 E_j、μ_j，软弱带厚度为 h_j，根据等效原则以及上述工程试验结果就可以算出 E_j（考虑到两种相近材料泊松比的变化较小，可采用 $\mu_j = \mu_b$）。再通过进一步的等效计算就可以确定横观各向同性体的 5 个弹性参数，横观各向同性体的物理方程如下

$$\boldsymbol{\varepsilon} = \boldsymbol{D}^{-1}\boldsymbol{\sigma} \tag{1}$$

$$\boldsymbol{\varepsilon} = (\varepsilon_{11}, \varepsilon_{22}, \varepsilon_{33}, \gamma_{11}, \gamma_{23}, \gamma_{31})^{T}$$

$$\boldsymbol{\sigma} = (\sigma_{11}, \sigma_{22}, \sigma_{33}, \tau_{12}, \tau_{23}, \tau_{31})^{T}$$

$$D^{-1} = \begin{bmatrix} \frac{1}{E_1} & -\frac{\mu_1}{E_1} & -\frac{\mu_3}{E_3} & 0 & 0 & 0 \\ -\frac{\mu_1}{E_1} & \frac{1}{E_1} & -\frac{\mu_3}{E_3} & 0 & 0 & 0 \\ -\frac{\mu_3}{E_3} & -\frac{\mu_3}{E_3} & \frac{1}{E_3} & 0 & 0 & 0 \\ 0 & 0 & 0 & \frac{2(1+\mu_1)}{E_1} & 0 & 0 \\ 0 & 0 & 0 & 0 & \frac{1}{G_3} & 0 \\ 0 & 0 & 0 & 0 & 0 & \frac{1}{G_3} \end{bmatrix} \tag{2}$$

式中：下角$_3$对应于纵向（即垂直于层面的方向），下角$_{1、2}$对应于横向（层面内任意两个相互垂直的方向）；E_1、μ_1 为横向弹性模量和泊松比；E_3、μ_3 为纵向弹性模量和泊松比；G_3 为纵横剪切模量。

为了解不同的 h_j 对最终得到的上面5个弹性参数的影响，所用计算模型为高1.5m的层状体，各层的厚度均为0.3m。计算分两步：第一步根据前述的工程试验资料，针对不同的 h_j 计算 E_j（假定 $\mu_j = \mu_b$），计算参数为：$E_b = 32\text{GPa}$，$h = h_b + h_j = 14\text{cm}$，$\mu_b = \mu_j = 0.2$，综合模量 $E_h = 20\text{GPa}$；第二步根据各组的 h_j、E_j、μ_j 以及 h_b、E_b、μ_b，按等效原则计算 5 个弹性参数。这里的计算均按有限元法进行，单元按层划分。

为确定不同的参数而采用的计算模型有 3 种（见图 1），计算结果见表 1。

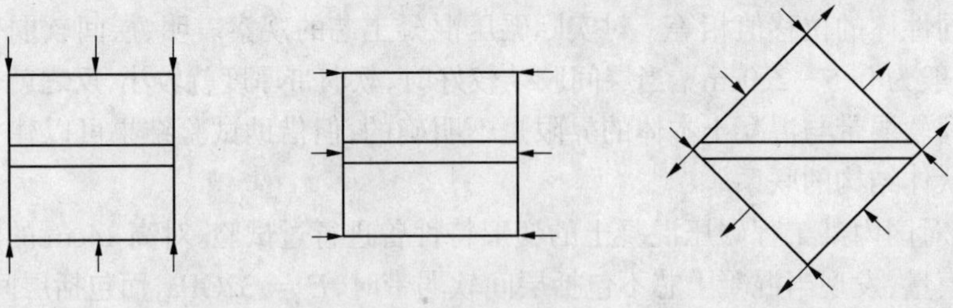

图 1　有限元计算模型

从表 1 可看出，尽管 h_j 对 E_j 的影响很大，但 h_j 与 E_j 的综合作用对 E_1、E_3、μ_1、μ_2 的影响很小。按图 1 中的第三种计算模型得到的 G_3 也有类似结果，即当 $v_j = 0.12$ 时，$G_3 = 10.9\text{GPa}$；当 $v_j = 0.033$ 时，$G_3 = 12.2\text{GPa}$。因此，在确定横观各向同性体的弹性参数时，

可以在一定范围内(比如 $h_j = 0.5 \sim 2.0$cm)选用,h_j 对结果影响不大。用 Aboudi[1] 公式预测弹性参数也可得到相近的结果。

表 1 不同夹层方案的横观各向同性体弹性参数

h_j(cm)	v_j	E_j(GPa)	E_1(GPa)	E_3(GPa)	μ_1	μ_3
2.0	8/150	5.75	31.6	26.2	0.2	0.163
1.0	4/150	3.22	31.8	26.3	0.2	0.164
0.5	2/150	1.72	31.9	26.4	0.2	0.165

注:v_j 为软弱夹层所占的体积比。

2 碾压混凝土坝的等效应力分析

2.1 坝体的宏观位移的计算

国内某碾压混凝土单曲拱坝,坝高 45.5m,最大底宽 13m,坝体碾压混凝土层厚 30cm,间歇层厚 1.5~1.8cm。在有限元计算中,除在周边由于布置方便的考虑而采用了数量不多的 15 结点三棱柱单元外,余者均用 20 结点 6 面体单元对坝体进行离散。坝体单元 380 个,基础 372 个。坝体单元高度一般为 6m。

由工程提供的坝体混凝土弹性模量 $E = 34$GPa,泊松比 $\mu = 0.17$,容重 $\gamma = 2.4\text{t/m}^3$。采用两种方案来计算坝体的宏观位移场:一种是将坝体混凝土按常规视为无缺陷的各向同性体;另一种是将坝体视为均质横观各向同性体,并假定 $h_j = 1.0$cm,按上一节叙述的方法,用有限元法确定横观各向同性体的弹性参数。

经过计算比较发现,在自重作用下,异性体方案给出的拱冠梁顶部位移偏大,表 2 中向下游的水平位移比同性体方案超出 10%,但应力差别不大。考虑到在水压的作用下,特别是重力坝失去两岸依托时,位移差别趋势只能加剧,故在进行碾压混凝土坝结构分析时,宜采用异性体方案。

表 2 拱冠梁顶部自重位移 (单位:mm)

位移		上游点	中点	下游点
水平(向右岸)	异性体	0.018	0.017 5	0.017 0
	同性体	0.017	0.016 4	0.016 2
水平(向下游)	异性体	3.083	3.084	3.084
	同性体	2.786	2.786	2.787
垂直(向下)	异性体	2.268	2.030	1.791
	同性体	2.100	1.893	1.684

2.2 坝体层状体应力分析

为了进一步得到层状体结构的内部应力,将坝体某处宏观应力较大的单元按层取出。在进行等效应力分析时,在坝体上下游方向布置了两个单元(见图 2)。

已知图示结点的位移值及单元所受外力(即单元 A 上游侧的水压力和两个单元的自重),将组合体按层厚 0.3m 划分成层状体,每层碾压混凝土本体用 20 结点等单元离散,

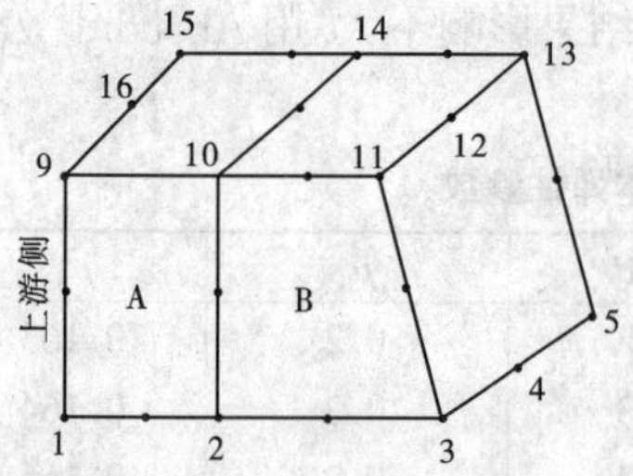

图 2　坝体单元示意图

夹层用 16 结点等单元离散，每一层面共划分 4×4=16 个单元。为考虑不同夹层厚度对层间应力的影响，采用了 4 种计算方案，即将组合单元视为均质体的方案以及夹层厚度分别为 2.0cm、1.0cm 和 1.5cm 的 3 个非均质体方案。现将分析计算结果分述如下。

2.2.1　成层体应力

成层体应力分为混凝土本体侧应力 σ_{ij}^{b} 和夹层侧应力 σ_{ij}^{j}。结果表明，层面应力分量 σ_z、σ_{yz}、τ_{zx} 满足连续条件。另外按均质体方案得到的应力与非均质体方案中的本体侧应力十分接近。表 3 列出 543 号单元的应力计算结果(其中非均质体方案夹层厚为 1cm)。但均质体应力和夹层应力相差较大。

表 3　均质体方案与非均质体方案的比较　（单位：kPa）

应力点位置	σ_x	σ_y	σ_z	τ_{xy}	τ_{yz}	τ_{zx}
均质体	−506	−185	−1 660	−21	−470	−1
本体侧	−522	−188	−1 700	−21.7	−485	−0.2
夹层侧	−444	−413	−1 710	−2	−496	0.4

假定层间应力满足平衡关系，层间位移满足 C_1 连续条件(即函数直至一阶导数连续)，则有

$$\begin{cases} \sigma_z^{b} = \sigma_z^{j} = \sigma_z \\ \tau_{yz}^{b} = \tau_{yz}^{j} = \tau_{yz} \\ \tau_{zx}^{b} = \tau_{zx}^{j} = \tau_{zx} \\ \varepsilon_x^{b} = \varepsilon_x^{j} = \varepsilon_x \\ \varepsilon_y^{b} = \varepsilon_y^{j} = \varepsilon_y \\ \gamma_{xy}^{b} = \gamma_{xy}^{j} = \gamma_{xy} \end{cases} \tag{3}$$

将式(3)代入各向同性弹性体的物理方程就可以得到本体侧层间应力与夹层侧层间应力的关系如下：

$$\sigma_x^{j} = \frac{1}{1-\mu_j^2}\left\{\frac{E_j}{E_b}[(1-\mu_b\mu_j)\sigma_x^{b} + (\mu_j-\mu_b)\sigma_y^{b}] + (1+\mu_j)\left(\mu_j - \frac{E_j}{E_b}\mu_b\right)\sigma_z\right\} \tag{4a}$$

$$\sigma_y^{j} = \frac{1}{1-\mu_j^2}\left\{\frac{E_j}{E_b}[(1-\mu_b\mu_j)\sigma_y^{b} + (\mu_j-\mu_b)\sigma_x^{b}] + (1+\mu_j)\left(\mu_j - \frac{E_j}{E_b}\mu_b\right)\sigma_z\right\} \tag{4b}$$

$$\tau_{xy}^{j} = \frac{G_j}{G_b}\tau_{xy}^{b} \tag{4c}$$

$$\varepsilon_z^{j} = \frac{1}{E_j}(\sigma_z - \mu_j\sigma_x^{j} - \mu_j\sigma_y^{j}) \tag{4d}$$

$$\tau_{yz}^{j} = \frac{1}{G_j}\tau_{yz}^{b} \tag{4e}$$

$$\gamma_{zx}^{j} = \frac{1}{G_j}\tau_{zx}^{b} \tag{4f}$$

经与有限元结果验证，式(4a)、式(4b)、式(4c)与有限元结果十分吻合，以式(4a)为例，用 $h_j=1.0$cm的计算参数(见表2)代入式(4a)得

$$\sigma_x^j = 0.095\,3\sigma_x^b + 0.002\,96\sigma_y^b + 0.229\,87\sigma_z^b \tag{5}$$

对单元639～640的250～306结点(相当于图2结点4～8的位置)，将有限元计算结果与根据有限元得到的 σ_b^j 再按式(5)计算得到的理论结果列入表4。可以看出，两种方法得到的 σ_x^j 十分接近，差别在中间部位最小，向上游(结点306)、下游(结点250)差异逐渐增大，但数量不大。

表4 不同方法得到的 σ_x^j 的比较 (单位:kPa)

方法	结点				
	250	264	278	292	306
有限元	-347	-193	-96.3	-72	-46.6
理论计算	-350.8	-192.4	-94.8	-69.9	-41.9
绝对差	3.8	0.6	1.5	2.1	4.7
相对差	1.1	0.31	1.56	2.92	10.08

2.2.2 夹层厚度与层间应力的影响

由表5(表中1400～1456为结点编号，位于图2中心从下游面依次向上游面的位置)数据可得两点结论，即夹层厚度对层间(本体侧或夹层侧)应力的绝对值影响不大；按均质异性体方案计算的夹层部位的应力与成层体应力场本体侧应力相近，但其与夹层侧应力相差较大。由于夹层材料强度较低，所以夹层侧应力的大小在坝体稳定分析中是很重要的。

3 层状体结构的自由边效应

层状复合材料的研究结果表明，这类材料受力后在结构边缘应力急剧上升，应力状态也变得十分复杂。在工程应用方面也经常发现这类材料在边缘处易于发生分层开裂破坏。这一现象是由沿层厚方向材料性质的不连续性以及顺层方向上结构几何形状的不连续性[2]所致。由于这种现象仅在结构边缘一个很小的范围内出现，所以称之为边界层效应或自由边效应。考虑到结构体的层间结合强度较低，尤其在往复荷载作用下结构的长期强度下降，自由边效应更容易破坏层状体结构。

对于碾压混凝土结构体的自由边效应的研究目前还较少。本文用有限元方法考察层状弹性体的自由边效应。被考察的层状体顺层向长240cm，厚31cm，中间夹有一层厚1cm的软弱夹层。夹层的弹性参数取表1中相应于 $h=1$cm 的参数，本体的弹性参数取某工程提供的数字 $E=34$GPa，$\mu=0.17$。计算采用8结点平面等参元进行。在边缘部位为加密单元区，总体划分720个单元、2 269个结点。计算采用3种加载情况；第一种为顺层向拉力 $p_x=10$MPa；第二种的沿层厚方向拉力 $p_y=10$MPa；第三种沿垂直层面的 z 向

施加均匀压应变 $\varepsilon_z = -120\times10^{-6}$。

表 5　各种方案的有限元结点应力计算结果　　　　(单位:kPa)

应力	类型	1400		1414		1428		1442		1456	
		本体	夹层	本体	夹层	本体	夹层	本体	夹层	本体	夹层
σ_x	$h=2.0$	−221	−276	−191	−214	−153	−121	−120	−67.5	−89.1	−57.9
	$h=1.0$	−225	−279	−191	−214	−153	−117	−117	−60.9	−85.9	−53.2
	$h=0.5$	−225	−281	−191	−213	−152	−113	−116	−57.5	−84.4	−48.7
	均质体	−228		−188		−149		−115		−83.5	
σ_y	$h=2.0$	−48.3	−248	−163	−210	−277	−141	−351	−106	−376	−105
	$h=1.0$	−57.6	−264	−166	−212	−277	−128	−343	−81.8	−367	−79.2
	$h=0.5$	−59.8	−272	−168	−212	−276	−119	−338	−68.5	−360	−62.3
	均质体	−5.80		−160		−275		−341		−365	
σ_z	$h=2.0$	−1 110	−1 110	−848	−846	−433	−436	−215	−212	−194	−192
	$h=1.0$	−1 120	−1 120	−847	−851	−442	−442	−211	−212	−186	−191
	$h=0.5$	−1 120	−1 120	−852	−850	−442	−439	−210	−214	−187	183
	均质体	−1 130		−838		−423		−208		−176	
τ_{zy}	$h=2.0$	−15.9	−2.6	−4.4	−0.7	7.5	1.2	12.6	2.1	13.8	2.3
	$h=1.0$	−15.5	−1.4	−4.2	−0.4	7.3	0.7	12.4	1.1	13.5	1.2
	$h=0.5$	−15.4	−0.8	−4.0	−0.2	7.5	0.4	12.2	0.6	13.1	0.6
	均质体	−14.9		−3.1		7.7		12.4		13.1	
τ_{yz}	$h=2.0$	−251	−252	−381	−382	−322	−323	−189	−187	−2.3	−10.6
	$h=1.0$	−253	−255	−386	−388	−325	−325	−189	−189	−6.4	−10.7
	$h=0.5$	−253	−258	−385	−388	−327	−327	−191	−190	−5.6	−10.5
	均质体	−251		−383		−332		−185		−12.2	
τ_{zx}	$h=2.0$	−21.6	−21.1	−17.1	−16.9	−21.2	−21.0	−25.4	−25.3	−35.0	−34.6
	$h=1.0$	−21.9	−21.5	−17.8	−17.6	−21.0	−20.8	−25.5	−25.4	−34.8	−34.3
	$h=0.5$	−21.6	−21.3	−17.6	−17.4	−20.8	−20.7	−25.7	−25.5	−35.1	−34.8
	均质体	−22.5		−13.8		−30		−23.1		−35.5	

计算结果表明,第三种加载情况无自由边效应现象,第一、二种情况则在自由边附近应力分量发生很大变化,而且还发生了很大的剪应力。按照复合材料自由边效应理论,层状体在平面荷载作用下,自由边附近有一个边界层,层内应力呈三维分布,层与层之间将出现很大的剪力。在均匀压应变作用下无自由边效应从另一角度也说明了这一点。如果把发生在均匀拉伸情况下出现 τ_{xy} 的区域定义为边界层,则第一、二种计算结果表明边界层厚度为 4.7cm。由于计算模型的弹性参数及层体相对厚度均由某工程情况确定,故可以认为通常碾压混凝土坝表面向内约 5cm 的范围将受自由边效应的影响。所以,成层碾压混凝土体比常规混凝土体易于在表面发生开裂。

4　结论

(1)横观各向同性体的弹性参数与假定的层状体软弱夹层厚度 h_j 无关。

(2)采用均质横观各向同性体计算的坝体位移比均质各向同性体计算的位移偏大。所以,进行碾压混凝土坝的应力位移分析时宜采用均质横观各向同性体假设进行。

(3)层状体本体侧的应力与均质横观各向同性体计算中相应部位的应力十分接近,所以可以采用后者估算前者。

(4)层状体中本体侧层间应力与夹层侧层间应力差别较大。式(4)建立的二者之间的关系具有足够的精度。

(5)坝体层间应力与假定的层状体软弱夹层厚度 h_j 关系不大。

(6)碾压混凝土层状体具有明显的边界层效应,在边界层内应力奇异,将导致出现塑性变形或断裂应力重分布。

(7)据此除边界层以外,本文建议的碾压混凝土层状体的简化计算方法如下:①根据工程提供的碾压混凝土本体的弹性参数以及含有软弱夹层的碾压混凝土复合体的弹性参数,估算均质横观各向同性体的弹性参数;②按均质横观各向同性体用有限元计算坝体应力,并把这一应力作为层状体本体侧的应力;③由层状体本体侧应力按式(4)计算层状体软弱夹层侧的层间应力,用这一应力分析是否发生层间破坏。

参 考 文 献

[1] Aboudi J. *Mechanics of composite materials*. A United Micromechanical Approach. Elsevier Sci Pub B V, 1991,107～109

[2] Wang S S, Choi I. *Boundary effects in composite materials*, part2, *free-edge stress solutions and basic characteristics*. ASME J of Appl Mech,1982,49:549～560

成层弹性介质的二维基本解

摘　要　成层碾压混凝土结构的内部应力和位移对其设计十分重要。根据刚度矩阵法的基本原理提出了一个建立成层弹性介质二维基本解的一般方法,基于这一方法可以建立用于进行有限尺寸成层结构体应力分析的半解析数值方法。另外,用叠加法解决了在层体内部力作用点附近 Fourier 积分收敛性不好的问题。在对叠加法进行数值检验中,还得到了具有刚性边界的无限长条形介质在内部集中力作用下的解。

关键词　刚度矩阵法　成层弹性介质　二维基本解

近年来用碾压混凝土来修建大体积混凝土水工建筑物已非常广泛。但工艺给碾压混凝土带来层面间的缺陷或弱面难以完全消除,尤其在不利的气候条件下,可能出现较大面积的弱面。混凝土坝蓄满水后,在渗流影响下,将直接威胁坝体(稳定破坏)安全。显然研究这种各向同性成层结构的变形性质和破坏过程是制定碾压混凝土结构准确设计方法的依据,也是保持快速简化施工工艺条件下改进结构的依据。

实测碾压混凝土在正常工艺下,弱面影响使垂直方向弹模比水平方向下降 20%～30%,沿弱面剪力剪切变形加大,显示出各向同性成层结构的特点。由于层面应力、变形突出以及碾压混凝土层通常只有 30～50cm 厚,和混凝土坝坝体宽度和高度相差数十到数百倍,给有限元法带来困难。采用解析解来处理应力变化率高区域的精度,结合数值方法来处理宏观及工程复杂边界条件问题,可以较好地了解各向均质成层结构内部应力和变形问题。本文介绍了各向均质成层材料解析数值方法及示例。

1　层状均质体的刚度矩阵法

弹性均质体内的 Fourier 变换式为

$$\overline{f}(\xi,y)=\int_{-\infty}^{\infty}f(x,y)\mathrm{e}^{i\xi x}\mathrm{d}x,\quad f(x,y)=\frac{1}{2\pi}\int_{-\infty}^{\infty}\overline{f}(\xi,y)\mathrm{e}^{-i\xi x}\mathrm{d}\xi \tag{1}$$

对用 Airy 应力函数 $\Phi(x,y)$ 表示的相容方程作上述变换可得常微分方程

$$\left(\frac{\mathrm{d}^2}{\mathrm{d}y^2}-\xi^2\right)^2\overline{\Phi}(\xi,y)=0 \tag{2}$$

其解为

$$\overline{\Phi}(\xi,y)=(A+By)\cosh(|\xi|y)+(C+Dy)\sinh(|\xi|y) \tag{3}$$

式中 A,B,C,D 为ξ的函数,可由边界条件确定。用弹性理论基本方程可导出应力位移与 $\overline{\Phi}(\xi,y)$ 的关系为

$$\overline{\sigma}_x(\xi,y)=\frac{\mathrm{d}^2}{\mathrm{d}y^2}\overline{\Phi}(\xi,y),\overline{\sigma}_y(\xi,y)=-\xi^2\overline{\Phi}(\xi,y),\overline{\tau}_{xy}(\xi,y)=i\xi\frac{\mathrm{d}}{\mathrm{d}y}\overline{\Phi}(\xi,y), \tag{4}$$

本文选自《清华大学学报(自然科学版)》1996 年第 1 期,作者还有郝巨涛。

$$2\mu\bar{u}(\xi,y)=\frac{i}{4\xi}\left[(k+1)\frac{\mathrm{d}^2}{\mathrm{d}y^2}\bar{\Phi}(\xi,y)+(3-k)\xi^2\bar{\Phi}(\xi,y)\right]$$

$$2\mu\bar{v}(\xi,y)=\frac{1}{4\xi^2}\left[(k+1)\frac{\mathrm{d}^3}{\mathrm{d}y^3}\bar{\Phi}(\xi,y)-(5+k)\xi^2\frac{\mathrm{d}}{\mathrm{d}y}\bar{\Phi}(\xi,y)\right]$$

式中 μ 为剪切模量，k 与泊桑比 ν 的关系为：对平面应变 $k=3-4\nu$；对平面应力 $k=(3-\nu)/(1+\nu)$。如令 $\cosh(|\xi|y)=c_y$，$\sinh(|\xi|y)=s_y$，将式(3)代入式(4)可得

$$\begin{Bmatrix}\bar{\sigma}_x\\ \bar{\sigma}_y\\ -i\bar{\tau}_{xy}\end{Bmatrix}=\begin{bmatrix}\xi^2c_y & \xi^2s_y & \xi^2yc_y+2|\xi|s_y & \xi^2ys_y+2|\xi|c_y\\ -\xi^2c_y & -\xi^2s_y & -\xi^2yc_y & -\xi^2ys_y\\ \xi|\xi|s_y & \xi|\xi|c_y & \xi|\xi|ys_y+\xi c_y & \xi|\xi|yc_y+\xi s_y\end{bmatrix}\begin{Bmatrix}A\\ B\\ C\\ D\end{Bmatrix} \tag{5}$$

$$2\mu\begin{Bmatrix}\frac{1}{i\xi}\bar{v}\\ \frac{-1}{|\xi|}\bar{v}\end{Bmatrix}=\begin{bmatrix}c_y & s_y & \frac{1+k}{2|\xi|}s_y+yc_y & \frac{1+k}{2|\xi|}c_y+ys_y\\ s_y & c_y & \frac{1-k}{2|\xi|}c_y+ys_y & \frac{1-k}{2|\xi|}s_y+yc_y\end{bmatrix}\begin{Bmatrix}A\\ B\\ C\\ D\end{Bmatrix} \tag{6}$$

一旦由边界条件确定了 $A\sim D$，由式(5)、式(6)，弹性场也就随之确定。设多层体中某层介质的上表面应力位移分量为 $\sigma_{ij}{}^{+}$、$u_i{}^{+}$，下表面为 $\sigma_{ij}{}^{-}$、$u_i{}^{-}$，则根据边界性质可把 $A\sim D$ 表示成这些量的各种组合的函数。在刚度法中是把 $A\sim D$ 表示成边界位移 $u_i{}^{+}$、$u_i{}^{-}$ 的函数，进而可由式(5)导出边界应力和位移之间的局部刚度矩阵。

设介质厚 $2b$，将局部坐标原点放在该层介质的中面上，则有：$\bar{\sigma}_{ij}(\xi,\pm b)=\bar{\sigma}_{ij}{}^{\pm}$，$\bar{u}_i(\xi,\pm b)=\bar{u}_i{}^{\pm}$。由式(6)可得(令 $c_b=\cosh(|\xi|b)$，$s_b=\sinh(|\xi|b)$：

$$\begin{Bmatrix}A\\ B\\ C\\ D\end{Bmatrix}=\boldsymbol{T}\begin{Bmatrix}-i\bar{\nu}^{+}\\ \bar{u}^{+}\\ -i\bar{\nu}^{-}\\ \bar{u}^{-}\end{Bmatrix},\quad \boldsymbol{T}=i\mu\begin{bmatrix}t_1 & t_5 & -t_1 & t_5\\ t_2 & t_6 & t_2 & -t_6\\ t_3 & t_7 & t_3 & -t_7\\ t_4 & t_8 & -t_4 & t_8\end{bmatrix} \tag{7}$$

式中：$\boldsymbol{T}$ 为转换矩阵，其元素为

$$t_1=\frac{1}{\Delta_1}\left(\frac{1+k}{2|\xi|}c_b+bs_b\right),\quad t_2=\frac{-1}{\Delta_2}\left(\frac{1+k}{2|\xi|}s_b+bc_b\right),\quad t_3=\frac{s_b}{\Delta_2},\quad t_4=\frac{-c_b}{\Delta_1},$$

$$t_5=-\frac{g}{\Delta_1}\left(\frac{1-k}{2|\xi|}s_b+bc_b\right),\quad t_6=\frac{g}{\Delta_2}\left(\frac{1-k}{2|\xi|}c_b+bs_b\right),\quad t_7=-g\frac{c_b}{\Delta_2},\quad t_8=g\frac{s_b}{\Delta_1},$$

$$\Delta_1=|\xi|b-kc_bs_b,\qquad \Delta_2=|\xi|b+kc_bs_b,\qquad g=\mathrm{sgn}(\xi)$$

式中 $\mathrm{sgn}(\xi)$ 为符号函数。将式(7)代入式(5)可得局部刚性关系如下：

$$\begin{Bmatrix}-i\bar{\sigma}_y{}^{-}\\ \bar{\tau}_{xy}{}^{+}\\ i\bar{\sigma}_y{}^{-}\\ -\bar{\tau}_{xy}{}^{-}\end{Bmatrix}=\boldsymbol{K}\begin{Bmatrix}-i\bar{\nu}^{+}\\ \bar{u}^{+}\\ -i\bar{\nu}^{-}\\ \bar{u}^{-}\end{Bmatrix},\quad \boldsymbol{K}=\mu|\xi|\begin{bmatrix}k_{11} & k_{12} & k_{13} & k_{14}\\ k_{12} & k_{22} & -k_{14} & k_{24}\\ k_{13} & -k_{14} & k_{11} & -k_{12}\\ k_{14} & k_{24} & -k_{12} & k_{22}\end{bmatrix} \tag{8}$$

式中 $\boldsymbol{K}$ 为局部刚度矩阵，其元素为

$$k_{11}=\frac{1+k}{2}\left(\frac{s_b^2}{\Delta_2}-\frac{c_b^2}{\Delta_1}\right),\qquad k_{13}=\frac{1+k}{2}\left(\frac{s_b^2}{\Delta_2}+\frac{c_b^2}{\Delta_1}\right),$$

$$k_{22}=\frac{1+k}{2}\left(\frac{c_b^2}{\Delta_2}-\frac{s_b^2}{\Delta_1}\right),\qquad k_{24}=-\frac{1+k}{2}\left(\frac{c_b^2}{\Delta_2}+\frac{s_b^2}{\Delta_1}\right),$$

$$k_{12}=g\left[\frac{1-k}{2}c_b s_b\left(\frac{1}{\Delta_1}-\frac{1}{\Delta_2}\right)+|\xi|b\left(\frac{1}{\Delta_1}+\frac{1}{\Delta_2}\right)\right]$$

$$k_{14}=g\left[\frac{1-k}{2}c_b s_b\left(\frac{1}{\Delta_1}+\frac{1}{\Delta_2}\right)+|\xi|b\left(\frac{1}{\Delta_1}-\frac{1}{\Delta_2}\right)\right]$$

有了局部刚度矩阵，就可按界面连续情况集合出整个层状体结构的总刚，进而求解这一结构。

2 含内部作用力的局部刚性关系

设某单层介质内部作用有集中力，该集中力把这层介质分为 u 区和 d 区，各区厚度为 h_u、h_d（见图1）。按分块写法，u 区和 d 区各自的刚性关系为

$$\begin{Bmatrix}\overline{\sigma}_u^{\,+}\\-\overline{\sigma}_u^{\,-}\end{Bmatrix}=\begin{bmatrix}K_{11}^u & K_{12}^u\\K_{21}^u & K_{22}^u\end{bmatrix}\begin{Bmatrix}\overline{\delta}_u^{\,+}\\\overline{\delta}_u^{\,-}\end{Bmatrix}\tag{9}$$

$$\begin{Bmatrix}\overline{\sigma}_d^{\,+}\\-\overline{\sigma}_d^{\,-}\end{Bmatrix}=\begin{bmatrix}K_{11}^d & K_{12}^d\\K_{21}^d & K_{22}^d\end{bmatrix}\begin{Bmatrix}\overline{\delta}_d^{\,+}\\\overline{\delta}_d^{\,-}\end{Bmatrix}$$

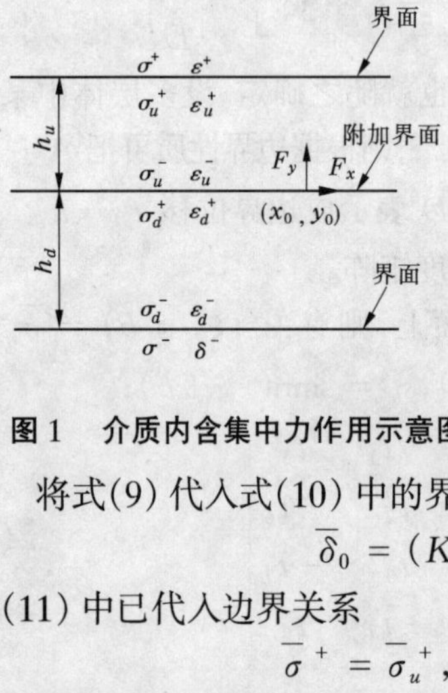

图1 介质内含集中力作用示意图

由 u 区和 d 区之间的界面连结情况知

$$\overline{\delta}_u^{\,-}=\overline{\delta}_d^{\,+}=\overline{\delta}_0,\quad \overline{\sigma}_d^{\,+}-\overline{\sigma}_u^{\,-}=\overline{F}=\begin{Bmatrix}-iF_y\\F_x\end{Bmatrix}e^{i\xi x_0}\tag{10}$$

将式(9)代入式(10)中的界面应力连续条件有

$$\overline{\delta}_0=(K_{22}^u+K_{11}^d)^{-1}(\overline{F}-K_{12}^d\overline{\delta}-K_{21}^u\overline{\delta}^+)\tag{11}$$

式(11)中已代入边界关系

$$\overline{\sigma}^{\,+}=\overline{\sigma}_u^{\,+},\ \overline{\delta}^{\,+}=\overline{\delta}_u^{\,+},\ \overline{\sigma}^{\,-}=\overline{\sigma}_d^{\,-},\ \overline{\delta}^{\,-}=\overline{\delta}_d^{\,-}\tag{12}$$

将式(11)代入式(9)，并从中消去界面位移 $\overline{\delta}_0$ 得

$$\begin{aligned}\overline{\sigma}^+=&[K_{11}^u-K_{12}^u(K_{22}^u+K_{11}^d)^{-1}K_{21}^u]\overline{\delta}^+-K_{12}^u(K_{22}^u+K_{11}^d)^{-1}K_{12}^d\overline{\delta}^-+\\&K_{12}^u(K_{22}^u+K_{11}^d)^{-1}\overline{F}\end{aligned}\tag{13}$$

$$\begin{aligned}-\overline{\sigma}^-=&-K_{21}^d(K_{22}^u+K_{11}^d)^{-1}K_{21}^u\overline{\delta}^++[K_{22}^d-K_{21}^d(K_{22}^u+K_{11}^d)^{-1}K_{12}^d]\overline{\delta}^-+\\&K_{12}^d(K_{22}^u+K_{11}^d)^{-1}\overline{F}\end{aligned}\tag{14}$$

当 $\overline{F}=0$ 时，式(13)、式(14)应与式(8)相同，故可得局部刚度矩阵等效关系如下：

$$\begin{aligned}&K_{11}=K_{11}^u-K_{12}^u(K_{22}^u+K_{11}^d)^{-1}K_{21}^u,\quad K_{12}=-K_{12}^u(K_{22}^u+K_{11}^d)^{-1}K_{12}^d\\&K_{21}=-K_{21}^d(K_{22}^u+K_{11}^d)^{-1}K_{21}^u,\quad K_{22}=K_{22}^d-K_{21}^d(K_{22}^u+K_{11}^d)^{-1}K_{12}^d\end{aligned}\tag{15}$$

由此可将式(13)、式(14)简写为

$$\begin{Bmatrix} \bar{\sigma}^{+} \\ -\bar{\sigma}^{-} \end{Bmatrix} = \begin{bmatrix} K_{11} & K_{12} \\ K_{21} & K_{22} \end{bmatrix} \begin{Bmatrix} \bar{\delta}^{+} \\ \bar{\delta}^{-} \end{Bmatrix} + \begin{Bmatrix} \bar{\sigma}_0^{+} \\ -\bar{\sigma}_0^{-} \end{Bmatrix}, \begin{Bmatrix} \bar{\sigma}_0^{+} \\ -\bar{\sigma}_0^{-} \end{Bmatrix} = -\begin{bmatrix} K_{12}(K_{12}^{d})^{-1} \\ K_{21}(K_{22}^{u})^{-1} \end{bmatrix} \bar{F} \tag{16}$$

此式就是含内部集中力作用时的层状体局部刚度矩阵。

3 含内部作用力时层状体的应力位移计算

同样采用分块矩阵写法。由图 1，当 $y \geqslant y_0$ 时有

$$\bar{\sigma} = (S_1^u \quad S_2^u) \begin{Bmatrix} \bar{\delta}^{+} \\ \bar{\delta}_0 \end{Bmatrix} \tag{17}$$

式中 S_1^u、S_2^u 为弹性矩阵元素，由式(5) 中矩阵与式(7) 的转换矩阵相乘求得。计算中，式(5) 矩阵中的 y 应取 u 区的局部坐标，式(7) 中的介质厚度 $2b$ 应取图 1 中的 h_u。将式(11) 代入式(17) 有

$$\bar{\sigma} = (S_1^u \quad S_2^u) \begin{bmatrix} 1 & 0 \\ -(K_{22}^u + K_{11}^d)^{-1} K_{21}^u & -(K_{22}^u + K_{11}^d)^{-1} K_{12}^d \end{bmatrix} \begin{Bmatrix} \bar{\delta}^{+} \\ \bar{\delta}^{-} \end{Bmatrix} + S_2^u (K_{22}^u + K_{11}^d)^{-1} \bar{F} \tag{18}$$

经过与上节类似的处理，式(18) 可简化为

$$\bar{\sigma} = (S_1 \quad S_2) \begin{Bmatrix} \bar{\delta}^{+} \\ \bar{\delta}^{-} \end{Bmatrix} + \bar{\sigma}_0, \quad \bar{\sigma}_0 = -(S_1 \quad S_2) \begin{Bmatrix} 0 \\ (K_{12}^d)^{-1} \end{Bmatrix} \bar{F} \tag{19}$$

同理当 $y \leqslant y_0$ 时，经过与上面类似的推导可得

$$\bar{\sigma} = (S_1 \quad S_2) \begin{Bmatrix} \bar{\delta}^{+} \\ \bar{\delta}^{-} \end{Bmatrix} + \bar{\sigma}_0, \quad \bar{\sigma}_0 = -(S_1 \quad S_2) \begin{Bmatrix} (K_{21}^u)^{-1} \\ 0 \end{Bmatrix} \bar{F} \tag{20}$$

经过适当处理，式(19)、式(20) 中的 $\bar{\sigma}_0$ 可以合并写成

$$\bar{\sigma}_0 = -(S_1 \quad S_2) \begin{Bmatrix} (1 - h_v)(K_{21}^u)^{-1} \\ h_v (K_{12}^d)^{-1} \end{Bmatrix} \bar{F} \tag{21}$$

式中 $h_v = y - y_0$，为阶梯函数。当 $u = y_0$ 时，式(21) 给出 u 区、d 区之间界面上下的 $\bar{\sigma}_0$ 值，它们满足关系式(10)。同理，计算位移场时，仅需将式(21) 中 S 按式(6) 代换即可。

4 方法验证

设有一层状体如图 2 所示，上下表面作用有集中力，层厚为 $2b$。该问题已有 Filon 解。这时有 $\bar{F} = \begin{Bmatrix} +i \\ 0 \end{Bmatrix} P$。对于上表面力有 $h_u = 0$，对于下表面力有 $h_d = 0$，由式(16) 按叠加原理有

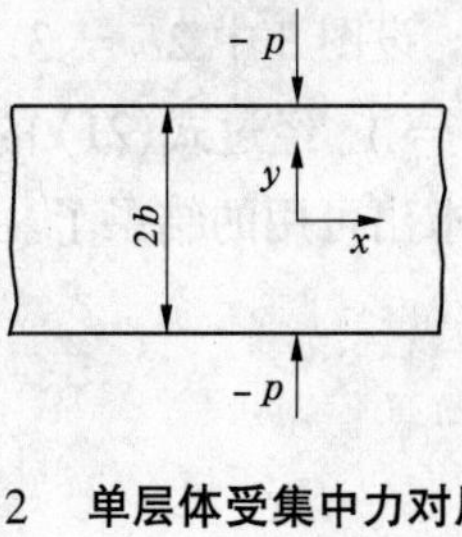

图 2 单层体受集中力对压

$$\begin{bmatrix} K_{11} & K_{12} \\ K_{21} & K_{22} \end{bmatrix} \begin{Bmatrix} \bar{\delta}^{+} \\ \bar{\delta}^{-} \end{Bmatrix} = \begin{Bmatrix} \bar{F} \\ \bar{F} \end{Bmatrix} \tag{22}$$

这里可把问题看成是层状体表面无外力作用，而内部有一对集中力，当集中力无限趋于表面时的情况，将式(22) 代入式(7) 得

$$\begin{Bmatrix} A \\ B \\ C \\ D \end{Bmatrix} = \boldsymbol{TK}^{-1}\begin{Bmatrix} \overline{F} \\ \overline{F} \end{Bmatrix} \tag{23}$$

$$\begin{Bmatrix} A \\ B \\ C \\ D \end{Bmatrix} = \boldsymbol{s}_b{}^{-1}\begin{Bmatrix} \overline{F} \\ \overline{F} \end{Bmatrix} \tag{24}$$

在导出式(8)的过程中已采用了关系式 $\boldsymbol{K} = s_b\boldsymbol{T}$, s_b 是式(5)应力分量 $\bar{\sigma}_y, \bar{\tau}_{xy}$ 当 $y = \pm b$ 时的应力系数矩阵。据此式(23)可写成式(24)。将式(24)代入式(5)可得所求应力场的 Fourier 变换式,求逆变换后有

$$\begin{aligned} \sigma_x &= \frac{P}{2\pi}\int_{-\infty}^{\infty} \frac{1}{c_b s_b + |\xi| b}[-c_y s_b + |\xi| b(bc_y c_b - ys_y s_b)]\mathrm{e}^{-i\xi x}\mathrm{d}\xi \\ \sigma_y &= \frac{P}{2\pi}\int_{-\infty}^{\infty} \frac{1}{c_b s_b + |\xi| b}[-c_y s_b - |\xi| b(bc_y c_b - ys_y s_b)]\mathrm{e}^{-i\xi x}\mathrm{d}\xi \\ \tau_{xy} &= \frac{iP}{2\pi}\int_{-\infty}^{\infty} \frac{\xi}{c_b s_b + |\xi| b}[bs_y c_b - yc_y s_b)]\mathrm{e}^{-i\xi x}\mathrm{d}\xi \end{aligned} \tag{25}$$

考虑上式被积函数的奇偶性,并令 $\xi b = u$,则式(25)变为 Filon 解的表达式。

5　成层弹性介质的二维基本解问题

前面已把集中力引入了层状体的局部刚性关系以及应力位移计算式。由此可按文献[1]中的程序来求解含内部作用的层状结构。但尚未解决式(21)是否满足 Fourier 积分条件,在进行层状体数值分析时要计算式(21)的 Fourier 逆变换,因此要关心它随 ξ 而变化的情况。而它正好对应于具有刚性边界条件的单层体含内部作用时的弹性场求解问题。

以图 3 为例考察式(21)的收敛情况。经分析发现,从理论上讲只要所求应力点 $y \neq y_0$(y_0 为作用点),Fourier 积分条件均成立。下面进行数值考察。

设图 3 中 $2b = 3.0$, $k = 1.2$,在坐标中心($x_0 = 0, y_0 = 0$)作用有集中力 $F_x = 0$, $F_y = 1$。经过式(21)的 Fourier 逆变换式进行数值积分发现,当 $|y - y_0| \leqslant 0.4$ 时,就很难求出可用的结果了。由此看出必须另找方法为式(21)赋值。

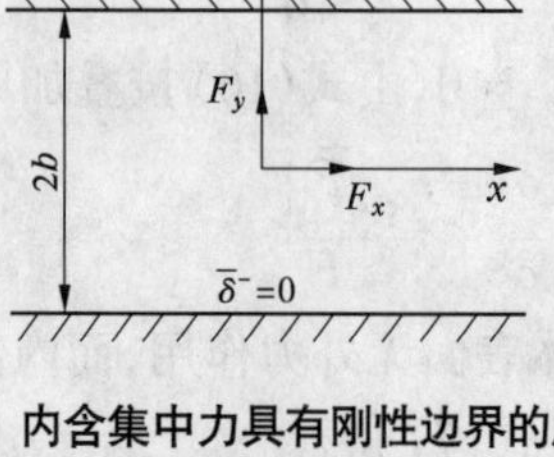

图 3　内含集中力具有刚性边界的层体

式(21)积分之所以收敛不好甚至发散是因为其中含有奇异成分,如果能将奇异部分

分离出去则可得好的数值积分结果。可能的方法有两个：其一是考察式(21) 被积函数当 $|\xi| \to \infty$ 时的极限形式，将奇异项分离出来，用奇异积分方法进行特殊处理；另一种方法是利用无限域已知的 Kelvin 的解，采用叠加原理消除奇异部分。本文采用后一种方法。叠加原理见图 4，图中 $\bar{\sigma}_0$ 为 F 在刚性边界处引起的反力(见式(16))，$\bar{\sigma}_1$ 为 F 在相应于上下边界位置处 Kelvin 解给出的应力。由图 4 看出，含内部集中力作用的刚性边界问题可分解成 Kelvin 弹性场与 $\bar{\sigma}_0 - \bar{\sigma}_1$ 弹性场的叠加。由 Kelvin 解可得

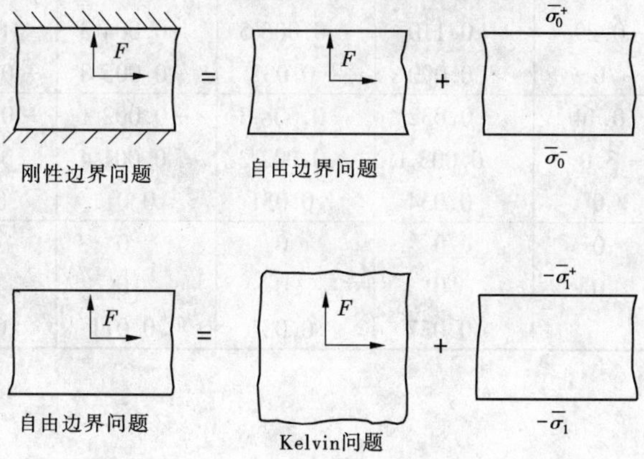

图 4　叠加法原理图

$$
\begin{Bmatrix} \bar{\sigma}_1^+ \\ -\bar{\sigma}_1^- \end{Bmatrix} = \begin{Bmatrix} -i\bar{\sigma}_y^+ \\ \bar{\tau}_{xy}^+ \\ i\bar{\sigma}_y^- \\ -\bar{\tau}_{xy}^- \end{Bmatrix}
$$

$$
= \frac{e^{-|\xi|b}}{2(1+k)} \begin{bmatrix} -(1+k+2|\xi|b) & -(1-k+2|\xi|b)g \\ -(1-k-2|\xi|b)g & -(1+k-2|\xi|b) \\ -(1+k+2|\xi|b) & (1-k+2|\xi|b)g \\ (1-k-2|\xi|b)g & -(1+k-2|\xi|b) \end{bmatrix} \begin{Bmatrix} -iF_y \\ F_x \end{Bmatrix} \tag{26}
$$

与第 4 节类似可得由 $\bar{\sigma}_0 - \bar{\sigma}_1$ 引起的应力场 σ_F 为

$$
\{\sigma_F\} = \frac{1}{2\pi}\int_{-\infty}^{\infty} s s_b^{-1} \begin{Bmatrix} \bar{\sigma}_0 - \bar{\sigma}_1^+ \\ -(\bar{\sigma}_0^- - \bar{\sigma}_1^-) \end{Bmatrix} e^{-i\xi x}\, d\xi \tag{27}
$$

表 1 是用叠加法得到的图 3 问题的解。经与数值积分结果对比后知，在 $|y - y_0| \geqslant 0.4$ 范围内两种方法给出的结果一致，同时在式(21) 无法求解的区域叠加法也能给出计算结果，这表明用叠加法解层状体在内部集中力作用下的弹性场是安全可行的。

应说明的是上面计算与采用的数值积分方法有关。本文采用 Richardson 外推法对 Filon 积分公式进行一次加速，使之具有较高积分精度。数值积分计算中相应的 Fourier 积分截断频率为 $\xi_m = 30$，叠加法计算中为 $\xi_m = 20$，两种方法的等分区间数均为 $2^{12} = 4\,096$。

表1 用叠加法得到的 $F_y = 1$ 的计算结果

y	应力	x					
		0	1	2	3	4	5
-0.5	σ_x	-0.001 4	0.110	0.036	0.008 7	0.001 2	-0.000 057
	σ_y	0.65	0.035	-0.009 1	-0.006 4	-0.001 9	-0.000 35
	τ_{xy}	0	-0.009 2	0.019	0.007 4	0.001 6	0.000 18
1.5	σ_x	-0.23	-0.088	-0.005 3	0.003 5	16	0.000 40
	σ_y	-0.29	-0.110	-0.006 5	0.004 3	0.002 0	0.000 49
	τ_{xy}	0	-0.090	-0.032	-0.005 8	-0.000 27	0.000 24
0.1	σ_x	0.14	-0.032	-0.008 3	-0.002 1	-0.000 31	0.000 0036
	σ_y	-3.0	-0.003 1	0.002 2	0.001 4	0.000 43	0.000 079
	τ_{xy}	0	0.034	0.031	0.011	0.002 4	0.000 26
0	σ_x	0	0	0	0	0	0
	σ_y	0	0	0	0	0	0
	τ_{xy}		0.037	0.031	0.011	0.002 5	0.000 26

参考文献

[1] Choi H J, Thanjitham S. *Stress analysis of multi - layered anisotropic elastic media*. ASME J of Appl Mech, 1991, 58: 382～387

[2] 郝巨涛. 成层结果及碾压混凝土坝的应力稳定分析方法:[学位论文]. 北京：清华大学水利水电工程系, 1995

整体碾压混凝土拱坝工艺及温度场仿真计算

摘　要　选用了整体碾压混凝土(RCC)拱坝的可行施工工艺,提供了混凝土坝施工期到运行期温度场的仿真计算方法和温度信息处理方法。利用我国某碾压混凝土坝的现场实测结果,对温度计算值及变化进行了验证,结果良好。数值计算用来预测我国拟建的某碾压混凝土拱坝从施工开始到长时间运行的仿真温度变化。仿真计算表明工艺对施工期温度变化影响大,对由施工末期到运行期温降值也影响较大。根据温度场的变化规律选择了碾压混凝土拱坝合理的施工工艺。

关键词　碾压混凝土拱坝　温度场　仿真计算

我国正在试探将碾压混凝土用于拱坝的技术,它的主要优点是碾压混凝土水泥用量较少,施工速度快。若利用自然低温季节(我国中部和南部冬季)快速浇筑混凝土,省去人工冷却,可以在一个枯水季完成80m以下高度的中小型拱坝工程。工程量减少,施工快,简化了导流等临时工程,因此它既保证了工程早日投入运行,又节约修建投资。

在窄河谷中,用整体碾压混凝土拱坝,不但可节省横缝或诱导缝分仓模板和埋设灌浆系统的费用并避免干扰,而且不需要等待冷却灌浆即可蓄水。有利于工程早日投入运行。其小型电站每提前一季度发电可回收1/10总投资,而原定2.5～3年完成的工程可在1年内完成。

整体碾压混凝土拱坝坝面平整,工程量小,有利于RCC施工,可满足月上升速度15～18m的要求。连续快速覆盖,间歇时间短,使上表面散热少,主要依靠上下游坝面散热,拱坝内部温度较高,施工期内外温差大,容易带来上下游表面拉裂。大量实测表明,当后期内部降温引起拉应力或外部升温拉应力区转向内部时,都将引起表面裂缝向内部发展而贯穿坝体。南非的两座碾压混凝土重力拱坝上下游预留了诱导缝,仍然出现了大量贯穿裂缝,缝宽从0.1～3mm不等。实际上整体碾压混凝土拱坝浇筑后,不论升温或降温,不但受梁向基础约束,更重要的约束来自拱向,它比通常拱坝在人工降温后才灌浆形成整体的拱向约束应力要大得多。因此,要实现碾压混凝土拱坝首先要认真解决坝体施工期和运行期的温度问题。通常柱状块温控计算和拱坝运行期的温度应力计算不足以反映整体碾压混凝土拱坝的温度应力。

整体碾压混凝土拱坝温度变化过程计算按温度应力变化特征可分为施工期[1](指混凝土坝开始浇筑,累计到坝体浇筑完蓄水前)和运行期(坝体浇筑完蓄水前到长时间运行期)。由于坝体浇筑过程已形成不同坝高的整体结构(它和常态混凝土拱坝分块条件下温降不同),因此施工期和运行期的任何温度变化都受到底部和两岸基础的约束形成较大的温度应力,需作仿真温度和应力计算。

本文选自《清华大学学报(自然科学版)》1996年第1期,作者还有张国新、刘志辉。

1 施工期温度场计算的基本方法

混凝土浇筑后,其温度场 $T(x,y,z,\tau)$ 应满足下列方程及边界条件:

$$\frac{\partial T}{\partial \tau} = a\left(\frac{\partial^2 T}{\partial x^2} + \frac{\partial^2 T}{\partial y^2} + \frac{\partial^2 T}{\partial z^2}\right) + \frac{\partial \theta}{\partial \tau} \tag{1}$$

当 $\tau = 0$ 时,$T = T_0(x,y,z)$;在 C_1 上:$T = T_b$;在 C_2 上:

$$\lambda_x \frac{\partial T}{\partial x} l_x + \lambda_y \frac{\partial T}{\partial y} l_y + \lambda_z \frac{\partial T}{\partial z} l_z + \beta(T - T_a) = 0$$

在边界 C_3 上满足绝热条件:$\partial T/\partial n = 0$。

以上诸式中:λ 为导热系数;a 为导温系数;β 为表面放热系数;θ 为混凝土绝热温升;T_a、T_b 为给定的边界气温和水温;n 为边界外法线方向;l_x、l_y、l_z 为边界外法线的方向余弦;T_0 为给定的初始温度。

上述热传导问题等价于泛函的极值问题,可用有限单元法求解。对结构求解区域 R 进行离散化,考虑泛函 $I(T)$ 的极值可得到如下方程:

$$\left[\boldsymbol{H} + \frac{2}{\Delta\tau}\boldsymbol{P}\right]\{T\}_{\tau} + \left[\boldsymbol{H} - \frac{2}{\Delta\tau}\boldsymbol{P}\right]\{T\}_{\tau-\Delta\tau} + \{Q\}_{\tau} + \{Q\}_{\tau-\Delta\tau} = 0 \tag{2}$$

式中:

$$\begin{cases} \boldsymbol{H} = \sum\limits_{e} \boldsymbol{H}^{e} = \sum\limits_{e} \iiint_{\Delta R} \left(a_x \dfrac{\partial N^{T}}{\partial x}\dfrac{\partial N}{\partial x} + a_y \dfrac{\partial \boldsymbol{N}^{T}}{\partial y}\dfrac{\partial \boldsymbol{N}}{\partial y} + a_z \dfrac{\partial \boldsymbol{N}^{T}}{\partial z}\dfrac{\partial \boldsymbol{N}}{\partial z}\right)\mathrm{d}R \\ \boldsymbol{Q} = \sum\limits_{e} \boldsymbol{Q}^{e} = \sum\limits_{e} \left\{\iiint_{\Delta R} \dfrac{\partial \theta}{\partial \tau}\boldsymbol{N}^{T}\mathrm{d}R - \iint_{\Delta C} \bar{\beta} T_a \boldsymbol{N}^{T}\mathrm{d}s + \iint_{\Delta C} \bar{\beta}\boldsymbol{N}^{T}\boldsymbol{N}\{T\}^{e}\mathrm{d}s\right\} \\ \boldsymbol{P} = \sum\limits_{e} \boldsymbol{P}^{e} = \sum\limits_{e} \iiint_{\Delta R} \boldsymbol{N}^{T}\boldsymbol{N}\mathrm{d}R \end{cases} \tag{3}$$

上式即为求解非稳定温度场的有限元法方程。只要给定 $\tau - \Delta\tau$ 时刻的温度场 $\{T\}_{\tau-\Delta\tau}$,解方程组(2)、(3) 可得到 τ 时刻的温度场 $\{T\}_{\tau}$,这样已知 $\tau = 0$ 时刻结构内的温度分布,可依次求出各时刻的温度分布。已编制的三维温度场计算程序 DTTS 可用微型计算机进行计算。

2 入仓温度的影响及计算与实测比较

当混凝土块浇筑在岩基上时,岩基表面初始温度可用浇筑前表面实测温度或日平均温度,若间歇后继续加高混凝土,则下层上表面采用计算值,上层混凝土用入仓温度作为初始状态,即实际上第一层混凝土未和第二层混凝土接触之前有不同温度值,一旦结合后,接触面就只有一个温度值。

某混凝土碾压试块 12m×12m×7.5m(5 层×1.5m 厚/层)。每层浇筑和间歇时间共 5d,各层入仓温度随气温上升为 10℃、11.5℃、13℃、14.5℃、16℃,绝热温升 $\theta_0 = 20.33$℃,放热速率 $m = 0.190$,500 个单元计算结果见图 1 ~ 图 3(温度按单元方式输入入仓温度,界面节点用下层混凝土计算的上表面温度,界面节点取下层计算温度和上层入仓温度平均值)。温度分布图均为第三层顶面温度分布,图中时间起点都是第一层混凝土浇筑开始。

用下层混凝土计算温度作为上下层界面初始温度输入所得累计温度远大于(约10℃)仿真单元输入的温度场。即使采用下表面计算值和入仓温度平均值内部最高温升值也比仿真温度高 2 ~ 2.5℃,仿真温度场计算宜用单元温度输入。

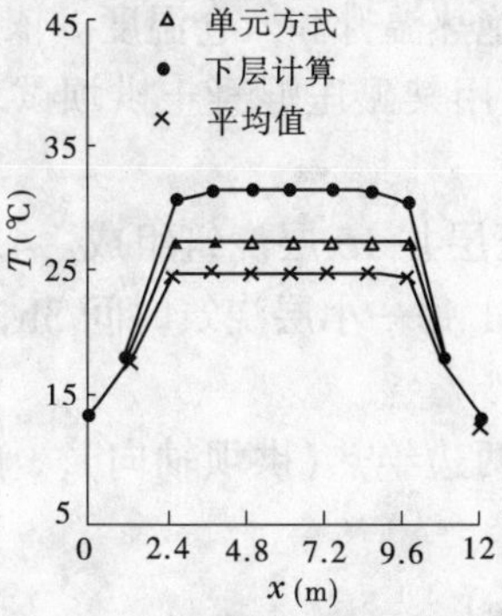

图 1　第 14d 温度分布

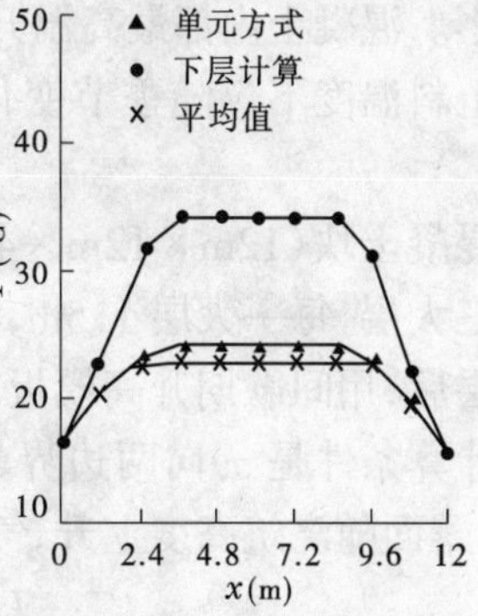

图 2　第 16d 温度分布

某碾压混凝土拱坝(分横缝)2[#] 坝段 134.9m 内部埋设温度计,在 134.9m 上下按实际浇筑各取一层混凝土(每层 1.8m)。实测记录下层浇筑日期为 5 月 11 日(气温 20℃),入仓温度为 14℃。上层混凝土浇筑日期为 6 月 2 日(气温 22℃),入仓温度为 21℃。上、下游及内部混凝土各龄期温升值按 $\theta = \theta_0(1 - e^{-m\tau})$ 分别拟合。表面散热系数 $\beta = 1.68$ kJ/(m^2 · d · ℃),其他热学参数见表 1。对比实测和计算结果(见表 2) 可以看出,两者变化规律相同。温度到达峰值的时间也相同,计算值略高于实测值。6 月 12 日差距最大达 1.8℃,由于未考虑 133.1m 以下混凝土传热作用(浇筑时间在 4 月 19 日前,到 5 月 11 日时已接近气温),致使上层混凝土计算结果偏高,考虑到计算中热学参数的精度影响,实用中温度计算可达到的精度也局限在 1 ~ 2℃。

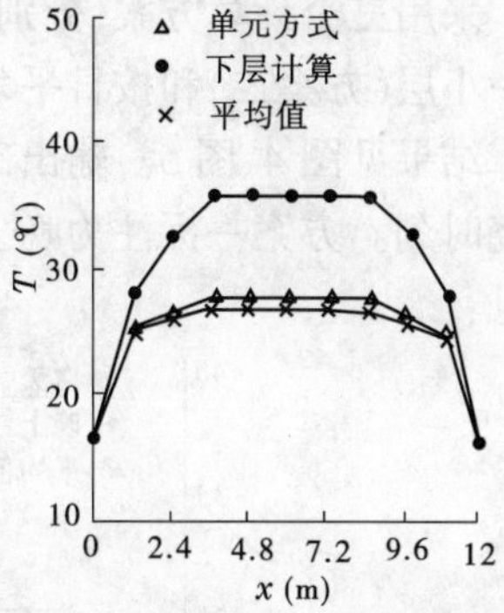

图 3　第 18d 温度分布

表 1　热学参数

混凝土	导温系数 a(m^2/d)	比热容 C(J/(kg·℃))
上游	0.100 8	0.943 58
内部	0.098 42	0.938 72
下游	0.093	0.992 27

表 2　计算值与实测值对比表

日　期(月 - 日)	06 - 04	06 - 05	06 - 06	06 - 07	06 - 08	06 - 10	06 - 12	06 - 14	06 - 16	06 - 19
计算值 T(℃)	29.0	30.4	30.7	30.8	30.5	29.7	28.8	27.9	27.2	26.4
实测值 T(℃)	28.5	29.2	30.5	30.6	30.2	26.2	27.0	26.2	26.0	26.0

3　碾压混凝土结构温度场和合理入仓时间选择

用 RCC 法浇筑碾压混凝土，由于上表面迅速覆盖，层间间歇时间短，表面散热对最高温升影响小。混凝土内部最高温升主要取决于混凝土绝热温升和入仓温度。依靠自然冷却的混凝土料温度不仅随季节变化而且随昼夜变化。用某碾压混凝土拱坝试块进行讨论。

碾压混凝土块(12m×12m×4.5m)，由 0.3m 碾压层共 15 层浇筑组成。4.5m 高混凝土块分三大层，每一大层 1.5m，浇筑和间歇时间共 5d，每一小层浇筑时间 3h，连续 15h 完成一大层后，用间歇期升高模板。

温度计算条件是 x 向两边界暴露于大气中，y 向两边绝热(拱坝轴向)，z 向底部绝热，顶部暴露面随浇筑高度上升，气温变化为

$$T = T_0 + T_m \sin(\omega t + \varphi) \tag{4}$$

式中：T_0 为日平均气温；T_m 为日最大温差；t 为时间。

采用三个计算方案，分别为下午 6 时开始浇筑第一小层(方案一)，上午 9 时开始浇筑第一小层(方案二)和按日平均温度浇筑各层混凝土(方案三)。计算时段间隔为 3～6h，计算结果见图 4、图 5。输出部位为第一大层顶面。图中所标时间计算起点均为第一小层开浇时刻。方案一标注为晚上，方案二标注为白天，方案三标注为平均值。由温度分布图可见：

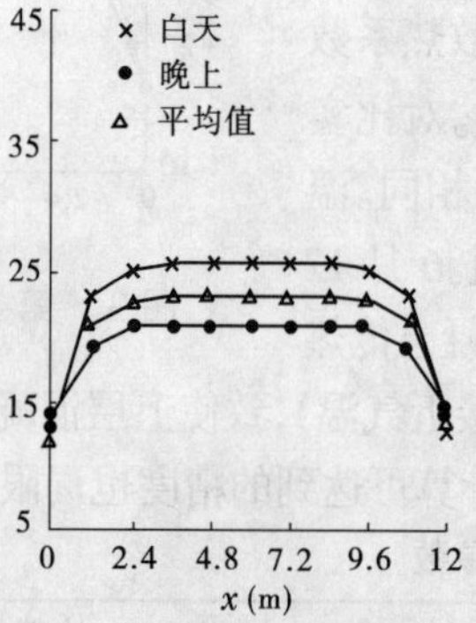

图 4　第 10d 温度分布

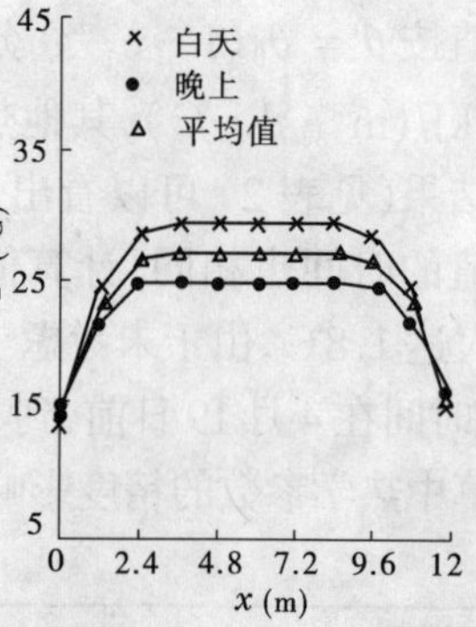

图 5　第 14d 温度分布

(1)采用白天入仓方案时混凝土的温度值比较高，一般比晚上入仓方案高出 3～4℃。因此，在工程实际中，应尽量利用晚上浇筑混凝土，避开白天高温期，以降低混凝土的温度值。

(2)采用日平均气温入仓方案得到的混凝土温度值介于白天和晚上入仓方案之间。这表明在混凝土非稳定积累温度场计算中采用日平均气温以简化计算的做法是可以接受的，其计算结果在工程实际中具有较好的应用价值。

4　碾压混凝土拱坝施工期坝体温度变化计算示例

某碾压混凝土拱坝地处北方，在初冬低温季节浇筑基础混凝土，冬季 12 月 5 日以后因冰冻停止浇筑。由于冬季最低温度为 −15～−20℃，为了保温，用水浸泡，以免过多超

冷(低于运行期温度)引起基础混凝土裂缝。待春季3月初解冻后继续浇筑混凝土,坝体拟在夏季前完成碾压混凝土高程162.0m,用DTTS程序计算典型结果如图6～图8所示。可见施工前期表面散热内部形成高温区,由于初冬入仓温度低(8.4℃),内部最高温度为18～20℃,远低于6月份入仓混凝土最高温升值35℃,随外界气温下降,浸水前内外温差加大到16℃。这里尚未计入寒潮影响,可见秋冬浇筑的混凝土要努力避免内外温差过大引起的表面裂缝。冬季虽然采用浸水保温,减少了内外温差,但是整体混凝土温度下降,施工期混凝土受基础约束大于运行期,可能超过按运行期拟定的温控约束应力,使表面裂缝向内延伸为贯穿裂缝。

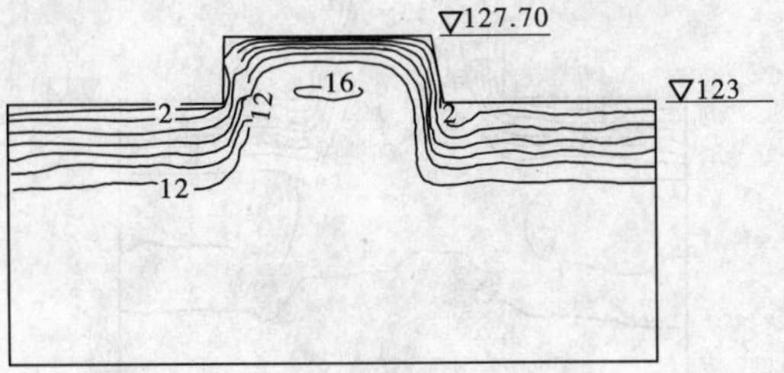

图6 中央坝段温度场(1992年12月5日,水温0℃)

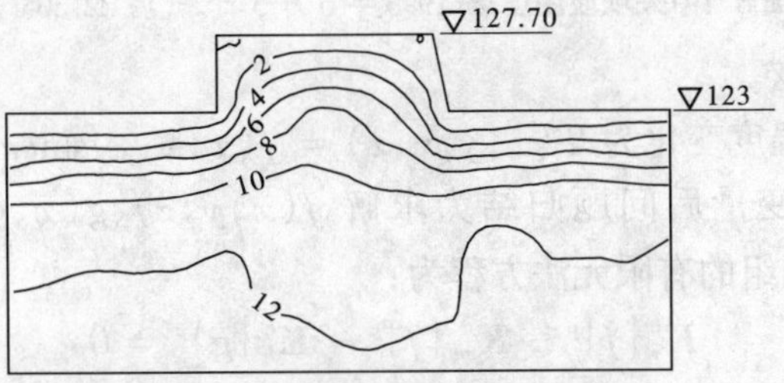

图7 中央坝段温度场(1993年3月1日,水温0℃)

5 运行期拱坝温度场计算

拱坝长期运行后混凝土水化热温升已很少,计算中可忽略不计($\theta=0$)。实际上当坝体厚度小于30m时整个拱坝都处于简谐变温场影响中(运行期不存在稳定温度场)。运行期结构变温场(因$\theta=0$)热传导方程为

$$\frac{\partial T}{\partial \tau}=a_x\frac{\partial^2 T}{\partial x^2}+a_y\frac{\partial^2 T}{\partial y^2}+a_z\frac{\partial^2 T}{\partial z^2} \quad (在域\ \Omega\ 内) \tag{5}$$

由于物体在不同的边界面分别作用有变幅不同但周期相同的简谐变化的温度时,域内任一点的温度均做同一周期的简谐变化,但振幅和相位随坐标而变。因此,问题的解可写成稳定温度场和简谐变温场。

边界条件:在C_1上(变温) $T=f_0\sin\omega\tau+g_0\cos\omega\tau+T_{01}$

在C_2上(恒温) $T=T_{02}$

在C_3上(绝热) $a_x\frac{\partial T}{\partial x}n_x+a_y\frac{\partial T}{\partial y}n_y+a_z\frac{\partial T}{\partial z}n_z=0$

式中:f_0、g_0为边界C_1上的温度变幅;T_{01}、T_{02}为边界C_1、C_2上的稳定温度;n_x、n_y、n_z为

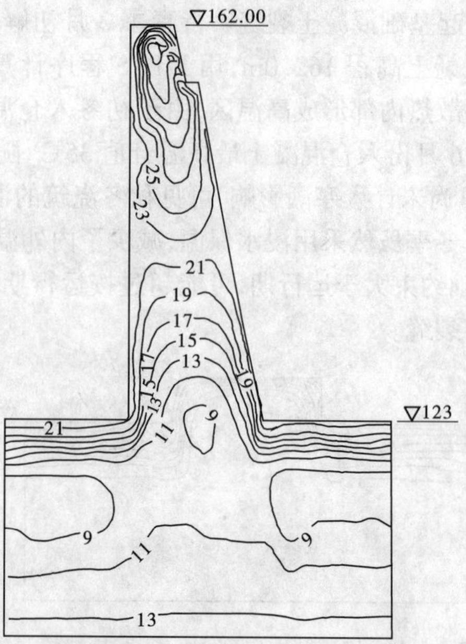

图 8　中央坝段温度场(1993 年 6 月 5 日,气温 22.30℃)

边界面法向的方向余弦。

设域内任一点的温度变化为 $T(x,y,z,\tau) = f(x,y,z)\sin\omega\tau + g(x,y,z)\cos\omega\tau + T_0(x,y,z)$,则分离变量后问题归结为求解 $f(x,y,z)$、$g(x,y,z)$、$T_0(x,y,z)$。用 Galerkin 方法求解方程组的有限元法方程为:

$$\begin{gathered}
\boldsymbol{K}_i^{\mathrm{e}}\{f\}^{\mathrm{e}} - \boldsymbol{K}_m^{\mathrm{e}}\{f\}^{\mathrm{e}} - \boldsymbol{K}_h^{\mathrm{e}}\{g\}^{\mathrm{e}} = 0 \\
\boldsymbol{K}_i^{\mathrm{e}}\{g\}^{\mathrm{e}} - \boldsymbol{K}_m^{\mathrm{e}}\{g\}^{\mathrm{e}} - \boldsymbol{K}_h^{\mathrm{e}}\{g\}^{\mathrm{e}} = 0 \\
\boldsymbol{K}_i^{\mathrm{e}} = \iiint_{\Omega^{\mathrm{e}}}\left(a_x \frac{\partial \boldsymbol{N}^{\mathrm{T}}}{\partial x}\frac{\partial \boldsymbol{N}}{\partial x} + a_y \frac{\partial \boldsymbol{N}^{\mathrm{T}}}{\partial y}\frac{\partial \boldsymbol{N}}{\partial y} + a_z \frac{\partial \boldsymbol{N}^{\mathrm{T}}}{\partial z}\frac{\partial \boldsymbol{N}}{\partial z}\right)\mathrm{d}\Omega \\
\boldsymbol{K}_m^{\mathrm{e}} = \iint_s \boldsymbol{N}^{\mathrm{T}}\left(a_x \frac{\partial \boldsymbol{N}}{\partial x}n_x + a_y \frac{\partial \boldsymbol{N}}{\partial y}n_y + a_z \frac{\partial \boldsymbol{N}}{\partial z}n_z\right)\mathrm{d}S \\
\boldsymbol{K}_h^{\mathrm{e}} = \iiint_{\Omega^{\mathrm{e}}} \boldsymbol{N}^{\mathrm{T}}\boldsymbol{N}\omega\,\mathrm{d}\Omega
\end{gathered} \tag{6}$$

式中:$\mathrm{d}\Omega = \mathrm{d}x\mathrm{d}y\mathrm{d}z$;$\Omega^{\mathrm{e}}$ 为单元的体积域。将边界条件代入,并将各单元集成得

$$\begin{gathered}
\boldsymbol{K}_i\{f\} - \boldsymbol{K}_h\{g\} = 0 \\
\boldsymbol{K}_i\{g\} + \boldsymbol{K}_h\{f\} = 0
\end{gathered} \tag{7}$$

式中:$\boldsymbol{K}_i = \sum_{i=1}^{m}\boldsymbol{K}_i^{\mathrm{e}}$;$\boldsymbol{K}_h = \sum_{i=1}^{m}\boldsymbol{K}_h^{\mathrm{e}}$;$\boldsymbol{K}_m = \sum_{i=1}^{m}\boldsymbol{K}_m^{\mathrm{e}} = 0$,$m$ 为单元个数。

联立求解方程组(7)可得$\{f\}\{g\}$,并求解稳定热传导方程求出 T_0,可得最终温度场。

用上述方法计算某碾压混凝土拱坝运行期简谐变温场示例如:坝体内部不同高程的温度变化见图 9。1 月份坝体温度场见图 10。将各时间温度场扣除施工期后期(蓄水前)温度场即得施工后期到运行期坝体温度变化值。施工期及运行期温度变化组成了混凝土结构温度变化全过程,它更接近坝体温度变化真实过程。

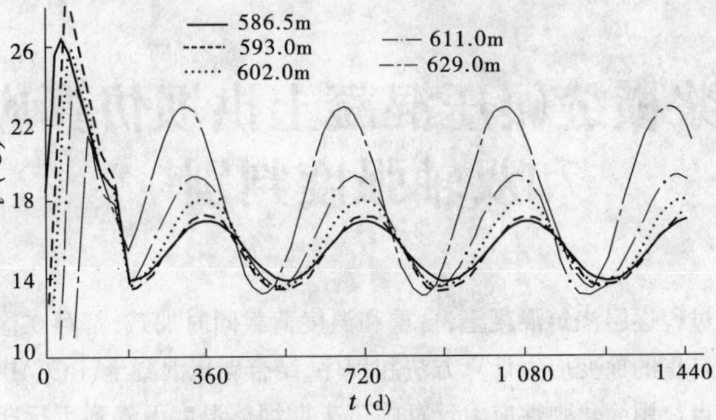

图 9　坝体内部温度变化过程图

6　讨论

(1)本文研究碾压混凝土拱坝温度变化全过程，由施工期(蓄水前)温度变化和运行期相对施工后期的温度变化组成更接近真实的温度仿真过程，也为仿真温度应力计算提供了条件。

(2)工艺对施工期温度变化及运行期温降总值影响大，仿真计算表明，不仅要限制运行期温降总值，也要限制施工期内外温差及超冷。

(3)本文提供的温度变化计算原理程序简明，现场温度计实测结果较确切，便于进行计算和实测比较。

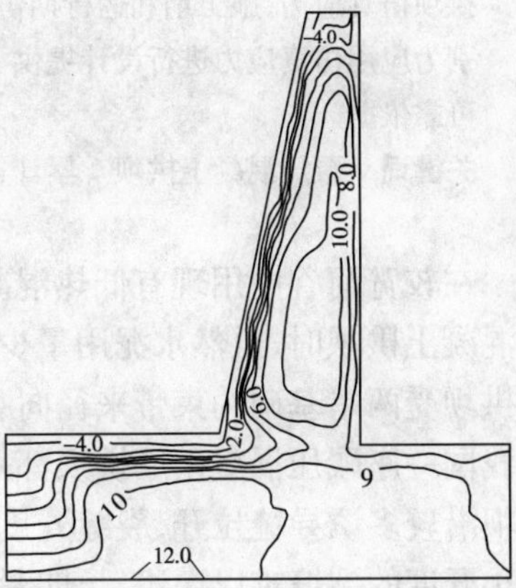

图10　1月份拱冠梁温度场

(4)实用计算中温度累计变化所需机时少，微型计算机即可胜任，便于在工程中广泛使用。

参 考 文 献

[1] 刘志辉. 碾压混凝土拱坝累积温度场和仿真应力场的研究：[学位论文]. 北京：清华大学水利水电工程系，1994

含灌浆横缝碾压混凝土拱坝仿真应力和双轴强度判别

摘　要　由于施工过程逐层浇筑混凝土，自重和温度荷载同时加载，都存在徐变效应。作者提供了累计温度和自重的徐变应力计算方法和程序，结合碾压混凝土(RCC)拱坝工程提供了施工期仿真应力特点。用简化弹性应力计算施工末期坝体温度下降到运行期坝体稳定变温场受河床及两岸基础和自身相对变形的约束应力，并和水压应力叠加取得运行期碾压混凝土拱坝仿真应力，施工期和运行期仿真应力形成最终组合应力。文中提供的混凝土双轴强度判别为应用仿真应力进行设计提供了条件，仿真计算为碾压混凝土拱坝设计和工程实践提供了可靠依据。

关键词　碾压混凝土拱坝　累计自重　徐变应力　仿真应力计算

在较宽河谷中用现有低热混凝土(绝热温升 11～15℃)以大仓面 RCC 法快速修建碾压混凝土拱坝时，虽然水泥用量少，温升小，可省去人工冷却措施，有时仍需设置横缝以防止拱坝受两岸基础约束带来径向裂缝破坏拱坝的整体性。南非两座碾压混凝土重力拱坝和我国一座碾压混凝土厚拱坝都采用径向诱导缝并在缝面设灌浆设施。运行后南非重力拱坝沿较多诱导缝拉开，裂缝开度 0.1～3mm，较宽的裂缝经灌浆处理改善了渗水状态，但小开度的裂缝难以灌浆，长期漏水。因重力拱坝受力以梁为主，裂缝破坏平面拱未引起失事。对于平面拱分载较多的碾压混凝土拱坝，这种径向缝加大上游坝踵梁向拉力，对坝体应力影响大，需认真研究。碾压混凝土拱坝设置灌浆横缝或诱导缝虽可避免其他失控的径向裂缝，但由于碾压混凝土工艺和埋设大量冷却水管干扰，内部往往不设冷却水管，仅依靠坝体表面散热，这样缓慢地降温到稳定温度变场需很长的时间，它影响拱坝横缝灌浆及投入运行的时间，若施工末期强行提前灌浆蓄水则坝体运行期进一步降温可能重新拉开灌浆缝。为此，需研究破坏整体拱作用后拱坝应力重分布的后果(另文讨论)。本文讨论仿真应力计算方法、碾压混凝土拱坝仿真应力规律和仿真强度判别。

1　仿真应力计算方法

近代力学的数值方法和计算机的发展提供了仿真计算的可能性，仿真应力计算和以往设计计算的不同之处在于：①施工期按混凝土浇筑过程逐块累计温度场及累计自重和温度徐变应力(因为自重和温度荷载实际上同时加载，变化的体型不断受到下部和两岸约束)；②施工末期坝体温度场缓慢下降到运行期坝体变温场的约束应力(包括蓄水前未灌浆和蓄水后灌浆成整体后温度下降的约束应力，后者往往引起较大拉应力)，将上述应力和水压应力叠加即为组合应力；③分别采用混凝土实测热学和力学参数以及混凝土双轴强度；④对于施工期或运行期超强度破坏部分进行应力重分布计算(即考虑局部超极限拉

本文选自《清华大学学报(自然科学版)》1996 年第 1 期，作者还有张国新、刘志辉。

压强度破坏过程及断裂后裂缝的延伸和影响,另文讨论)。

目前用有限元法计算水压应力和温降弹性应力的程序已经是成熟的。施工期累计温度变化、施工末期温度场和运行期坝体温度变场差值另文刊出,以下介绍累计温度及自重徐变应力计算。

(1) 徐变变形分析[1]。前期混凝土受力变形(温度、自重)与固化过程的温度状态有关,碾压混凝土常用大比例掺合料并在低温季节(月平均 5 ~ 15℃)浇筑,徐变变形和标准 20℃ 条件的混凝土徐变曲线相差较多,宜用相近温度的徐变曲线进行变形分析。将时间离散成 N 个子区间,为减少计算量,在任一子区间 $[t_{i-1}, t_i](i = 1,2,\cdots,N)$ 上取 $\partial\sigma/\partial t$ 为常数,则从 t_0 时刻加载到 t 时的混凝土徐变变形为

$$\varepsilon^c(t) = \int_{t_0}^{t} c(t,\tau)\frac{\partial\sigma}{\partial\tau}\mathrm{d}\tau = \sum_{i=1}^{N}\int_{t_{i-1}}^{t_i} c(t,\tau)\frac{\partial\sigma}{\partial\tau}\mathrm{d}\tau = \sum_{i=1}^{N}\omega_i \tag{1}$$

式中:σ 为应力;τ 为龄期;徐变度为

$$c(t,\tau) = c(\tau)[1 - \mathrm{e}^{-k(t-\tau)}] \tag{2}$$

由相邻时段徐变变形关系得

$$\omega_{n+1} = \omega_n \mathrm{e}^{-k\Delta\tau_n} + \Delta\sigma_n c_n f_n \mathrm{e}^{-k\Delta\tau_n},\quad \omega_0 = \Delta\sigma_0 c_0 \tag{3}$$

式中:$f_n = (\mathrm{e}^{-k\Delta\tau_n} - 1)/k\Delta\tau_n$;$\Delta\tau_n = t_n - t_{n-1}$。对于复杂应力状态

$$\{\Delta\varepsilon_n^c\} = (1 - \mathrm{e}^{-k\Delta\tau_n})\{\omega_n\} + \boldsymbol{Q}\{\Delta\sigma_n\}c_n(1 - f_n\mathrm{e}^{-k\Delta\tau_n}) \tag{4}$$

式中:$\{\omega_n\} = \mathrm{e}^{-k\Delta\tau_n}\{\omega_{n-1}\} + \boldsymbol{Q}\{\Delta\sigma_{n-1}\}c_{n-1}f_{n-1}\mathrm{e}^{-k\Delta\tau_{n-1}} \quad \{\omega_1\} = \boldsymbol{Q}\{\Delta\sigma_0\}c_0$

$$\boldsymbol{Q} = \begin{bmatrix} 1 & -\nu & -\nu & 0 & 0 & 0 \\ -\nu & 1 & -\nu & 0 & 0 & 0 \\ -\nu & -\nu & 1 & 0 & 0 & 0 \\ 0 & 0 & 0 & 2(1+\nu) & 0 & 0 \\ 0 & 0 & 0 & 0 & 2(1+\nu) & 0 \\ 0 & 0 & 0 & 0 & 0 & 2(1+\nu) \end{bmatrix}$$

$$\boldsymbol{D} = \frac{\boldsymbol{E}_n(1-\nu)}{(1+\nu)(1-2\nu)}\begin{bmatrix} 1 & \frac{\nu}{1-\nu} & \frac{\nu}{1-\nu} & 0 & 0 & 0 \\ 0 & 1 & \frac{\nu}{1-\nu} & 0 & 0 & 0 \\ 0 & 0 & 1 & 0 & 0 & 0 \\ 0 & 0 & 0 & \frac{1-2\nu}{2(1-\nu)} & 0 & 0 \\ 0 & 0 & 0 & 0 & \frac{1-2\nu}{2(1-\nu)} & 0 \\ 0 & 0 & 0 & 0 & 0 & \frac{1-2\nu}{2(1-\nu)} \end{bmatrix}$$

(2) 徐变应力分析。以平面应力问题说明,若第 n 个时段某单元的应变增量为

$$\{\Delta\varepsilon_n\} = \{\Delta\varepsilon_n^e\} + \{\Delta\varepsilon_n^c\} + \{\Delta\varepsilon_n^\tau\} + \{\Delta\varepsilon_n^o\} \tag{5}$$

式中:$\{\Delta\varepsilon_n^e\}$ 为弹性应变增量;$\{\Delta\varepsilon_n^c\}$ 为温度、自重等徐变变形增量;$\{\Delta\varepsilon_n^\tau\}$ 为温差应变增量;$\{\Delta\varepsilon_n^o\}$ 为自生体积变形增量。由式(4)、式(5) 知

$$\{\Delta\sigma_n\} = \overline{\boldsymbol{D}}_n(\boldsymbol{B}\{\Delta\delta_n\} - \{\omega_n\}(1 - \mathrm{e}^{-k\Delta\tau_n} - \{\Delta\varepsilon_n^{\mathrm{T}}\} - \{\Delta\varepsilon_n^{o}\} \tag{6}$$

式中：

$$\overline{\boldsymbol{D}}_n = \frac{\boldsymbol{D}_n}{1 + c_n(1 - f_n \mathrm{e}^{-k\Delta\tau_n}) \cdot E_{(t_{n-1}+\frac{1}{2}\Delta\tau_n)}}$$

$\boldsymbol{B}$ 为应变和位移转换矩阵。由虚功原理可得

$$\boldsymbol{K}^e\{\Delta\delta_n\} = \{\Delta P_n^c\}^e + \{\Delta P_n^T\}^e + \{\Delta P_n^o\}^e + \{F\}^e \tag{7}$$

式中：$\boldsymbol{K}^e = \boldsymbol{B}^{\mathrm{T}}\overline{\boldsymbol{D}}_n\boldsymbol{B}A$ 为单元刚度阵，A 为单元面积；$\{\Delta P_n^c\}_{\mathrm{T}}^e = \boldsymbol{B}^{\mathrm{T}}\overline{\boldsymbol{D}}_n\{\omega_n\}(1 - \mathrm{e}^{-k\Delta\tau_n})A$ 为单元温度、自重等徐变变形所产生的当量荷载增量；$\{\Delta P_n^{\mathrm{T}}\}^e = \boldsymbol{B}^{\mathrm{T}}\overline{\boldsymbol{D}}_n\{\Delta\varepsilon_n^{\mathrm{T}}\}\mathrm{d}x\mathrm{d}y$ 为单元温差荷载增量；$\{\Delta P_n^o\}^{\mathrm{e}} = \boldsymbol{B}^{\mathrm{T}}\overline{\boldsymbol{D}}_n\iint\{\Delta\varepsilon_n^o\}\mathrm{d}x\mathrm{d}y$ 为自生体积变形产生的当量荷载增量；$\{F\}^e$ 为单元外力列阵。由式(7)对全部单元集成可得总体矩阵方程

$$\boldsymbol{K}\{\Delta\delta_n\} = \{\Delta P_n^c\} + \{\Delta P_n^{\mathrm{T}}\} + \{\Delta P_n^o\} + \{F\} \tag{8}$$

解上式得$\{\Delta\delta_n\}$，再由式(6)可算应力。

为拟合混凝土徐变试验资料及方便应力分析中的数学运算，本文采用$\sum_{j=1}^{r} c_i^{(j)}[1 - \mathrm{e}^{-k_j(t-\tau)}]$类型函数表示混凝土徐变度。当$\gamma = 1$时复杂应力状态下隐式解中混凝土徐变变形见式(4)，相应应力按式(6)计算；对一般情况 $\gamma \neq 1$ 时徐变变形为

$$\{\Delta\varepsilon_n^c\} = \sum_{j=1}^{\gamma}\{\omega_n^{(j)}\}(1 - \mathrm{e}^{k_j\Delta\tau_n}) + \boldsymbol{Q}\{\Delta\sigma_n\}c_n^{(j)}(1 - f_n^{(j)}\mathrm{e}^{-k_j\Delta\tau_n}) \tag{9}$$

式中：

$$\{\omega_n^{(j)}\} = \{\omega_{n-1}^{(j)}\}\mathrm{e}^{k_j\Delta\tau_{n-1}} + \boldsymbol{Q}\{\Delta\sigma_{n-1}\}c_{n-1}^{(j)}(1 - f_{n-1}^{(j)}\mathrm{e}^{-k_j\Delta\tau_{n-1}})$$

$$\{\omega_1^{(j)}\} = \boldsymbol{Q}\{\Delta\sigma_0\}c_0^{(j)}$$

徐变应力：

$$\{\Delta\sigma_n\} = \overline{\boldsymbol{D}}_n(\boldsymbol{B}\{\Delta\delta_n\} - \sum_{j=1}^{\gamma}\{\omega_n^{(j)}\}(1 - \mathrm{e}^{-k_j\Delta\tau_n}) - \{\Delta\varepsilon_n^{\mathrm{T}}\} - \{\Delta\varepsilon_n^o\}) \tag{10}$$

式中：

$$\overline{\boldsymbol{D}}_n = \frac{\boldsymbol{D}_n}{1 + E\left(t_{n-1} + \frac{1}{2}\Delta\tau_n\right)\sum_{j=1}^{\gamma}\{c_n^{(j)}\}(1 - f_n^{(j)}\mathrm{e}^{k_j\Delta\tau_n})}$$

由虚功原理，式(8)仍然成立，但相应公式中$\{\Delta P_n^c\} = \boldsymbol{B}^{\mathrm{T}}\overline{\boldsymbol{D}}_n\sum_{j=1}^{\gamma}\{\omega_n^{(j)}\}(1 - \mathrm{e}^{k_j\Delta\tau_n})A$，对全部单元集成解出$\{\Delta\delta_n\}$后由式(10)计算应力。

用 FORTRAN77 语言编制了大坝三维累积温度与仿真应力场计算通用计算机程序 DTTS，用计算机可解大型结构问题。

2　混凝土承受能力

由混凝土试验的极限拉伸，7d、28d、90d 抗压强度和弹模以及混凝土双轴强度规律，可确定混凝土施工期和运行期的强度判据：施工前期应力单调变化用极限破坏强度；单轴拉力极限用极限拉伸乘 1/2 弹模，双轴拉力用 0.9 倍单轴拉力强度；超过 90d 龄期用后期相应极限破坏强度。双轴压力比 σ_2/σ_3 为 0.05 ～ 0.2 时，最大压应力 σ_3 允许值增大 10% ～ 40%；拉压应力状态时，侧压力增长 10% ～ 50%，最大拉应力 σ_1 允许值下降 10% ～ 50%。应力单调变化时允许拉应力用混凝土极限拉伸值乘相应后期弹模。

运行期仍以 28d 和 90d 抗压强度和极限拉伸作为基本参数，按双轴强度规律换算双轴强度参数。考虑到长期荷载及疲劳作用，混凝土按内部未出现微裂缝损伤的强度(35%极限强度) 作为设计强度进行水压和累计自重荷载应力判别。组合应力(包括温度荷载)仍用 70% 极限强度判别，超载后温度应力因裂缝松弛按应力重分布计算。

3 含横缝碾压混凝土拱坝仿真应力算例

在不利的(干燥、温度变幅大)中国北方气候条件下(夏季月平均气温 20℃以上占 4 个月，冬季月平均温度在零度以下占 3 个月)修建碾压混凝土拱坝，坝址河谷呈 U 形，坝顶长 176m，坝高 47.5m(见图 1、图 2)，底宽 13m。

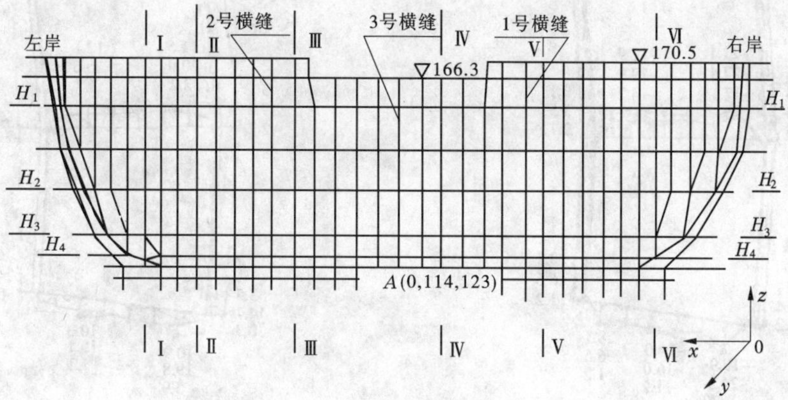

图 1 拱坝计算网格上游立视图(无水平裂缝)

拱坝中部分三条横缝，间隔 30m。两岸各设诱导缝 1 条，缝面预留灌浆设施。混凝土工程量 6.2 万 m^3，浇筑混凝土将连续浇筑至层高为 1.5～1.8m，间歇 5d。拱坝由 1992 年春季浇筑常规混凝土垫层开始到 1994 年底完成。未采取人工温控措施，冬季和夏季停止施工。

1992 年 10 月 30 日开始浇筑垫层混凝土。由于入仓及外界气温较低(8.4℃)，浇筑后坝体内部最高温升较低，两层浇筑后内部最高温度为 18℃，上游二级配的混凝土局部最高温度达 22℃。计算和实测都表明施工前期典型温度分布是内部高表面低。由于基础约束内部形成较大压应力(见图 3)，最大达 −2.74MPa，外部为拉应力，达 0.93MPa，数值由下而上迅速衰减。冬季保温注水后，坝块温度下降，基础约束引起 12 月的内部压力由 $\sigma_x = -2.11$MPa 减少到 1.1MPa(σ_x 为沿坝轴方向)，表面拉应力增大到 2.56MPa，随着坝体温度进一步降低，内部应力由压应力变为拉应力。1993 年 3 月(见图 4)在坝轴方向全部变为拉应力，最大达 2.2MPa。由现场可观察到 30m 间距拱坝横缝实际张开达 3mm。由于坝段内拉应力尚小于碾压混凝土应力反向变化的极限抗拉能力，坝段中(工

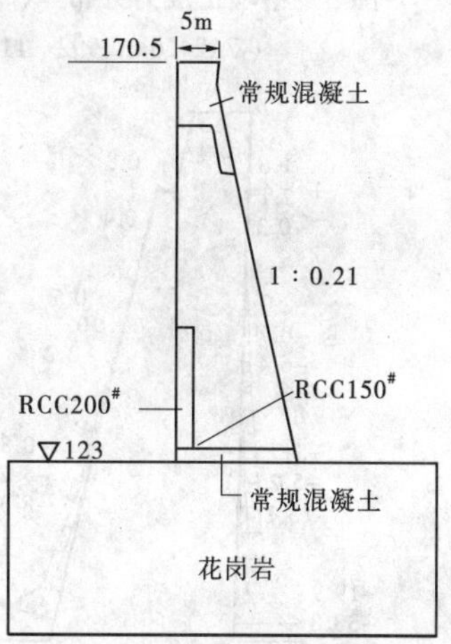

图 2 坝体剖面和材料分区示意图

程中)未发现新的裂缝,因此利用低温季节浇筑混凝土以降低最高温升仍然是必要的。施工期超冷未出现破坏,运行期内部温度较高亦可保证安全。春季3月中以后浇筑的混凝土由于表面气温不断升高,减少了内外温差,有时超过前期最高温度。6月5日在▽127.5m表面拱向σ_x甚至出现-0.64MPa的压应力(见图5),自重压力影响加大,σ_z铅垂压力达-2.02MPa。▽150m以上尽管浇筑后温升值高,但约束少,应力较小,均小于0.4MPa。上述温度和应力变化过程实际上是春季和秋季浇筑碾压混凝土的典型过程。

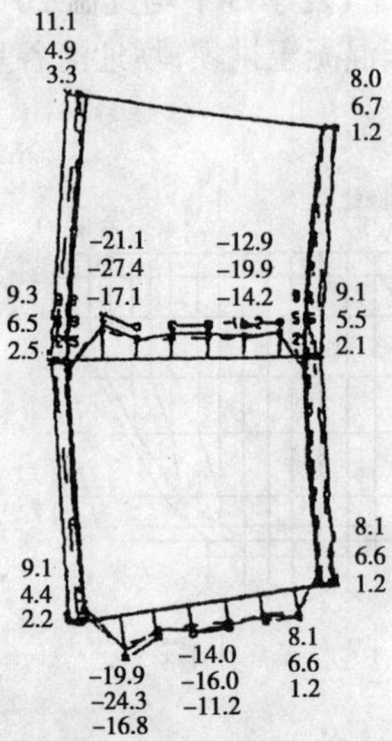

图3　中坝正应力分布　(单位:0.1MPa)
(▽124.6m,1992-11-05)

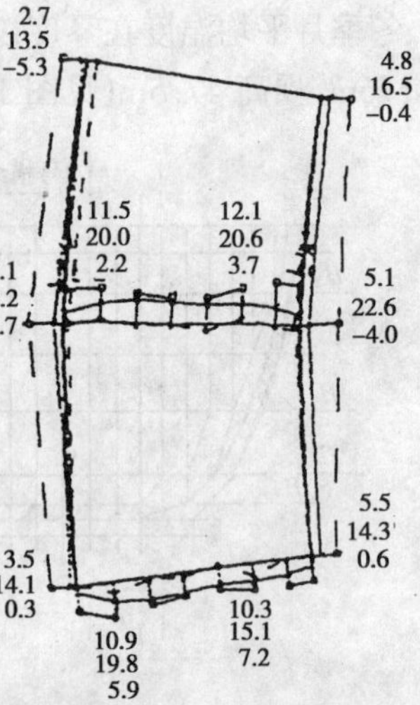

图4　中坝正应力分布　(单位:0.1MPa)
(▽124.6,1993-03-01)

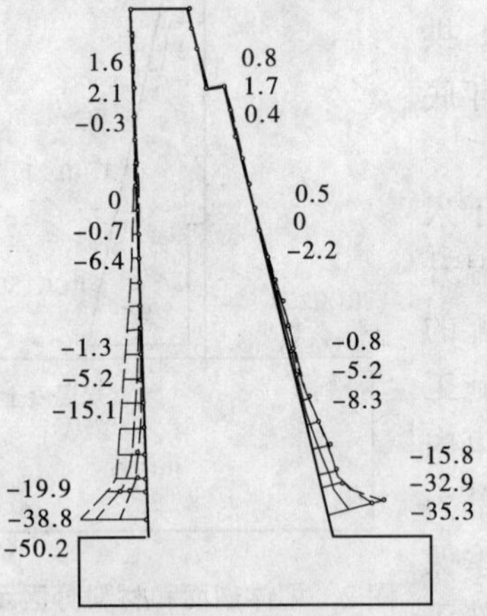

图5　中坝上下游正应力分布　(单位:0.1MPa)
(1993-06-05)

若1993年6月拱坝浇筑完即进行横缝灌浆形成整体以满足汛期拦洪拱坝传力要求,则从6月初温度场变化到运行期简谐变温场引起较大拉应力,和水压应力叠加如图6、图7所示。坝址最低月平均温度为-7℃(1月份),最高为28℃,坝体较薄,计算和实测都表明整个坝体都处于变温场中。1月份拱冠上游▽127.5m拱向拉力σ_x达+2.6MPa,下游达+4.75MPa,抵消了夏季的压力储备,上部拱圈应力减小。夏季受库水温影响,▽140m以下的上游面仍有拱向拉力,▽127.5m达+1.93MPa,下游面气温加热后拱向为压应力,▽127.5m达-3.86MPa,拉应力区转向坝体内部(见图8),最大σ_x值亦达+2.76MPa。冬季表面裂缝在夏季可向内部延伸,推迟灌浆时间可以降低灌浆时坝体温度,明显降低上游拱向拉应力,但坝体自然降温时间缓慢,明显影响拱坝灌浆期整体作用时间。拱坝下游面拱向温度应力的拉应力变幅达8.

7MPa,难以用坝段降温后灌浆来消除,需作钢筋混凝土或其他保温防护。

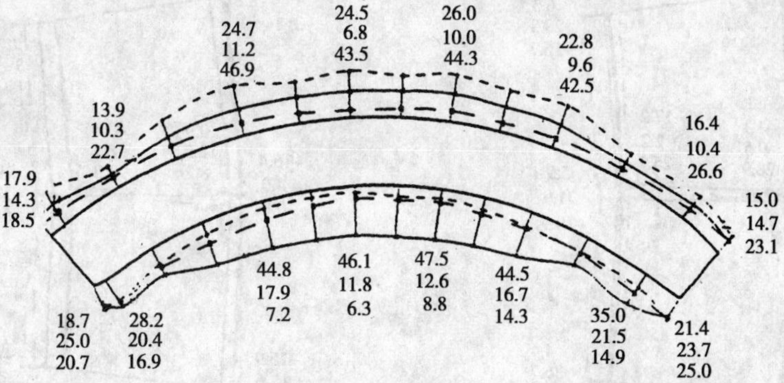

图 6　1 月正应力分布(▽127.5m)　(单位:0.1MPa)

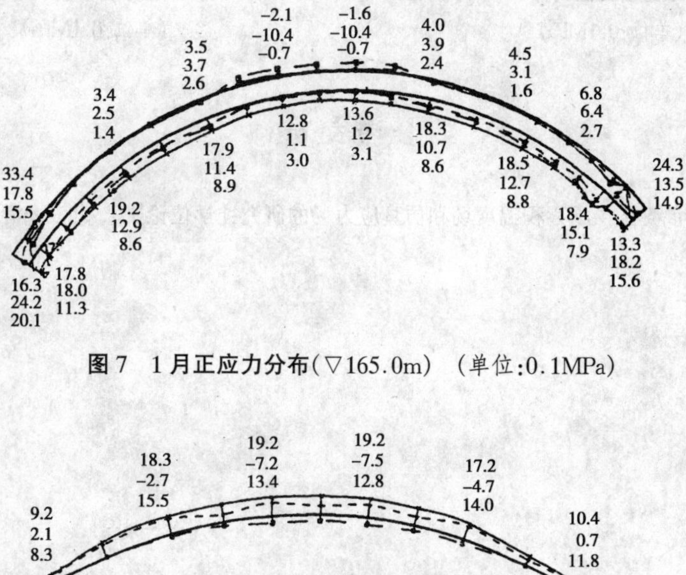

图 7　1 月正应力分布(▽165.0m)　(单位:0.1MPa)

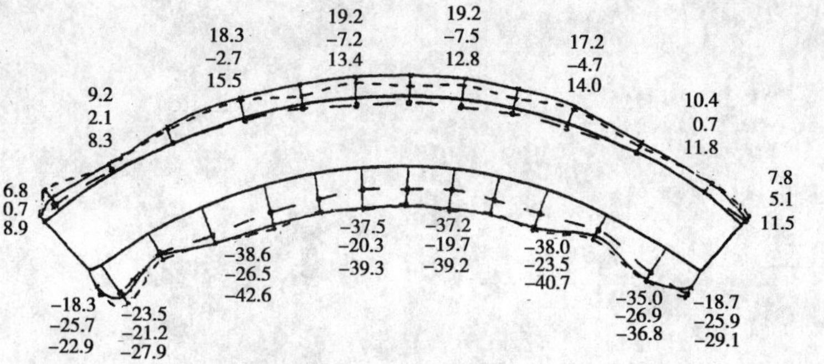

图 8　7 月正应力分布(▽127.5m)

施工末期和运行期应力叠加形成坝体各时间的组合应力,可见碾压混凝土拱坝应力中温降拉应力在组合应力中占主要部分。由图 9、图 10 可见,1 月份拱冠上游坝踵梁向拉应力 σ_z 达 2.89~3.6MPa,易于出现水平裂缝。7 月份下游坝踵 σ_z 达 −6.6MPa,冬季或夏季即使变位较大的上部拱作用力也不大,都有待降低坝体温度后灌浆以消减冬季的上游坝踵梁向拉力。

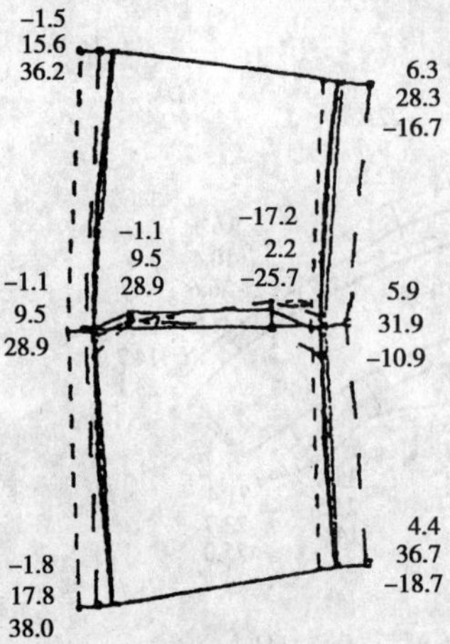

图 9　1 月份中坝组合正应力分布(▽127.7m)
(单位:0.1MPa)

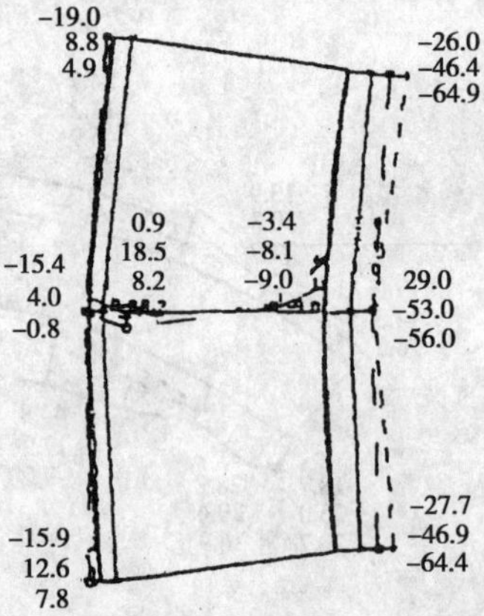

图 10　7 月份中坝组合正应力分布(▽127.7m)
(单位:0.1MPa)

参 考 文 献

[1] 刘志辉. 碾压混凝土拱坝累积温度场和仿真应力场的研究:[学位论文]. 北京:清华大学水利水电工程系,1994

含横缝碾压混凝土拱坝的变形和应力重分布

摘　要　研究含横缝碾压混凝土拱坝工作状态。含横缝碾压混凝土拱坝未灌浆前若出现洪水强迫蓄水,横缝或诱导缝在施工末期(汛前)灌浆,由于蓄水后坝体进一步降温重新拉开灌浆缝都会破坏拱坝整体性。当缝宽不大时(＜0.5mm),在水压自重作用下梁向变位加大,可将部分拱重新压紧,形成应力重新分布。作者用体积向量提高简化计算中缝的变形场精度。坝踵水平裂缝出现后,拱作用逐渐加大,梁向大变位和接触形成新拱可使水平裂缝停止扩展。

关键词　碾压混凝土拱坝　应力重分布　体积向量　横缝

整体碾压混凝土拱坝内部温度较高,降温时往往受两岸基础约束,容易引起径向裂缝,如两座南非碾压混凝土重力拱坝和我国一座碾压混凝土拱围堰都出现较多径向裂缝。当拱坝含有各种裂缝时,其受力和变化特性与完整坝体相比有很大变化。裂缝的存在将对坝体的安全运行起不利作用[1~3]。因此,研究含横缝碾压混凝土拱坝的缝宽和拱变形限制,研究应力重分布后局部破坏范围和稳定性,不仅是研究已有开裂拱坝工作状态的需要,也是为更广泛使用碾压混凝土拱坝提供条件。

1　计算方法

由于拱坝尺寸大,而缝宽相对较小,本文将用体积向量提高缝面接触判别精度。

1.1　横缝的力学模型

(1)当横缝宽 $\Delta>0$ 时,缝面间均不能传递拉、压、剪力。

(2)当横缝面受力变形接触合并时,缝面间能传递压、剪力,但不能传递拉力。

(3)当横缝面处切向剪应力 $\tau>\sigma_n f$(σ_n 为缝面法向正应力,f 为摩擦系数)时,已经接触合并的缝面允许产生剪切错动。

1.2　计算处理

根据 1.1 所采用的力学模型,在计算中对缝面作如下处理:当横缝保持张开,缝宽 $\Delta>0$ 时,缝面处设置双排节点,不传力,缝面相当两处独立的边界。

当横缝受力变形,缝宽 $\Delta=0$ 时,双排节点合并为一节点,节点能承受压、剪作用。此时,当节点沿缝面出现法向拉应力,这节点又重新分开成双排节点;当节点处沿缝面剪应力 $\tau>\sigma_n f$(σ_n,f 如 1.1 中所定义)时,双排节点可以沿缝面产生错动。

(1)缝面接触合并的判断。如图 1、图 2 所示,缝面处单元节点编号,需要判断缝面 1234 和缝面 5678 是否接触。

对于三维问题,每个节点都有三个位移分量。采用右手法则,四面体体积 $V_{1245}=(\overline{12}\cdot\overline{14})\times\overline{15}$,当 $V_{1245}>0$ 时,节点 5 在缝面 124 外,否则节点 5 和缝面 124 接触。对缝面的所有节点进行这样的判断处理,即可得到当前状况下缝面的接触合并情况。

本文选自《清华大学学报(自然科学版)》1996 年第 1 期,作者还有邱德隆。

(2)已接触合并的缝面双节点因出现拉应力或剪切力过大而分开或产生错动的判断。如图 3 所示,缝面 1234 和缝面 5678 在外力(增量)作用下已经接触合并,仅考虑 1 节点处应力状态,1 节点处缝面外法向 $\overline{n}=\overline{12}\times\overline{14}$,则由 1 节点处应力状态 σ_x、σ_y、σ_z、τ_{xy}、τ_{yz}、τ_{xz} 即可得出垂直缝面法向正应力 σ_n 和切向剪力 τ。当 $\tau>\sigma_n f$ 或 $\sigma_n>0$ 时,1、5 节点将重新分开成双排节点,此时错动的 1、5 节点按两独立节点计算。否则,1、5 节点维持原状。本文用 FORTRAN 语言编制了三维弹性有限元程序。

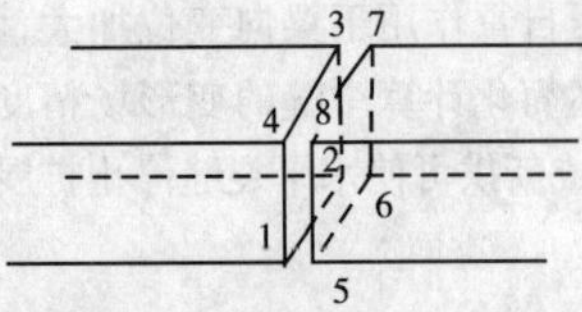

图 1　缝面单元节点

图 2　位移向量

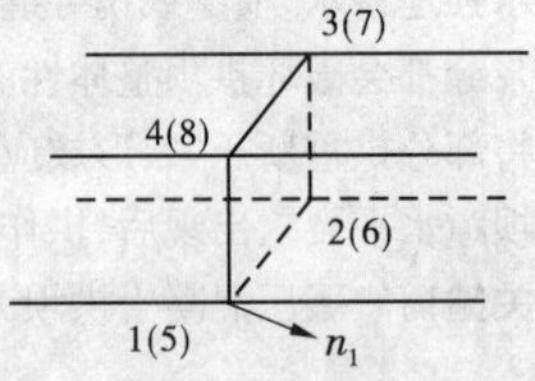

图 3　缝面接触

2　含横缝碾压混凝土拱坝受力变形和应力规律

2.1　计算条件和内容

2.1.1　基本资料

某碾压混凝土拱坝前缘总长 187.867m,由 4 个坝段组成,中间设有 3 条横缝,其中中间横缝位于拱坝中心线,两侧各一条,距中间横缝各为 30m,如图 4 所示。三条横缝均从坝底高程延伸到坝顶处,坝体最大中心角为 103.5°,坝顶高程为 170.5m,坝基最低高程为 123.0m,最大坝高为 47.5m,基础宽 13.61m。

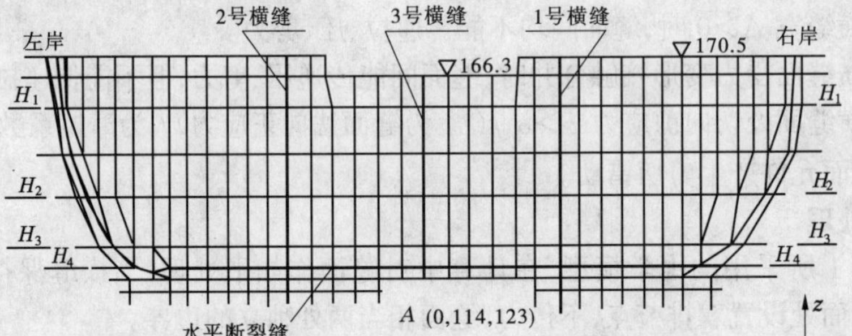

图 4　拱坝计算网格上游立视图(含水平断裂缝)

2.1.2　计算类型和工况

计算分以下三种情况:①坝体无横缝为整体时,作用水压加自重载荷;②坝体有横缝且原始缝宽为 1mm 时,作用水压加自重载荷(无水平断裂缝);③坝体内横缝原始宽为 2mm 时,作用水压加自重载荷(无水平断裂缝)。

计算工况(温度应力另行考虑):坝体作用自重和水压载荷,坝体薄而且上游做防渗处理,不计算渗透压力。

其中自重应力是按梁单独承受方式计算，水压载荷分四级，水位高程分别为 140.0m、150.0m、160.0m、166.3m(正常蓄水位高程)。

2.2　含缝拱坝的变形和应力重分布

2.2.1　位移分布

当坝体内无横缝时，顺河向最大位移发生在下游面拱冠梁处，值为 $v_{max}=6.1$mm，水平方向最大位移为 $u_{max}=1.1$mm；当坝体横缝原始宽为 1mm 时，$v_{max}=14.9$mm，$u_{max}=5.0$mm；当横缝原始宽为 2mm 时，$v_{max}=17.7$mm，$u_{max}=5.4$mm，。

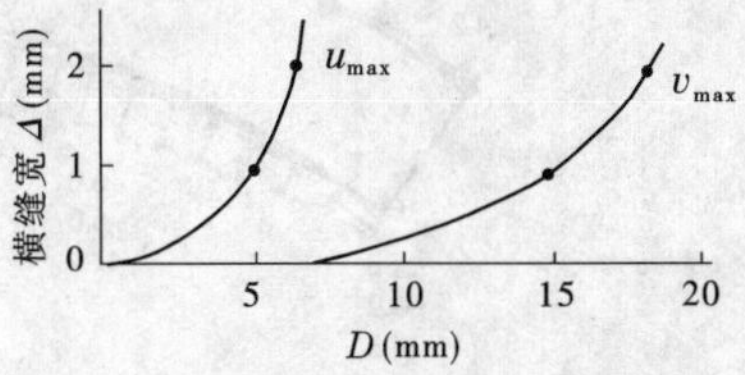

图 5　最大位移随横缝宽变化图
(v 为顺河向位移，u 为垂直河向水平位移)

由图 5 可见，坝体变形对横缝的存在是很敏感的，v_{max} 由无横缝时的 6.1mm 增到 1mm 缝宽时的 14.9mm，增加了 1.4 倍，而 u_{max} 由 1.1mm 增到 5.0mm，增加了近 4 倍。

2.2.2　应力分布

三种计算类型典型高程(125.0m)拱圈应力分布如图 6～图 8 所示。当坝体无横缝时，坝体整体上应力处于良好状态，最大拉应力发生在 125.0m 高程上游面处，为 $\sigma_z=1.01$MPa，剪应力最大值为 $\tau_{yz}=1.14$MPa，最大压应力为 $\sigma_z=-2.60$MPa，拱坝坝肩处拉应力值小于 0.50MPa，其范围在坝肩 15m 以内。

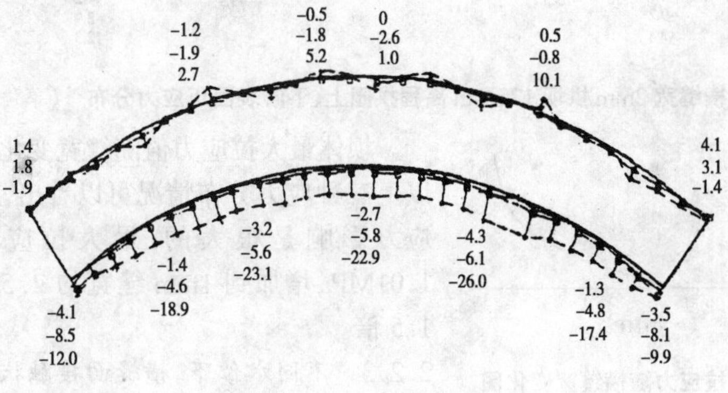

图 6　无缝拱坝 125.0m 高程拱圈上、下游表面正应力分布　(单位:0.1MPa)

当坝体横缝原始缝宽为 1mm 时，中央坝段上游面出现较大拉应力值，最大拉应力值发生在横缝周围区域高程 125.0m 处，值为 $\sigma_z=2.57$MPa，超过混凝土尤其碾压混凝土层面抗拉强度，剪应力最大值为 $\tau_{yz}=1.64$MPa；下游坝趾压应力最大值达 $\sigma_z=-4.84$MPa。从截面应力分布看，拉应力区在坝厚方向 1/4 坝厚以内(约 3m)，即拉应力沿坝厚方向变化梯度很大，在拱坝肩处有 0.82MPa 左右的拉应力，其范围在坝肩 20m 以内。

当缝宽为 2mm 时，应力分布情况与 1mm 缝宽相似，但最大应力值均有增加，最大拉力值为 $\sigma_z=2.74$MPa，最大剪应力为 $\tau_{yz}=1.82$MPa，最大压应力为 $\sigma_z=-4.99$MPa，左右坝肩有约 0.85MPa 大小的拉应力，其范围在 20m 内。

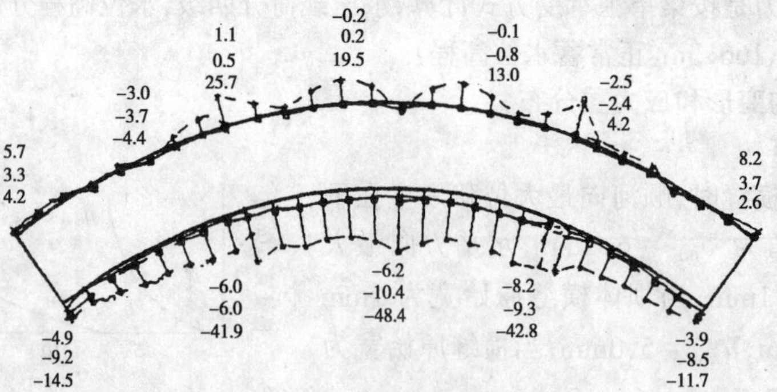

图 7　横缝宽 1mm 拱坝 125.0m 高程拱圈上、下游表面正应力分布　(单位:0.1MPa)

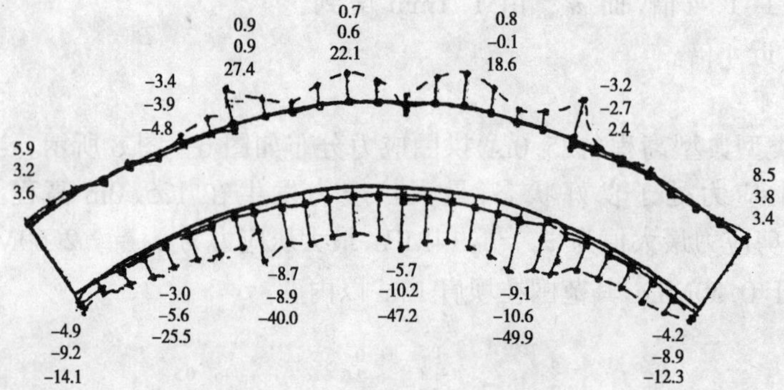

图 8　横缝宽 2mm 拱坝 125.0m 高程拱圈上、下游表面正应力分布　(单位:0.1MPa)

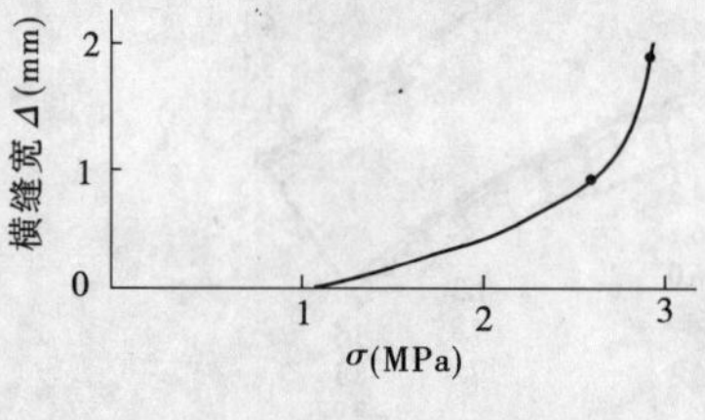

图 9　最大拉应力随横缝宽变化图

坝体最大拉应力值随缝宽变化如图 9 所示。从以上三种应力分布情况可以看出,坝内含有横缝对应力影响是很大的,最大拉应力值从无缝的 1.01MPa 增加到 1mm 缝宽的 2.57MPa,增加了约 1.5 倍。

2.2.3　不同水位下,横缝面接触状况

横缝原始缝宽为 1mm 时,缝面接触情况随水位变化情况如图 10 所示。

当水位为 140.0m 高程时,三条缝面均不接触;水位为 150.0m 高程时,左右缝面上部已有较大的接触面积。此时,上部拱圈能传递压剪力而形成一定的拱效应。当水位为 160.0m 高程时,中间横缝面大部缝面接触,而两侧缝面有局部因过大的剪应力而产生错动。但水位为正常蓄水位 166.3m 高程时,两侧错动的横缝又在加大的压力作用下重新压紧。此时中上部横缝面均接触压紧形成拱效应,但下部横缝面仍张开。横缝原始宽为 2mm 时,接触变化情况如图 11 所示。当水位为 150.5m 高程时,只有 2 号横缝面顶端稍有接触,显然由于缝宽的增加使得在相同水位下横缝面难以接触;当水位为 160m 高程时,三条横缝上部都接触压紧,但下部缝面保持张开状态;当水位为 166.3m 高程时,接触面又有增加,但与1mm缝宽相比接触面积要小。

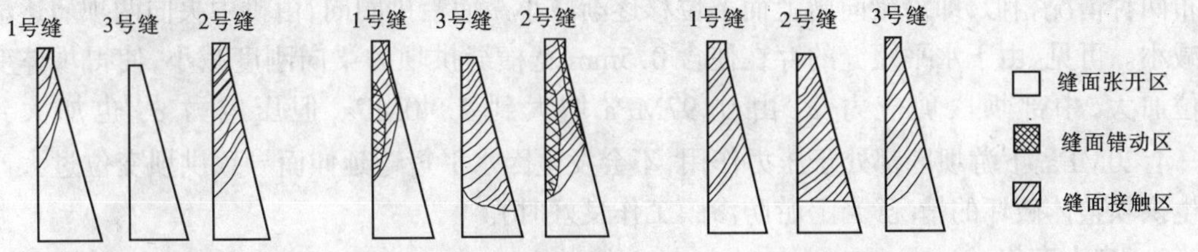

(a)150m高程　(b)160m高程　(c)166.3m高程(正常蓄水位)

图10　不同水位缝面接触图(1mm缝)

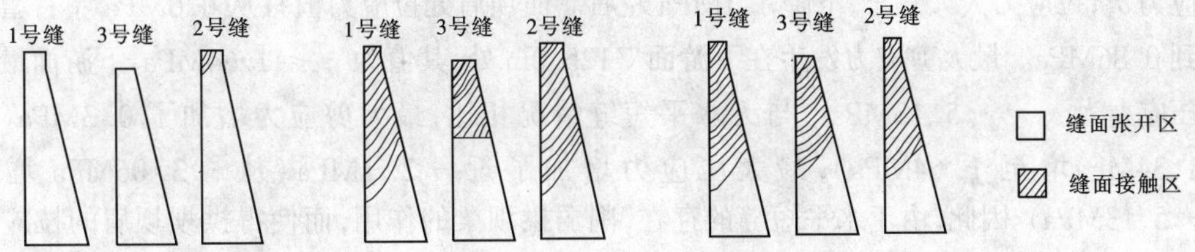

(a)150.5m高程　(b)160m高程　(c)166.3m高程(正常蓄水值)

图11　不同水位缝面接触图(2mm缝)

综上所述可见:

(1)有横缝时坝顶位移值(尤其中央坝段)比无缝拱坝上部位移值增大(达2~5倍),横缝大大地削弱拱的作用,加大梁的变位。

(2)横缝面接触时压力不大,不引起局部压碎破坏。

(3)横缝面随着水位增高逐步接触压紧,接触部位从上部向下部发展,但水位即使达到正常蓄水位,由于拱坝下部断面大,刚度大,离基础高度小,变位小,横缝面仍有部分保持不接触状态,破坏平面拱作用,而上部拱作用过大对坝肩稳定不利。

(4)当横缝宽在1mm以上(3条横缝)时,仅水压和自重作用下拱坝中央坝段上游坝踵▽127.5m的梁向拉力 σ_z 增大到2.6MPa左右,大大超过无横缝的1MPa。若和运行期1月份降温拉应力叠加(达4.9MPa),远超过碾压混凝土层面极限抗拉强度。因此,蓄水前不灌浆将使拱坝中部上游坝踵拉裂,拉裂缝充水又加大缝面水压,更增强裂缝扩展能力。

(5)若把缝宽减小到0.5mm以下(0.5mm以上缝宽蓄水前春季灌浆,限制温降重新拉开缝宽小于0.5mm等),并在上游坝踵(见图4)设有止水的人工水平短缝(1/4坝厚度),以防止压力水进入水平缝面,降低梁的刚度,可以加大拱的作用,改善拱坝的应力。

3　上游坝踵设水平人工短缝对含横缝碾压混凝土拱坝应力的影响

对坝体含宽0.5mm横缝、无水平短缝和有水平短缝时位移、应力分布情况进行比较。

3.1　位移变化

当坝体悬臂梁底部存在水平短缝(横缝宽为0.5mm时),与不含水平短缝情况位移相比,位移均有增加:v、u 分别由 10.3mm 增至 15.4mm、由 4.5mm 增至 4.9mm。位移分布两种情况相似,即沿梁向由上而下位移逐渐减小。而沿拱圈向,由拱中央向两坝肩逐渐减小。可见,由于水平短缝的存在使含 0.5mm 宽横缝拱坝的梁向刚度减小,使得坝体变位加大,中部坝段剪应力 τ_{yz} 由 0.97MPa 增大到 1.40MPa,但压应力 σ_z 也加大到 -4.20MPa。下游坝区都处于压力作用,不会发生因水平短缝延伸而导致拱坝变位过大产生拱坝整体破坏的情况(当上游防渗膜工作良好时)。

3.2 应力变化

有水平短缝的应力分布比无水平短缝变化较大,在▽125.0m 处,最大拉应力发生在拱坝左坝肩处,其值为 $\sigma_x = 0.86$MPa,而在水平短缝周围仅有 0.6MPa 左右的 Z 方向拉应力 σ_z,拉应力大大减小,下降了 1MPa 左右。而坝肩处拉应力值只从 0.6MPa 左右增加到 0.86MPa。最大剪应力发生在下游面▽125.0m 处,其值为 $\tau_{yz} = 1.64$MPa,下游面最大压应力为 $\sigma_z = -5.13$MPa。与无水平短缝情况相比,最大剪应力增加了 0.3MPa(从 1.34MPa 增至 1.64MPa),最大压应力增加了近 -2.1MPa(从 -3.06MPa 增至 -5.13MPa)。因此,由于水平短缝的存在,削弱拱坝梁的作用,而使得拱坝坝肩的拉应力增大,但坝中央梁向拉应力值大为减小,说明水平短缝的存在使梁向拉应力释放,坝体应力重分布,而增加坝肩拉应力。

在▽160.0m 处,正应力分布基本对称,左、右坝肩有约 0.6MPa 的拉应力值,比无水平短缝情况增加 0.15MPa;拉应力区沿拱圈向范围为 15m,其余部分处于小于 -1MPa 的压应力区,压应力反而减小。另外,在横缝附近应力值稍有减小。剪应力分布呈反对称分布,其值较小,均为 0.6MPa 以下。

从坝体横缝宽 0.5mm 不含水平短缝和含有水平短缝时,在自重和水压作用下坝体的位移和应力分布计算结果分析,以及横缝面的接触变化情况可以得出以下结论:

(1)当坝体仅有 3 条 0.5mm 宽横缝(无水平短缝)时,在自重和水压作用下,坝体在▽125.0m 上游面横缝周围沿梁向仍将出现大于碾压混凝土层面极限抗拉强度的拉力,虽然由于横缝宽的减小(和 1mm、2mm 相比)有利于横缝面的合并接触而形成拱坝整体作用,但是出现过大的梁向拉应力仍会产生拉裂的水平裂缝(此时最大拉应力方向为垂直于水平面)。说明当坝体温降收缩,人工灌浆后如坝体横缝宽仍有 0.5mm,坝体仍将沿梁向拉裂而且可能发生在上游坝踵区约▽125.0m 处。

(2)当坝体有 0.5mm 宽横缝,在▽125.0m 处人工预留(含止水)水平短缝(缝长度为此处坝厚的 1/4)时,在自重和水压作用下,坝体应力将重分布,其结果是在▽125.0m 处水平短缝缝端周围梁向应力 σ_z 将大大小于无水平短缝时上游面 σ_z 值,而且其值仅为 0.6MPa 左右,在碾压混凝土允许应力范围内。短缝缝端下游混凝土处于压力区,即水平短缝不会沿坝厚方向扩展开裂而保持原状(此时上游面应有良好止水)。同时,梁向释放的 σ_z 应力大都较均匀地分散到拱肩处的应力区中,使得在▽125.0m 坝肩处出现最大为 0.86MPa 的拉应力 σ_x,但从整体上并不引起拱肩的拉裂。因此,在▽125.0m 上设水平短缝释放梁向应力可以使拱坝整体应力得到改善。

(3)在有水平短缝时,从位移计算结果来看,并不会因为梁向刚度的削弱使得大坝变位大幅度地增加。中间坝段在水压作用下,上部横缝能很好地接触合并,发挥拱的效应,而阻止梁向变位继续加大。因此,当水压载荷均匀地逐渐增加时,大坝不会因为变位过大而出现不正常工作状态。

(4)显然,由于水平短缝的存在使横缝面在正常蓄水位下(▽166.3m),横缝面几乎全部接触,使拱坝从坝底到坝顶形成整体作用,有利于坝体的受力。另外从应力计算可以得出,在横缝压紧接触的区域不会因为压应力过大而产生局部受压破坏。

参 考 文 献

[1] 张富德,刘光廷. 含缺陷坝体的强度和变形. 清华大学学报, 1991, 31(5): 1~10
[2] 陈式慧,李广远. 混凝土坝横向缝对应力影响的研究. 水力发电学报, 1989, 3: 45~51
[3] 刘观标,潘林. 重力坝纵缝并缝对坝体结构性态的影响. 水利学报, 1992(5): 71~82

缝端奇异边界单元和界面裂缝的应力强度因子计算

摘　要　虽然不同材料的界面裂缝缝端应力情况很复杂，但是在拉剪荷载作用下，仍然存在主导缝端奇异特性的特征参数——应力强度因子，且其主导奇异项仍为1/2，因此可以采用1/4奇异边界单元模拟缝端的位移场和应力场。作者沿界面引用边界元，在界面裂缝周围引入1/4奇异边界元，给出了计算异弹模界面缝复应力强度因子的计算格式，定义了界面裂缝的等效能量释放率，探讨了界面裂缝的断裂差别指标，并应用于混凝土坝与岩石地基的界面裂缝扩展分析中，得到一些有关坝工安全的重要提示。

关键词　界面裂缝　应力强度因子　边界元方法　重力坝

混凝土坝和基础岩体界面由于形状、材料和应力分布的迅速变化，往往形成工程弱面，长期以来，重力坝设计都以这个界面作为控制断面进行应力稳定安全判别。实际上坝体滑移破坏不取决于剪力全面超强度，而往往由于局部超强度破坏后应力重分布引起的裂缝延伸造成全面破坏。因此，设计上将混凝土及岩体作为宏观分区均质体来计算界面裂缝的应力强度因子(SIF)和测定断裂韧性(若存在较稳定的数值)。以判别剪力裂缝的稳定性，更真实地表征坝体稳定安全程度。

1　界面裂缝的SIF解析式

1988年，Rice[1]从两种不同均质材料在共同的界面上位移相等、面力平衡和缝面受力为零的边界条件出发，提出了界面缝端复应力强度因子解析式，当振荡接触区相对于缝长很小时(大多数工程材料均满足此条件)，复应力强度因子仍然是主导缝端奇异特性的一个特征参数。

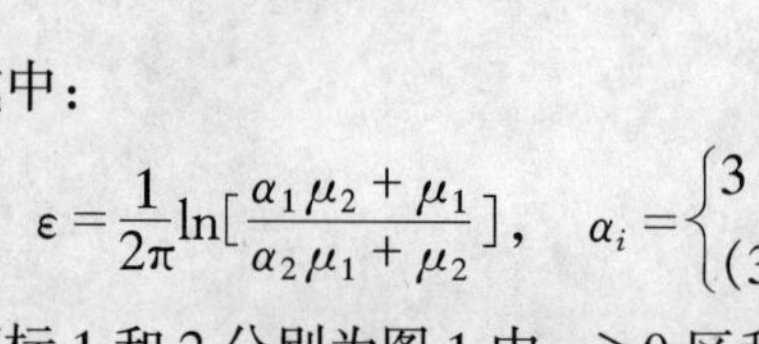

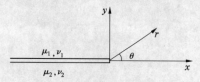

图1　界面裂缝

对于图1界面裂缝问题，裂缝前端的振荡奇异场为

$$(\sigma_{yy}+\sigma_{xy})|_{\theta=0}=\frac{K}{\sqrt{2\pi r}}r^{i\varepsilon} \tag{1}$$

式中：

$$\varepsilon=\frac{1}{2\pi}\ln\left[\frac{\alpha_1\mu_2+\mu_1}{\alpha_2\mu_1+\mu_2}\right],\quad \alpha_i=\begin{cases}3-4\nu_i & (平面应变)\\(3-4\nu_i)/(1+\nu_i) & (平面应力)\end{cases}\quad (i=1,2)$$

下标1和2分别为图1中 $y>0$ 区和 $y<0$ 区；ν 为泊松比；μ 为剪切模量。

由式(1)可见，不同材料界面裂缝的主导奇异性仍为1/2奇异性(ε 振荡项数很小)。沿裂缝表面张开位移为

本文选自《清华大学学报(自然科学版)》1996年第1期，作者还有王宗敏、周鸿钧。

$$(u_y + iu_x)_{\theta=\pi} - (u_y + iu_x)_{\theta=-\pi} = \frac{C_1 + C_2}{2(1+2i\varepsilon)\cosh(\pi\varepsilon)}\sqrt{\frac{r}{2\pi}}Kr^{i\varepsilon} \tag{2}$$

式中：$C_i = (1+\alpha_i)/\mu_i (i=1,2)$。

界面裂缝的能量释放率为

$$G = (C_1 + C_2)k\bar{k}/16\cosh^2(\pi\varepsilon) \tag{3}$$

以上诸式中，复应力强度因子 $K = K_{\mathrm{I}} + \mathrm{i}K_{\mathrm{II}}$，其实部和虚部不是经典意义下的Ⅰ型和Ⅱ型应力强度因子。

对于远处均匀应力场 $\sigma_{yy}^{\infty} + i\sigma_{xy}^{\infty}$，界面内含 L 长度裂缝时的复应力强度因子解析式为

$$K = (\sigma_{yy}^{\infty} + i\sigma_{xy}^{\infty})(1+2i\varepsilon)L^{-i\varepsilon}\sqrt{\pi L/2} \tag{4}$$

由 Evans 等细观力学分析，界面裂纹的断裂韧性与界面混合度 $\psi = \tan^{-1}(K_{\mathrm{II}}/K_{\mathrm{I}})$ 有关，界面断裂韧性

$$G_{\mathrm{c}}(\psi) = G_{\mathrm{c}}^0(1+\tan^2\psi) \tag{5}$$

式中：G_{c}^0 为材料固有的断裂韧性，由界面裂缝Ⅰ型载荷实验测得，即当

$$K_{\mathrm{II}} \approx 0,\ \tan\psi = 0,\ G_{\mathrm{c}}(\psi) = G_{\mathrm{c}}^0$$

由式(3)和式(5)，可得到界面裂纹的起裂准则为 $G^* \geqslant G_{\mathrm{c}}^0$，式中 G^* 为等效能量释放率，$G^* = (C_1 + C_2)K_{\mathrm{I}}^2/(16\cosh^2(\pi\varepsilon))$。

2 不同材料界面裂缝的边界元和奇异边界元

不同区域材料界面裂缝边界元的本质是沿界面和裂缝的多区域离散，使得裂缝面分属不同的区域，且使除裂缝外的界面满足连续协调条件。

如图 2 将整个区域分成子域 $\Omega^{(k)}$，其边界为 $\Gamma^{(k)}$ $(k=1,2)$，则边界积分方程可写为

$$C_{ij}^{(k)}(p)u_j^{(k)}(p) = \int_{\Gamma^{(k)}} u_{ij}^{s(k)}(p,q)t_j^{(k)}(q)\mathrm{d}\Gamma^{(k)}(q) - \int_{\Gamma^{(k)}} T_{ij}^{s(k)}(p,q)u_j^{(k)}(q)\mathrm{d}\Gamma^{(k)}(q) \tag{6}$$

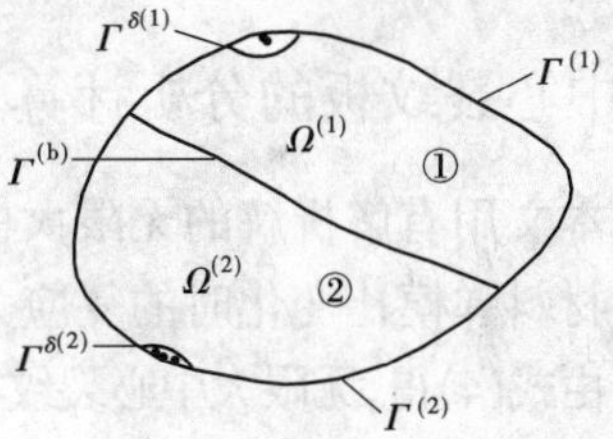

图 2 不同材料区域

式中：$C_{ij}^{(k)}(p) = \lim\limits_{\delta\to 0}\int_{\Gamma^{\delta(k)}} T_{ij}^{s(k)}(p,q)\mathrm{d}\Gamma^{\delta}(q)$，对于光滑边界 $C_{ij}^{(k)}(p) = 0.5\delta_{ij}$，$u_{ij}^{s(k)}(p,q)$ 和 $T_{ij}^{s(k)}(p,q)$ 分别是面力和位移基本解，是在 P 点 i 方向施加单位力引起的 q 点 j 方向的位移和面力分量。子域 $\Omega^{(1)}$ 和 $\Omega^{(2)}$ 的界面点的位移连续和面力平衡的条件为

$$u_i^{(1)}(p) = u_i^{(2)}(p),\quad t_i^{(1)}(p) = -t_i^{(2)}(p) \tag{7}$$

将边界进行离散化，引入面力和位移边界条件和式(7)的界面约束条件，即可将边界积分方程(6)化为代数方程。

在进行边界离散化时，当忽略界面缝尖附近小范围的振荡和缝面贯穿时，缝端单元必须能够模拟式(2)的 $\sqrt{r}$ 位移场和式(1)的 $1/\sqrt{r}$ 面力场。参照有限元构造 1/4 奇异元的方法，将二次等参元的中节点移到距缝端奇点 1/4 单元边长处(见图 3)，构造位移和面力插值函数：

$$u(r)=\sum_{i=1}^{3}N_iu_i=a_1+a_2\sqrt{rl^{-1}}+a_3rl^{-1}$$

$$t(r)=\sum_{i=1}^{3}N_i\sqrt{rl^{-1}}\,t_i=\overline{a_1}\sqrt{rl^{-1}}+\overline{a_2}+\overline{a_3}\sqrt{rl^{-1}}$$

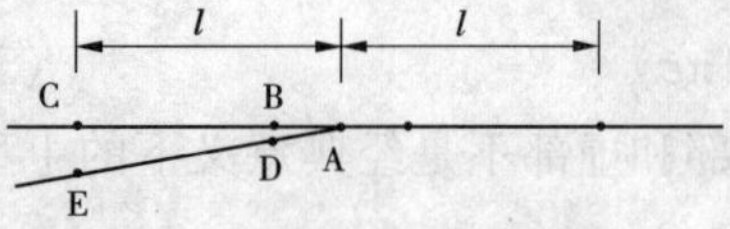

图 3 缝端 1/4 奇异元

式中：a_1、a_2、a_3 是节点位移值的函数；$\overline{a_1}$、$\overline{a_2}$、$\overline{a_3}$ 是节点面力值的函数；l 为裂缝单元的长度。

这种面力插值函数被修正的 1/4 奇异元，称为面力 1/4 奇异元，它满足了缝端位移场和面力场的要求。

3 应力强度因子的计算

对于异弹模界面裂缝，可利用缝面相对位移来进行应力强度因子计算，由式(2)得到复应力强度因子的实部和虚部为

$$K_{\mathrm{I}}=\lim_{r\to0}H\sqrt{2\pi r^{-1}}\left[\Delta u_y(\cos\beta+2\varepsilon\sin\beta)-\Delta u_x(2\varepsilon\cos\beta-\sin\beta)\right]$$

$$K_{\mathrm{II}}=\lim_{r\to0}H\sqrt{2\pi r^{-1}}\left[\Delta u_x(\cos\beta+2\varepsilon\sin\beta)+\Delta u_y(2\varepsilon\cos\beta-\sin\beta)\right] \tag{8}$$

式中：$H=2\cosh(\pi\varepsilon)/(C_1+C_2)$；$\beta=\varepsilon\ln r$。$\Delta u_x$，$\Delta u_y$ 在文献[2]中，直接采用上下缝面 1/4 点处的相对位移，即 $\Delta u_i=u_i^B-u_i^D$，而本文根据 1/4 奇异元的位移插值公式

$$u_i=u_i^A+(-u_i^C+4u_i^B-3u_i^A)\sqrt{rl^{-1}}+(2u_i^A-4u_i^B+2u_i^C)rl^{-1}$$

得
$$\Delta u_i=\left[4(u_i^B-u_i^D)-(u_i^C-u_i^E)\right]\sqrt{rl^{-1}} \tag{9}$$

式中：u_i^A、u_i^B、u_i^C、u_i^D、u_i^E 分别为图 3 中 1/4 奇异元节点处的位移值；l 为 1/4 单元的长度；i 分别代表 x 和 y 方向。

4 中心裂纹板的分析计算

本文用有解析解的无限大中心裂纹板来检验界面裂纹复应力强度因子的计算精度及两种材料弹模比变化时的复应力强度因子。

由式(4)得，无限大中心裂纹板在无穷远处作用载荷 $\sigma_{yy}^{\infty}+\mathrm{i}\sigma_{xy}^{\infty}$ 下的复应力强度因子为

$$K=K_{\mathrm{I}}+\mathrm{i}K_{\mathrm{II}}$$

式中：

$$K_{\mathrm{I}}=\sqrt{\pi a}\,(p_1\sigma_{yy}^{\infty}-p_2\sigma_{xy}^{\infty}),\quad K_{\mathrm{II}}=\sqrt{\pi a}\,(p_1\sigma_{xy}^{\infty}+p_2\sigma_{yy}^{\infty})$$

$$p_1=\cos\hat{\beta}+2\varepsilon\sin\hat{\beta},\ p_2=2\varepsilon\cos\hat{\beta}-\sin\hat{\beta},\ \beta=\varepsilon\ln2a$$

$2a$ 为裂纹的长度。

由于本文中心裂纹板的计算是取有限尺寸，相当于在具有解析解的无限大板中取出一部分，因此需要修正 x 方向边界力，以使和解析解边界条件一致。有限尺寸板 x 方向修正边界力为

$$(\sigma_{xx})_2=\begin{cases}E_2E_1^{-1}(\sigma_{xx})_1+[\nu_2-E_2E_1^{-1}\nu_2]\sigma_{yy} & (\text{平面应力})\\ \dfrac{E_2}{E_1}\left[\dfrac{1-\nu_1^2}{1-\nu_2^2}\right](\sigma_{xx})_1+\left[\dfrac{\nu_2}{1-\nu_2}-\dfrac{E_2\nu_1(1+\nu_1)}{E_1(1-\nu_2^2)}\right]\sigma_{yy} & (\text{平面应变})\end{cases}$$

由于问题的对称性，取板的一半进行分析，计算简图见图4，计算结果见表1。

表1 中心裂纹板的应力强度因子计算比较

E_2/E_1	ν_2	解析解		文献[2]方法				本文			
		K_{I}	K_{II}	K_{I}	$e_{K\text{I}}$	K_{II}	$e_{K\text{II}}$	K_{I}	$e_{K\text{I}}$	K_{II}	$e_{K\text{II}}$
1	0.25	2 170.8	0.00	2 171.0	0.01	0.00	0.0	2 179.4	0.40	0.00	0.00
3	0.25	2 180.7	104.46	2 173.5	−0.33	121.93	16.7	2 186.6	0.27	105.38	0.88
11	0.20	2 198.2	172.77	2 177.3	−0.95	199.89	15.7	2 200.4	0.10	172.90	0.08
98	0.25	2 211.0	208.47	2 179.9	−1.41	239.12	14.7	2 210.6	−0.02	205.13	−1.60
1 198	0.25	2 212.6	212.62	2 180.6	−1.45	243.74	14.6	2 211.9	−0.03	208.93	−1.74

注： 1. 表中相对误差 $e=[(K_{数值}-K_{解析})/K_{解析}]\times100$；

2. 计算中缝端奇异元的长度取 $0.2a$；

3. K 的单位为 kPa。

由表1可见，本文提出的方法，SIF的计算相对误差很小，最大的 K_{II} 相对误差仅为1.74%，而文献[2]的 K_{II} 最大误差达16.7%。事实上，当将式(9)代入式(8)中时，影响SIF计算精度的 $1/\sqrt{r}$ 恰好被消去，这是本法计算精度高的原因。

5 工程应用

重力坝是一种大体积混凝土结构，在浇筑过程中产生水化热，温降后，上游坝踵产生了较高的温度剪应力，综合水压作用，上游坝踵产生拉应力集中。由于碾压混凝土重力坝层面形成弱面，更增加上游坝踵沿层面开裂的可能性。这种裂缝在运行期各种载荷作用下是否扩展，其扩展规律如何，无疑对重力坝的安全和稳定是至关重要的。为此，本文对图5重力坝坝踵裂缝进行了计算分析，计算结果见表2和图6。表中负值的 K_{I} 表示缝面压紧，超出了一般弹性界面断裂力学的适用范畴，属于压剪状态。

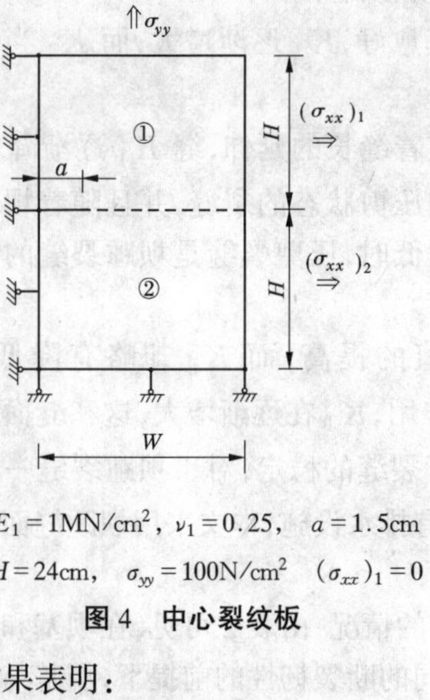

$E_1=1\text{MN/cm}^2$，$\nu_1=0.25$，$a=1.5\text{cm}$

$H=24\text{cm}$，$\sigma_{yy}=100\text{N/cm}^2$ $(\sigma_{xx})_1=0$

图4 中心裂纹板

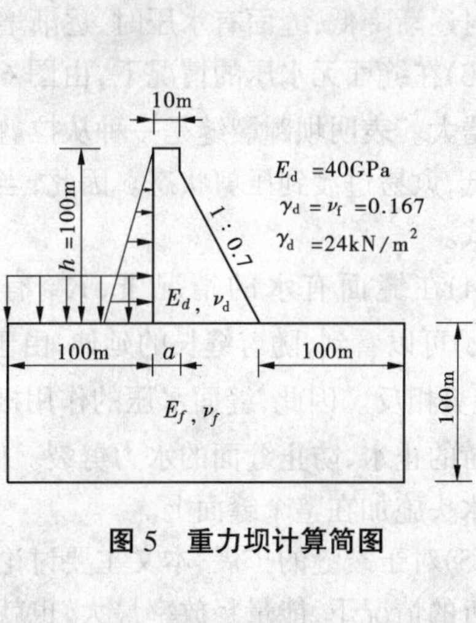

图5 重力坝计算简图

结果表明：

(1)在其他条件不变的情况下，由 K、G 表达式可见，界面裂纹的复应力强度因子仅与两种材料的弹模比有关,而与弹模的具体量值无关,但能量释放率却与二者皆有关系。

表 2　坝踵界面裂缝的应力强度因子及等效能量释放率

E_f/E_d		$a=1$cm		$a=2$cm		$a=3$cm		$a=5$cm	
		无	有	无	有	无	有	无	有
0.25	K_{I}	437.8	2 820.9	−295.8	3 208.7	−973.0	3 428.7	−2 094.8	3 801.2
	K_{II}	2 980.1	2 402.4	3 269.4	2 585.9	3 411.0	2 698.9	3 550.7	2 858.5
	G^*	0.001 1	0.045 6		0.059 0		0.067 3		0.082 7
0.5	K_{I}	1 166.3	3 622.4	553.9	4 131.1	−100.3	4 374.9	−1 228.4	4 739.1
	K_{II}	2 810.1	2 441.6	3 110.3	2 623.3	3 280.3	2 749.1	3 504.5	2 943.8
	G^*	0.004 9	0.047 0	0.001 1	0.061 1		0.068 5		0.080 4
1.0	K_{I}	1 865.1	4 371.9	1 421.4	5 053.8	816.4	5 346.5	−296.3	5 723.5
	K_{II}	2 696.8	2 603.9	2 968.8	2 746.3	3 144.1	2 862.3	3 439.9	3 073.7
	G^*	0.008 5	0.046 5	0.004 9	0.062 1	0.001 6	0.069 5		0.079 6
2.0	K_{I}	2 448.5	4 967.4	2 205.2	5 864.1	1 669.2	6 226.8	588.9	6 637.9
	K_{II}	2 639.7	2 832.8	2 856.6	2 914.3	3 013.0	2 998.1	3 354.8	3 203.5
	G^*	0.010 7	0.044 2	0.008 7	0.061 6	0.005 0	0.069 4	0.000 6	0.078 9
3.0	K_{I}	2 716.8	5 228.2	2 591.2	6 254.2	2 098.6	6 662.2	1 041.1	7 099.1
	K_{II}	2 619.6	2 958.6	2 803.8	3 006.8	2 942.4	3 066.1	3 299.3	3 260.0
	G^*	0.011 5	0.042 5	0.010 4	0.060 8	0.006 9	0.069 0	0.001 7	0.078 4
1 000	K_{I}	3 495.3	5 934.9	3 815.6	7 460.6	3 510.7	8 070.6	2 561.0	8 636.1
	K_{II}	2 528.3	3 311.6	2 617.6	3 274.9	2 664.5	3 218.1	3 031.8	3 331.9
	G^*	0.012 5	0.036 0	0.014 9	0.056 9	0.012 6	0.066 6	0.006 7	0.076 3

注: K 的单位为 $\mathrm{kPa\cdot mm^{\frac{1}{2}}}$, G 的单位为 N/m, a 为缝长,“有”“无”为有无缝水。

(2)随着坝基与坝体弹模比的逐渐增高,即坝基愈好,K_{I} 逐渐增大;而 K_{I} 当缝面无水压时逐渐降低,缝面有水压时,逐渐增高。

(3)在缝面无水压的情况下,由图 6(a)可见,随着缝长的延伸,缝 K_{I} 逐渐降低,K_{II} 逐渐增大。表明坝踵裂缝是一种从拉剪状态过渡到压剪状态的裂缝,并且随着坝基弹模的降低,愈易过渡到压剪状态。因此,当坝基弹模较低时,压剪裂缝是坝踵裂缝的主要裂缝形式。

(4)在缝面有水的情况下,K_{I} 有了较大幅值的提高,而 K_{II} 却略有降低,且由图 6(b)可以看到,随着缝长的延伸,由于水力劈裂作用,K_{I} 在逐渐增大,这和缝面无水的 K_{I} 趋势相反。因此,缝面水压的作用极大地影响了裂缝的稳定,对于坝踵裂缝一定要做好上游的止水,防止缝面的水力劈裂。假定缝端没有排水设施,本文采用坝踵缝面的水压为全水头施加在整个缝面上。

(5)对于裂缝的扩展,本文主要讨论缝面有水时的情况,由表 2 可见,在坝基和坝体弹模相近的情况下,能量释放率最大,也就是说,在相同的断裂韧性的前提下,坝基与坝体弹模相近时,愈易开裂扩展。

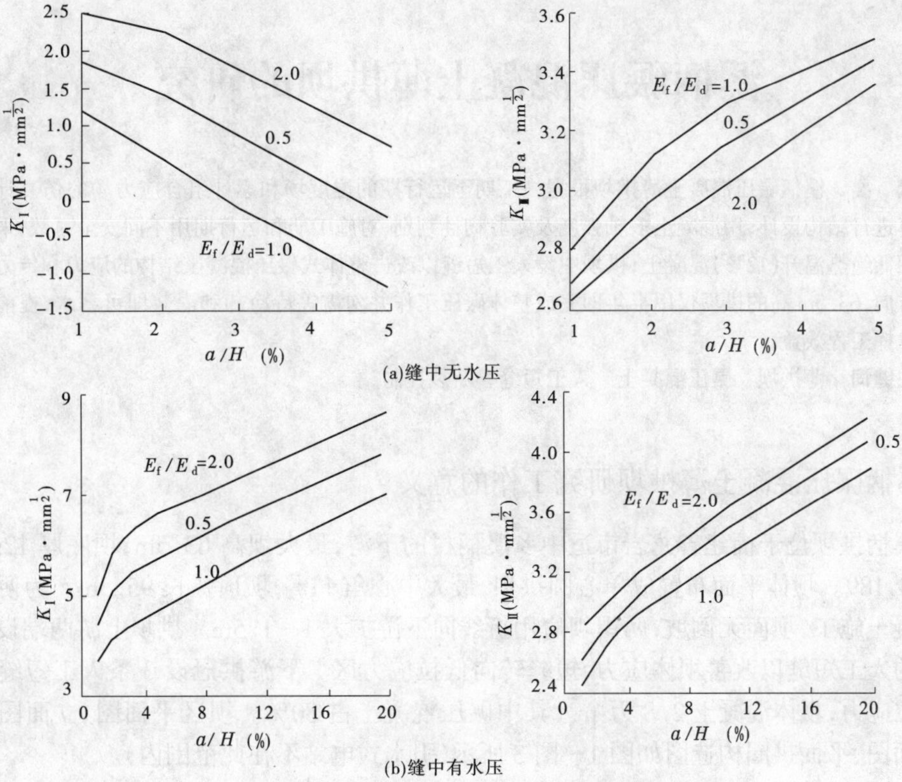

图6 应力强度因子随缝长和坝基与坝体弹模比的变化

6 结语

本文采用不同材料界面裂缝解析解和分区耦合边界单元法及面力1/4奇异元来分析界面裂缝问题,计算界面裂缝复应力强度因子。它既具有通常解析数值方法的高精度,又具有能满足复杂边界条件的长处。当裂缝延伸时,边界元准备工作量少、便于工程应用的优点,是碾压混凝土坝基础面抗滑稳定仿真计算的有效方法。

在坝基弹模低于坝体,且缝面无水压力时,重力坝坝踵界面裂缝易处于压剪状态。因此,压剪裂缝是重力坝坝踵界面裂缝的主要形式之一,关于压剪裂缝的研究应是坝踵裂缝研究的一个主要方向。但是当缝面有较大的水压作用时,K_{I} 应力强度因子大幅度地提高,形成了较危险的拉剪状态。因此,防止上游水渗入缝面,做好止水设施,可有效地防止裂缝的扩展,从而增加重力坝的抗滑稳定性。

参考文献

[1] Rice J R. *Elastic fracture mechanics concepts for interfacial cracks*. J of Appl Mech, 1988, 55: 98～103

[2] Raveendra S T, Banerjee P K. *Computation of stress intensity factor for interfacial cracks*. Engng Fracture Mech, 1991,40:89～103

溪柄碾压混凝土薄拱坝的研究

摘　要　溪柄碾压混凝土薄拱坝根据施工期至运行期的温度场和累计组合应力场的仿真计算进行结构设计,用混凝土多轴强度及实验韧性判别,对施工期和运行期用不同安全系数,采用低绝热温升(12℃)混凝土,拱坝中设人工短缝以改进整体式碾压混凝土结构的应力和传力方向,63.5m高的拱坝仅用半年即完成整体碾压工作并勿需等待冷却和灌浆即可蓄水,提前发挥工程效益。

关键词　薄拱坝　碾压混凝土　人工短缝　断裂控制

1　溪柄碾压混凝土薄拱坝研究工作的意义

溪柄拱坝位于福建省龙岩市适中乡溪柄村的下游,最大坝高63.5m,坝底厚12m,厚高比0.189。坝体平面布置成单心圆拱坝,最大中心角114°,坝顶弧长95.5m。为便于碾压混凝土施工,坝面无倒坡,两岸坝肩用折线向下游扩大1～1.5m。拱坝上游两端设置有止水的人工短缝以改善坝体应力,短缝转向低拉应力区。下游拱冠设3条人工短缝削减局部拉应力,坝体混凝土2.8万m^3,其中碾压混凝土占80%。坝区平面图、立面图和典型剖面图、平面拱圈构造图如图1～图3所示(引水式电站不在此范围内)。

碾压混凝土工艺简单,施工速度快,若用于工程量少的拱坝,在一个冬春低温枯水期碾压完毕,可以简化围堰和导流工程,大大缩短整个工程的全部建造工期;另外,拱坝以拱为主的传力方式将荷载传至两岸,减小碾压混凝土层间弱面破坏所造成的威胁。

常规混凝土拱坝水泥用量多,混凝土的水化热温升大,需多设横缝,在坝体内大量埋设冷却水管及灌浆系统,干扰大,人工冷却和灌浆费用大,工艺复杂,影响蓄水日期。溪柄碾压混凝土由于水泥用量少,水化热温升较低,在低温季节或入仓温度较低的条件下进行整体式大仓面施工。拱冠设置3条、拱端设置2条人工短缝,不设横缝,而仅在较高部位设置一条贯通横缝,可连续快速施工。不等待坝体降温灌浆即可蓄水,大大提前运行日期。

整体式大仓面碾压混凝土拱坝设计需要进行仿真计算,即:按建造过程加载,采用按实际变化的材料热学力学性能参数及约束条件,以了解更接近真实的受力变化过程;采用相应的安全度判别及控制人工短缝的稳定措施。

2　计算条件与计算结果

由于碾压混凝土拱坝在施工期间弹性模量、温度场和徐变因素等都在不断地变化,坝体逐渐加高并起拱的作用,其应力等和通常柱状块浇筑后灌浆的应力相差甚多。为此,溪柄拱坝模仿施工过程、温变过程和加载过程,并考虑混凝土的徐变,用三维八节点等参元的有限元法计算坝体及基础的温度场变化和应力场变化,为正确的工程结构设计和合理

本文选自《水力发电学报》1997第2期,作者还有麦家煊、张国新。

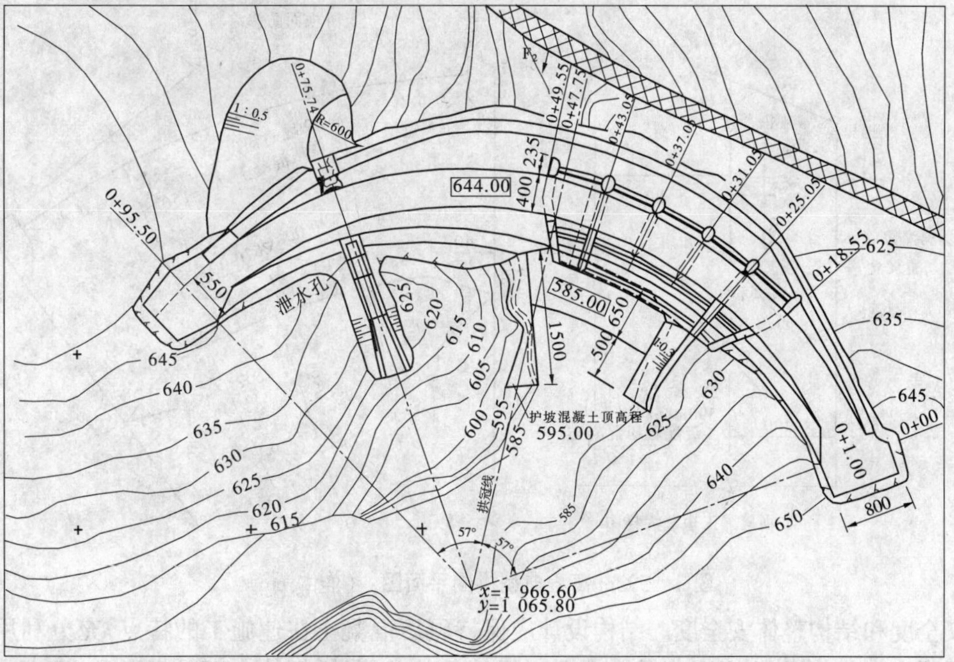

图1　溪柄碾压混凝土拱坝平面布置图

（高程、桩号、坐标单位为 m，其余尺寸单位为 cm）

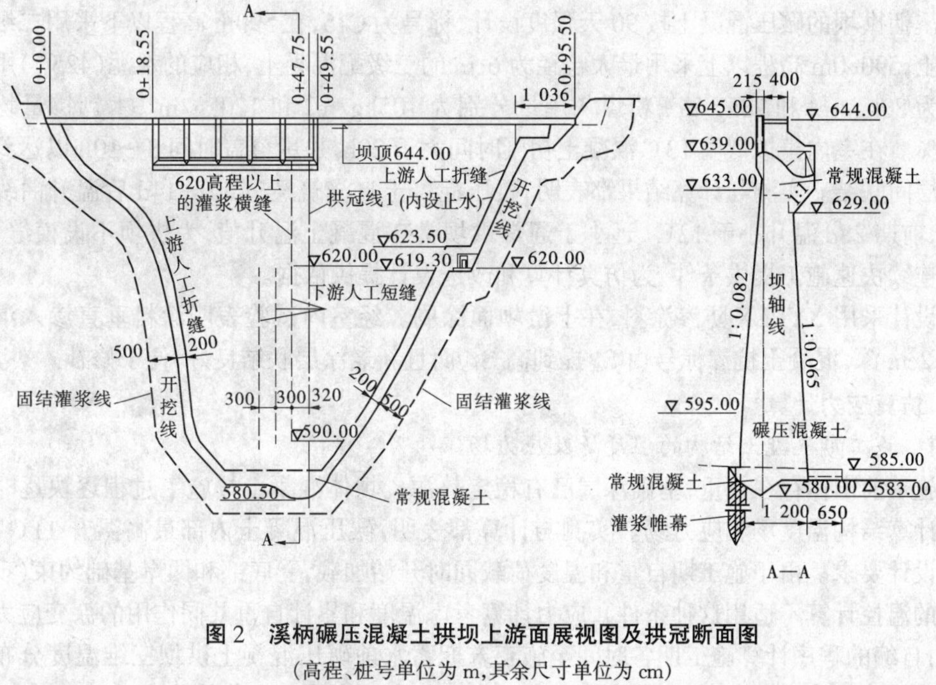

图2　溪柄碾压混凝土拱坝上游面展视图及拱冠断面图

（高程、桩号单位为 m，其余尺寸单位为 cm）

的工程进度提供依据。显然相对材料承受能力也采用更接近真实的多轴强度和断裂韧性判别，进行人工短缝缝端应力强度因子的计算，考虑混凝土内部损伤及损伤延伸来确定局

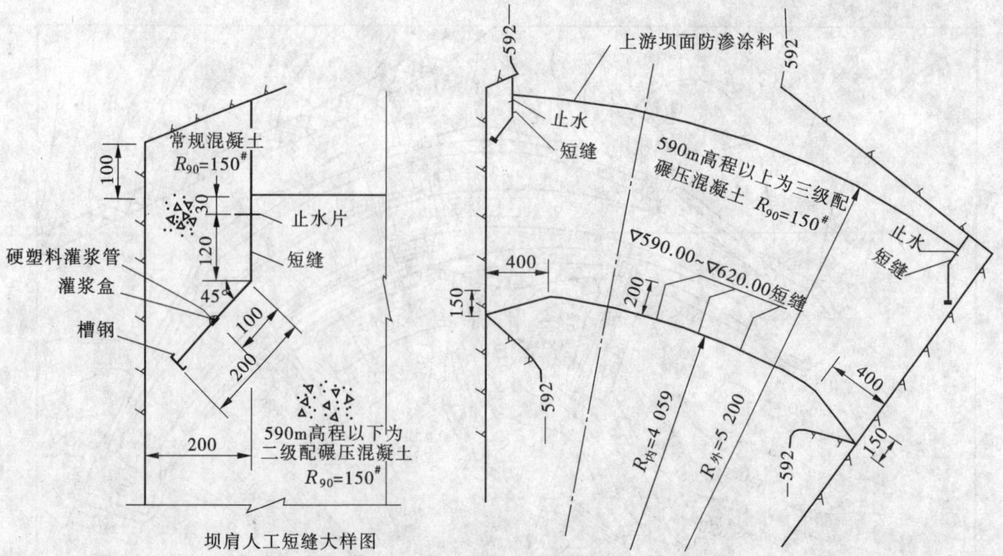

图3　592m高程典型拱圈平面图　(单位:cm)

部安全度和结构整体安全度。结构设计应保持碾压混凝土快速施工的特点,充分利用碾压混凝土水化热温升小,冬春季入仓温度低的条件,以降低坝体内部最高温升,省去人工温控费用,保证坝体质量。

2.1　溪柄工程碾压混凝土材料

溪柄拱坝的碾压混凝土按90天强度设计,标号为C15,在590m高程以下采用二级配混凝土,590.0m高程以上采用最大粒径为6cm的三级配混凝土,相应的水泥(425#)用量分别为80kg/m^3 和78kg/m^3,粉煤灰用量分别为105kg/m^3 和120kg/m^3,木钙掺量均为0.25%。在室内模拟低温13℃混凝土初凝时间大于20h,采用覆盖时间8～10h以达到较好的层间联结。实测与计算结果都表明,碾压混凝土自浇筑经过12～14d后温升曲线已平缓,前期28d温升小于12℃,远小于通常拱坝常态混凝土温升值,为拱坝不设横缝、大仓面连续快速施工提供条件,为仿真计算和改进设计提供依据。

设计采用XYPEX防渗涂料,在上游坝面涂刷。经室内试验表明涂料垂直渗入混凝土约2cm深,混凝土抗渗标号由S_4 提到高S_8,而且新老涂层联结良好,便于修补。

2.2　仿真应力计算

2.2.1　*施工期混凝土结构的温度场及应力场*

施工前山体存在自重,基础深层已有稳定热源。坝体混凝土按施工过程逐块逐时段累计计算结构温度场和应力场。实测与计算都表明,碾压混凝土内部最高温升11℃,可满足设计要求。由于施工期自重和温度荷载同时开始加载,受底部和两岸基础约束(现有规范的温控计算不适用这种条件),应力计算考虑温度和累计自重共同作用的徐变应力变化,由自编的程序计算施工期各时间至施工末期蓄水前碾压混凝土拱坝三维温度分布及三维累计徐变应力分布[1],缝端应力强度因子变化由组合受力位移差计算。

冬季自然条件下浇筑的混凝土因内部升温,上下游表面散热形成内外温差,表面拉应力不断增大,连续浇筑的碾压混凝土最大内部温升较常态混凝土小,内外温差形成的前期最大表面拉应力小于 1MPa,不致引起拉裂。随着散热时间延长,春季内部温度逐步下降,受约束混凝土块内部压力下降,转向拉力,而表面气温上升,减少内外温差,表面拉应力减小,施工末期转入夏季,表面已变为压应力区,内部出现大面积拉应力区,最大值达 1.21MPa,仍小于极限拉伸应力。

2.2.2 施工末期温度场变化到运行期稳定变温场产生的温度应力

整体碾压混凝土拱坝浇筑完成后,运行期坝体和基础都因蓄水后温度场改变而变形。整体变形受两岸基础约束,产生较大的温度应力。

由于运行期坝和基础边界受气温、水温影响作相似周期简谐变形,将运行期坝体温度较低(或较高)的时候对应的温度场减去施工末期(蓄水前)温度场即得到施工末期到运行期坝体温度变化值,由有限元程序求得约束应力场。

2.2.3 水压作用下的应力

水压作用下的应力由通常的三维有限元程序计算,这里不再叙述。上述应力叠加可得到运行期库满时水压、累计自重及温度应力的组合应力。

2.2.4 组合应力

水压和温度荷载都在上游拱座产生拉应力,所以上述各种应力组合(见图 4)在 620.0m高程以下的拱座出现 1.6～2.6MPa 拉应力,可能引起拉裂,620.0m 高程以上的拱座仍然有 0.97MPa 拉应力,下游面拱冠区仍有较大面积的拱向拉应力区,其拉应力数值为 0.61～1.09MPa,600.0m 高程以下拱坝内部中截面有较大拉应力区,最大拱向拉应力为 1.45MPa。

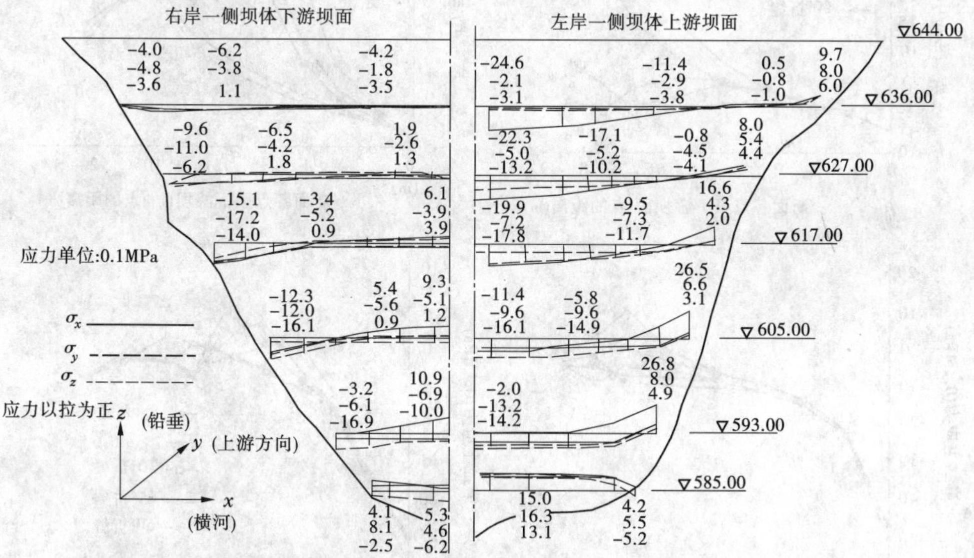

图 4 拱坝(无人工缝)运行期(库满)1 月份组合正应力分布 (单位:0.1MPa)

3 人工短缝对薄拱坝应力的改进

拱坝在水压作用或温降时通常容易在上游坝肩和下游拱冠产生较大的拉应力。在上游拱端设置有止水的人工短缝(见图3),不但可以削减或释放局部拉应力,而且通过调整短缝的长度和形状,改变有效传力断面,可以改变水压作用下主应力的传力方向,使外形上便于碾压施工的无倒悬、小曲率的单曲拱坝,起到加大曲率的双曲拱受力的作用。设置短缝不超过坝厚的1/4,以免加大坝肩剪应力。人工短缝是构造缝(不是温度诱导缝),需要控制缝端断裂能以防止缝延伸。上游坝肩人工短缝使坝肩上游部位的拉应力区转移到内部缝端,用折缝将缝端转入低压应力区,也减小缝和内部主拉应力方向的交角,以消减缝端断裂能,在缝端区埋设抗裂能力高的材料,以增大韧性,阻止裂缝发展。拱冠下游短缝用木板隔成,伸入坝体深2m。

3.1　上游坝面人工短缝对拱坝应力的改进

上游坝面人工短缝设置止水,缝内有排水管,不计缝内水压作用。以611.0m高程的拱圈为例,上游坝肩四种形状的短缝(直缝、30°折缝、45°折缝、60°折缝)和未设缝的整体结构,对坝肩区域应力分布的影响如图5、图6所示。缝长 ac = bd = 1.5m, ce = de = 2.0m。图中5条曲线分别代表:①无缝整体结构;②径向直缝 $\theta=90°$;③折缝 $\theta=30°$;④折缝 $\theta=45°$;⑤折缝 $\theta=60°$。以上算例单独考虑上游面短缝对应力的影响,未考虑下游面中间三条人工短缝。

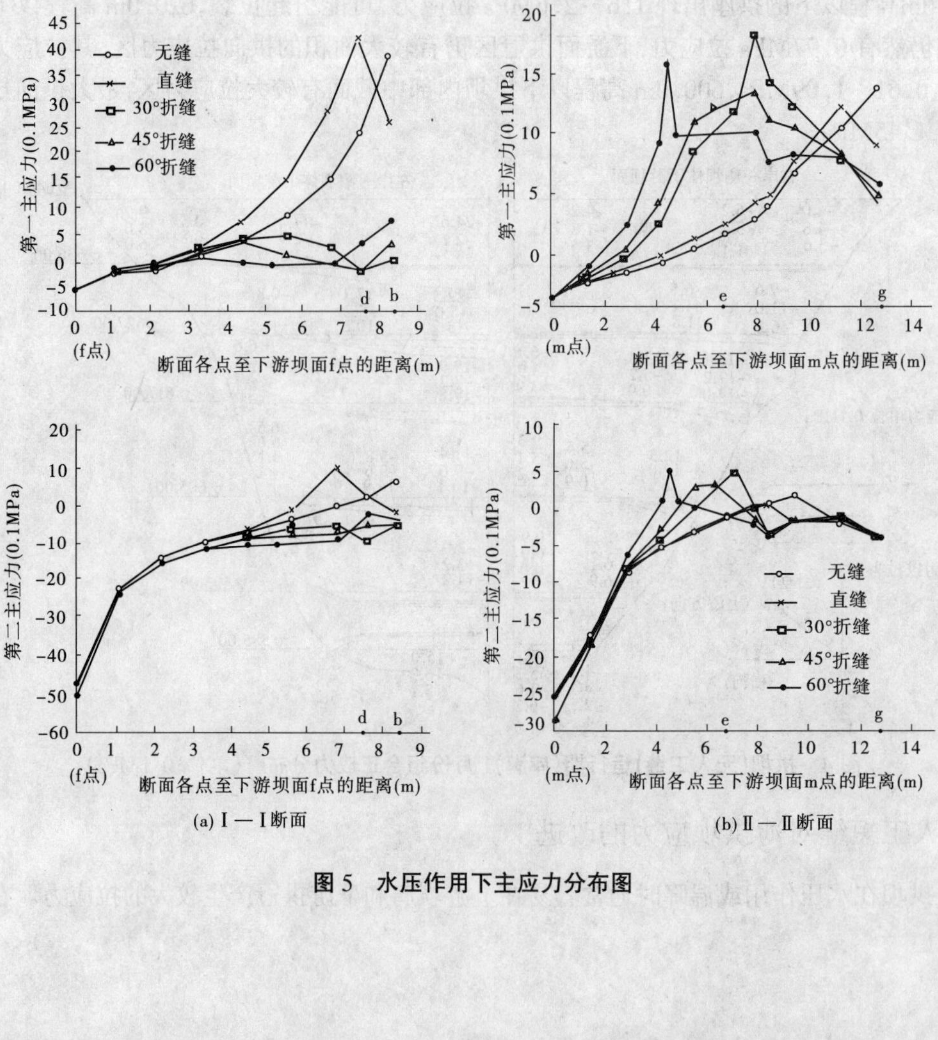

(a) Ⅰ—Ⅰ断面　　(b) Ⅱ—Ⅱ断面

图5　水压作用下主应力分布图

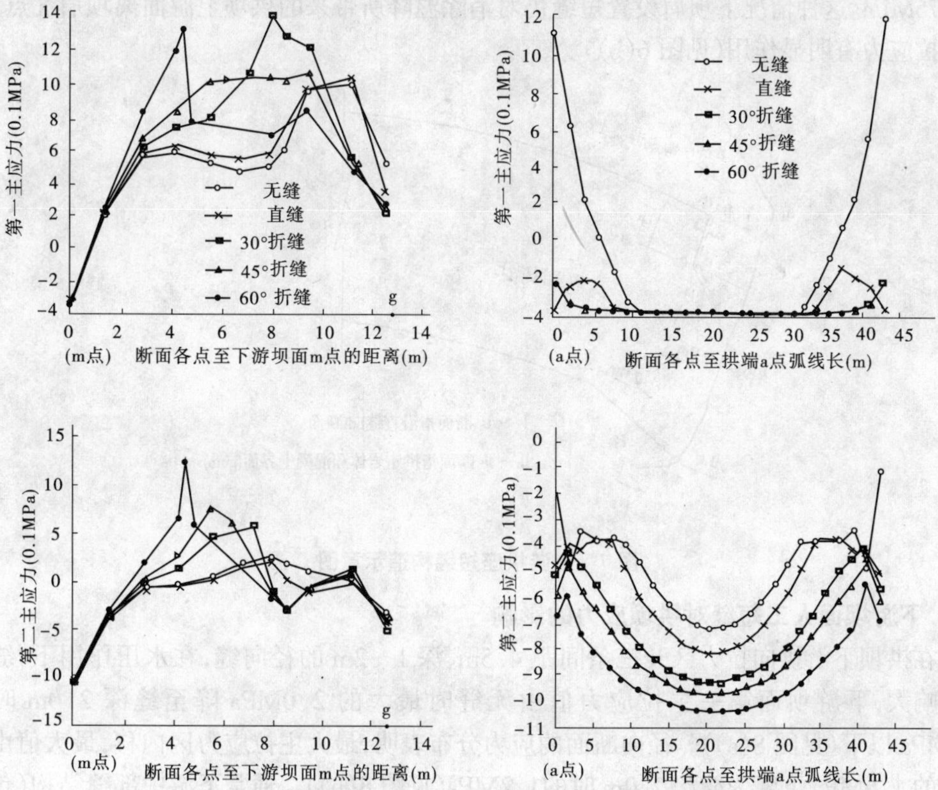

(a)拱座沿Ⅱ—Ⅱ断面　　(b)611m高程拱圈沿上游坝面

图6　运行期3月份综合温度场主应力分布图

由图5(a)中见:Ⅰ—Ⅰ断面无缝时,b(或a)点第一主拉应力达+3.9MPa,超出混凝土承受能力;设直缝时(c、d点重合),虽然b点的主拉应力下降,但是d点(直缝缝端)最大主拉应力达+4.2MPa,d点和f点之间的主拉应力也加大,因此更加不利;45°折缝不仅b点第一主拉应力下降为+0.3MPa,第二主应力由无缝时的+0.9MPa下降为-0.4MPa,而且d点及整个Ⅰ—Ⅰ断面第一主拉应力都下降到安全值以内。

至于拱座基岩表面(Ⅱ—Ⅱ断面),由于45°折缝的缝端移到Ⅱ—Ⅱ断面附近(参见图7),沿Ⅱ—Ⅱ断面(图5(b))最大主拉应力加大到+1.4MPa,它和无缝时Ⅱ—Ⅱ断面上游端g点应力相近,第二主应力无缝时最大为+0.2MPa,与45°折缝的+0.34MPa很相近。在水压作用下,45°折缝虽然对Ⅱ—Ⅱ断面最大应力影响小,但它可大大改善Ⅱ—Ⅱ断面的应力分布,使最大主拉应力由上游面转到缝端(e点)附近,使上游面(g点)在无人工短缝时的最大主拉应力1.4MPa降低到45°折缝时的0.5MPa,防止在上游面结合处开裂。

综合考虑施工期温度徐变应力以及从施工末期温度下降到运行期变温场的应力(3月份拉应力最大),由于内部总温降值较大,拉应力场加大,折缝缝端拉应力集中也加剧。由图6(a)所示的Ⅱ—Ⅱ断面应力可见,45°折缝缝端区最大温度主拉应力达+1.02MPa,和无缝时的+1.0MPa相近,第二主拉应力由无缝时的+0.3MPa增大到45°折缝的

+0.75MPa。这种情况下坝肩设置短缝仍对消除温降所带来的拱坝上游面离坝肩 a 点 5m 宽的拉应力有明显作用(见图 6(b))。

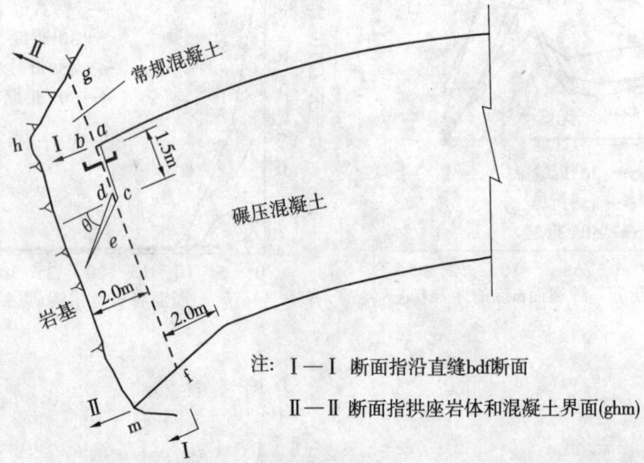

图 7　上游拱座短缝构造示意图

3.2　下游坝面人工短缝对拱坝应力的影响

在拱坝下游拱向拉力区开三条间距 4.5m、深 1～2m 的径向缝,在水压作用下,缝深度影响大,下游坝面第一主拉应力值由无缝时最大的 2.0MPa 降至缝深 2.0m 时的 0.5MPa 以下(见图 8(a))。径向断面的应力分布表明,最大主拉应力区内移,最大值由无缝时的 1.6MPa 下降为缝深 2.0m 时的1.2MPa(见图 8(b))。通常下游中部缝结构(包括缝间距和缝深)对应力的影响是局部的,对整体应力分布的影响不大。拱坝下游面拱冠区设缝,主要对减小下游拱冠区拉应力有利。

3.3　上、下游坝面人工短缝以及徐变应力因素的共同作用

上游两岸坝肩设置 45°折缝,下游拱冠自 590.0m 高程至 620.0m 高程的拉应力区设 3 条 2m 深的短缝,考虑徐变作用,计算得拱坝的应力重分布如图 9 所示。

比较图 4 及图 9,表明设置人工短缝后,沿拱坝上游坝肩宏观拉应力大大下降为微压,下游拱冠拉应力大大下降。但拱坝内部仍存在拉力区。若沿内部坝轴方向放置冷却水管,或将膨胀系数大的砂岩骨料掺用石灰岩骨料(590.0m 高程以下采用),降低混凝土温度变形值,都可以降低内部拉应力,使内部混凝土的变形保持在极限拉伸值以内,也可以阻止内部裂缝出现。

溪柄工程在上游拱座人工短缝内设灌浆系统,目的是在运行期需要时也可以利用灌浆改变作用力方向,以增强拱座稳定。按设计正常情况本可不灌浆,但考虑到部分止水埋设质量较差,只好在坝体温降之后蓄水之前对止水质量较差的部分作了灌浆处理。这些部位的人工折缝对于施工期温度应力仍然起到了较好的释放作用。

3.4　缝端应力强度因子的计算

应力集中区尤其缝端计算应力值只是在相对比较时才有意义,缝端的破坏能可由离缝端已知点坐标及其位移场(或应力场),直接求得应力强度因子。通常用缝面结点位移差计算断裂能精度较好[2]。溪柄工程在缝端单元尺寸减小到 0.5m,环绕缝端的 4 个三维

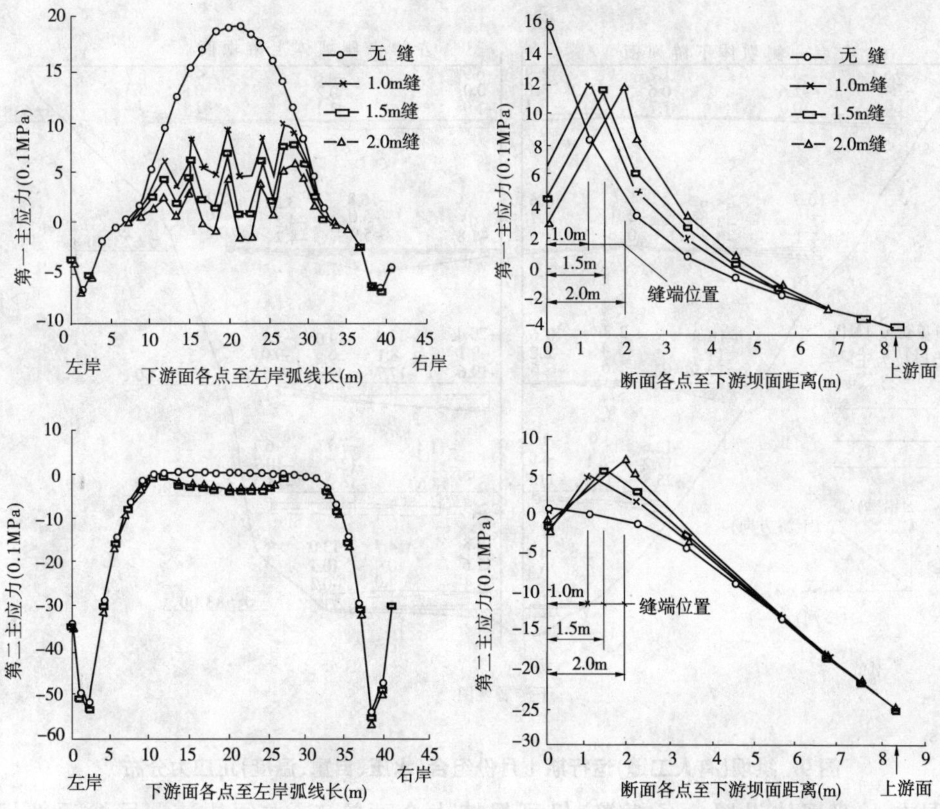

(a)沿拱圈下游面　　(b)下游中部右侧短缝断面

图 8　下游中部短缝水压作用下主应力分布图

等参元中,取含缝的上下单元缝面结点的位移值,直接计算位移差,可以求得 K_{I}、K_{II}、K_{III}。

溪柄薄拱坝下游拱冠三条短缝缝端 K 值都小于 $1\mathrm{MN/m^{\frac{3}{2}}}$,短缝是稳定的。上游 45°折缝在 590.0～610.0m 高程区间 K 值较大,水压作用下 $K_{\mathrm{I}}=0.52\mathrm{MN/m^{\frac{3}{2}}}$,$K_{\mathrm{II}}=0.02\mathrm{MN/m^{\frac{3}{2}}}$,缝保持稳定,但水压和温度荷载组合应力时最大值。

3 月份:$K_{\mathrm{I}}=2.68\mathrm{MN/m^{\frac{3}{2}}}$　　$K_{\mathrm{II}}=-0.22\mathrm{MN/m^{\frac{3}{2}}}$

7 月份:$K_{\mathrm{I}}=3.02\mathrm{MN/m^{\frac{3}{2}}}$　　$K_{\mathrm{II}}=-0.26\mathrm{MN/m^{\frac{3}{2}}}$

对于这些高程,K_{I}、K_{II} 组合应力强度因子超过断裂韧性时,在缝端埋设抗裂材料以阻止裂缝发展,如图 3 所示的缝端槽钢。

4　结语

(1)溪柄碾压混凝土拱坝设置了人工短缝改善水压及温度荷载的应力。

(2)溪柄碾压混凝土薄拱坝的研究与实践结果都表明,因修建的中低型碾压混凝土薄拱坝,水泥用量少,在冬春低温季节碾压,采用人工短缝释放拉应力的方法,可不设横缝,

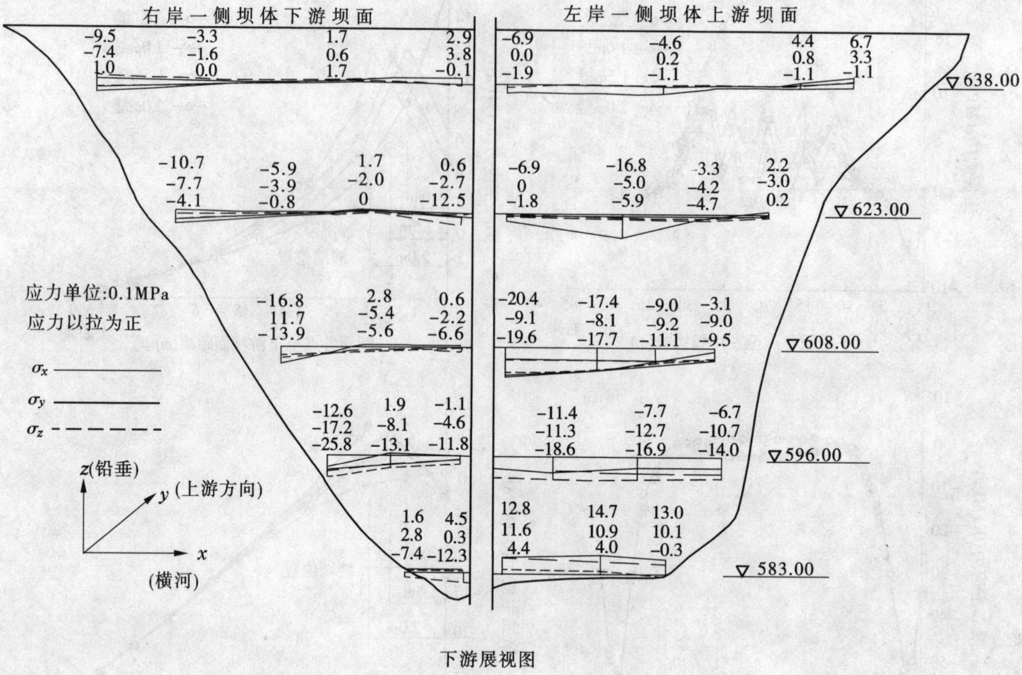

图 9　拱坝(有人工缝)运行期 1 月份组合(水压、自重、温度)正应力分布

或只是在上部坝体设置一条横缝,仍可保持大仓面施工,方便快速。虽然顶部坝厚4～5m,卡车及铲斗散料和碾压设备有干扰,降低了速度,又由于前期施工机械不足,多次停工,但溪柄拱坝仍在一个枯水期内完成了大坝主体工程全部碾压混凝土的施工。

(3)溪柄坝体温度分布实测和计算相近(误差小于1.0～1.5℃),薄拱坝温度下降到稳定变温场后,坝体未出现径向约束裂缝。大坝建成后的当年7月底经受了20年一遇的洪水,上游水位上升至624.0～625.0m高程。第二年8月2日经受了50年一遇的大洪水,水位达设计洪水位642.5m并正常泄洪,现已正常发电,效益显著。

参 考 文 献

[1] 刘光廷,张国新,刘志辉.含灌浆横缝碾压混凝土拱坝仿真应力和双轴强度判别.清华大学学报,1996(1)

[2] Pekau, O.A., Z.X. Zhang, G.T. Liu. *Constitutive Model for Concrete in Strain Space*. A.S.C.E. Journal of Engineering Mechanics, Vol.118 No.9, Sept. 1992

溪柄碾压混凝土薄拱坝运行期位移预测和实测

摘　要　溪柄碾压混凝土薄拱坝设计采用了仿真的材料热学参数。这些参数是在预测的施工温度条件下进行的材料实验中测定的。设计模拟了施工全过程，进行坝体的累计温度及自重徐变应力计算，提供施工期末初应力。本文提供运行期某一时刻水压和温度下相对施工期末的简易计算位移，并把计算值和短系列的原型观测数据进行比较修正。上述两者应力叠加即为该时全应力值。运行期位移突变或向下游变位过大都不安全。

关键词　位移　稳定温度场　边界条件

通常设计对工程都保留一定的安全度，当实测和设计预测结果相近时可认为工程满足安全要求。

溪柄一级电站大坝为碾压混凝土薄拱坝(最大厚度 12m)，坝顶弧长 90.5m，最大坝高 63.5m，1995 年完工蓄水[1]。拱坝设置人工短缝，采用有限元仿真计算进行设计，即按预期施工条件测定材料热学参数和模拟坝体施工过程的累计温度及自重徐变应力作为施工期末坝体初应力和初始温度场。施工期在不同坝体高程沿水平坝面设温度测点，监测坝体温度[2]，为后期调整施工手段以限制各区最高温升提供依据。相应的修正模拟计算过程和初应力另文刊出。受经济限制，在拱冠坝顶设有两个位移测点。用视准线法观测，测线总长约 200m，精度尚好[3]。施工期末建立位移初读数，运行期用计算和实测来判定由水压和温度改变引起位移(应力)变化。本文提供运行期碾压混凝土薄拱坝设计计算位移，并通过计算位移和短系列实测位移的比较来初步判定坝体的工作状态。

薄拱坝下部混凝土在冬季无温控施工，高掺粉煤灰 425# 低含量水泥的混凝土在 10～13℃条件下放热速度慢，试验绝热温升低(12℃)。工程实测温升 11℃。坝址平均气温(包括日照影响)达 20.2℃。因此，实测坝体最高温升值只比年平均温度高 2～4℃。实测表明坝体运行 3 年后内部测点温度在年平均温度附近摆动，接近稳定变温场，可供计算和实测比较。运行期自重不变，对顺河向变形改变影响小，变形改变主要是由水位变化和温度变化引起的。考虑到坝体的变形以弹性为主，可以采用荷载叠加的方法。将施工期末测点坐标作初读数，记录相应的温度水位作初始值，用运行期任一时刻的温度水位相对初始值变化的计算位移叠加，即可得到位移预测。

本研究工作建立的三维有限元模型，计 11 492 个结点，9 087 个单元，混凝土温度参数值采用和施工现场相近条件下的混凝土实验值，岩石弹模采用高水位岩体综合弹模，计算参数如表 1 所示。

观测点的位置在坝顶(▽644.0m)下游面，具体分布如图 1 所示。

本文选自《水力发电学报》2002 年第 1 期，作者还有叶源新。

表 1

计算参数	基础	常态混凝土	碾压混凝土
弹性模量 E(MPa)	左岸及基础 1.5×10^4 右岸 0.2×10^4	3.10×10^4	3.49×10^4
泊松比 ν	0.22	0.181	0.160
混凝土空气的散热系数 β(kJ/(m^2·d·℃))		1 046.0	1 046.0
比热 C(kJ/(kg·℃))	0.836 8	0.920 5	0.938 1
导温系数 α(m^2/d)	0.10	0.096	0.098 4
环境及初始温度为 13℃的绝热温升 过程测定值 θ(℃)		25.0	12.0(425$^{\#}$ 水泥 75kg/m^3 混凝土)
线膨胀系数(砂岩骨料)α(1/℃)	8.9×10^{-6}	8.5×10^{-6}	8.5×10^{-6}
散热速率 m_1		0.30	0.10
容重 γ(kN/m^3)		24.2	24.0

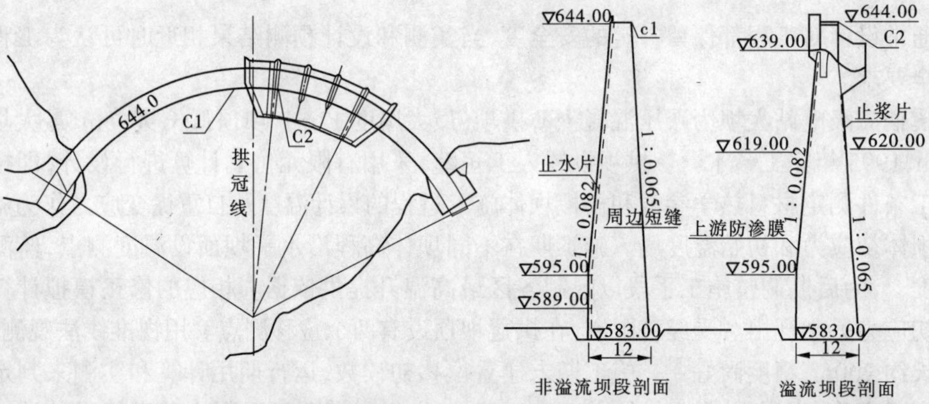

图 1　拱坝平面、剖面测点位置　(单位:m)

纯水压荷载下的坝体位移通常是确定的。把所计算的点(C1,C2)的位移和水位之间的关系用图 2 表示如下,因为实测主要提供大坝顺河向(Y 向)的位移,所以只画出顺河向位移随水位变化的规律。采用 SDJ336—89《混凝土大坝安全监测技术规范》,水平位移正负号为:向下游和左岸为正,反之为负。

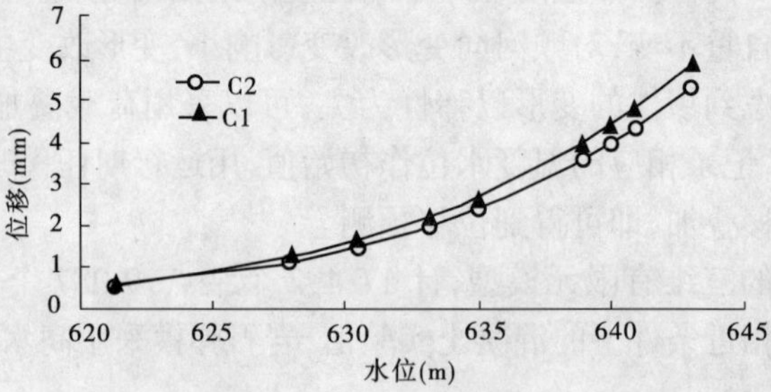

图 2　C1、C2 点位移与水位关系曲线

再利用三维模型计算温度荷载作用下坝体的变形规律。

根据大坝的有关气候的资料选定多年月平均气温(见表 2)为参考温度计算。我们知道这样得到的位移只有相对意义,但是并不影响数值的相对大小,也就是说可以看出坝体测点的位移变化趋势,再根据原型观测的值来修正参考零点,就得到实际意义上的位移变化趋势和大小。

表 2 坝址月平均气温及太阳辐射热

月份	1	2	3	4	5	6	7	8	9	10	11	12	年平均
气温(℃)	9.5	11.0	14.4	18.4	21.7	23.7	25.6	25.1	23.4	19.5	15.0	11.1	18.2
太阳辐射能 (kJ/(h·m^2))	400.2	373.9	418.8	506.3	513.3	518.6	726.8	708.2	628.3	574.0	477.8	452.7	525.0

坝顶、下游坝面温度:

$$T_a(\tau) = A\sin\omega(\tau - \tau_0) + B \tag{1}$$

实测拟合:$A = 8.0$℃,$\tau_0 = 4$,$B = 20.2$℃(考虑日照影响)。

库水温度分布变化规律和实测相似,拟合后取以下参数:

$$T_w(y,\tau) = T_{wm}(y) + A_w(y)\cos\omega[\tau - 7 - \varepsilon(y)] \tag{2}$$

式中:$T_w(y,\tau)$ 为深度 y 处、时间 τ 的水温,℃;$T_{wm}(y)$ 为深度 y 处的年平均水温;$T_{wm}(y) = 9.57 + 10.63e^{-0.04y}$;$A_w(y) = 8.0e^{-0.033y}$(℃);$\varepsilon(y) = 2.15 - 1.3e^{-0.085y}$(月);$\omega = 2\pi/12$。

3 年后对于运行中的碾压混凝土薄拱坝,混凝土的水化及散热已经基本完成,温度实测表明坝体内部温度在年平均温度上下摆动。运行期坝体各部分的温度变化是由外界的温度变化引起的。当年温度变化相近时,相同月份气温变化引起坝体位移也相近,可由稳定变场计算相应的位移变化。计算中采用的边界条件主要考虑了以下三种:

(1)坝体和空气接触的部分,按公式(1)取值。

(2)坝体和水接触的部分,按库水温度分布公式(2)取值。

(3)选取三维计算模型时,蓄水前后深层岩体温度变化很小,取定值;山体的表面和水或者空气相接触,温度随外界的温度周期性变化而变化。则岩体的温度的分布是两者共同作用的结果,实测统计简化如图 3 所示。在埋深 20m 处,可认为岩体温度恒定在年平均气温,由此可以根据埋深推算计算模型的山体深层部分的人工边界的温度值。

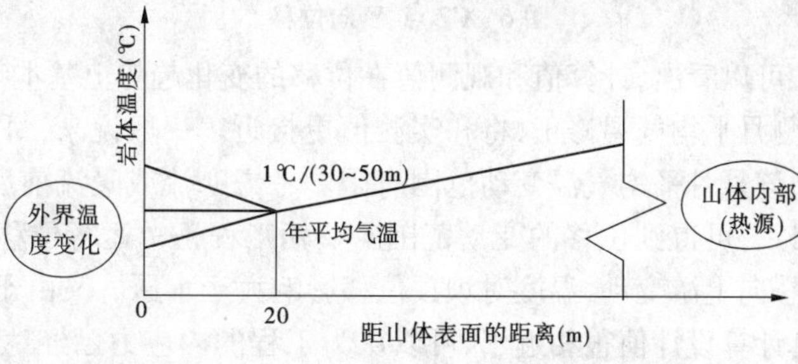

图 3 深层岩体温度分布示意图

在这里,我们取库水的平均水深来确定与水接触部分的边界。该工程的水位年变化并不大,多在 637m 附近,上下波动一般在 5m 之内,为简便起见把水库在大多数情况下的库水位值带入计算，与实际相差不大。用多年实测温度进行拟合月平均温度过程，得到温度变化引起的各测点的 Y 向位移变化如图 4 所示。

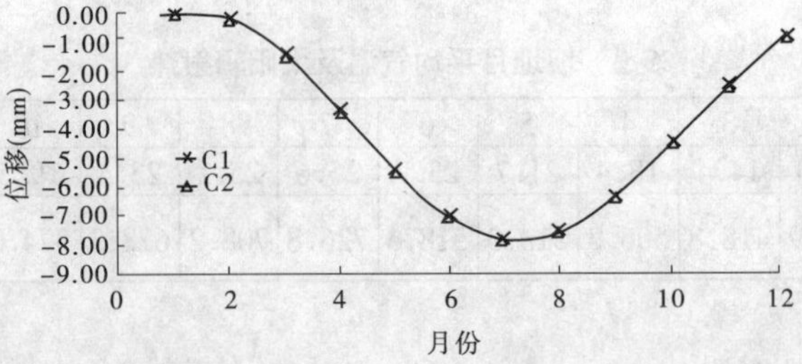

图 4　运行期温度引起的 Y 向位移曲线

这样，只要给定水位值和时间，通过图 2 和图 4 查得对应的水压和相应月份的温度引起的位移，把两者叠加就可得到该状态下坝体应有的位移，再和原型观测值作比较（见图 5 和图 6）。

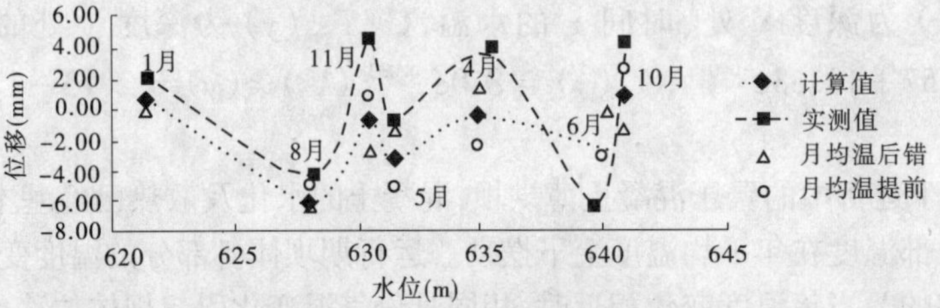

图 5　C1 点 Y 向位移

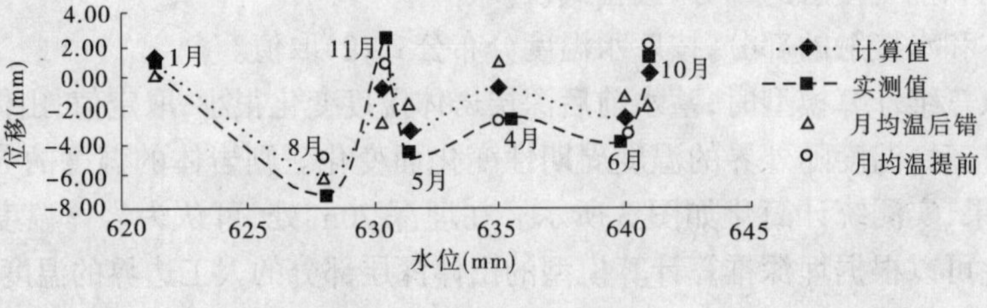

图 6　C2 点 Y 向位移

从图 5 和图 6 可以看出，计算值和观测值在位移的变化趋势上基本吻合，在数值上也接近；若用当年实测月平均气温修正，将和实测值更接近。一般说来，每年实际的某月月平均气温和多年的该月月平均气温变动范围有限。考虑寒流或暖流前后错动，对计算位移值进行简单的修正，可得到位移的变动范围。溪柄工程正常运行位移变幅为 6mm，冬季向下游变位，夏季向上游变动，温度对坝顶位移影响大于水压。又由于 641m 水位下的实测值已经和仿真计算设计值很相近了，可以认为工程的内应力已经达到或略超过了设计值。实际上溪柄工程为增加发电量连续 4 年超校核洪水位蓄水，经常超高 2～4m 蓄水，降低了工程的安全裕度，是不可取的。

虽然本文的方法对坝体所受荷载进行了较大的近似简化，但比较结果说明按照该方法计算运行期水压及稳定温度变场作用下混凝土薄拱坝的变形是可行的，而且操作简便快捷,在工程实际中具有较好的应用价值。

参考文献

[1] Liu G. T., Mai J. X., Zhang G. X.. *Research and Practice on Xi-Bing Roller Compacted Concrete Thin Arch Dam*, *Proceedings of Int. Symp*. Santander. Spain. on 2～4 October 1995 Vol 1. p413～426

[2] 张富德,薛慧,陈凤岐,等.碾压混凝土坝非稳定温度场计算预测与工程实测的比较.清华大学学报,1998,38(1)

[3] 曹乐安,朱丽如.建筑物及其基础的安全监测.葛洲坝工程丛书之7.北京:水利电力出版,1990

RESEARCH AND PRACTICE ON XI-BING ROLLER COMPACTED CONCRETE THIN ARCH DAM

Abstract In present paper a special structure of roller compacted concrete thin arch dam with stress-release artificial short joints is introduced, which has the advantages of greatly reducing the constructing period of arch dam with smaller concrete volume and simplifying the flood-release structures during construction. Technology of roller-compacted concrete is suitable for broad concrete placing area, which induces strong restraint by rock foundation in both banks and causes an intensive tensile stress for any temperature drop to the arch dam without transverse joint. Therefore the actual similar calculations of stress field and multiaxial strengths of concrete, which is more close to the actual state, are introduced in the design. Degrees of formation inner crack in concrete mass are considered for determining the coefficient of safety. The continued constructional technology in spring 1995 on Xi-Bin roller-compacted concrete thin arch dam offered a rise of 0.75～0.9m height of arch dam per day in average. Engineering practice confirms the advantages of little interference, simple technology and high speed in construction.

1 Brief Introduction

Roller-compacted concrete has a simple technology and high speed in construction, which will greatly reduce the constructing period of arch dam with smaller concrete volume and simplify the flood-release structures during construction. Since the plan-arch serves as main style of transmitting forces, the weaken layers of roller-compacted concrete play less important role in stability of dam. Conventionally, arch dam is made of separated block and grouted after drawing down the concrete temperature by artificial cooling pipe. The complicated form works for transverse joints and waiting for heat divergence or workable strength of concrete also cause a loss of time. Therefore, higher costs, more complicated technology and longer constructing period are carried out by conventional technology. The technology of roller-compacted concrete is suitable for broad concrete-placing area. It has an unfavorable interference with installation of great amount cooling pipes, form works in transverse joints and grouting system. The low cement content in concrete bring an important benefit to lower temperature rise of roller-compacted concrete during construction. But the strong restraint of both sides abutments causes an intensive tensile stress for any temperature drop to the arch dam without transverse joint. Canceled the cooling pipe system, the temperature of concrete should go down very slowly in later period and delay the date of pounding, if the grouting of transverse joints or cracks is necessary. Technology of rapid placing concrete makes a large temperature difference between inner part and outer part of concrete structure, which will

本文选自《Materlals, Planning and Design》1995 年 10 月，作者还有 Mai Jiaxuan, Zhang Guoxin。

cause cracks on the upper and down stream faces of dam. These cracks always propagate through inner tensile region in summer time and radial through-cracks will happen after all. It is unsafe to build concrete thin arch dam with broken arch. In order to keep integrity of arch dam, transverse joints or cracks must be grouted usually. Since the widths of joints increase slowly with descending of concrete temperature and they are out of control, these grouted joints may open again later. Date of normal service of arch dam evidently delays (even later than conventional technology). Therefore, in order to keep off upper describing discomposure the actual-similar stress calculation is necessary for the favorable design of roller-compacted arch dam, especially concrete thin arch dam. Loads are exerted step by step according to constructing process. Thermal and mechanical parameters of concrete materials were measured both for winter and standard conditions (20℃). Changes of structural figure and its restraint conditions are considered for the various construction stages. So the information of stress in any parts of structure and its foundation are more close to the actual state. According to experimental results Multi-axial strength of concrete with corresponding criteria of safety were suggested. The energy of propagation and toughness of concrete beyond artificial short joints under thermal load (study on thermal toughness of concrete was published in another paper) are compared. The structural improvement and engineering measures for prevention of crack propagation were made. The upper described method of design was used in practice under the guard of the Ministry of Water Resources and also supported by the Ministry and National Natural Science Faundation of China. In spite of various unfavorable condition: Delay of arrival of main construction equipment, frequently constructional breaks for repair of machine, abnormal gravel supply and etc., the concrete thin arch dam was completed within one low water season. Engineering practice shows that the continued constructional technology in winter offers a rise of 0.75~0.9m height of arch dam per day in average. The continued placing concrete causes an interior maximum temperature rise about 11℃, which is under the limit of design. Practice confirms also that the broad placing concrete area has the advantages of little interference and less preparation work, simple technology and high speed in construction.

Xi-Bin Roller-Compacted Concrete thin arch Dam has a maximum. height 63.5m with 12m thickness at bottom of dam and concrete volume about 33 000m^3. Three typical figures (Figs. 1~3) including: general layout plan of concrete thin arch dam. Upstream elevation with profile of arch crown and arch plan with joints are given as following.

2 Method of Design

Using RCC Method with broad placing area, the plan arch without transverse joints is strictly restrained by rock foundation of both side abutments during temperature change which is the main source of formation radial cracks. Self-weights of concrete layers are supported by rock foundation of both bank and river bed also. The stress-distributions in arch

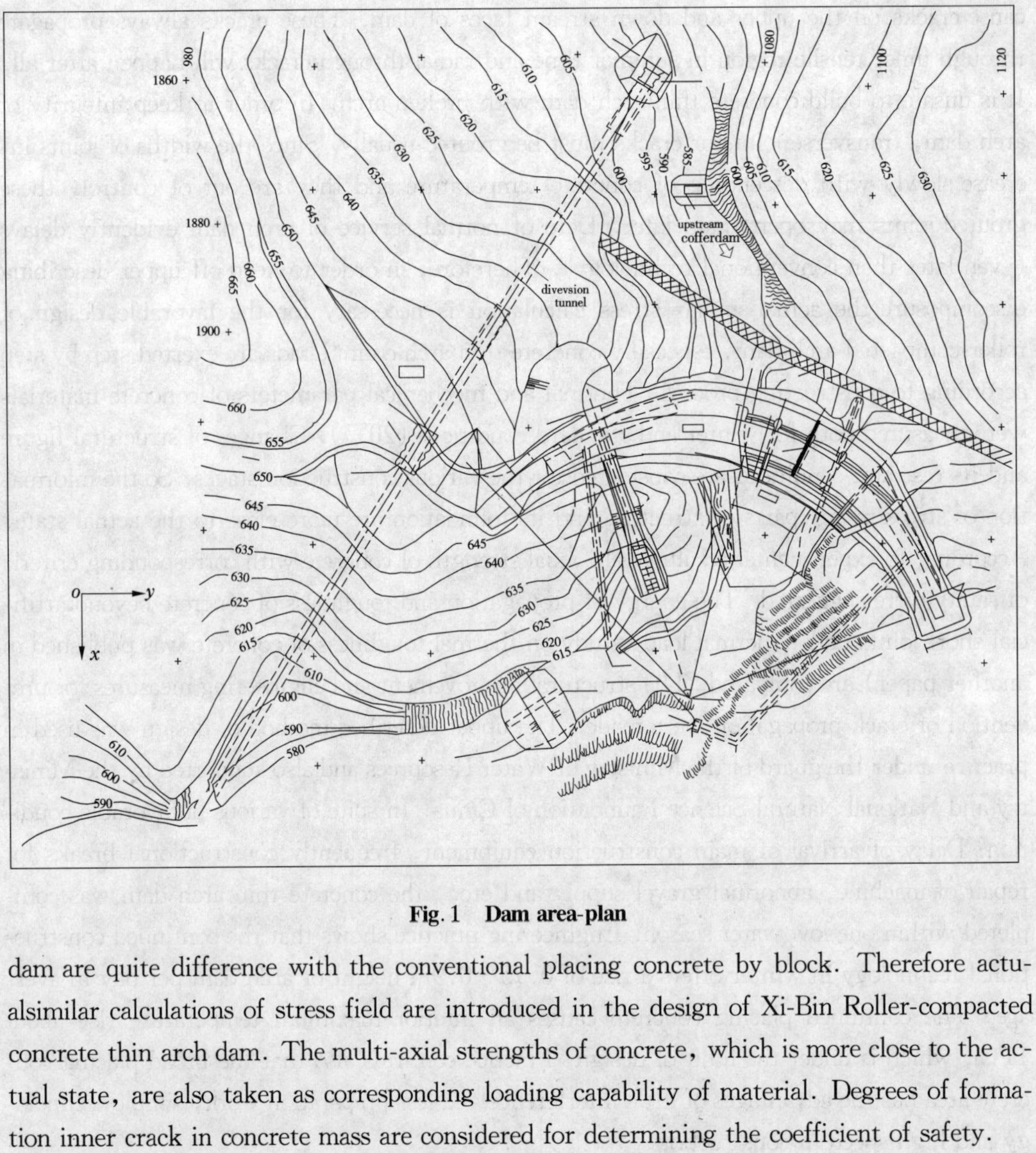

Fig. 1　Dam area-plan

dam are quite difference with the conventional placing concrete by block. Therefore actualsimilar calculations of stress field are introduced in the design of Xi-Bin Roller-compacted concrete thin arch dam. The multi-axial strengths of concrete, which is more close to the actual state, are also taken as corresponding loading capability of material. Degrees of formation inner crack in concrete mass are considered for determining the coefficient of safety.

2.1　The Calculation of Actual Similar Stress

3-D F. E. M with isoparametric elements were used for the calculation of temperature and stress-field. According to process of placing concrete during construction, the variation of temperature field in structure is calculated by accumulating block. Since the load by weight and thermal load begin to exert on structure at the same time, the displacements are restrained by foundation of both shores and concrete underneath. Creep due to both thermal load and accumulated weight must be considered in stress calculation throughout the construction period.

The integrated (without transverse joints) RCC arch dam and foundation continue their deformations after ponding for the temperature drop of structure. The restraint caused by deformation difference between foundation and integrated concrete dam will produce a certain large thermal stress in dam (conventionally, arch dam is separated into block during this temperature drop. This kind of stress is not important). For this purpose harmonic vibration of temperature field in dam and its foundation during operation period must be calculated. The thermal stress field caused by the difference between temperature field at the end of construction and long term after ponding is finally obtained.

Stress fields of dam due to hydraulic pressure after ponding are also given by F. E. M. Summarized the upper described stresses, the combined stresses of hydraulic load, accumulated weight and all the thermal stress during construction and operation are obtained. Evidently the main parameters of material for calculation are taken directly from experiments with similar conditions. For examples: Coefficient of thermal expansions of local rocks and concrete, adiabatic thermal rise of placing concrete in lower temperature, etc.

2.2 Capability of Taking Load for Roller Compacted Concrete

The biaxial strengths of concrete are used, which are more close to the actual extreme state. The maximum strength of concrete is used for checking temporary stress during construction period. The cracked elements and elastic-plastic elements are considered for stress-redistribution calculation when the stress go over the maximum. strength of material. 35% maximun. strength of concrete (stress intensity corresponding to initial micro crack growth in concrete) is used for the criteria of variable stresses during operation.

2.3 The Stability of Artificial Short Joints

The S. I. F. is obtained from the stress-field beyond the tip of crack. The average value 2 000kN/$m^{3/2}$, measured in field, is used for criteria of fracture toughness during outer loads and combined stresses. But strain toughness from experimental value $15\times10^{-6}m^{1/2}$ is taken for checking criteria of thermal fracture. For the safety of dam special technology and measure of crack-prevention were used for the local region where stress intensity and S. I. F. grow over the criteria of strength and toughness.

3 The Structure of Roller-compacted Thin Arch Dam

Intensive tensile stress happened usually at upstream arch abutment and downstream arch crown during hydraulic load or homogeneous temperature drop of arch dam. The installation of artificial short joints with water tight in these places will reduce or release the tensile stress and change the direction of transmission force of hydraulic load. So the simple for roller compacted technology arch dam with outline of single curve and short joints will work as double curved (from the view of transmission force) arch dam with enlarged curvatures. The artificial short joints at upstream dam abutment make a transfer of tensile stress region from abutment to the tip of joints and cause the new regions of stress concentration near the tips. The curved artificial joints with buried tip located at low stress intensity region near the foundation reduce the energy of fracture. The anti-fracture material is installed beyond the

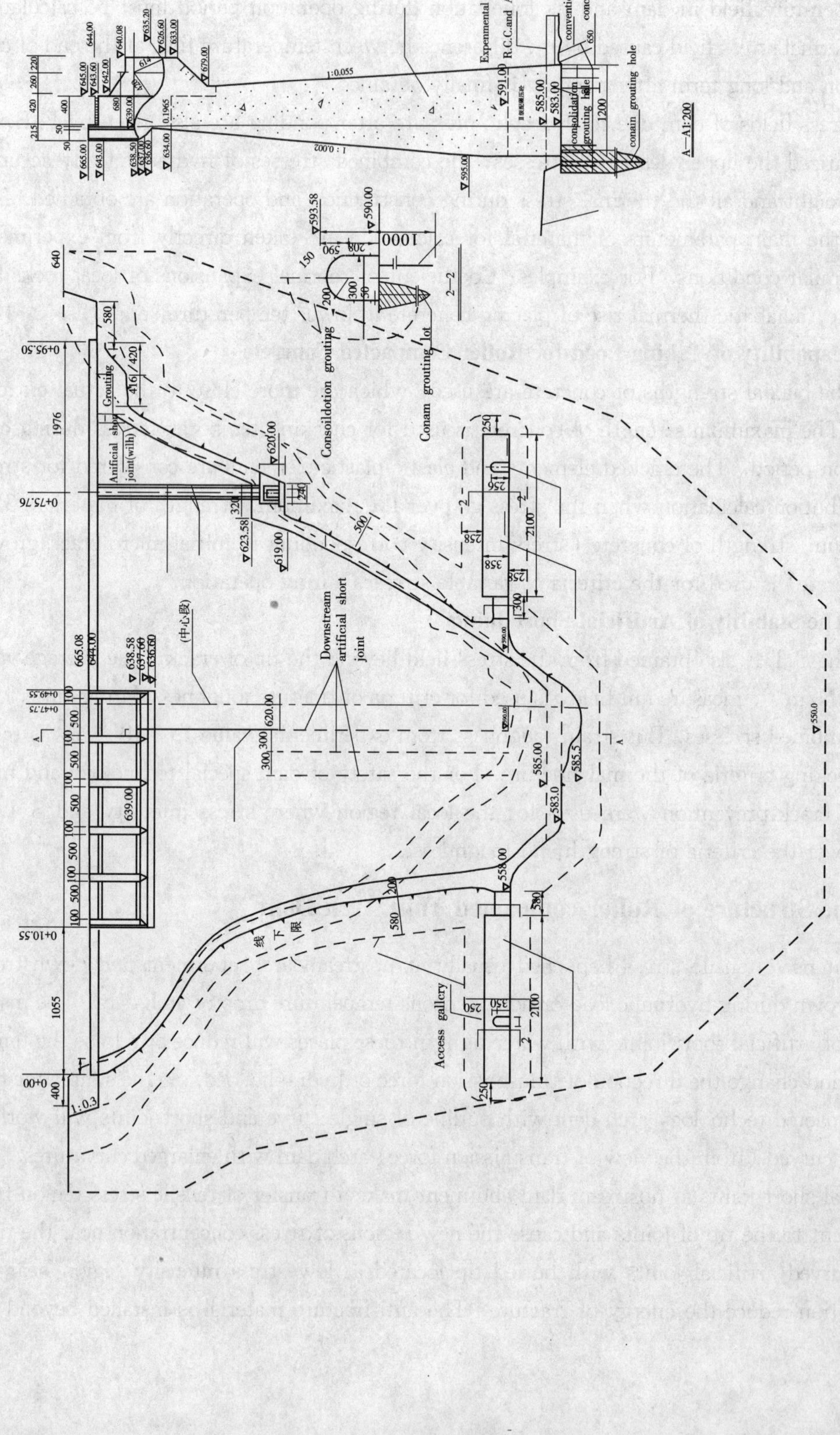

Fig. 2 Upstream face (developed) elevation

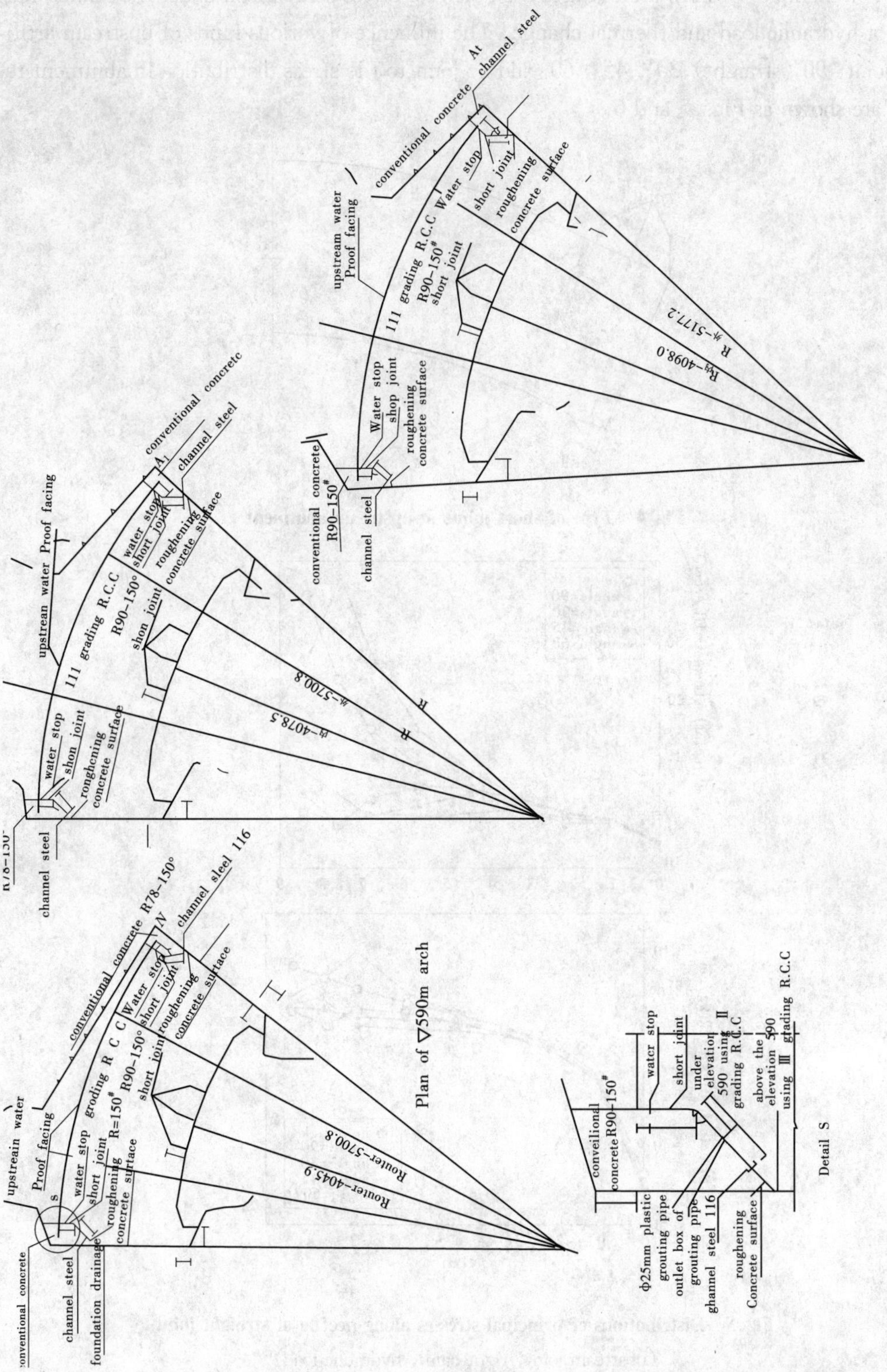

Fig. 3 Arch – Plan

tip of joints for the prevention of crack propagation.

For example ▽611.0 arch (Fig.4) is taken for stress comparison under the same condition of hydraulic load and thermal change. The influence of various kinds of upstream artificial joint: 90°(straight), 30°, 45°, 60° and no joint to the stress distribution in abutment region are shown as Figs.5 and 6.

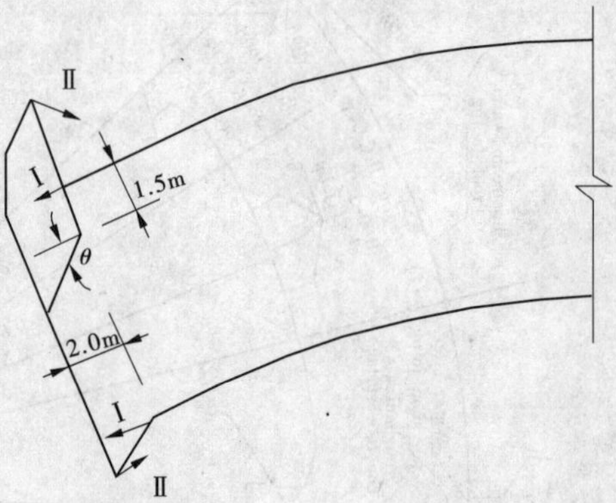

Fig.4　Type of short joints at upstream abutment

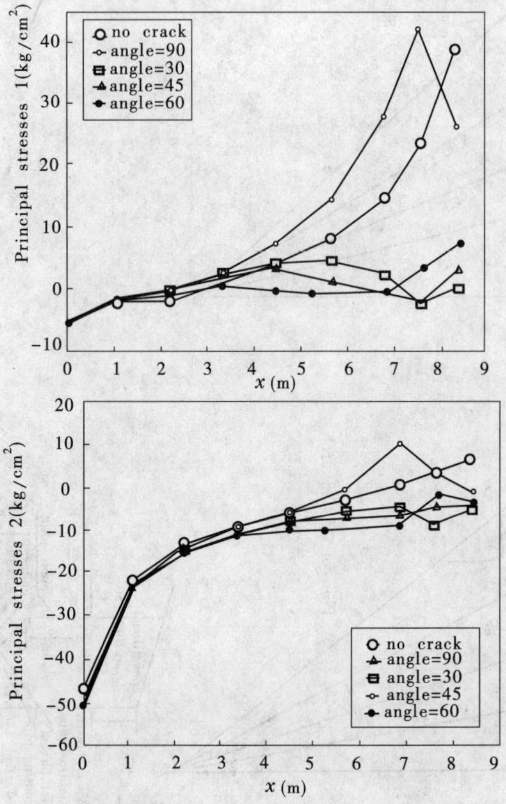

Fig.5　Distributions of principal stresses along profile of straight joint

(upstream joint, right bank, hydraulic load)

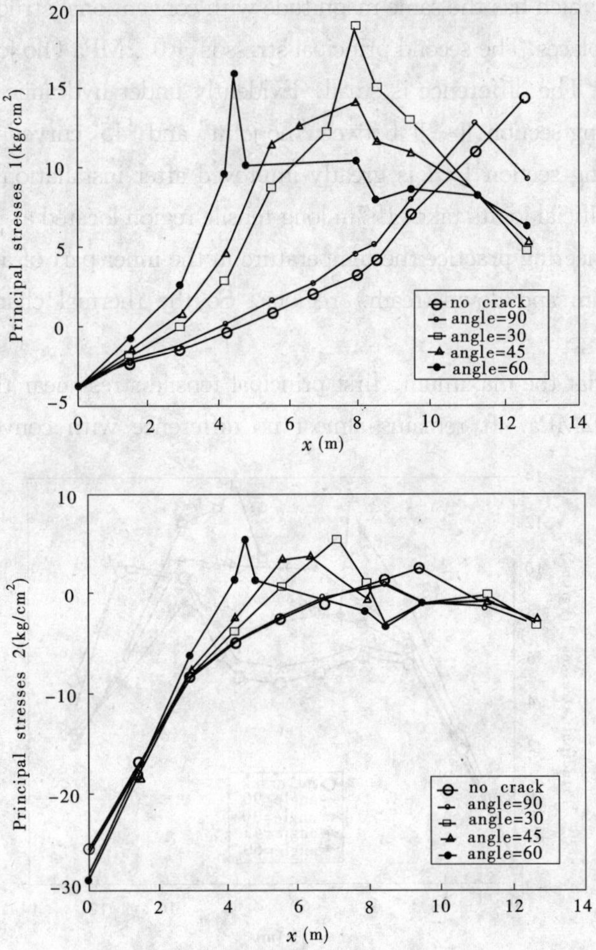

Fig. 6 Distributions of principal stresses along contact surface between rock and concrete in abutment(upstream joint, right bank, hydraulic load)

1) conventional integrated structure (no joint).

2) straight joint, 1.5m long.

3) curved joint $\theta=30°$, $a_1=1.5$m, $a_2=2.0$m.

4) curved joint $\theta=45°$, $a_1=1.5$m, $a_2=2.5$m.

5) curved joint $\theta=60°$.

In order to lay out the influence of upstream joint to the stress of arch individually, the artificial joints at downstream arch crown were eliminated during calculation.

In section Ⅰ—Ⅰ along the direction of radial joint, the principal tensile stress decrease from +3.9MPa (no joint) to +0.3MPa (45° curved joint) during hydraulic load. The second principal stress decrease also from tensile stress +0.9MPa (no joint) to −0.4 compression (45° curved joint). Since the tip of 45° curved joint located at section Ⅱ—Ⅱ of rock surface, the maximum. principal tensile stress of section Ⅱ—Ⅱ grows up to +1.4MPa

(45° curved joint) which has the same magnitude with conventional structure (no joint), but locates at different places. The second principal stress is +0.2MPa (no joint) and +0.3MPa (45° curved joint). The difference is small. Evidently under hydraulic load the maximun. stress difference along section Ⅱ—Ⅱ between"no joint" and "45° curved joint" is very small. But the stresses along section Ⅰ—Ⅰ is greatly improved after installation joints. It is shown from Fig. 6 that artificial joints take off 7m long tensile region located at upstream face of "no joint"arch. In engineering practice the temperature in the inner part of arch is usually higher than outer (upstream and downstream) regions. So the thermal change near tip of 45° curved joint is enlarged.

Fig. 7 shows that the maximum. first principal tensile stress near the tip of 45° curved joint go up +1.02MPa. It remains almost no difference with conventional (on joint)

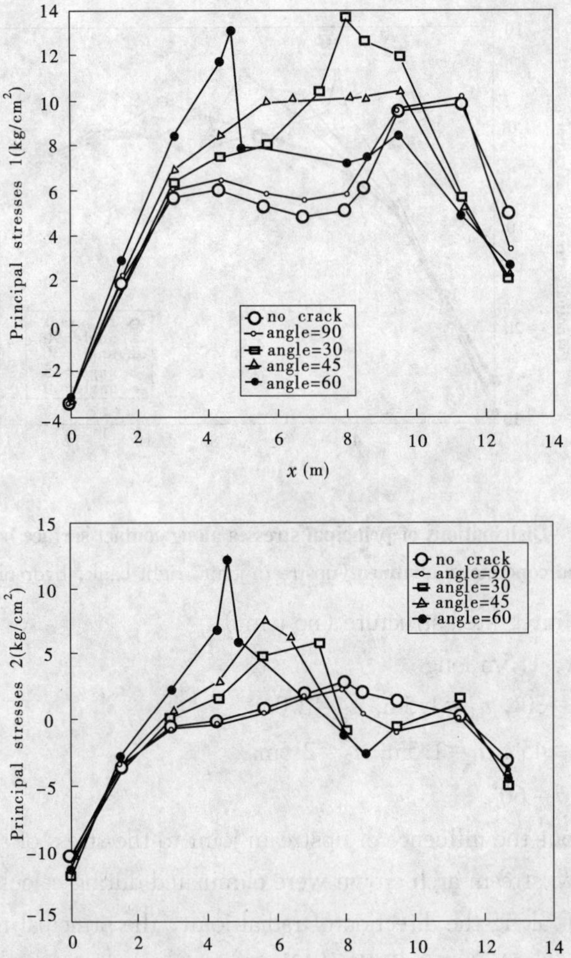

Fig. 7 Distributions of principal stresses along contact surface between rock and concrete in abutment(upstream joint, combined thermal field in March, right bank)

+1.0MPa. The second principal stress increases from +0.3MPa (no joint) to +0.75MPa (45° curved joint). Nevertheless artificial joints clean out the 5m tensile stress region in upstream surface during this thermal change (Fig. 8). Therefore cutting down the maximum thermal rise in the inner part of arch during construction has the advantage not only for reducing temperature difference between inner part and surface of arch, but also for improving the tensile stress concentration at tip of joint. The artificial short joints installed in downstream region of arch crown offer a reduction of tensile stress at downstream arch crown.

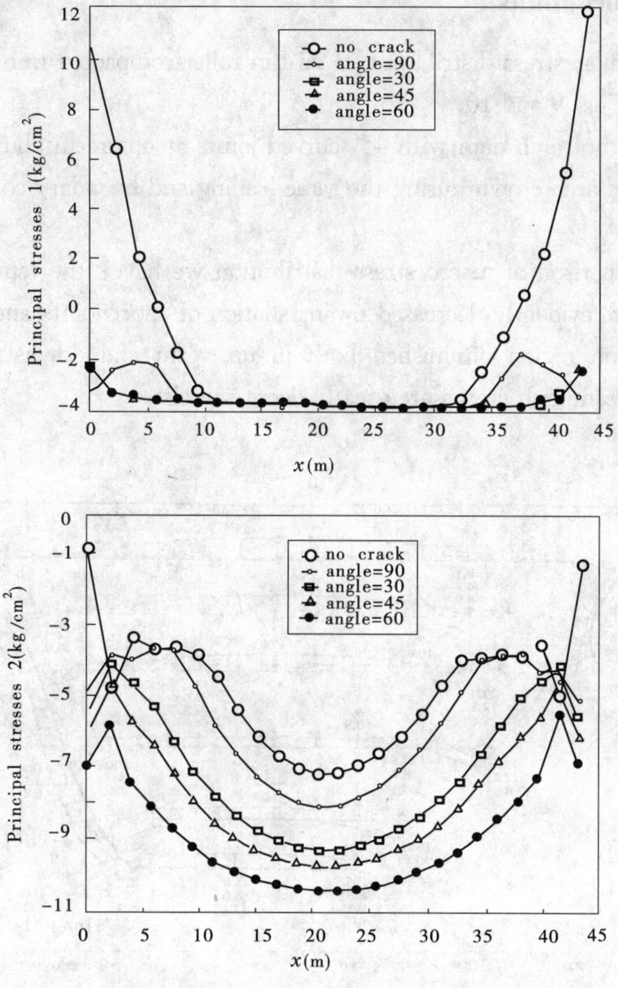

Fig. 8 Distributions of principal stresses along upstream surface of arch (upstream joint, combined thermal field in March, right bank)

Stress-concentration region, especially stress value at tip region has the meaning only for relative comparison. S. I. F. value is used for detecting the state of crack propagation. Stress field of known point beyond the tip offers the information of S. I. F. For 45° curved joint in right bank due to hydraulic load $K_{I}=0.52MN/m^{3/2}$, $K_{II}=0.02MN/m^{3/2}$ combined stress of hydraulic pressure and thermal load (March) $K_{\mathrm{I}} = 2.68\mathrm{MN/m^{3/2}}$, $K_{\mathrm{II}} = -0.22\mathrm{MN/m^{3/2}}$, (July) $K_{\mathrm{I}} = 3.02\mathrm{MN/m^{3/2}}$, $K_{\mathrm{II}} = -0.26\mathrm{MN/m^{3/2}}$. Some of them are not involved in the toughness limit of outer load and thermal fracture. For safety's sake crack prevention material should be installed beyond the crack tip when the combined value of K_{I} and K_{II} goes over the limit of toughness at certain elevation.

4 The Stress Redistribution of Roller-compacted Concrete Thin Arch Dam with Artificial Short Joints

The actual similar stress distribution of Xi-Bin roller-compacted thin arch dam without joints is shown in Figs. 9 and 10.

The stress field of arch dam with 45° curved joints at upstream abutment and straight joint at downstream arch crown during the same loading and boundary conditions is gives in Figs. 11 and 12.

From the comparison of macro stress distribution we have: the tensile stresses at upstream abutment are evidently decreased by installation of short joints and even change into compression, tension region diminished both in upstream and downstream face, tensile stresses at downstream arch crown are greatly decreased also.

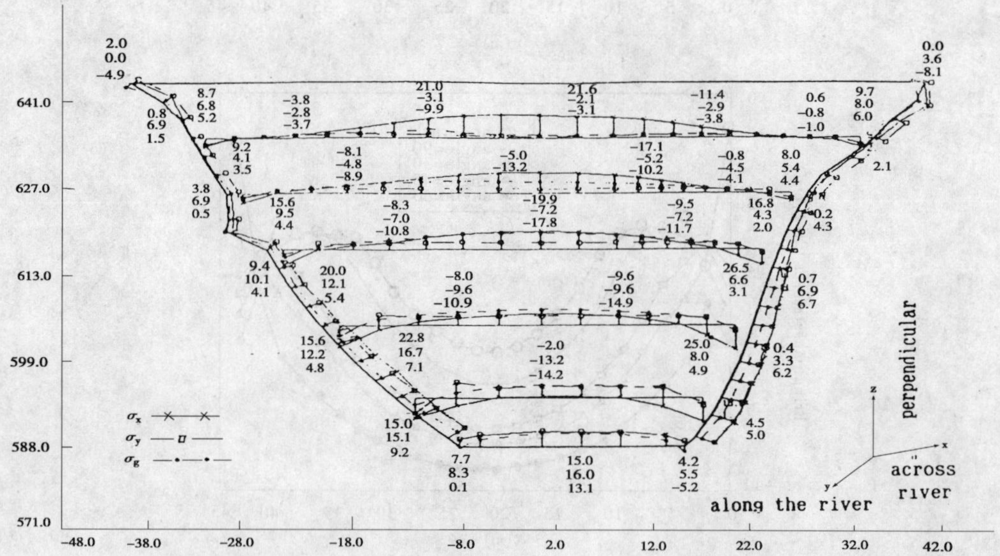

Fig. 9 Combined normal stresses at upstream face of arch dam in Jan. during operation (no joint)

Compared Fig. 13 and Fig. 14, there exists a certain tension region in the inner part of arch dam. These tension stress can be effectively reduced if the artificial cooling faces could be created along the inner dam axis or in stead of sand stone gravel with large coefficient of expansion we add some of limestone gravel for decreasing the deformation of inner concrete. Both of the upper described measures were used in present engineering successfully. Keep the

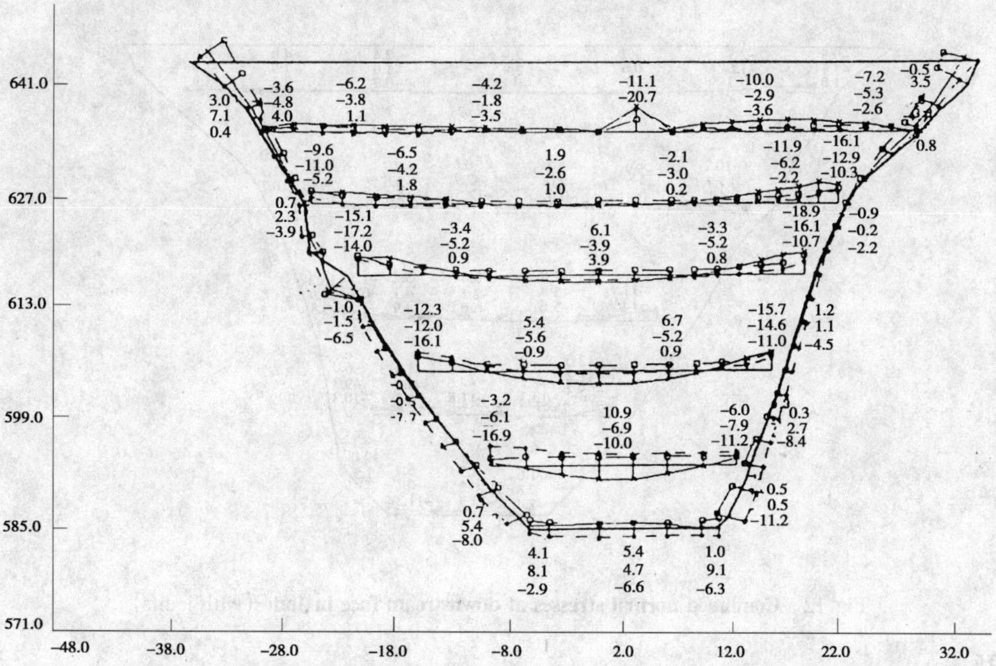

Fig. 10 Combined normal stresses at downstream face of arch dam in Jan. during operation(no joint)

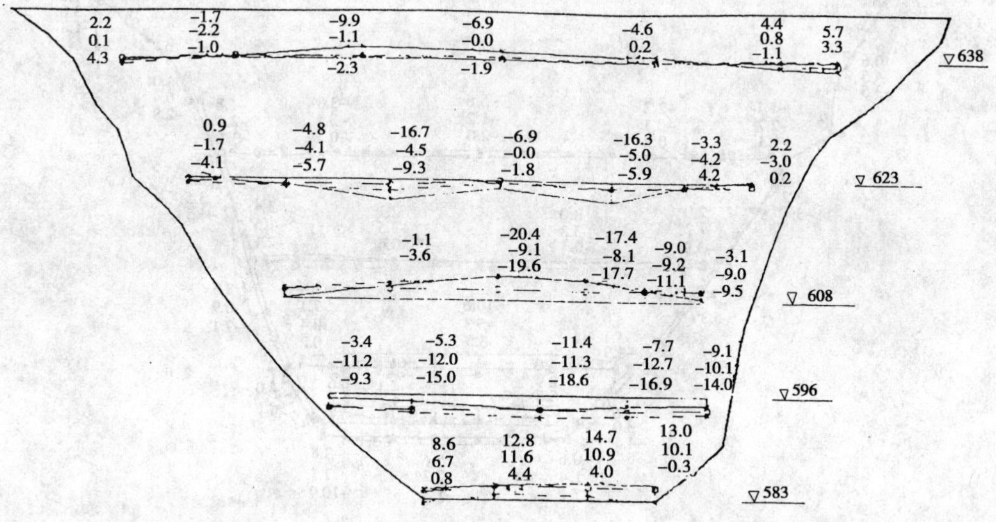

Fig. 11 Combined normal stresses at upstream face in Jan (with joints)

upstream and downstream faces of dam in compression state (without crack), the inner crack may not happened, if stress of inner part concrete of dam remains under the limit value of tension. Grouting systems are installed in artificial short joints, which can be used for adjusting the direction of transmission force if necessary and improving the stability of abutment during operation.

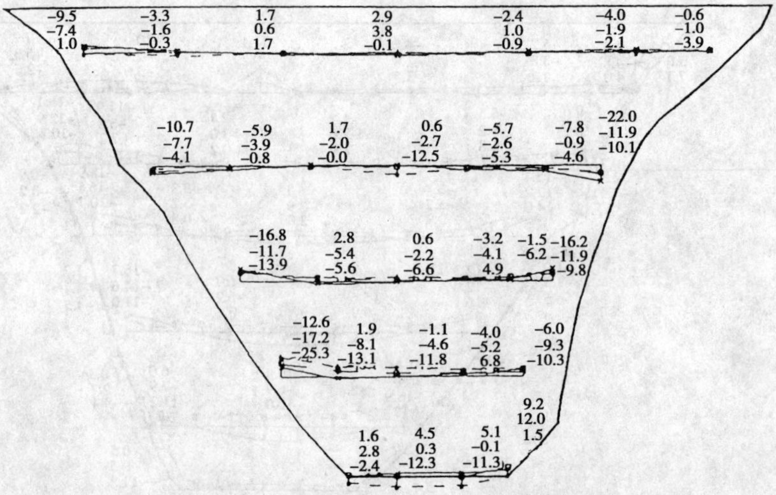

Fig. 12　Combined normal stresses at downstream face in Jan. (with joints)

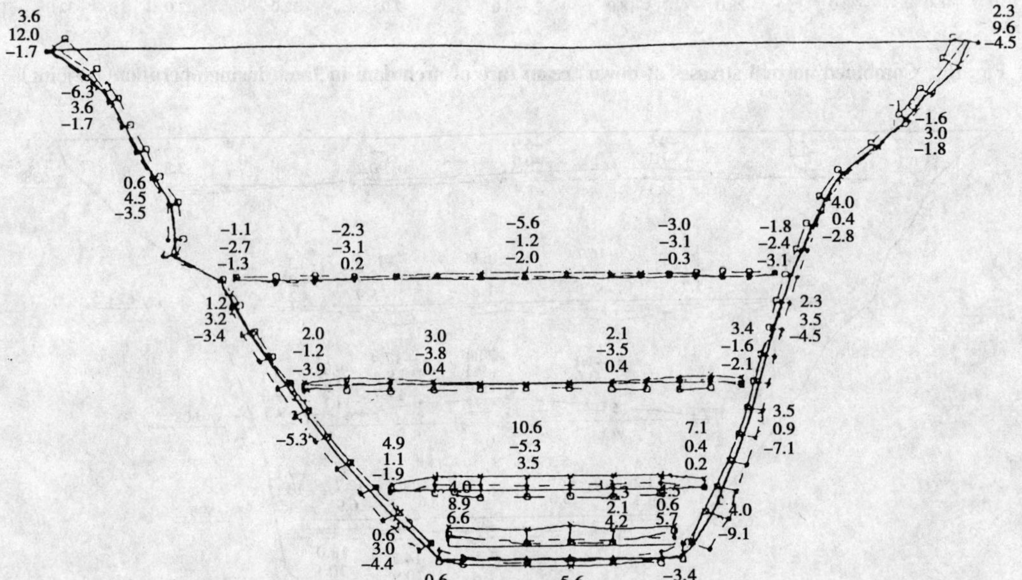

Fig. 13　Combined normal stresses in the center part of arch dam in Jan. during operation (no joint)

Acknowledgements

The research work was supported by the Ministry of Water Resources and National Natural Science Foundation.

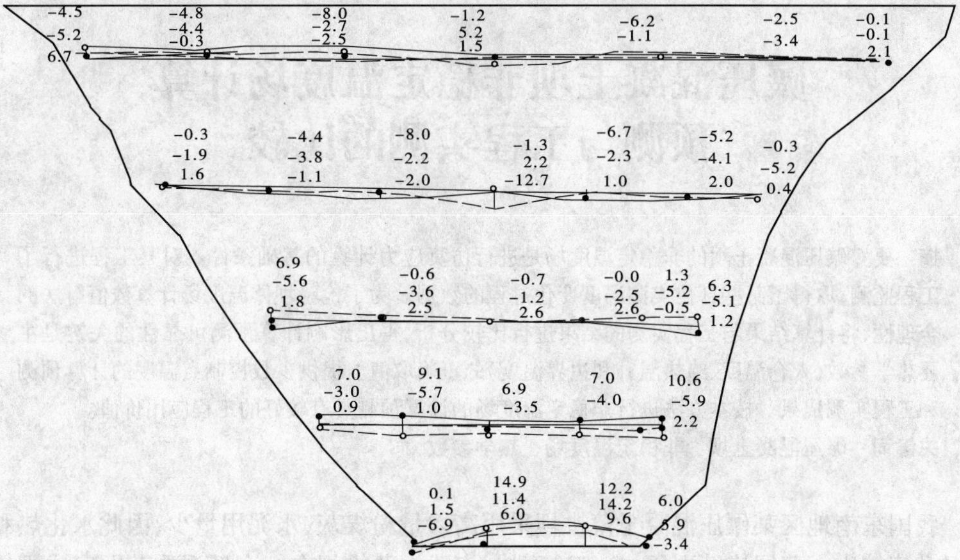

Fig. 14 Combined normal stresses in the center part of arch dam in Jan. during operation(with joints)

碾压混凝土坝非稳定温度场计算预测与工程实测的比较

摘　要　碾压混凝土坝的非稳定温度场是进行仿真应力计算的基础条件。对某工程进行了工程监测,取得了某些部位实测温度变化过程的数据。为了检验坝体温度场计算数值解法的合理性,将计算结果与工程实测的结果进行比较分析,得出影响计算预测可靠性的关键是主要热学参数(入仓温度、绝热温升和边界温度)的正确取值。提供少数控制点温度的计算预测和工程实测成果。按本方法进行非稳定温度场的计算预测具有较好的工程应用价值。

关键词　碾压混凝土坝　非稳定温度场　热学参数

我国东南地区某碾压混凝土薄拱坝采用高掺量粉煤灰,水泥用量少,因此水化热和绝热温升值较小。薄层连续碾压,施工速度快,实践中薄拱坝在一个低温季节即完成坝体浇筑的工程量。由于碾压混凝土层间间歇时间较短,上表面散热少,混凝土的入仓温度和绝热温升将直接影响坝体的温度状态,依靠上下游坝面散热温降慢,因此坝体实际升温仍能达到一定数值。

在浇筑碾压混凝土薄拱坝的过程中,由于水泥水化热和外界环境条件的影响,坝内的温度将随时间和空间而变化,属于三维非稳定温度场问题,坝体边界条件复杂,只能采用数值解法。为了检验其解法的可靠性和热学参数的敏感性,可直接比较原型观测结果和计算预测结果。

1　三维非稳定温度场的计算原理

根据热传导理论,碾压混凝土薄拱坝在施工期的三维非稳定温度场 $T(x,y,,z,t)$ 应满足下述偏微分方程和边界及初始条件[1,2](见图 1)

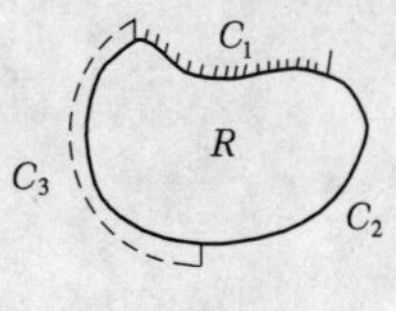

图 1

$$\frac{\partial T}{\partial t} = a\left(\frac{\partial^2 T}{\partial x^2} + \frac{\partial^2 T}{\partial y^2} + \frac{\partial^2 T}{\partial z^2}\right) + \frac{\partial \theta}{\partial t} \tag{1}$$

初始条件:当 $t = 0$ 时,

$$T = T_0(x,y,z)$$

在边界 C_1 上为第一类边界,

$$T = T_b$$

在边界 C_2 上为第三类边界,

$$\lambda_x \frac{\partial T}{\partial x} l_x + \lambda_y \frac{\partial T}{\partial y} l_y + \lambda_z \frac{\partial T}{\partial z} l_z + \beta(T - T_a) = 0$$

在边界 C_3 上为绝热边界,

$$\partial T / \partial n = 0$$

本文选自《清华大学学报(自然科学版)》1998 年第 1 期,作者还有张富德、薛慧、陈凤岐、缪丽斌。

式中：λ 为导热系数；a 为导温系数，$a = \lambda / c\rho$；c 为比热；ρ 为容重；β 为表面放热系数；θ 为混凝土的绝热温升；T_a、T_b 为给定的边界气温和水温；n 为边界外法线方向；l_x、l_y、l_z 分别为边界外法线的方向余弦；T_0 为给定的初始温度。

适当选择 β 值后，上述第一类边界条件和绝热条件均可用第三类边界条件形式代替，于是由变分原理，上述的热传导问题等价于下列泛函的极小值问题。

$$I(T) = \iiint_R \left\{ \frac{1}{2}\left[\left(\frac{\partial T}{\partial x}\right)^2 + \left(\frac{\partial T}{\partial y}\right)^2 + \left(\frac{\partial T}{\partial z}\right)^2 \right] + \frac{1}{a}\left(\frac{\partial T}{\partial t} - \frac{\partial \theta}{\partial t}\right) T \right\} \mathrm{d}R + \iint_C \left(\frac{\bar{\beta}}{2} T^2 - \bar{\beta} T_a T \right) \mathrm{d}s \tag{2}$$

式中：$\bar{\beta} = \beta / \lambda$。

泛函 $I(T)$ 的极值问题可用有限单元法求解。对三维结构 R 域进行离散化得到以下方程组：

$$\left[\boldsymbol{H} + \frac{2}{\Delta t}\boldsymbol{P} \right] \{T\}_t + \left[\boldsymbol{H} - \frac{2}{\Delta t}\boldsymbol{P} \right] \{T\}_{t-\Delta t} + \{\boldsymbol{Q}\}_t + \{\boldsymbol{Q}\}_{t-\Delta t} = 0 \tag{3}$$

式中

$$\boldsymbol{H} = \sum_e \boldsymbol{H}^e = \sum_e \iiint_{\Delta R} \left(a_x \frac{\partial \boldsymbol{N}^T}{\partial x}\frac{\partial \boldsymbol{N}}{\partial x} + a_y \frac{\partial \boldsymbol{N}^T}{\partial y}\frac{\partial \boldsymbol{N}}{\partial y} + a_z \frac{\partial \boldsymbol{N}^T}{\partial z}\frac{\partial \boldsymbol{N}}{\partial z} \right) \mathrm{d}R$$

$$\boldsymbol{Q} = \sum_e \boldsymbol{Q}^e = \sum_e \left\{ -\iiint_{\Delta R} \frac{\partial \theta}{\partial t} \boldsymbol{N}^T \mathrm{d}R - \iint_{\Delta C} \bar{\beta} T_a \boldsymbol{N}^T \mathrm{d}s + \iint_{\Delta C} \bar{\beta} \boldsymbol{N}^T \boldsymbol{N} \{T\}^e \mathrm{d}s \right\}$$

$$\boldsymbol{P} = \sum_e \boldsymbol{P}^e = \sum_e \iiint_{\Delta R} \boldsymbol{N}^T \boldsymbol{N} \mathrm{d}R$$

这样，给定 $t - \Delta t$ 时刻的温度场 $\{T\}_{t-\Delta t}$，解方程组可得到 t 时刻温度场 $\{T\}_t$，已知 $t = 0$ 时刻结构内温度（如入仓温度）分布。可依次求得各时刻的温度分布。本课题组已编制的计算三维非稳定温度场 DTTS 程序适用计算机计算。

2 碾压混凝土的浇筑工艺和热学参数的取值

碾压混凝土按薄层连续施工模式，每层 30 ~ 35cm 厚即进行碾压，取初凝时间（某工程为 16h）的一半（即 8h）为层间间隔时间，以保证上、下层混凝土的联结质量。原计划连续浇 3m 厚，再间歇 5 ~ 6d，以满足升高模板和仓面凿毛等工序要求。实际施工中采用模板连续上升（未因模板而停歇），但由于诸多原因（如设备多次故障、资金不到位等）致使浇筑工期拖长，从 1994 年 12 月 28 日开仓至 1995 年 7 月 5 日完成，施工进度见图 2。

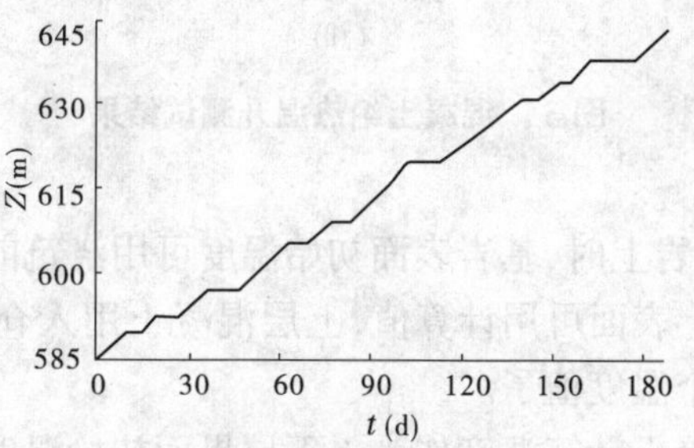

图 2 施工进度

按照碾压混凝土薄拱坝的实际浇筑过程，即分层浇筑(薄层连续碾压)，其温度场逐渐变化，混凝土材料的热学性能参数也在逐渐变化。经过热学参数的敏感性分析，发现对温度场变化规律起主要作用而且随材料性质及现场情况而变化的参数是绝热温升、入仓温度、边界气温与辐射热。

2.1　绝热温升

混凝土的绝热温升过程不但取决于水泥品种、水泥用量和骨料岩性，而且与混凝土固结过程的绝对温度有关。

本课题组研制的混凝土绝热温升测试仪，是利用计算机进行自动控制与采集，并自动完成试验。与从国外进口的同类仪器相比，它在测试原理上进行了改进 —— 采用二级自动跟踪系统和多通道采集处理，提高了仪器的精度和可靠性。可按照混凝土试验规程进行28d 混凝土绝热温升曲线跟踪测试。在进行某薄拱坝碾压混凝土的测试之前，已顺利完成了华北地区某拱坝和中南地区某重力坝采用混凝土的绝热温升的测试，其中华北地区某拱坝已完建，其实测的大坝内部混凝土最高温度值和利用绝热温升值进行仿真计算的成果基本吻合。

取用某薄拱坝的三级配混凝土的原材料，按工程选定的配合比(每立方米混凝土用料公斤数为：水 93.75；水泥 75；粉煤灰 112.5；砂 705；小石 600；中石 600；大石 300；木钙 0.469) 制备试件，试件为圆柱体，高 320mm，直径 300mm，原材料拌和后分 3 层装入试模并用振动台振实[3]。成型过程中在试件内部测温部位放置热电偶。密封成型后立即放入绝热室内开机试验，并进行二级跟踪控制。试件的初始温度为 16.45℃，连续测试了 28d。

混凝土的绝热温升随时间的变化规律惯用下述表达式：

$$\theta = \theta_0(1 - e^{-mt})$$

式中：θ_0 为最终绝热温升值；m 为由试验测定的因数；t 为时间。

根据测试结果用非线性最小二乘法得到了上述表达式中的 θ_0 为 10℃，m 为 0.16，见图 3。

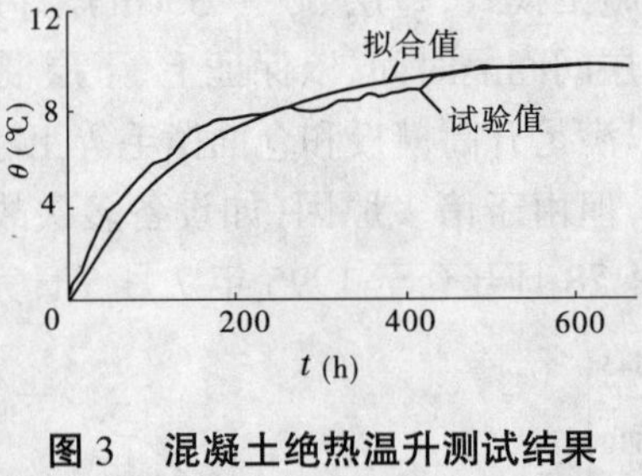

图 3　混凝土绝热温升测试结果

2.2　入仓温度

当混凝土块浇筑在基岩上时，基岩表面初始温度可用浇筑前实测表面温度。若间歇后继续加高混凝土，则下层上表面可用计算值，上层混凝土用入仓温度作为初始温度，一旦结合后，接触面就只有一个温度值了。

计算表明，用下层混凝土计算温度作为上下层界面初始温度输入，所得的累计温度远高于实测仿真单元的温度场(高约 10℃)。即使采用下表面计算值和上层入仓温度平均值,内部最高温升值也比仿真温度值高出 2 ~ 2.5℃,所以在计算仿真温度场时新浇的上层混凝土的入仓温度需要用单元温度输入。某工程实测的入仓温度见表 1。其值与坝址区的月平均气温相近。

表 1　入仓温度 T_{in}

Z(m)	单元号 N	T_{in}(℃)
583.0 ~ 585.0	1 ~ 1 032	18.2
585.0 ~ 587.5	1 033 ~ 1 112	15.0
587.5 ~ 590.0	1 113 ~ 1 156	14.3
590.0 ~ 592.4	1 157 ~ 1 208	13.4
592.4 ~ 597.0	1 209 ~ 1 260	11.0
597.0 ~ 599.0	1 261 ~ 1 320	10.9
599.0 ~ 602.0	1 321 ~ 1 384	10.2
602.0 ~ 605.5	1 385 ~ 1 456	10.2
605.5 ~ 609.3	1 457 ~ 1 528	13.0
609.3 ~ 611.0	1 529 ~ 1 608	10.6
611.0 ~ 614.0	1 609 ~ 1 688	11.8
614.0 ~ 617.0	1 689 ~ 1776	12.1
617.0 ~ 620.0	1 777 ~ 1 868	16.4
620.0 ~ 623.0	1 869 ~ 1 964	17.4
623.0 ~ 626.0	1 965 ~ 2 064	17.4
626.0 ~ 629.0	2 065 ~ 2 168	19.6
629.0 ~ 631.0	2 169 ~ 2 276	19.6
631.0 ~ 634.0	2 277 ~ 2 388	20.5
634.0 ~ 638.0	2 389 ~ 2 504	20.7
638.0 ~ 641.0	2 505 ~ 2 624	22.5
641.0 ~ 644.0	2 625 ~ 2 748	22.7

2.3　边界温度

施工期从下往上逐层浇筑混凝土时,上下游边界暴露于大气中,拱坝轴向两侧面为绝热,顶部暴露面随浇筑高度上升。

依靠自然冷却的碾压混凝土块的温度随气温及辐射热的变化而变化。某薄拱坝工地每天 3 次(早、中、晚)实测坝区气温,用三次测量数据的平均值作为日平均气温,考虑春季和夏季的日照作用,按实测取辐射热的影响为 4℃。

碾压混凝土其他的热学参数取值: 山谷中风小, 混凝土 / 空气的散热系数 β 为

1 675kJ/(m^2·d·℃)；比热 C 为0.938 77kJ/(kg·℃)；导温系数 a 为0.098 4m^2/d；线膨胀系数 α(砂岩骨料，由试验测试得到) 为 8.5×10^{-6}/℃。

3　计算预测值与工程实测值的比较

将上述热学参数代入非稳定温度场基本方程式，即可用编制的有限元程序在计算机上求解。根据某薄拱坝实际开挖与浇筑的体形，共计离散为2 748个六面体或五面体(过渡) 等参单元，3 894个节点，计算得到施工期非稳定温度场的累计变化过程。

在浇筑大坝混凝土的过程中，进行了坝体内部安全监测仪器的布置和埋设，并进行施工期监测，取得了较为可靠的实测成果。实测点与计算点的对应关系见表2。可见计算点与实测点的位置接近。

表2　实测点与计算点的对应关系

实测部位	实测点号	仪器埋设高程(m)	仪器埋设日期
左坝肩	S1－1R	593	1995－01－25
右坝肩	S2－1R	593	1995－01－25
实测部位	计算节点号	计算点高程(m)	浇筑日期
左坝肩	1 928	592.4	1995－01－24
右坝肩	1 892	592.4	1995－01－24

计算和实测的温度变化规律见图4和图5。可以看出浇筑后的计算预测与实测的温度过程线的起始位置和上升段基本一致，最高温度的发生时间都在浇筑后的第10～12d，最高温度的差值在1～2℃，降温过程线的变化趋势也基本相同，其数值相差也在1～2℃，说明决定计算预测可靠性的关键是热学参数(入仓温度、绝热温升和边界温度等) 的正确取值。

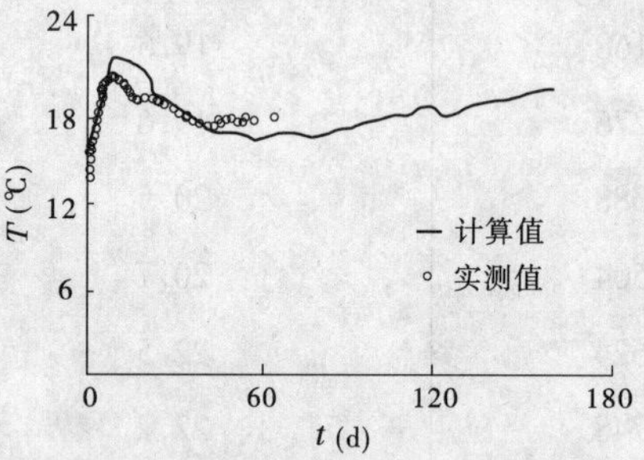

图4　S1－1R 温度变化过程线

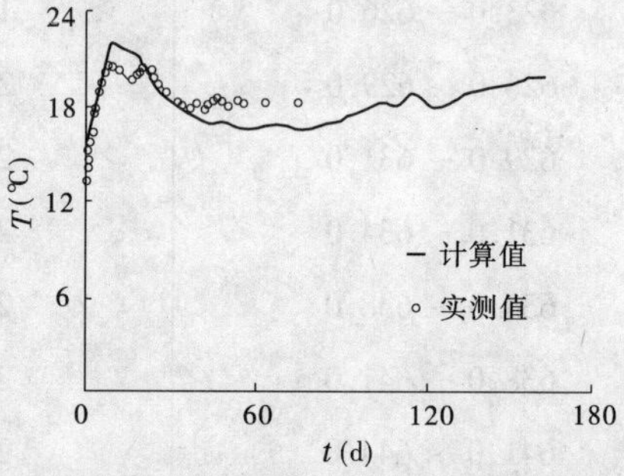

图5　S2－1R 温度变化过程线

在设计阶段，如果能正确测试大坝混凝土的绝热温升曲线，根据施工进度安排确定浇筑期内逐层变化的入仓温度和边界气温与辐射热等热学参数，则按本文方法计算混凝土非稳定温度场的变化过程，其计算预测在工程实际中具有较高的应用价值。

参考文献

[1] 刘志辉. 碾压混凝土拱坝累积温度场和仿真应力场的研究：[硕士学位论文]. 北京：清华大学水利

水电工程系,1994
[2] 张国新,刘光廷,刘志辉. 整体碾压混凝土拱坝工艺及温度场仿真计算. 清华大学学报,1996,36(1):1~7
[3] 中华人民共和国水利电力部. 水工混凝土试验规程. SD105—82. 北京:水利电力出版社,1983

层体边界元法在二维层体断裂分析中的应用

摘　要　在刚度矩阵法的基础上建立了用于进行二维多层体结构断裂分析的边界单元法(BEMLM)。由于BEMLM的基本方程中已经包含了层体表面和裂纹缝面的边界条件,因而不需要对这些边界进行单元离散,从而其断裂分析可望有较好的精度。通过与柯西积分方程法进行结合,算例表明BEMLM是可靠并有效的。

关键词　边界元　多层体结构　刚度矩阵法

1　含裂纹的刚度矩阵法

设有一界面相互平行的二维多层体弹性介质,取层面方向为 x 向,垂直界面方向为 y 向。按照文献[1]中所述,在Fourier变换域中,层体的位移和应力可以写成式(1),而每层介质的界面应力与界面位移之间都存在一个对应关系式(2),式(2)中各变量的含义及表达式见文献[1]。

$$\overline{\delta} = \{-i\overline{v}, \overline{u}\}^{\mathrm{T}},\ \overline{\sigma} = \{-i\overline{\sigma}_y, \overline{\sigma}_x\}^{\mathrm{T}} \tag{1}$$

$$\begin{Bmatrix} \overline{\sigma}^+ \\ -\overline{\sigma}^- \end{Bmatrix} = \begin{bmatrix} K_{11} & K_{12} \\ K_{21} & K_{22} \end{bmatrix} \begin{Bmatrix} \overline{\delta}^+ \\ \overline{\delta}^- \end{Bmatrix} \tag{2}$$

设多层体中某层介质内含有一顺层面方向的裂纹(如图1所示),裂纹中的分布位错为 $d(x) = \{-d_y(x), d_x(x)\}^{\mathrm{T}}$,位置在 $x \in (-a, a)$ 范围内。该裂纹在 y 向所在的位置将该层介质分为 u 区和 d 区两部分,相应的高度为 h_u、h_d。按照文献[1]中的思路,在裂纹所在位置引入一附加界面,根据文献[2]的结果,附加界面上的连接条件为

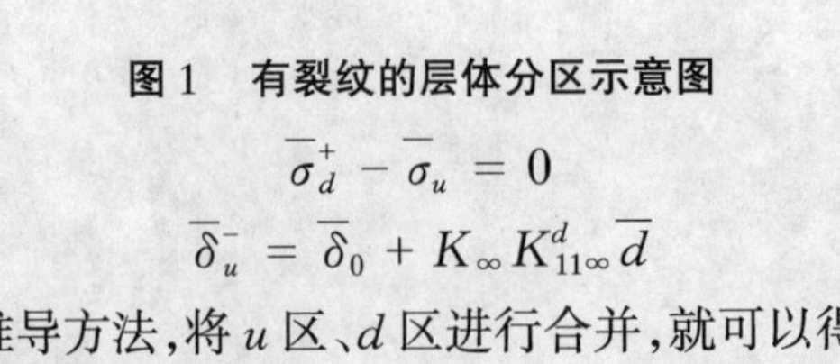

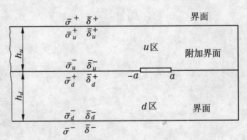

图1　有裂纹的层体分区示意图

$$\overline{\sigma}_d^+ - \overline{\sigma}_u = 0 \tag{3}$$

$$\overline{\delta}_u^- = \overline{\delta}_0 + K_\infty K_{11\infty}^d \overline{d} \tag{4}$$

按照文献[1]中的推导方法,将 u 区、d 区进行合并,就可以得到裂纹所处该层介质的局部刚性关系式(5)和应力场计算公式(6):

本文选自《力学学报》1998年第5期,作者还有郝巨涛。

$$\begin{Bmatrix} \overline{\sigma}^+ \\ -\overline{\sigma}^- \end{Bmatrix} = \begin{bmatrix} K_{11} & K_{12} \\ K_{21} & K_{22} \end{bmatrix} \begin{Bmatrix} \overline{\delta}^+ \\ \overline{\delta}^- \end{Bmatrix} + \begin{pmatrix} K_{12}^u & CK_{11}^d \\ -K_{21}^d & CK_{22}^u \end{pmatrix} \overline{d} \tag{5}$$

$$\overline{\sigma} = (S_1\ S_2) \begin{Bmatrix} \overline{\delta}^+ \\ \overline{\delta}^- \end{Bmatrix} + \overline{\sigma}_0, \overline{\sigma}_0 = \begin{cases} S_2^u CK_{11}^d \overline{d}, & y > y_d, \\ -S_1^d CK_{22}^u \overline{d}, & y < y_d, \end{cases} \quad C = (K_{11}^d + K_{22}^u)^{-1} \tag{6}$$

注意上式中在计算 S_1^d 和 S_2^u 时,转换矩阵应采用相应于 u 区和 d 区的尺寸参数。

2 应力场公式(6)存在的问题及其处理方法

与含内部作用的刚度矩阵法[1]类似,式(6)中 $\overline{\sigma}_0$ 项在应用中也存在Fourier积分收敛性不好的问题,这是由位错基本解的奇异性质决定的。今设在 (x_c, y_c) 处有一集中位错 d_c ($d_c = \{-id_y, d_x\}^{\mathrm{T}} H(x - x_c)$;$H(x)$ 为阶梯函数),同时该层体的上下层面边界为刚性边界,$y = y_c$ 将该层介质分为 u 区 d 区两部分。由于边界位移为零,其弹性场按式(6)可写为式(7):

$$\{\overline{\sigma}\} = \begin{cases} S_2^u CK_{11}^d \overline{d}_c, & y > y_c, \\ -S_1^d CK_{22}^u \overline{d}_c, & y < y_c, \end{cases} \quad \overline{d}_c(\xi) = \frac{i}{\xi} e^{i\xi x_c} d_c \tag{7}$$

与文献[1]中的处理方法类似,这里采用叠加法来改善式(7)的Fourier积分收敛性。按照叠加法原理,在 d_c 作用下的刚性层面边界弹性场式(7)(原场)等于在 d_c 作用下的自由层面边界弹性场(A 场)与仅边界作用有 $\overline{\sigma}_0^{\pm}$ 的弹性场(B 场)的叠加($\overline{\sigma}_0^{\pm}$ 为 d_c 在刚性层面边界处引起的反力,可以由式(7)令[S]中的 y 分别等于上下边界得到);而 A 场又等于在 d_c 作用下的无限大平面弹性场(C 场,有理论解)与仅边界作用有 $-\overline{\sigma}_1^{\pm}$ 的弹性场(D 场)的叠加($\overline{\sigma}_1^{\pm}$ 为 C 场在上下层面边界处应力)。据此有:原场 = B 场 + C 场 + D 场。

表1给出了当位于坐标原点的集中位错为 $d_x = 1/2\beta$(β 为Dundurs弹性参数),$d_y = 0$ 时,式(7)的结果与叠加法结果的比较。从中可以看出,当 $y = 0.3$ 时,两种方法的结果还比较一致,当 $y < 0.3$ 并趋于 $y = 0$ 时,两种方法结果的差别越来越大,当 $y = 0, x \neq 0$ 时,由 d_x 引起的应力 σ_x 应为零,但式(7)却仍然给出了不小的值。

表1 式(7)与叠加法的 σ_x 比较结果($d_x = 1/2\beta, d_y = 0$)

y	应力	方法	$x=0$	$x=2$	$x=4$	$x=6$	$x=8$	$x=10$
0.3	σ_x	式(7)	0.47×10^{0}	0.21×10^{-1}	0.24×10^{-3}	-0.47×10^{-4}	-0.17×10^{-4}	0.13×10^{-4}
		叠加法	0.47×10^{0}	0.21×10^{-1}	0.26×10^{-3}	-0.58×10^{-4}	0.30×10^{-5}	0.56×10^{-5}
0.0	σ_x	式(7)	0.87×10^{1}	-0.44×10^{-1}	0.42×10^{-1}	-0.39×10^{-1}	0.34×10^{-1}	-0.29×10^{-1}
		叠加法	—	0	0	0	0	0

注:σ_x 关于 $x = 0$ 对称。

3 有限大成层体结构的断裂力学分析

3.1 含内部分布力和不连续位移的刚度矩阵法

设有一 N 层成层结构,其中第 j 层含有一不连续位移 d_j,同时各层还含有各种均布内部力作用。除第 j 层以外,其他各层介质的局部刚性关系可以用含均布内部力的刚性关系导出,第 j 层介质的局部刚性关系可以用含均布内部力的刚性关系与含内部不连续位移的局部刚性关系的叠加求出,即

$$\begin{Bmatrix} \overline{\sigma}_j^+ \\ -\overline{\sigma}_j^- \end{Bmatrix} = \begin{pmatrix} K_{11}^j & K_{12}^j \\ K_{21}^j & K_{22}^j \end{pmatrix} \begin{Bmatrix} \overline{\delta}_j^+ \\ \overline{\delta}_j^- \end{Bmatrix} - \sum_{i=1}^{m_j} \begin{pmatrix} G_{jd}^i \\ G_{ju}^i \end{pmatrix} P_j^i + \begin{pmatrix} K_{12}^{ju} & C^j K_{11}^{jd} \\ -K_{21}^{jd} & C^j K_{22}^{ju} \end{pmatrix} \overline{d}_j \tag{8}$$

式中:$\overline{d}_j = \{-i\overline{d}_{jy}\overline{d}_{jx}\}^{\mathrm{T}}$ 为第 j 层介质中的不连续位移;$P_j^i(i = 1 \sim m_j)$ 为第 j 层介质所含的第 i 个虚拟均布力。

3.2　总刚方程的建立

利用式(8),结合各层介质之间的界面连续条件,可以建立下面多层体的总体刚度方程:

$$K_{11}^1\overline{\delta}_1 + K_{12}^1\overline{\delta}_2 = \overline{f}_U + \sum_{i=1}^{m_1} G_{1d}^i P_1^i$$

$$K_{21}^k\overline{\delta}_k + (K_{22}^k + K_{11}^{k+1})\overline{\delta}_{k+1} + K_{12}^{k+1}\overline{\delta}_{k+2} = \sum_{i=1}^{m_k} G_{ku}^i P_k^i + \sum_{i=1}^{m_{k+1}} G_{(k+1)d}^i P_{k+1}^i$$

$$(k = 1,2,\cdots,(j-1),(j+2),\cdots,(N-1)) \tag{9}$$

$$K_{21}^{j-1}\overline{\delta}_{j-1} + (K_{22}^{j-1} + K_{11}^j)\overline{\delta}_j + K_{12}^j\overline{\delta}_{j+1} = \sum_{i=1}^{m_{j-1}} G_{(j-1)u}^i P_{j-1}^i + \sum_{i=1}^{m_j} G_{jd}^i P_j^i - K_{12}^{ju} C^j K_{11}^{jd}\overline{d}_j$$

$$K_{21}^j\overline{\delta}_j + (K_{22}^j + K_{11}^{j+1})\overline{\delta}_{j+1} + K_{12}^{j+1}\overline{\delta}_{j+2} = \sum_{i=1}^{m_j} G_{ju}^i P_j^i + \sum_{i=1}^{m_{j+1}} G_{(j+1)d}^i P_{j+1}^i + K_{21}^{jd} C^j K_{22}^{ju}\overline{d}_j$$

$$K_{21}^N\overline{\delta}_N + K_{22}^N\overline{\delta}_{N+1} = -\overline{f}_L + \sum_{i=1}^{m_N} G_{Nu}^i P_N^i$$

式中:$\overline{f}_U$ 和 $\overline{f}_L$ 分别为层体上下表面作用外力的Fourier变换;$\overline{\delta}_i$ 为 $i(i = 1 \sim (N+1))$ 界面的位移。

3.3　虚拟力方程

这里的虚拟力方程与Crouch虚拟力方程[4]的区别在于必须考虑第 j 层介质不连续位移对虚拟力方程的影响。设各边界单元均为无应力边界,则虚拟力方程可以写成 $AP + \sigma_f + \sigma_d = 0$ 的形式,其中 A 为 $2(m \times m)$ 阶边界虚拟力影响系数矩阵,A_{ij} 表示 j 单元的单位虚拟力在 i 单元处产生的面力;σ_f 为层体结构上下表面外荷载 f_u、f_L 在各单元处产生的面力,σ_d 为不连续位移在各单元处产生的面力。所有这些系数均可以由文献[1]中的式(19)、式(20)以及本文的式(6)结合总刚方程(9)得出。

3.4　缝面积分方程

这里的积分方程是针对缝面应力给出的。在对积分方程的奇异性进行处理时,既可以采用叠加法,也可以采用借助考察积分核的渐近性质进行奇异性分离的方法,本文采用后一种方法。根据式(6)同时考虑单元虚拟力对缝面应力的影响,下缝面应力经推导可以写成式(10),其中 $M(\xi)$ 为 2×2 阶矩阵,反映缝面不连续位移 $\overline{d}_j$ 对 $\overline{\sigma}_{jd}^+$ 的影响;L_{ij} 为总刚矩阵(9)逆阵的子阵;$\mu(\xi)$ 为 f_u、f_L 的影响;Q_{jd} 为单位虚拟力产生的缝面应力,可以由式

(9) 得到。

$$\overline{\sigma}_{jd}^{+} = \boldsymbol{M}(\xi)\overline{d}_j + \mu(\xi) + Q_{jd}P, \quad \boldsymbol{M}(\xi) = -\boldsymbol{K}_{11}^{jd}C^j\boldsymbol{K}_{22}^{ju} + \sum_{n=0}^{1}\boldsymbol{K}_{1(n+1)}^{js}\boldsymbol{H}_n \tag{10}$$

式中:

$$\boldsymbol{H}_n = -\boldsymbol{L}_{(j+n)j}\boldsymbol{K}_{12}^{ju}C^j\boldsymbol{K}_{11}^{jd} + L_{(j+n)(j+1)}\boldsymbol{K}_{21}^{jd}C^j\boldsymbol{K}_{22}^{ju} \quad (n = 0,1)$$

$$\boldsymbol{\mu}(\xi) = \sum_{n=0}^{1}\boldsymbol{K}_{1(n+1)}^{js}(\boldsymbol{L}_{(j+n)1}\overline{\boldsymbol{f}}_u - \boldsymbol{L}_{(j+n)(N+1)}\overline{\boldsymbol{f}}_L)$$

将虚拟力方程代入式(10),消去虚拟力 $\boldsymbol{P}$,再代入缝面应力边界条件,就可以得到求解有限尺寸成层体结构断裂力学问题的积分方程。对该方程进行奇异性分离后可得式(11):

$$\overline{\sigma}_{jd}^{+} = \frac{2\mu_j}{\pi(1+k_j)}\int_{-a}^{a}\frac{\boldsymbol{I}\cdot\Phi(t)}{t-x}\mathrm{d}t + \int_{-a}^{a}\left\{\frac{i}{2\pi}\int_{-\infty}^{\infty}\left(\frac{1}{\xi}\boldsymbol{M}(\xi) + \boldsymbol{M}_{\infty}\right)\mathrm{e}^{i\xi(t-x)}\mathrm{d}\xi - Q_{jd}\boldsymbol{A}^{-1}R\right\}$$

$$\Phi(t)\mathrm{d}t + \frac{1}{2\pi}\int_{-\infty}^{\infty}\mu(\xi)\mathrm{e}^{i\xi x}\mathrm{d}\xi - Q_{jd}\boldsymbol{A}^{-1}\sigma_f; \quad \boldsymbol{M}_{\infty} = \frac{2\mu_j}{1+k_j}\boldsymbol{I}\cdot\mathrm{sign}(\xi) \tag{11}$$

其中:$\Phi(t)$ 为位错密度函数(即 d_j 沿缝面的导数);μ_j、k_j 为 j 层介质的弹性参数;I 为 2 阶单位矩阵;$\mathrm{sign}(\xi)$ 为符号函数。式(11) 就是柯西型奇异积分方程组,其求解方法见文献[5]。

4 算例及结论

根据式(11) 编制了数值积分程序,用图 2 模型对其进行检验,并与文献[6]、[7] 进行比较,对比参数为 $F_{\mathrm{I}} = K_{\mathrm{I}}/(\sigma\sqrt{\pi a})$,$F_{\mathrm{II}} = K_{\mathrm{II}}/(\sigma\sqrt{\pi a})$,$K_{\mathrm{I}}$、$K_{\mathrm{II}}$ 为 Ⅰ、Ⅱ 型应力强度因子。对比结果见表 2。表 2 还列出了文献[7] 无侧边界的结果,模型中 $E_1 = 4.5\times10^5\psi$, $E_2 = 10^7\psi$, $v_1 = 0.35$, $v_2 = 0.3$, $a/W = 0.1$,模型边界仍采用 20 个边界单元离散。由表 2 可以看出,本文的结果与文献[6] 略有差异,同时两个结果均比文献[7] 的结果大,由此反应出边界的影响。另外,随着模型 h 的减小,F_{I} 也越来越小,表明界面对 F_{I} 的作用越来越强。

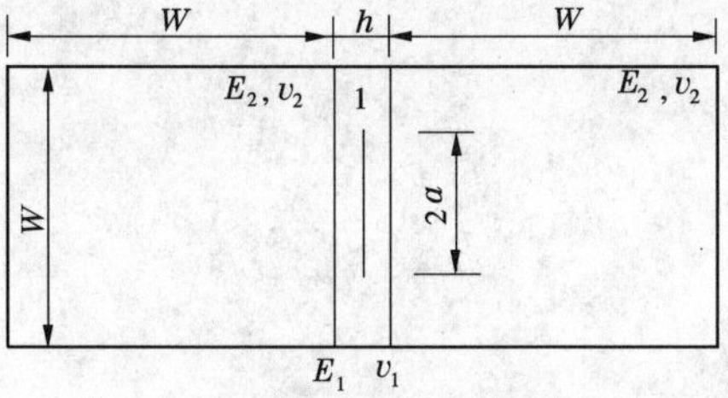

图 2　含软弱夹层的计算模型

表 2　计算模型(图 2)的 F_{I} 验证结果

h/a	本文	文献[6]	文献[7]	h/a	本文	文献[6]	文献[7]
4.0	1.057	1.045	0.92	0.75	0.604	0.543	0.55
3.0	1.020	0.988	0.87	0.50	0.514	0.463	0.46
2.0	0.969	0.860	0.78	0.25	0.388	0.374	0.37
1.0	0.697	0.616	0.60	0.20	0.360	0.348	0.33

上面的结果表明,本文采用的方法是正确、有效的,用本文方法分析层体断裂力学问题时,仅需对层体的侧边界进行离散,上下表面及缝面均不需离散,因而所用单元较少,精度较高。应当说明的是,文献[6]只能求解含一个夹层的对称问题或只有一个界面的非对称问题,本文的方法在这方面没有限制。

参 考 文 献

[1] 刘光廷,郝巨涛. 成层弹性介质的二维基本解. 清华大学学报,1996,36(1):71~77

[2] Thangjitham S,Choi Hj. *Interlaminar crack problems of a laminated anisotropic medium*. Int J Solids Structures, 1993,30(7):963~980

[3] 郝巨涛. 成层结构及碾压混凝土坝的应力稳定分析方法:[博士论文].北京:清华大学,1995

[4] Crouch SL et al.. *Boundary Element Method in Solid Mechanics*. George Allen & Unwin Pub Ltd, 1983

[5] Erdogan F, Gupta GD, Cook TS. *Numerical Solution of Singular Integral Equations*. Mechanics of Fracture I, Sih GC edn, Noordhoff Int Pub,1973

[6] Yuuki R. *Usefulness of Hetenyi's Solution for Boundary Element Analysis of Crack Problems in Dissimilar Materials*, Role of Fracture Mechanics in Modern Technology, Sih GC et al. edn, Elsevier Sci Pub BV, North-Holland, 1987,823~834

[7] Erdogan F, Gupta GD. *Stress analysis of mutilayered composites with a flaw*. Int J Solids Structures, 1971,7:39~61

三维热弹性力学问题的混合边界元法

摘　要　本文给出了三维无限大域内点热源作用下的位移、应力场基本解。采用基于虚拟热源法的间接边界元法和直接边界元法的混合边界元法求解三维有限域热弹性力学问题，有效地避免了热弹性力学问题中域内积分的处理。数值计算表明混合边界元法求热弹性力学问题具有简单方便、精度较高的优点。

关键词　热弹性力学　混合边界元法　虚拟热源

采用边界元法求解三维非耦合热弹性力学问题，自边界元法应用以来就得到了广泛的重视[1~4]。解非耦合热弹性力学问题，首先是根据热传导方程以及温度边界条件求解热传导问题，由此根据温度场和物体温度变形特性，将温度作用视为初应变或温度荷载(体积力)，而求解与之对应的弹性力学问题[5~8]。由于边界元法是在所关心的域边界上进行离散求解，当引入温度荷载(体积力)时，需要进行域内积分的处理。为了避免对域内的离散化，很多学者进行了较深入的研究，其中方法之一是利用格林积分定理将域内体积积分转化成边界积分。

本文利用热弹性位移势的概念，导出三维无限大域内单位强度点热源作用的位移、应力解，将三维热弹性力学问题的求解分解成基于虚拟热源法的间接边界元法求热传导问题和采用直接边界元法求解相应弹性力学问题的联合求解。这种采用间接边界元法和直接边界元法联合求解的混合边界元法可以有效地避免热弹性力学问题中由于温度项引起的域内体积积分，同时由于基本解的引入，本方法具有较高的精度和简单的形式。

1　三维无限域内单位强度点热源产生的位移、应力场基本解

如图1所示，无限大均质域原点 O 处作用单位强度稳态点热源，则域内任意点 P 处满足热弹性方程：

$$\Delta u_i + \frac{1}{1-2\nu}e_{,i} + \frac{\rho}{\mu}f_i - \frac{2(1+\nu)}{1-2\nu}\lambda T_{,i} = \frac{\rho}{\mu}u_i \qquad (i = 1,2,3) \tag{1}$$

式中：Δ 为 Laplace 算子；u_i 为 i 方向位移；$e_{,i}$ 为体积应变；ν 为泊松比；μ 为剪切模量；λ 为热膨胀系数；f_i 为 i 方向体积力；ρ 为密度。

不考虑体积力的作用，仅考虑温度场产生的位移和应力，式(1) 简化成

$$\Delta u_i + \frac{1}{1-2\nu}e_{,i} = \frac{2(1+\nu)}{1-2\nu}\lambda T_{,i} \qquad (i = 1,2,3) \tag{2}$$

考虑到问题的对称性，引入 Goodier, J. N. 提出的热弹性位移势 Φ，式(2) 可变成

$$\Delta\Phi = \frac{1+\nu}{1-\nu}\lambda T \qquad (i = 1,2,3) \tag{3}$$

本文选自《工程力学》1999 年第 6 期，作者还有邱德隆。

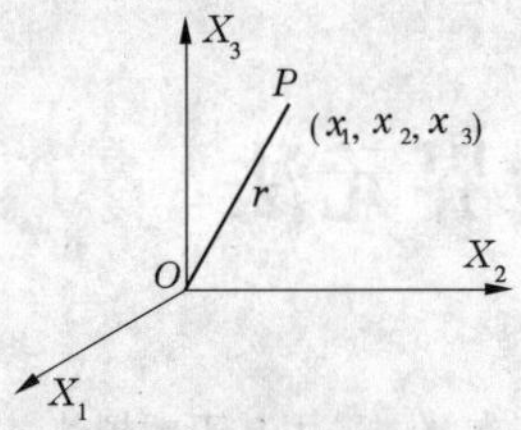

图1　点热源示意图

已知 $T = \dfrac{1}{4\pi k}\dfrac{1}{r}$,代入式(3)中得到

$$\Phi(r) = \frac{1}{4\pi k}\frac{1+\nu}{1-\nu}\lambda\frac{1}{r} \qquad (i = 1,2,3) \tag{4}$$

解此方程得到:

$$\Phi(r) = \frac{m}{2}r - \frac{c_1}{r} + c_0 \qquad (i = 1,2,3) \tag{5}$$

式中:$m = \dfrac{1}{4\pi k}\dfrac{1+\nu}{1-\nu}\lambda$;$c_1$、$c_0$ 为常数。

由于 $r = 0$ 时,$\Phi(r)$ 有意义,则 $c_1 = 0$,c_0 对位移无贡献,取 $c_0 = 0$,则可得

$$\Phi(r) = \frac{m}{2}r \qquad (i = 1,2,3) \tag{6}$$

这样得到三维无限域内单位强度点热源作用产生的位移、应力场基本解为

$$u_i = \frac{\partial\Phi}{\partial x_i} = \frac{m}{2}\frac{x_i}{r} \qquad (i = 1,2,3) \tag{7}$$

$$\sigma_{ij} = \frac{2\nu\mu}{1-2\nu}\gamma_{kk}\delta_{ij} + 2\mu\gamma_{ij} - \beta T\delta_{ij} \qquad (i = 1,2,3) \tag{8}$$

式中:γ 为应变;$\gamma_{ij} = \Phi_{,ij} = \dfrac{m}{2r^3}(r^2\delta_{ij} - x_i x_j)$;$\beta = \dfrac{2(1+\nu)}{1-2\nu}\mu\lambda$。

展开得到

$$\left.\begin{aligned} u_1 &= \frac{m}{2}\frac{x_1}{r} \\ u_2 &= \frac{m}{2}\frac{x_2}{r} \\ u_3 &= \frac{m}{2}\frac{x_3}{r} \end{aligned}\right\} \tag{9}$$

$$\left.\begin{aligned} \sigma_{11} &= -\frac{m}{r^3}\mu(r^2 + x_1^2) \\ \sigma_{22} &= -\frac{m}{r^3}\mu(r^2 + x_2^2) \\ \sigma_{33} &= -\frac{m}{r^3}\mu(r^2 + x_3^2) \\ \sigma_{12} &= -\frac{m}{r^3}\mu x_1 x_2 \\ \sigma_{23} &= -\frac{m}{r^3}\mu x_2 x_3 \\ \sigma_{13} &= -\frac{m}{r^3}\mu x_1 x_3 \end{aligned}\right\} \tag{10}$$

2　混合边界元法求解热弹性力学问题基本原理

如式(1)所表示的热弹性方程,待定的位移由两部分组成,一部分是方程(1)的特解

u_i^T,它是由温度荷载产生的;另一部分是式(1)对应齐次方程的解 u_i^M,它与温度场不直接相关。所谓的齐次方程是隐含了由于温度荷载而产生的位移、应力条件的常规弹性力学方程(不考虑常规体积力作用)。真实的位移解由 u_i^T 和 u_i^M 叠加得到,即

$$u_i = u_i^T + u_i^M \qquad (i = 1,2,3) \tag{11}$$

这样热弹性方程的求解可以分成两步:第一,采用热弹性位移势法求出已知温度场所产生的 u_i^T;第二,按弹性力学方法求包括隐含温度场作用产生的位移、面力以及常规外载作用下产生的 u_i^M。u_i^T 和 u_i^M 叠加后的 u_i 既满足域内热弹性方程又满足给定域边界位移、面力边界条件,此解 u_i 即是热弹性力学问题的全解。

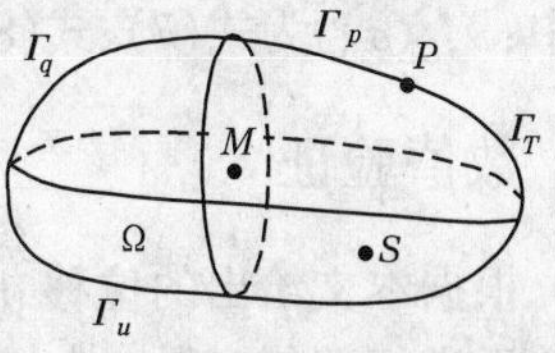

图 2　有限域 Ω 边界条件示意图

如图 2 所示,设域 Ω 满足温度边界条件 Γ_T、Γ_q 和位移、面力边界条件 Γ_u、Γ_p。采用间接边界元法格式可以求出满足给定温度边界条件边界上作用的虚拟热源值 $\Psi(S)$[9]。根据式(7)、式(8)中给出的位移、应力场基本解,利用叠加原理,则域 Ω 内任意点 M 仅由温度作用产生的位移、应力解为

$$u_i^T(M) = \int_\Gamma u_i^*(M,S)\Psi(S)\mathrm{d}\Gamma(S) \qquad (i = 1,2,3) \tag{12}$$

$$\sigma_{ij}^T(M) = \int_\Gamma \sigma_{ij}^*(M,S)\Psi(S)\mathrm{d}\Gamma(S) \qquad (i = 1,2,3) \tag{13}$$

式中:$u_i^*(M,S)$、$\sigma_{ij}^*(M,S)$ 即是无限大域内 S 点作用单位强度点热源时,域内产生的位移、应力场基本解。

相应地,边界上点 P 的位移、面力值为

$$u_i^T(P) = \int_\Gamma u_i^*(P,S)\Psi(S)\mathrm{d}\Gamma(S) \qquad (i = 1,2,3) \tag{14}$$

$$p_i^T(P) = n_j\sigma_{ij}^T(P) = f_\Gamma \sigma_{ij}^*(P,S)\Psi(S)\mathrm{d}\Gamma(S) \qquad (i = 1,2,3) \tag{15}$$

式中:f_Γ 表示取其主值意义下的积分值。

通常情况下,由式(14)、式(15)给出的边界位移、面力值并不满足给定的边界条件:

$$u_i(P) = \overline{u}_i(P) \qquad (P \in \Gamma_u \quad i = 1,2,3) \tag{16}$$

$$p_i(P) = \overline{p}_i(P) \qquad (P \in \Gamma_p \quad i = 1,2,3) \tag{17}$$

为了得到原热弹性力学问题的全解,需另求解一对应的弹性力学问题,其边界条件应为

$$\overline{u}_i^M(P) = \overline{u}_i(P) - u_i^T(P) \qquad (P \in \Gamma_u \quad i = 1,2,3) \tag{18}$$

$$\overline{p}_i^M(P) = \overline{p}_i(P) - p_i^T(P) \qquad (P \in \Gamma_p \quad i = 1,2,3) \tag{19}$$

根据直接边界元法求解弹性力学问题原理和方法。即可求得满足边界条件式(18)、式(19)下,此对应弹性力学问题全域边界 Γ 上相应的位移 u_i^M 和面力 p_i^M。

返回到式(11),得到原热弹性力学问题的位移、应力场全解分别为

$$u_i(M) = u_i^T(M) + u_i^M(M)$$
$$= \int_\Gamma u_i^*(M,S)\Psi(S)\mathrm{d}\Gamma(S) + \int_\Gamma [u_{ik}^*(M,S)p_k^M(S) -$$

$$p_{ik}^{*}(M,S)u_{k}^{M}(S)]\mathrm{d}\Gamma(S) \quad (i=1,2,3) \tag{20}$$

$$\sigma_{ij}(M)=\sigma_{ij}^{T}(M)+\sigma_{ij}^{M}(M)=\int_{\Gamma}\sigma_{ij}^{*}(M,S)\Psi(S)\mathrm{d}\Gamma(S)+$$
$$\int_{\Gamma}[\sigma_{kij}^{*}(M,S)p_{k}^{M}(S)-t_{kij}^{*}(M,S)u_{k}^{M}(S)]\mathrm{d}\Gamma(S) \quad i=1,2,3 \tag{21}$$

式中：u_i^*、σ_{ij}^* 为式(7)、式(8)给出的基本解；u_{ik}^*、p_{ik}^*、σ_{kij}^*、t_{kij}^* 为 Kelvin 解。

3 数值验证

根据本文给出的位移、应力场基本解及混合边界元法基本原理和方法，采用二次非协调单元进行数值离散[9,10]，对以下两个简例进行验证计算。

3.1 两端轴向固定长方柱沿轴向受线性分布的温变

如图3所示，截面为10m×10m、长为100m的长方柱，其两端沿轴向固定，长方柱沿轴向受线性分布温升。长方柱侧面为自由面。其材料参数为 $\lambda=10^{-5}/℃$，$E=10^{6}\mathrm{N/m^2}$，$\nu=0.2$，$k=1\mathrm{W/m℃}$。

采用8节点四边形单元。柱端面划分1个单元，侧面沿轴向划分10个单元。计算值和解析值比较如图4、图5、图6所示。从中可以看出计算值和解析值吻合很好，最大误差不超过1%。

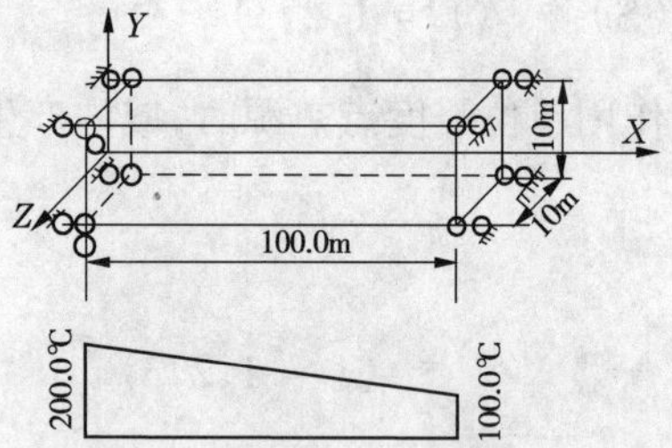

图3 计算简图

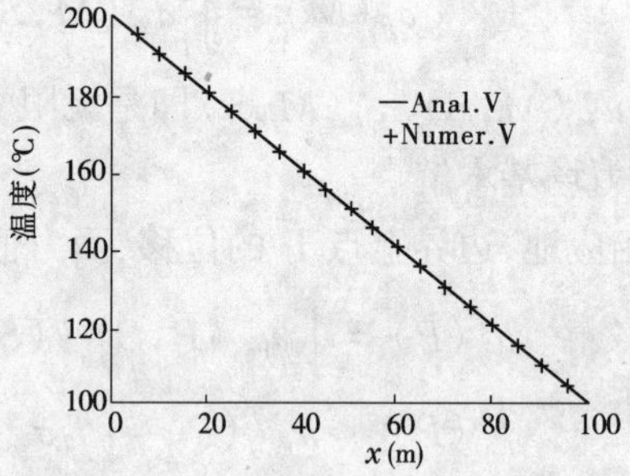

图4 温度沿 ox 轴分布图

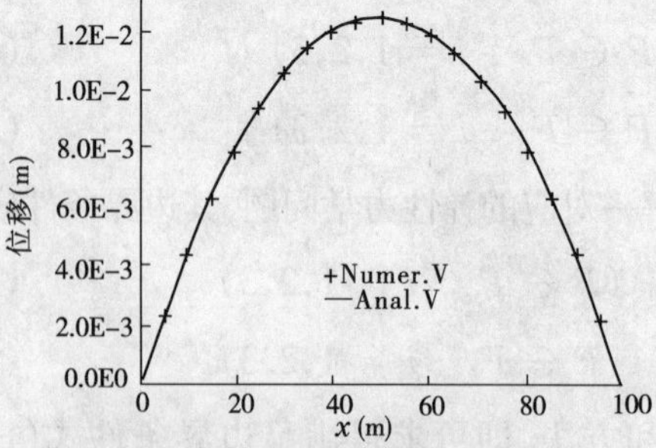

图5 位移沿 ox 轴分布图

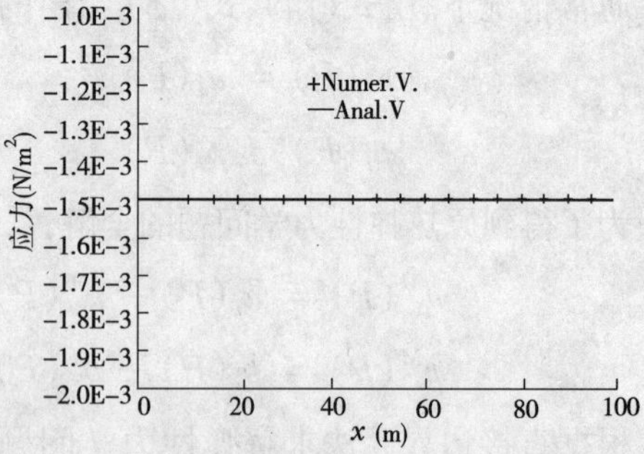

图6 应力沿 ox 轴分布图

3.2 表面自由圆盘受内外温差作用

如图7所示，表面自由圆盘内半径 $R_a=2\mathrm{m}$，外半径 $R_b=4\mathrm{m}$，厚为1.5m；内侧面温

升 100℃,外侧面温升为 0。材料参数同上长方柱。取 1/4 圆盘计算,采用 8 节点四边形单元,沿周向划分 6 个单元,径向 4 层单元,沿厚度划分 3 层单元。计算值与按平面应力情况解析值比较如图 8、图 9、图 10 所示。从中也可看出计算值与解析值吻合良好,误差小于 5%。

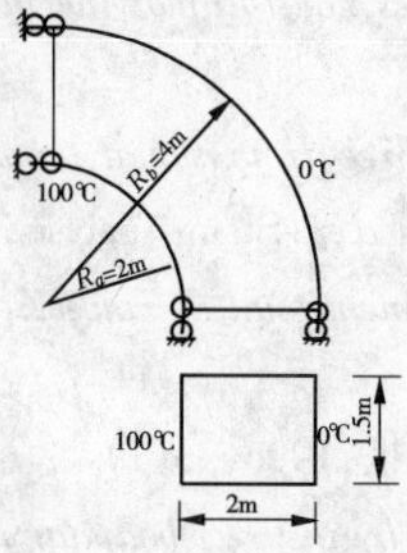

图 7　计算简图

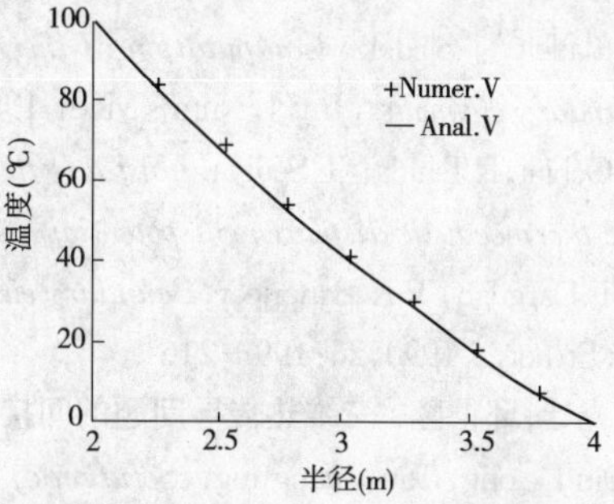

图 8　圆盘温度沿半径分布图

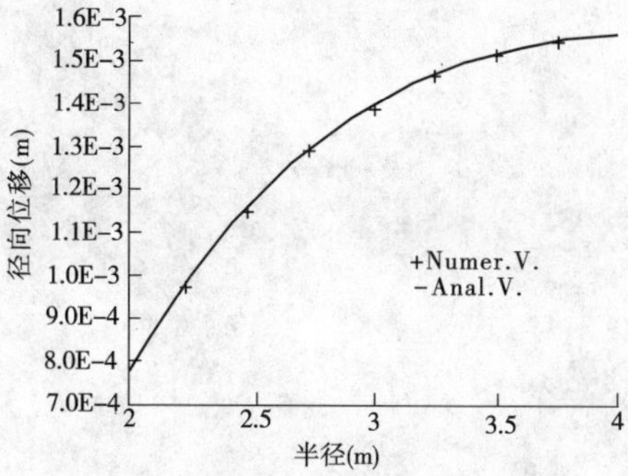

图 9　圆盘径向位移沿半径分布图

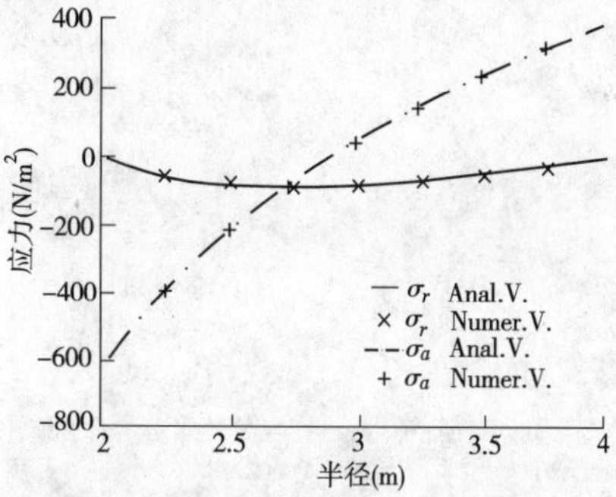

图 10　圆盘径向、周向应力沿半径分布图

4　结论

本文给出三维无限大域内点热源作用下的位移、应力基本解,利用混合边界元法的基本原理和方法,将热弹性力学问题分解成用基于虚拟热源法的间接边界元法解热传导问题和直接边界元法解与之相对应的弹性力学问题的叠加求解,有效地避免了域内积分。

计算结果表明,本方法具有简单方便和精度较高的优点。

参考文献

[1] H D Bui. *Some remarks about the formulation of three dimensional thermoelastic problems by integral equation*. Int. J. Solids and Struct, 1978, 14: 935～939

[2] F J Rizzo, D J Shippy. *An advanced boundary integral equation method for three-dimensional thermoelasticity*. Int. J. Num. Meth. Eng., 1977, 11: 1753～1768

[3] V Sladek, J Sladek. *Boundary integral equation method in two-dimensional thermoelasticity*. Eng. Anal,

1984,1:135～148

[4] A Chaudouet. *Three-dimensional transient thermoelastic analysis by boundary integral equation method*. Int. J. Num. Meth. Eng., 1986,24:25～45

[5] S Sharp, S L Crouch. *Boundary integral method in thermoelasticity problem*. J. Appl. Mech., 1986, 53:298～302

[6] V Sladek, J Sladek. *Computation of thermal stress in quasic statics nonstational thermoelasticity using boundary elements*. Int. J. Num. Meth,1989,28:1131～1144

[7] Y Ochiai,R Ishida, T Sediya. *Unsteady thermal stress analysis in three-dimensional problem by means of the thermoelastic displacement potential and boundary element method*. J. Stain Analysis,1990,25:9～14

[8] G F Dargush, P K Banerjeer. *Boundary element method in three-dimensional thermoelasticity*. Int. J. Solids Struct., 1990,26:199～216

[9] 刘光廷,邱德隆. 三维热传导问题的间接边界元法. 清华大学学报,1996,36(1)

[10] Qiu Delong, Liu Guangting. *Solution of periodic heat conduction by indirect boundary element method based on fictitious heat source*. Com. Num. Meth. Eng.,1996,12:673～682

碾压混凝土坝的等效连续本构模型

摘　要　本文根据变形等效的基本原理,导出了一个等效连续的本构模型,并给出了碾压混凝土层间真实应力的估算式,为复杂成层结构的应力分析提供了一条系统的简化计算技术路径。

关键词　碾压混凝土　变形等效原理　本构模型

碾压混凝土是利用强力振动和碾压的共同作用,对超干硬性混凝土进行压实的一种混凝土施工新方法。应用这种新技术修建混凝土坝,将给坝工设计、筑坝材料和施工技术带来转折性的重大变化,实质上是把混凝土坝结构与材料和土石坝施工方法两者的优越性加以综合,经过择优改进、相互结合而形成的一种新筑坝技术。与传统的常态混凝土筑坝方法相比,它具有水泥用量少、施工速度快、工程造价低、温度控制简单、施工设备通用性强等优点。

为了充分发挥碾压混凝土坝快速施工的特点,越来越多的工程采用了大面积不设纵缝,放宽横缝间距,甚至不设横缝、全断面碾压、薄层通仓浇筑、连续上升的筑坝方法。如果施工组织设计完善,工程量不太大的中等高度的坝有可能经过一个枯水季节即可基本完成,这对于加快水利水电坝工建设,是任何一种坝型所难以比拟的。但是这种方法也使得坝体成为一个层状结构物,对这类层状结构物的数值模拟,可以用有限单元法把结构离散成许多单元,层间采用无厚度的节理单元来进行应力变形分析,我们不妨称之为“精确法”。这在理论上是可行的,但是由于碾压混凝土坝的层厚一般为20～80cm,对于坝高几十米甚至上百米的高坝,特别是三维拱坝,计算工作量之大是可以想见的,甚至是难以实现的。因此,发展一种层状结构物的等效连续模型是很有必要的。

如图1(a)所示的某一碾压混凝土坝,我们可以从中找出一个足够大的包含多个层面的代表性单元,这个代表性单元和工程尺度相比又足够小,我们试图对这个代表性单元进行深入分析,根据等效原理,得出该代表性单元的本构关系,并应用于碾压混凝土坝工程。

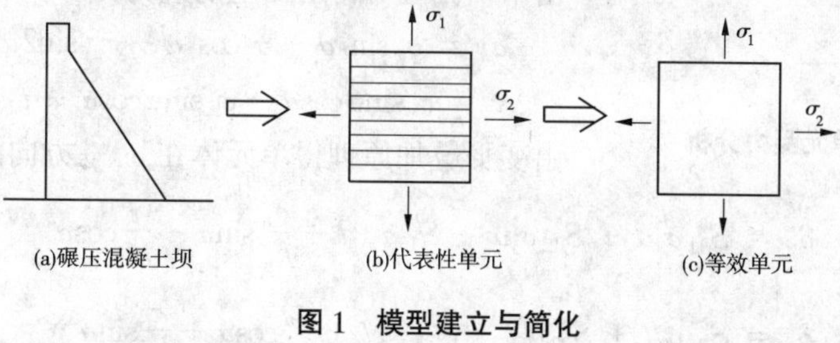

图1　模型建立与简化

从已有的文献看,所有“等效”方法的基本思路是在考虑本构模型时,根据一定的等效原则,笼统地考虑层面对单元力学特性的影响,将整个层面均匀化、连续化,得出一套本

本文选自《工程力学》1996年第2期,作者还有王宗敏。

构模型,然后再利用数值分析得出整体结构的力学特性。基于这种思想,文献[4]根据等效模量理论提出了一种均质横观各向同性体等效连续模型,该模型对于含不同数量弱面的代表性单元,需要计算不同的等效模量,应用于整体结构的有限元计算中,意味着剖分不同大小的网格,就需要计算相应网格的等效模量,这是不方便的。本文根据变形等效所得的本构模型,改进了上述模型,是便于工程结构有限元计算的一种等效连续模型。

1　变形等效连续模型

变形等效的基本原理就是假设连续体与层状体单元在同样荷载作用下变形相等,由此推导出等效单元与代表性单元之间的材料常数关系,这个等效单元可依据不同的实际情况,假定为各向同性体、正交各向异性体、横观各向同性体或一般的各向异性体。本文将等效单元作为一般的各向异性体看待。

在平面情况下的各向异性材料的应力应变关系为

$$\begin{Bmatrix} \sigma_x \\ \sigma_y \\ \tau_{xy} \end{Bmatrix} = \begin{bmatrix} c_{11} & c_{12} & c_{13} \\ c_{21} & c_{22} & c_{23} \\ c_{31} & c_{32} & c_{33} \end{bmatrix} \begin{Bmatrix} \varepsilon_x \\ \varepsilon_y \\ \gamma_{xy} \end{Bmatrix} \tag{1}$$

由于 $c_{ij} = c_{ji}(i,j = 1,2,3)$,其独立的常数为6个。只要能够确定这6个参数,则进行有限元的弹性计算将无困难,但是要测定这种各向异性的弹性常数很不方便。本文的思路是:既然这种层状体可以看做是由各向同性本体与层面组成的,则可以通过分别测定本体的弹性常数 E_b、V_b 和有厚度的层面的弹性常数 E_j、V_j 或无厚度的层面刚度系数 K_n、K_s 以及几何参数(层厚、间距等),然后按照变形等效的方法来推导等效单元的变形参数。

不失一般性,假定代表性单元为平面含有一条贯穿整个单元的无厚度弱面的单元,如图2所示,本体为一般各向异性体,其弹性本构关系可以表示为

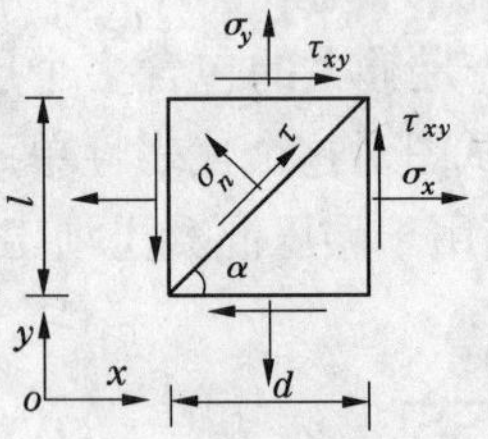

图2　代表性单元受力分析

$$\begin{Bmatrix} \varepsilon_x \\ \varepsilon_y \\ \gamma_{xy} \end{Bmatrix} = \begin{Bmatrix} S_{11}^b & S_{12}^b & S_{13}^b \\ S_{21}^b & S_{22}^b & S_{23}^b \\ S_{31}^b & S_{32}^b & S_{33}^b \end{Bmatrix} \begin{Bmatrix} \sigma_x \\ \sigma_y \\ \tau_{xy} \end{Bmatrix} \tag{2}$$

由平衡方程可得层面上的应力为

$$\begin{aligned} \sigma_n &= \sigma_x \sin^2\alpha + \sigma_y \cos^2\alpha - \tau_{xy}\sin 2\alpha \\ \tau &= \sigma_y \sin\alpha\cos\alpha - \sigma_x \sin\alpha\cos\alpha - \tau_{xy}\cos 2\alpha \end{aligned} \tag{3}$$

由变形叠加原理得单元体在 x、y 方向的位移为

$$\begin{aligned} \delta_x &= S_{11}^b\sigma_x d + S_{12}^b\sigma_y d + S_{13}^b\tau_{xy} d + \frac{\sigma_n}{k_n}\sin\alpha - \frac{\tau}{k_s}\cos\alpha \\ \delta_y &= S_{21}^b\sigma_x l + S_{22}^b\sigma_y l + S_{23}^b\tau_{xy} l + \frac{\sigma_n}{k_n}\cos\alpha + \frac{\tau}{k_s}\sin\alpha \end{aligned} \tag{4}$$

将式(3)代入式(4),整理得

$$\delta_x = \left(S_{11}^b d + \frac{1}{k_n}\sin^2\alpha\sin\alpha + \frac{1}{k_s}\cos^2\alpha\sin\alpha\right)\sigma_x +$$

$$\left(S_{12}^{b} d - \frac{1}{k_n}\cos^2\alpha\sin\alpha - \frac{1}{k_s}\cos^2\alpha\sin\alpha\right)\sigma_y +$$

$$\left(S_{13}^{b} d - \frac{1}{k_n}\sin2\alpha\sin\alpha + \frac{1}{k_s}\cos2\alpha\cos\alpha\right)\tau_{xy} \tag{5}$$

$$\delta_y = \left(S_{21}^{b} l + \frac{1}{k_n}\sin^2\alpha\cos\alpha - \frac{1}{k_s}\sin^2\alpha\cos\alpha\right)\sigma_x +$$

$$\left(S_{22}^{b} l + \frac{1}{k_n}\cos^2\alpha\cos\alpha + \frac{1}{k_s}\sin^2\alpha\cos\alpha\right)\sigma_y +$$

$$\left(S_{23}^{b} l - \frac{1}{k_n}\sin2\alpha\cos\alpha - \frac{1}{k_s}\cos2\alpha\sin\alpha\right)\tau_{xy}$$

另一方面,等效单元的弹性本构关系为

$$\begin{Bmatrix}\varepsilon_x\\ \varepsilon_y\\ \gamma_{xy}\end{Bmatrix} = \begin{bmatrix}S_{11} & S_{12} & S_{13}\\ S_{21} & S_{22} & S_{23}\\ S_{31} & S_{32} & S_{33}\end{bmatrix}\begin{Bmatrix}\sigma_x\\ \sigma_y\\ \tau_{xy}\end{Bmatrix} \tag{6}$$

在和代表性单元同样荷载条件下,等效单元的变形为

$$\begin{aligned}\delta_x^e &= S_{11}\sigma_x d + S_{12}\sigma_y d + S_{13}\tau_{xy} d\\ \delta_y^e &= S_{21}\sigma_x l + S_{22}\sigma_y l + S_{23}\tau_{xy} l\end{aligned} \tag{7}$$

根据变形等效原理,即 $\delta_x = \delta_x^e$, $\delta_y = \delta_y^e$, 可得等效体的弹性常数:

$$\left.\begin{aligned}S_{11} &= S_{11}^{b} + \left(\frac{1}{k_n d}\sin^2\alpha + \frac{1}{k_s d}\cos^2\alpha\right)\sin\alpha\\ S_{12} &= S_{12}^{b} + \left(\frac{1}{k_n d}\cos^2\alpha - \frac{1}{k_s d}\cos^2\alpha\right)\sin\alpha\\ S_{13} &= S_{13}^{b} + \left(\frac{1}{k_s d}\cos2\alpha\cos\alpha - \frac{1}{k_n d}\sin2\alpha\sin\alpha\right)\\ S_{21} &= S_{21}^{b} + \left(\frac{1}{k_n l}\sin^2\alpha - \frac{1}{k_s l}\sin^2\alpha\right)\cos\alpha\\ S_{22} &= S_{22}^{b} + \left(\frac{1}{k_n l}\cos^2\alpha + \frac{1}{k_s l}\sin^2\alpha\right)\cos\alpha\\ S_{23} &= S_{23}^{b} - \left(\frac{1}{k_s l}\cos2\alpha\sin\alpha + \frac{1}{k_n l}\sin2\alpha\cos\alpha\right)\end{aligned}\right\} \tag{8}$$

由图 2 有 $l = d\tan\alpha$,可以推导出 $S_{12} = S_{21}$。从本构关系的对称性出发,不难得到 $S_{31} = S_{13}$, $S_{32} = S_{23}$,并近似假定 $S_{33} = S_{33}^{b}$。至此,等效单元(一般各向异性体)的本构关系所需的 6 个参数已全部求出。

对于含两个弱面的代表性单元,根据式(8)计算出含一条弱面时的 S_{ij},然后将式(8)中的 S_{ij}^{b} 用 S_{ij} 代替,重复式(8)的计算,即得含两个弱面时的本构关系。多条弱面的情况依此类推。

为了碾压混凝土坝有限元分析实际应用方便起见,这里给出 $\alpha = 0$,代表性单元含 m 条材料性质相同的无厚度弱面时的等效本构关系:

$$\begin{Bmatrix}\varepsilon_x\\ \varepsilon_y\\ \gamma_{xy}\end{Bmatrix}=\begin{bmatrix}S_{11}^b & S_{21}^b & S_{31}^b+\dfrac{m}{k_sd}\\ S_{21}^b & S_{22}^b+\dfrac{m}{k_nl} & S_{32}^b\\ S_{31}^b+\dfrac{m}{k_sd} & S_{32}^b & S_{33}^b\end{bmatrix}\begin{Bmatrix}\sigma_x\\ \sigma_y\\ \tau_{xy}\end{Bmatrix} \tag{9}$$

对于含有一定厚度弱面的代表性单元，根据以上变形等效原理，不难推导出相应的本构关系，这里仅给出代表性单元含 m 条材料性质相同、层厚为 h_j 的弱面时的等效本构关系：

$$\begin{Bmatrix}\varepsilon_x\\ \varepsilon_y\\ \gamma_{xy}\end{Bmatrix}=\begin{bmatrix}S_{11}^b+S_{11}^j & S_{21}^b+S_{21}^j & S_{31}^b+S_{31}^j\\ S_{21}^b+(S_{21}^j-S_{21}^b)\dfrac{mh_j}{l} & S_{22}^b+(S_{22}^j-S_{22}^b)\dfrac{mh_j}{l} & S_{23}^b+(S_{23}^j-S_{23}^b)\dfrac{mh_j}{l}\\ S_{31}^b+S_{31}^j & S_{23}^b+(S_{23}^j-S_{23}^b)\dfrac{mh_j}{l} & S_{33}^b\end{bmatrix}\begin{Bmatrix}\sigma_x\\ \sigma_y\\ \tau_{xy}\end{Bmatrix} \tag{10}$$

2　本构模型的进一步简化与层间应力的计算

式(9) 和式(10) 所给出的碾压混凝土本构模型是一种变形等效的连续模型，但是遗憾的是式(10) 为一非对称的柔度矩阵，这在有限元计算中是十分不方便的。很自然产生两个问题：一是当弱面具有一定尺寸厚度，但是当厚度很小时，能否将对称的式(9) 应用于有厚度弱面的情况，以代替式(10)，这种情况下的刚度系数 k_n、k_s 如何确定；另一个是弱面层的层间真实应力如何得到。本节将论述这两个问题。

由弱面的弹性模量 E_j、泊松比 ν_j 和剪切模量 G_j 及弱面的厚度 h_j，根据文献[5] 不难近似地推得符合本文模型(9) 的弱面刚度系数 k_n、k_s 值。

$$k_n=\frac{E_0}{h_j}\qquad k_s=\frac{G_j}{h_j} \tag{11}$$

其中：

$$E_0=\frac{E_j(1-\nu_j)}{(1+\nu_j)(1-2\nu_j)}\qquad \text{(对于平面应变)}$$

$$E_0=\frac{E_j}{1-\nu_j^2}\qquad \text{(对于平面应力)}$$

这样，根据本文的等效模型，即可得到结构的宏观力学行为。然而在实际应用中，工程界往往关心的是某处较危险部位的层间内部真实应力。为解决这一问题，一种方法是在整体结构中取出某一局部结构进行有限元网格细化，来分析层间真实的应力场[6]；另一种方法是一种层间应力的算法[4]，根据层间应力的平衡，层间位移满足 C_1(即函数直至一阶导数连续件) 连续条，得到层间应力的算式：

$$\left.\begin{aligned}&\sigma_x^j=\frac{E_j}{E_b}\sigma_x^b+\left(\nu_j-\frac{E_j}{E_b}\nu_b\right)\sigma_y^b && \text{(对于平面应变)}\\ &\sigma_x^j=\frac{E_j}{E_b}\left(\frac{1-\nu_b^2}{1-\nu_j^2}\right)\sigma_x^b+\left(\frac{\nu_j}{1-\nu_j}-\frac{E_j\nu_b(1+\nu_b)}{E_b(1-\nu_j^2)}\right)\sigma_y^b && \text{(对于平面应力)}\\ &\sigma_y^j=\sigma_y^b,\ \tau_{xy}^j=\tau_{xy}^b\end{aligned}\right\} \tag{12}$$

式中：σ_{ij}^{j} 表示层间应力；σ_{ij}^{b} 表示碾压混凝土本体应力。

根据文献[4] 的计算，认为本体应力近似地等于按等效模型所求得的应力 σ_{ij}，即 $\sigma_{ij}^{b} \approx \sigma_{ij}$。

3 算例

在实际的碾压混凝土坝的施工过程中，很多工程采用 RCC 浇筑法，为了模拟实际施工过程，文献[7] 对某一工程的施工过程进行了仿真累积自重及温度应力计算，考虑到计算机容量限制及计算时间、费用等因素，采用了 3m 厚的均质连续单元来进行计算。然而实际上施工中是每上升 30cm 间歇 4 ~ 5h，可能造成一定的弱面。为考虑弱面的影响，本文取出一 3m 厚的代表性单元，将之分别考虑为各向同性的模型和本文的无厚度弱面等效模型(9)，来考察两个模型的差别。

如图 3 所示，一个长 × 宽 = 3m × 3m 的代表性单元，包含 9 条间距 30cm 的弱面，每条弱面的厚度分别假定为 0.5cm、1.0cm、2.0cm。在如图示的简单荷载作用下，根据本文无厚度弱面等效模型(9) 和文献[7] 的各向同性均质模型来分别计算该代表性单元的垂直层面方向的位移，并和该结构分层细化网格的有限元解对比如表 1 所示。

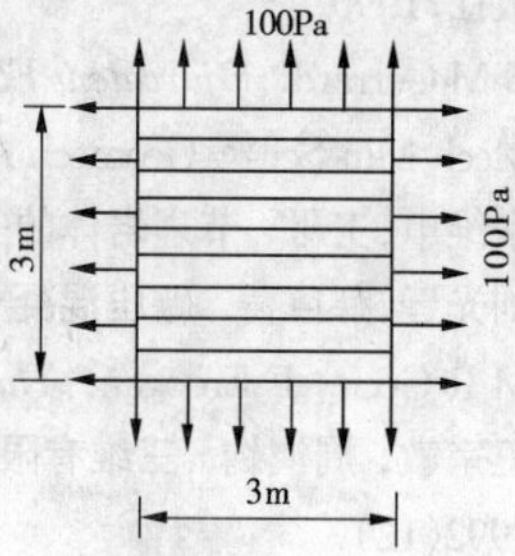

图 3　代表性单元

$E_b = 100\,000\text{Pa}, E_j = 10\,000\text{Pa}$

$\nu_b = \nu_j = 0.2$

表 1　等效模型(9)、各向同性均质模型差别考核

模型	层厚 $h=0.5$(cm)		层厚 $h=1.0$(cm)		层厚 $h=2.0$(cm)	
	位 移 (cm)	相对误差 (%)	位 移 (cm)	相对误差 (%)	位 移 (cm)	相对误差 (%)
等效模型	0.400 5	1.98	0.441 0	3.54	0.522 0	5.84
均质模型(无弱面)	0.360 0	11.9	0.360 0	21.2	0.360 0	35.1
有限元解	0.408 6		0.457 2		0.554 4	

由表 1 可以看出，忽略碾压混凝土坝层间弱面的影响，将坝看成各向同性均质连续体来进行模拟，随着弱面层厚的增加，其变形差别较大。而本文的无厚度弱面的变形等效模型，即使模拟有一定厚度弱面的结构，只要弱面的厚度小于 2cm，是可以满足工程精度要求的。

4 结语

(1)由等效连续模型来模拟成层状碾压混凝土结构，可以大大减小计算工作量，是一种便于实际工程应用的简化计算法。

(2)本文所采用的变形等效连续模型，仅仅需要知道弱面数量，在原有的柔度矩阵或刚度矩阵中略加修改,这对于已具有有限元结构分析程序的部门,仅需要略加变动即可模拟碾压混凝土成层结构物,并且在剖分网格时不必顾虑网格的大小,通用性强,精度满足工程需要。

(3)本文等效方法十分容易推广到三维情况。

参考文献

[1] 能源部、水利部碾压混凝土筑坝推广领导小组. 碾压混凝土筑坝——设计与施工. 北京:电子工业出版社,1990

[2] C M Gerrard. *Equivalent Elastic Moduli of a Rock Mass Consisting of Orthorhombic Layers*. Int J Rock Mech Min Sci & Geomech Abstr, 1982,19:9~14

[3] 朱维申,王平. 节理岩体的等效连续模型与工程应用. 岩土工程学报,1992,14(2):1~11

[4] 刘光廷,郝巨涛. 碾压混凝土拱坝坝体应力简化计算的研究. 清华大学学报,1996,(1)

[5] M R Gecit, F Erdogan. *The interface crack in tension field*. ASME J Appl Mech,1978,54

[6] 王宗敏, 周鸿钧. 三维有限元局部网格细化边界条件插值计算与数据自动采集. 郑州工学院学报,1992(12)

[7] 刘光廷,等. 含灌浆横缝碾压混凝土拱坝应力规律研究. 清华大学学报,1995(6)

水管冷却效应的有限元子结构模拟技术

摘　要　本文提出了水管冷却效应的有限元子结构模拟技术，将冷却水管所在单元视为子结构，给出了相应的有限元计算公式和计算步骤。结果表明，子结构法的引入解决了计算机存储量、单元网格的处理等一系列问题，从而具有很大的优越性。

关键词　混凝土结构　冷却水管　温度分析　有限元法　子结构

冷却水管温度效应的计算总体上可以分为两大类：第一类是解析法[1]，第二类是数值法[2~5]。解析法因其实用性不大这里不再多述。数值法通常是通过有限元法来实现[2~5]，可以分为以下几种：

(1)在每一个冷却水管的周围布置密集的单元[2,3]。从总体上说，布置密集单元的方法大大地增加了计算量和计算机存储量。

(2)采用较粗的网格进行整体性分析[4]。显然这种整体性分析不易正确地反映出冷却水管的效果，也无法考虑温度变化的局部效应。

(3)多重网格法[5]。这种方法的优点在于计算量不太大，效率较高，可以反映出冷却水管的冷却效果，但仍有以下不足之处，如无法精确地计算冷却水管周围的温度和应力，无法反映出水管内水的流量与管径对冷却效果的影响以及无法连续进行二期冷却效应分析等。

综上所述，为兼顾精度和效率，有效地计算出水管冷却对温度和应力的影响，提出一种新的数值计算方法显然已十分有必要。

1992 年，王镭等人首次针对岩土工程渗流分析中排水孔效应的数值分析问题，提出了排水子结构法[6]。文献[6]所研究的是稳定渗流场问题，对应于温度问题相当于是稳定温度场，而对于不稳定温度场问题要复杂得多，笔者尚未见到有关文献，本文也因此将首次对该问题进行研究。

1　温度场计算的常规有限元公式

不稳定温度场的定解方程为

$$\left.\begin{aligned}&\frac{\partial T}{\partial t}=a\nabla^2 T+\frac{\partial \theta}{\partial t} &&\text{(结构内部)}\\ &T\big|_{t=0}=T_0(x,y,z) &&\text{(初始条件)}\\ &\left.\frac{\partial T}{\partial n}\right|_a=-\frac{b}{\lambda}(T-T_a) &&\text{(边界条件)}\end{aligned}\right\}\qquad(1)$$

式中：a 为导温系数；b 为表面放热系数；λ 为导热系数；T_a 为环境温度；T_0 为初始温度；θ 为绝热温升。根据变分原理，不难得到以下有限元列式：

本文选自《水利学报》1997 年第 12 期，作者还有刘宁。

$$([K_1]+\frac{2}{\Delta\tau}[K_2])\{T\}_{\tau}+([K_1]-\frac{2}{\Delta\tau}[K_2])\{T\}_{\tau-\Delta\tau}+\{Q\}_{\tau-\Delta\tau}+\{Q\}_{\tau}=0 \quad (2)$$

式中：

$$\left.\begin{aligned}[K_1] &= \sum_e \left[a \iiint_e \left(\frac{\partial N_i}{\partial x}\frac{\partial N_j}{\partial x} + \frac{\partial N_i}{\partial y}\frac{\partial N_j}{\partial y} + \frac{\partial N_i}{\partial z}\frac{\partial N_j}{\partial z} \right) \mathrm{d}x\mathrm{d}y\mathrm{d}z + a \iint_{\sigma} \frac{b}{\lambda} N_i N_j \mathrm{d}s \right] \\ [K_2] &= \sum_e \iiint_e N_i N_j \mathrm{d}x\mathrm{d}y\mathrm{d}z \\ \{Q\} &= \sum_e \left(-\iint_e \frac{\partial\theta}{\partial t} N_i \mathrm{d}s + a \iint_{Ce} \frac{b}{\lambda} [N_i][N] T_a \mathrm{d}s \right) \end{aligned}\right\} \quad (3)$$

2　冷却水管温度效应的有限元子结构解法

2.1　有限元子结构模拟技术的基本思想及其优越性

为能方便地在原有的有限元网格(不考虑冷却水管时的有限元网格)的基础上有效地模拟出冷却水管,可以设想将冷却水管所在之处的单元视为子结构。冷却水管的冷却效应通过子结构内部结点效应向出口结点凝聚,而后由常规有限元计算而获得。子结构的形式根据冷却水管排列的密集程度、结构大小以及计算规模而定,可选用单管子结构(见图1)、双管子结构(见图2)或多管子结构。

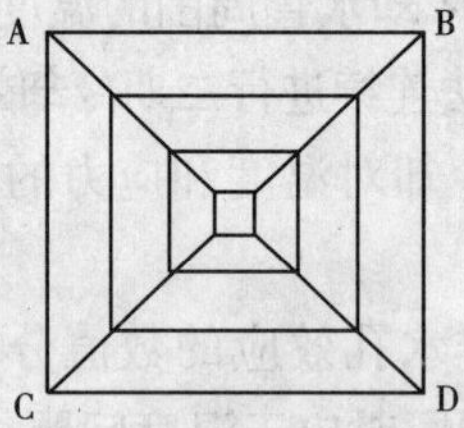

图1　单管子结构示意

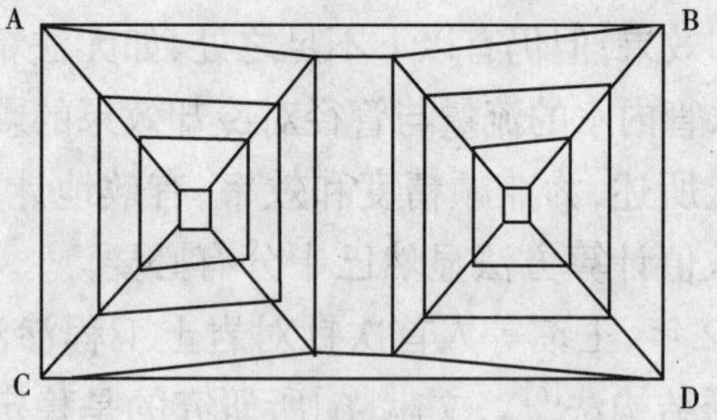

图2　双管子结构示意

不难看出,子结构的引入,使水管冷却的整体效应可以通过出口结点值反映,而子结构的内部结点值能有效地反映出冷却水管的局部效应,从而具有以下的优越性:

(1)无需网格加密,结构单元总数不增加,从而不增加劲度矩阵的维数,大大地节省了计算机存储量。

(2)可以较为准确地计算出冷却水管管径及水的流量对冷却效果的影响。

(3)对于结构下部冷却水管已停止通水的混凝土浇筑层,只需将子结构单元视为常规单元,无需变动网格或采用多重网格,进行二期冷却效应分析时,只需重新将某些常规单元视为子结构单元,模拟十分方便。

(4)由于无需加密网格或变动网格,给有限元前后处理带来了很大的方便。

2.2　冷却水管温度效应有限元子结构模拟法的计算公式

将冷却水管外缘作为第一类边界条件时,不难得出子结构的有限元计算公式:

$$([K_{S1}]+\frac{2}{\Delta\tau}[K_{S2}])\{T_S\}_{\tau}+([K_{S1}]-\frac{2}{\Delta\tau}[K_{S2}])\{T_S\}_{\tau-\Delta\tau}+\{Q_S\}_{\tau-\Delta\tau}+\{Q_S\}_{\tau}=0 \quad (4)$$

式中：下标 S 表示子结构；$[K_{S1}]$、$[K_{S2}]$以及$\{Q_S\}$的表达式类同式(3)。由于将子结构结点分离为内部结点和外部结点，$[K_{S1}]$、$[K_{S2}]$、$\{Q_S\}$以及$[T_S]$应表示为

$$\left.\begin{aligned}&[K_{S1}]=\begin{bmatrix}K_{S1}^{11} & K_{S1}^{12}\\ K_{S1}^{21} & K_{S1}^{22}\end{bmatrix}\quad [K_{S2}]=\begin{bmatrix}K_{S2}^{11} & K_{S2}^{12}\\ K_{S2}^{21} & K_{S2}^{22}\end{bmatrix}\\ &\{Q_S\}=\begin{Bmatrix}Q_S^1\\ Q_S^2\end{Bmatrix}\qquad \{T_S\}=\begin{Bmatrix}T_S^1\\ T_S^2\end{Bmatrix}\end{aligned}\right\} \tag{5}$$

式中：上标 1 表示出口结点；上标 2 表示内部结点。

将式(5)代入式(4)可得

$$([K_{S1}^{11}]+\frac{2}{\Delta\tau}[K_{S2}^{11}])\{T_S^1\}_\tau+([K_{S1}^{12}]+\frac{2}{\Delta\tau}[K_{S2}^{12}])\{T_S^2\}_\tau+([K_{S1}^{11}]-\frac{2}{\Delta\tau}[K_{S2}^{11}])\cdot$$
$$\{T_S^1\}_{\tau-\Delta\tau}+([K_{S1}^{12}]-\frac{2}{\Delta\tau}[K_{S2}^{12}])\{T_S^2\}_{\tau-\Delta\tau}+\{Q_S^1\}_{\tau-\Delta\tau}+\{Q_S^1\}_\tau=0 \tag{6}$$

$$([K_{S1}^{21}]+\frac{2}{\Delta\tau}[K_{S2}^{21}])\{T_S^1\}_\tau+([K_{S1}^{22}]+\frac{2}{\Delta\tau}[K_{S2}^{22}])\{T_S^2\}_\tau+([K_{S1}^{21}]-\frac{2}{\Delta\tau}[K_{S2}^{21}])\cdot$$
$$\{T_S^1\}_{\tau-\Delta\tau}+([K_{S1}^{22}]-\frac{2}{\Delta\tau}[K_{S2}^{22}])\{T_S^2\}_{\tau-\Delta\tau}+\{Q_S^2\}_{\tau-\Delta\tau}+\{Q_S^2\}_\tau=0 \tag{7}$$

由式(7)可得

$$\{T_S^2\}_\tau=[M_2]^{-1}\{S_2\} \tag{8}$$

式中：

$$[M_2]=[K_{S1}^{22}]+\frac{2}{\Delta\tau}[K_{S2}^{22}]$$

$$\{S_2\}=-([K_{S1}^{21}]+\frac{2}{\Delta\tau}[K_{S2}^{21}])\{T_S^1\}_\tau-([K_{S1}^{21}]-\frac{2}{\Delta\tau}[K_{S2}^{21}])\{T_S^1\}_{\tau-\Delta\tau}-$$
$$([K_{S1}^{22}]-\frac{2}{\Delta\tau}[K_{S2}^{22}])\{T_S^2\}_{\tau-\Delta\tau}-\{Q_S^2\}_{\tau-\Delta\tau}-\{Q_S^2\}_\tau$$

将式(8)代入式(6)可得

$$[M_1]\{T_S^1\}_\tau=\{S_1\} \tag{9}$$

式中：

$$[M_1]=[K_{S1}^{11}]+\frac{2}{\Delta\tau}[K_{S2}^{11}]-([K_{S1}^{12}]+\frac{2}{\Delta\tau}[K_{S2}^{12}])[M_2]^{-1}([K_{S1}^{21}]+\frac{2}{\Delta\tau}[K_{S2}^{21}])$$

$$\{S_1\}=-([K_{S1}^{11}]-\frac{2}{\Delta\tau}[K_{S2}^{11}])\{T_S^1\}_{\tau-\Delta\tau}-([K_{S1}^{12}]-\frac{2}{\Delta\tau}[K_{S2}^{12}])\{T_S^2\}_{\tau-\Delta\tau}+$$
$$([K_{S1}^{12}]+\frac{2}{\Delta\tau}[K_{S2}^{12}])[M_2]^{-1}(([K_{S1}^{21}]-\frac{2}{\Delta\tau}[K_{S2}^{21}])\{T_S^1\}_{\tau-\Delta\tau}+$$
$$([K_{S1}^{22}]-\frac{2}{\Delta\tau}[K_{S2}^{22}])\{T_S^2\}_{\tau-\Delta\tau}+\{Q_S^2\}_{\tau-\Delta\tau}+\{Q_S^2\}_\tau)-$$
$$\{Q_S^1\}_{\tau-\Delta\tau}-\{Q_S^1\}_\tau$$

$[M_1]$和$\{S_1\}$即为子结构出口劲度矩阵和出口右端项。将所有子结构的出口劲度矩阵$[M_1]$和常规单元的单元劲度矩阵$[K_e]$组装，即可得整体劲度矩阵：

$$[K]=\sum[K_e]+\sum[M_1] \tag{10}$$

同时,将所有子结构的出口右端项$\{S_1\}$和常规单元的右端项$\{Q_e\}$组装,即可得整体右端项列阵

$$\{Q\} = \sum\{Q_e\} + \sum\{S_1\} \tag{11}$$

由于冷却水管外缘是按第一类边界条件处理,因而需知每一时段冷却水管内水的温度。文献[2]给出了计算水温增量的3种计算方法,为方便起见,可采用以下计算公式:

$$T_{wi+1} = T_{wi} + \Delta T_{wi} \qquad \Delta T_{wi} = \frac{\lambda \Delta L_i}{c_w \rho_w q_w}\left(\int_{C_0} \frac{\partial T}{\partial r}\mathrm{d}s\right)_i \tag{12}$$

式中:c_w、ρ_w、q_w 分别为水的比热、密度和流量;ΔL_i 为两截面的间距;$\partial T/\partial r$ 为水管外缘的混凝土径向温度梯度;C_0 为水管外缘。

按式(12)计算的关键是求出 $\partial T/\partial r$。文献[3]采用杂交单元求解时,可直接计算出冷却水管外缘的 $\partial T/\partial r$。文献[2]采用的是常规单元,故采用了在孔口附近布置密集单元的方法,按此方法,为保证计算精度,孔口附近布置的单元数不能太少[2],这样势必大大增加工作量。按本文子结构方法,可以根据精度要求在子结构内部随意地部置内部结点的层数。

式(12)中,$\int_{C_0} \frac{\partial T}{\partial r}\mathrm{d}s$ 可以采用下式计算[2]:

$$\int_{C_0} \frac{\partial T}{\partial r}\mathrm{d}s \approx \Delta s \sum_{j=1}^{m} (\partial T/\partial r)_j \Big|_{r=r_0} \tag{13}$$

式中:m 为位于圆周上的结点数。

上式事实上假定了圆周上相邻两点之间 $\partial T/\partial r$ 为一常数,当 m 较大时,这一假定不会引起太大的误差。当采用图1或图2的子结构模拟方案时,是将圆形水管模拟成了方管,相应于在式(13)中 $m=4$。为减小误差,可将式(13)改为下式:

$$\int_{C_0} \frac{\partial T}{\partial r}\mathrm{d}s \approx \frac{1}{2}\Delta s \sum_{j=1}^{m} \left[\left(\frac{\partial T}{\partial r}\right)_{j-1} + \left(\frac{\partial T}{\partial r}\right)_j\right] \Big|_{r=r_0} \tag{14}$$

上式隐含着 $\partial T/\partial r$ 在圆周相邻两结点之间呈线性变化的假定。如果进一步在水管圆周多布置一些结点,以更精确地模拟出圆形水管,可以选用其他形式的子结构,如图3(a)、(b)所示。

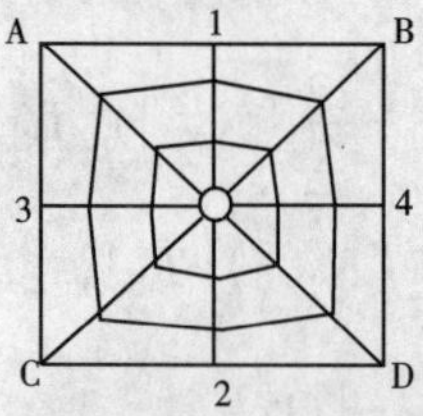

(a)中间有过渡点

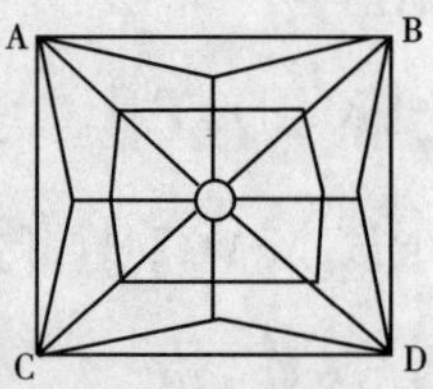

(b)中间无过渡点

图3 模拟圆形水管时的两种子结构

图3(a)中仍是只有A、B、C、D为出口结点,1、2、3、4只是过渡结点,此时前述子结构有关公式需作修改,修改方法可参见文献[6],但前提是温度在ABCD单元内的变化较为

平缓,以便可进行线性插值,这无疑会给最终计算结果带来一定的误差。图 3(b)所示子结构的优点是没有过渡点,缺点是单元形态不太好,含三棱柱单元,编程相对复杂。

2.3 有限元子结构解法的计算步骤

(1)在冷却水管通水的初始时刻 t_0,混凝土温度为 $\{T\}_0$,令冷却水管内水温为:$T_{wi}^0 = T_{w0}(i=1,2,\cdots)$,式中上标 0 表示 t_0 时刻,T_{w0} 为冷却水管进水口处的水温。

(2)分别形成常规单元的单元劲度矩阵和子结构的出口劲度矩阵,并组装得到整体劲度矩阵。同时,分别形成常规单元的右端项和子结构的出口右端项,并组装得到整体右端项。

(3)求解出结点温度列阵 $\{T\}_1$ 后,再求出子结构内部结点温度 $\{T_S^2\}_1$。由此可进一步计算出各子结构内冷却水管外缘的温度梯度 $\partial T/\partial r$,从而可求出 t_1 时刻冷却水管内的水温 $T_{wi}^1(i=1,2,\cdots)$。

(4)由子结构内部结点温度 $\{T_S^2\}_1$ 和冷却水管内水的温度 T_{wi}^1,可进一步计算出下一时刻子结构的出口劲度矩阵和出口右端项,再进行有限元组装,计算出结点温度列阵 $\{T\}_2$。

3 程序及算例

根据前述理论和方法,笔者编制了"可考虑水管冷却效应的大体积混凝土结构三维不稳定温度场大型通用计算程序 TECOP"。该程序可模拟施工过程,考虑各种实际影响因素(如入仓温度、气温、水管冷却效应等)的影响,进行施工期和运行期的温度场计算。在计算水管冷却效应时,该程序还可有效地反映出水管通水时间、水流换向频率的影响。以下给出两个算例进行验证。

3.1 算例 1——无限长圆柱域的冷却问题

取文献[1]中无限长圆柱域的冷却问题,圆柱直径取为 $D=1.5\text{m}$,内部水管边界为 0℃,外边界为绝热,混凝土初始温度取为 $T_0=10℃$,水管直径为 $d=D/100=0.015\text{m}$。按文献[5]的方法,以正方形区域近似代替圆形域(如图 4所示),可以认为这两种区域中断面上的平均温度是近似相等的。有限元网格采用 5×5 的网格。图 5 和图 6 给出了本文子结构解与理论解的对比结果。图 5 中,T_m 为断面平均温度,a 为导

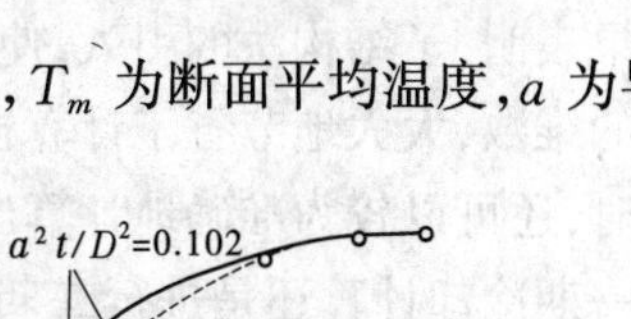

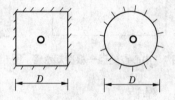

图 4 圆柱域的冷却

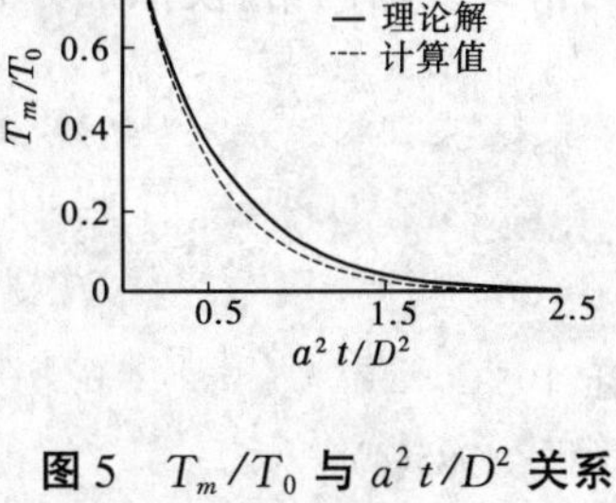

图 5 T_m/T_0 与 a^2t/D^2 关系

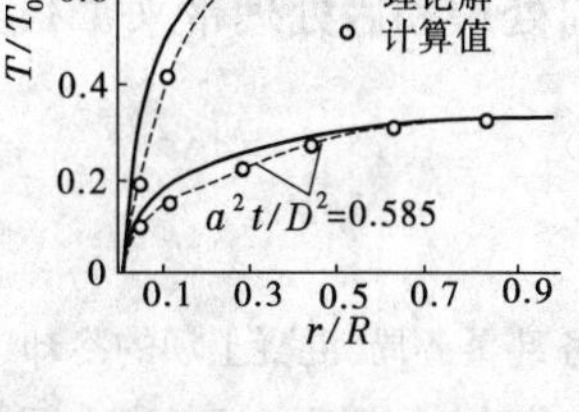

图 6 T/T_0 与 r/R 的关系

温系数。图 6 中 r 为考察点距中心点的距离，R 为圆柱的半径，T 为考察点处的温度。从图 5、图 6 可以看出，采用 5×5 的网格已能得出较为满意的结果。误差产生的原因主要是以正方形域代替了圆形域以及以方管（外切）代替了圆形冷却水管。

3.2 算例 2——混凝土浇筑块的冷却问题

考虑一 3m×3m×3m 的混凝土浇筑块，底部恒温在 10℃（按第一类边界条件），其余各面暴露在 10℃ 的大气中（按第三类边界条件），混凝土导温系数、导热系数和表面放热系数分别为：$a=0.1\text{m}^2/\text{d}$，$\lambda=237.0\text{kJ}/(\text{m}\cdot\text{d}\cdot℃)$，$\beta=1\ 184.9\text{kJ}/(\text{m}^2\cdot\text{d}\cdot℃)$。混凝土绝热温升表达式选为 $\theta=\theta_0(1-e^{-m_1 t})$，其中：$\theta_0=25.0℃$，$m_1=0.397$。冷却水入口处水温为 3℃，流量为 $21.6\text{m}^3/\text{d}$，水管直径为 0.04m。本文分别按两种情况进行计算：①浇筑块中心点处通一根冷却水管；②浇筑块中间层面布置一蛇形管。图 7 和图 8 给出了水管周围局部增加常规单元的方法（示意）。图 9 给出了与断面中心点相距 0.5m 处的平均温度计算结果，其中，虚线为无冷却水管时的温度值，曲线 1 和曲线 2 分别为通一根冷却水管和布置蛇形管时的计算结果，实线为本文子结构解法所得结果，圆圈为按常规加密单元法所得结果，两者几乎完全吻合，可以看出，子结构解法在无需常规加密单元、不增加劲度矩阵容量的情况下仍能达到较好的精度。

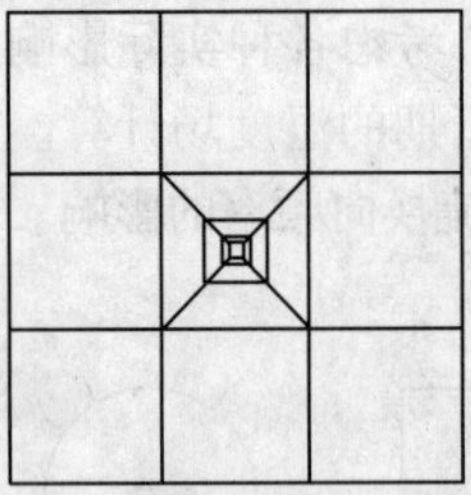

图 7　中心点处通一根冷却水管

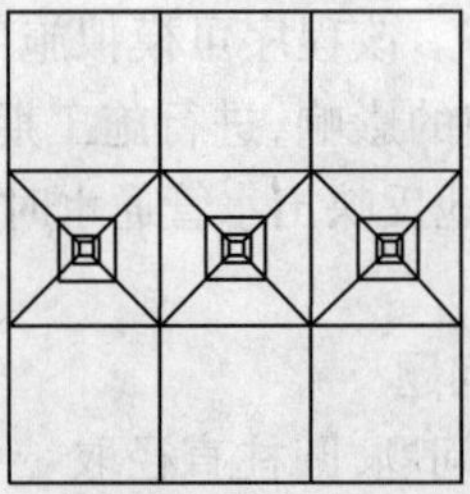

图 8　中间层面布置一蛇形管

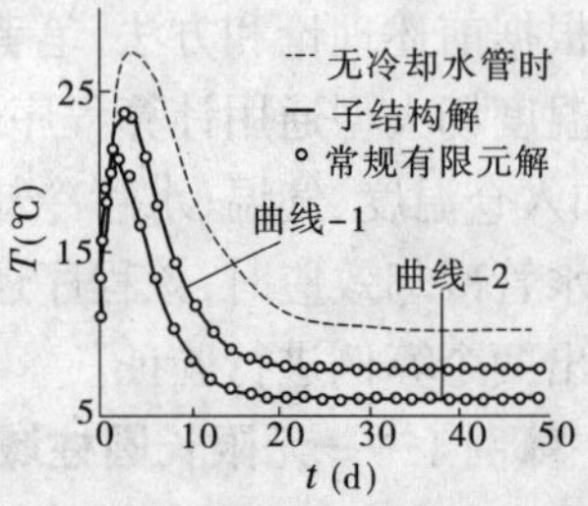

图 9　与中心点相距 0.5m 处的平均温度

4　结语

本文首次提出了水管冷却效应的有限元子结构模拟技术，编制了相应的计算机程序。结果表明，子结构法的引入，使在计算水管冷却效应时，无需加密网格，从而不增加劲度矩阵的维数，大大地节省了计算机存储量，使大型实际混凝土结构温度场的计算成为可能，同时，还可以较为准确地计算出冷却水管管径及水的流量对冷却效果的影响。无论是进行一期冷却计算还是进行二期冷却分析，都无需加密网格或变动网格，模拟十分方便，且给有限元前处理和后处理带来了很大的方便。

参考文献

[1] 美国内务部垦务局. 混凝土坝的冷却. 北京：水利电力出版社，1958
[2] 朱伯芳，蔡建波. 混凝土坝冷却效果的有限元分析，水利学报，1985(4)
[3] 蔡建波. 用杂交元求解有冷却水管的平面不稳定温度场. 水利学报，1984(5)

[4] 潘家铮.重力坝设计. 北京:水利电力出版社,1987
[5] 陈里红，傅作新.采用一期水管冷却的混凝土坝施工期数值模拟. 河海大学学报，1991,19(3)
[6] 王镭，刘中，张有天.有排水孔幕的渗流场分析. 水利学报，1992(4)

阶梯形变截面圆拱和圆环稳定计算的有效方法

摘　要　利用等截面圆弧曲杆的稳定微分方程和本文导出的弯矩一般表达式，建立了静水压力作用下阶梯变截面圆拱和圆环稳定分析的代数方程组，得到了解析计算临界载荷的特征方程。算例表明本文方法简单有效。

关键词　阶梯截面　圆拱　圆环　稳定计算

曲杆结构稳定计算是土木、桥梁和水利等工程设计分析中的重要内容[1]。对于各类等截面圆弧曲杆的稳定分析，已有多种精确计算方法[1~3]，然而对于阶梯变截面圆弧曲杆的稳定分析，目前只能采用数值方法计算。为此，本文利用等截面圆弧曲杆位移解析解，以阶梯截面径向位移为基本未知量，建立了在静水压力作用下两铰圆拱和圆环稳定计算的代数方程组和特征方程，由此可解析求得最小临界载荷。

1　圆弧曲杆的稳定微分方程

薄壁曲杆在外部压力作用下会出现曲折失稳问题。如果不计轴向变形的影响，运用弹性小变形理论可以得到在静水压力作用下等截面圆弧曲杆平面弯曲时用位移和用弯矩表示的稳定微分方程[2,3]

$$\frac{\mathrm{d}^2 w}{\mathrm{d}\theta^2} + w = -\frac{Mr^2}{EI} \tag{1a}$$

$$\frac{\mathrm{d}^3 M}{\mathrm{d}\theta^3} + \frac{\mathrm{d}M}{\mathrm{d}\theta} = -\frac{qr^3}{EI} \cdot \frac{\mathrm{d}M}{\mathrm{d}\theta} \tag{1b}$$

式中：w、M、EI 分别为曲杆 θ 截面的径向位移、弯矩和抗弯刚度，其中 ω 以指向圆心为正，M 以使圆弧初始曲率减小为正；r 为平均半径；θ 为极角；q 为静水压力。

将式(1a) 代入式(1b) 式可得

$$\frac{\mathrm{d}^3 M}{\mathrm{d}\theta^3} + \frac{\mathrm{d}M}{\mathrm{d}\theta} = qr\left(\frac{\mathrm{d}^3 w}{\mathrm{d}\theta^3} + \frac{\mathrm{d}w}{\mathrm{d}\theta}\right) \tag{2}$$

解此方程得圆弧曲杆弯矩一般表达式

$$M(\theta) = A + B\sin\theta + C\cos\theta + qrw(\theta) \tag{3}$$

式中：A、B、C 为积分常数，可由曲杆边界约束条件和变形对称性条件确定。

2　圆拱的稳定计算

圆拱结构分两铰拱、三铰拱和无铰拱等，其稳定分析方法相似。下面以两铰拱为例介绍阶梯截面圆拱的稳定计算方法。

在静水压力作用下，n 段阶梯形变截面两铰圆拱如图 1(a) 所示。Timoshenko[2] 指出

本文选自《力学与实践》1997 年第 1 期，作者还有朱先奎。

在均匀外压力作用下等截面两铰圆拱失稳时呈反对称变形。假定该结论对于常见的对称型阶梯圆拱仍然成立，则式(3) 中 $A = C = 0$，由边界条件 $M(\pm\varphi) = w(\pm\varphi) = 0$ 得 $B = 0$。因此，两铰圆拱失稳时弯矩为

$$M(\theta) = qrw(\theta) \tag{4}$$

将式(4) 代入式(1a) 得第 i 段阶梯圆拱的稳定微分方程

$$\frac{d^2 w}{d\theta^2} + k_i^2 w = 0, \quad k_i^2 = 1 + \frac{qr^3}{EI_i} \tag{5}$$

对于任意相邻两段阶梯圆弧单元如图 1(b) 所示，因第 i 和第 $i+1$ 段的抗弯刚度 EI_i 和 EI_{i+1} 为常量，方程(5) 为分段常系数微分方程，其通解为

$$\omega(\theta) = C_1^i \sin(k_i\theta) + C_2^i \cos(k_i\theta) \quad (-\alpha_i \leqslant \theta \leqslant 0) \tag{6}$$

$$\omega(\theta) = C_1^{i+1} \sin(k_{i+1}\theta) + C_2^{i+1} \cos(k_{i+1}\theta) \quad (0 \leqslant \theta \leqslant \alpha_{i+1}) \tag{7}$$

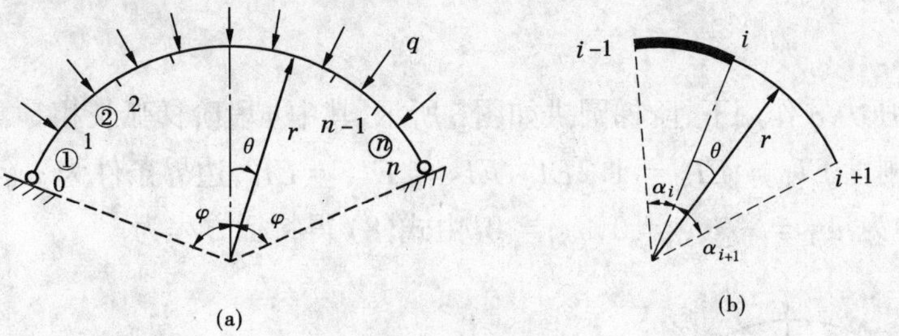

图 1

利用结点位移 w_{i-1}、w_i、w_{i+1} 和结点 i 变形连续条件 $w(0^-) = w(0^+)$，$\left.\frac{dw}{d\theta}\right|_{\theta=0^-} = \left.\frac{dw}{d\theta}\right|_{\theta=0^+}$，由式(6)、式(7) 消去常数 C_1^i、C_2^i、C_1^{i+1}、C_2^{i+1} 后得圆拱阶梯截面位移代数方程

$$w_{i-1} - a_i w_i + b_{i+1} w_{i+1} = 0 \tag{8}$$

式中

$$\left.\begin{aligned} a_i &= \cos(k_i\alpha_i) + b_{i+1}\cos(k_{i+1}\alpha_{i+1}) \\ b_{i+1} &= \frac{k_{i+1}}{k_i} \cdot \frac{\sin(k_i\alpha_i)}{\sin(k_{i+1}\alpha_{i+1})} \end{aligned}\right\} \tag{9}$$

而且 $i = 1 \sim n$，注意到 $w_0 = w_n = 0$，将所有方程组合起来得如下位移矩阵方程：

$$[K]\{w\} = \{0\} \tag{10}$$

式中：$\{w\} = [w_1, w_2, \cdots, w_{n-1}]^{\mathrm{T}}$；$\{0\}$ 为零向量；

$$[K] = \begin{bmatrix} -a_1 & b_2 & 0 & \cdots & 0 & 0 & 0 \\ 1 & -a_2 & b_3 & \cdots & 0 & 0 & 0 \\ 0 & 1 & -a_3 & \cdots & 0 & 0 & 0 \\ \vdots & \vdots & \vdots & \vdots & \vdots & \vdots & \vdots \\ 0 & 0 & 0 & \cdots & -a_{n-3} & b_{n-2} & 0 \\ 0 & 0 & 0 & \cdots & 1 & -a_{n-2} & b_{n-1} \\ 0 & 0 & 0 & \cdots & 0 & 1 & -a_{n-1} \end{bmatrix} \tag{11}$$

由于圆拱失稳时位移向量$\{w\}$非全零,因此方程(10)系数矩阵的行列式必须为零,即

$$\det[K] = 0 \tag{12}$$

上式就是阶梯截面两铰圆拱稳定计算的特征方程,由此可解析求得临界载荷的大小。

3 圆环的稳定计算

工程中的圆管屈折稳定分析常按圆环计算,图2所示为在静水压力作用下n段阶梯截面圆环。Timoshenko[2]研究表明,等截面圆环失稳时呈对称变形。假定常见对称型阶梯截面圆环失稳变形也是对称的,则圆环临界失稳的弯矩和两铰圆拱临界失稳的弯矩式(4)相同[2],因此上节导出的位移代数方程(8)本节仍然适用。不过对于圆环$w_0 = w_n \neq 0$,位移向量变为$\{w\} = [w_1, w_2, \cdots, w_n]^T$,相应的特征方程与式(12)稍有不同。

4 算例

(1)静水压力q作用下,阶梯圆拱如图3所示。其中4段阶梯弧长相等,各段圆心角$\alpha_i = \varphi/2$,抗弯刚度$EI_1 = EI_4 = 1.2EI_0$,$EI_2 = EI_3 = EI_0$,边界条件为$w_0 = w_4 = 0$,反对称变形条件为$w_1 = -w_3 \neq 0$,$\omega_2 = 0$。由式(8)得特征方程为

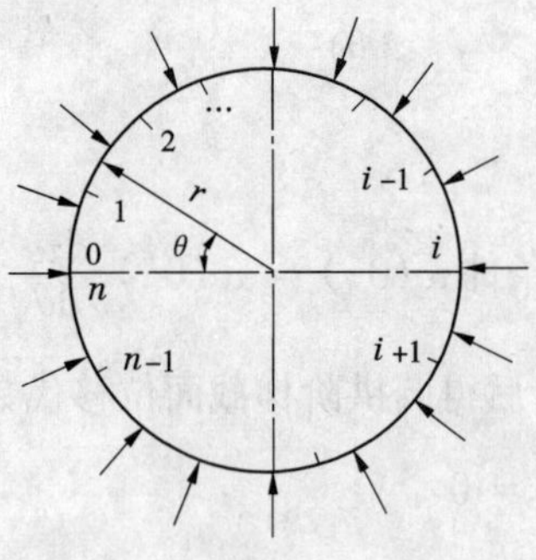

图2

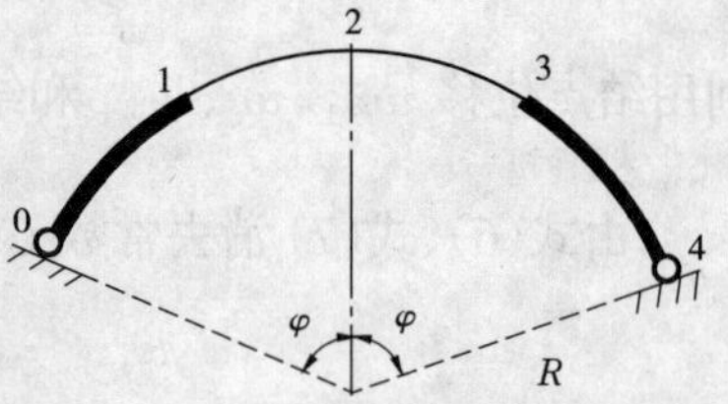

图3

$$\cos\frac{k_1\varphi}{2} + \frac{k_2}{k_1}\sin\frac{k_1\varphi}{2}\cos\frac{k_2\varphi}{2} = 0 \tag{13}$$

式中:$k_1^2 = 1 + qR^3/(1.2EI_0)$;$k_2^2 = 1 + qR^3/(EI_0)$。

解此方程即得最小临界载荷q_{cr},如当$\varphi = \pi/3$时,$q_{cr} = 8.710\,9EI_0/R^3$。

如果该拱为等截面圆拱,则$k_1^2 = k_2^2 = 1 + qR^3/(EI_0)$,式(13)变为$\cos\dfrac{k_1\varphi}{2} = 0$,由此得$q_{cr} = \left[\left(\dfrac{\pi}{\varphi}\right)^2 - 1\right]\dfrac{EI_0}{R^3}$,这与精确结果[1~3]相同。当$\varphi = \pi/3$时,$q_{cr} = 8EI_0/R^3$。由此可见。等截面拱在两端拱脚增大刚度后其临界载荷随之增加,这表明本文结果合理。

(2)静水压力q作用下,阶梯圆环如图4所示。其中8段阶梯弧长相等,各段圆心角$\alpha_i = \pi/4$,抗弯刚度$EI_1 = EI_3 = EI_5 = EI_7 = 1.1EI_0$,$EI_2 = EI_6 = EI_0$,$EI_4 = EI_8 = 1.2EI_0$。因圆环失稳变形对称,则$w_1 = w_2 = w_5 = w_6$,$w_3 = w_4 = w_7 = w_8$,独立

位移只有 w_1 和 w_8。由式(8)得该圆环稳定特征方程为

$$(1-a_8)(b_2-a_1)-b_1=0 \tag{14}$$

式中：$a_1=\cos(k_1\alpha_1)+b_2\cos(k_2\alpha_2)$；$a_8=\cos(k_8\alpha_8)+b_1\cos(k_1\alpha_1)$。其中 $k_1^2=1+\dfrac{qR^3}{1.1EI_0}$，$k_2^2=1+\dfrac{qR^3}{EI_0}$，$k_8^2=1+\dfrac{qR^3}{1.2EI_0}$，$b_1=\dfrac{k_1}{k_8}\cdot\dfrac{\sin(k_8\alpha_8)}{\sin(k_1\alpha_1)}$，$b_2=\dfrac{k_2}{k_1}\cdot\dfrac{\sin(k_1\alpha_1)}{\sin(k_2\alpha_2)}$。解此方程得最小临界载荷 $q_{cr}=3.283\,6EI_0/R^3$。

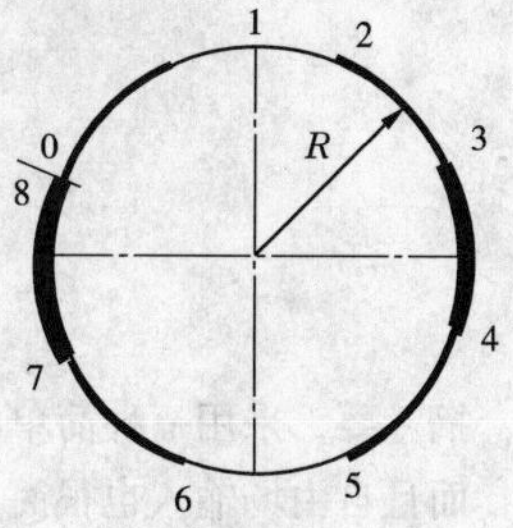

图 4

如果该圆环为等截面，则 $k_1^2=k_2^2=k_8^2=1+qR^3/(EI_0)$，式(14)变为 $\cos(k_1\alpha_1)[\cos(k_1\alpha_1)-1]=0$，由此得 $q_{cr}=3EI_0/R^3$，这就是等截面圆环的精确解[1~3]。

5 结语

本文采用静力法建立了静水压力作用下阶梯形变截面两铰圆拱和圆环稳定计算的代数方程组和特征方程，解决了解析计算其临界载荷的问题。算例表明本文方法简单有效，结果合理。所给特征方程便于电算分析。

对于等截面圆拱和圆环，本文结果和其他方法得到的精确结果完全一致。对于任意变截面圆拱和圆环，可采用文献[4]的刚度折算法将任意变化的刚度折算成若干阶梯刚度，然后用本文方法可以方便地进行稳定分析计算。

参考文献

[1] Bazant Z P, Cedolin L. *Stability of Structures*. Oxford University Press, 1991:108～118

[2] Timoshenko S. *Theory of Elastic Stability*. McGraw-Hill Book Company, Inc:1936. 204～238

[3] 龙驭球，包世华. 结构力学(下册). 北京：人民教育出版社，1981:288～295

[4] 朱先奎. 任意变刚度梁变形的通用方程. 力学与实践，1993，15(3)：58～60

拱坝河谷自由场反应

摘　要　采用一种简单的模型计算拱坝河谷平面内反应,使地基的动力刚度不但容易确定,而且自由场输入也很简单。对P和SV波在不同入射情况的河谷反应进行了频域求解。结果表明,这种计算模型能有效地反应河谷两岸山体的放大效应、幅差和相差。程序的计算过程简单,便于工程应用。

关键词　子结构　结构—土相互作用　自由场

拱坝河谷自由场地震反应是拱坝抗震设计的关键问题[1~5]。传统的确定方法,如有限元、有限差分法对这类波散射问题不是很有效;无限元法在波动计算方面辐射参数确定还有很大的困难[6];自动满足波辐射条件的边界元法,需要位移和应力基本解,工作应用受到很大限制[7]。本文将河谷平面内自由场问题转化为子结构动力相互作用问题。这种方法不但容易确定规则自由场输入,而且能解析确定半无限地基动力刚度,便于应用现有有限元程序。最后,对不同入射P波和SV波的河谷自由场进行了分析。

1　基本方法

将河谷平面内自由场散射问题转化为结构相互作用问题,图1所示计算模型是半无限空间与两山体形成河谷的断面。

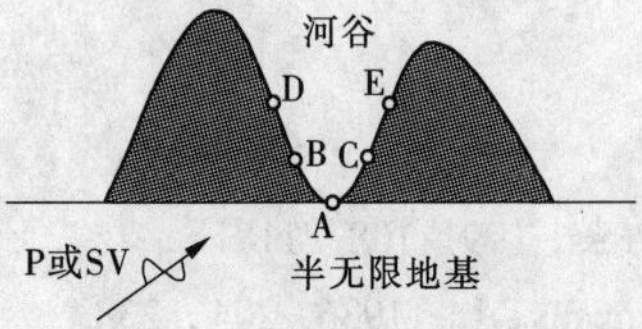

图1　河谷计算模型

1.1　山体子结构动力刚度

山体子结构(有限部分)应用有限元法离散,这样可以模拟任何不规则河谷形状。子结构的动力刚度为

$$\boldsymbol{S}_s(\omega) = \boldsymbol{K} - \omega^2\boldsymbol{M} + i\omega\boldsymbol{C} \tag{1}$$

式中:$\boldsymbol{K}$、$\boldsymbol{M}$和$\boldsymbol{C}$分别是山体的刚度、质量与阻尼矩阵;ω是激励频率;$i=\sqrt{-1}$。

为了区分子结构相互作用节点,将式(1)表示为如下分块的形式:

$$\boldsymbol{S}_s(\omega) = \begin{bmatrix} S_{ss}(\omega) & S_{sb}(\omega) \\ S_{bs}(\omega) & S_{bb}(\omega) \end{bmatrix} \tag{2}$$

式中下标s与b分别表示结构与地基。

1.2　半无限地基动力刚度

对于黏弹性匀质半无限地基,应有波动方程可以解析地确定动力刚度[8]。首先,如图2所示原点0单位应力引起m节点的复位移为

$$F_m = \begin{bmatrix} F_m^{11} & F_m^{12} \\ F_m^{21} & F_m^{22} \end{bmatrix} \tag{3}$$

本文选自《水利学报》1999第9期,作者还有刘天云。

式中上标 1 和 2 表示平面内两个方向位移与应力。

由式(3)不难形成所有节点的柔度矩阵 $\boldsymbol{F}(\omega)$。应用虚位移原理,可以确定半无限地基子结构的动力刚度矩阵 $\boldsymbol{S}_f(\omega)$ 为

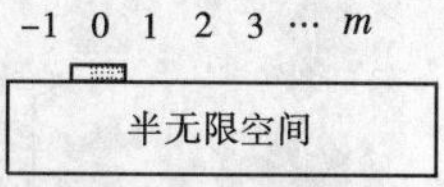

图 2 半无限地基

$$\boldsymbol{S}_f(\omega) = \boldsymbol{D}^{\mathrm{T}}[\boldsymbol{D}\boldsymbol{F}(\omega)]^{-1}\boldsymbol{D} \tag{4}$$

其中矩阵 $\boldsymbol{D}$ 是简单的位移传递矩阵。由上式可见半无限地基的动力刚度矩阵是对称的。

1.3 子结构动力相互作用

半无限地基自由场位移为 u_f,与地基联结的山体子结构节点位移向量为 u_b,相对位移为 $u_b - u_f$,山体子结构的其余节点位移向量为 u_s,则山体子结构平衡方程为

$$\begin{bmatrix} S_{ss} & S_{sb} \\ S_{bs} & S_{bb} \end{bmatrix}\begin{Bmatrix} u_s \\ u_b \end{Bmatrix} = \begin{Bmatrix} 0 \\ -S_f(u_b - u_f) \end{Bmatrix} \tag{5}$$

将上式进一步表示为

$$\begin{bmatrix} S_{ss} & S_{sb} \\ S_{bs} & S_{bb} + S_f \end{bmatrix}\begin{Bmatrix} u_s \\ u_b \end{Bmatrix} = \begin{Bmatrix} 0 \\ S_f u_f \end{Bmatrix} \tag{6}$$

式(6)表示激励作用在山体与半无限地基之间,适应于平面内 P、SV 和 Rayleigh 波输入的激励。自由场输入 u_f 可由文献[9]中方法解析确定。这样,通过上式可以在频域内求解河谷自由场位移$[u_s u_b]^{\mathrm{T}}$。

2 应用

在有限元程序 DDJ－W 的基础上,作者开发了计算半无限地基的动力刚度的子程序 BDSTIF。下面针对新疆石门子碾压混凝土拱坝河谷:$c_s = 500.0\mathrm{m/s}$, $\gamma = 0.333$, $\xi = 0.05$,左右山体底宽各 600m,左山高 480m,右山高 420m;A、D、E 点水平间距 120m,高差 240m。分析 P 与 SV 波不同入射情况时平面内自由场的反应。

2.1 P 波入射

当单位幅值 P 波以不同角度入射时,图 3 所示是河谷两岸不同高程的自由场反应幅值放大系数—频率曲线。由图可见,河谷各点的反应明显不均匀,沿高度有显著的放大效应,尤其是右岸相对较小山体,P 波入射会产生较大的水平反应;由于河谷两岸山体不对称,即使 P 波垂直入射,河谷中点也存在水平位移;行波效应使河谷中高频反应对入射角很敏感,尤其是左岸山体的节点(如 D 点)。与水平反应相比,竖向反应峰值比较集中,尤其是山体较高部位,放大 3～6 倍。与水平位移不同的是河谷两岸的放大对于不同的入射角是不一样的:左岸随入射角增大而减小,河谷中点与左岸类似;右岸则随入射角增大而趋于增大。无论水平还是竖向反应幅值,高频激励河谷反应都不显著。

2.2 SV 波入射

图 4 是单位幅值 SV 波以不同角度入射时河谷位移放大系数—频率曲线。$\theta = 0°$和$\theta = 30°$入射时,都只有水平方向位移激励,只是幅值与视波速不同,河谷中点位移在高频域幅值变化趋势相反,放大较大(2～4 倍)。$\theta = 45°$是只有竖向位移激励的情况,但结构的不对称使得河谷中点仍有水平位移。$\theta = 60°$基本与 $\theta = 45°$入射时位移反应基本一致。山体只是在中低频段放大效果显著,而高频反应量很小。同样,由于不对称,垂直入射波

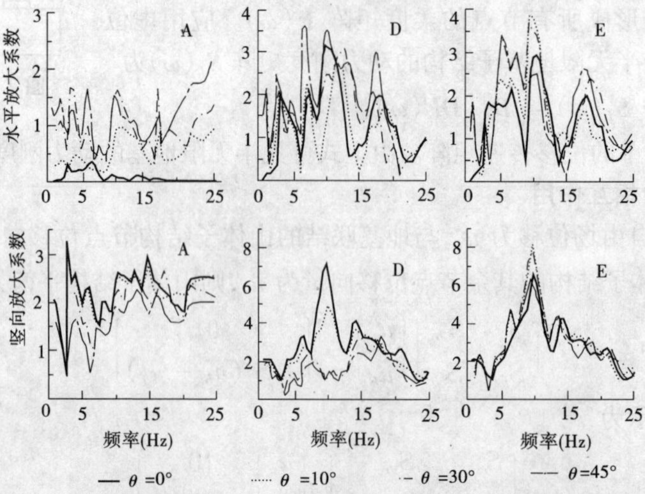

图 3　P 波激励下河谷自由场水平与竖向放大系数—频率关系

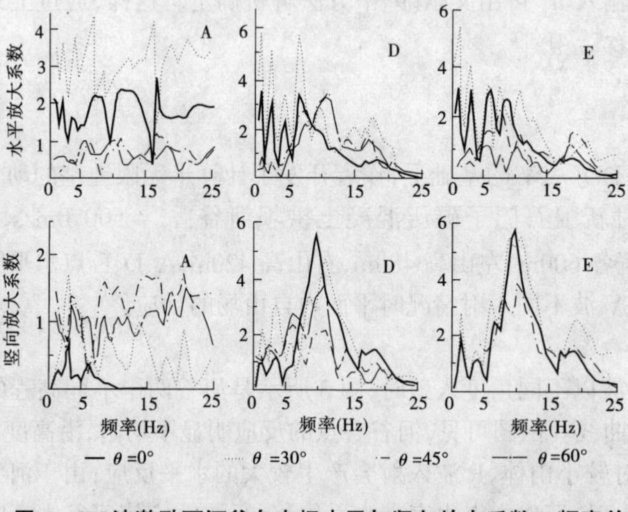

图 4　SV 波激励下河谷自由场水平与竖向放大系数—频率关系

引起 A 点竖向位移，且随入射角增大而增大。相比而言，山体基本是前两种激励情况反应较大。在中低频段，两岸都有局部放大现象，以小角度入射为主。而高频域两岸则出现不同的反应幅值，尤其是山体较高的部位。

总之，入射波的波型与入射角对河谷自由场的反应影响很大，尤其是山体自振频率 $f=9.76$Hz附近，出现山体不同程序的放大现象，这能有效地反应河谷自由场散射的情况。

3　结语

通过子结构动力相互作用法，本文分析了不同入射波激励河谷的自由场反应。结果表明入射波型与入射角对河谷自由场反应有重要影响。两岸山体有不同的放大效应，尤其是较高部位节点。这对于拱坝抗震分析十分重要。本文采用简单的方法确定半无限地基动力刚度,应用现有有限元程序,很容易实现结构—土相互作用分析。这种拱坝自由场分析方法便于工程技术人员掌握与应用。

参 考 文 献

[1] 中美拱坝抗震学术讨论会论文集.北京:万国学术出版社,1987

[2] Earthquake Engineering for Concrete Dames: Design, *Performance and Research Needs*. National Academy Press, Washington, D.C.1990

[3] Clough R W, Penzien J. *Dynamics of structures*. McGraw-Hill, 1975

[4] Nowak P S, Hall J F. *Arch dam response to non-uniform seismic input*. J. of Engrg. Mech. ASCE, 1990, 116(1)

[5] 陈厚群,侯顺载,王均.拱坝自由场地震输入和反应.地震工程与工程振动,1990,10(2)

[6] 赵崇斌,张楚汉,张光斗.用映射动力无限元求解地基中三维波动问题.中国科学(A),1988(10)

[7] 林皋,关飞.用边界元法研究地震波在不规则地形处的散射问题.大连理工大学学报,1990,30(2)

[8] Dasgupta G, Chopra K. *Dynamic stiffness matrices for viscoelastic half planes*. J. of Engrg. Mech. ASCE 1979,105(5)

[9] Wolf J P. *Dynamic soil-structure interaction*. Prentice-Hall, 1985

拱坝河谷三维地震动分析

摘　要　应用半无限相似单元模拟远场,通过动量守恒定理确定辐射阻尼,建立了有限元离散近场的三维波动计算模型。采用中心差分法,可形成显式积分格式,整个近场域具有相同的精度与稳定性。对于规则半无限域数值计算结果与理论值符合很好,说明本文模型是有效的。最后,将此应用于半圆形及不规则拱坝河谷,计算结果表明地形影响显著,特别是薄弱山体地震动放大现象严重。

关键词　人工边界　地震波动　拱坝河谷

河谷地震动分析是拱坝结构抗震分析的关键问题。确定河谷地震自由场的实质是三维半无限域动力求解问题,而复杂地形与非均匀地质条件使问题很难求得解析解,因此数值方法得到了广泛应用[1~3]。人们研究结果与工程应用经验表明[3,4],对于复杂场地问题,有限元—人工边界条件的波动仿真是切实可行的方法。妥善处理低频漂移与高频振荡问题后,这套方法具有明显优势[5,6]。本文目的是建立有效三维波动计算模型,并应用于拱坝河谷地震动自由场分析。

本文推导出半无限相似单元静力刚度,单元辐射阻尼应用动量守恒定理确定。结合近场有限元离散模型建立有限元—半无限相似单元计算模型。在地震波输入情况下,对现有有限元程序只需添加上述单元,即可相当简单地通过中心差分法进行波动时程分析。

1　半无限相似单元

近场不规则地形与非均匀地质的有限部分采用有限元离散,远场空间采用半无限相似单元模拟。无限小相似单元法是文献[4]发展的新方法。其基本思想是利用单元节点坐标的比例关系建立半无限空间的动力刚度,如图1所示。无限小相似单元静力刚度展开为

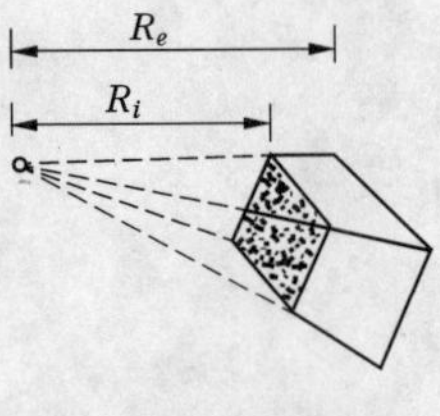

图1　三维相似单元

$$K = \frac{1}{\omega}K_0 + K_1 + \omega K_2 \tag{1}$$

式中:$\omega = (R_e - R_i)/R_i$,是无量纲单元厚度;R_i、R_e 分别为单元内外尺寸;K_i 为相似单元的各阶静力刚度分量,详见文献[4]。

由式(1)可见,当 $\omega \to 0$ 时,与右端第一项相比,后两项可忽略。于是式(1)可表示为

$$K = \frac{1}{\omega}K_0 = \frac{1}{\omega}\begin{bmatrix} E_0 & -E_0 \\ -E_0 & E_0 \end{bmatrix} \tag{2}$$

式中:$E_0 = \int_{-1}^{+1}\int_{-1}^{+1} B^{\mathrm{T}}DB \mid J \mid \mathrm{d}\eta \mathrm{d}\xi$,为无限小相似单元端刚度[4]。

本文选自《水利学报》2000年第9期,作者还有刘天云。

三维相似单元刚度具有线性比例特性

$$K_0^{i+1} = (1+\omega)K_0^i \tag{3}$$

由式(2)和式(3),半无限域单元静力刚度 S_∞ 可表示为无穷个小相似单元级数

$$\begin{aligned} S_\infty^{-1} &= \omega E_0^{-1}[1 + (1+\omega)^{-1} + (1+\omega)^{-2} + (1+\omega)^{-3} + \cdots + (1+\omega)^{-j} + \cdots] \\ &= \omega E_0^{-1}\sum_{i=0}^{\infty}(1+\omega)^{-i} \end{aligned} \tag{4}$$

对于任意 $\omega>0$,上式级数都是收敛的,且当 $\omega\to 0$ 时可得

$$S_\infty = E_0 \tag{5}$$

由此可见,半无限域静力刚度计算只需在其边界处离散进行,问题降低一维,且在空间上具有局部(单元)特性,便于数值分析。式(5)半无限域静力刚度的本质是应用无限长的有限个柱来模拟远场空间。

2 辐射阻尼的确定

半无限空间具有辐射阻尼效应是由于介质的惯性强于弹性的结果,即导致波前的介质不断被扰动,形成波辐射现象[4]。对于给定的介质,波通过介质振动来辐射能量,可以由动量守恒原理来确定其辐射阻尼。

对于垂直截面 $\mathrm{d}A$ 的 P 波,在时间 $\mathrm{d}t$ 内扰动范围的质量为

$$M_0 = \rho\cdot \mathrm{d}A\cdot C_p\mathrm{d}t \tag{6}$$

式中:ρ 为介质的密度;C_p 为纵波波速。

介质 M_0 以速度 $v(t)$ 振动的动量为

$$M_0 v(t) = \rho\cdot \mathrm{d}A\cdot C_p\mathrm{d}t\cdot v(t) \tag{7}$$

此时的冲量定义为 $F(t)\cdot\mathrm{d}t$,则根据动量守恒原理得与速度相关的作用力为

$$F(t) = \rho\cdot \mathrm{d}A\cdot C_p\cdot v(t) \tag{8}$$

上式确定了速度 $v(t)$ 与作用力 $F(t)$ 的关系,即辐射阻尼系数或黏性边界。同理,只需将相应的横波与面波波速代入式(8)即可确定相应的辐射阻尼系数。

根据式(8),综合节点的三个方向速度,单元节点辐射阻尼矩阵定义为

$$C_0 = \rho\cdot \mathrm{d}A\begin{bmatrix} C_p & & \\ & C_s & \\ & & C_s \end{bmatrix} \tag{9}$$

式中:C_s 为横波波速。

3 有限元计算模型

近场进行有限元划分,远域采用具有黏性 C_0 的半无限相似单元模拟。因此,结合这两类单元建立这种计算模型动力平衡方程为

$$M\ddot{u} + C\dot{u} + Ku = P \tag{10}$$

式中:M、C、K 分别是计算模型的质量阵、阻尼阵和刚度阵,且节点黏滞阻尼采用 $c'_i = \alpha m_i$,其中 α 为阻尼系数,m_i 为节点质量;$\ddot{u}$、$\dot{u}$、u 分别为网格节点运动的加速度、速度和

位移向量；P 为外力向量，可以是作用在有限元内部节点的力，亦可以是人工边界节点上的波动输入。

本文采用文献[6]中建议的波动输入方法，即

$$P = E_0 u_f + C_0 \dot{u}_f + \sigma \tag{11}$$

式中：u_f、$\dot{u}_f$ 分别为规则自由场中与半无限相似单元节点相应的位移与速度向量，可以解析地确定；σ 为相应的应力状态。

为了进行波动仿真分析，采用中心差分法显式格式为

$$\left(\frac{1}{\Delta t^2}m_i + \frac{1}{\Delta t}c_i\right)u_{ij}^{t+\Delta t} = p_{ij}^t - r_{ij}^t + \frac{2}{\Delta t^2}m_i u_{ij}^t - \left(\frac{1}{\Delta t^2}m_i - \frac{1}{2\Delta t}c_i\right)u_{ij}^{t-\Delta t} \tag{12}$$

式中：下标 i 表示节点，j 表示位移方向；Δt 为时间积分步长。

由于半无限相似单元及辐射阻尼具有空间局部特性，计算节点恢复力 r_{ij} 时只是单元级的计算。另外，式(12)为显式格式，当满足数值积分稳定性条件的时空步长时，内点与边界点计算是同等稳定的，不会发生低频漂移与高频振荡发散现象，非常适应地震波长时间分析。

4　规则半无限空间

对于二维问题，黏弹性人工边界(或双渐进人工边界)的精度已有详尽的分析[4,6]。为了研究本文三维计算模型的效果，下面仅以 SH 面波入射规则半无限空间为例，分析波以不同方位角和倾角的入射情况。P 与 SV 波入射的精度效果与 SH 波相当。

图 2 所示截取的有限体积尺寸为 175m×175m×87.5m，有限元网格尺寸为 17.5m×17.5m×17.5m，采用八节点的等参块元，半无限相似单元为四节点单元。介质参数为：$C_p = 2\,600.0$m/s，$C_s = 1\,500.0$m/s，波速比 $\mu = 0.25$。入射的 SH 波及入射状况见图 2，时间积分步长取 $\Delta t = 0.005$s，不考虑材料阻尼，当波以不同方位角 ϕ 与倾角 θ 入射时，可根据半空间弹性动力学解析确定波场中任一点的波动状态依此检验计算模型的精度。图 3～图 5 是波以不同方位角与入射角入射时，有限模型 4 种不同部位节点的位移时程曲线。

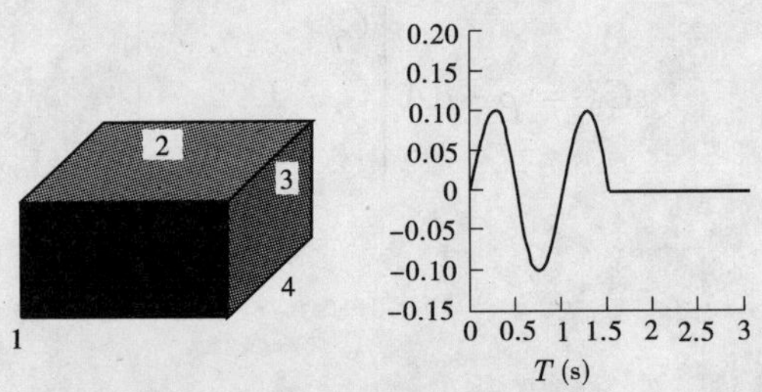

图 2　半无限空间有限体模型及输入

图中三种曲线是节点的位移，三种点标为本文计算结果。图 3 是垂直入射的情况，只有 v 单方向水平位移，具有放大现象且与精确解吻合很好；节点 2 与节点 3 略有行波延迟现象。图 4 是倾角、方位角都是 30°时的情况，由于方位角的作用，水平方向有 u 与 v

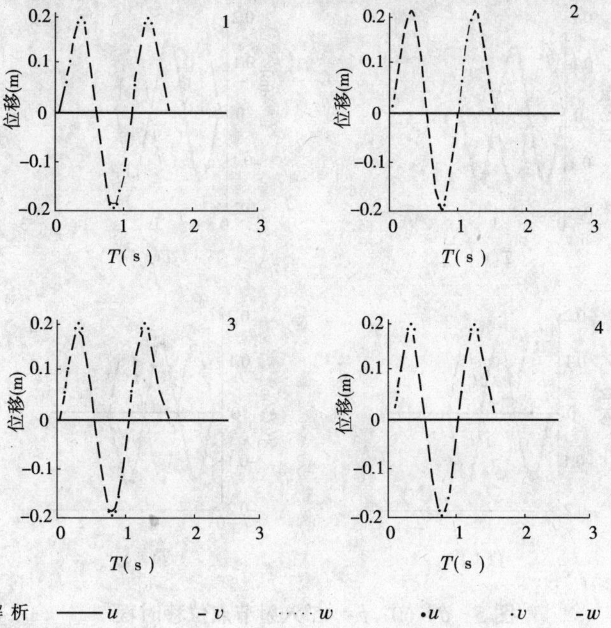

图 3 $\theta=0°$,$\phi=0°$入射节点位移时程

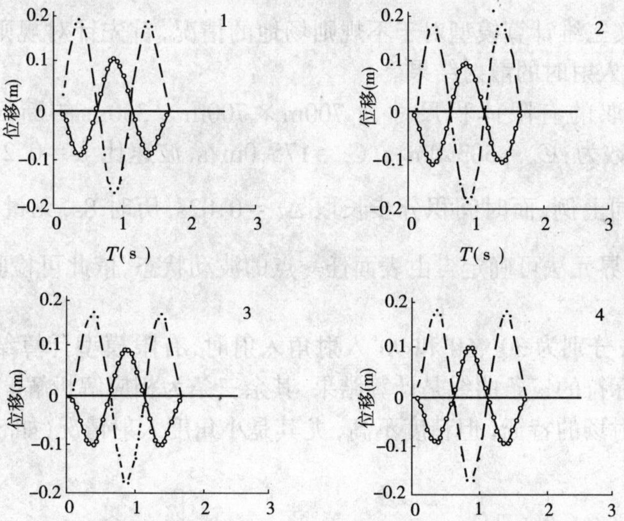

图 4 $\theta=30°$,$\phi=30°$入射节点位移时程

两种位移,且都与解析解吻合。图 5 是入射角与方位角分别为 60°与 45°时情况,这时两水平位移相等,仍然没有竖向位移。总之,不论入射 SH 波以任何方位角与倾角入射,节点位移向量计算结果都与精确解符合得很好;另一方面,在入射波结束时没有振荡现象。这说明本文采用的黏弹性边界即黏性半无限相似单元对于波的透射是很有效的。

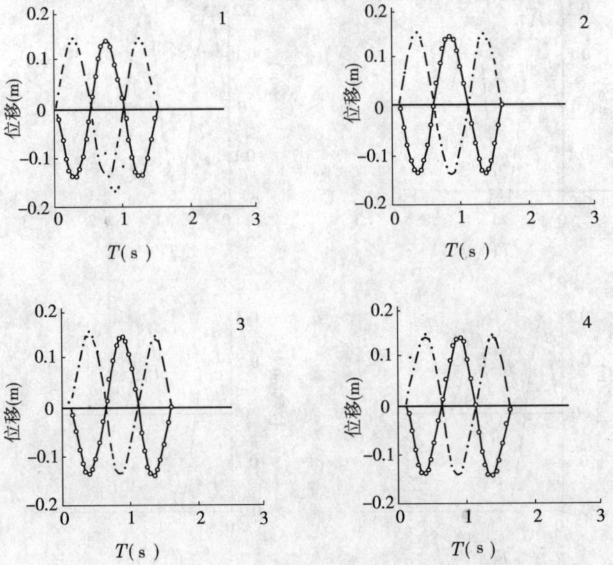

图 5　$\theta = 60°$，$\phi = 45°$入射节点位移时程

5　半圆形河谷地震散射

为了研究本文三维计算模型对于不规则场地的情况，首先针对规则半圆形河谷分析 SH 波以不同倾角入射时的散射结果。

图 6 所示截取的有限体积尺寸为 700m × 700m × 350m 的断面，半圆半径 $a = 175.0$m。介质参数为：$C_p = 303.0$m/s，$C_s = 175.0$m/s，波速比 $\mu = 0.25$。有限元网格尺寸及入射波状况同上例，而时间积分步长取 $\Delta t = 0.02$s，历时 8s，无量纲频率 $\eta = \dfrac{\omega a}{\pi c_s} = 2.0$。根据间接边界元法可确定自由表面任一点的波动状态，依此可检验三维计算模型的精度[7,8]。

图 7 是 SH 波分别为 30°、60°和 90°入射角入射时，有限模型计算结果幅值与精确解的比较。其中带标符的三条曲线是计算结果，其余三条为相应解析解。由图可见，计算模型基本能体现散射场的特征，但精度不高，尤其是小角度入射情况(如 30°角)。这可能有

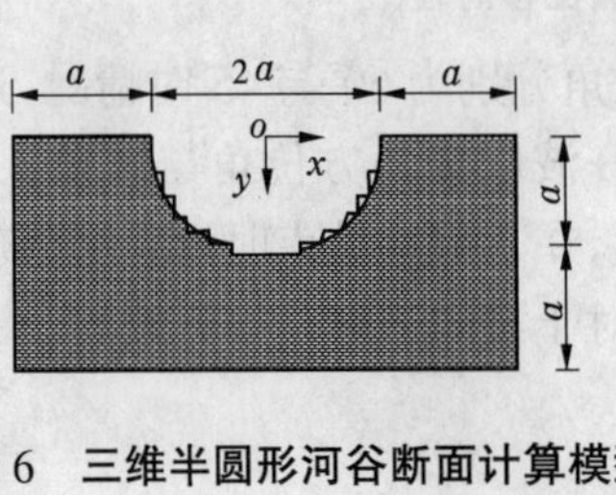

图 6　三维半圆形河谷断面计算模型

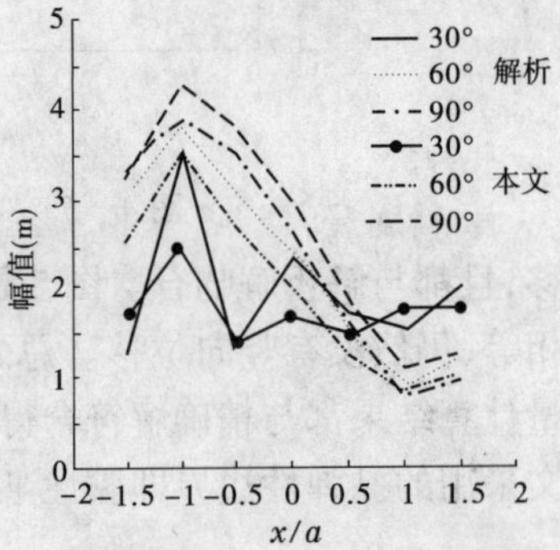

图 7　半圆形河谷表面散射辐射

两方面原因：①由于有限元离散比较粗糙，没能充分体现半圆形状以及幅值曲率变化大的情况；②取有限体的尺寸太小，目前仅为两倍半圆范围。如何进一步验证，困难是计算效率问题。

6　不规则拱坝河谷的地震响应

采用有限元与黏弹性边界计算模型，目的是计算不规则自由场的地震反应，尤其能考虑各种河谷地形与地质情况，对于建高坝极为重要。新疆石门子拱坝河谷，两岸山体极不规则，尤其左坝肩小，山体薄弱，是抗震研究的重点。

本文采用图8所示的河谷模型，其尺寸为490m×280m×210m，有限元网格尺寸，时间积分步长与介质参数同前例，材料阻尼5%，以新疆乌恰地震记录（取幅值5%）作为SH波输入。由于坝址附近断裂带比较明确，因此取入射波方位角 $\phi=11°$。下面对不同倾角入射情况，计算河谷建基面中五个典型节点的位移地震响应时程，如图9～图11所示。由图可见，计算结果有几个明显特点：首先，虽然地震波长时间激励，节点响应却稳定性很好，没有漂移与高频振荡现象；其次，不同节点的位移响应明显不同，呈现出不规则地形对地震波输入的严重影响，散射出竖向位移，尤其是河谷左岸山体比谷底与右岸放大效应显著，且竖向位移也很突出；第三，同规则半空间一样，SH波对于入射倾角的变化不敏感，这是无量纲频率很小的结果，这可能是SH波的特点。

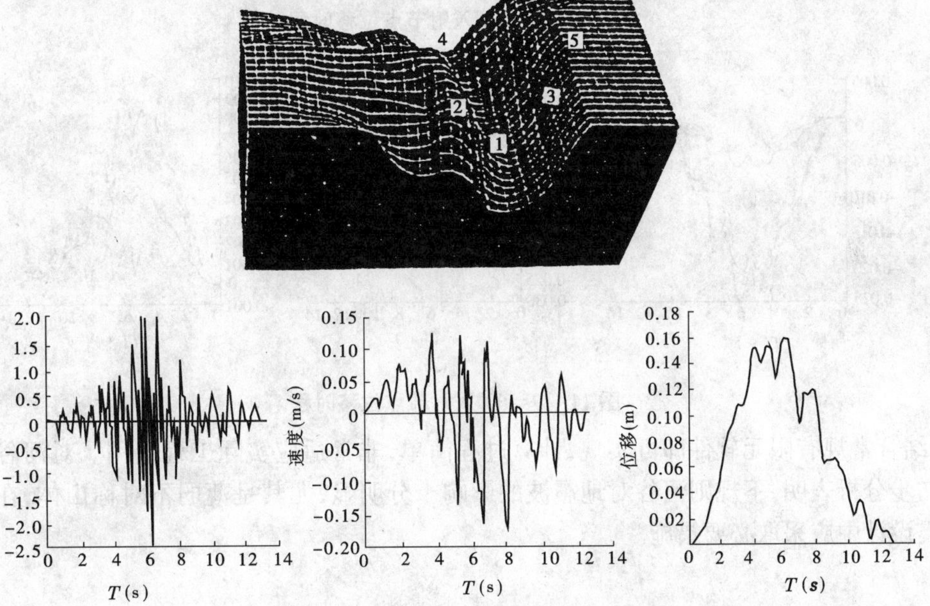

图8　三维拱坝河谷模型及输入时程

7　结语

本文计算结果表明，采用有限元与黏性半无限相似单元计算模型研究河谷地震波动问题是十分有效的，尤其在稳定性方面能得到保证。本文三维波动计算模型物理概念明

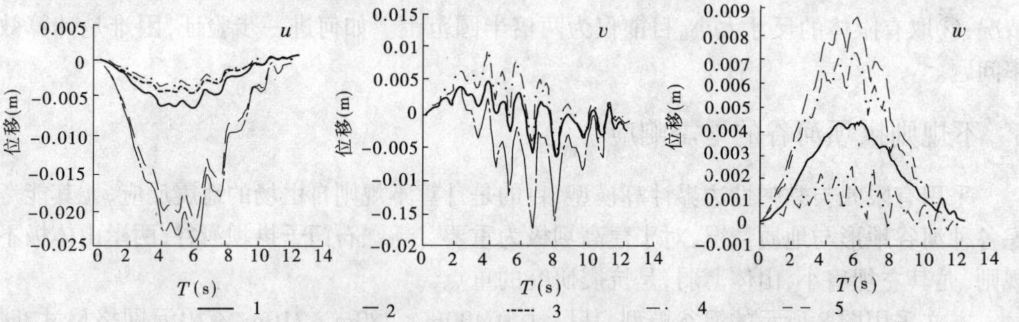

图 9　$\theta=0°$入射节点位移时程

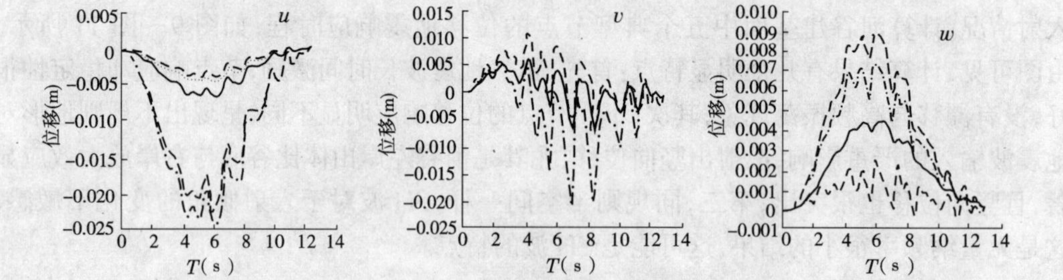

图 10　$\theta=30°$入射节点位移时程

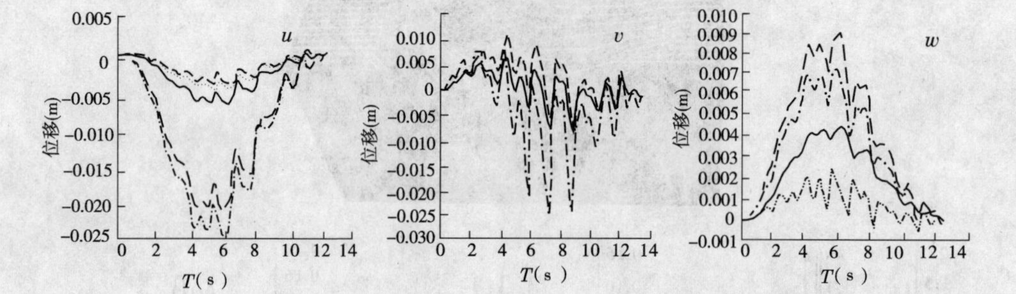

图 11　$\theta=60°$入射节点位移时程

确，结合常规有限元软件即可实现，计算过程简单，非常适应实际工程应用。对河谷地震动初步分析表明，不规则河谷对地震波的影响十分明显，尤其是薄弱不对称山体，在工程抗震设计中应采取必要措施。

参 考 文 献

[1] 廖振鹏. 工程波动理论导引. 北京：科学出版社，1996

[2] 林皋，张楚汉，王光纶. 地下结构与水坝动力学. 现代力学与科技进步，1997(8)：124～238

[3] 陈厚群. 当前我国水工抗震中的主要问题和发展动态. 振动工程学报，1997，10(3)：253～257

[4] Wolf J P, Song Ch M. *Finite-element modelling of unbounded media*. John Wily & Sons Lid, England,

1996
[5] 杜修力,陈厚群,侯顺载.拱坝—地基系统的三维非线性地震反应分析.水利学报,1997(8):7~14
[6] 刘晶波,吕颜东.结构—地基动力相互作用问题分析的一种直接方法.土木工程学报,1998,31(3):55~64
[7] Sanchez-Sesma F J, Rosenblueth E. *Ground motion at canyon of arbitrary shape under incident SH waves*. EESD,1979,7:441~450
[8] Trifunac M D. *Scattering of plane SH waves by a semi-cylindrical canyon*. EESD, 1973,1:267~281

碾压混凝土拱坝设人工短缝的应力释放及止裂作用

摘　要　大仓面碾压混凝土拱坝横缝少,整体性好,仓面准备工作量少,浇筑工艺简化,施工速度快,省水泥和温控措施,但施工期内外温差约束强,运行期均匀温降及温差应力大。拱结构研究表明:在上游坝肩拉力区设人工折缝,将折缝缝端置于低应力区,下游面拱冠设径向短缝,可以大大减少或消除温度和水压引起的拉力;从近缝两侧有限元节点位移差直接求得缝端应力强度因子,和缝端止裂措施组合韧性比较,可以保证人工构造缝的稳定。该设计已用于碾压混凝土工程,实测表明,在超高水位下运行时人工短缝张开小于1mm,止裂措施后实测应变小于37个微应变,止裂效果好,人工缝保持稳定。

关键词　碾压混凝土拱坝　人工短缝　应力释放　断裂控制

大仓面碾压混凝土拱坝减少了仓面准备工作,简化浇筑工艺,大大加快施工速度[1]。碾压混凝土拱坝虽然水化热温升较常态混凝土低,但冷却水管和碾压工艺相互干扰,少用或不用冷却水管,后期温度下降仍带来拱坝大面积受拱向拉力。通常拱坝尤其薄拱坝即使人工冷却到稳定温度场后灌浆,运行期冬春季温度下降仍受拉力,夏秋季温度上升加大拱座推力,由于温度通过变形产生荷载。因此,人工缝提供自由变形面,对释放温度应力最敏感,其实混凝土固化收缩和干缩也会引起类似的拉伸体积力,水压作用下小曲率拱或深梁在固端上游面引起拉应力集中,它加大了温度荷载在上游拱座的拉力[2]。在拉力区设人工短缝可以大大削减拱坝拉力,将难以确定位置的拉力区裂缝限制在有上游止水和下游止裂的人工短缝上。

1　拱座上游人工短缝及拱冠下游区设人工缝对拱坝宏观边缘应力的改进

某碾压混凝土拱坝上游温降17℃,下游温降13℃,拱厚25m,跨度180m,上游面水压80m水头。水压加温降荷载时平面拱主应力如图1所示。σ_1 上游拱座拉应力达4.0MPa,下游拱冠拉力达2.5MPa;σ_2 下游拱座压应力达-7.0MPa,上游拱冠压力达-6.0MPa。在上游拱座切缝深2.5m时,水压加温降荷载平面拱主应力如图2所示。由 σ_1 分布可见上游拱座拉力区几乎消失,下游拱冠拉力也下降为0.5MPa,但下游拱座压力仍保持-7.0MPa(因为它主要由水压荷载引起)。可见,上游拱座设缝可以大量削减拱座拉力区。

拱座下游设中央径向缝[3],缝长10m,可使缝端应力强度因子下降到0.4MPa·$m^{1/2}$(混凝土断裂韧性)以下(如图3所示),也可以在缝端设止裂结构而减少缝的长度。

由图4可见下游拱冠设10m缝使拉应力区向缝的两侧转移,拉力下降到1.5MPa,拱座上下游应力不变。继续在拱冠下游两个拉力区设3m缝,拉力可下降到0.5MPa以下。

本文选自《水利学报》2002年第5期,作者还有谢树南、李鹏辉、张富德。

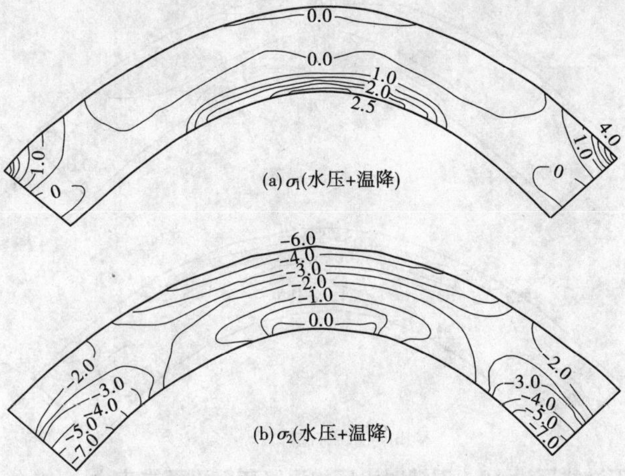

图 1 水压加温降荷载时平面拱主应力 （单位:MPa）

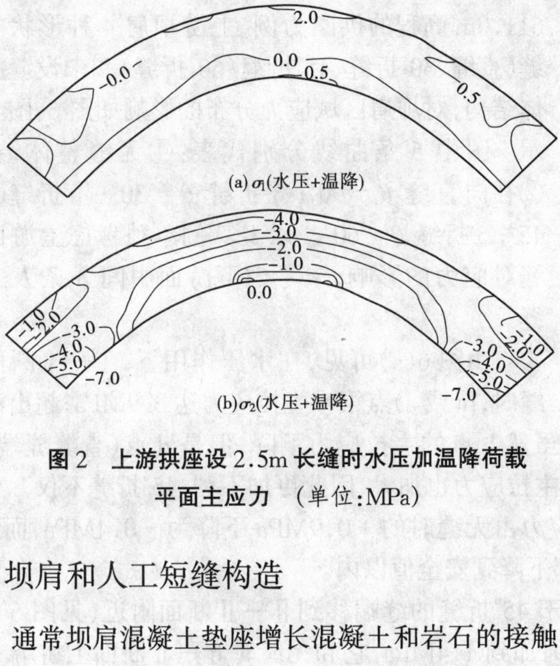

图 2 上游拱座设 2.5m 长缝时水压加温降荷载平面主应力 （单位:MPa）

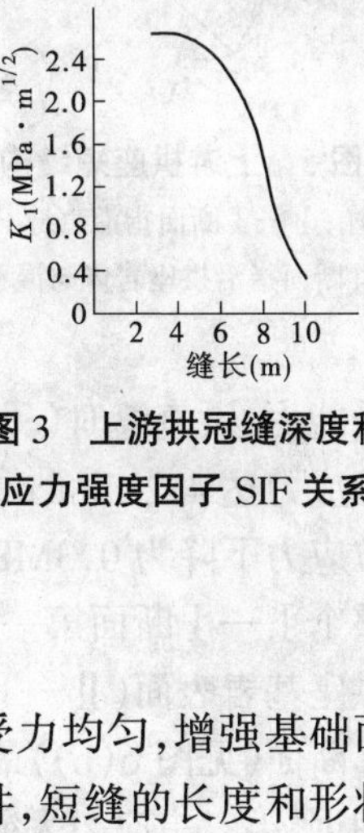

图 3 上游拱冠缝深度和应力强度因子 SIF 关系

2 坝肩和人工短缝构造

通常坝肩混凝土垫座增长混凝土和岩石的接触面使岩石受力均匀,增强基础面抗剪能力,也增加上游抗绕渗能力,便于埋设拱座人工短缝的预埋件,短缝的长度和形状改变有效传力断面,可以改变水压作用下主应力的传力方向,使外形上便于碾压施工的无倒悬,对小曲率的单曲拱坝起到加大曲率的双曲拱受力的作用。设置短缝不超过坝厚的1/4,以免加大坝肩剪应力。人工短缝是构造缝(不是温度诱导缝),需要控制缝端断裂能以防止缝延伸。上游坝肩人工短缝使坝肩上游部位的拉力区转移到内部缝端,用折缝将缝端转入低应力区,也减少缝和内部主拉应力方向的交角,以削减缝端断裂能,在缝端区埋设抗裂能力高的材料,以增大韧性,阻止裂缝发展。拱冠下游短缝用木板隔成,伸入坝体,缝端设止裂材料以减少缝深。

某碾压混凝土薄拱坝典型拱圈拱座设缝构造示意如图 5 所示。上游坝面人工短缝设

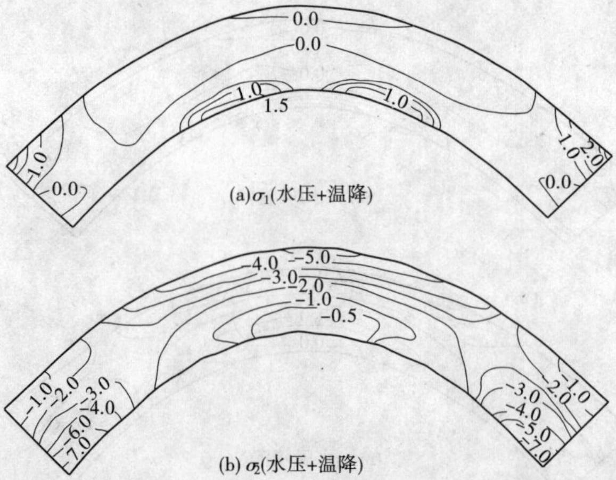

(a)σ_1(水压+温降)

(b) σ_2(水压+温降)

图 4　下游拱冠设 10m 深缝时水压加温降荷载平面主应力　(单位:MPa)

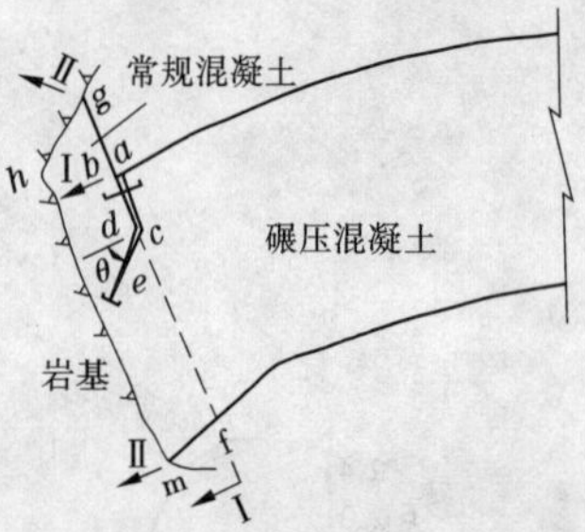

图 5　上游拱座短缝构造示意

注:Ⅰ—Ⅰ断面指沿直缝 bdf 断面;

Ⅱ—Ⅱ断面指沿拱座岩体与混凝土 ghm 断面

置止水,缝内有排水管,不计缝内水压作用。以 611.0m 高程的拱圈为例,上游坝肩 4 种形状的短缝(直缝、30°折缝、45°折缝、60°折缝)和未设缝的整体结构,对坝肩区域应力分布的影响如图 6、图 7 所示。图中 5 条曲线分别代表:①无缝整体结构;②径向直缝 $\theta=90°$;③折缝 $\theta=30°$;④折缝 $\theta=45°$;⑤折缝 $\theta=60°$。以上算例单独考虑上游面短缝对应力的影响,未考虑下游面中间 3 条人工短缝。

由图 6(a)可见,在水压作用下,Ⅰ—Ⅰ断面无缝时,b(或 a)点第一主拉应力达 3.9MPa,超出混凝土承受能力;设直缝时(c、d 点重合),虽然 b 点的主拉应力下降,但是 d 点(直缝缝端)最大主拉应力达 4.2MPa,d 和 f 之间的主拉应力也加大,因此更加不利;45°折缝不仅 b 点第一主拉应力下降为 0.3MPa,第二主应力由无缝时的 +0.9MPa 下降为 −0.4MPa,而且 d 点及整个Ⅰ—Ⅰ断面第一主拉应力都下降到安全值以内。

拱座基岩表面(Ⅱ—Ⅱ断面),由于 45°折缝的缝端移到Ⅱ—Ⅱ断面附近(见图 5),沿Ⅱ—Ⅱ断面(见图 6(b))最大主拉应力加到 1.4MPa,它和无缝时Ⅱ—Ⅱ断面上游端 g 点应力相近,第二主应力无缝时最大为 0.2MPa,与 45°折缝的 0.34MPa 很相近。水压作用 45°折缝虽然对Ⅱ—Ⅱ断面最大应力影响小,但它可大大改善Ⅱ - Ⅱ断面的应力分布,使最大主拉应力由上游面转移到缝端(e 点)附近,使上游面(g 点)在无人工短缝时的最大主拉应力 1.4MPa 降低到 45°折缝时的 0.5MPa,防止在上游面结合处开裂。

综合考虑施工期温度徐变应力以及从施工末期温度下降到运行期变温场的应力(3 月份拉应力最大),由于内部总降温值较大,拉应力场加大,折缝缝端拉应力集中也加剧。由图 7(a)所示的Ⅱ—Ⅱ断面应力可见,45°折缝缝端区最大温度主拉应力达 1.02MPa,和无缝时的1.0MPa 相近,第二主拉应力由无缝时的 0.3MPa 增大到 45°折缝的 0.75MPa。坝肩设置短缝仍对消除温降所带来的拱坝上游面离坝肩 a 点 10m 宽的拉应力有明显作用(见图 7(b))。

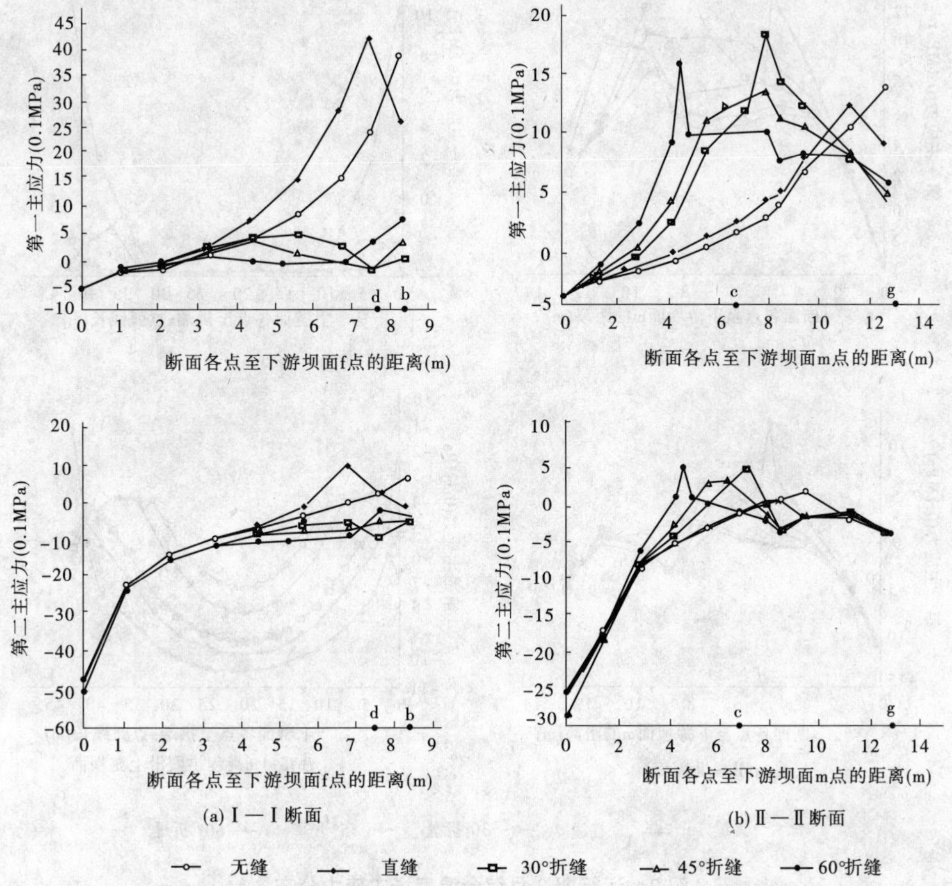

图 6 水压作用下主应力分布

3 下游坝面人工短缝对拱坝应力的影响

在拱坝下游拱向拉力区开 3 条深度为 1～2m 的径向缝,在水压作用下,缝深度影响大,下游坝面第一主拉应力值由无缝时最大的 2MPa 降至缝深 2m 时的 0.5MPa 以下(见图 8(a)),径向断面的应力分布表明,最大主拉应力区内移,最大值由无缝时的 1.6MPa 下降为 1.2MPa(见图 8(b))。通常下游中部缝结构(包括缝间距和缝深)对应力的影响是局部的,对整体应力分布的影响不大。拱坝下游面拱冠区设缝,主要对减小下游拱冠区拉应力有利。

4 缝端应力强度因子计算和止裂

应力集中区,尤其缝端计算应力值在相对比较时才有意义,缝端的破坏能可由离缝端已知点坐标及其位移场(或应力场)直接求得应力强度因子[4]。通常用缝面结点位移差计算断裂能精度较好。某工程在缝端单元尺寸减小到 0.5m,环绕缝端的 4 个三维等参元

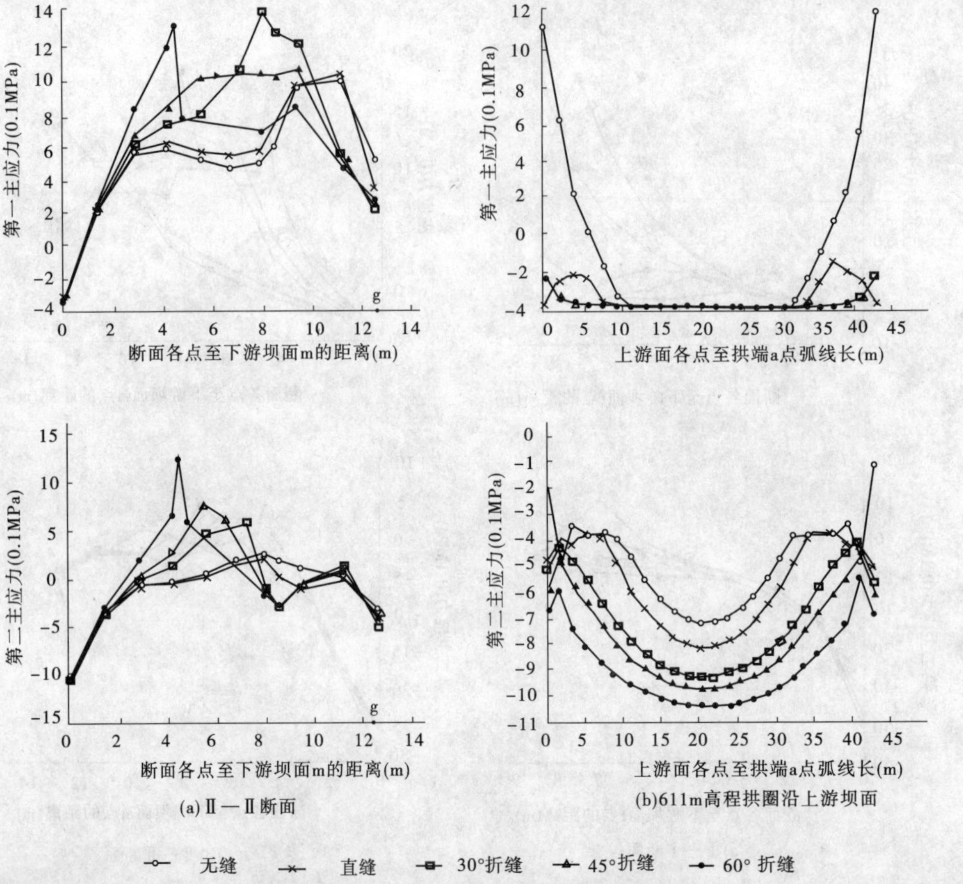

图7　运行期3月综合温度场主应力分布

中,取含缝的上、下单元缝面结点的位移值,可以求得 K_{I}、K_{II}、K_{III}。水压外力断裂仍用应力强度因子,温度断裂用稳定的应变强度因子按后期弹模折算后叠加,不同高程组合应力强度因子为 0.50~1.80MN/$m^{3/2}$,接近三级配混凝土断裂韧性。人工短缝可用槽钢增强止裂,用三点弯曲梁测定 3cm 小槽钢止裂增强作用已经很明显。

断裂试验试件的长×宽×高为 850mm×100mm×200mm(见图9),配合比如表1所示,水泥为 525# 硅酸盐水泥,采用规程 408—80“混凝土拌和物室内拌和方法”。

表1　混凝土材料配合比　(单位:kg/m^3)

水	水泥	粉煤灰	石粉	砂	小石(5~20mm)	中石(20~40mm)	DH_9 溶液	JG_4 溶液
120	153	65	83	607	693	693	1.74	6.25

注:①二级配,小石:中石=50:50;②DH_9 溶液浓度为 1%,JG_4 溶液浓度为 10%;③粉煤灰除注明外均为Ⅱ级灰。

由表2可见,龄期增长,梁的承载力和抗裂能力提高,4cm 和 6cm 缝高(有 3cm 小槽钢时)影响不大。有槽钢比不设槽钢的梁最大承载力大 25%~32%。断裂能大 23%~

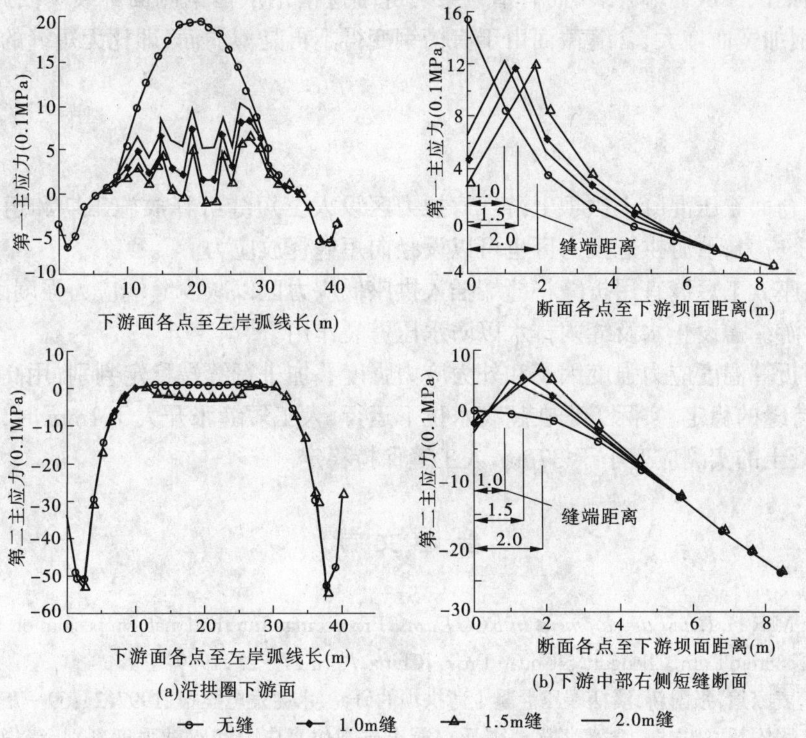

图 8 下游中部短缝水压作用下的主应力分布

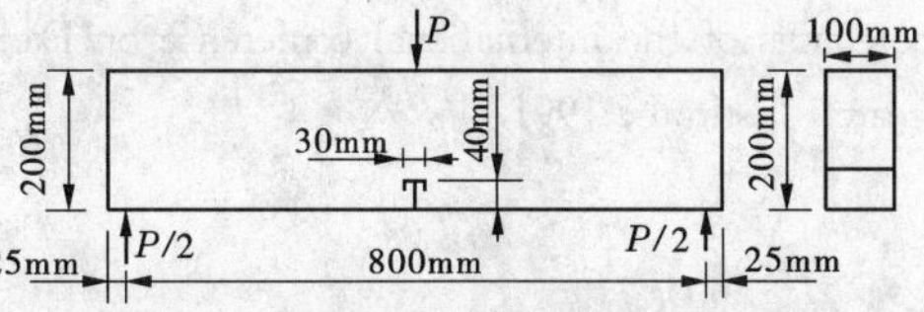

图 9 带槽钢三点弯曲梁试件尺寸

表 2 三点弯曲梁试验结果

试件编号	缝长 a_0 (cm)	缝长/梁高 a_0/ω	龄期 (d)	槽钢	P_{max} (kN)	C_F (N/m)	K_{IC} ($MN/m^{3/2}$)
A1	4	0.2	44	有	7.369 9	313.6	
A2	4	0.2	44	无	6.332 6	256.7	0.66
B1	4	0.2	24	有	6.808 6	247.6	
C1	6	0.3	35	有	4.270	207.6	
C2	6	0.3	35	无	3.245	99.9	0.44
D1	6	0.3	44	有	6.374	170.7	
D2	6	0.3	44	无	5.075	148.3	0.69
D3	6	0.3	44	无	4.797	131.1	0.65

30%,无槽钢试件从缝端开裂,而有槽钢梁裂缝绕过槽钢从槽钢侧面开裂。因此,实际增强将随槽钢加宽而增大,含缝截面由于有槽钢变得不再是薄弱面,即比无短缝的断面抵抗能力更强。

5 结语

(1)大仓面碾压混凝土拱坝上游坝肩拉力区设人工短缝可释放施工期和运行期温度应力和水压应力,下游拱冠拉力区也可以设径向短缝释放应力。

(2)拱座人工短缝宜用折缝将缝端插入拱座低应力区以减少缝端应力强度因子,防止缝延伸,上游缝需设止水及缝内排水以防水压劈裂作用。

(3)用折算温度应力强度因子和外力应力强度叠加进行缝端稳定判别,用高韧性材料止裂可保持缝的稳定,实际工程在超高水位下运行,人工短缝张开大于1mm时,采取止裂措施后混凝土的实测应变小于37μm,人工缝保持稳定。

参 考 文 献

[1] Dunstan M R H. *Latest development in RCC Dams*. Proceedings International symposium on Roller Compacted Concrete Dam. Chengdu,SiChuan Prov.,China. April 21～25,1999

[2] 刘光廷,麦家煊,张国新.溪柄碾压混凝土薄拱坝的研究.水力发电学报,1997(2):69～75

[3] 刘光廷,张国新,刘志辉.含灌浆横缝碾压混凝土拱坝仿真应力和双轴强度判别.清华大学学报,1996,36(1):3～19

[4] Guangting Liu. *Study on the curved and branch cracks in massive concrete structures*. V. Saouma, R. Dunger, D. Morris, Proceedings of the international conference on Dam Fracture. Boulder, Colorado USA, Electric Power Research Institute, 1991

石门子碾压混凝土拱坝温度场实测与仿真计算

摘　要　碾压混凝土坝的非稳定温度场是进行仿真应力计算和设计的基础。根据理论分析和数值计算，分析各热学参数和非热学参数对非稳定温度场的影响。通过对石门子工程（在建）进行工程实际监测，取得了一些高程测点实测温度变化过程，并与仿真计算结果相比较。为模拟混凝土中粉煤灰后期放热，提出双 e 曲线模型，使仿真计算结果更符合实际。按所提出的方法进行非稳定温度场的计算预测，从而对大坝后期浇筑作指导，具有较好的工程应用价值。

关键词　碾压混凝土坝　非稳定温度场　工程实测　热学参数

塔西河水利枢纽工程位于新疆维吾尔自治区昌吉州玛纳斯县西南塔西河中游"石门"峡谷段，峡谷长约 350m，河谷呈 U 形，谷底宽 80m，布置 109m 高的碾压混凝土拱坝。

坝址地区冬季寒冷，月平均气温在 0℃ 以下长达 5 个月，夏季气温最高达 38℃；工地日变幅常达 15～19℃。这不仅缩短了混凝土的良好浇筑时间，而且还给混凝土温控带来较大困难。

面对恶劣的自然条件，在快速施工方面，用低热混凝土连续大仓面浇筑兼用保温与降温措施；在结构方面，在坝肩设人工短缝、拱冠设中缝以释放拱坝温度应力，并在拱坝上游早期降温区设"铰点"，使拱坝在拱向温度收缩的同时能保证平面拱向整体作用[1,2]。为提前蓄水提供安全保障。

1　参数分析

影响坝体温度场的因素有很多，其中主要有混凝土浇筑层厚度、边界气温及浇筑间隙期内部温控措施、混凝土入仓温度、混凝土绝热温升 θ_0 及混凝土放热系数 m 等，见表 1[3]。各部分参数作用耦合在一起。

表 1　材料热学参数

β (kJ/(m²·d·K))	c (kJ/(kg·K))	α (m²/h)	θ_0 (℃)	m
0.80	0.94	0.004 1	17	0.16

注：表中各参数取值均来自工程实测资料，β 为表面散热系数，c 为比热容，α 为导温系数。

1.1　混凝土厚度的影响

温度实测表明，边界的影响在 1m 范围之内较显著。如果浇筑间歇期小于 6～10d，超过 2m 深度处的混凝土温度受外界影响很小，所以单从温度场来看，在浇筑过程中，将每次累积层厚度定为小于 2m，对散热有利。为了减少层间间隔，加快施工进度及考虑到模板工艺，石门子工程采用 3m 浇筑层。

本文选自《清华大学学报（自然科学版）》2002 年第 4 期，作者还有胡昱、王恩志、陈凤岐、高虎。

1.2　边界条件

边界条件变化有两种:散热系数的变化以及边界气温值的变化。第一种变化影响较大,可以说是改变了热交换条件,如固气交换变成固液交换等;第二种情况较普遍,如周围空气温度上升、下降等。

1.2.1　散热系数变化的影响

本文比较的两种散热条件:一种是用河水养护(比初始边界气温低 8℃,初始边界气温为 15℃);一种是靠边界空气散热(散热系数 β 取 0.8,初始边界气温为 15℃,气温降温幅度为 -1℃/d)。计算条件:入仓温度 15℃,水化热温升 17℃,混凝土放热系数 0.16。计算结果为:12d 后,在 1m 深处,河水冷却条件下,混凝土温度要多降低 4℃左右。

1.2.2　气温值变化

石门子工程所在山区气温日变幅较大。图 1 为 ±9℃时混凝土温度场的变化图。可以看出,日变幅对后期混凝土温度场影响较小,1m 深处混凝土只有 0.2℃的变幅,即使在 0.5m 深处也只有 0.5℃左右的变化。不管是白天还是夜晚对最后结果影响不大。但由于夜间周围气温较低,对骨料散热有利;再加上在运输路上及入仓后的混凝土不受太阳直射,所以其入仓温度比白天要低,也就降低了混凝土浇筑块温度。所以,在实际工程施工中,一般在夜间浇筑混凝土。

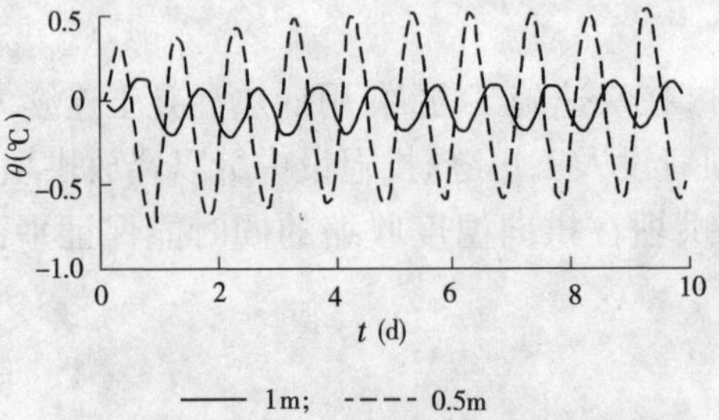

图 1　日变幅 9℃温度场变化(散热系数 0.8)

1.3　入仓温度

其他条件不变,入仓温度提高 1℃,6d 后在 1m 深处,仍维持升高 0.8℃,12d 后仍有 0.6℃。而在周围气温变化不大的情况下,通过浇筑面散热,6d 才散热 1.4℃。也就是说,只要入仓温度高 2℃,由 6d 散热的效果就会被抵消。石门子工程属于快速施工间歇期较短的情况,因此必须注意混凝土入仓温度的控制。

1.4　混凝土的绝热温升

由于混凝土绝热温升曲线常用表达式为 $\theta=\theta_0(1-e^{-mt})$,绝热温升 θ_0 的影响是成比例关系。若放热系数不变,取 0.16,边界为固气热交换,则绝热温升增加 1℃,在混凝土 3m 深处,混凝土温度值增加 1℃在右;1m 深处 6d 为0.5℃,12d 为 0.60℃。

通常水泥绝热温升 e 曲线拟合,曲线前期值上升较快,后期(1 个月左右)持平。而在工程中用的粉煤灰后期水化发热,拟合采用双 e 曲线更好。图 2 是我国南方某一工程混凝土绝热温升测试结果及曲线模拟,可以看出,采用双 e 曲线更能符合实际情况[4]。

1.5　放热系数

为了研究混凝土放热系数对混凝土温度的影响,在计算中,放热系数 m 分别取 0.16

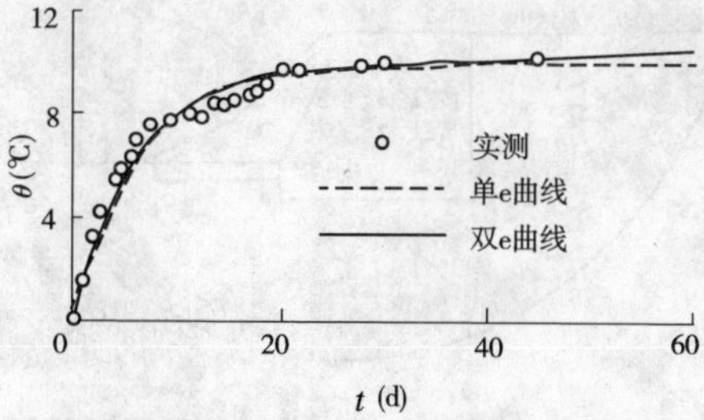

图 2　混凝土绝热温升测试拟合图

和0.32。其他计算条件相同,即边界散热系数取 0.8,浇筑块入仓温度 0℃,绝热温升 17℃。计算表明,混凝土的放热系数大时,早期放热快,所以在一定时间歇期内散出热量也多,12d 后,1m 深处,放热系数 0.32 要比放热系数 0.16 散热多,达 1.3℃。

1.6　层间间隙时间的影响

边界气温升高、降低速率假设为±1℃/d。表 2 中所列温度下降值均是相对于混凝土在绝热温升条件下正常温升的差值。

表 2　各种边界条件下 1m 深处混凝土温度变化

间隙时间(d)	温度变化(℃)			
	气温升高	气温不变	气温降低	河水冷却
6	−1.0	−1.4	−1.8	−6.0
12	−1.7	−4.3	−6.9	−10.9

注:河水冷却时,河水温度比混凝土入仓温度低 8℃。

由表 2 可以看出,如果外界日平均气温上升,又无冷却措施,6d 后浇筑第二层和 12d 后浇筑第二层两者相差不大,不到 1℃左右。所以,对这种情况间歇期的降温效果不大。

但如果日平均气温不变或降低,12d 后要比 6d 后散热效果好得多,即以时间代价换取混凝土温度值的降低。

如果既想温度下降快,又不想时间拖得太长,就只能用河水冷却或其他冷却方式。

为减少层间缺陷,简化工艺,加高模板,加快施工进度,石门子工程采用 3m 浇筑混凝土,间歇期间散热采用低温河水浸泡方式。

2　三维仿真数值计算

图 3 是石门子碾压混凝土拱坝 1 295m 高程温度计埋设位置图。仿真计算所用边界温度值、混凝土入仓温度以及材料热学参数均是实测资料。因为在实测数据时间段内,大坝没有蓄水,所以计算中不考虑大坝渗流的影响。

根据石门子拱坝实际开挖与浇筑的体形,共计离散为 3 352 个六面体或五面体(过渡)等参单元,4 580 个节点,计算得到施工过程仿真非稳定温度场的累计变化过程[5,6]。

2.1　边界条件

施工期从下往上逐层浇筑混凝土时,上下游边界暴露于大气中。拱坝上游面基坑有上游渗水,所以边界条件为第一类边界条件。由于水是上游天山雪水,所以水温较低

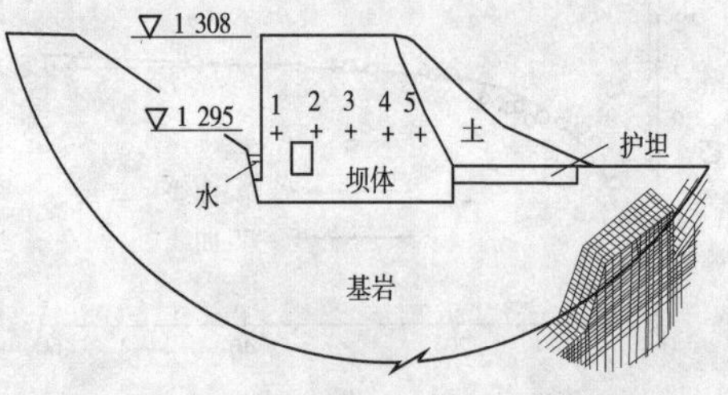

图 3　1 295m 高程温度测点位置图及计算网

(7℃)且变化值不大。拱坝顶部暴露面随浇筑高度上升,依靠自然冷却的碾压混凝土块的温度随气温及辐射热的变化而变化。在早期坝混凝土浇筑过程中,为了施工方便,用土堆了上坝道路,如图 3 所示。土对混凝土散热产生了一定的负面影响,但在严冬中可起一定的保护作用。

2.2　混凝土入仓温度

加高混凝土,实际上可以说是一个新过程的开始。对老混凝土来说,只是改变了边界条件,其初始条件为:老混凝土的当时温度作为初温,还有剩余的没有散发的水化热,也就是在水化热方程中时间参数要减去一个初值;对于新混凝土,其初始温度便是浇筑温度。所以在有限元计算时,用单元温度,即用单元离散混凝土的温度[3,4]。

2.3　混凝土热学参数

由于抗渗性、抗冻耐久性等要求不同,石门子拱坝各部位混凝土配合比也不尽相同。大坝内部三级配混凝土含水泥 60kg、粉煤灰 110kg,θ_0 为 17℃,m 为 0.16;外部抗渗二级配混凝土含水泥 90kg、粉煤灰 110kg,θ_0 为 23℃,m 为 0.32。其中热学参数由本课题组研制的混凝土绝热温升测试仪(同温绝热)测出。该仪器可按照混凝土试验规程,进行长时间混凝土绝热温升曲线跟踪测试。

3　计算预测值与工程实测值的比较

计算和实测的温度变化规律见图 4(a)～图 4(f)。

(1)计算预测与实测的温度过程线的曲线走势和值大小基本一致。走势均有两个高峰期,第一个出现在上面混凝土覆盖之前,第二次出现在覆盖之后。对于覆盖之后,离上下游散热面较近的测点 1 和测点 5 的第二个高峰期的温度比第一次要低,而对于中间散热条件较差的点,情况正好相反,第二次高峰期温度要比第一次高。测点 2 由于离廊道较近,所以其后期温度没有 3、4 测点上升得高;5 号测点因为后期有土覆盖,所以其温度变化形式与 1 号测点也不一致。

(2)从各测点温度计算与实测比较图中不难发现,虽然在前段两条曲线非常符合,但都在后期出现计算值偏低的情况。分析原因正如前文所述,混凝土中含大量活性大的Ⅰ级粉煤灰,其放热比较缓慢,不像水泥那样快,而我们原来计算中采用的公式是单 e 曲线,$\theta=\theta_0(1-e^{-mt})$,难免会有误差。将公式改写成 $\theta=\theta_1(1-e^{-m_1t})+\theta_2(1-e^{-m_2t})$,按试验测定分别计入粉煤灰放热量(525# 水泥 60kg,Ⅰ级粉煤灰 110kg),热学参数如下:θ_1(水泥)15℃,(粉煤灰)6℃,m_1(水泥)0.18,m_2(粉煤灰)0.025。计算结果如图 4(f)所示

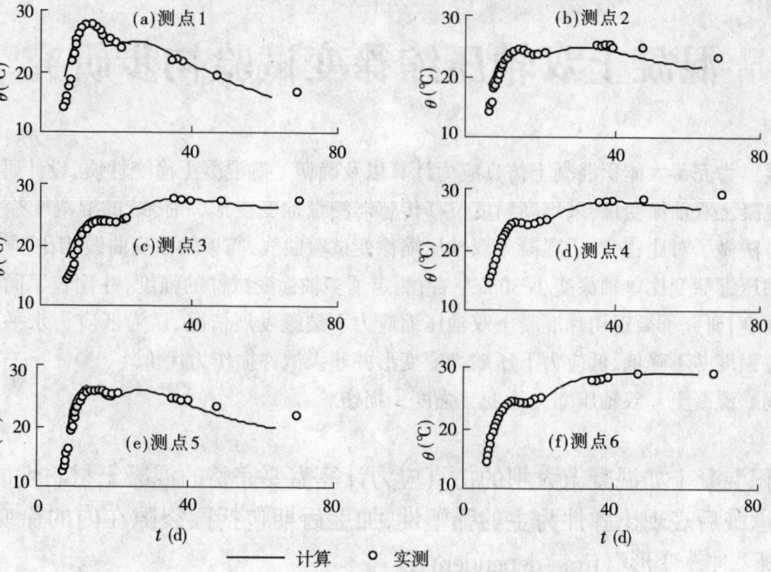

图4 各测点温度计算、实测比较图

(以测点6为例)符合得很好,在温度计算中要注意混凝土的后期放热。

4 结语

本文经过理论分析和数值计算,分析了各热学参数和非热学参数对非稳定温度场的影响。对比实测和仿真计算结果,说明决定计算预测可靠性的关键是热学参数(入仓温度、绝热温升和边界温度等)的正确取值。除需获得工地实际气温变化情况和施工进度,还要正确测试和模拟大坝混凝土的绝热温升曲线。文中为了模拟碾压混凝土中粉煤灰后期放热,采用双e曲线模型,取得较好效果。在大坝设计阶段,能获得准确的仿真温度场,对研究坝体应力分布、调整施工计划及采取温控措施要求,都是很有实际工程价值的。

参考文献

[1] Dunstan M R H. *Recent developments in RCC dams*. Int J Hydropower & Dams, 1999,6(1):40~45

[2] 张国新,刘光廷,刘志辉.整体碾压混凝土拱坝工艺及温度场仿真计算.清华大学学报,1996,36(1):1~7

[3] 刘光廷,邱德隆.含横缝碾压混凝土拱坝的变形和应力重分布.清华大学学报,1996,36(1):20~26

[4] 张富德,薛慧,陈凤岐,等.碾压混凝土坝非稳定温度场计算预测与工程实践的比较.清华大学学报,1998,38(1):75~78

[5] 刘光廷,麦家煊,张国新.溪柄碾压混凝土薄拱坝的研究.水力发电学报,1997,57(2):19~28

[6] ZHENG G R, YANG S C. *Solution of steady periodic heat conduction by the FEM*. Numerical Heat Transfer, 1989, 15: 525~534

混凝土双轴压缩徐变试验初步研究

摘　要　为完善大体积混凝土仿真应力计算以及确切了解混凝土徐变性质，设计研制了机电伺服混凝土双轴徐变仪，采用高精度位移传感器测量徐变变形，和传统的混凝土徐变测量仪器及方法做了对比；获得了混凝土双轴压缩徐变试验曲线，与单轴徐变曲线相比，早龄期混凝土双轴压缩徐变比单轴徐变小30%左右；测定了多轴徐变试件的强度，并比较了同龄期未受力的强度；研究了微观切片混凝土双轴压缩应力下裂缝发展情况，认为低应力水平下压缩徐变试件强度并不降低，低应力下压缩徐变变形并非以试件损伤为代价。

关键词　混凝土　双轴压缩　徐变　强度　损伤

大体积混凝土如混凝土大坝的仿真应力计算需要完整的混凝土材料性能曲线。混凝土在瞬时承载后表现出弹性为主的弹塑性，加上后期包括微裂隙在内的徐变变形成为完整的混凝土"时效变形"(time-dependent)。

目前大体积混凝土仿真应力计算，多轴徐变应力多是根据单轴的试验结果拟合计算参数。通过叠加原理应用于多轴的情况，和实际相差甚远。而国内徐变试验都是单轴型式[1]，操作过程也是人工手动进行，影响试验精度。文献[2]介绍了双轴徐变仪器，将单轴弹簧式拓展到双轴方向，但这会影响到加载时的精度。文献[3]甚至研制过三轴徐变试验机，用油压千斤顶3个方向调整荷载，这十分不方便。另外在测量相对面压板之间的变形时，由于减磨材料的变形会使测量不准。3向加载使得试件没有裸露的表面，无法观测试件的表面变形。为此研制了机电伺服混凝土双轴徐变试验机，实现了微机自动控制记录徐变过程。本文着重研究了双轴压缩应力下混凝土前期受荷(龄期14d)及后期受荷下(龄期60d)的徐变变形行为。

1　徐变试验机性能介绍

混凝土双轴徐变试验机由长春试验机研究所与清华大学水利系共同设计，并由前者开发制造。这是我国第一台混凝土双轴徐变试验机。该机由主机和控制柜两大部分组成(主机如图1所示)。

仪器采用机电伺服机构控制垂直和水平方向的加载，将轮幅式测力传感器放置在试样的一端，分别测量垂直和水平方向的轴向荷载，测量精度为±1%示值(从量程10%开始)；加载能力为垂直方向(压)500kN、水平方向(压)300kN。

变形的测量采用高精度差动式位移传感器，变形测量范围为±5mm，精度为±0.5%满量程，分辨率是1μm。变形测量方式如图2所示。

仪器的水平轴具有特殊的浮动功能，这是为了减少垂直轴与水平轴加载之间的相互影响。在水平轴加载头与压板之间采用滚动连接，滚动摩擦因数 $\mu<2\%$；水平轴加载框架能在水平方向滑动，以消除横向附加力；在传感器一端的压头上还设计了球面支撑，以

本文选自《清华大学学报(自然科学版)》2001第11期，作者还有高虎、陈凤岐。

保持荷载的均匀。机器的压板和试件之间放置有两层聚四氟乙烯减磨材料，以减少压板的局部应力集中。

图 1 混凝土双轴徐变试验机主机

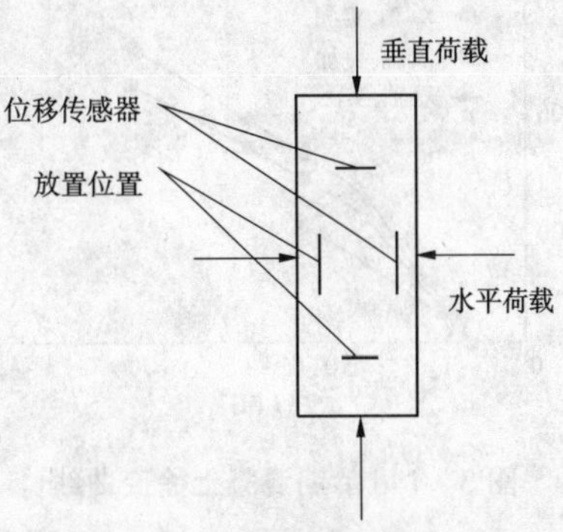

图 2 变形测量示意图

试验机加载系统具有锁定功能，当意外停电后，荷载变化平均速率小于每小时 1%。另外试验机配备有 UPS 外挂电源，用于意外停电时保持计算机和主机工作正常。

计算机能按照规定的采样程序采集试验数据(包括荷载及变形)并进行处理，试验结果可在屏幕上显示或在打印机上打印。

2 徐变试验及其结果

试验机放置在密封房间中，用空调保证温度恒定，用加湿仪控制湿度恒定。由于房间全部密封，试验期间数据的记录由计算机自动完成，并且荷载与变形均由数显表显示，透过房间的双层玻璃即可观察。因此，试验期间温度和湿度保持很好，温度变化幅度为 ±0.5℃，湿度变化幅度为 ±5%。该压缩试验的应力水平为极限强度的 30%。

徐变试件进行了湿筛，试件尺寸为 100mm×100mm×300mm，混凝土配比见表 1。

表 1 试验的混凝土配比

材料	配比 (kg/m^3)	材料	配比 (kg/m^3)	材料	配比 (kg/m^3)
水	78	砂	673	DH9	3.2
水泥	60	小石	465	JG4	4.8
粉煤灰	100				

注：按照新疆某碾压混凝土拱坝工程的材料配比。

2.1 试验曲线

进行了单轴和双轴混凝土徐变试验，试验曲线如图 3、图 4 所示，作为比较，图中也画出了按照叠加原理得到的结果。

图中按照叠加原理计算得到的双轴徐变是按照如下公式计算的：

$$\varepsilon'_y = \varepsilon_y - \nu\varepsilon_x$$

式中：ε_x 为 x 方向单轴加载时 x 方向应变；ε_y 为 y 方向单轴加载时 y 方向应变；ε'_y 为考虑泊松效应后，双轴加载时 y 方向应变；泊松比 ν 取 0.17；经有限元计算得到 $\varepsilon_x = 0.735\varepsilon_y$。

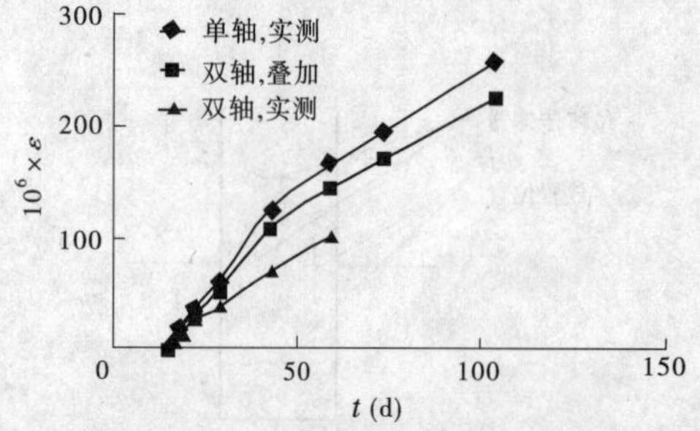

图 3　14d 龄期混凝土徐变曲线

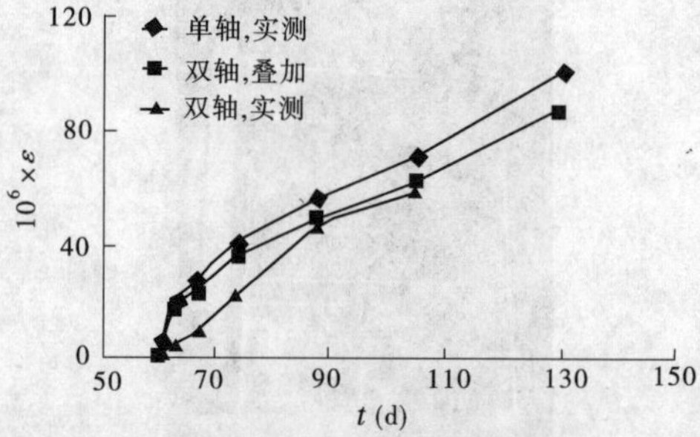

图 4　60d 龄期混凝土徐变曲线

比较试验结果可知，在同样龄期与养护条件下，双轴徐变和单轴徐变总变形差别很大。即使与利用叠加原理后得到的变形曲线相比较，这种差别也仍然明显存在。早龄期最为明显（如图 3 所示），根据单轴徐变的数据，利用叠加原理修正后得到的变形比双轴徐变试验仍然要大 30%左右；晚龄期混凝土的差别要小些（见图 4），但在开始加荷时差别也比较大，在后期变小，利用叠加原理后得到的变形略高于实测双轴变形。可以看出，在早期混凝土强度比较低、水化仍在进行时，单轴徐变和双轴徐变有很大的区别，而在晚龄期水化过程基本结束后，这种差别变小。大体积混凝土前期承受很高的温度及自重徐变应力，裂缝在前期也非常容易产生，因此仿真应力计算非常依赖于前期混凝土的弹塑性及徐变变形的研究。

另外，从伺服电机反馈得到的荷载维持曲线来看，机电伺服自动控制荷载非常成功，试验中荷载变化远小于 1%；从变形曲线来看，传感器的测量很平稳；UPS 电源在试验中起到了很好作用：试验中动力电源出现了两次停电，UPS 电源供电的启动时间为 0.1ms，这期间荷载没有任何变化。由于机器有多项保护装置，其中“破断”项是在荷载变化剧烈时自动停机，故机器除了徐变试验，还可以做强度试验，在最后破坏阶段荷载剧烈下降，仪器自动停止加载，通过试验记录就得到了破坏曲线和破坏荷载。

2.2　试验试件强度

测量了徐变试验前后试件的强度，结果如表 2 所示。

根据徐变试件强度试验结果，在低应力水平下（30%极限强度），徐变试件的强度和徐变之前相比，除 C2 外都稍微有些增强，60%应力水平下的试件强度稍有降低。排除试件强度随龄期增加以及试件随机性的影响，至少可以得到以下结论：低应力水平下（30%极限荷载）徐变混凝土的强度并没有因徐变而降低，即低压应力水平下徐变变形并非是以强度损伤为代价。这和以往的混凝土徐变损伤理论有所差别。“微裂缝理论”[4] 及“徐变损伤理论”[5] 认为混凝土在受荷时就存在损伤，损伤发展的速率和应力水平有关。文献[6]区分线性徐变的应力水平为 40%，认为在低于该值时混凝土内部损伤的裂缝主要是砂浆裂缝，而高于该值则存在骨料及砂浆的界面裂缝。

表 2 徐变试件强度测量结果

编号	徐变试验形式	加荷龄期 (d)	持荷时间 (d)	徐变试件平均强度 (MPa)	同龄期非徐变试件强度 (MPa)
A2	双轴	14	45	—	8.20
A4	双轴	60	90	14.43	11.30
B1	双轴	30	28	10.83	5.46
B2	双轴	60	30	10.75	7.00
C1	单轴	60	12	19.70	18.35
C2	双轴	75	12	19.84	23.24
C3	高应力双轴	90	18	19.82	20.90

注：试验中 C3 高应力为 60%极限强度，其余为 30%极限强度。

为此，我们研制了小型的混凝土双轴加载设备，通过微观试验观察了在双轴徐变应力条件下切片混凝土内部裂缝的发展。该加载装置可以提供 x 方向、y 方向的压缩应力；观察设备采用 Questar 公司生产的长焦距光学显微镜，该显微镜工作距离可达 20mm，放大倍数 200～2 000 倍，连续变焦。为观察方便，试件采用一级配，尺寸为 100mm×100mm×10mm，打印试验结果放大倍数为 400 倍，见图 5、图 6、图 7。试验过程中保持试件表面的湿润，以模仿混凝土内部水分的迁移。由图 5 可见，加荷瞬时在混凝土内部产生沿 y 方向的裂缝，该裂缝主要沿着砂浆、骨料的界面发展；该裂缝在 72h 后，在双轴压缩徐变应力作用下逐渐萎缩，趋于愈合(如图 6 所示)，裂缝的痕迹已不明显。图 7 为加载 13d 后再卸载，然后再加载时原裂缝位置处的情况。图中显示砂浆裂缝基本愈合，骨料和砂浆之间的界面裂缝也明显愈合。即该切片试件原来存在的裂缝在再次加载的情况下，并没有再次张开，说明在双轴压缩徐变应力下，混凝土内部裂缝愈合了，而且裂缝再次胶结，并具有一定的强度。

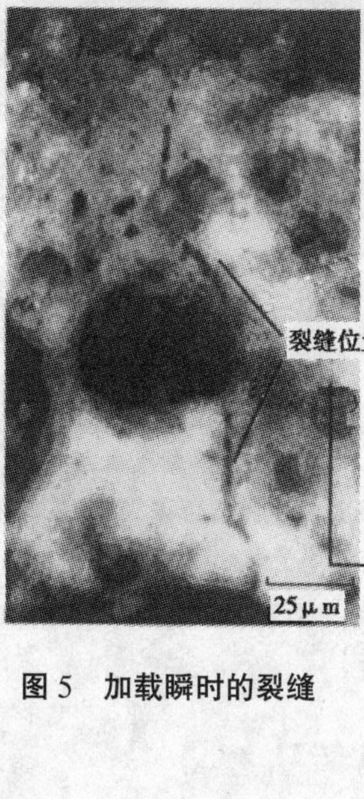

图 5 加载瞬时的裂缝

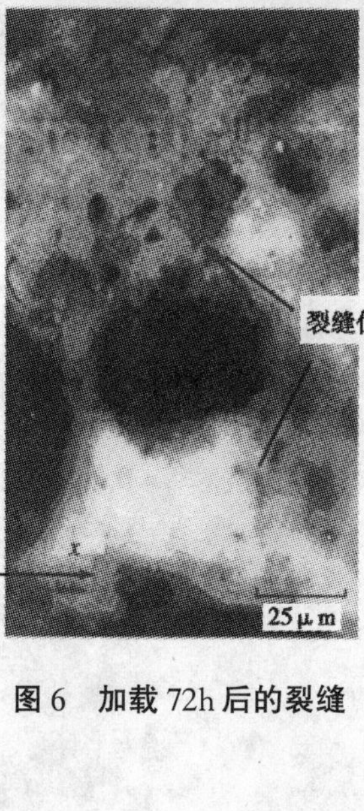

图 6 加载 72h 后的裂缝

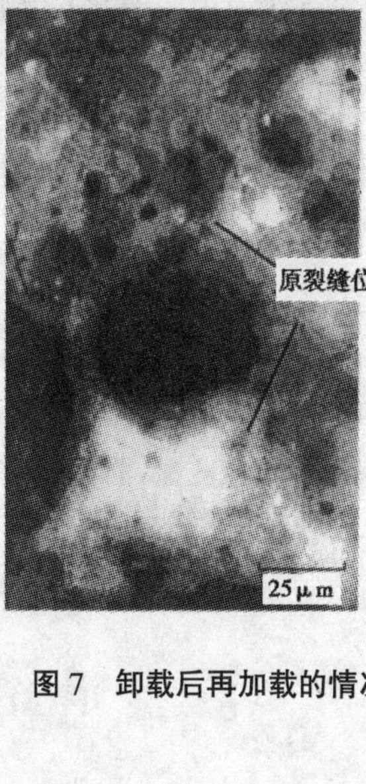

图 7 卸载后再加载的情况

因此,在双轴压缩应力作用下,混凝土的徐变变形中也包含着微裂缝闭合的部分,即在双轴徐变应力下混凝土强度是有可能增强的。文献[7]也发现低压应力下徐变试件的强度可能会增加。我们可以假设混凝土在双轴徐变低压缩应力下的徐变变形包括:内部骨料、砂浆以及孔隙的密实,在压力作用下骨料和砂浆界面裂缝愈合以及水泥水化引起的自身体积变形。当然由于混凝土材料的复杂性,徐变变形包含许多因素,裂缝的扩展所造成的变形只是其中的一部分,而在高应力的作用下,裂缝的扩展则是引起徐变变形和徐变损伤破坏的最主要因素[7]。

3　结语

(1)该双轴徐变仪器可以很好地实现荷载稳定以及变形的测量。

(2)混凝土双轴徐变和单轴徐变差别比较大,用叠加原理计算不能完全反映这种差别,故有必要进一步研究,尤其是前期混凝土承受荷载后的弹塑性变形及徐变变形研究。

(3)低应力水平下混凝土的双轴压缩徐变变形可能并非是以损伤为代价。

参考文献

[1] 唐崇钊.混凝土的徐变和徐变试验.北京:水利电力出版社,1982

[2] Ross A D. *Experiments on the creep of concrete under two-dimensional stressing*. Magazine of Concrete Research,1954,(6):3～10

[3] Gopalakrishnan K S, Neville A M. *Creep Possion's Ratio of Concrete Under Multiaxial Compression*. ACI Journal, 1969,66(90): 1006～1019

[4] Neville A M, Dilger W H, Brooks J J. *Creep of plain and structural concrete*. Contribution Press. London and New York, 1983

[5] 于骁中,等.岩石和混凝土断裂力学.长沙:中南工业大学出版社,1991

[6] 李兆霞.高应力下混凝土的徐变和徐变破坏.河海大学学报,1988,16(1):105～108

[7] 惠荣炎,黄国兴,易冰若.混凝土的徐变.北京:中国铁道出版社,1988

老化黏弹性蠕变本构方程中的热力学条件

摘　要　针对具有老化特性的黏弹性材料,从不可逆热力学角度给出了其本构关系应该满足的条件;以混凝土材料为例,对某些蠕变关系式进行探讨,指出了老化材料蠕变方程应该满足的关系。

关键词　热力学　本构模型　黏弹性　蠕变　老化

黏弹性材料分为两类(恒温条件下),一类材料的参数不随时间而改变,而另一类则随时间的发展而呈现出变化,称之为“老化”(Ageing)。老化又区分为两种,一种是材料特性随时间逐渐“劣化”,而另一种则逐渐“增强”。作为黏弹性材料的一种,水泥基材料和其他工程材料的不同之处就在于老化特性。混凝土从浇筑开始,随着内部水化过程的继续,其材料特性如弹性模量、强度等都会随时间大大增强。通过对水坝等大体积混凝土结构的研究可以发现,这一过程可以持续很久。另一方面,混凝土材料在高温下(高于120℃)、砾岩等岩石在长期泡水情况下它们的特性则呈现出“劣化”性质,这正是核反应堆及拱坝坝肩等结构需要解决的问题。

作者根据黏弹性材料的特点,着重研究老化与非老化材料随时间相关本构关系式的不同,并讨论了恒温条件下混凝土蠕变关系式中需要满足的热力学条件。

1　黏弹性材料本构模型

先从最简单的模型着手[1]。黏弹性材料最基本的模型有两种,分别由一个弹簧及一个阻尼器串联和并联组成,构成如图1所示的Maxwell模型和Kelvin模型。

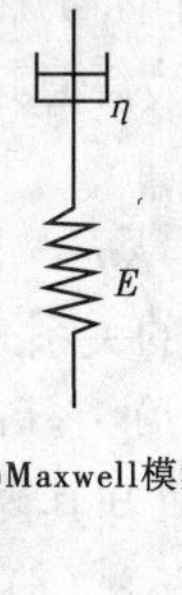

(a)Maxwell模型

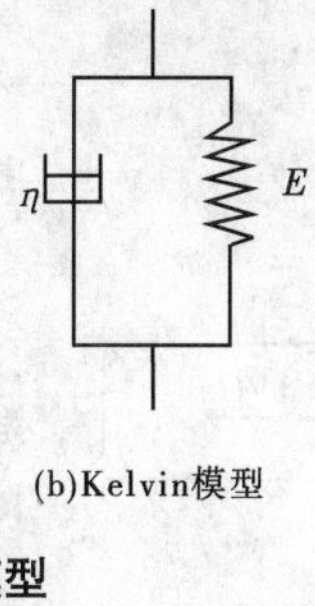

(b)Kelvin模型

图1　黏弹性材料基本模型

模型中的弹簧和黏壶分别代表理想弹性和理想黏性行为,它们分别满足关系式

$$E \geqslant 0, \quad \eta \geqslant 0 \tag{1}$$

$$\sigma = E \cdot \varepsilon, \quad \sigma = \eta \cdot \varepsilon \tag{2}$$

其中:E 为弹簧的弹性模量;η 为黏壶的黏性。

本文选自《固体力学学报》2003年第2期,作者还有高虎、胡昱。

公式(1) 从模型本身的物理概念上很容易理解,从能量方面考虑则是热力学第一定律的要求。不难得出两个模型的本构关系式

Maxwell:　$\sigma(t) = E\varepsilon_0 e^{-Et/\eta}$　(ε_0 为常应变)　(3a)

Kelvin:　$\varepsilon(t) = \dfrac{\sigma_0}{E}(1 - e^{-Et/\eta})$　(σ_0 为常应力)　(3b)

公式(3a) 的 Maxwell 模型对应于常应变情况下的松弛试验,而式(3b) 的 Kelvin 模型对应于常应力下的蠕变试验。由于实验室中应力要比应变容易控制,因此一般采取控制应力的蠕变试验。以下的讨论也针对 Kelvin 模型进行。

将以上 Kelvin 模型公式表示成 $\varepsilon(t) = J(t) \cdot \sigma_0$,称

$$J(t) = \frac{1}{E}(1 - e^{-t/(\eta/E)}) \tag{4}$$

为"蠕变柔量函数"(Creep Compliance Function)。

2　老化黏弹性材料本构关系

老化材料的特点是随时间的变化,其内部成分、组成、比例也发生变化。水泥颗粒遇水发生水化,生成以水化硅酸钙为主体的凝胶体结构,该凝胶体也就是混凝土表现出黏弹性特性的主要结构[2]。随着水化过程的进行,水化产物逐渐增多,混凝土的力学特性也逐渐发生变化,其弹性模量和强度逐渐增加,外荷载下的蠕变曲线也发生变化,即蠕变柔量产生了变化。混凝土的这一特点可以用"固结理论"[3] (Solidification Model) 表示,如图 2 所示。

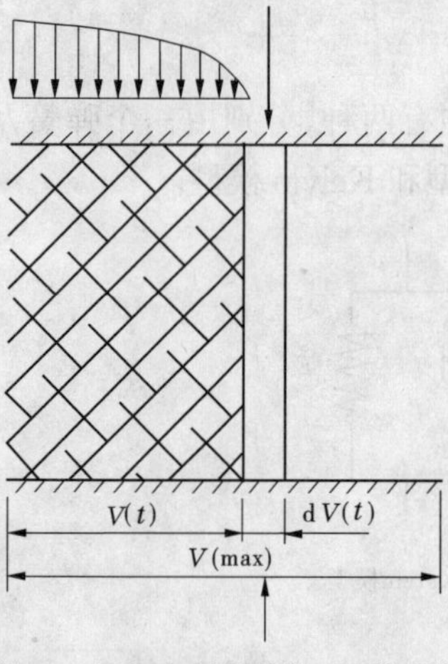

图 2　混凝土材料的"固结模型"

图 2 中假定所有水化了的产物平均承担外部荷载,且水化产物自身的特性是不随时间而改变的。这就使得老化特性反映在水化产物有效体积变化上面(既包括水化产物体积的增长,也包括水化产物之间的联结建立),从而使蠕变模型变得非常简单。仍然可以采用 Kelvin 单元来表示混凝土的黏弹性行为,但其中的弹簧和黏壶随时间而变化[4]:

$$E = E(t), \quad \eta = \eta(t) \tag{5}$$

假设仍然用公式(1) 中的关系来表示水化情况下混凝土的性能,即 $\sigma(t) = E(t) \cdot \varepsilon(t)$,先考查等温过程 Kelvin 单元中的理想弹簧,可知其内能为

$$U(t) = \frac{\sigma^2(t)}{2E(t)} \tag{6}$$

其内能变化率为

$$\dot{U} = \dot{W} + \dot{D}_i \tag{7}$$

其中

$$\dot{W}(t) = \frac{\sigma\dot{\sigma}}{E(t)},\ \dot{D}_i(t) = -\frac{\sigma^2\dot{E}(t)}{2E^2(t)} \tag{8}$$

瞬时可逆的 $\dot{W}$ 代表外力机械功率,而不可逆的 $\dot{D}_i$ 代表内部成分的变化导致的材料耗散

能。根据热力学第二定律,所有的耗散能率一定不为负,即 $\dot{D}_i(t) \geqslant 0$,从而得到

$$\dot{E}(t) \leqslant 0 \tag{9}$$

即弹簧的弹性模量是逐渐减小的,而这显然不符合常温下混凝土随水化过程的进行弹性模量增加的情况,所以关系式(2) 不再适用于“固结” 老化材料[5~7]。

事实上,从图 2 的固结模型中可以归纳得到固结材料应该满足的本构关系式(先考虑图中凝胶体的弹性行为)。设 t 时刻水化产物对应的弹性模量为$E(t)$,在 $t + \mathrm{d}t$ 时刻微量体积 $\mathrm{d}v(t)$ 自由固结(即 $\sigma_0 = 0$),此时弹性模量为 $E(t + \mathrm{d}t)$,$\mathrm{d}t$ 时间内的应变变化为 $\mathrm{d}\varepsilon$,则对应应力变化为

$$\mathrm{d}\sigma = E(t + \mathrm{d}t)\mathrm{d}\varepsilon + \sigma_0 \approx E(t)\mathrm{d}\varepsilon \tag{10a}$$

即

$$\dot{\sigma} = E(t)\dot{\varepsilon} \tag{10b}$$

该式为老化黏弹性材料根据热力学定律以及材料的老化本质得到的弹性关系所应满足的式子[7]。故对于固结老化材料来说,弹簧的虎克弹性关系仅仅适用于增量式(10a) 的形式。如将式(10b) 积分则得到

$$\sigma(t) = \int_0^t E(\tau)\mathrm{d}\varepsilon(\tau) + \sigma_0 \tag{10c}$$

可见式(10c) 这种形式的本构关系和非老化材料黏弹性式(2) 是完全不同的。

但是很多的文献在建立模型时往往忽略了以上不同。如文献[8] 在研究混凝土“自收缩徐变力学模型” 时,采用 Burger 模型表示混凝土随时间相关(Time-dependent) 的变形,将模型中弹簧的变形表示为弹性;黏性表示为不可恢复变形,并给出了模型本构关系式

Maxwell 单元: $$\sigma(t) = E_m(t)\varepsilon_m(t) = \eta_m(t)\frac{\mathrm{d}\varepsilon_m(t)}{\mathrm{d}t} \tag{11a}$$

Kelvin 单元: $$\sigma(t) = E_k(t)\varepsilon_k(t, t_0) + \eta_k(t)\frac{\mathrm{d}\varepsilon_k(t, t_0)}{\mathrm{d}t} \tag{11b}$$

由前推导可知,式(11a) 及式(11b) 中前一个关系式对于水化进行中的混凝土来说,在热力学方面是欠考虑的。事实上该式表达的正是“劣化” 老化材料的关系式,它满足的是式(9)。

再以图 2 为例考查 Kelvin 单元中老化黏壶的本构关系式。考虑图中凝胶体的黏性特性,已知 t 时刻已水化体积为$v(t)$,黏性为 $\eta(t) = \eta_0 v(t)$,$\mathrm{d}t$ 时刻内体积变化为 $\mathrm{d}v(t)$,设单位体积变化造成的黏性应力变化相同,则 $\mathrm{d}v(t)$ 形成的应力变化为 $\mathrm{d}\sigma'(t) = \sigma'(t) \cdot \mathrm{d}v(t)/v$,从而

$$\mathrm{d}\sigma(t) = \eta(t)\mathrm{d}\dot{\varepsilon}(t) + \sigma(t)\frac{\mathrm{d}v(t)}{v(t)} \tag{12}$$

$$\Rightarrow \quad \eta_0\mathrm{d}\dot{\varepsilon}(t) = \frac{\mathrm{d}\sigma(t)}{v(t)} - \sigma(t)\frac{\mathrm{d}v(t)}{v^2(t)} = \mathrm{d}\left[\frac{\sigma(t)}{v(t)}\right]$$

$$\Rightarrow \quad \eta_0\dot{\varepsilon}(t) = \frac{\sigma(t)}{v(t)} + \text{const} \quad \text{(设 const = 0,不影响推导)}$$

$$\Rightarrow \quad \sigma(t) = \eta(t)\dot{\varepsilon}(t) \tag{13}$$

由此可得到式(10) 和式(13) 即为“固结” 老化材料需要满足的黏弹性本构关系式。组

合起来得到老化 Kelvin 单元的本构关系式

$$\dot{\sigma}_e = E(t)\dot{\varepsilon},\ \sigma_\eta(t) = \eta(t)\dot{\varepsilon}(t)$$

$$\Rightarrow \quad \dot{\sigma}(t) = \dot{\sigma}_e + \dot{\sigma}_\eta(t) = E(t)\dot{\varepsilon} + \frac{\mathrm{d}[\eta(t)\dot{\varepsilon}(t)]}{\mathrm{d}t}$$

$$\Rightarrow \quad \ddot{\varepsilon} + \left[\frac{E(t)}{\eta(t)} + \frac{\dot{\eta}(t)}{\eta(t)}\right]\dot{\varepsilon} = \frac{\dot{\sigma}}{\eta(t)} \tag{14}$$

由于式(12) 中 $\mathrm{d}v(t)$ 可正可负，因此式(13) 可适用于所有的“老化”材料。同样，整理式(2) 和式(13) 可得到“劣化” 老化材料 Kelvin 单元本构关系为

$$\sigma(t) = E(t)\varepsilon(t) + \eta(t)\dot{\varepsilon}(t) \tag{15}$$

由式(14)、式(15) 可见，“固结” 老化材料本构关系是含有二阶的微分方程，而“劣化” 老化材料的本构关系则和非老化黏弹性材料的相同。对老化 Maxwell 单元同样可以推导出相应的公式，其结果是一个一阶的微分方程式。

3　老化材料蠕变本构关系

在表示老化黏弹性材料的蠕变关系式时，需要考虑“加载时间” 的影响，对于混凝土来说是用“龄期”τ 这个概念表示。利用叠加原理，蠕变关系式用 Volterra 积分[9] 关系表示为

$$\varepsilon(t) - \varepsilon^0(t) = \sigma(\tau_0)J(t,\tau_0) + \int_{\tau_0}^{t} J(t,\tau)\mathrm{d}\sigma(\tau) \tag{16}$$

其中蠕变柔量 $J(t,\tau) = 1/E(t) + c(t,\tau)$，$c(t,\tau)$ 为单位荷载下的蠕变变形即“蠕变度”。将式(16) 中积分关系式分步积分，并利用 $c(t,\tau) = 0$ 后得到

$$\varepsilon(t) - \varepsilon^0(t) = \frac{\sigma(t)}{E(t)} + \int_{\tau_0}^{t} \sigma(\tau)L(t,\tau)\mathrm{d}\tau \tag{17}$$

式中 $L(t,\tau) = \dfrac{\partial J(t,\tau)}{\partial \tau}$，称为“冲量记忆函数”[7]。

为了混凝土结构数值计算的需要，有些文献[10] 采用 Dirichlet 级数展开式来表示冲量记忆函数，即

$$L(t,\tau) = \sum_{u=1}^{n} \frac{1}{\eta_u(t)} \mathrm{e}^{-(t-\tau)/\tau_u} \tag{18}$$

对应的冲量记忆函数也和式(18) 有相同的表达式。将式(18) 代入式(17) 中得

$$\varepsilon(t) = \frac{\sigma(t)}{E(t)} + \sum_u \varepsilon_u,\ \varepsilon_u(t) = \int_0^t \frac{\sigma(\tau)}{\eta_u(\tau)} \mathrm{e}^{-(t-\tau)/\tau_u}\mathrm{d}\tau \tag{19}$$

而

$$\dot{\varepsilon}_u(t) = -\frac{1}{\tau_u}\int_0^t \frac{\sigma(\tau)}{\eta_u(\tau)} \mathrm{e}^{-(t-\tau)/\tau_u}\mathrm{d}\tau + \frac{\sigma(t)}{\eta_u(t)}$$

于是得到

$$\varepsilon_u + \tau_u \cdot \dot{\varepsilon}_u(t) = \tau_u \cdot \frac{\sigma(t)}{\eta_u(t)}$$

即

$$\frac{\eta_u(t)}{\tau_u}\varepsilon_u + \eta_u(t)\dot{\varepsilon}_u(t) = \sigma(t) \tag{20}$$

可见式(20) 和“劣式” 老化材料的本构关系式式(15) 都是一阶微分方程。Umehara[12] 在研究早期混凝土的温度应力时，用两个串联的具有非老化参数的 Kelvin 单元表示蠕变；

事实上,当采用非老化的广义 Kelvin 链来表示混凝土材料的黏弹性行为时,ε_u 表示为每个 Kelvin 单元的应变,其蠕变柔量函数可由式(4) 得到:

$$J(t) = \sum_u \frac{1}{E_u}(1 - \mathrm{e}^{-t/(\eta_u/E_u)}) \tag{21}$$

仔细发现式(21) 微分后也可以得到和式(18) 相同的表达式,其中 $\tau_u = \eta_u/E_u$ 与 Kelvin 链的阻尼相同。由于式(20) 形式上和式(15) 完全相同,都是一阶微分方程,从式(18) 可推导得到与"劣化" 老材料完全相同的本构关系式。从而可知式(18) 的"冲量记忆函数" 对于"固结" 老化材料来说是违反热力学基本定律的,这也解释了为何混凝土老化理论在用方便简单的指数形式式(19) 拟合实际的蠕变数据时,总是存在巨大的偏差,因为它所表示的其实是"劣化" 材料的本构关系式。采用具有老化参数的广义 Kelvin 链和弹性老化蠕变理论进行蠕变计算时,由于满足二阶微分方程式,因而在数据拟合时偏差较小,适用范围更广。

有时将混凝土材料归为岩土材料,多是从承载能力及短期变形方面考虑,蠕变影响可以忽略不计[13]。但当考虑到持续荷载下变形的影响时,就不能忽视混凝土老化特性与普通岩土材料的不同,因此岩土材料中诸如蠕变弹性后效的公式(根据图 3 中 Burger 体)[14]

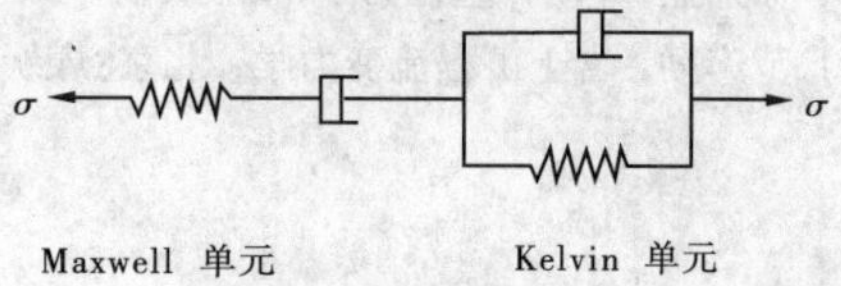

图 3　文献[8] 的混凝土自收缩力学模型
(Burger 模型)

$$\varepsilon(t) = \frac{\sigma}{2}\left\{\frac{t_1}{\eta_m} + \frac{1}{E_k}\left[1 - \exp\left(-\frac{E_k}{\eta_k}\right)t_1\right]\exp\left(-\frac{E_k}{\eta_k}\right)(t - t_1)\right\} \tag{22}$$

就不能适用于混凝土材料(其中 t_1 为卸载时间)。在实际应用中一定要注意这点。

4　总结

作者以水泥基材料为例研究了具有"老化" 特性的黏弹性材料本构模型,从热力学角度给出了其本构方程需要满足的基本条件;以混凝土为例讨论了其蠕变方程式应该受到的限制。在用公式总结"老化" 材料的蠕变等与时间相关的特性时,一定要注意满足材料热力学方面的条件。混凝土材料由于自身构成的复杂性,经验公式很多,这方面尤其需要重视。

参 考 文 献

[1] 杨挺青. 黏弹性力学. 武汉:华中理工大学出版社,1990

[2] 惠荣炎,黄国兴,易冰若. 混凝土的徐变. 北京:中国铁道出版社,1988

[3] Bazant Z P, Prasannan S. *Solidification theory for concrete creep I: formulaton*. J Eng Mech,1989, 115:1691～1703

[4] Carl I, Bazant Z P. *Viscoelasticity with aging caused by solidification of non-aging contituent*. J of Eng Mech,1993,119(11):2252～2269

[5] Carl I,Bazant Z P. *Solidification theory: A rational and effective framework for constitutive modeling*

of aging viscoelasticity. *Proceedings of the fifth international RILEM Symposium*: *On creep and shrinkage of concrete*. E·FN Spon, London, U K, 1993:177～188

[6] Bazant Z P. *Thermodynamics of solidifying or melting viscoelasticity material*. J Eng Mech, 1979, 106(6):933～952

[7] 朱伯芳.大体积混凝土的温度应力和温度控制. 北京:中国电力出版社,1999

[8] 安明喆. 高性能混凝土自收缩的研究.清华大学学位论文,1999,60～65

[9] Bazant Z P, Wittmann F H. *Creep and shrinkage in concrete structures*. Wiley-interscience Publication, New York, 1982,183～187

[10] Creus G J. *Viscoelasticity-Basic theory and applications to concrete structures*. Springer-Verlag. Berlin,1986, 118～121

[11] 唐崇钊. 混凝土的徐变和徐变试验.北京:水利电力出版社,1982

[12] Umehara H,Uehara T,Iisaka T. *Effect of creep in concrete at early ages on thermal stress*. *Thermal cracking in concrete at early ages*. Edited by R. Springenschmid, E & FN Spon. London,1994,79～86

[13] 徐秉业.应用弹塑性力学. 北京:清华大学出版社,1995

[14] 范广勤. 岩土工程流变力学. 北京:煤炭工业出版社,1993

考虑温度对于弹模影响效应的大体积混凝土施工期应力计算

摘　要　阐述了水泥水化反应遵循物理化学反应中 Arrhenius 方程的规律，用“等效龄期”的概念考查了温度对于混凝土弹性模量的影响。进行了某碾压混凝土拱坝施工期温度场的计算，并利用该温度场及“等效龄期”进行了应力场的计算，该应力计算中包含了温度及自重徐变应力。对比了 20℃定温下弹模变化的应力场。考虑温度对于混凝土弹模影响的计算结果是趋于危险情况的。

关键词　温度　水化反应　等效龄期　弹性模量　碾压混凝土

大体积混凝土仿真应力计算中，混凝土的弹性模量值是个十分重要的基本量，计算中一般认为混凝土弹性模量是随龄期增长的，最后达到一个终值，而弹模的测量也是在常温（一般是 20℃的范围）下进行的，没有考虑温度对于混凝土弹模的影响。

混凝土的弹性模量增长是和水泥的水化程度直接相关的。水泥水化程度不仅依赖于龄期，也依赖于周围环境的温度。温度增加，水化速度加快，温度降低，水化速度下降。大体积混凝土由于水化温升和周围环境的影响，各处的温度场一般并不均匀，这样就导致了同一龄期混凝土的弹性模量的差异。本文则着重考虑了温度对于混凝土弹性模量的影响。

1　Arrhenius 公式和活化能

Arrhenius 通过对溶液反应速率常数与温度关系的研究，在 Van't Hoff 的启发下，于 1889 年提出了一个表述反应速度系数的公式：

$$k = A\exp\left(-\frac{E_a}{RT}\right) \tag{1}$$

并引入活化分子概念。其中 E_a 为反应活化能；R 为大气常数；T 为温度；A 为指前因子。人们称此公式为 Arrhenius 公式。该公式是控制物理化学反应方程的基本公式之一[1]。

该公式的提出，使人们定量地明白了温度是如何影响反应速率的。公式中一个重要的概念是活化能。Arrhenius 对于它的解释是一般分子发生反应成为活化分子需要吸收的最低能量。“简单碰撞理论”和“过渡状态理论”分别对于它作过解释，Tolman 于 1920 年给出比较合理的说法，Arrhenius 的定义是不确切的，“活化能”是活化分子的平均能量与全部反应物分子的平均能量之差，是一个宏观统计量，可通过实验获得。它的准确性表现在由它结合不同理论模型导出的公式和理论结果是一致的，成为目前普遍接受的定义。

由实验观察，大部分化学反应，在一定温度范围内，服从 Arrhenius 公式，包括基元反应、总包反应、均相和多相反应、催化和非催化反应等，水泥基材料的化学反应也包含在

本文选自《工程力学》2001 第 6 期，作者还有高虎。

内[1,4]。

2　水泥水化活化能

水泥水化的过程是复杂的化学物理变化,必然受到温度变化的影响,而水泥老化性质正是由水化过程控制的。早龄期混凝土的弹性模量、极限强度等机械特性更是容易受到温度影响。大体积混凝土施工期仿真应力计算中除了考虑弹性模量等性质随龄期的变化,还应考虑水泥水化热以及外界环境温度的变化对于混凝土性质的影响。

人们通过研究发现,活化能 E_a 并非是常数,而是和温度有关,但这种情况一般在1 000K以上的温度范围[1]时出现,与此相比,混凝土坝坝体中温度变化相对不是很剧烈,故可以认为“在温度比较低,温度变化范围比较窄时,E_a 近似为常数”[1]。

Verbeck[5]根据水化放热的过程,做了大量的研究水泥活化能的实验,通过实验发现,虽然在水泥水化中存在很多化学反应,并且各反应的活化能并不完全相同,但是水化反应总的活化能在0～100℃之间大致为常数,并由实验得到 $E_a/R\approx 2\ 700\text{K}$,这也就是目前广泛使用的实验数据[1,2,3]。

3　大体积混凝土仿真应力计算

大体积混凝土的温度及应力计算在考虑温度对于弹性模量的影响时,需要知道施工期过程中的温度分布,按照浇筑计划分步计算各个浇筑层在外界边界气温以及水化发热下的温度历程。获得施工期的温度历史后,再计算温度对于弹性模量的影响就比较容易实现了。

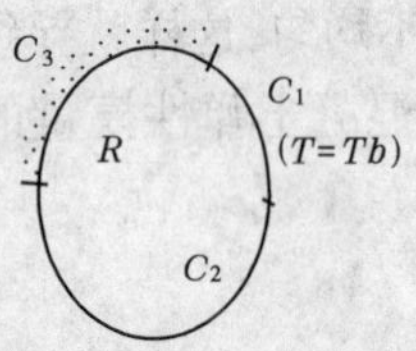

图1　温度边界条件

施工期变化温度场 $T(x、y、z、t)$应满足下述方程及初始和边界条件(如图1):

$$\frac{\partial T}{\partial t}=a\left(\frac{\partial^2 T}{\partial x^2}+\frac{\partial^2 T}{\partial y^2}+\frac{\partial^2 T}{\partial z^2}\right)+\frac{\partial\theta}{\partial t} \tag{2}$$

当 $t=0$ 时,$T=T_0(x、y、z)$; 在 C_1 上:$T=T_b$; 在 C_2 上:

$$\lambda\frac{\partial T}{\partial x}l_x+\lambda\frac{\partial T}{\partial y}l_y+\lambda\frac{\partial T}{\partial z}l_z+\beta(T-T_a)=0 \tag{3}$$

在绝热边界 C_3 上:

$$\frac{\partial T}{\partial n}=0 \tag{4}$$

式中:c 为比热;γ 为容重;a 为导温系数;λ 为导热系数;β 为表面放热系数;θ 为绝热温升;n 为边界法线方向;T_0 为给定的初始温度;T_a、T_b 为给定的边界气温和水温;l_x、l_y、l_z 为边界外法线的方向余弦。

适当选择 β 值后,上述第一类边界条件和绝热条件均可用第三类边界条件形式代替,于是由变分原理,上述的热传导问题等价于下列泛函的极值问题:

$$I(T)=\iiint_R\left\{\frac{1}{2}\left[\left(\frac{\partial T}{\partial x}\right)^2+\left(\frac{\partial T}{\partial y}\right)^2+\left(\frac{\partial T}{\partial z}\right)^2\right]+\frac{1}{a}\left(\frac{\partial T}{\partial t}-\frac{\partial\theta}{\partial t}\right)T\right\}\mathrm{d}R+\iint_C\left(\frac{\bar{\beta}}{2}T^2-\bar{\beta}T_aT\right)\mathrm{d}s \tag{5}$$

考虑泛函极值并对结构 R 域进行离散化得到以下方程组：

$$[H+\frac{2}{\Delta t}P]\{T\}_t+[H-\frac{2}{\Delta t}P]\{T\}_{t-\Delta t}+\{Q\}_{t-\Delta t}+\{Q\}_t=0 \tag{6}$$

其中：

$$[H]=\sum_{e}[H]^e=\sum_{e}\iiint_{\Delta R}(a_x\frac{\partial[N]^T}{\partial x}\frac{\partial[N]}{\partial x}+a_y\frac{\partial[N]^T}{\partial y}\frac{\partial[N]}{\partial y}+a_z\frac{\partial[N]^T}{\partial z}\frac{\partial[N]}{\partial z})dR \tag{7}$$

$$[P]=\sum_{e}[P]^e=\sum_{e}\iiint_{\Delta R}[N]^T[N]dR \tag{8}$$

$$[Q]=\sum_{e}[Q]^e=\sum_{e}\left\{-\iiint_{\Delta R}\frac{\partial\theta}{\partial t}[N]^T dR-\iint_{\Delta c}\bar{\beta}T_a[N]^T ds+\iint_{\Delta c}\bar{\beta}[N]^T[N]\{T\}^e ds\right\} \tag{9}$$

式中 $\bar{\beta}=\beta/\lambda$。这样，对于结构进行有限元划分后，给定 $t-\Delta t$ 时刻的温度场 $\{T\}_{t-\Delta t}$，解方程组可得到 t 时刻温度场 $\{T\}_t$。已知 $t=0$ 时结构内温度（入仓温度）分布，可依次求得各时刻的温度分布。已编制的 SAP 程序适应于计算机计算[6]。计算的温度场为各节点的温度值。用“等效龄期”τ_e 代替真实龄期 τ[2,3]，τ_e 表示为

$$\tau_e=\int_0^{\tau}\alpha_T dt' \tag{10}$$

式中：$\alpha_T=\exp\left[\frac{U_h}{R}(\frac{1}{T_0}-\frac{1}{T})\right]$。其中 $\frac{U_h}{R}\approx 2\,700$K；$T$ 为绝对温度 $273+t$K，是时间的函数，T_0 为参考温度，取实验室温度 296K。

对式(10)进行离散可得

$$\tau_e=\sum_{i=1}^{n}\Delta\tau_i\exp\left(\frac{2\,700}{296}-\frac{2\,700}{\overline{T}_i}\right) \tag{11}$$

由于每个单元的温度均不相同，因此对于每个单元均要建立这样的等效龄期公式，而式中的 $\overline{T}_i$ 为每一计算时段前后该单元温度的平均值。

计算参数按照新疆某碾压混凝土拱坝工程的试验参数，混凝土弹模为 2.0×10^6 t/m^2，泊松比 ν 为 0.167，散热系数 β 为 837.36kJ(m^2·d·℃)，导温系数为 0.098，容重为 2.4t/m^3，最高绝热温升为 13℃，线膨胀系数为 6.5×10^{-6}。

计算中在考虑施工期温度及自重徐变应力的基础上（详见文献[7]），在仿真程序中加入温度对于混凝土弹模的影响。成果图为施工过程中三个高程上游坝面的应力分布。计算结果有两部分，一部分是没有考虑温度对于弹性模量的影响，另外一部分是考虑了温度的影响。计算的时间安排按照工程的浇筑计划摘引时段半年(1999 年 4 月 1 日～9 月 14 日)。

4 计算结果及分析

计算结果打印了 3 个浇筑高程(1 294m、1 329m、1 333m)，均为上游坝面应力。(应力图中每个节点的应力大小从上而下分布为 σ_x、σ_y、σ_z)由该 3 个高程的结果，可以看到：

(1)春季浇筑的混凝土在早期温度低,弹模比较小,上游因气温上升而受压力,考虑了温度对于弹性模量的影响后,应力变化不是很大(见图 2、图 3)。

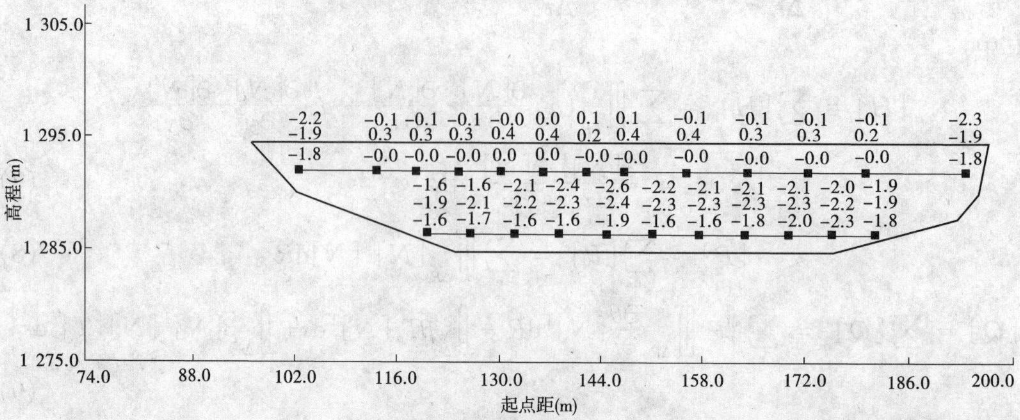

图 2　1999 年 5 月 1 日 1 294m 高程上游正应力图(未考虑温度效应)　(单位:0.1MPa)

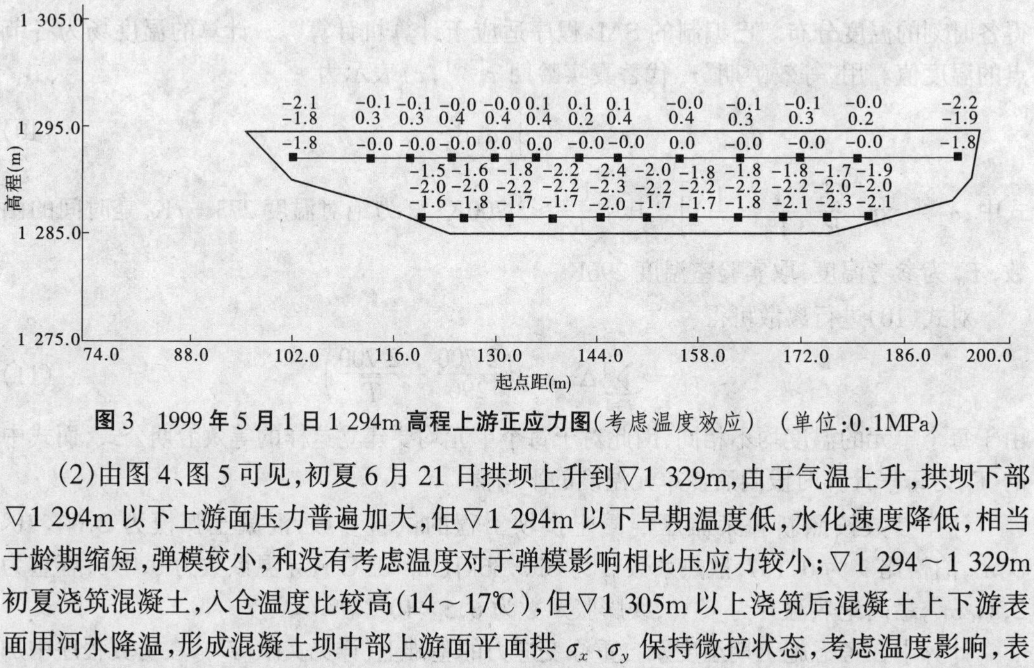

图 3　1999 年 5 月 1 日 1 294m 高程上游正应力图(考虑温度效应)　(单位:0.1MPa)

(2)由图 4、图 5 可见,初夏 6 月 21 日拱坝上升到▽1 329m,由于气温上升,拱坝下部▽1 294m 以下上游面压力普遍加大,但▽1 294m 以下早期温度低,水化速度降低,相当于龄期缩短,弹模较小,和没有考虑温度对于弹模影响相比压应力较小;▽1 294～1 329m 初夏浇筑混凝土,入仓温度比较高(14～17℃),但▽1 305m 以上浇筑后混凝土上下游表面用河水降温,形成混凝土坝中部上游面平面拱 σ_x、σ_y 保持微拉状态,考虑温度影响,表面温度低,弹模小,拉应力也小,只有 σ_z 由自重引起了相应的徐变压力,它受弹模影响小。

(3)由图 6、图 7 可见,即使温度和标准温度相差±5℃,夏季浇筑时 6 月 21 日～9 月 14 日坝体由▽1 329m 上升到▽1 342m,由于弹模快速增长,考虑温度弹模效应,使新浇混凝土▽1 333m 平面拱的应力约增长一倍;同时考虑温度对于弹性模量的影响后,坝肩的应力,尤其拉应力加大,部分由压应力变化成拉应力,拉应力最大值由 0.36MPa(见图 6)变化至 0.47MPa(见图 7),变化幅度为 31%,最大值位置也同时发生了变化;变化剧烈的是由 -0.08MPa(图 4)到 0.15MPa(见图 5),变化大小为 0.23MPa。

(4)以上为温度变化小的碾压混凝土的温度弹模效应(20℃±5℃),当温度远离 20℃

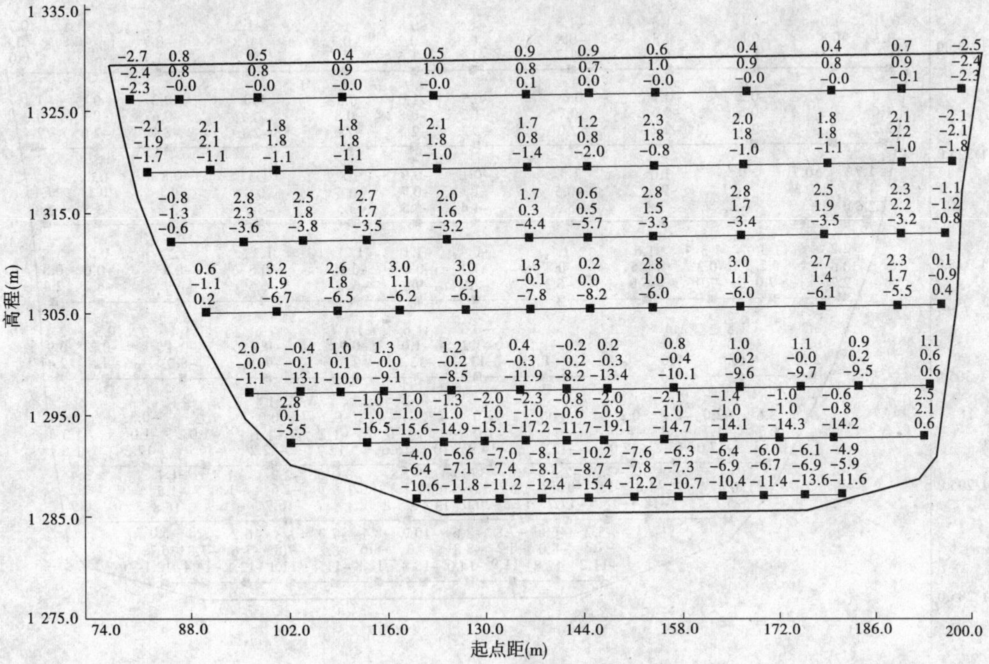

图 4　1999 年 6 月 21 日 1 329m 高程上游立面图(未考虑温度效应)　(单位:0.1MPa)

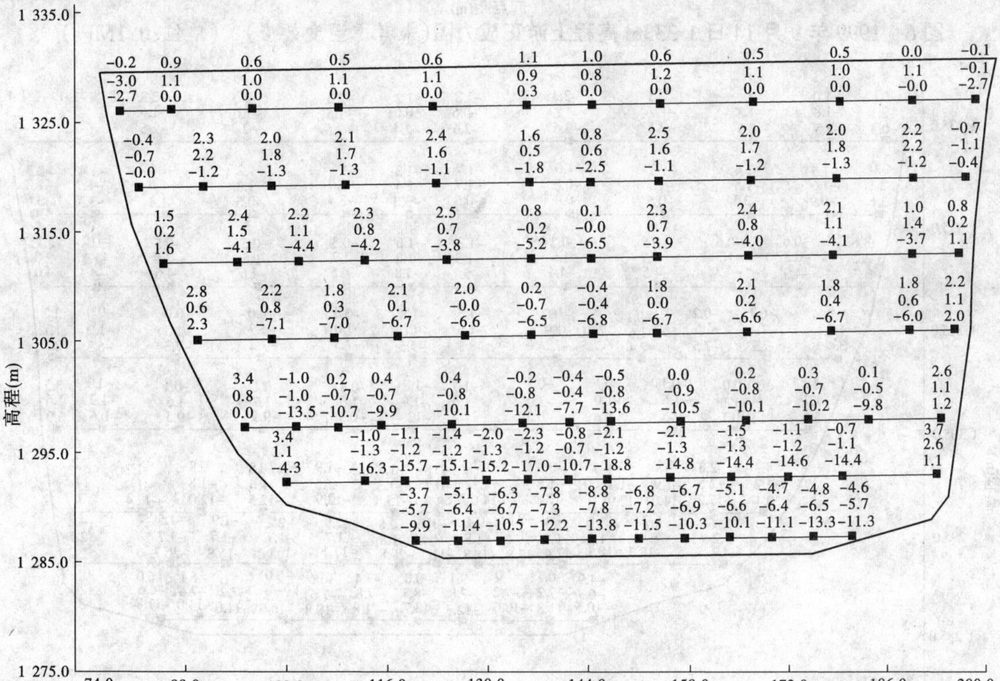

图 5　1999 年 6 月 21 日 1 329m 高程上游正应力图(考虑温度效应)　(单位:0.1MPa)

时,如秋季气温下降引起拉应力增大,再考虑温度弹模效应,应力会更加恶化。

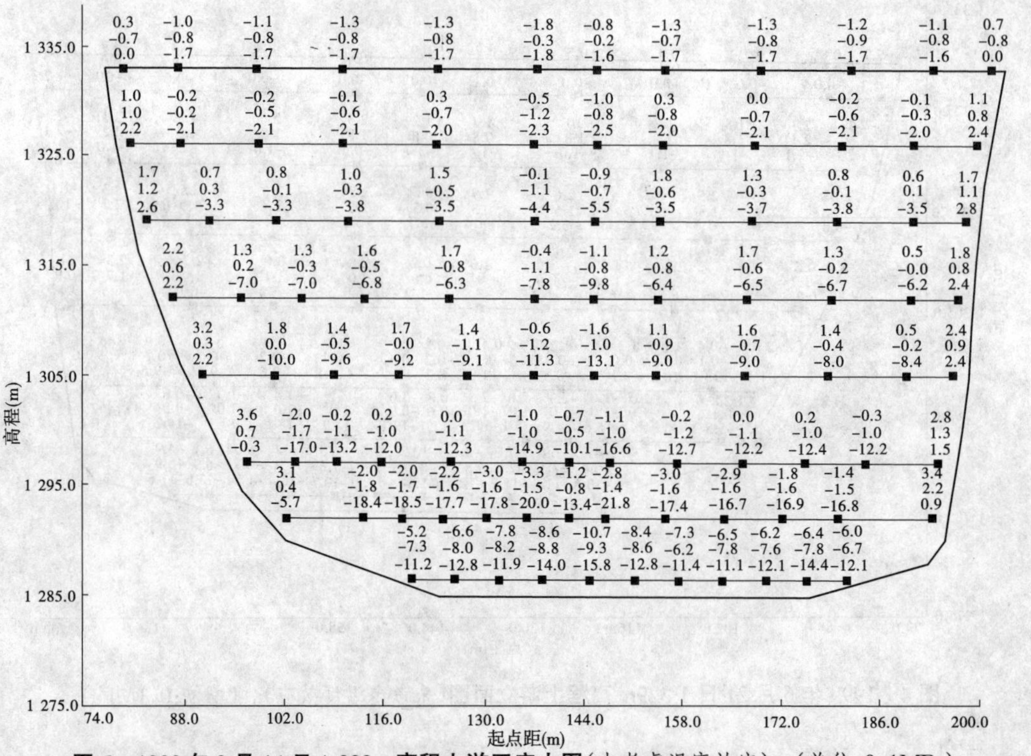

图 6　1999 年 9 月 14 日 1 333m 高程上游正应力图(未考虑温度效应)　(单位:0.1MPa)

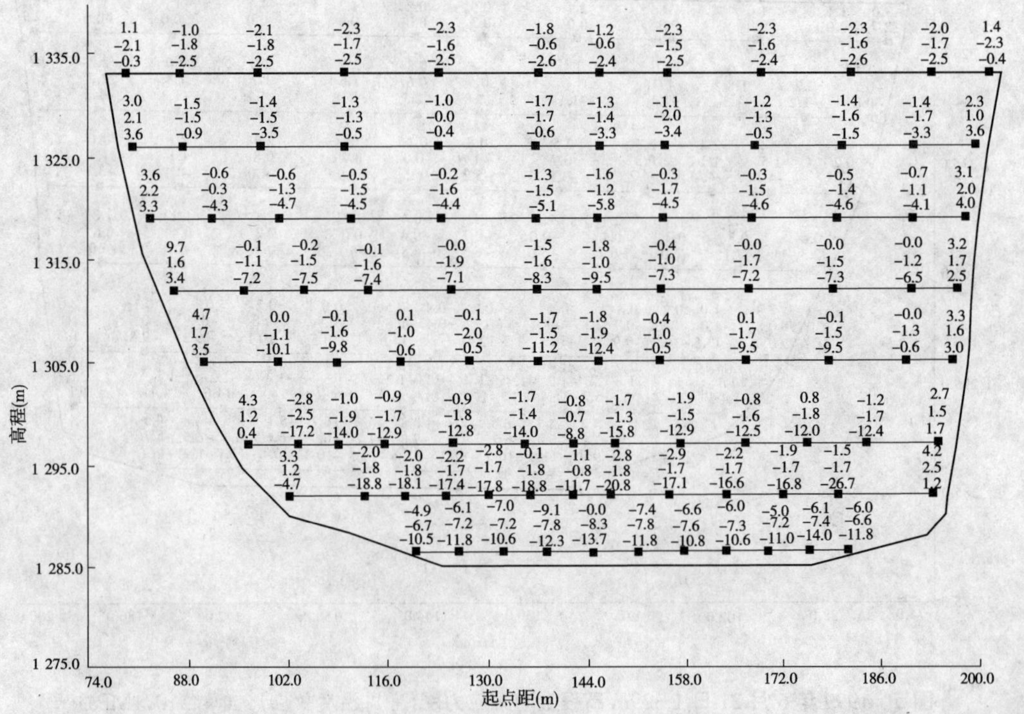

图 7　1999 年 7 月 14 日 1 333m 高程上游正应力图(考虑温度效应)　(单位:0.1MPa)

因此,温度对于弹性模量的影响对本工程是一种较为危险的情况。不同的温度场对应不同的弹性模量变化,故不同的工程温度对弹性模量的影响对工程本身的效果是不同的。考虑温度对于弹性模量的影响,对了解大体积混凝土的应力分布是有益的,将有利于采取措施以防止裂缝的发生。

参 考 文 献

[1] 夏少武. 活化能及其计算.北京:高等教育出版社,1993

[2] Z P Bazant, F H Wittmann. *Creep and shrinkage in concrete structures*. Wiley-Interscience Publication, 1982

[3] 杜崇江.大体积混凝土结构施工累计应力计算方法及碾压混凝土坝的应力研究.清华大学,1988

[4] Z P Bazant. *Thermo-viscoelasity of Aging Concrete*. J. of Engrg Mech,1974,100(6):575~597

[5] Copeland, Verbeck. *Chemistry of Hydration of Portland Cement*. Proceedings, Fourth International Symposium on the Chemistry of Cement, Washington, D.C, 1960,429~465

[6] 张国新,刘光廷.整体碾压混凝土拱坝及温度场仿真计算.清华大学学报,1996,36(1):2~6

[7] 刘光廷,麦家煊,张国新.溪柄碾压混凝土薄拱坝的研究.水力发电学报,1997,(2):19~28

自生体积变形试验方法研究及应用

摘　要　提高混凝土的自生体积膨胀变形量,补偿混凝土的温度收缩变形,对于混凝土抗裂很有意义。从混凝土的细观结构研究出发对混凝土自生体积变形的基准值问题进行了初步探讨。在对比和分析了国内外自生体积变形测定方法的基础上提出了一种更为合理的自生体积变形测定方法:高精度位移传感器法。应用建立的试验方法探索了微膨胀碾压混凝土的自生体积变形,试验表明,水泥生产中均匀外掺氧化镁碾压混凝土的自生体积收缩变形明显减小。

关键词　自生体积变形　基准值　微膨胀混凝土

大体积整体结构内部温度较高,降温时受基础约束,会产生较大的温度应力[1],研究和实践表明,在不影响混凝土强度和耐久性情况下适当提高混凝土的自生体积膨胀变形量,补偿混凝土的温度收缩变形,可简化温控、降低成本和提高筑坝速度。50 多年前 Davis 就认识到了自生体积变形的现象[2],它会影响混凝土内部的初始受力状态。20 世纪 80 年代人们发现过去对自生体积变形的测定由于不能真正保持试件绝湿状态,不能测量早期变形,造成试验数据不准确[3]。考虑控制大坝混凝土温降产生收缩裂缝的多种原因,微膨胀混凝土开始受到人们的关注。

1　自生体积变形基准值的确定

在混凝土自生体积变形的测定和计算中,基准值的选定直接影响变形的绝对值。试验中如果基准值选定的时间较早,混凝土处于全塑性,量测仪器刚度相对过大,测定的自生体积变形波动较大,试验数据的代表性就较差;如果基准值选定的时间较晚,则会丢失一部分测量变形值,造成测定值偏小,不能代表真实的自生体积变形。我国《水工混凝土试验规程》(SD105—82)规定:除有特殊要求外,一般以成型后 24h 作为测定自生体积变形的基准值,尚值得商榷。

自生体积变形是胶凝材料的水化作用引起的,而胶凝材料水化是在混凝土拌制中就开始发生的。晶体构架未形成之前处于塑性阶段,由于其良好的触变复原性能,在这个阶段水化收缩并不产生应力,混凝土结构不产生损伤。随着进一步水化,胶凝材料颗粒在水分子的作用下相互搭接,晶体构架随晶体的不断生成逐渐形成,水泥浆体中空隙加大,混凝土逐渐减少触变复原的能力,强度逐渐升高。晶体构架完全形成后水化反应引起的自生体积变形由于受到晶体构架的约束而产生应力,从而对已形成的晶体构架造成不可恢复的破坏,必然引起混凝土内部的损伤,故作者认为应以晶体构架的形成时间作为自生体积变形的基准值。为此,利用高倍连续变焦显微技术研究胶凝材料的水化,以考察自生体积变形的基准值。

在放大 1 000 倍的显微镜下,刚配置好的砂浆表面有明显的胶凝材料颗粒,多显现为

本文选自《清华大学学报(自然科学版)》2001 第 11 期,作者还有李鹏辉、高虎、陈凤岐。

不规则的卵石状,颜色灰暗,它被水形成的粗大网状结构包围(见图 1(a))。然后大部分水迅速被胶凝材料吸收,少许水蒸发到空气中,水形成的网状结构迅速变细,胶凝材料颗粒在水分子作用下相互搭接,且开始水化,一些胶凝材料颗粒已开始变为半透明晶体。约10min 后水的网状结构已完全消失,透明晶体颗粒初步形成。之后随水化反应透明晶体颗粒逐渐增多,此时的砂浆表面结构包括未水化的胶凝颗粒、正在水化的半透明晶体和已水化的透明晶体(见图 1(b))。

由于砂浆表面胶凝材料较多,结构相对比较致密,在 0.5h 后观察砂浆内部结构。从40min 的观察结果发现砂浆内部结构较疏松,胶凝材料之间有明显的空隙,透明晶体颗粒尺寸较表面大,晶体轮廓也较表面清楚(图 1(c))。1h 后水化反应缓慢,晶体的形成和发展仍在继续,晶体轮廓更加清晰。由于水分被吸收,胶凝材料颗粒无明显的移动。2h 时晶体生成基本完成,晶体颗粒轮廓清楚,相互之间已构成骨架。随后每小时拍摄一幅图片,对比可以看出晶体颗粒基本不变化。图 1(d)为 7h 时的图片。

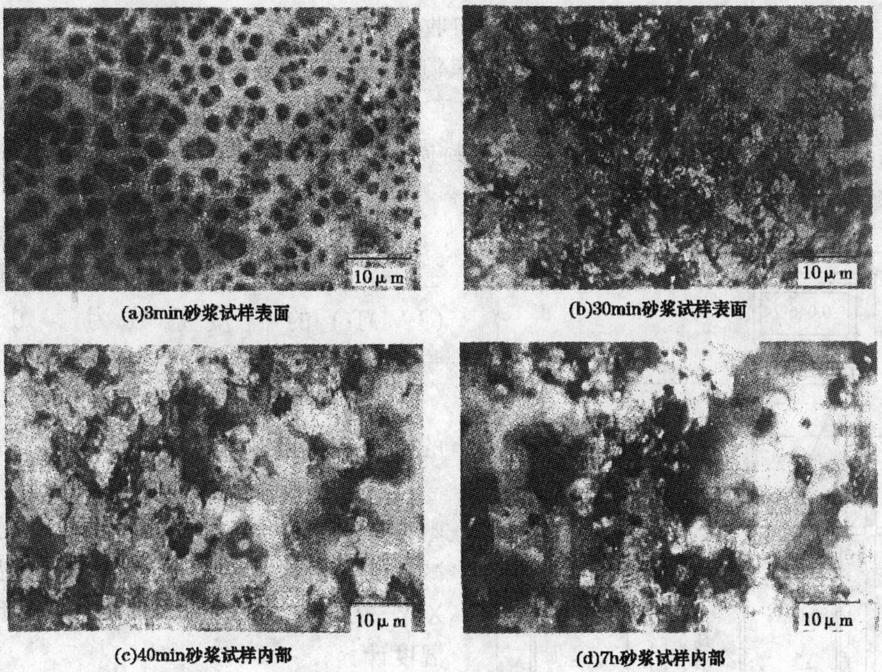

(a)3min砂浆试样表面　(b)30min砂浆试样表面

(c)40min砂浆试样内部　(d)7h砂浆试样内部

图 1　细观砂浆观察图片

细观观察与配合比试验同步进行宏观凝结试验,测定砂浆的初凝时间约为 5.6h。和晶体构架形成的时间 2h 相比,晶体构架的形成时间早于宏观的初凝时间,且晶体构架在初凝前后未发现明显变化。

综上可以看出:以成型后 24h 或初凝作为测量自生体积变形的基准值均不恰当,而以混凝土内部晶体构架的形成时间作为测定自生体积变形的基准值更为合理。

2　自生体积变形测定方法的改进

混凝土的自生体积变形是指在恒温绝湿条件下,由于胶凝材料(水泥加混合材)的水化作用引起的体积变形，它不包括混凝土受外荷载、温度、外界湿度和碱活性骨料影响所引起的体积变形。自生体积变形在早期变化较大，但是到后期变形逐渐缓慢。因此，对自生体积变形的测定必须注意以下问题：

(1)在整个测试过程中系统的密封状况要良好，即必须保证试件在整个测试过程中保持恒重，不允许有透气透水现象。

(2)由于自生体积变形的早期变形较大，要求在早期弹模很低晶体构架形成时就开始测定，所以对测定仪器的精度要求较高(μm 级)。

(3)由于温度引起的变形大，测量中一定要包含测量试件内部温度以及线胀系数的仪器(该量测仪器应少干扰局部变形)，以在试验结果处理中扣除温度的影响。

目前国内外对自生体积变形的测量方法主要有应变计法和千分表法两种。测定水工混凝土自生体积变形的应变计法最大的不足之处就是在早期由于混凝土弹性模量很低，应变计和混凝土变形不同步，早期混凝土的自生体积变形不能准确测量。国内外最近研究表明，混凝土的早期自生体积变形很大[4]，由于不能测量而忽略这个阶段的变形是不恰当的。建筑混凝土[4,5]采用千分表法测定自收缩(自生体积变形)，可测定早期的自生体积变形，但由于自生体积变形的量级很小，其测量精度不能很好地满足试验要求。

为此，本文以高精度位移传感器法实现了对自生体积变形的合理测定。这套测定装置包括高精密数字位移计、支架、混凝土密封模具桶以及测温设备 4 部分(见图 2)，和高倍显微技术相互配合应用。

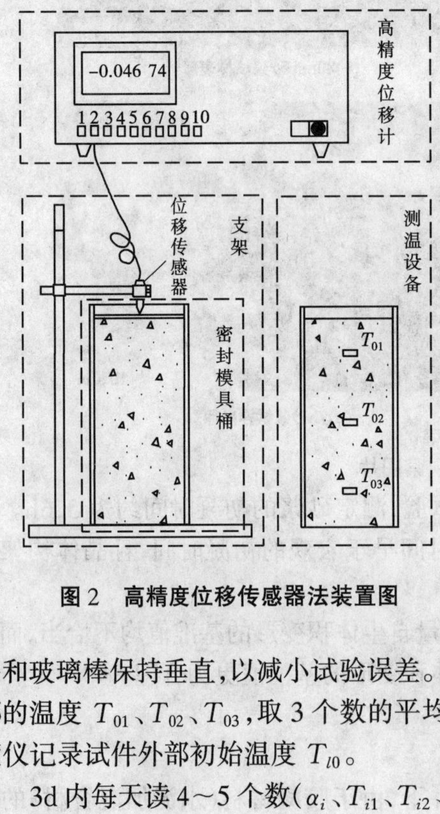

图 2　高精度位移传感器法装置图

高精密数字位移计的测量范围为 ±1mm，分辨率为 0.000 1mm；差动变压器(LVDT)的温度系数为 −0.01 ~ −0.05%/℃，具有较强的抗干扰能力。

设计加工的专用支架可消除传感器本身的松弛，适应不同尺寸试件的测量需要。

混凝土密封模具桶用镀锌铁皮制作，用塑料布、黄油和 2mm 厚橡皮贴于铁桶内壁，减小侧面变形约束。混凝土内部测温采用 XJY—0162 智能巡检仪，外部测温采用数字温度计。

试件成型后立即置于预先调好试验温度的恒温室中。测量试件的原始长度 l_0，试件顶部放置玻璃板，玻璃板上垂直放置石英棒(石英棒对温度的敏感性远小于混凝土本体，从而减少测量中温度的影响)。传感器的探头和玻璃棒保持垂直，以减小试验误差。调零后读取位移初始值 α_0，同时读取混凝土内部的温度 T_{01}、T_{02}、T_{03}，取 3 个数的平均值作为混凝土内部的温度初值 T_0，并用数字温度仪记录试件外部初始温度 T_{l0}。

3d 内每天读 4~5 个数(α_i、T_{i1}、T_{i2}、T_{i3}及 T_{il})，以后每天读 3 个数。

混凝土自生体积变形由下式计算：

$$\varepsilon_i = \frac{(\alpha_i - \alpha_0)}{l_0} + C_1(T_i - T_0) + C_2(T_{il} - T_{l0})$$

式中：ε_i 为混凝土的自生体积变形；C_1 为混凝土的线膨胀系数；C_2 为 LVDT 的线膨胀系数；$T_i=(T_{i1}+T_{i2}+T_{i3})/3$；$T_0=(T_{01}+T_{02}+T_{03})/3$；$T_{il}$ 为 LVDT 所处的外部环境温度。

高精度位移传感器法具有以下特点：①传感器测量精度高，可达 0.1μm 量级，较千分表精度高出 10 倍；②由于传感器不是埋入式的，没有和混凝土温度变形不同步的问题，所以测量不受混凝土弹性模量的影响，可以测量早期的自生体积变形；③密封桶具有良好的密封性，保证试件的绝湿状态；④通过对温度影响的修正，可消除温度对自生体积变形以及传感器的影响；⑤传感器可重复使用，长期试验成本相对较低；⑥密封桶内衬以橡胶皮、黄油和塑料薄膜，降低了模具对混凝土的约束作用。

3 工程应用

恰当地改善混凝土的自生体积膨胀变形特性，可补偿大体积混凝土结构温降引起的收缩变形，以达到简化温控、提高混凝土质量的目的。利用建立的高精度位移传感器法，结合某碾压混凝土拱坝中采用的碾压混凝土配合比，在 16℃ 养护和试验温度条件下进行了外掺氧化镁（外掺量为水泥用量的 3%）和不掺氧化镁两种微膨胀碾压混凝土自生体积变形的初步试验研究，测定试验结果见图 3（图中正值为膨胀，负值为收缩）。

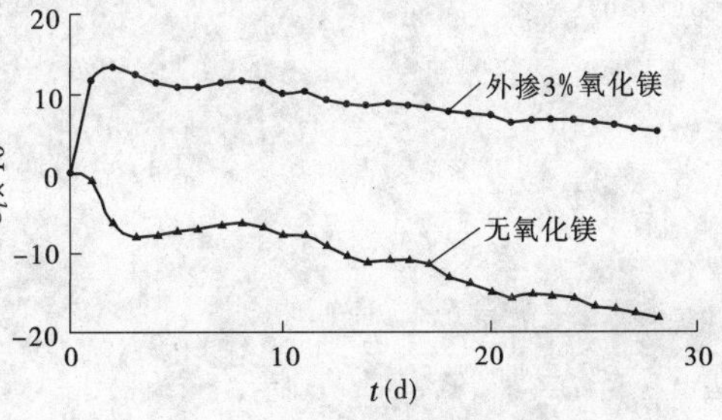

图 3 碾压混凝土的自生体积变形与龄期的关系

由图 3 可以看出，在 16℃ 试验温度条件下不外掺氧化镁碾压混凝土自生体积变形为收缩型；而外掺水泥用量 3% 氧化镁碾压混凝土的自生体积变形前期膨胀，后期才收缩，但是前期的膨胀变形相对后期收缩变形大，总体表现为膨胀。氧化镁混凝土的自生体积变形表现为膨胀还是收缩不仅取决于胶凝材料的水化作用，还取决于氧化镁的水化膨胀作用。早期混凝土的水化反应速度快，弹性模量较小，故早期的变形速率较大。总之，外掺氧化镁碾压混凝土的自生体积变形相对于不外掺氧化镁的碾压混凝土收缩变形明显减小。

4 结语

自生体积变形基准值的确定在自生体积变形的试验中具有举足轻重的作用，根据细观试验研究，认为以混凝土晶体构架形成初应力累计开始的时间作为自生体积变形测量的基准值较为合理。在对比和分析了国内外自生体积变形测定方法的基础上建立了更加合理的自生体积变形测定方法：高精度位移传感器法。外掺氧化镁和不外掺氧化镁碾压混凝土试验结果表明：早期的自生体积变形速率大，外掺氧化镁碾压混凝土的自生体积变形相对于不外掺氧化镁的碾压混凝土收缩变形小，有利于提高早期混凝土质量。

参 考 文 献

[1] 刘光廷，张国新，刘志辉. 含灌浆横缝碾压混凝土拱坝仿真应力和双轴强度判别. 清华大学学报，1996，36(1)：3～19

[2] Davis H E. *Autogenous volume change of concrete*. Proc of ASTM. 1940，40：1103～1110

[3] 关英俊. 混凝土自生体积变形试验研究. 见：中国水电科学研究院科学研究论文集. 北京：中国水电科学研究院，1982，138～146

[4] Tazawa E，Miyazawa S. *Experimental study on mechanism of autogenous shrinkage of concrete*. Cement and Concrete Research，1995，25(8)：1633～1638

[5] 安明喆，覃维祖，朱金铨. 高强混凝土的自收缩试验研究. 山东建材学院学报，1998，12(1)：139～143

RCC ARCH DAMS: CHINESE RESEARCH AND PRACTICE

Abstract Chinese research and design practice in RCC arch dam construction is reviewed, including: the use of short artificial joints to relieve thermal and hydraulic stress; the application of high-strength anti-crack materials; measures adopted to strengthen abutments; and the concept of a flexible arch for dams on weak rock foundations.

Adopting the large placement area in RCC dam construction can reduce the preparation work necessary for the monoliths in traditional concrete dams, and can increase the speed of construction. However, in complex construction conditions, defects at the joints between the layers can occur in the dam at the same elevation, decreasing the safety of a gravity-type structure, especially in the case of a high dam. An enlarged section is always recommended, to ensure the safety of a gravity-type structure. As a result, the material quantity, cost, equipment and amount of construction work are increased, and the construction period can be prolonged. Clearly, developments in engineering must include not only new materials and technology, but also new types of structure, calculations which simulate actual conditions more precisely, and new design methods.

If it is assumed that forces transfer mainly horizontally, an arch can remove the danger caused by any defects at the joints between the layers under hydraulic pressure. The stresses in a structure can be calculated accurtely to improve its design and its overall safety by simulation of the material properties and of the structure itself. The RCC arch dam has the advantages of a smaller volume, and hence a potential lower cost. This modern technique can offer the advantages of rapid construction, earlier impounding and good performance in terms of crack prevention. Extending the application of arch dams to cases of adverse climatic and geological conditions would represent valuable new progress in dam construction.

In 1990, research was carried out on the stresses of a multiple layer structure in the case of the Wenquanpu RCC arch dam. Based on the characteristics of the RCC, the calculations took into account temperature generation and creep (including the initial stress) and the development of multi-axial strength[1].

Research was carried out on: the stress distribution of the layered RCC structure[2] and the shear stress concentration at the edges of layers; deformation and stress redistribution of an arch dam with transverse joints; the stable depth of crack propagation at the arch dam heel (with installed seals for preventing hydraulic fracture); and stress redistribution in the

本文选自《Hydropower & Dams》2002 年第 3 期,作者还有 Li Penghui, Xie Shunan。

dam body.

The intervals between the transverse joints of the monolith in this case were 30m, which caused interference between spreading of the concrete and the roller compaction process. Concrete works and grouting continued for three years. Impounding was delayed to allow for gradual cooling of the dam.

1 The Xibing Thin Arch Dam

On the basis of research on multiple cracking in a dam body[3], three-dimensional fracture and thermal fracture, the research group studying stress and stability of high dams in the Department of Hydraulics and Hydropower Engineering, Tsinghua University, suggested in 1987～1988 that the problem of the tensile area in a large placement area of a RCC arch dam could be solved by providing artificial short joints to release stress, and by using high strength material at the tip of the joint to stabilize the cracks.

The first thin RCC arch dam (Xibing, in Fujian province) was designed in 1993 with a new shape based on simulation calculations. The dam height is 63.5m, the maximum thickness at the base is 12m, and the height-to-thickness ratio is 1∶0.189 (see Figs. 1 and 2).

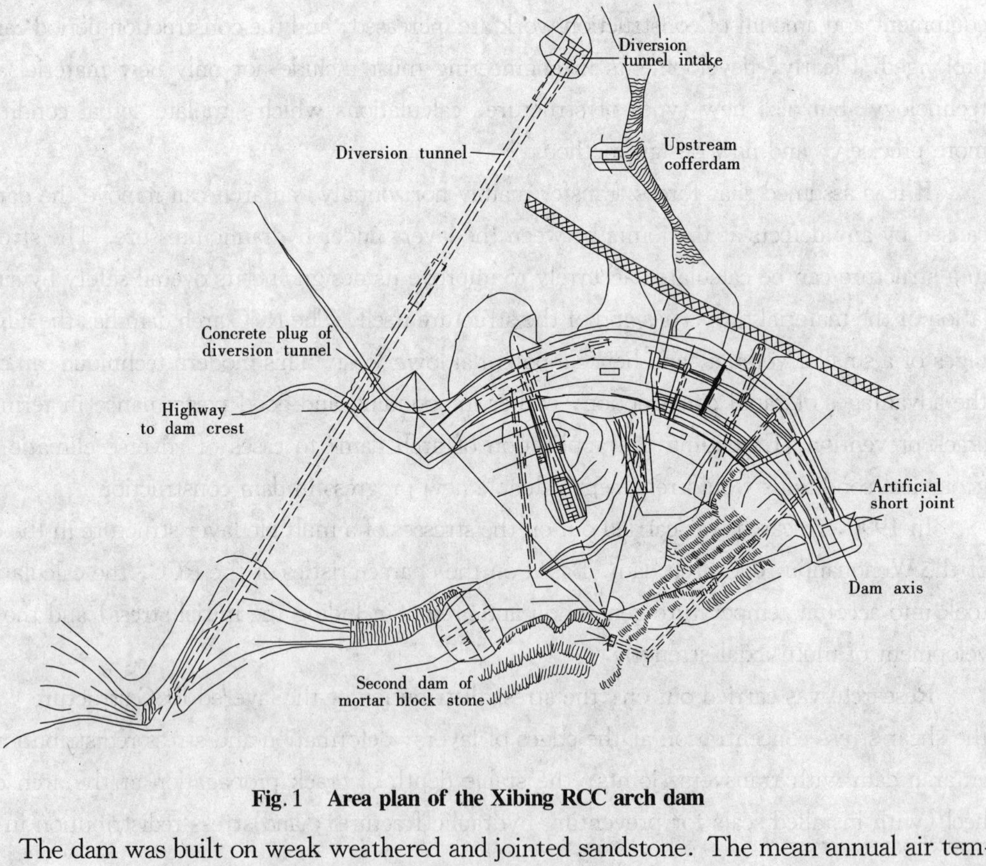

Fig. 1　Area plan of the Xibing RCC arch dam

The dam was built on weak weathered and jointed sandstone. The mean annual air temperature at the dam site, which is in a rainy area, is 18℃. There is a transverse joint in the

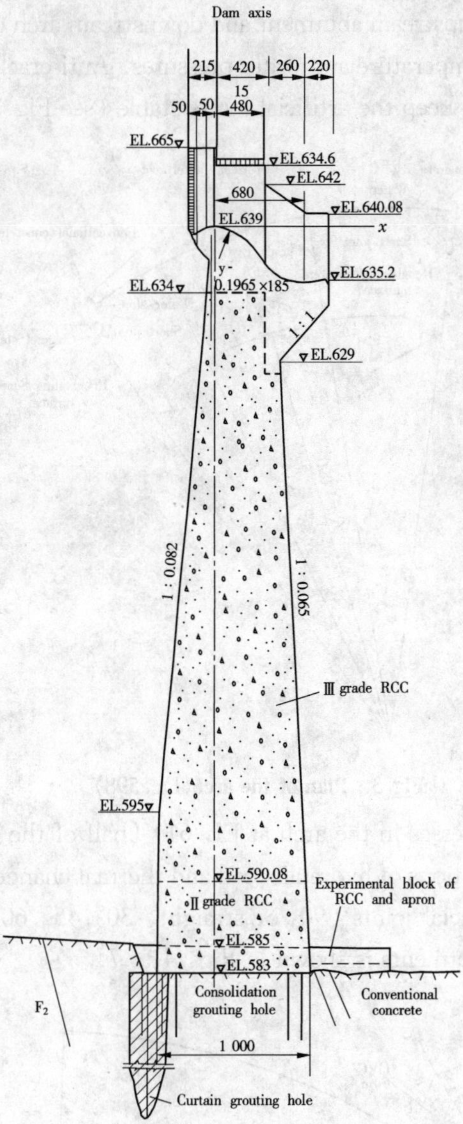

Fig. 2 The spillway profile

upper part of the dam. It is located at about two-thirds of the dam's height, but there are no other through joints in the lower part of the structure. The dam was rapidly built to two-thirds of its eventual height for flood protection. Concrete containing Grade 425 cement and a high flyash content was used, with a view to obtaining a low-temperature, high-strength RCC. This allowed continuous placement without relying on heat loss through the concrete surfaces. Substituting fine aggregates with a lower coefficient of thermal expansion into the normal aggregate decreased the stresses in the tensile area. The studies on the new structure and the characteristics of the new material provided the inputs for the 3D simulation of the temperature rise and development of stress within the dam during the various stages of construction[4]. To reduce tensile stress and to integrate any cracks into the structure, artificial joints were provided at the upstream abutment and downstream arch crown. These joints can release stresses caused by temperature and water pressures. Anti-crack measures were provided at the tip of the joints to keep the artificial joints stable (see Fig. 3).

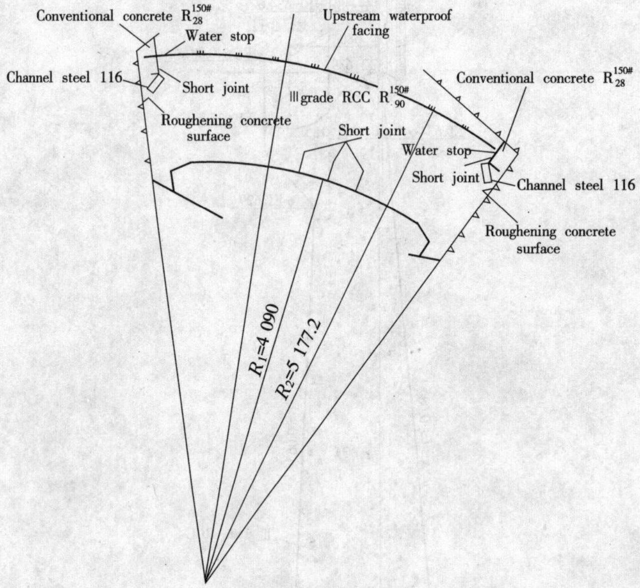

Fig. 3 Plan of the arch(EL. 598)

As an example, the stresses in the arch at EL. 611 (half of the dam height) have been compared for the same conditions of hydraulic load and thermal change. The influence of various kinds of upstream artificial joints (90° or straight, 30°, 45°, 60° and no joint) on the stress distribution in the abutments is shown in Figs. 4 to 7.

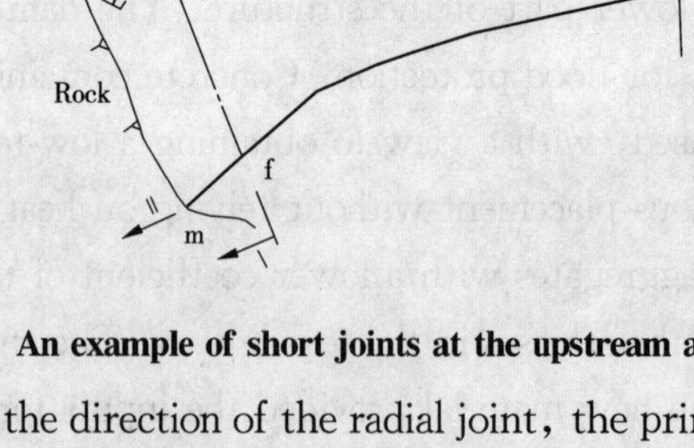

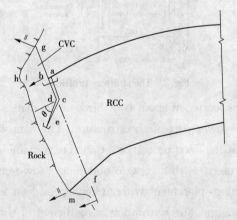

Fig. 4 An example of short joints at the upstream abutment

In section Ⅰ—Ⅰ along the direction of the radial joint, the principal tensile stress decreases from +3.9 MPa (no joint) to +0.3MPa(45°, curved joint) during hydraulic loading. The second principal stress also decreases from tensile stress +0.9MPa (no joint) to

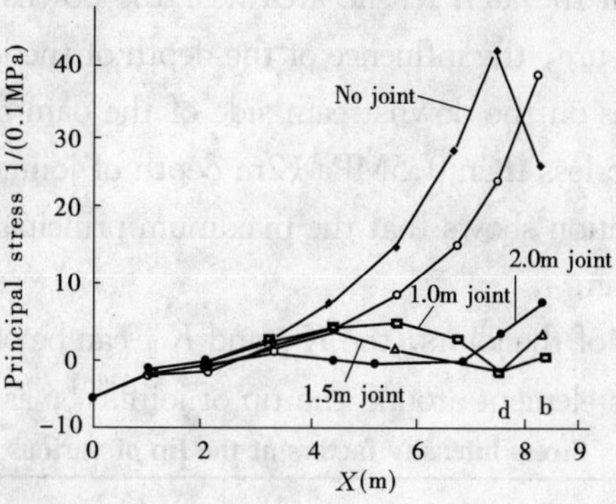

Fig. 5 Distribution of principal stresses along the profile of a straight joint

(upstream joint Ⅰ—Ⅰ, right bank, hydraulic load)

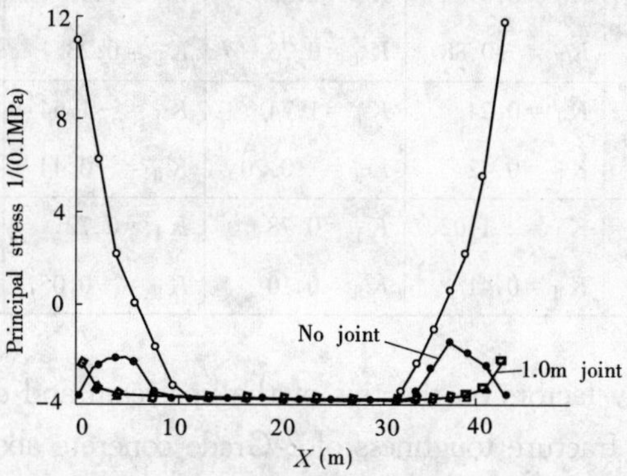

Fig. 6 Distribution of principal stresses along upstream surface of arch

(upstream joint, combined thermal field in March, right bank)

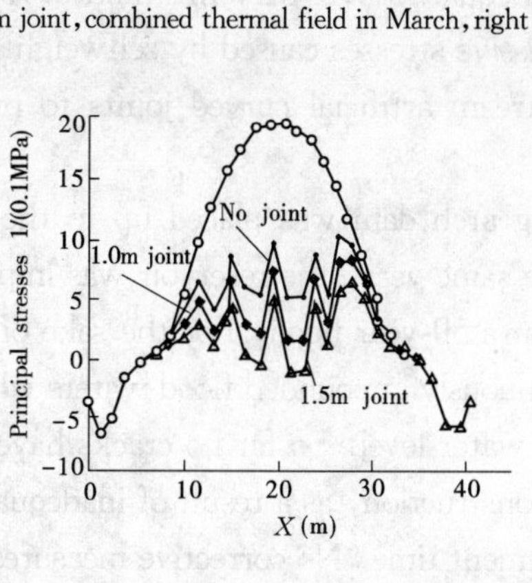

Arch length from the points on the downstream surface to the left bank

Fig. 7 Stresses along the downstream face of the arch (hydraulic load)

−0.4MPa in compression (45°, curved joint). The artificial joint reduces the tensile stress to zero in the 5m region near the upstream surface during these thermal changes (Fig. 6).

The influence of the downstream artificial joints on the stress in the arch is as follows.

Radial joints are arranged in the arch tensile area near the downstream surface of the arch dam. Under hydraulic pressure, the influence of the depth of the joints is considerable. The first principal tensile stresses on the downstream side of the dam decrease from a maximum value of 2MPa(no joints) to less than 0.5MPa (2m depth of joints), see Fig. 7. The stress distribution in the radial section shows that the maximum principal tensile stress area moves towards the centre of the dam.

Regarding the stability of the joints, the K_{I} and K_{II} can be obtained by the gauss-point stresses of the isoparametric element around the tip of joints[5], as shown in the Table 1.

Table 1 Stress intensity factors at the tip of various joints (unit: $MN/m^{3/2}$)

		Upstream artificial curved joints		Downstream crown artificial short joints		
		Left	Right	Left	Middle	Right
Combined load (including water pressure and thermal load)	March	$K_{\mathrm{I}}=0.69$	$K_{\mathrm{I}}=2.25$	$K_{\mathrm{I}}=0.59$	$K_{\mathrm{I}}=0.85$	$K_{\mathrm{I}}=-0.29$
		$K_{\mathrm{II}}=-0.88$	$K_{\mathrm{II}}=0.75$	$K_{\mathrm{II}}=0.23$	$K_{\mathrm{II}}=0.28$	$K_{\mathrm{II}}=0.24$
	July	$K_{\mathrm{I}}=0.24$	$K_{\mathrm{I}}=1.74$	$K_{\mathrm{I}}=-1.64$	$K_{\mathrm{I}}=-1.35$	$K_{\mathrm{I}}=-2.54$
		$K_{\mathrm{II}}=0.42$	$K_{\mathrm{II}}=-0.20$	$K_{\mathrm{II}}=-0.44$	$K_{\mathrm{II}}=0.15$	$K_{\mathrm{II}}=-0.58$
Only water pressure		$K_{\mathrm{I}}=-1.02$	$K_{\mathrm{I}}=0.78$	$K_{\mathrm{I}}=0.72$	$K_{\mathrm{I}}=0.75$	$K_{\mathrm{I}}=-0.08$
		$K_{\mathrm{II}}=0.41$	$K_{\mathrm{II}}=0.10$	$K_{\mathrm{II}}=-0.05$	$K_{\mathrm{II}}=-0.15$	$K_{\mathrm{II}}=0.20$

The stress intensity factors on the tips of the upstream and downstream joints are less than 1 $MN/m^{3/2}$. The fracture toughness of 3-Grade concrete above No. 200 is up to 2.0 $MN/m^{3/2}$; therefore the joints are stable. But the maximum value of K_{I} and K_{II} under complex loading in March is equal to 2.25$MN/m^{3/2}$ and 0.75$MN/m^{3/2}$ (not taking into account the favourable compressive stresses caused by selfweight). The high strength material was used at the tip of upstream artificial curved joints to prevent the propagation of the joints.

The RCC at the Xibing arch dam was placed up to the crest of the arch in only six months in 1995. During the same year, the reservoir was impounded and retained a 20-year flood, and the following year a 50-year flood. For the sake of increasing power production, for four years the dam continuously impounded flood waters which brought the reservoir level higher than the exceptional water level. So far no cracks have been found. Defects between the layers occurred during construction, as a result of inadequate construction equipment and the prolonged concrete placement time. No corrective measures were taken. The influence of these defects on the transfer of arch stress is not considered significant. The defects were grouted, however, to prevent leakage later.

2 The Shimenzi RCC Arch Dam

In 1997 this 109m-high RCC arch dam, with similar artificial short joints was constructed in a very cold area of North Xinjiang (the annual mean temperature is 4.1℃) and on weak foundations (arigillo-calcareous cemented conglomerate, the elastic modulus of which is only 4GPa). Limited by the carrying capacity of the rock, the maximum thickness of the arch dam foundation was enlarged to 30m. The height-to-width ratio is 1:0.27, and the valley is U-shaped. The silt-laden interlayers on both banks with a downstream orientation and the rudite foundation rocks divided by faults along the valley, created an unstable rock mass on both abutments, see Figs. 8 and 9.

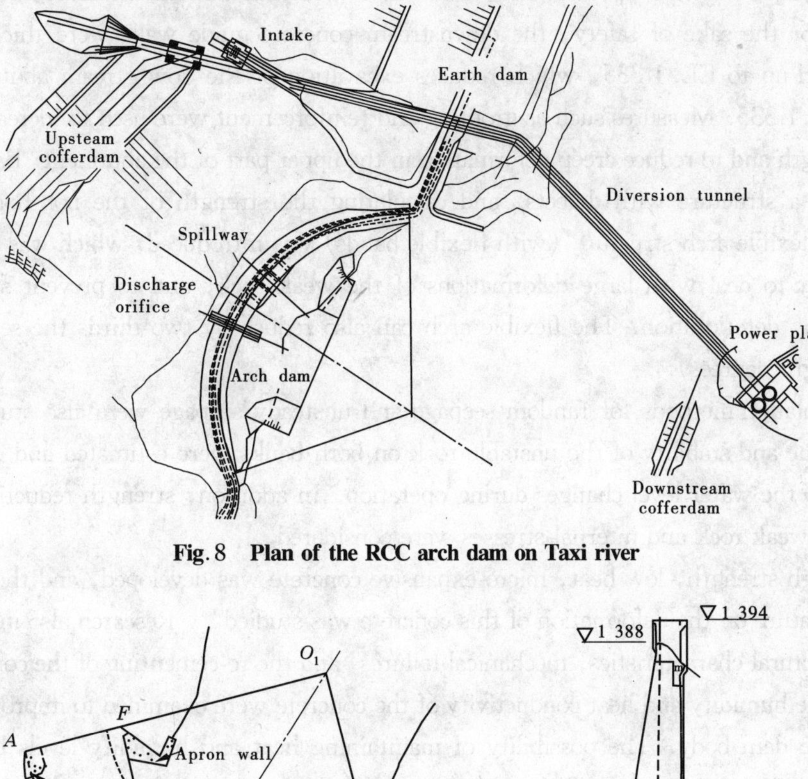

Fig. 8 Plan of the RCC arch dam on Taxi river

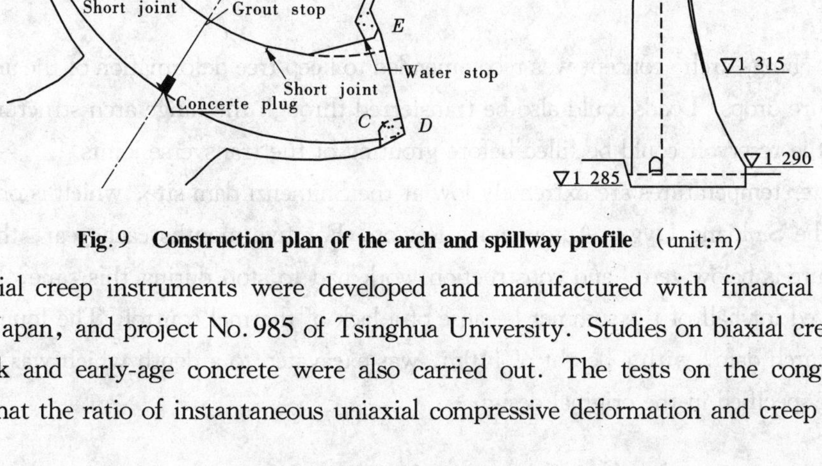

Fig. 9 Construction plan of the arch and spillway profile (unit:m)

Biaxial creep instruments were developed and manufactured with financial aid from JICA of Japan, and project No. 985 of Tsinghua University. Studies on biaxial creep of the weak rock and early-age concrete were also carried out. The tests on the conglomerates showed that the ratio of instantaneous uniaxial compressive deformation and creep deformation (viscoplasticity) was (2.0～2.6) : 1. The increasing rate in the long term is up to (1.5～1.2):1, and μ varies from 1/6.4 (small load, less than 30 per cent of ultimate strength) to 1/2.6 (large load, less than 50 per cent of the ultimate strength). There are only a few yielding elements on the right bank according to an FEM analysis of 3D visco-plasticity, and these are mainly distributed in the abutment between ELs. 1 284 and 1 310 and the upstream boundary of the F6 fault at the same level. The experiments showed that the strain of the biaxial compressive creep clearly decreases compared with the uniaxial compressive creep, which is up to 1:2.6, and this consideration could eliminate the yield elements. For the sake of safety, the downstream concrete guide walls were thickened and heightened up to EL. 1 335, which reduces excavation of the downstream abutment rock above EL. 1 335. Measures such as grouting and reinforcement were used to increase the lateral strength and to reduce creep deformation in the upper part of the abutment. Based on research on a structure with defects, and calculating the strength of the non-homogeneous body, a 'flexible arch structure' (with flexible bands) was introduced, which was considered appropriate to deal with large deformations of the weak rock, and to prevent stress from causing any deterioration. The flexible arch can also reduce by two-thirds the seismic arch stress (eight degrees).

Calculation methods for random seepage and unsteady seepage were also studied. The seepage line and stability of the unstable rock on both banks were estimated and checked in relation to the water level changes during operation. In addition, strength reductions in the saturated weak rock and internal stresses were considered.

A high strength, low heat, micro-expansive concrete was developed, and the influence of temperature on the deformation of this concrete was studied[6]. Research also included the microstructural characteristics, mechanical failures, and the re-cementing of the concrete material. The humidity and heat conductivity of the concrete were examined to improve dissipation in the dam body. The possibility of maintaining heat and humidity levels by using a polyurethane material was studied and monitored at the construction site, with a view to reducing the difference of temperature and humidity in the block during summer and winter time.

The 'hinge arch' concept was recommended to keep free deformation of the arch during temperature drops. Loads could also be transferred through the hinge arch structure, ensuring that the reservoir could be filled before grouting of the transverse joints.

Winter temperatures are extremely low at the Shimenzi dam site, which is on the Taxi river in the Sinkiang Uygur Autonomous Region. For five months each year, the average temperature is below zero, and construction work had to stop during this time. Work was also delayed for half of the summer because of a lack of thermal control. The foundation for the RCC arch dam, with a height of 110m, was excavated to a depth which was 1.0m less than that specified in the original design.

Work on the foundation concrete (EL. 1 285) began in June 1999. The arch dam reached EL. 1 365m in eleven months (despite some days when the placement was delayed in the summer). The maximum monthly placement rate was equivalent to 15m of the dam's height. To avoid deformations during the decrease in temperature in the dam, an expansive concrete was used to fill a joint in the dam to form the hinge arch. The reservoir was filled up to EL. 1 348(63m deep) for the irrigation season in the spring after completion. Concrete was placed up to the crest elevation in 15 months. No cracking occurred during the winter as a result of protection with sand, water or a polyurethane foam layer. Cracks occurred in the gallery (at EL. 1 289m) because the placing temperature of the concrete exceeded the required temperature by 6℃. These were repaired by grouting. The present unit cost of the RCC per unit volume is 180 Chinese yuan, which is cheaper than the cost of conventional concrete with the same strength (260 Chinese yuan). More than 10 per cent was thus saved on investment costs for the project.

3 Conclusions

The experience which has been described shows that, if topographical conditions and the available materials are suitable for a concrete dam, an RCC arch dam can be built with enlarged concrete blocks. This has the advantages of: transferring forces through the horizontal arch to eliminate the effect of any horizontal joint defects; ensuring an overall improved quality for the structure; reducing preparation work; achieving a faster construction time, thus allowing for earlier filling of the reservoir; reducing the amount of cement required; simplifying thermal control; and, reducing costs. It would therefore be valuable to refine this technique further, to allow for its wider application.

References

[1] Liu Guangting, Zhang Guoxin, Liu Zhihui. *Simulation stresses of RCC arch dam with transverse joints and biaxial strength criteria*. Journal of Tsinghua University (in Chinese), Beijing, China, 1996(1)

[2] Liu Guangting, Hao Jutao. *Simplified numerical method in stress analysis of RCC arch dam with layer structure*. Journal of Tsinghua University(in Chinese), Beijing, China, 1996(1)

[3] Liu Guangting, Zhou Ruizhong. *Strength of a finite body with multiple cracks*. Engineering Fracture Mechanics, No. 35, 1990

[4] Liu Guangting, Mai Jiaxuan, Zhang Guoxin. *Research on XiBing Roller Compacted Concrete Thin Arch Dam*. Journal of Hydroelectric Engineering(in Chinese), Beijing, 1977

[5] Pekau, O. A., Zhang, Z. X., Liu, G. T. *Constitutive model for concrete in strain space*. Journal of Engineering Mechanics. 1992(9)

[6] Liu Guangting, Li Penghui, Hu Yu. *The RCC arch dam structure on taxi river and water storage measure during construction*. Proceedings, International Symposium on RCCD, ChengDu, China, 1999

RCC ARCH DAM STRUCTURE ON THE TAXI RIVER AND WATER STORAGE MEASURE DURING CONSTRUCTION

Abstract　The new structure of roller compacted concrete (RCC) arch dams is presented for extremely cold and earthquake prone areas. The influence of construction plans and improved materials on the stresses in the Taxi River dam is also given. Earlier impoundment of water is shown to not only benefit the engineering design but also improve the stresses during construction in winter. Low cement content in the concrete and artificial short joints improved the monolithic structure and the transmitted forces. The concrete plug installed in the first cooled part of the arch dam provides excellent force transmission in the arch, which increases the monolith of the earlier arch, reduces the increasing thermal stresses that occur later, and improves the deformation flexibility of the dam.

Key words　roller compacted concrete (RCC) arch dam; artificial short joint; concrete plug

1　Introduction

The Taxi River Hydraulic Project is located in the Shimen Gorge section in the middle section of the Taxi River in Manasi County, Xinjiang Uygur Autonomous Region. The gorge is about 350m long with a U-shaped valley and is about 70～80m wide at the bottom. The roller compacted concrete (RCC) arch dam is 109m high. The penstock tunnel for the 6.4MW hydropower station and the diversion tunnel pass through the long and narrow mountain ridge in the middle of the riverbed. There is an old river channel on the left bank, comprised of porous sand pebbles. Therefore, a sloping core earth-fill dam with a non-porous concrete wall was built on the foundation there.

The bank and riverbed are comprised of caesious and red rudite. When soaked, the deformation modulus of red rudite is 4 GPa and some samples collapse, so the dam should have a flexible structure to allow for deformation. The stratified conglomerate angles downstream at about 30° to the riverbed. The stratified conglomerates have several mud interlayers. A sharp declined fault F_6 in the abutment to the right bank extends from upstream to downstream. The fault and the mud interlayer make up the unstable part of the right bank. Therefore, the abutment needs to be nonporous and fixed against sliding.

Strong earthquakes frequently occur at the dam site, so the arch dam is designed for an earthquake intensity of more than 8° on the Richter scale.

本文选自《Tsinghua Science and Technology》2002 年第 3 期，作者还有 Li Penghui，Hu Yu，Zhang Fude，Xie Shunan。

The winter is extremely cold at the dam site with five months annually when the average temperature is below 0℃. The summer temperatures can reach 38℃, so the good concrete placing time is short. Therefore, the thermal stresses and the tensile stress concentrations caused by the water pressure are reduced using artificial short joints at the abutment and the middle joint at the arch crown. The upstream area of the dam where the temperature drops earlier has a concrete hinge, which can maintain the horizontal shape of the arch as the temperature drops. Water storage began seven months after construction of the RCC dam. The RCC arch dam was finished after one and a half years.

2 Taxi River RCC Arch Dam

The RCC arch dam is 109m high; the arch length at the crest is 176.5m. For construction convenience, there is no inverse slope. The dam is multi-centered. In areas with a poor foundation, the dam contact area with the foundation rock is enlarged and thickened to reduce stresses. The thickest part at the intrados is 31m and $H:V=0.284$. The crest elevation is 1 394m and the crest width is 5m. The softening of the rock which occurs when it is soaked with water is reduced by taking effective anti-penetration measures and by adding drainage facilities to keep the rock dry and stabilize the foundation. The project layout is shown in Fig. 1.

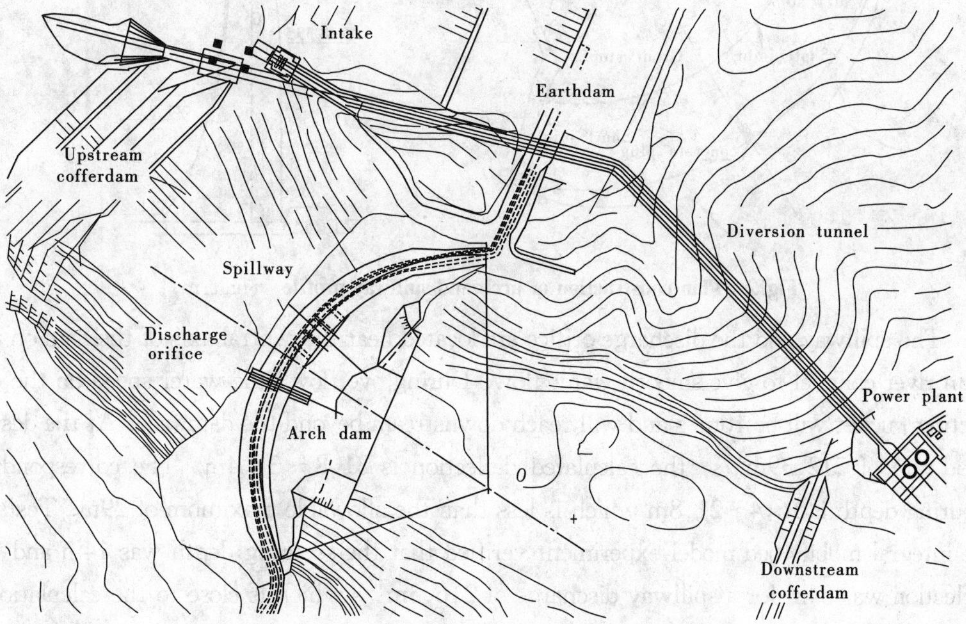

Fig. 1 The layout of the Taxi river RCC arch dam

To take advantage of the continuous placement of concrete on a broad surface used in the RCC construction method to reduce stresses in the dam, during construction a transverse joint was installed above EL. 1 288m. A concrete plug was installed close to the upstream end of the transverse joint to transfer the arch force as water was stored during construction. A grout system was installed at the edge of the plug and in the transverse joint for later grouting. An artificial short joint was installed upstream of both abutments to reduce the tensile stresses caused by the water pressure and the temperature drop. The joint is 2～4m long and extends radially towards the lower stress area. The upstream end of the joint has a watertight seal and the downstream end has 16# channel steel to prevent cracking. Above EL. 1 295m, the dam has downstream artificial short joints 25m apart from the middle axis. The joints extend radially and are 1.5m deep and also reduce the downstream arch tensile stresses due to the water load and the temperature drop in the middle part of the dam. The upper part of the dam (EL. 1 375～1 394m) has transverse joints to permanently reduce thermal stresses during operation which compensate for the downstream cantilever tensile stress at the middle part of the dam, due to the water storage which bends the dam from the upper part, as shown in Fig. 2.

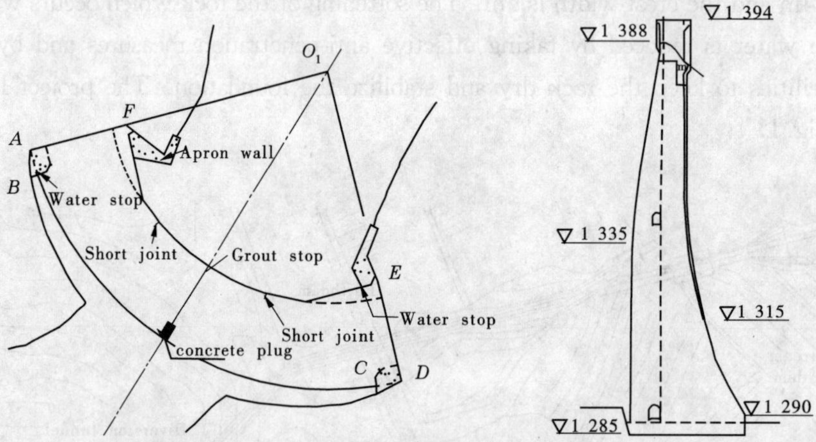

Fig. 2 Plan construction of arch and spillway profile (unit: m)

The spillway and the discharge orifice are located near the central axis of the dam on the main river channel to give smooth water flow. During overflow, the water speed on the deflecting bucket will be 10m/s and will reach downstream beyond the dam face. At the design flood rate of 212.39m^3/s, the calculated deflection is 31.8～38.4m. The corresponding scouring depth is 16.4～21.8m which is less than the allowable maximum of 29m. Tests in the integral mobile bed model experiment verified that the scouring depth was 14m and the deflection was 34m for a spillway discharge of 216.3m^3/s which is close to the calculational value.

The discharge orifice works in special flood conditions, during construction, when emptying the reservoir or when providing irrigation water in dry years. The orifice lies on the right side of the spillway of crest. The central axis of the discharge orifice and the central axis of the arch dam intersect at an angle of 9° to direct the water flow in the main channel direction. In very dry years, the irrigation water flow rate must be more than $30m^3/s$, so the drainage orifice opening must be 2.0m×2.0m. The level of the orifice central axis is at 1 334.0m.

3 RCC Arch Dam Construction Materials and Techniques

Aggregate gravel was readily available 1.8~2.5km from the dam site and transport was convenient. The aggregates generally met the specifications except that the mud content in the fine aggregates was somewhat high. Silicate 525# cement produced by a local cement factory for the dam had the proper shrinkage as verified by experiments for the concrete autogenous volume change. Class Ⅱ flyash was provided by the Manasi power plant. The cement content of the RCC concrete in the inner part of the dam was limited to $60kg/m^3$ with a content of cement and flyash exceeding $170kg/m^3$ [1]. The cement content of the external anti-seepage and anti-freezing concrete was less than $90kg/m^3$. MgO was mixed with the cement to compensate for the concrete autogenous volume deformation to reduce cracking.

Steel molds with 3.6m height were used for continuous placement of the RCC. They rose in a continuously alternating pattern with the spacing adjustable. Each layer was always 30~35cm thick unless the placing area was 27cm. The allowable interval between layers was eight hours. Below EL. 1 344m the concrete was directly transported by trucks to the placing areas with a bulldozer assisted by a loader used to even it. The concrete was then compacted by a 11-t vibratory roller. Above EL. 1 344m, a vacuum chute on the left side of the bank transported the concrete. The concrete was first transported by trucks from the mixer plant to the left bank of the dam along a temporary road. Then the concrete was loaded into the hopper from which it was sent to the placing area by the vacuum chute. The concrete was then also evened by the bulldozer or loader and compacted by the vibrating roller.

The RCC of the main dam was placed on April 1, 1999. By June 25, the dam height was at EL. 1 333m. The concrete plug in the transverse joint was grouted at EL. 1 300m. When the air temperature was above 14℃, the concrete placing and curing temperatures were kept at 14℃ by cooling the aggregate or curing with river water. Heat insulation was not installed on the downstream face of the dam during this period. The concrete construction was stopped during the summer. From Sept. 11 to Nov. 5, the dam was raised to EL. 1 365m, with an upstream water level of 1 357.5m and a downstream water level of 1 319.0m. Heat insulation was applied up to EL. 1 365m on the downstream face of the dam. The plug in the transverse joint was filled to EL. 1 360m before the end of March 2000. Before May 31, 2000 the level was EL. 1 394m, which is the top of the dam with the concrete plug up to 1 375m. All of the middle joint was grouted before March 2001.

4 Effect of Construction Plan and Material Characteristics on Dam Stresses

A simulation was used to analyze the temperature and load accumulated during the actual concrete placement process. The analysis considered the change of the arch dam shape and the mechanical and thermal parameters. The creep stresses including the thermal stress and the accumulated weight stress were considered. The water stored during construction not only applied hydraulic pressure to the dam but also changed the temperature boundary condition, which must be considered for accurate simulation of the stresses.

4.1 Influence of Water Storage on the RCC Arch Dam Stresses

Water storage began when the dam reached EL. 1 365m in the winter of 1999. From EL. 1 286.5m to EL. 1 288m, the upstream water pressure and the restraints of the foundation caused the tensile stresses at the dam heel. However, the temperature inside the concrete increased after placement so compressive stresses caused by the increased temperature nearly compensated the tensile stresses due to the water pressure, which reduced the tensile stresses near the foundation to a maximum tensile stress of less than 1.0MPa.

The middle part of the dam was placed in June when the temperatures were high, so the placing temperature and the maximum concrete temperature increase was high. After the end of Oct. 1999, the thermal differences between the outside and the inside of the concrete increased. If the reservoir was empty, tensile stresses occurred at both the upstream and downstream surfaces from EL. 1 319m to EL. 1 333m, even in the presence of the thermal insulation protection. In Jan. 2000, the tensile stresses continued to increase to a maximum arch tensile stress of 1.74MPa near EL. 1 330m(Fig. 3).

If the reservoir water level was kept at EL. 1 357.5m in the winter of 1999, the stress at the upstream surface in Jan. 2000 would be acceptable with the tensile stresses replaced by compressive stresses. Moreover, the tensile stresses at the downstream surface were also greatly reduced, with a maximum of 1.17MPa, less than the allowable tensile strength. The simulation stress criterion during the construction is controlled by the ultimate strength. When the weather became warm in the spring of 2000 and dam height increased to the crest, the stresses were better (Fig. 4).

Therefore, storage of water in advance greatly benefited not only the spring irrigation in 2000, but also the stresses in the dam.

4.2 RCC Arch Dam Stresses at the End of Construction

At the end of the construction phase, the water was filled to EL. 1 390m in May 2000 when the dam height was EL. 1 394m and the concrete plug was backfilled to EL. 1 375m.

On the dam foundation, from EL. 1 286.5m to EL. 1 288.0m, the water pressure generates large tensile stresses. The maximum transversal tensile stress σ_x is 2.2MPa. However, the creep stresses due to the temperature and the accumulated weight generated large compressive stresses at the same place, which reduces part of the tensile stresses[2]. Consequently, the combined transversal tensile stresses σ_x is decreased to 1.25MPa and σ_y (opposite to the water flow direction) is 1.74MPa. The micro-expansion concrete will prevent cracks in the concrete foundation. Therefore, the placing arch dam foundation must be care-

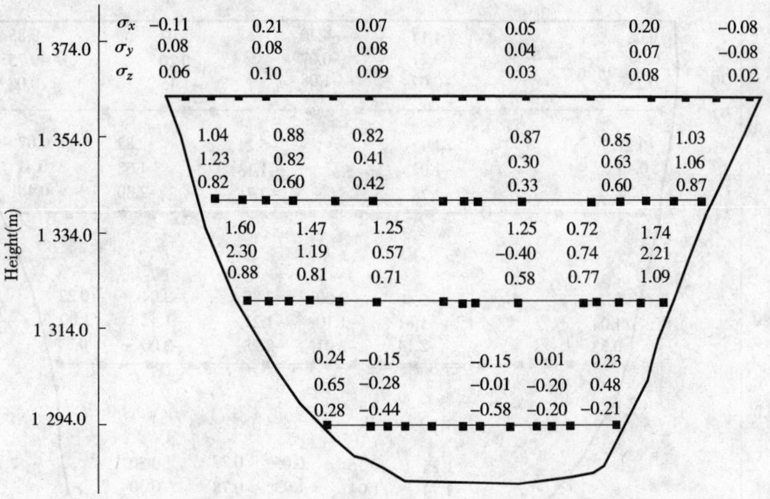

Fig. 3 Normal stresses on downstream face, Jan. 20, 2000
(Concrete plug: EL. 1 300m; temperature + weight, unit: MPa)

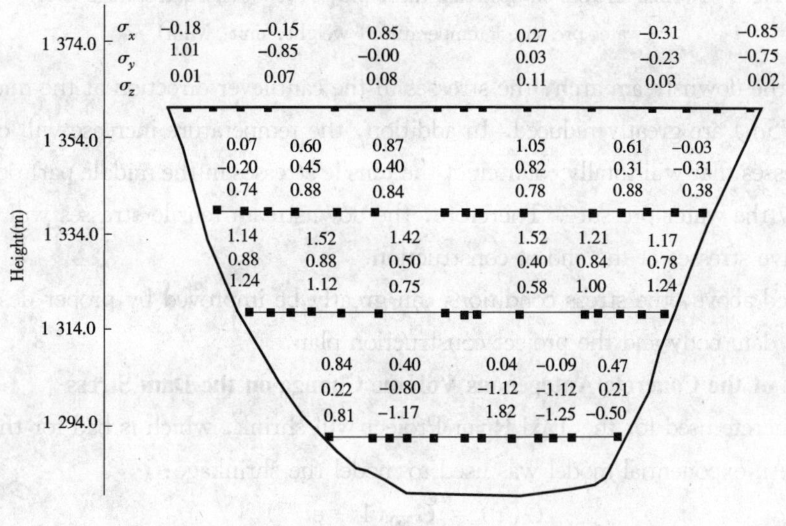

Fig. 4 Normal stresses on downstream face, Jan. 20, 2000
(Concrete plug: EL. 1 300m; water pressure + temperature + weight, unit: MPa)

fully timed to reduce the tensile stresses.

For the middle part of the dam (EL. 1 314~1 375m), as the temperature increases and the concrete plug in the middle joint is backfilled to EL. 1 375m, local stress concentration at the arch crown due to the water pressure is −5.21MPa at EL. 1 354m (Fig. 5).

At the top of the dam, the transverse joints greatly relieve the stresses so that large tensile stresses do not occur (except for dynamic loads). Some tensile stresses occur on the downstream dam surface due to the water pressure[3]. Because the moments generated by the water pressure due to the transverse joints on the dam top and the radial artificial short joints

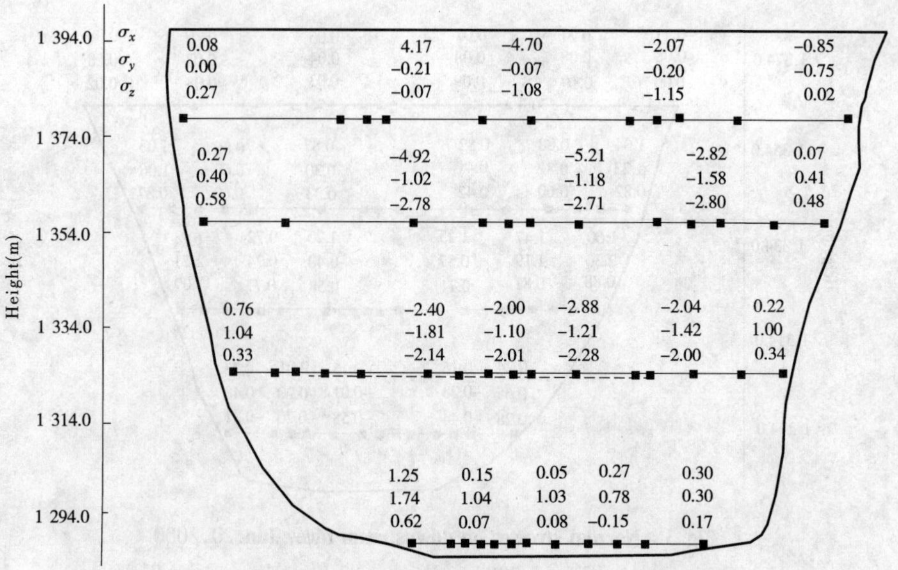

Fig. 5　Normal stresses on upstream face, May 31, 2000 (normal storage level)

(water pressure + temperature + weight, unit: MPa)

are set into the downstream arch, the stresses in the cantilever direction at the middle (EL. 1 314~1 375m) are greatly reduced. In addition, the temperature increase will cause compressive stresses that will totally counteract the tensile stresses in the middle part downstream generated by the water pressure. Therefore, the downstream tensile stresses will all change to compressive stresses at the end of construction.

As stated above, the stress conditions can greatly be improved by proper design of the joints in the dam body and the project construction plan.

4.3　Effect of the Concrete Autogenous Volume Change on the Dam Stress

The concrete used for the Taxi River Project will shrink, which is bad for the concrete stresses[4]. An exponential model was used to model the shrinkage:

$$G(\tau) = G_{360}(1 - e^{-m\tau})$$

where $G(\tau)$ is the concrete autogenous volume change (m^3) at time τ, τ is the age (day), m is the rate of the deformation coefficient ($=0.035\text{day}^{-1}$), G_{360} is the total concrete autogenous volume change.

The advantage of this model is that it requires little memory, does not need the stress history and the coefficient is easily determined.

The date in Table 1 shows that the concrete autogenous volume change mainly affects the arch stresses and has little influence on the stresses in the cantilever direction. The maximum effect is about 0.2MPa, especially at the upstream abutment. Since the stresses are large near the bottom of the RCC arch dam, MgO was added to the cement for elevations less than 1 334.0m to improve the stresses.

Table 1 Stresses with and without concrete autogenous volume change (unit: MPa)

Condition		Upstream dam face		Downstream dam face		Concrete inside dam	
		Left abutment	Right abutment	Left abutment	Right abutment	Left abutment	Right abutment
With							
concrete	σ_x	0.66	0.51	-0.01	0.00	0.28	0.43
autogenous	σ_y	0.45	0.27	0.03	0.03	0.21	0.35
volume change	σ_z	0.56	0.29	0.01	0.01	0.17	0.31
Without							
concrete	σ_x	0.59	0.34	-0.07	-0.11	0.18	0.29
autogenous	σ_y	0.40	0.19	-0.06	-0.13	0.17	0.31
volume change	σ_z	0.53	0.28	0.07	0.00	0.16	0.31

Note: The data assume the dam begins at EL. 1 294.0m on Jan. 20, 1999 according to the concrete placement plan.

5 New Arch Dam Desing with Improved Stresses

5.1 Stress Improvement for Arch Dam with Artificial Short Joints

The water pressure and the temperature decrease with the constrained abutment will generate tensile stress concentrations on the upstream abutment. Therefore, an artificial short joint with a water stop was added to the upstream abutment (Fig. 2) to reduce or eliminate the local tensile stresses and change principal stress directions with the water pressure.

The arch at EL. 1 335.0m will be used as an example for the hydraulic pressure analysis. Water stops are installed near the upstream end of the short joints. Since the joints have drainage pipes, the pressure in the joints is eliminated. The artificial short joints in both abutments are 45° bending joints[5]. Concrete is backfilled in an excavation upstream and downstream of the abutment to make a rigid end of the arch. The calculated results are shown in Table 2.

Table 2 Stresses with and without 45° bending joint (unit: MPa)

Condition	Stresses	*A*	*B*	*C*	*D*	*E*	*F*
With 45° bending joint	σ_x	-0.51	1.13	0.87	-0.56	-1.87	-1.83
	σ_y	0.44	1.62	1.14	0.22	-3.55	-3.49
	σ_z	0.01	0.46	0.33	-0.07	-1.10	-1.11
Without 45° bending joint	σ_x	-0.52	4.77	4.20	-0.56	-1.87	-1.82
	σ_y	0.68	2.10	1.67	0.34	-3.50	-3.45
	σ_z	0.07	1.13	0.98	-0.01	-1.10	-1.10

As shown in Table 2, the maximum tensile stress is at point *B* (or *C*) with a value of 4.8MPa without the 45° bending joints, which exceeds the concrete bearing capacity. With the artificial short joints in both abutments, the maximum tensile stress is reduced to 1.1MPa. The tensile stresses in the other two directions are also greatly reduced. The principal stress is transferred along the artificial short joint to the end of the joint which is located in a lower stress region. 16# channel steel is embedded in the joint end to prevent crack propagation. These methods could also be used to improve the tensile stress concentration in the upstream abutments (The strain intensity factor and the combined concrete toughness with the channel steel will be published in another paper).

5.2 Effect of the Middle Joint and Concrete Plug on Dam Body Stresses

To facilitate continuous placement of RCC on a broad surface and to reduce the thermal stresses in the dam, a transverse joint was installed above the height of 1 288.0m. The concrete plug in the transverse joint near the upstream will cool faster and will transfer the arch force when the reservoir is storing water during construction. The grouting system is near the concrete plug boundary and in the transverse joint for grouting later. The transmission mechanism of the arch force by the concrete plug was studied by analyzing several different regions of the concrete plug for a normal water level of 1 390.0m. The different regions of the expanded concrete plug are shown in Fig. 6. The calculational results are listed in Table 3.

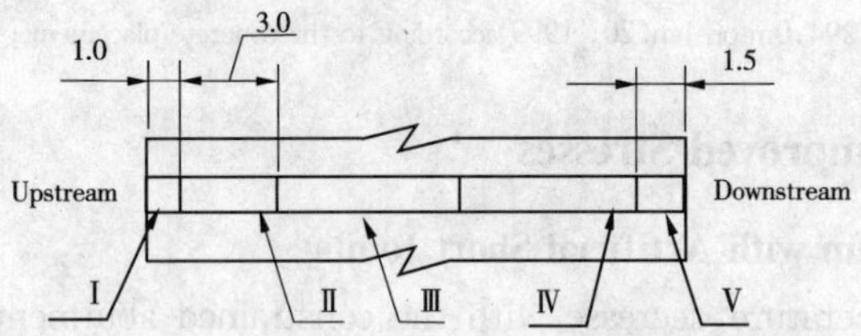

Fig. 6 Calculational area of the expanded concrete (unit: m)

Table 3 Stresses with different concrete plug lengths (unit: MPa)

Condition	Stresses	Ⅰ	Ⅰ+Ⅱ	Ⅰ+Ⅱ+Ⅲ	Ⅰ+Ⅱ+Ⅲ+Ⅳ	Ⅰ+Ⅱ+Ⅲ+Ⅳ+Ⅴ
Maximum upstream compressive stress at EL. 1 365.0m	σ_x	-8.51	-2.30	-3.34	-3.77	-3.81
	σ_y	1.14	-0.32	-0.26	-0.28	-0.28
	σ_z	-0.34	-0.04	-0.26	-0.36	-0.36
Maximum upstream compressive stress at EL. 1 343.0m	σ_x	-7.40	-2.66	-3.43	-3.76	-3.78
	σ_y	1.00	-0.61	-0.47	-0.48	-0.48
	σ_z	-1.15	-0.80	-1.08	-1.19	-1.20
Maximum upstream compressive stress at EL. 1 312.0m	σ_x	-5.46	-2.19	-2.37	-2.36	-2.35
	σ_y	-0.00	-1.03	-0.91	-0.19	-0.91
	σ_z	-0.58	-0.26	-0.27	-0.91	-0.18
Maximum downstream tensile stress at EL. 1 365.0m	σ_x	0.43	-0.67	-1.13	-1.28	-1.29
	σ_y	-0.01	-0.04	-0.08	-0.08	-0.08
	σ_z	0.50	0.28	0.12	0.09	0.08
Maximum downstream tensile stress at EL. 1 343.0m	σ_x	1.45	0.62	-0.22	-0.57	-0.58
	σ_y	0.17	0.15	0.10	0.07	0.07
	σ_z	1.09	0.97	0.76	0.71	0.71
Maximum downstream tensile stress at EL. 1 312.0m	σ_x	0.71	0.60	0.38	0.47	0.48
	σ_y	-0.15	-0.15	-0.17	-0.17	-0.17
	σ_z	-0.37	-0.23	-0.25	-0.23	-0.22
Maximum compressive stress on right downstream abutment at EL. 1 354.0m	σ_x	-2.68	-2.45	-2.36	-2.33	-2.33
	σ_y	-3.15	-2.86	-2.74	-2.71	-2.71
	σ_z	-0.65	-0.55	-0.51	-0.50	-0.49

Concrete plugs are installed only up to EL. 1 375m. Consider the date at EL. 1 365.0m and EL. 1 343.0m as an example.

(1) If the concrete plug is too thin, for example, 1.0m in case Ⅰ, the stress concentration will be much larger in the upper part of the arch dam with a maximum compressive stress of −8.5MPa at the height of 1 365.0m. However, with the thick concrete plug, for example, 4.0m in case Ⅰ+Ⅱ, the stress concentration on the upstream arch crown will be much less than the maximum compressive strength. If the concrete plug is thicker, the maximum compressive stress on the upstream arch crown increases compared to case Ⅰ+Ⅱ because of the action of the arch. When the concrete plug fills the whole transverse joint, the maximum compressive stress is −3.8MPa.

(2) On the downstream surface, when the concrete plug thickness is just 1.0m, the tensile stresses in the middle part of dam body are quite large with the maximum arch tensile stress of 1.45MPa at an elevation of 1 343m. For a concrete plug thickness of 4.0m, the tensile stress on the downstream face is reduced to only 0.62MPa with the tensile stresses in the cantilever direction also reduced. When the concrete plug thickness increases further, the arch tensile stress at the same point gradually changes to a compressive stress. When the concrete plug fills the whole transverse joint, the maximum arch compressive stress will be −0.58MPa with the tensile stresses in the cantilever direction reduced to 0.7MPa.

Therefore, a concrete plug with a thickness of 4m is quite enough to transfer the arch force in the arch dam. Therefore, partial grouting of the arch on the upstream side and water storage during construction will benefit the engineering design.

(3) The data in Table 3 shows that when the concrete plug only partially fills the arch section, the stresses in two cases (Ⅰ+Ⅱ and Ⅰ+Ⅱ+Ⅲ+Ⅳ+Ⅴ) are very close with the hydraulic load. Therefore, concrete could be grouted into just part of the transverse joint during construction instead of the whole joint to maximize transfer of the arch force by the concrete plug during water storage. The plug will also increase the flexibility of the arch dam which will improve the thermal stresses caused by the temperature decrease later.

6 Simulation of the Combined Stresses in the RCC Arch Dam

The 3-D temperature and creep-stress fields in the RCC arch dam were simulated from the beginning to the end of construction[6]. The temperature stress will then change from the end of construction to the steady-state temperature field during operation. The combined stresses are the sum of the accumulated thermal stresses, the weight and the water pressure during operation.

The stresses in Fig. 7 show that tensile stresses occur on the upstream abutment and on both lower parts of the upstream and downstream faces in March during operation. In the arch dam foundation, the maximum σ_x tensile stress on the dam heel is 1.4MPa, and the radial σ_y tensile stress is 1.88MPa. Micro-expansion concrete is used to reduce the tensile

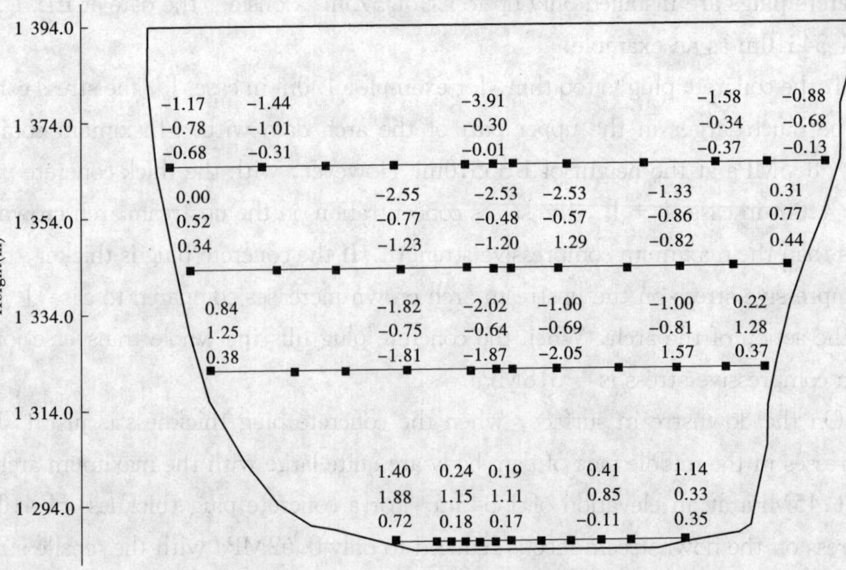

Fig. 7 Normal stresses on the upstream face during operation in March (unit: MPa)

stress. Some tensile stresses will occur in the dam toe, but all values are less than 1.2MPa.

Although PF consumes more time/memory as the number of particles grows, PF is a powerful tool for dealing with nonlinear filtering problems such as INS alignment.

References

[1] Huillet T, Salut G. *Interpretation des équations du filtrage non-linéaire*. In Séances du GDR Automatique du CNRS (Póle non-linéaire), Paris, Nov.8,1989

[2] Gordon N J, Salmond D J, Smith A F M. *Novel approach to nonlinear/non-Gaussian Bayeaian state estimation*. In: IEEE Proceedings, Pt. F,140,2(Oct.1992), 107~113

[3] Del Moral P. *Resolution particulaire des problémes d'estimation et d'optimisation non-linéaires*. Thése de 1'Université Paul Sabatier, LAAS-CNRS, Toulouse, 1994

[4] Carvalho H, Monin A, Sault G. *Filtrage optimal non-linéaire du signal GPS NAVSTAR en recalage de centrales de navigation*. Report LAAS 94534, 1994

[5] Carvalho H, Moral P. *Optimal nonlinear filtering in GPS/INS integration*. IEEE Trans. AES, 1997, 33(3): 835~849

[6] Dmitriyev S P, Stepanov O A. *Nonlinear filtering methods application in INS alignment*. IEEE Tran. AES, 1997, 33(1): 260~271

[7] Kong Xiaoying, Eduardo M N, Hugh D W. *Development of a nonlinear psi-angle model for large misalignment errors and its application in INS alignment and calibration*. In: Proceedings of the 1999 IEEE International Conference on Rootics & Automation. Michigan: Detroit, 1999: 1430~1435

[8] Arshal George. *Error equations of inertial navigation*. Journal of Guidance, Control and Dynamics, 1987,10: 351~358

[9] Bar-Itzhack Itzhack Y, Berman N. *Control theory approach to inertial navigation systems*. Journal of Guidance, 1988, 11(3): 147~152

RESEARCH AND PRACTICE OF ROLLER-COMPACTED CONCRETE ARCH DAMS

Abstract In present paper messages of research, design and practice of three RCC arch dams since 1990 are introduced. New structures with artificial short joints were induced for thermal and hydraulic stress release. Anticrack (high toughness) materials were installed at the end of joint for stability of crack. Studies on biaxial creep of weak rock and early-age concrete show evidently increasing in strength and reducing deformation in compare with uniaxial. Artificial side restraints (concrete wall support or shallow anchored rock) were used to strengthen bank. The mechanical and thermal parameters used for 3-D actual simulated program were measured corresponding to constructional conditions. Flexible arch was introduced for large deformation of arch dam on weak rock foundation without stress deterioration and "hinge arch" for early filling reservoir before grouting transverse joint was recommended.

1 Introduction

With the progress of the material and technology of concrete in recent years, dry concrete with less cement and a faster roller compacted method are adopted for the construction of concrete dam. Comparing with conventional concrete, the technology of vibro-compaction and thermal control may be simplified. The roller compacted work on large placing area may reduce the preparing works of concrete blocks and increase the speed of construction. However, during complicate construction conditions, the layer defects may occur in dam and on the same level, so that unsafety will happen to gravity type structure, especially high gravity dam. Enlarged section is always advised in order to keep the safety of gravity type construction. In result, the quantity, cost, equipment and strength of construction are increased and the construction period is prolonged. Obviously the development of engineering need not only new material and new technology but also the corresponding new structure and more similar to practice calculation and new design method. Suppose that the forces transfer mainly through horizontal arch may remove the danger caused by the layer surface defect under hydropressure. The real stress of structure may be obtained to improve the design and the safety of whole dam by the actual simulating measure of the material property and the simulating calculation of structure. RCC arch dam has advantages of smaller engineering volume, less unit cost. The modern technique will conduct to rapid construction, earlier ponding and good

本文选自《International Conference in RCC Dam Construction on Middle East》2002 年第 4 期，作者还有 Li Penghui, Xie Shunan。

quantity with crack prevention. Enlarging the applicability of arch dam in worse temperature and geologic condition will create new progress in dam construction.

2 Wenquanpu RCC Arch Dam

On bases of research on multi-crack body[1], three-dimension of fracture and thermal fracture, the research group of the stress and stability of high dam, the department of Hydraulic and Hydropower Engineering in Tsinghua University suggested in 1987 ~ 1988 that the problem of the tensile area in large placing region of RCC arch dam can be solved by setting artificial short joint for releasing stress and installing material with high toughness at tip of joint for stability of crack. In 1990 research on the stress of multiple layer structure Wenquanpu RCC arch dam (smaller blocks with 30m long, see Fig. 1) was carried out.

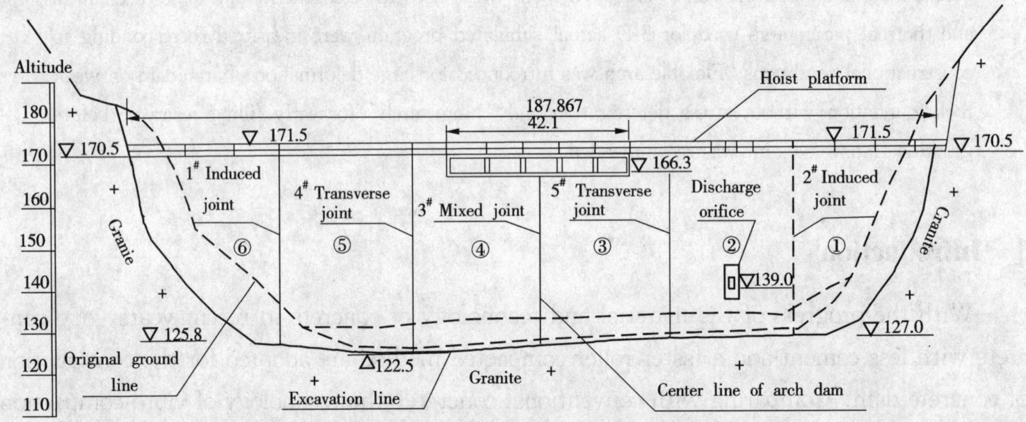

Fig. 1 The upstream sectional view of Wenquanpu RCC arch dam (unit: m)

The arch dam is 48m high and the crest length is 188m long. The crest length-height ratio is 3.9:1, and the constructional transverse joints are necessary. The dam is located in the region of granite and the geologic condition is good. The mean annual air temperature is 10 degrees and the minimum average ten-days air temperature is −7.4 degrees. The cement content is a little high for meeting the need of frost resistance and impermeability. The adiabatic temperature rise of 20℃ to 26℃ is lower than those of conventional concrete. The intervals between transverse joints of monolith are 30in. The placing concrete regions on both sides of arch increase to 60m for the convenient of Roller-compacted technology, but remain the induced joints at the place of 30m.

According to the characteristic of RCC arch dam, the simulating calculations including accumulated temperature and weight creep-stresses (considering the initial stress) and the criteria of multi-axial strength were considered[2]. The research on the stress distribution of layered structure[3] (RCC) and the shear stress concentration at the edges of layers, the deformation and stress redistribution of arch dam with transverse joints and the stable depth of crack propagation at the arch dam heel (with installed water seal for preventing hydraulic break) and stress redistribution of dam body were carried out.

3 Xibing RCC Thin Arch Dam

The first RCC thin arch dam (i.e. XIBING engineering in FUJIAN Province) were designed in 1993 by using actual simulating calculation, the dam height is 63.5m, the maximum thickness at bottom is 12.0m and the height-thickness ratio is 1:0.189 (see Figs. 2 and 3).

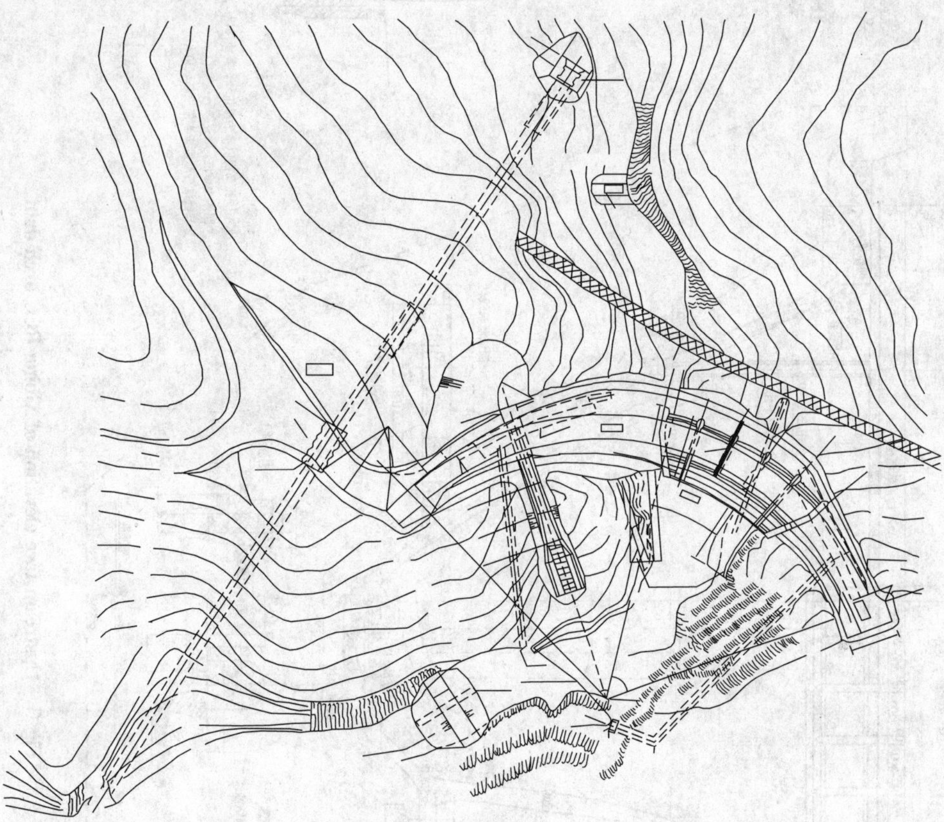

Fig. 2 The Xibing RCC arch dam area-plan

The arch dam was built on weak weathered sandstone with joints. The mean annual air temperature at the dam site of rainy area is 18℃. A middle joint (i.e. transverse joint) is remained in the upper part, it is about one third high of whole arch dam, and no joint is in the lower part of dam which is about two thirds high of whole arch dam for flood retard during construction stage. The concrete with $425^{\#}$ cement and high flyash content was studied for providing lower temperature, high strength RCC and condition of continuous placement without relying on heat loss through the block surfaces. Substituting small aggregate with lower expansion into common aggregate decreased the stresses of tensile area. The studies on new structure and characteristic of new material served the fundamental parameters for 3-D

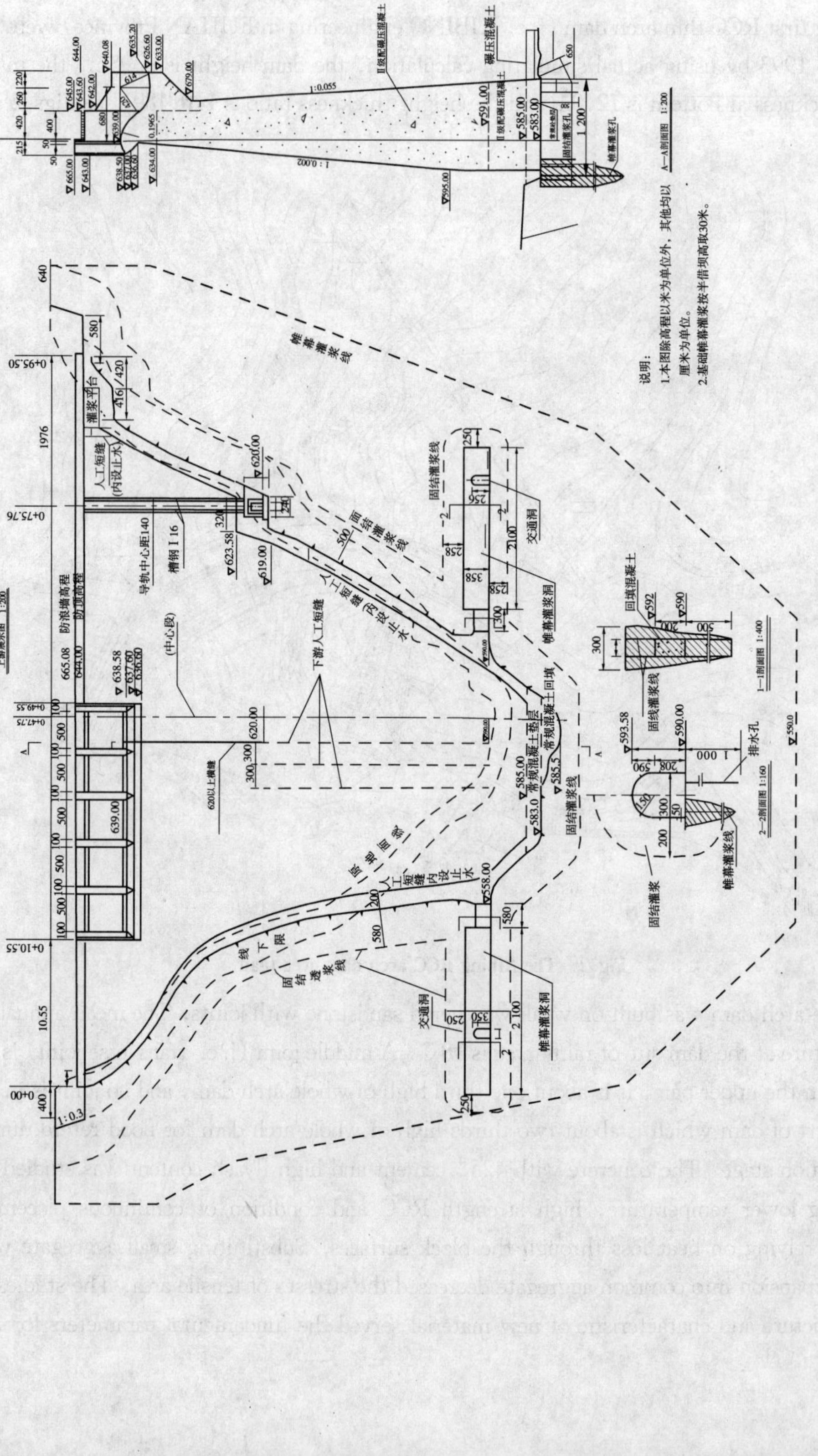

Fig. 3 Upstream face elevation of xibing RCC arch dam

simulating accumulated calculation of temperature field and stress field corresponding to the stages of construction[4]. In order to reduce tensile stress and make the cracks to be a part of the structure, the artificial joints were set at the upstream abutment and the downstream arch crown, which can obviously release stresses caused by temperature and water pressure. The measures of anti-crack at the tip of the joints were made to keep the artificial joints stable (as shown in Figs. 4 to 9).

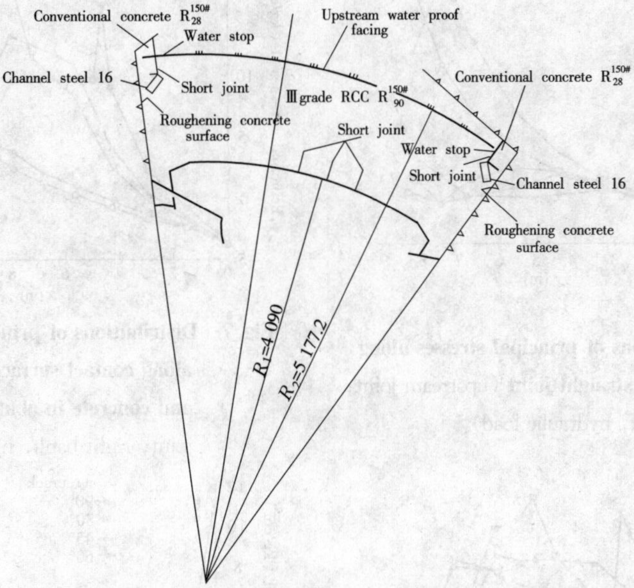

Fig. 4 Plan of ▽598 arch

For example ▽611.0 arch (1/3 dam height) is taken for stress comparison under the same condition of hydraulic load and thermal change. The influence of various kinds of upstream artificial joint: 90° (straight), 30°, 45°, 60° and no joint to the stress distribution in abutment region are shown as Figs 6 to 9.

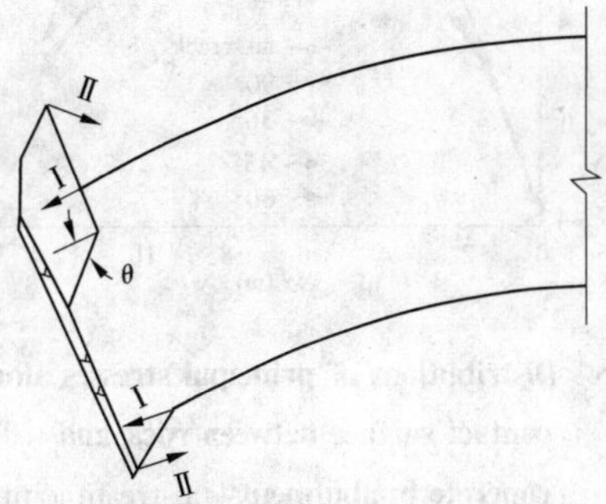

Fig. 5 Type of short joints at upstream abutment

In section Ⅰ—Ⅰ along the direction of radial joint, the principal tensile stress decrease from +3.9MPa (no joint) to +0.3MPa (45° curved joint) during hydraulic load. The second principal stress decrease also from tensile stress +0.9MPa (no joint) to −0.4MPa compression (45° curved joint). Since the tip of 45′ curved joint located at section Ⅱ—Ⅱ of rock surface, the maximum. principal tensile stress of section Ⅱ—Ⅱ grows up to +1.4MPa (45° curved joint) which have the same magnitude with conventional structure (no joint) but locates at different places.

For thermal stress: Fig. 8 show that the maximum. first principal tensile stress near the tip of 45° curved joint goes up +1.02MPa. It remains almost no difference with conventional (no joint) +1.0MPa. The second principal stress increases from +0.3MPa (no joint) to +0.75MPa (45° curved joint). Nevertheless artificial joint cleans out the 5M tensile stress region in upstream surface during this thermal change (Fig. 9).

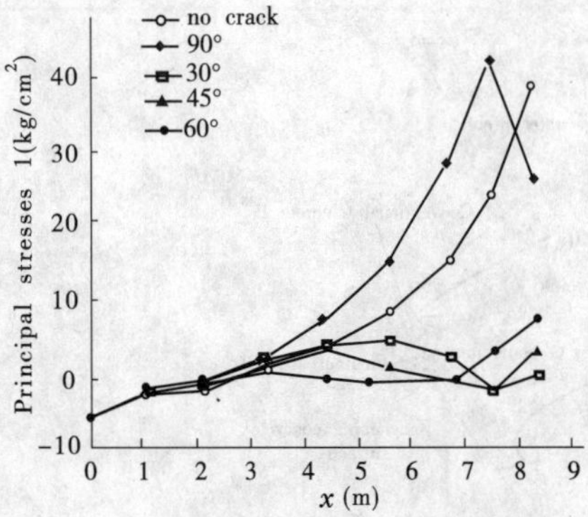

Fig. 6　Distributions of principal stresses along profile of straight joint (upstream joint, right bank, hydraulic load)

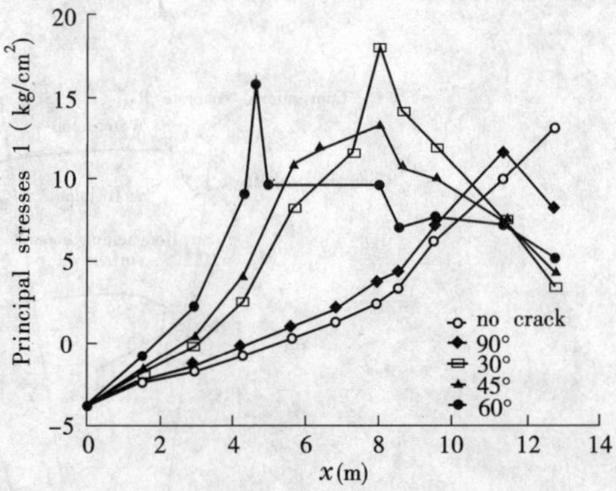

Fig. 7　Distributions of principal stresses along contact surface between rock and concrete in abutment (upstream joint, right bank, hydraulic load)

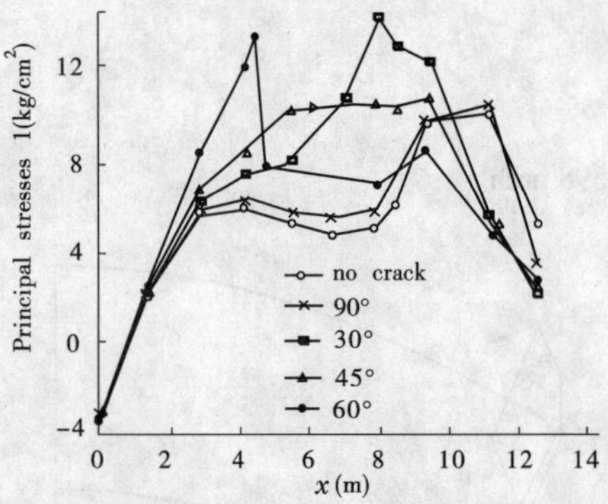

Fig. 8　Distributions of principal stresses along contact surface between rock and concrete in abutment (upstream joint, combined thermal field in March, right bank)

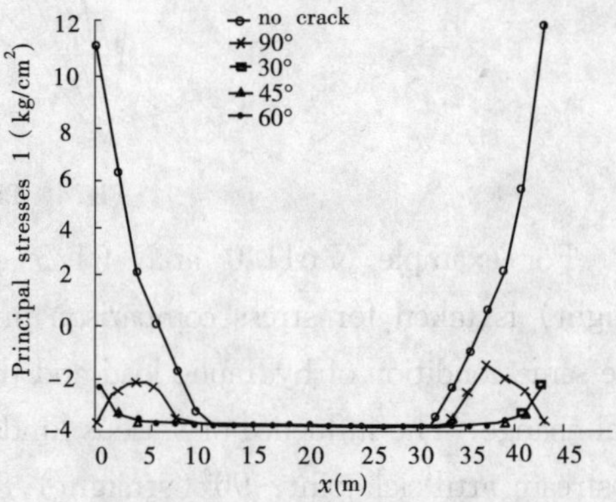

Fig. 9　Distributions of principal stresses along upstream surface of arch (upstream joint, combined thermal field in March, right bank)

The influence of the downstream artificial joints to the stress of arch dam:

Radial joints are arranged in arch tensile area near downstream surface of arch dam. Under the hydro-pressure, the influence of the joints depth is remarkable. The first principal tensile stresses on the downstream of dam decrease from maximum, value of 2.0MPa (no joints) to less than 0.5MPa (2m depth of joints) (Fig. 10). The stress distribution of radial section shows that the maximum. Principal tensile stress area moves toward inside of dam, the maximum, value reduces from 1.6MPa (no joint) to 1.2MPa (Fig. 11). The influence of the downstream joints structure in the middle part of dam (including the interval and depth of joints) on the stress distribution of whole dam isn't important. But it can greatly improve the stresses of downstream crown.

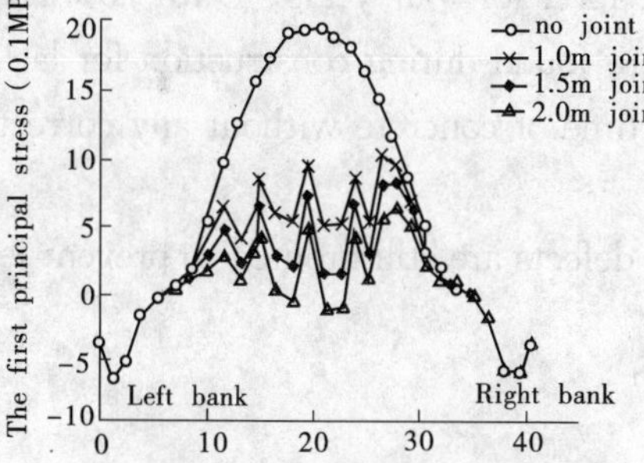

Fig. 10 The arc length from the points on the downstream surface to left bank

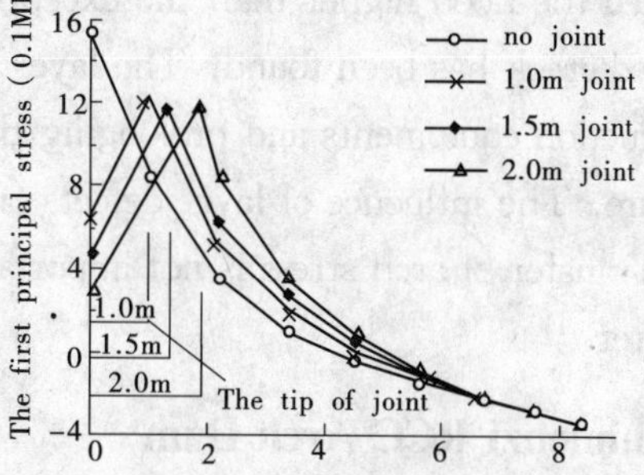

Fig. 11 The distance from the points of section to the downstream surface

The stability of joints: The K_{I} and K_{II} can be obtained by the gauss-point stresses of iso-parametric element around the tip of joints[5] (as shown in Table 1).

Table 1 The stress intensity factors at the tip of various joints (611.0 for illustration) under different cases (unit: $MN/m^{3/2}$)

Case	K	The upstream artificial curved joints		The downstream crown artificial short joints		
		left	right	left	middle	right
Composed load (including water pressure and thermal load)	March	$K_{\text{I}}=0.69$ $K_{\text{II}}=-0.88$	$K_{\text{I}}=2.25$ $K_{\text{II}}=0.75$	$K_{\text{I}}=0.59$ $K_{\text{II}}=0.23$	$K_{\text{I}}=0.85$ $K_{\text{II}}=0.28$	$K_{\text{I}}=-0.29$ $K_{\text{II}}=0.24$
	July	$K_{\text{I}}=0.24$ $K_{\text{II}}=0.42$	$K_{\text{I}}=1.74$ $K_{\text{II}}=-0.20$	$K_{\text{I}}=-1.64$ $K_{\text{II}}=-0.44$	$K_{\text{I}}=-1.35$ $K_{\text{II}}=0.15$	$K_{\text{I}}=-2.54$ $K_{\text{II}}=-0.58$
Single water pressure		$K_{\text{I}}=-1.02$ $K_{\text{II}}=0.41$	$K_{\text{I}}=0.78$ $K_{\text{II}}=0.10$	$K_{\text{I}}=0.72$ $K_{\text{II}}=-0.05$	$K_{\text{I}}=0.75$ $K_{\text{II}}=-0.15$	$K_{\text{I}}=-0.08$ $K_{\text{II}}=0.20$

The stress intensity factors on the tips of upstream and downstream joints are less than $1.0MN/m^{3/2}$. The fracture toughness of three grades concrete above 200# is up to $2.0 MN/m^{3/2}$. So the joints are stable. But the maximum value K_{I} and K_{II} under complex load in March is equal to $2.25MN/m^{3/2}$ and $0.75MN/m^{3/2}$ (not including the favorable compressive stresses caused by self weight). The high toughness material was installed at the tip of upstream artificial curved joints to prevent the propagation of the joints. The experimental beams with small channel steels about 3.0cm width are installed at the tip of joints for toughness studies. The tests show that the carrying capacity of short joint can increase more than 30%. The beams failed from other section with new fractures beside artificial joint. The 16# channel steels are used in factual engineering. The measurements in situ showed that the strain of RCC behind the channel steels was 37μ, which could keep the structure safe when the artificial short joints opened more than 1.0mm. The roller compacted work of XIBING RCC thin arch dam had been placed up to the crest of arch dam only half a year in 1995. In the same year arch dam impound and retard twenty-year flood and fifty-year flood in the second year. For the sake of increasing electric energy, the arch dam had continuously impounded the flood higher than the exceptional water level for four years. Until now no restrained crack has been found. The layer defects were found during construction for lack of construction equipments and prolonging the placing time of concrete without any correcting measure. The influence of layer detects on.

Transfer of arch stress is not important. These defects are still grouted to prevent leakage later.

4 Shimenzi RCC Arch Dam

In 1997 the RCC arch dam with the height of 109m was built in severe cold area of North Xinjiang (the annual mean temperature is 4.1℃) and on the weak foundation (arigillo-calcareous cement conglomerate, the elastic modulus is only 4 000MPa). Limited by the carrying capacity of rock, the maximum thickness of arch dam foundation was enlarged to 30m. The height-width ratio is 1∶0.27 and the shape of valley is "U". The silt-laden interlayers in both banks with downstream trend and rudite rocks divided by faults along valley make the unstable rock body in both banks. See Figs. 12 and 13.

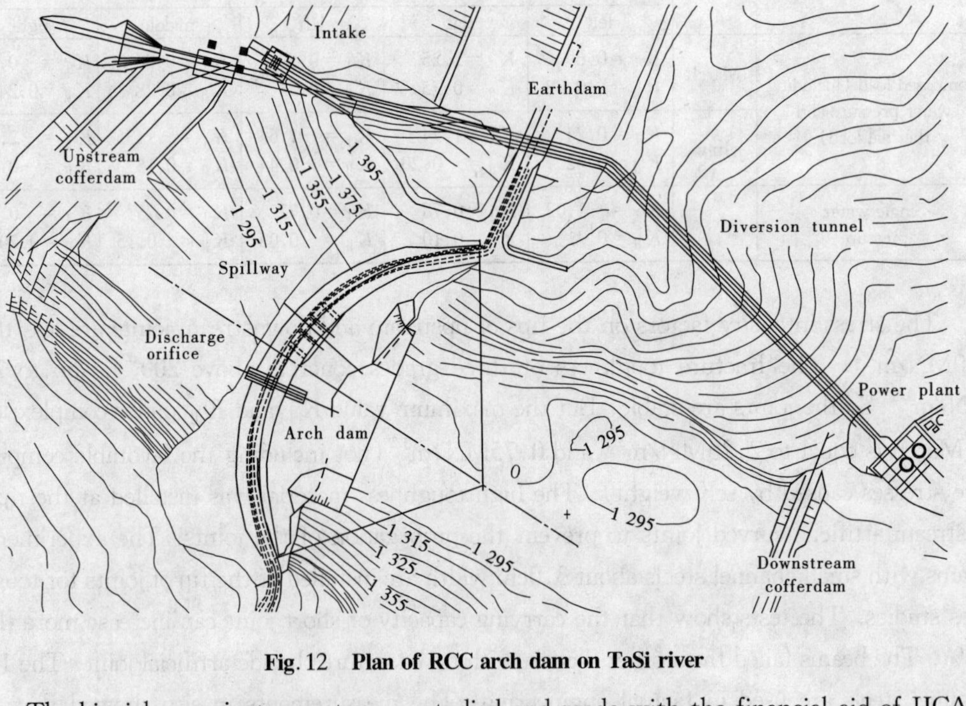

Fig. 12 Plan of RCC arch dam on TaSi river

The biaxial creep instruments were studied and made with the financial aid of JICA of Japan and '985' project of Tsinghua University, and studies on biaxial creep of weak rock

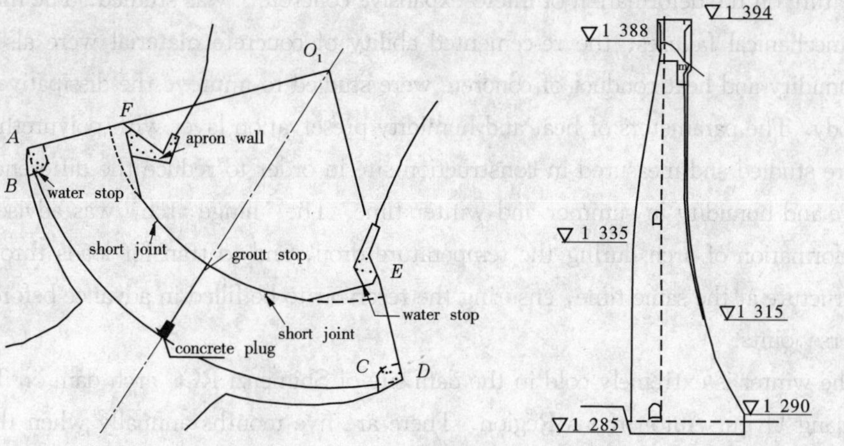

Fig. 13 Plan construction of arch and spillway profile (unit: m)

and early-age concrete were carried out. The tests of conglomerate showed that the ratio of instantaneous uniaxial compressive deformation (elasticity) and creep deformation (visco-plasticity) is (2.0~2.6):1, the increasing rate of long term is up to (1.5~1.2):1, and μ varies from 1/6.4 (small load, less than 30% of ultimate strength) to 1/2.6 (big load, less than 50% of ultimate strength). There are few yielding elements of right bank by the analysis of 3-D visco-plasticity FEM, which mainly distribute in the abutment of ▽1 284 ~ 1 310mand the upstream boundary of F_6 fault on the same level. The experiments showed that the strain of the biaxial compressive creep decreases obviously comparing with uniaxial compressive creep, which is up to 1:2.6 and this consideration can remove those yield elements. For the sake of safety, the downstream concrete guide walls are thickened and heightened to ▽1 335m, which reduce the excavation of downstream abutment rock above ▽1 335m.

The measure of grouting, cohere and reinforce are used to increase the lateral restraint and reduce the creep deformation of upper part abutment. Based on the research of the structure with defects and the calculating strength of nonhomogeneous body, the "flexible arch structure" with flexible bands was introduced to suit the large deformations of weak rock, and prevent stress from causing deterioration. And the flexible arch can also reduce by two thirds of seismic arch stress (eight degrees). Transfer force through increasing part elastic moduli of the abutment may guide the thrust into deep layer of 3-d compressive field. The mathematic models and the calculating method of the random seepage and unsteady seepage were also studied. The simulating seepage line and stability of the unstable rock on both banks were estimated and checked according to the water level changes during operation. In addition, strength discounts on saturated weak rock and internal force wreck problem were studied.

The high strength, low heat, micro-expansive concrete was developed. The influence of temperature on the deformation of micro-expansive concrete[6] was studied. The micro-structural, mechanical failures, the re-cemented ability of concrete material were also studied. The humidity and heat conduct of concrete were studied to improve the dissipative ability in dam body. The parameters of heat and humidity preservation layer with polyurethane material were studied and measured in construction site in order to reduce the difference of temperature and humidity in summer and winter time. The 'hinge arch' was advised to keep free deformation of arch during the temperature drop, and to transfer loads through hinge arch structure at the same time, ensuring the reservoir to be filled in advance before grouting transverse joints.

The winter is extremely cold in the dam site of Shimenzi RCC arch dam on Taxi River in Xinjiang Uygur Autonomous Region. There are five months annually when the average temperature is below 0℃. Thus the construction work was stopped. The construction work was delayed half time in summer for lack of thermal control. The foundation of RCC arch dam with the height of 110m was excavated 1.0m less than that of the original design for satisfying the requirement already. The foundation concrete (▽1 285m) began in June 1999. The arch dam grew up to ▽1 365.0m after eleven months (including those days when the placement were delayed in summer). The actual maximum placement height monthly was up to 15m. In order to keep the free deformation during temperature drop of dam, we filled the slight expansive concrete plug into the reserved well to form the hinge arch which filled the reservoir up to ▽1 348.0m (63m deep) for irrigation in next spring. The RCC arch dam had gone up to the crest after concrete placing of 15 months. No constraint crack occurs during winter under protection of sand, water or polyurethane foaming layer. Cracks occurred in the gallery (▽1 289.0m) since the placing temperature of concrete was 6℃ exceed required temperature, grouting repair was made.

Therefore, if the conditions of topography and building material are suitable for concrete dam, RCC arch dam can be built with enlarged concrete blocks, which has the advantages of transferring force by horizontal arch to get rid of layer defect, ensuring the better quality of whole dam, reducing the preparation work, constructing dam much rapidly, earlier filling reservoir, reducing amount of cement, simplifying the measure of thermal control and reducing cost. So it is valuable to be improved further and used widely.

References

[1] Liu Guangting, Zhou Ruizhong. *Strength of a finite body with multiple cracks*. Engineering Fracture Mechanics, 1990,35,1～3

[2] Liu Guangting, Zhang Guoxin, Liu Zhihui. *Simulation stresses of RCC arch dam with transverse joints and biaxial strength criteria*. Journal of Tsinghua University, Beijing, 1996, 36(1), 13～19. (in Chinese)

[3] Liu Guangting, Hao Jutao. *Simplified numerical method in stress analysis of RCC arch dam with layer structure*. Journal of Tsinghua University, Beijing, 1996,36(1), 2733(in Chinese)

[4] Liu Guangting, Mai Jiaxuan, Zhang Guoxin. *Research on XiBing Roller Compacted Concrete Thin Arch Dam*. Journal of Hydroelectric Engineering, Beijing,1997, 57(2),19~28 (in Chinese)

[5] Pekau, O.A., Zhang, Z.X., Liu, G.T.. *Constitutive model for concrete in strain space*. Journal of Engineering Mechanics,(1992)118(9), 1907~1927

[6] Liu Guangting, Li Penghui, Hu Yu. *The RCC Arch Dam Structure on Taxi River and Water Storage Measure During Construction*. Proceedings Int. Symp. on RCCD, ChengDu, SE.1, (1999)86~110

碾压混凝土拱坝的铰结拱研究

摘　要　本文介绍的碾压混凝土铰结拱式拱坝是在拱坝低温区中缝上设置混凝土塞,可以在水压作用下传递拱作用力而不明显增加坝体的应力,且能松弛拱坝运行期坝体混凝土温降引起的拉应力,可不必等待横缝灌浆即可蓄水,从而提前发挥工程效益。“铰结拱”已成功用于高百米以上、软基、高寒的某碾压混凝土拱坝,2000 年 10 月水库已成功蓄水。

关键词　铰结拱　膨胀混凝土塞　碾压混凝土拱坝

常态混凝土拱坝为防止温度裂缝,往往沿拱轴每 20m 左右设横缝,常用预冷混凝土材料和坝内埋设冷却水管等措施以降低前期最高温升,并采用后期强制降温等措施来满足灌浆形成整体拱要求。相比之下碾压混凝土拱坝简化浇筑工艺,便于大仓面(40～80m 长)施工,大仓面也减少横缝模板及灌浆系统等仓面准备工作量,施工速度快。由于碾压混凝土单位水泥含量少,绝热温升小,它不仅节约温控费用,而且因常用不等待上表面冷却的快速施工,大大加快了工程进度[1]。实践表明,碾压工艺和上下游变态混凝土区(震捣施工)埋设塑料冷却水管不干扰,但和坝内(碾压施工)冷却水管埋设有干扰(水管有时被压裂,漏水,堵塞)[2],而坝内无冷却水管使大体积混凝土内部降温缓慢,难以依靠多次灌浆形成整体拱,推迟碾压混凝土拱坝投入运行日期。采用“铰结拱”则可消除这个缺点。碾压混凝土拱坝浇筑后虽然温升较小,但仍形成上下游散热冷却区(加上变态混凝土区可埋设人工冷却水管),在中缝上游表层冷却区回填混凝土塞形成“铰结拱”结构。在水压作用下铰结拱(除局部压力加大外)和整体拱应力相近,人工缝端保持稳定,可提前蓄水。

1　碾压混凝土拱坝的铰结拱

高寒地区软弱地基上修建的某碾压混凝土拱坝,坝高 109m,河谷底宽近百米,拱推力大,为减少软弱地基压力强度和变位,拱坝剖面梁最大底宽扩大为 30m,典型平面拱及中央剖面示意如图 1 所示。

在各平面拱上游拱座及下游拱冠拉力区设人工短缝,以释放温度和水压应力。为削减两岸岩体对平面拱降温约束,拱坝中央设横缝(简称中缝)[3,4]形成左右两大仓面,各 50～85m 长。内部碾压混凝土绝热温升限制在 14℃,坝内最高控制温度不超过 25～26℃,控制失误使实测值达 28～30℃。中缝上游区设 4.0m 长的铰结井,第一年夏秋季浇筑的混凝土越冬后(为了经济,冬、春季月平均气温在 0℃以下的 5 个月停工,上游蓄水,下游砂砾料覆盖保温材料,或用喷涂聚氨酯材料保温,第一年冬季实测混凝土表面温度为 4～7℃),拱坝上游已形成 7～8℃的冷却区(仿真计算和实测差值小于 2℃,见图 2)。若利用施工期的冷却区用膨胀混凝土填铰结井,即可形成铰结拱传力结构。铰结井左右两侧预留灌浆系统,以保证后期拱向紧密结合。中缝可以较长时间保留,以减少拱坝中下游坝体温度下降的约束力。在水压作用下,铰结拱和整体拱应力相近,因此可以提前蓄水,

---

本文选自《水利学报》2002 第 6 期,作者还有李鹏辉、谢树南、张富德。

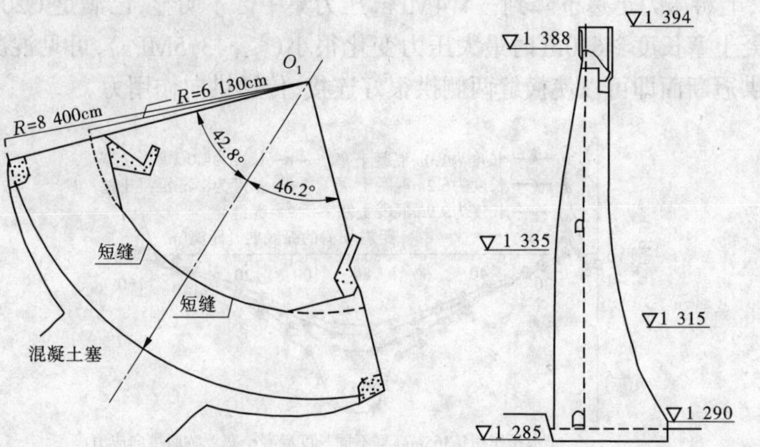

图1 典型平面拱及中央剖面 (单位:m)

而不必等待坝体全部降温中缝灌浆后才蓄水。

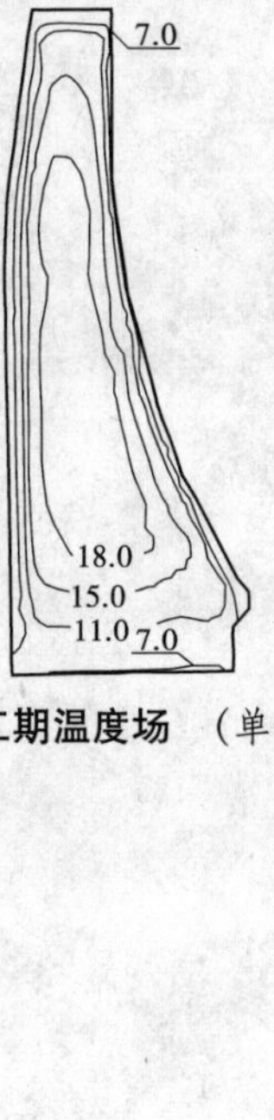

图2 施工期温度场 (单位:℃)

2 水压作用下铰结拱传力作用分析

采用9 532个八节点六面体单元,12 072个节点对碾压混凝土拱坝在正常高水位1 390.0m下进行应力计算。比较中缝上游含不同长度的混凝土塞(即铰结点,参见图1)的拱坝应力,取1 365.0m高程拱平面上、下游拱向应力和含混凝土塞中央剖面拱向应力作为典型规律比较。

从图3可见,不同混凝土塞长度在拱冠上游面▽1 335~1 375m(拱坝高度1/3~2/3区间)出现最大拱向压力,混凝土塞1.0m时压力大(其值大于－7.0MPa),混凝土塞长度6.0m以上时压力变化不大,其值均小于－3.5MPa。

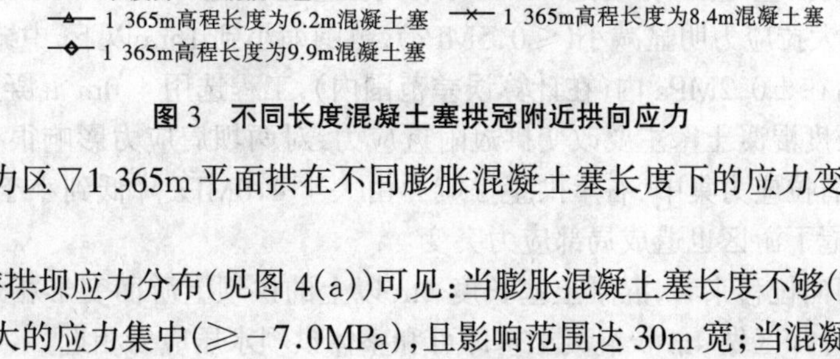

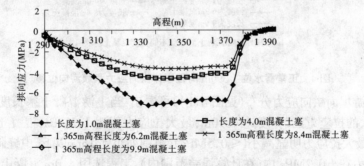

图3 不同长度混凝土塞拱冠附近拱向应力

取稳定压力区▽1 365m平面拱在不同膨胀混凝土塞长度下的应力变化规律进行分析(见图4)。

(1)从上游拱坝应力分布(见图4(a))可见:当膨胀混凝土塞长度不够(≤1.0m)时,拱冠上游处产生大的应力集中(≥－7.0MPa),且影响范围达30m宽;当混凝土塞长度增大到4.0m时，上游压力迅速下降到－4.4MPa，压力集中区不明显，已满足C20混凝土强度要求；当混凝土塞长度≥6.0m时最大压力变化很小（≤－3.5MPa），可见混凝土塞（铰结点）占部分拱冠断面即可以使横缝两侧拱很好连接，传递拱向作用力。

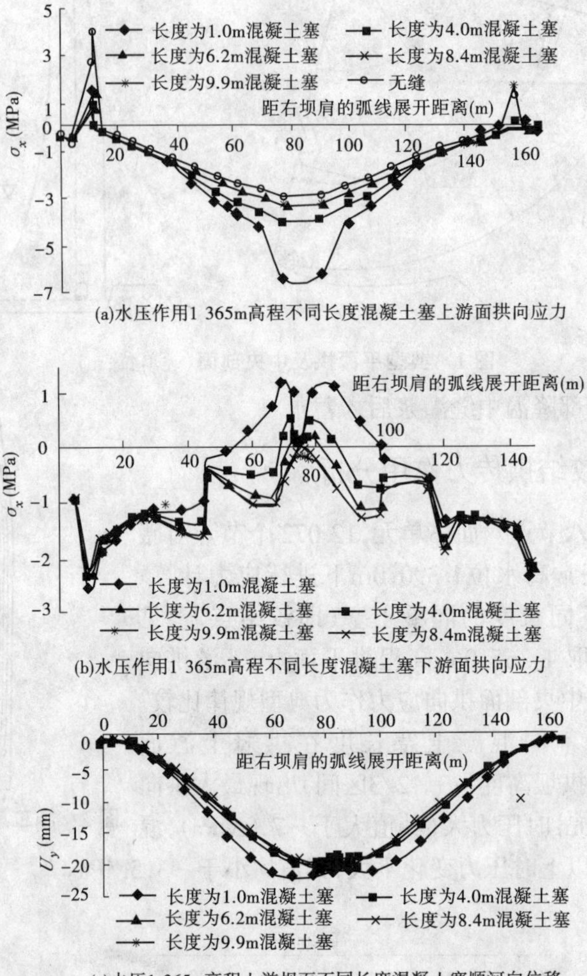

(a)水压作用1 365m高程不同长度混凝土塞上游面拱向应力

(b)水压作用1 365m高程不同长度混凝土塞下游面拱向应力

(c)水压1 365m高程上游坝面不同长度混凝土塞顺河向位移

图4　正常蓄水位1 390m高程坝体拱向应力和顺河向位移

(2)从下游坝面拱向应力分布（见图4(b)）可看出：当上游混凝土塞长度1.0m时，拱冠下游出现大的拉应力区，宽度达46.0m，最大拉应力值达1.2MPa，混凝土塞长度增大到4.0m时，最大拉应力明显减小（≤0.5MPa），范围缩小到16m以下，中缝附近即使全封闭，下游面应力在±0.2MPa内（在计算误差范围内），工程选用4.0m混凝土塞。

(3)不同长度混凝土塞主要改变拱冠附近应力，对两坝肩应力影响很少，上游人工短缝大大削减坝肩拉应力集中，右岸拱座拉应力由大于4.0MPa降低到小于1.2MPa，下游人工短缝在拱冠下游区也造成局部应力突变。

(4)从顺河向位移来看，混凝土塞长度4m以上的拱坝上游面变形相近，因此利用中缝上游混凝土冷却区做4m长混凝土塞即可和整体拱坝水压应力相近。

3 拱坝后期温降及铰结拱对坝体应力影响

拱坝处于高寒地区，年平均温度 4.3℃，回填混凝土塞后坝体平均温度为 14.5℃（上游混凝土塞 7℃），取均匀温降 10℃ 的拱坝温度应力进行铰结拱和整体拱应力比较。

(1)后期拱坝温降时，坝肩由于受强约束，上游面拱向出现 0.5MPa 拉力（见图 5(a)）。坝肩设置上游人工短缝，拱向可自由变形以释放温降收缩应力，拉力突变明显下降。混凝土塞长短对坝肩应力影响不大，主要影响拱冠区。上游混凝土塞长度 1m 时受拉均匀，长度大于 4m 时，在拉力和弯矩压力作用下上游坝面出现微压，按坝体施工期实际不均匀温度分布（混凝土塞区 7℃），当下降为稳定变场温度时上游坝面均为压应力。

(2)拱坝降温时，下游面大部分处于拉力区，铰结拱处混凝土塞长度愈大，中缝刚度就愈大，自由变形就愈小，拱冠下游面拉力区和最大拉力值也就愈大（只有中缝下游局部因未全封闭时应力接近零），中缝全封闭的整体拱拱冠下游面温降应力最不利，拉力最大（见

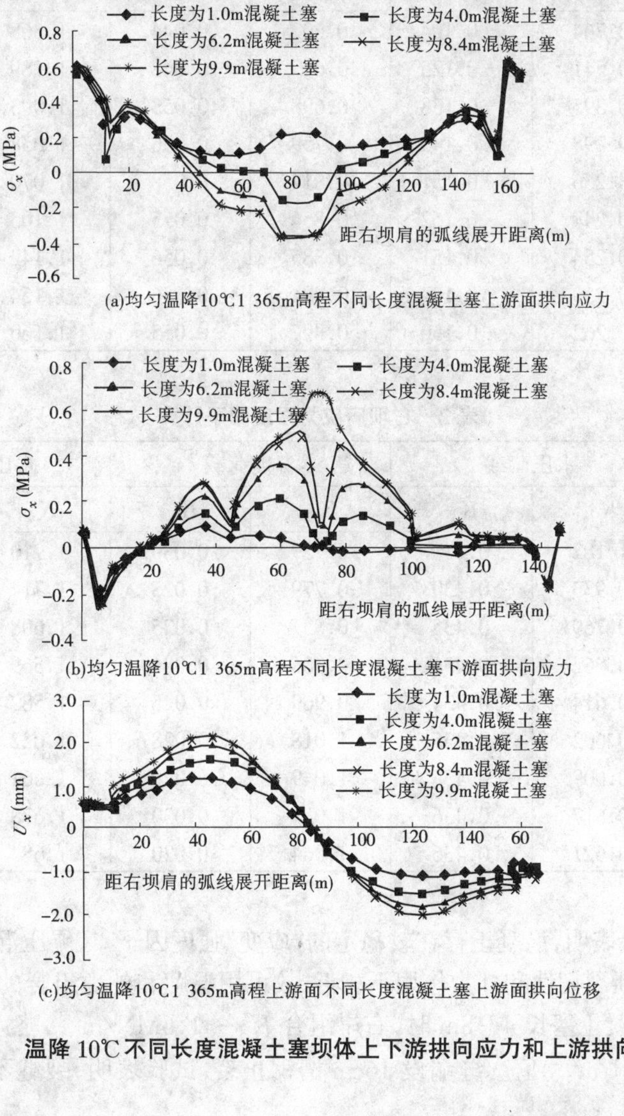

(a)均匀温降10℃1 365m高程不同长度混凝土塞上游面拱向应力

(b)均匀温降10℃1 365m高程不同长度混凝土塞下游面拱向应力

(c)均匀温降10℃1 365m高程上游面不同长度混凝土塞上游面拱向位移

图 5 温降 10℃ 不同长度混凝土塞坝体上下游拱向应力和上游拱向位移

图 5(b))。由此可见,中缝的中下游面敞开的铰结拱结构可以释放后期拱坝下游面的温降应力,中缝混凝土塞(铰结点)短有利于拱坝降温。综合考虑前期蓄水水压作用下拱的传力以及后期拱坝降温时不破坏拱作用又可释放温度应力的需要,工程选用 4m 长混凝土塞以形成铰结拱。

4　铰结拱长度与坝肩人工折缝稳定性

铰结拱混凝土塞的选择还应能保证释放拱坝应力的上游坝肩人工折缝和下游人工短缝的安全,以便使它们能共同作用而达到改善坝体应力的目的。任取 1 335m 高程水压荷载大的拱平面应力,表 1、表 2 列出不同长度混凝土塞对坝肩人工短缝稳定性的影响。

表 1　左坝肩应力强度因子计算　　(单位:$MN/m^{3/2}$)

混凝土塞长度(m)	水压荷载		温度荷载		水压+温度荷载	
	K_I	K_{II}	K_I	K_{II}	K_I	K_{II}
1.000	0.764	−0.104	0.602	0.044	1.368	−0.069
2.650	0.541	−0.125	0.647	0.048	1.189	−0.086
4.395	0.395	−0.138	0.698	0.053	1.093	−0.081
6.391	0.298	−0.140	0.759	0.056	1.058	−0.082
8.387	0.256	−0.151	0.814	0.058	1.070	−0.080
10.383	0.248	−0.152	0.856	0.055	1.105	−0.093
12.379	0.254	−0.151	0.885	0.056	1.142	−0.102
13.659	0.259	−0.144	0.894	0.056	1.154	−0.095
15.209	0.262	−0.150	0.897	0.055	1.160	−0.094

表 2　右坝肩应力强度因子计算　　(单位:$MN/m^{3/2}$)

混凝土塞长度(m)	水压荷载		温度荷载		水压+温度荷载	
	K_I	K_{II}	K_I	K_{II}	K_I	K_{II}
1.000	1.182	0.411	0.729	0.030	1.910	0.443
2.650	0.933	0.430	0.779	0.028	1.714	0.457
4.395	0.769	0.435	0.837	0.025	1.608	0.460
6.391	0.062	0.436	0.906	0.026	1.569	0.462
8.387	0.614	0.434	0.969	0.026	1.582	0.459
10.383	0.602	0.435	1.018	0.028	1.622	0.462
12.379	0.609	0.435	1.049	0.029	1.661	0.463
13.659	0.617	0.436	1.051	0.030	1.678	0.464
15.029	0.621	0.436	1.064	0.030	1.684	0.466

温度断裂试验表明,混凝土存在较稳定的“应变”强度因子[5],碾压混凝土后期弹模达 30 000MPa,温度断裂韧性和外力作用下相近,故可用温度和外力组合的断裂应力强度因子进行比较,当混凝土塞长 4～8m 时,右岸组合 $K_I \approx 1.6MN/m^{2/3}$,略大于 K_{IC}(对三级配混凝土取$1.5MN/m^{2/3}$)值。缝端设 16cm 槽钢止裂,试验表明,裂缝不能穿行槽钢,即

使绕行槽钢 K_{IC} 远远大于 $2.0MN/m^{2/3}$。工程采用上游 7℃冷却区回填混凝土塞，减少拱坝上游坝面温降值及其 K_I 值。

5 结语

碾压混凝土拱坝进行大仓面快速施工，大大缩短施工期，且水化热温升低，前期混凝土内外温差小，易于抗裂保证质量。当内部不埋设冷却水管时，可利用混凝土坝表层前期冷却区设置膨胀混凝土塞以形成"铰结拱"，提前蓄水。后期拱坝降温时，下游拉力区因中缝保留自由变形可消除拉力，中缝可以等待拱坝降温到稳定场后再灌浆。中缝灌浆前可由"铰结拱"代替"整体拱"挡水，由于"铰结拱"和"整体铰"应力相近，不影响拱坝提前投入运行日期，提前发挥工程效益。

参 考 文 献

[1] 刘光廷，张国新，刘志辉．含灌浆横缝碾压混凝土拱坝仿真应力和双轴强度判别．清华大学学报，1996，36(1)：3～19

[2] 三峡水利枢纽混凝土工程温度控制研究编辑委员会．三峡水利枢纽混凝土工程温度控制研究．北京：中国水利水电出版社，2001

[3] Zeng Zhaoyang, Ma Qian. *Study on the structure joints in the high RCC Arch Dam*. Shuili fadian/Water Power, 1988, (1): 273～285

[4] 刘光廷，麦家煊，张国新．溪柄碾压混凝土薄拱坝的研究．水力发电学报，1997(2)：69～75

[5] Guangting Liu. *Study on the curved and branch cracks in massive concrete structures*. Proceedings of the international conference on Dam Fracture. Boulder, Colorado USA, 273～285

裂缝在压剪条件下的应力场和扩展能

摘　要　用无缝宽的光测模型试验和位移不连续边界元法研究了压剪条件下缝面和缝端的能量分配和敏感性。试验和计算表明,压剪裂纹在缝端存在强烈的应力集中区,属于断裂问题,应由韧性判别,由试验得到的应力场和计算应力场在整体上很相近,但在缝端相差较大,压剪缝延伸可用离缝端一定距离的应力当量韧性来判断。

关键词　宏观应力场　裂隙体　压剪荷载

水工建筑物和自然界的岩体常处于压剪状态,很多建筑物例如混凝土重力坝的极限状态是压剪控制[1]。对于压剪断裂破坏问题,目前研究得还不成熟。人们通常沿用拉剪的线弹性破坏机理来求解压剪问题,计算假定是否正确尚有待测定和检验。

由于在压剪状态下裂纹面闭合,其接触面阻力对整体应力场分布尤其缝端初应力场有很大影响,所以在分析压剪问题时,试验和计算的裂纹面初始状态的正确模拟十分重要,这正是与拉剪问题的重要不同之处。如混凝土坝水平裂缝常由应力超限而产生,其裂纹"初始宽度"可视为零,故为了正确反映压剪状态下的应力场,在试验和数值分析压剪问题时,应使裂纹的初始宽度趋于零。

目前压剪试验的试块大多采用锯缝形式制作裂纹,其裂缝宽度有时达 3mm,尖端附近也在 0.3mm 以上,因此其受力方式、裂纹面和裂纹尖端的应力分布将受很大影响。要正确地模拟裂纹压剪状态下的受力规律,试验和计算须很好地解决初始裂纹宽度和阻力模拟问题。确定宏观裂纹扩展能力和方向以及研究压剪缝延伸判别问题。

本文用含斜边裂纹板块所研制的初始裂纹宽度接近零的光弹试验以及砂浆混凝土试验(另文发表)来研究压剪断裂时缝面和缝端应力场分布规律问题,并用按摩尔库仑原则考虑裂纹面接触和摩擦效应的边界元数值方法进行比较,得到应力分布规律相近的缝面应力和相似的缝端应力场,用等效应力场数值方法提供了工程初裂缝延伸能力计算。

1　压剪条件下断裂能数值分析

将裂纹作为不连续位移边界之一,不考虑裂纹面上的压剪效应,由积分方程:

$$\overline{u}_i(P) = \int_s \overline{u}_{ik}(P,Q)D_k(Q)\mathrm{d}s(Q)$$

$$\overline{t}_{ik}(P,Q) = \int_s \overline{T}_{ik}(P,Q)D_k(Q)\mathrm{d}s(Q) \tag{1}$$

式中:$\overline{T}_{ik}(P,Q)$、$\overline{u}_{ik}$ 分别为 Q 点(见图 1)i 方向作用一单位不连续位移在 P 点 j 方向的应力和位移;$D_k(Q)$为 Q 点的不连续位移值;$\overline{u}_i(P)$、$\overline{t}_i(P)$为 P 点在 i 方向的位移和应力值。

经离散化后,可得到边界元的支配方程组:

本文选自《清华大学学报(自然科学版)》1996 第 1 期,作者还有涂金良、张镜剑。

$$\begin{bmatrix} A \\ B \end{bmatrix} \begin{Bmatrix} D_1 \\ D_2 \end{Bmatrix} = \begin{Bmatrix} P_1 \\ u_1 \end{Bmatrix} \tag{2}$$

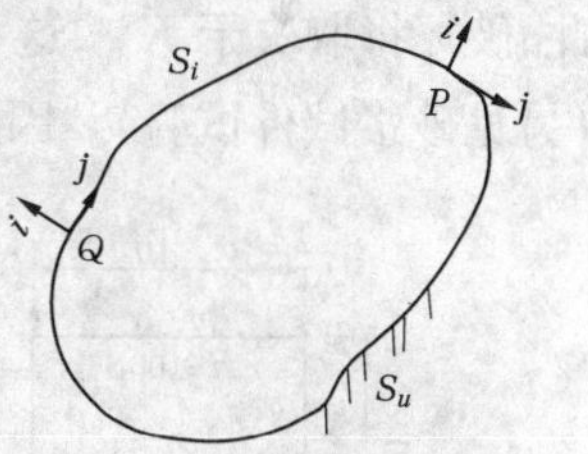

图1　方程符号示意图

我们注意到,裂纹面上的边界条件均为应力边界条件,并且首次迭代计算时,裂纹面无应力存在。

由式(2)可解得不连续位移向量 D,从而求解到裂纹面上的应力 F_s、F_n,粗略地假定裂纹面(包括缝端裂纹处)摩擦符合库仑定律,则对于裂纹面上的各单元处有下述三种状态之一:

(1)接触状态:$D_n=0, D_s=0, |F_s|<|F_n|f$;

(2)滑移状态:$D_n=0, D_s\neq 0, |F_s|\geqslant|F_n|f$;

(3)脱开状态:$D_n>0, F_s=F_n=0$。

式中:f 为摩擦系数;F_s、F_n 为裂纹面上的剪切、法向应力;D_s、D_n 为不连续位移值。

实际判断时,把与上述状态不符量作为不协调量进行迭代。首先把各裂纹面上单元的 D_s 值及 $D_n<0$ 的 D_n 值反号并乘以一迭代因子 ω,作为准不协调位移向量,由此求出裂纹面上相应的准不协调力向量 ΔF_n 及 ΔF_s,对各裂纹面上的单元作下列判断:

(1)如果 $D_n>0, \Delta F_n+F_n>0$,此单元为张开状态:

$$F_s=F_n=0$$

(2)如果 $\Delta F_n+F_n\leqslant 0, |F_s+\Delta F_s|<|\Delta F_n+F_n|\cdot f$,则此单元为接触状态:

$$F_s=-\mathrm{sgn}(D_s)\cdot|F_n+\Delta F_n|,\quad F_n=F_n+\Delta F_n$$

(3)如果 $\Delta F_n+F_n\leqslant 0, |F_s+\Delta F_s|\geqslant|\Delta F_n+F_n|\cdot f$,则此单元处于滑移状态:

$$F_s=-\mathrm{sgn}(D_s)\cdot|(F_n+\Delta F_n)\cdot f|,\quad F_n=F_n+\Delta F_n$$

上述过程已把不协调量叠加到裂纹边界上的应力中,把求得的裂纹面上的应力作为应力边界条件代入式(2)或重新迭代计算并判断,直至满足收敛条件为止。收敛条件为

$$\|\{F_{i+1}\}-\{F_i\}\|/\|F_{i+1}\|\leqslant\varepsilon$$

式中:ε 为给定允许误差;$\{F_i\}$为第 i 次迭代的右端项;$\{F_{i+1}\}$为第 $i+1$ 次迭代的右端项。

上述迭代过程不必重新分解方程组,但迭代因子 ω 的选取至关重要。本文将 ω 作为下山因子,初始值 ω_0 取 0.8～1.0,每当第二次算出的不平衡误差 $\varepsilon_i>\varepsilon_{i-1}$ 时,ω_{i+1} 取 $0.7\omega_i$,以保证收敛,本文数值计算表明其收敛性很好。

2　算例

含有斜边裂纹的矩形板,尺寸及受荷情况见图2,计算结果见表1。不压缝时 K_{I}、K_{II} 值为不考虑压剪情况下缝面变位限制及缝面摩擦阻力时的计算应力强度因子。

(1)压剪荷载下当缝面不接触(缝有一定宽度)时,K_{I} 为负值,在缝端有压剪应力集中区,压剪破坏形式和 K_{II} 不同。

(2)缝端厚趋近零,计算假定理想的缝面完全闭合,缝面法线方向反力使 $K_{\mathrm{I}}=0$。因

此,破坏将取决于 $K_{Ⅱ}$,这和实际砂浆试验裂纹方向不一致。压剪不宜单纯由 $K_{Ⅱ}$ 确定,(另见砂浆试件试验)。因此,压剪破坏指标应另作研究。

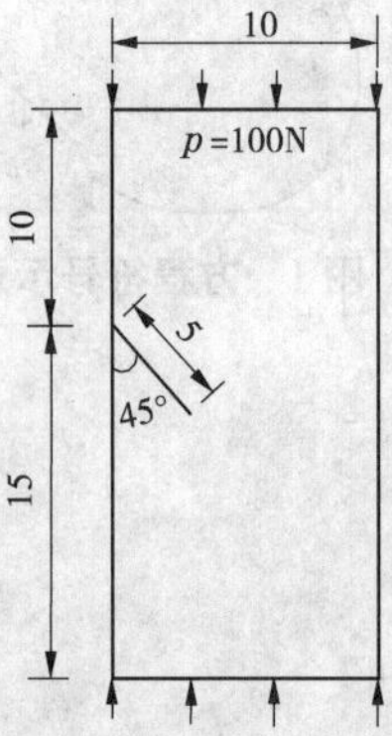

图 2 斜裂纹矩形板 (单位:cm)

表 1 边裂纹的压剪分析 (单位:N/cm$^{3/2}$)

计算情况	$K_{Ⅰ}$	$K_{Ⅱ}$
不压缝	-48.14	22.86
$f=0$	-0.000	22.86
$f=0.2$	-0.004	18.13
$f=0.4$	-0.014	13.55
$f=0.6$	-0.012	9.13
$f=0.8$	-0.006	4.90
$f=1.0$	-0.001	0.680
$f=1.2$	-0.001	0.002

(3)随缝面摩擦阻力增大,$K_{Ⅱ}$ 减小,缝端断裂能迅速下降,f 的取值误差直接影响 $K_{Ⅱ}$ 的值。

3 均质材料压剪试验

用光弹环氧板研制近似无缝模型,研究缝面和缝端能量分配。

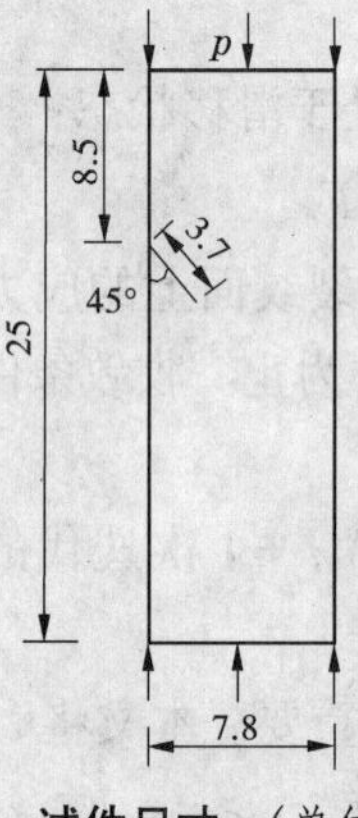

图 3 试件尺寸 (单位:cm)

3.1 试件尺寸

光测试验试件的长度较大,以消除均布加力的不均匀效应,冻结加力后离板端 3~4cm 处有条纹均匀区,保证了远场为均匀的应力场。试件尺寸见图 3,宽 L 为 7.8cm,裂纹倾斜角为 45°,裂纹长 a 为 3.7cm。由于加力冻结时环氧板变形较大且加力前缝面已接触,初始缝宽可视为零。

3.2 加力和参数测定

为确保两边加力的均匀性,试件置于光滑玻璃板及滑粉纸垫层上,砝码绕过三角架上的滑轮,通过垫块加力于两端。实测表明,滑轮及玻璃板加滑粉纸的摩擦力损失小于 5%,精度满足试验要求。

3.3 试件参数测定

试件的初应力及黏结冻结初应力等于小于 0.1 级/cm 厚。重复试验结果相近。

光学参数随试验一同测定,结果:弹模为 23.5MPa,光学常数 f 为 0.034 5MPa,摩擦系数 f 为 0.65。摩擦系数 f 是在冻结温度 110℃以下测定的。

4 试验和数值计算结果

本文采用相对错位间接边界元法。压剪情况下,假定缝的上、下岸不相互侵入,因此

$K_{\mathrm{I}}=0$,缝面若遵守摩尔库仑法则$|\tau| \leqslant f \cdot \sigma$(实际形式 $\tau=f\sigma+c$),f 计算值往往偏大。小块体压剪试验得平均应力场 σ 值偏小,反算 f 值偏大。

对试件的计算表明,考虑裂纹面的摩擦阻力效应后,缝端 K_{II} 减少至 4.667N/cm$^{3/2}$。本次试验加外力 σ 为 6.12N/cm^2,外力经 2cm 距离传递后,呈较均匀分布,试验校正测定 σ 的平均值为 5.8N/cm^2(较实际加力小 5%)。对计算条件进行修正。

4.1 裂纹上下两边的相对位错值

试验中试件的裂纹上下边的沿缝方向相对错动值用精度 0.01mm 显微镜测定。试验和计算的相对错动值的对比见图 4。由图 4 可看出试验值和考虑压剪摩擦效应的计算值沿缝长分布相近,试验值较大,尤其开口端位错较计算值累计大约大 12%,即计算中缝面阻力偏大。试验沿缝面位移略大于计算值。

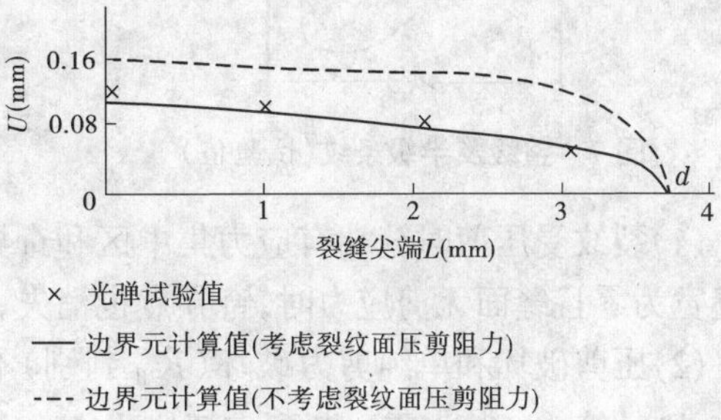

图 4 裂纹面上错动位移分布试验值与计算值对比

4.2 裂纹面的接触应力

图 5 为裂纹面上压应力试验值和数值解的对比。图 6 为裂纹面上摩擦力(剪应力)的试验值和数值解的比较。可见,试验值和数值解的正应力(压力)规律相同,数值也相近,但图 6 中可见开口端试验剪力值较计算值小,而缝末端试验剪力值较计算值加大 25%。近末端的缝面应力分配偏离按摩尔库仑原则计算值较多,不宜作断裂能计算依据。

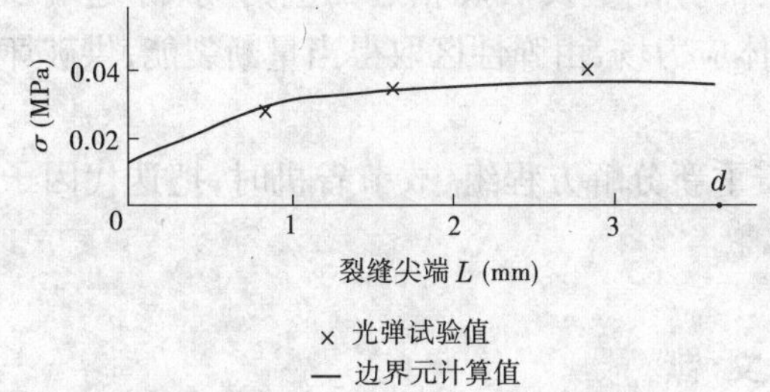

图 5 裂纹面上正应力分布计算和试验值的对比

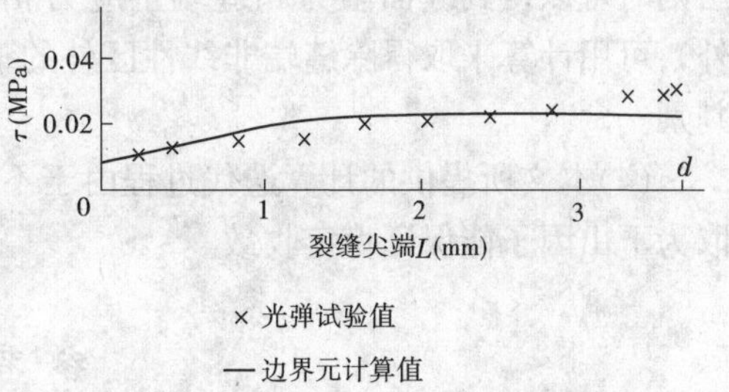

图 6 裂纹面上剪应力分布试验值与计算值的对比

4.3 裂纹尖端应力及整体应力场

图 7 为等差线试验描图,图 8 为计算结果图。比较试验和同条件计算结果可见缝面变形、应力场相近,缝端应力场分布形状相似,整体应力场的试验值和计算值相近。按线弹性边界元计算宏观应力场,可提供工程初步计算当量断裂能,即取非线性区外的已知点的弹性应力反推缝端当量断裂能,用砂浆和混凝土试件的起裂点,由同条件边界元计算其 K 值作为断裂韧性,进行断裂延伸差别。

5 结语

由试验和数值计算分析可见,初始缝宽近似为零的压剪问题有以下特点:

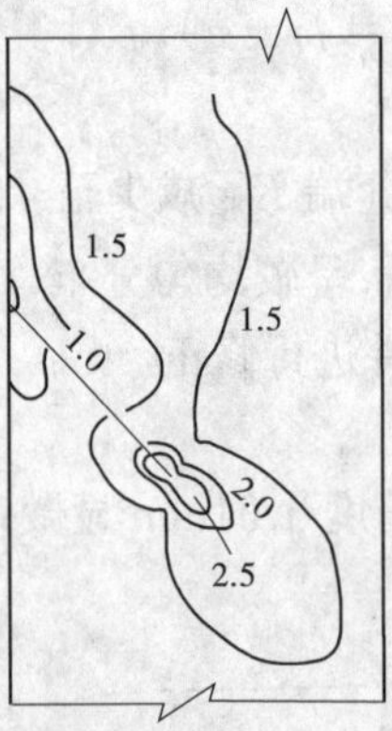

图 7　整级及半级条纹(试验值)

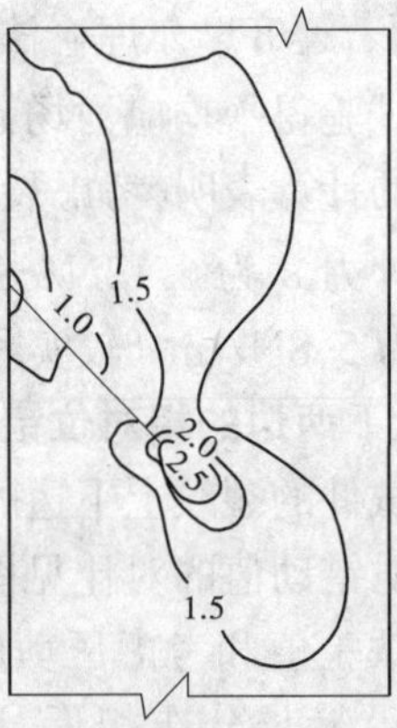

图 8　整级及半级条纹(计算值)

(1)裂纹受压剪时缝端有应力集中区和奇异点属断裂延伸问题,宜按韧性判别。当理想缝宽为零且缝面无剪应力时,奇异点也消失,破坏由常规应变(或应力)确定。

(2)压剪破坏和单纯剪力破坏(K_{II} 判别)不同,当裂纹缝宽为零,压剪时缝宽仍为零不变,则计算中 K_{I} 为零。断裂破坏应由 K_{II} 确定,但这和砂浆压剪断裂试验破坏方向不一致(另文刊出)不宜单纯用 K_{II} 作为压剪破坏指标。压剪问题的缝面压力直接影响 K_{II} 的大小,压力增大缝面接触压力和摩擦力增大,则缝端剪力减小,压剪问题中缝端缝面能量分配直接影响缝端起裂。

(3)压剪缝端实际上是一个接触非线性问题,试验应力场和考虑接触摩擦效应的边界元断裂力学应力场分布规律相似,但近缝端剪应力值有差异,当裂纹表面摩擦用摩尔库仑法则时可以得到缝面阻力和缝端正应力相近的分配值及宏观相近的应力场(除缝端以外),可用计算来取得除缝端非线性区外的整体应力场,由弹性区取得当量断裂能,供破坏判别。

(4)本文所提供的计算迭代过程由于不需重新分解方程组,故节省机时,把迭代因子取为下山因子能保证稳定收敛。

参 考 文 献

[1] 徐道远,傅新苟.压剪断裂问题的有限元分析.河海大学学报,1987(4):46~53

[2] 池元.直缝多裂隙体的通用解析数值法及其工程应用:[学位论文].福州:福州大学土木工程系,1989

碾压混凝土重力坝结构改进和仿真应力

摘　要　因坝高百米以上的碾压混凝土重力坝往往存在坝体下部抗剪能力和基岩内稳定安全度不足的问题,所以作者探讨一种结构改进措施:坝体下部采用不分永久性横缝只设人工短缝的整体式结构;坝体上部采用变高度分横缝的悬臂梁式结构。通过对我国中南地区某工程实例的仿真应力计算,即施工期的温度场和温度与累计自重徐变压力,运行期温度场和温差应力的计算,其结果表明,采用上述结构改进措施是有明显效果的。

关键词　碾压混凝土　重力坝　整体结构　人工短缝　仿真应力

1　高碾压混凝土重力坝简述和结构改进

通常对于宽河谷(平面拱作用较小)或两岸地质较弱的坝址,混凝土坝宜选用直线重力坝布置,这可减短坝轴线的长度,避免泄洪的径向集中。重力坝是以悬臂梁挡水,随着坝高的加大,梁下部的剪力也加大。当混凝土采用碾压混凝土工艺快速施工时,不论是工艺上人为的因素还是气候等客观因素引起的较大面积层间弱面都将直接威胁坝体的稳定安全。国外用加大碾压混凝土坝剖面来保安全(如日本的玉川坝和岛地川坝等),但剖面加大多少才能保证安全并没有科学依据或足够的经验统计,且过多增大剖面,工程量大,势必丧失碾压混凝土筑坝的快速经济优越性。碾压混凝土坝有平整的大仓面便于施工,目前沿上下游方向坝底宽达百米仍不设纵缝,主要依靠混凝土低温升和后期混凝土强度上升降低基础约束系数来实现抗裂,但仍采用和通常重力坝相近的横缝以防止垂直坝轴线方向的裂缝。试验表明,混凝土在单轴和双轴受拉时承受能力差别不显著,而碾压混凝土低温升和后期降温约束系数的下降同样有利于坝体内部垂直坝轴线方向的抗裂,碾压混凝土水泥用量少内部温升低也减少施工期混凝土坝的内外温差,且短时间的内外温差冲击是可以用工程措施来消除的,可见在不增加新的工程措施前提下,碾压混凝土坝的横缝间距可以加大(便于碾压施工),以至在窄河谷的坝体下部可以采用整体式[1]。

国内某直线布置的碾压混凝土重力坝坝高 128m,横缝间距 21～33m,河谷底部宽约 85m,坝顶长 335m,即使坝剖面底宽加大到 107.3m,其抗剪能力仍不足。该坝基岩石呈规则的层状结构,向下游倾斜,其倾角约 38°,并有 10 余层厚薄不均的层间错动,不能承受水压自重组合在坝踵区的主拉应力。将坝体下部改为不分永久横缝(只设人工短缝)的整体结构,上部为变高度悬臂梁,见图 1～图 5。这种碾压混凝土重力坝新结构的特点是保持碾压混凝土重力坝直线布置,坝下部为不设永久横缝的整体结构,它将水压作用下坝下部的平面深梁通过人工短缝实现平面拱传力。为了经济可将坝底宽减少到 97.5m,但垂直坝轴线的坝体侧面在压剪条件下可提供更大的抗剪能力,并随碾压层面的减弱(变形加大)而增大抗剪阻力,这样仍可满足稳定安全要求。坝体中部和上部随河谷加宽使平面拱

本文选自《清华大学学报(自然科学版)》1996 第 1 期,作者还有张富德、张明丽。

作用减弱，横缝设置在上游坝面是从▽146.0m 往上，下游坝面是从▽155.0m 往上(见图 5)，这种上游低、下游高的悬臂梁有利于抗滑稳定，它与碾压混凝土的层间弱面形成交角。坝体下部整体结构降温慢，可预留一条备用分区灌浆横缝以保持温度变形后整体作用的可靠性。碾压混凝土工艺用于大体积混凝土结构的优点已被工程实践所证实，但急需改进结构和设计方法，改进传力方式以削减层间弱面的不利影响。

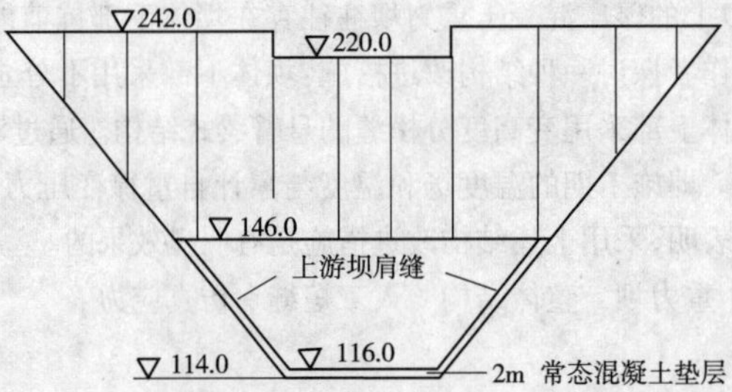

图 1　下部整体式结构上游坝肩缝位置示意

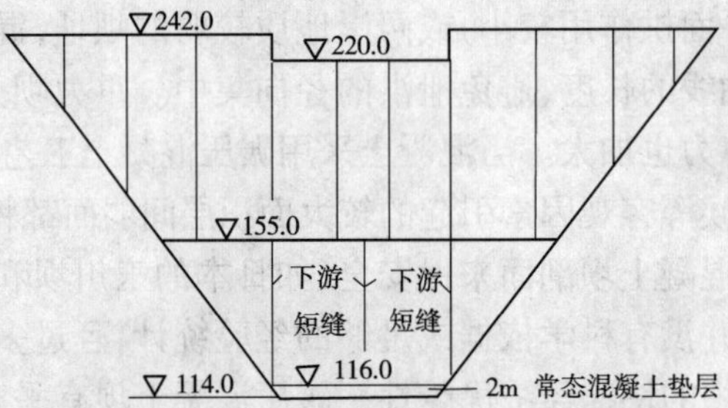

图 2　下部整体式结构下游短缝位置示意

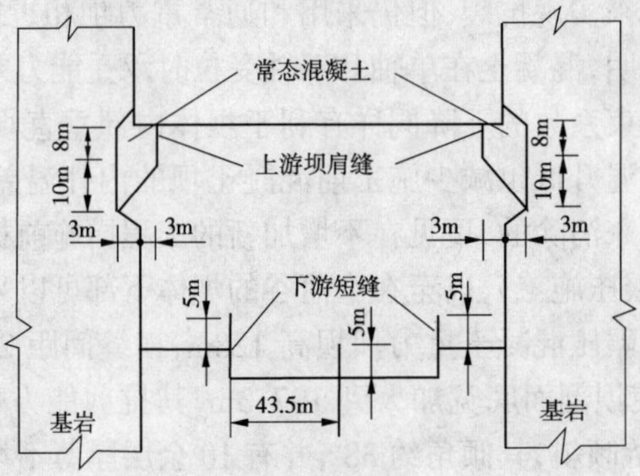

图 3　人工短缝平面布置示意

2　碾压混凝土重力坝施工期温度与累计自重应力及运行期温度应力

自重通常在重力坝(碾压混凝土或常规混凝土)上下游面产生有利的垂直压应力，仿真应力表明它参与徐变过程的压应力值略降低。

碾压混凝土水泥用量少，绝热温升低，我国筑坝实践中常用的碾压混凝土已做到绝热温升值为 10～15℃，这对减少坝体内外温差、防止施工期表面裂缝有利，实例的温度场变化(尚未采用人工冷却措施)如图 6、图 7 所示。

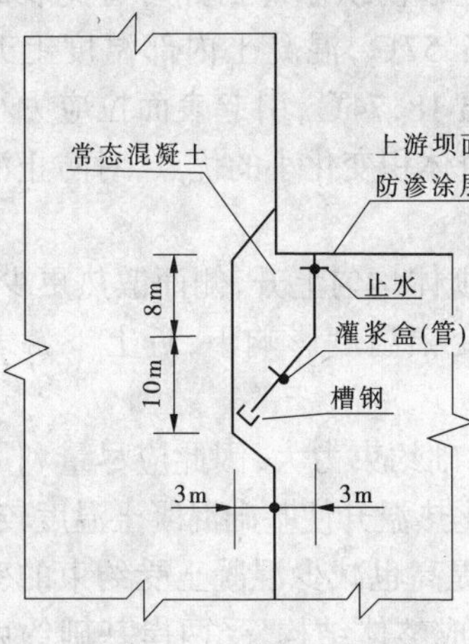

图 4 人工短缝构造示意

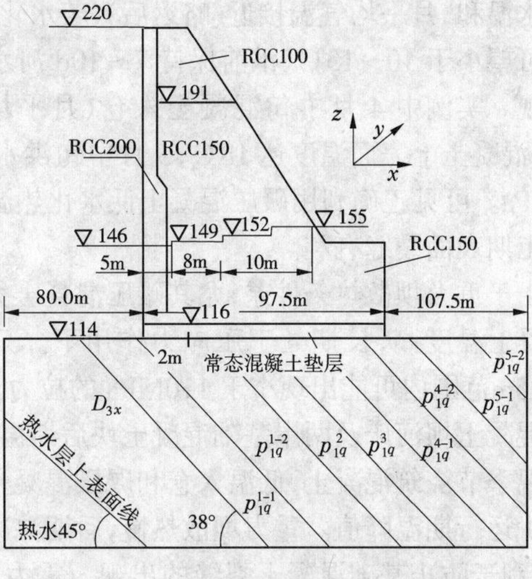

图 5 下部整体式结构溢流坝典型横剖面示意

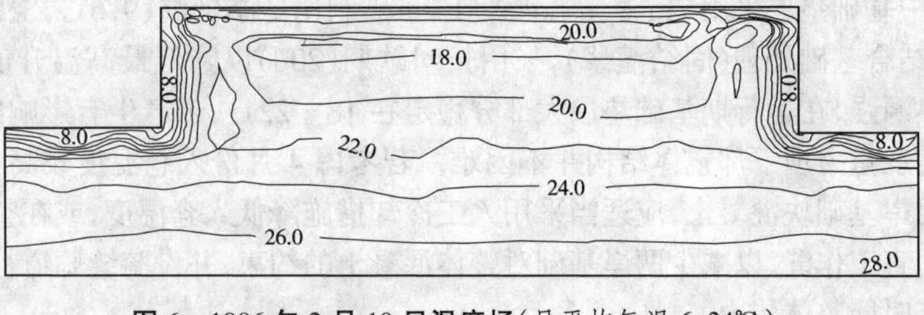

图 6 1996 年 2 月 10 日温度场(月平均气温 6.34℃)

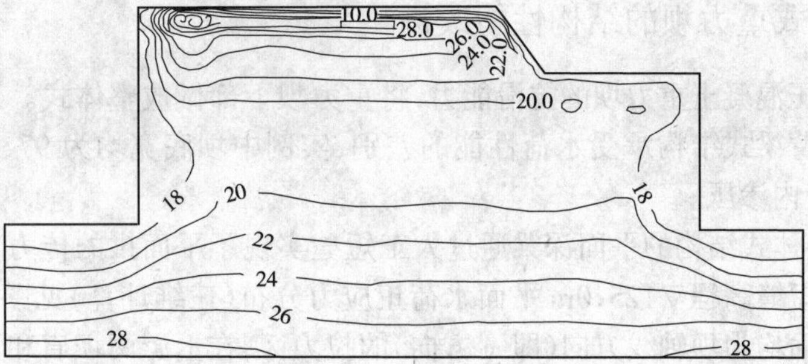

图 7 1996 年 4 月 20 日温度场(月平均气温 16.57℃)

连续碾压时混凝土上下层温度接近连续变化,因此内应力较小。间歇期间主要由坝体上下游面及上表面散热,上表面温度梯度较大,但碾压混凝土绝热温升小,温度梯度也减小,短期间歇的碾压混凝土上表面温度拉应力通常在 0.3~0.5MPa,实例中最大(冬季)可达 1.0MPa(无覆盖),实践表明注意在寒流期覆盖和湿养护即使在冬季也不致引起裂缝。为加快施工进度,常需在温度较高的初夏和秋季浇筑碾压混凝土,坝体在秋季入仓(较高温度)的混凝土到冬季低温时会形成坝体内部与上下游坝面间较大的温差值,好在散热时间长,温度梯度已降低,表面温度拉应力与自重压应力叠加后,在上游坝面拉力值为0.63MPa,下游坝面略大一些,为1.02MPa。初夏按月平均气温入仓的碾压混凝土,由于河水温和,月平均气温接近(略迟后),若水化热温升小,度汛时水温和碾压混凝土温度差距可望小于10~13℃,汛前保持7~10d河水低温养护以防洪水冷击亦可避免表面裂缝出现。实例中4月中旬混凝土入仓(月平均气温)16.57℃,混凝土内部温度上升到30℃,混凝土上表面温度达18℃,5月中旬洪水平均水温18.74℃,引起表面拉应力小于0.5MPa。可见正确利用碾压混凝土低水化热温升和自身体积变化小的优点,对防止混凝土施工期表面裂缝有利。

由于重力坝散热条件差,尤其碾压混凝土大仓面使坝体均匀上升,侧面散热更少,内部混凝土温度高,长期处于压应力作用下。只有在年变幅温度影响下,近上下游表面10~15m范围内可能出现小于1.0MPa的拉力。

混凝土坝河床及两岸基础混凝土块后期温降时受基础约束力大,因此应尽量利用冬季低温季节浇筑混凝土,低温入仓和碾压混凝土的低水化热温升使基础混凝土温度较低,以减少运行期温降值。重力坝散热慢,后期混凝土强度提高也减少混凝土受约束的变形值,有利于防止基础混凝土裂缝的出现。重力坝下部做成整体结构,受两岸基础约束力大,因此整体结构的混凝土应利用低温季节浇筑低温升值的碾压混凝土以减少后期温降变形,实例中基础垫层采用2m厚常态混凝土,虽然利用冬季低温(9.6℃)浇筑,但水化热温升大,可结合基础处理(固结灌浆),采用长间歇期(20d)以降低最高温升值(达22℃)。该工程地热源强,在运行期基础垫层大部分稳定在18~22℃,未产生有影响的拉力,因此在该工程实现重力坝下部整体结构并不困难。若考虑4月份入仓温度较高(16.57℃)的季节浇筑两岸基础块混凝土,应适当采用人工冷却措施降低入仓温度,或在整体混凝土中增加中央垂直工作缝,以减少两岸基础对整体混凝土的约束,并设骑缝廊道补灌浆以保持运行期温降时能整体传力。

3 下部整体式重力坝的结构性能改进

为增强碾压混凝土重力坝的抗滑能力,将重力坝下部做成整体式。下面分析下部整体式结构与悬臂梁式结构承受水荷性能的差别,实例中坝底宽均为97.5m,短缝内设排水,故不考虑缝内渗压。

(1)下部整体式结构的平面深梁通过人工短缝实现了平面拱的传力特性。下部整体式结构设人工短缝高程▽125.0m平面水荷正应力分布(三维计算)见图8。在未设人工短缝时上下游面均为坝轴线方向(即 y 方向)的拉力区,在上游两坝肩和下游面的中间部位拉应力数值较大,而设置了人工短缝(见图3)之后,上游面形成了坝轴线方向的压力区,下游面亦为微压力区。下游面中间部位的三条短缝采用直缝形式,上游两坝肩的短缝采用折缝形式,使其缝端伸入到坝肩基岩中,以便预先进行加固处理。

(2)下部整体式结构在垂直坝轴线的坝体侧面形成了剪应力(τ_{xy}),并随碾压层面的减弱可逐渐增大,以承受水压荷载。▽125.0m平面两坝肩可提供剪应力 $\tau_{xy}>0.3$MPa。中央坝段两侧面在下部整体部位也能提供剪应力 τ_{xy} 为0.01~0.04MPa,如果存在碾压层间弱面,则 x 方向的变形加大,其剪应力 τ_{xy} 会迅速增加,对承受水压荷载是非常有利的。

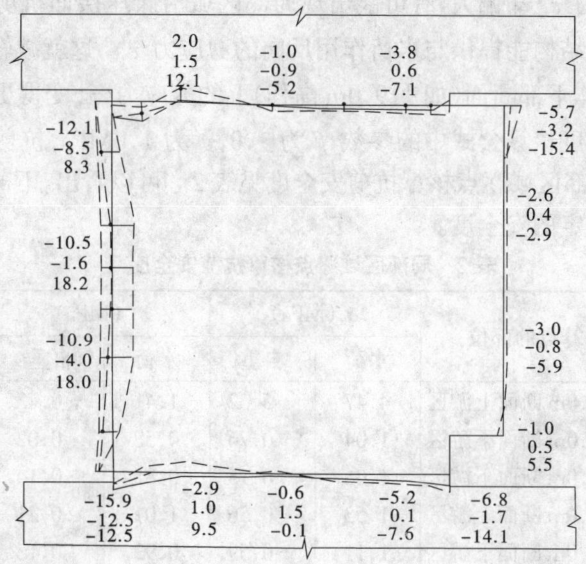

图 8　下部整体式结构设人工短缝▽125.0m 平面水荷正应力分布　(单位:0.1MPa)

(3)下部整体式结构在下部碾压层面上的顺河向剪应力 τ_{zx} 值下降。在坝基▽119.0m 断面上,下部整体式结构的剪应力 τ_{zx} 值比悬臂梁式结构减小了约 0.1MPa,这对减轻高碾压混凝土重力坝坝下部的抗剪负担是很有利的。

(4)下部整体式结构的下部梁向正应力 σ_z 下降,比悬臂梁式结构在上游坝踵的拉应力下降了 0.37MPa,在下游坝趾的压应力下降了 −0.29MPa,因此下部整体式结构大大降低了由水压荷载引起的在上游坝踵区的拉剪破坏和下游坝趾区的压剪破坏,改善了应力状态。

(5)人工短缝缝端的稳定性。两坝肩人工短缝采用折缝形式使其缝端伸入到坝肩基岩中。在水荷作用下,缝端单元高斯点的应力一般均小于 1.0MPa,而缝端处则为 1.0~3.0MPa(由于划分单元很小,且采用了奇异单元)。用应力法求得缝端应力强度因子 K_{I} 和 K_{II} 值列于表 1,可以看出 K_{I} 值在 2.0MN/m$^{3/2}$ 以下,而 K_{II} 值更小,因此人工短缝是稳定的。由于缝端裂缝前沿断裂带很小,当 K_{I} 与 K_{II} 组合值略大于 K_{IC} 时亦可在缝端埋设抗裂能力大的材料(如槽钢)。

表 1　水压作用下缝端应力强度因子　(单位:MN/m$^{3/2}$)

K	上游坝肩缝		下游中部短缝		
	左	右	左	中	右
K_{I}	1.946	1.876	−1.183	−1.678	−1.798
K_{II}	−0.89	0.306	−0.38	0.187	0.182

4　坝体层间抗滑稳定和基岩内的主拉应力分析

在水压和自重荷载作用下,悬臂梁式结构坝体下部的部分区域内竖向压应力 σ_z 不大,而顺河向的剪应力 τ_{zx} 却偏大,有可能出现局部区域沿碾压层面抗剪强度安全度不足的问题。下部整体式结构能提供与水荷作用反向的剪应力 τ_{xy},这就减轻了层间剪力的负担,整体作用还使坝体下部断面(如 119.0m 高程)上的剪应力 τ_{zx} 变得更趋均匀。根据工程实测值取抗剪断强度核算公式中的参数 f' 为 1.0,c' 为 1.0MPa,抗剪强度核算公式中的参数 $f=0.7$,对局部区域逐点核算抗剪安全度见表2。可以看出,下部整体式结构能有效地提高层间抗滑稳定的安全度。

表2 局部区域逐点核算抗剪安全度

结构形式	荷载组合	核算点的部位	σ_z(MPa)		τ_{zx}(MPa)		$\frac{f'\sigma_z+c'}{\tau_{zx}}$	$\frac{f\sigma_z}{\tau_{zx}}$
			水荷	自重	水荷	自重		
下部整体式	自重+校核水荷	▽119.0m 断面上游区	4.47	−5.32	1.41	−0.43	1.88	0.61
		▽119.0m 断面下游区	−1.04	−0.76	0.58	0.02	4.75	2.15
		▽140.0m 断面下游区	−1.06	−0.15	0.85	0.14	2.23	0.87
		▽155.0m 断面上游区	−1.53	−0.56	1.01	0.21	2.53	1.20
		▽155.0m 断面下游区	−1.11	−0.59	0.92	0.13	2.57	1.13
悬臂梁式	自重+校核水荷	▽119.0m 断面上游区	4.84	−4.86	1.50	−0.53	1.01	0.01
		▽119.0m 断面下游区	−1.57	−0.81	0.74	0.07	4.17	2.06
		▽140.0m 断面下游区	−1.00	−0.18	0.88	0.15	2.12	0.80
		▽155.0m 断面上游区	−1.44	−0.23	0.99	0.15	2.34	1.03
		▽155.0m 断面下游区	−1.08	−0.27	0.94	0.12	2.22	0.89

考虑从施工期到运行期的温度荷载以后,其组合应力在悬臂梁式结构的坝体下部部分区域内出现了"拉剪区"或压剪安全度不足的区域,而下部整体式结构在坝体下部区域内,σ_z 均为压应力,不会出现"拉剪区",而且压剪安全度得到普遍提高。

在水压和自重荷载作用下,悬臂梁式结构的基岩内部,坝踵区附近的岩石层面上,顺河向正应力 σ_x 为拉应力,实际的岩石层面不能承担与其垂直的拉应力作用,而且岩石层面的张开将直接危及防渗帷幕的安全。基岩内防渗帷幕区及其上下游邻近区域内均出现主拉应力,对倾向下游倾角为38°的基岩的应力和稳定是不利的。采用下部整体式结构,基岩内的主拉应力值普遍减小,见表3(其中 φ 为 σ_1 与 x 的夹角),其改善效果是明显的。

表3 基岩内局部区域逐点核算主拉应力值 (单位:MPa)

结构形式	核算点的部位	σ_x	σ_y	σ_z	τ_{xy}	τ_{yz}	τ_{zx}	σ_1	σ_2	σ_3	φ(°)
下部整体式	▽109m 帷幕上游侧	0.98	0.03	−1.01	0	0	0.61	1.16	0.03	−1.19	15.7
	▽109m 帷幕下游侧	0.37	−0.02	−1.43	0	0	0.69	0.61	−0.02	−1.66	18.7
	▽94m 帷幕上游侧	0.05	−0.05	−1.99	0	0	0.31	0.09	−0.05	−2.03	8.4
	▽94m 帷幕下游侧	0.18	0.06	−1.79	0	0	0.46	0.28	0.06	−1.89	12.5
悬臂梁式	▽109m 帷幕上游侧	1.12	−0.03	−1.31	−0.03	0	0.50	1.22	−0.03	−1.40	11.2
	▽109m 帷幕下游侧	0.51	−0.41	−1.88	−0.03	0	0.64	0.67	−0.41	−2.04	14.1
	▽94m 帷幕上游侧	0.20	−0.55	−2.28	−0.01	0.02	0.20	0.22	−0.55	−2.3	4.6
	▽94m 帷幕下游侧	0.32	−0.58	−2.25	−0.01	0.02	0.35	0.37	−0.58	−2.3	7.6

参考文献

[1] 张明丽．碾压混凝土重力坝结构措施及应力与稳定问题的研究:[学位论文]．北京:清华大学水利水电工程系,1995

柔性拱和软弱地基上的碾压混凝土拱坝

摘　要　为改善软弱基础上修建碾压混凝土拱坝的结构设计，通过对水压和温度荷载作用下坝体的应力和位移分析，提出了适应软弱基础拱坝变位大但应力不恶化的"柔性拱"及简易止裂措施，已用于修建新疆石门子碾压混凝土拱坝。坝体设人工短缝加大拱的变位，可削减水压和温度作用下的拉应力集中；扩大拱座降低坝肩软弱岩面上的压应力和剪应力，拱座考虑侧约束减少拱座在水压作用下的变位，也增加坝肩绕渗途径。

关键词　柔性拱　刚性拱　碾压混凝土拱坝　人工短缝　软弱基础　刚性基础

通常修建拱坝理想的地址条件是在基岩性能良好（均匀、完整、足够强度、透水性小等）的刚性基础上。在高寒地区、软弱基础上修建拱坝尤其是较薄的碾压混凝土拱坝易使坝体的变位过大，局部应力集中恶化，以至于造成坝体不稳定和坝体破坏。因此，尽管修建碾压混凝土拱坝工程量少，工艺简化，施工速度快[1,2]，但在高寒地区、软弱基础上建造碾压混凝土拱坝还有很多技术难题尚待解决[3~5]。

1　新疆石门子碾压混凝土拱坝简介

石门子水利枢纽工程位于新疆维吾尔自治区昌吉州玛纳斯县境内的塔河中游河段上，是一项以灌溉为主，兼有防洪、发电和改善生态环境等综合效益的中型水利枢纽工程。

石门子工程主坝采用高 110m 的碾压混凝土拱坝。该工程的两岸和河床为青灰色和红色砾岩，砾岩为泥钙质胶结，其中红色砾岩浸水软化后的变形模量为 4GPa，个别样品浸水后散塌。成层砾岩有夹泥层 J_3，右坝肩有陡倾角的断层 F_6，断层沿上下游方向延伸，并和斜夹泥层组成右岸不稳定体，同时，在左坝肩上存在 $F_5 \sim J_3$ 组成的不稳定体。

坝址处于强震多发区，地震设计烈度 8 级，设计采取相应的减震措施。

坝址地处高寒地区，月平均气温在 0℃以下长达 5 个月，且年温度变幅高达 60℃。碾压混凝土拱坝未设后期的冷却措施，需采取专门措施削减后期坝体温降应力。

在石门子工程中，采用在坝肩设人工短缝、拱冠设中缝、下游面设人工短缝等措施以降低坝体的刚度，限制拱座变位及加大拱坝变位，达到释放温度应力及减少水压作用下的拉应力集中，也就是采用柔性拱的方法来改善坝体应力，作用十分明显。

石门子碾压混凝土拱坝拉力区即在坝肩上游面处设人工短缝，由于组合应力断裂强度因子已接近混凝土韧度值，缝端设止裂结构。同时坝体中央横缝（简称中缝）灌浆时在下游面预留 1m 的部位不灌浆，在▽1 380m 以上中缝留温度通缝不灌浆；在坝体下游面拉力区 G'、F'两点处设立沿径向 1.5m 深的人工短缝，▽1 380m 以上处设横缝。这种设人工短缝的方法可降低坝体刚度，起柔性拱作用。同时在坝体靠近坝肩部位加宽坝体厚度以增加坝体与软弱岩体的接触面积，降低下游拱座最大压应力水平，尤其是 B'、D'点

本文选自《清华大学学报（自然科学版）》2002 年第 10 期，作者还有徐增辉、李鹏辉。

压力值(如图1所示)。

2 水压荷载作用下柔性拱对于坝体应力场和位移场的影响

2.1 水压情况下的计算模型和材料参数

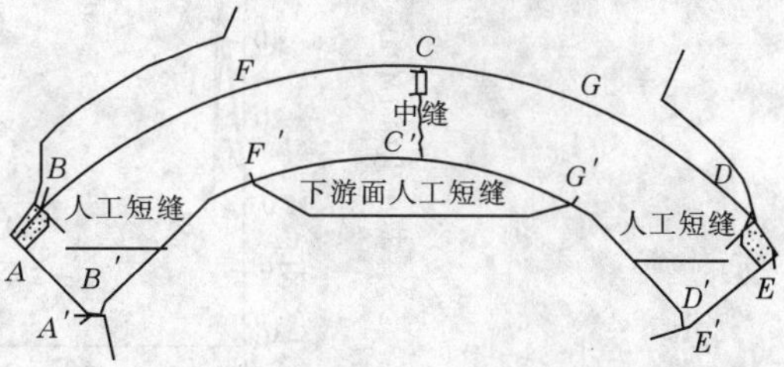

图1 拱圈的人工短缝示意图

计算以坝轴线中点为原点,横河向(指向左岸为正)为 x 轴,顺河向(逆水流方向为正)为 y 轴,铅直方向(向上为正)为 z 轴。为保证计算精度,共划分14 330个单元,17 748个节点。

不同高程岩石弹性模量采用石门子工程软弱基础实测值,但在刚性基础比较计算时,岩石弹性模量 E_r 取为20GPa(如表1所示)。

表1 软弱地基、刚性地基岩石计算弹性模量

岩石基础	高程(m)	E_r(GPa)
软弱	<1 319	4
	1 319~1 351	6
	>1 351	10
刚性	—	20

注:软弱基础岩石数据来自新疆石门子工程的实测材料参数。

在柔性拱计算中,考虑拱坝及人工短缝,缝端应力强度因子用加密单元位移差计算[4],而在刚性拱计算中不设缝。由于护坦和导墙是先浇筑的,其弹性模量取和坝体混凝土最终弹性模量相同。在仿真计算中采用了水库正常蓄水位▽1 391m,下游面水位▽1 320m,同时考虑坝体上游淤沙到▽1 342m的淤沙压力。任取典型高程的应力和位移进行讨论比较。

2.2 柔性拱对坝体水压下应力场和位移场的影响

首先对石门子碾压混凝土拱坝在水压作用下的应力场和位移场进行计算,比较讨论在软弱基础和刚性基础条件下柔性拱的作用,任取典型高程仿真计算结果如图2~图4所示。

从图2、图3可以清楚地看出,拱坝坝体应力在柔性拱和刚性拱情况下的差别相当明显。上游两坝肩和岩石之间由于混凝土轮廓外延,增加上游绕拱肩渗流途径,也使得坝肩 A、E 点上游拉应力集中部位外移至 B、D 两点(见图2(a))。无论是软弱基础还是刚性基础,采用柔性拱都可以减少两坝肩上游处的拱向拉应力集中,坝体下部(约1/4高)拱的拉应力从5~6MPa减少到1MPa左右,减少了75%~85%,拱冠部位的压应力增大0.3~0.5MPa(但不大于2.5MPa)。由图2(b)可知,软弱基础上柔性拱减少了拱坝下游面拱向压力,但未增加下游拱座 B'、D' 两点的最大压应力值(小于刚性基础最大压应力值),因此坝体应力得到了明显的改善。这主要是由于柔性拱适应了柔性基础的较大变位。

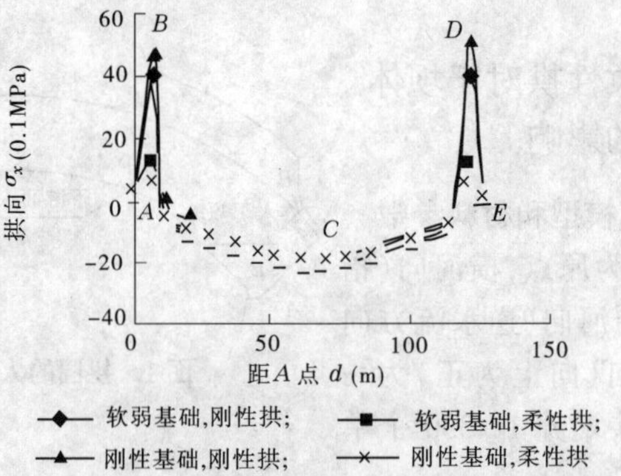

(a)水压荷载下 ▽1 308m上游面 σ_x

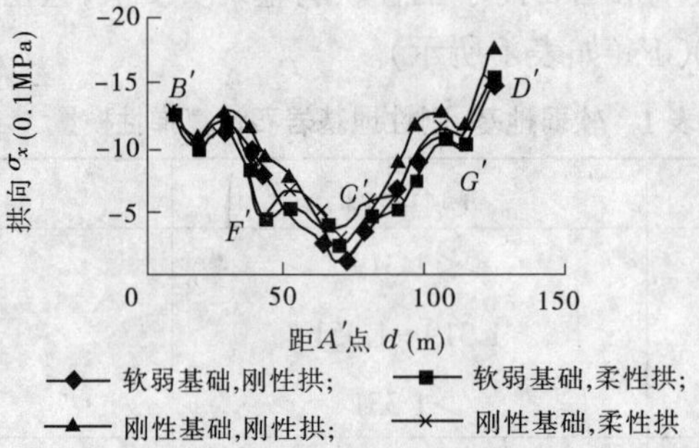

(b)水压荷载下 ▽1 345m上游面 σ_x

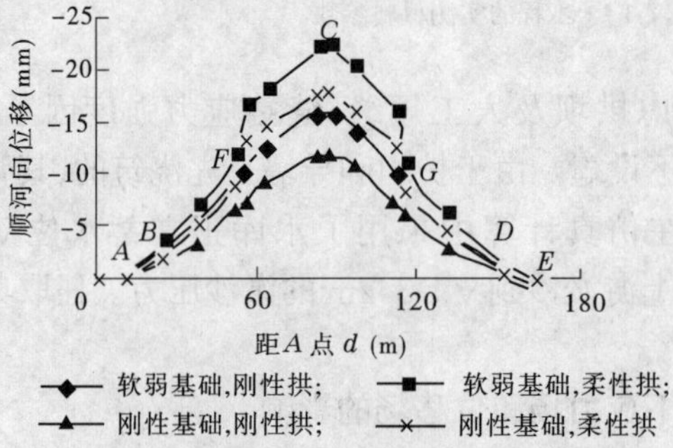

(c)水压荷载下 ▽ 1 394m顺河向位移图

图 2　水压荷载下坝体的拱向 σ_x 和顺河向位移图

坝体的下游面开了人工短缝后,下游面的开缝部位 G'、F'两点附近的拱向压应力有一明显的降低,降低到采用刚性拱时压应力的 1/4～1/2。

从图 3 可以看到坝肩处 AA'的拱向应力和顺河向位移,在坝肩扩大后坝体应力比较小,下游拱座最大只有 2～3MPa 压应力,都在岩石和混凝土的承载范围内。采用柔性拱或刚性拱无论是对于坝肩压应力分布还是对于坝肩位移都没有明显影响。影响坝肩应力和位移的主要原因是基础的岩石刚度,尤其对于坝肩的位移(见图 3(b)),基础的好坏有决定性影响。软弱基础下,坝肩的压应力比刚性基础大 0.5MPa 左右(见图 3(a));而位移则几乎是刚性基础的 1 倍,但总的来说,最大为 4mm 左右。这也正体现了软弱基础变位

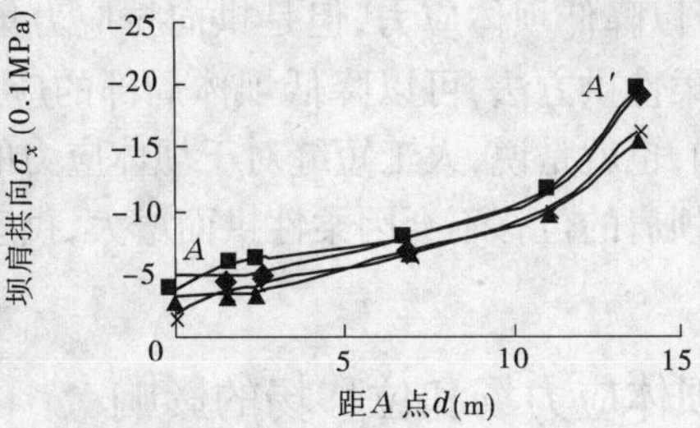

(a)水压荷载下 ▽1 355m右坝肩

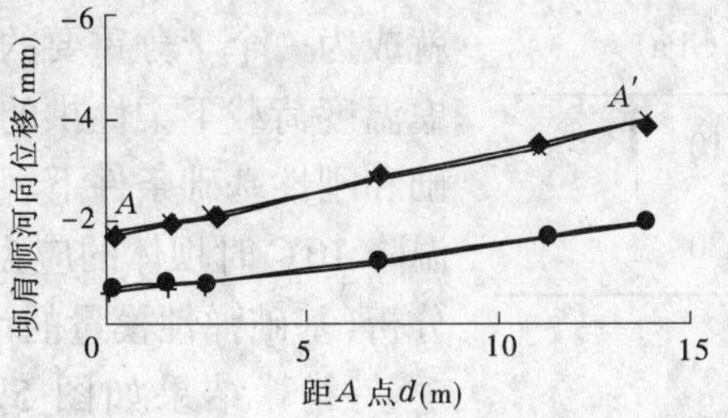

(b)水压荷载下 ▽1 355m右坝肩顺河向位移

图 3 右坝肩拱向 σ_x 和顺河向位移图

大的特点。

从图 2(c)看水压作用下坝体的拱冠部位位移,刚性拱位移比柔性拱位移小,这是由于柔性拱的坝体设人工短缝和▽1 380m以上温度横缝使坝体刚度降低所致。刚性拱的最大位移产生于坝体上部拱冠,为 19.6mm,而此处柔性拱位移仅 20.5mm,增大 5%;柔性拱的最大位移产生于坝体顶部,为 22.4mm,刚性拱顶部位移为 16.2mm,柔性拱位移增大 1/3 左右。

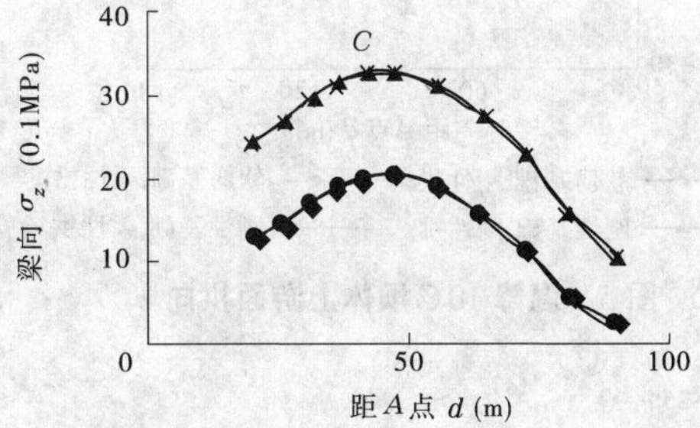

图 4 水压荷载下坝体▽1 291m 上游面梁向 σ_z

柔性拱顶部位移较大的原因是坝体▽1 380m以上中缝留横缝,同时,1/4 缝在▽1 380m以上留横缝,导致拱向作用降低,梁的顺河向位移加大。图 2(c)中显示出柔性拱位移比刚性拱位移在拱冠部位增量最大(主要是在坝体的▽1 380m以上),坝肩部位位移增加总量不大。虽然软弱基础坝体位移较刚性基础明显增大,增大 20%~30%,但总量不大。可见,坝体位移柔性拱较刚性拱要大,而软弱基础较刚性基础要大。

从图 4 可以看到上游面拱冠区的梁向拉应力主要取决于上下拱圈的相对变位,比较刚性基础上刚性拱和软弱基础上柔性拱,尽管后者变位大但上游梁向的拉应力明显减小。当然,这里也包括了软弱基础由下到上岩石弹性模量 E_r 值增大所带来的好处。

由此可见,增大拱座厚度,可以降低坝体应力,但是拱向拉应力集中则没有改善。而设立人工短缝,降低坝体刚度的柔性拱方法,可以降低坝体局部的应力集中,但对于坝体的其他部位应力不会有大的影响,也就是说,人工短缝对于坝体应力的影响是局部的。坝体中部的位移会有所增加,但是坝肩的位移不会因柔性拱而增大,拱座及坝体的应力得到了改善。

3　温度荷载下柔性拱对于坝体应力场和位移场的影响

对于厚度不大的拱坝来说,特别是在年温度变化剧烈,或未设后期冷却水管的碾压混凝土拱坝及未分缝全坝段碾压混凝土拱坝,如何控制坝体的后期温降产生的拉应力集中就成为一个十分重要的问题。在这里主要考虑温度荷载下柔性拱的作用。考虑在软弱基础和刚性基础条件下坝体上部单层拱圈整体温降 10℃时坝体的应力和位移,并进行对比分析(基础弹性模量的计算参数见表 2)。

表 2　基础弹性模量的计算参数

基础	E_r(GPa)
柔性	10
刚性	20

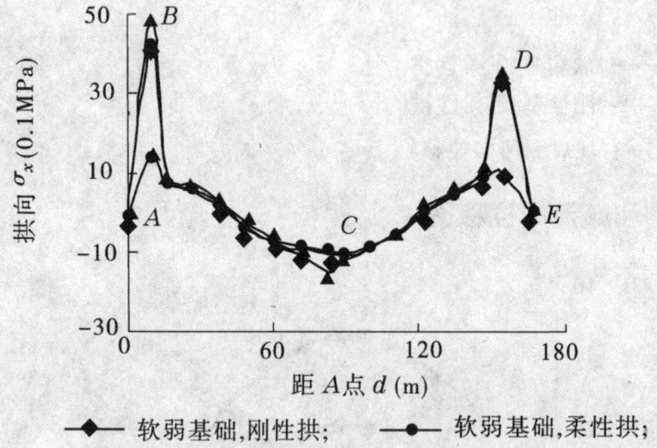

图 5　温降 10℃坝体上游面拱向 σ_x

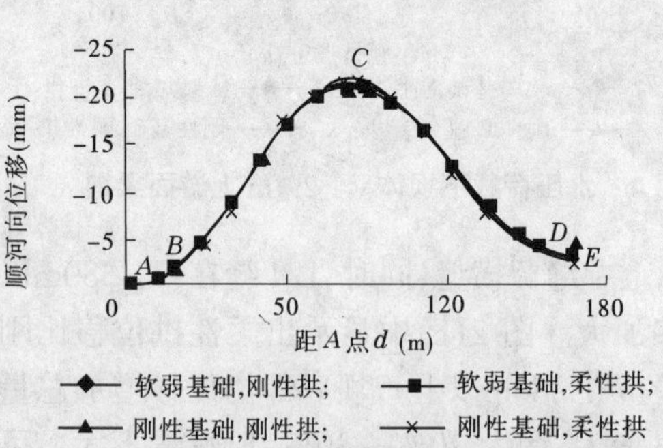

图 6　温降 10℃坝体上游面顺河向位移

计算结果如图 5、图 6 所示。可以看出:当坝体整体温降 10℃后,在坝体和岩石交界面产生了很大的应力集中,无论是软弱基础还是刚性基础,都会出现这种应力集中。在采用柔性拱时,坝肩上游面的拉应力从刚性拱的 4.86MPa 降到 1.48MPa,降低了 2/3 左右。下游面的 1/4 缝处的拉应力也下降 0.5～1MPa,下游面中缝留的人工短缝降低了下游拱冠拉应力的峰值。可见,柔性拱可以降低坝体的拉应力集中,使处在内部低应力区的缝端大大降低了应变强度因子,保持在止裂结构允许范围(在文献[6]中已发表)。这主要是由于柔性拱坝体刚度降低,变位增大,适应了坝体温降时的变位,降低了基础对于坝体的约束,释放了部分温度应力所致。文献[6]指出,碾压混凝土薄拱坝人工短缝对施工期温度徐变应力和施工末期温度下降到运行期变温场的应力释放的效果显著,缝端应力强度因子也下降到止裂结构容易承受的范围内[6]。本项工程的应力强度因子计算结果也都在 2.0 以内,和文献[6]中的结论相同。

由图 6 可见,坝体在温降时拱冠的位移较大(往往较水压作用下变位大),随坝体地基情况好坏,采用柔性拱还是刚性拱均有改变,但是变化不大。坝肩的温度位移也有同样的规律。

由此可知,在温度荷载下,采用柔性拱,坝体的应力集中特别是拉应力集中得到了很大的改善,而坝体位移并不会恶化。

4 结语

从坝体在水压和温度荷载作用下结果可以看出,在坝体设人工短缝以降低坝体刚度的柔性拱可以降低坝体应力集中,从而大大改善坝体应力。水压作用下软弱基础的拱肩位移加大,柔性拱坝体中部位移虽然在水压情况下有所增加,但是应力并不会恶化;增大坝肩的厚度虽不能改善坝肩上游面应力集中,增大了坝体和岩石的接触面积,可以减少坝体和岩石接触面的压应力和剪应力。因此,柔性拱结合坝体的坝肩加厚的方法可以解决在软弱基础上建造拱坝时坝体位移加大引起应力恶化的问题。由此可见,在软弱基础上修建拱坝不难通过采用结构措施来做到。

参考文献

[1] Dunstan M R H. *Recent developments in RCC dams*. Int J Hydropower & Dams, 1999,6(1):40~45

[2] Sembeneli K, Shengpe W. *Chinese experience in the design and construction of RCC arch dams*. Int J Hydropower & Dams, 1998,5(5):95~100

[3] 曾昭扬,马黔. 高碾压混凝土拱坝中的构造缝问题研究. 水力发电,1998(1):273~285

[4] Liu Guangting, Lin Guoyu. *Study on the curved and branch cracks in massive concrete structures*. Proc Int Conf Dam Fracture, 1991,(11):19~28

[5] 李守义,杜效鹄,王选平. 拱圈形状对应力和坝肩稳定的影响. 西安理工大学学报,1998(1):75~79

[6] 刘光廷,麦家煊,张国新. 溪柄碾压混凝土薄拱坝的研究. 水力发电学报,1997(2):69~75

侧约束对拱坝坝体应力和位移的影响

摘　要　结合某碾压混凝土拱坝的拱座,在减弱和加强侧约束时,即在坝体部分高程的破碎软弱岩石减弱坝体侧约束以及坝体下游边墙和护坦增强坝体侧约束的情况下,研究侧约束对于坝体应力和位移的影响。从仿真计算结果可以看出,减弱侧约束时,坝体会自动地进行应力调整,实现坝体的应力重分布,不会产生应力的集中;同时由于拱向应力的增大,即增大了抗剪面剪应力,抵消了坝体下游破碎岩石的影响。而增强侧约束,可以减少坝体位移,特别是坝肩位移。

关键词　侧约束　碾压混凝土拱坝　护坦　边墙　破碎岩石

拱坝通常是修建在岩石完好的地基之上的。在坝肩地基岩石情况差的坝址修建拱坝,特别是在坝肩有缺陷情况下修建碾压混凝土拱坝,需了解坝肩应力是否满足要求、坝肩是否稳定及加强拱座的有效办法[1~4]。

本文结合了某碾压混凝土拱坝工程实际地质情况,即在右坝肩▽1 370～1 380m 的下游部位出现软弱破碎岩石,甚至已经威胁到坝肩,研究该状态对坝肩应力分布和坝体安全的影响。结合坝体下游护坦和边墙增强侧约束来研究侧约束对坝体应力和位移的影响,探讨加强拱座的有效方法[5,6]。

1　某碾压混凝土拱坝简介

某碾压混凝土拱坝工程主坝坝高 110m,该工程两岸和河床为青灰色和红色砾岩,砾岩为泥钙质胶结。其中下部红色砾岩浸水软化后的变形模量为 4GPa,坝肩中部和上部岩石弹性模量分别为 6GPa 和 10GPa。成层砾岩有夹泥层 J_3,右坝肩有陡倾角的断层 F_6,左坝肩有 F_5 和 F_3。断层沿上下游方向延伸,并和斜夹泥层组成左右岸不稳定体,即 F_6～J_3、F_5～J_3 及 F_3～J_3 组成的不稳定体。在断层和夹泥层中设混凝土键以保持整体稳定。

施工过程中还发现,在右坝肩下游靠近坝顶▽1 394m 的▽1 370～1 380m 存在一个软弱破碎岩体。这个软弱破碎岩体甚至影响到了拱坝坝肩,可能对坝体产生不利的影响。

坝体下游的边墙和护坦对于加强坝体侧约束是否有效,特别是在该工程的下游边墙较厚而基础岩石软弱的情况下是否有效,意义很大。因此,需要研究水压作用下的拱坝坝肩应力位移变化和有效的加固方式。

2　坝肩岩石缺失对坝体应力和位移的影响

为了更加直观地看出右坝肩软弱破碎岩石对于坝体应力的影响,采用整体仿真结构拱坝及岩基的水压荷载三维有限元计算。取其典型高程 1 374m(破碎岩带)、1 332m(最大拱应力区)、1 293m(强侧约束区)的应力和位移。具体计算情况如图 1 所示。

本文选自《清华大学学报(自然科学报)》2002 年第 11 期,作者还有徐增辉、胡昱。

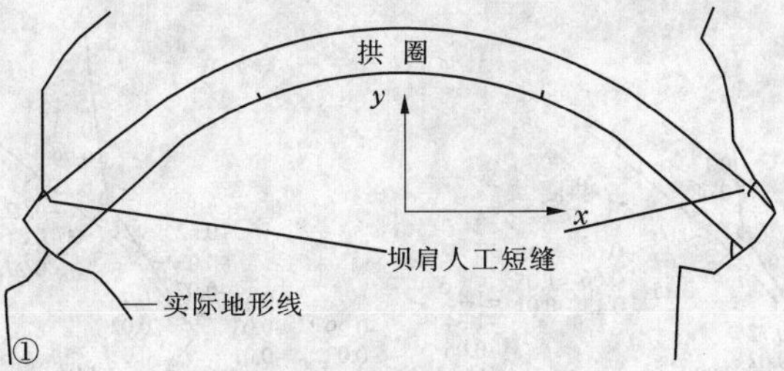

①坝体右坝肩下游面部分岩石缺失，已影响到坝肩

图1 坝肩计算拱圈简图

比较两种坝肩岩体在正常水位水压荷载作用下的正应力可以看出（见图2(a)、图2(b)），最敏感的拱座混凝土和岩石界面压应力集中区只有5～10m范围；坝肩存在局部破碎岩石的情况下，坝肩拱向正应力增加，σ_x 由 -0.74MPa 增加到 -1.3MPa，但顺河向压应力 σ_y 由 -1.70MPa 下降到 -0.53MPa，合力转向岩石内部。这是由于坝体顺河向岩石破碎，引起顺河向约束降低，导致顺河向应力下降。当拱座有缺陷时，拱座压力出现内移，出现有利的应力重分布。拱座界面内部和岩体内部应力较小，拱向应力增加；坝肩主应力方向也发生了改变，从倾向下游面向着岩石内部转移，这对于坝肩的应力是有好处的。也就是说，在坝肩出现局部岩石破碎的情况下，拱座及岩体内应力会自行转向岩石内部，且坝肩混凝土和岩石接触面及岩石内拱向压应力均略有增加，坝肩上游面人工短缝处顺河向拉应力少量增加。

从坝体位移计算结果可以看出，由于拱坝整体受力，在坝肩局部岩石破碎情况下坝体位移增加受到限制，拱座位移增大15%左右（整体统计）。由于此处位置在坝体的中上部，水压作用力较小，总体位移并不大，最大拱座位移2.1mm。

从图2(c)、图2(d)可以看出，水压荷载主要引起坝肩剪应力 τ_{xy}，在下游拱座处出现了剪应力集中，并且由外向内逐渐减少；坝肩缺陷使内部 τ_{xy} 剪应力少量增加，但是均小于0.1MPa；顺河向剪应力 τ_{xy} 小于拱向压力 σ_x 增值，拱座应力并未恶化。

可见，坝肩局部岩石存在缺陷，较为软弱，甚至由于挖深不够、表层有缺陷使承载力减弱，坝肩应力会出现内移现象。坝肩应力存在着一个自适应、自调整过程，应力会内移至弹模相对较高、岩石较好的地方，应力集中区也相应内移；但 τ_{xy} 最大值由 -0.67MPa 下降到 -0.61MPa，未引起坝肩应力恶化。

同时，从计算结果可以看出，坝肩存在局部缺陷的情况下，对于下部远离缺陷的1 332m高程，应力变化极小，在坝肩处加大10kPa，其余地方应力没有影响。可见，局部缺陷影响的范围有限，只是在缺陷周围20m高程内。

从上面的分析可以看出，坝肩岩体表层出现局部破碎岩石，不会造成坝体应力极度恶化而导致破坏。坝体自身可以通过调整主应力方向和内力分布来适应这种变化，同时通过抗剪面正应力增加来弥补由于下游坝肩局部软弱所造成的剪应力下降，从而避免了坝体应力恶化，因此影响是局部的。

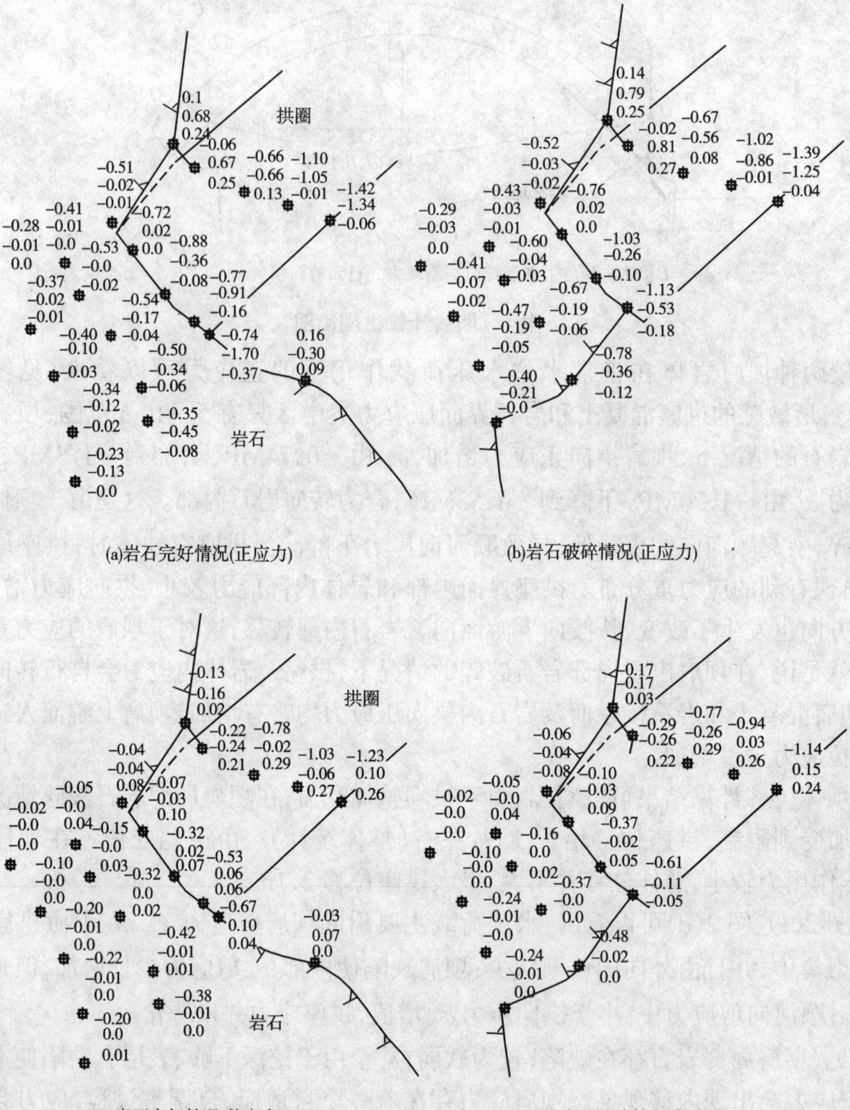

(a)岩石完好情况(正应力)　　(b)岩石破碎情况(正应力)

(c)岩石完好情况(剪应力)　　(d)岩石破碎情况(剪应力)

图2　▽1 370～1 380m 坝肩存在缺陷时▽1 374m 右坝肩岩石应力　(单位:MPa)

3　护坦和边墙等人工侧约束对于坝体应力和位移的影响

对于建在软弱基础上的拱坝,坝体护坦和较厚边墙形成人工侧约束来影响坝体应力和位移以改善拱座受力状态。基础岩石软弱了,护坦和边墙的约束作用相应更加明显。

从图3(a)和图3(b)可以看出,护坦和边墙增强了坝基侧约束,也增加了下部拱的支撑力,对局部应力改善明显,拱座压力 σ_y 由 -0.84MPa 下降到 -0.58MPa。有边墙时应力集中外移至坝体与边墙交点处,σ_y 由 -0.84MPa 增大到 -1.67MPa,但由混凝土和软

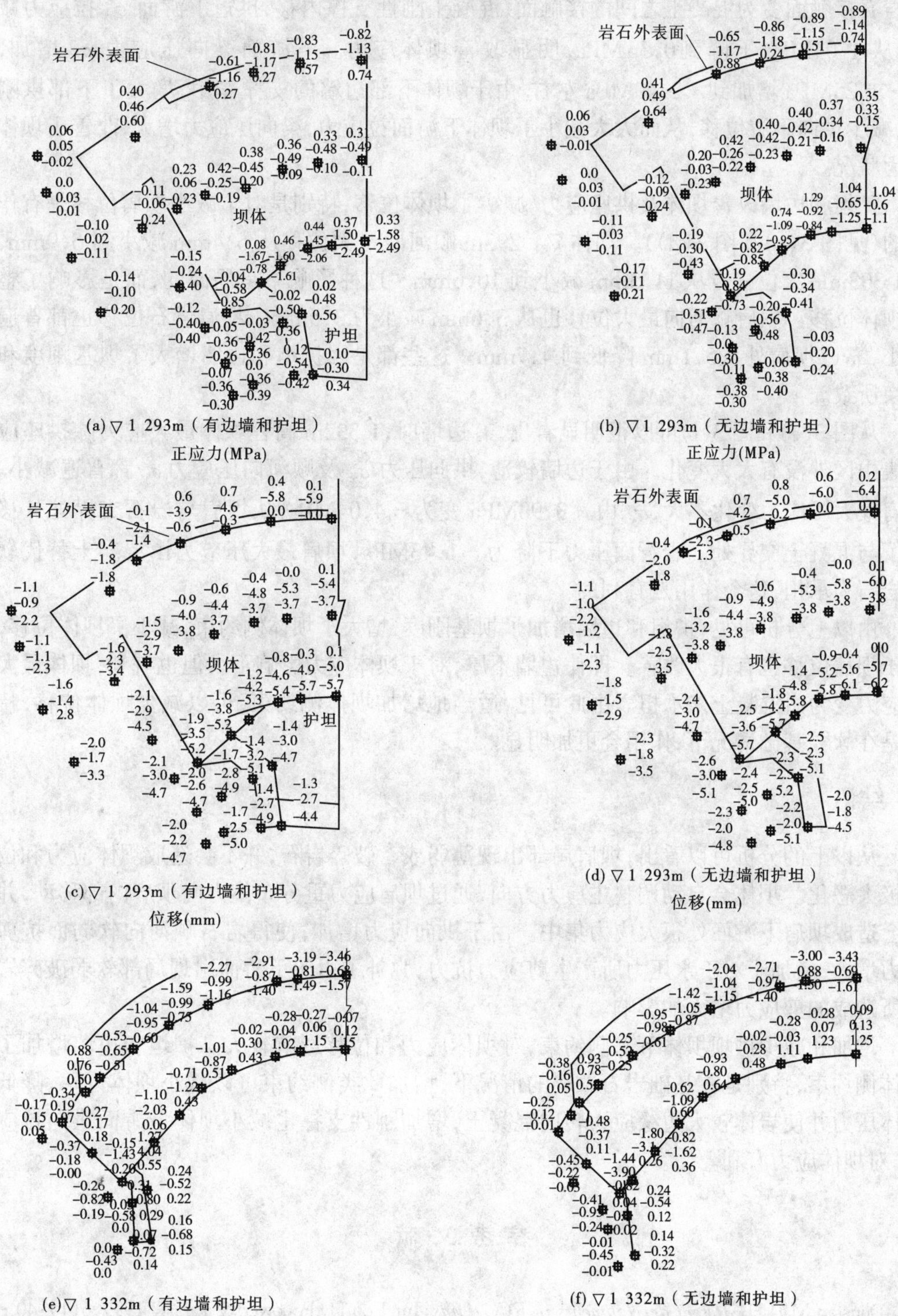

(a) ▽ 1 293m（有边墙和护坦）
正应力(MPa)

(b) ▽ 1 293m（无边墙和护坦）
正应力(MPa)

(c) ▽ 1 293m（有边墙和护坦）
位移(mm)

(d) ▽ 1 293m（无边墙和护坦）
位移(mm)

(e) ▽ 1 332m（有边墙和护坦）
正应力(MPa)

(f) ▽ 1 332m（无边墙和护坦）
正应力(MPa)

图 3　坝体正应力和位移

弱岩石接触面变为混凝土之间的接触面;混凝土刚性支撑内移,拱冠下游面 σ_x 拉应力减小,从 1.04MPa 下降到0.33MPa,明显改善坝体应力。下游面梁向压应力 σ_z 增加,从 -1.25MPa 增加到 -2.49MPa 左右。由于坝体下部边墙的支撑作用,增大了下部拱刚度,减少拱向下游位移,从而大大减小了坝体下游面拉应力,梁向压应力增大,改善了坝体应力状况。

护坦和边墙改善坝体及拱座应力,减少了坝体位移,特别是对于减小坝肩位移是有作用的(见图 3(c)和图 3(d))。坝体▽1 293m 顺河向最大位移从 6.4mm 减小到 5.9mm,▽1 308m最大位移也从 11.3mm 减小到 10.6mm。这种影响不是局部的,而是影响了整个坝体位移。坝肩顺河向最大位移也从 3.6mm 减小为 3.5mm。坝肩岩石位移也都普遍减小,靠近坝肩处从5.1mm 降低到 4.7mm。这些都是因护坦和边墙增大了坝基刚度和约束所致。

从图 3(e)和图 3(f)可以很明显看出,有边墙时,1 332m 高程坝体最大应力除拱座应力集中区外没有太大变化。由于边墙较薄,拱向压力 σ_x 及顺河向压应力 σ_y 都普遍减小。坝肩最大压应力变化不大,σ_y 由 -3.90MPa 变为 -4.04MPa,从坝肩与岩石交界处外移到了与混凝土交界处。岩石面压力下降为 -1.43MPa,坝肩最大压应力由混凝土替代软弱岩石为承担,这个作用是有利的。

由以上分析可见,护坦和边墙增加了坝基刚度,增大了坝体侧约束,减小了坝体位移,对于坝肩位移也有很大改善。即使边墙不厚,对于坝体应力影响不大但也有利,坝体最大压应力变为由混凝土来承担。由此可见,适当地增加坝体侧约束,可以减少坝体位移,特别是在软弱基础情况下,作用会更加明显。

4　结语

从以上的分析可以看出,坝肩局部出现薄弱或者破碎岩石,并不会造成坝体应力和位移极大恶化。坝体会自动调整主应力方向,通过坝肩应力重分布使力向坝肩内部移动,并不会造成坝肩下游面处很大应力集中。由于拱向应力增加,使得岩石顺河向软弱面抗剪能力增大,增加了对于水压力所产生剪应力抗力,弥补了由于下游面出现局部软弱破碎岩石所造成的剪应力增大的影响。

增加和减少拱坝坝体下部侧约束,对坝体应力和位移影响较大。护坦和边墙增加了坝体侧约束,特别是在基础岩石软弱的情况下,增加此类侧约束可以减小坝体位移,降低岩体压力并使岩体较大边缘应力转向混凝土,增加刚性支撑也减小坝体下游面拱向拉应力,对坝体应力有利。

参考文献

[1] Dunstan M R H. *Recent developments in RCC dams*. Int J on Hydropower & Dams, 1999,6(1):40～45

[2] Sembeneli K, Shengpe W. *Chinese experience in the design and construction of RCC arch dams*. Int J on Hydropower & Dams, 1998,5(5):95～100

[3] 刘光廷,麦家煊,张国新．溪柄碾压混凝土薄拱坝的研究．水力发电学报,1997(2):69～75

[4] Liu Guangting, Lin Guoyu. *Study on the curved and branch cracks in massive concrete structures*. Proceedings of Int Conf on Dam Fracture, 1991,11:19～28

[5] 李守义,杜效鹄,王选平．拱圈形状对应力和坝肩稳定的影响．西安理工大学学报,1998(1):75～79

[6] 董羽蕙．香溪口工程坝肩软弱夹层的处理及其应力分布．贵州工学院学报,1995,24(2):34～37

MICROSTUDY ON CREEP OF CONCRETE AT EARLY AGE UNDER BIAXIAL COMPRESSION

Abstract An interesting phenomena of crack restoration and increasing strength of concrete under biaxial compression creep were described in this paper. A small loading apparatus was prepared and a long work distance optical microscope with variable focus was used for studying the cracks. It was found from the micrographs that these cracks diminished under biaxial compression creep. There were increases in the strength of the creep specimens under the sustained biaxial compression load compared with the free companion ones. Multiaxial compression caused by the early temperature rise inside the mass concrete may strengthen the concrete and reduce the tensile cracks during and after temperature drop.

Key words creep; microcracking; concrete; crack detection; hydration

1 Introduction and Objective

Scientists have studied a lot about the microstructure of cement paste[1]. However, little has been done about the mortar structure change when concrete is under sustained loads.

The conventional optical microscope is restricted in studying the properties of the slice concrete for their short work distance as well as small magnification. The electron microscopes themselves require the dry specimens (Scan Electron Microscopes) or the small and thin slices (Transmission Electron Microscopes), which are not suitable for us to study the long-term changes of the cement hydration under multiaxial sustained load. In this paper, a long variable focus and high magnification optical microscope (QHS-2005C) is used in the experiment. The microscope lens can work 15mm away from the specimen even at 1 000 times magnification. The highest magnification is 4 000 times. So it is suitable for us to study the interior configuration deformation and the crack changes in the cement paste and mortar under multiaxial stresses.

2 Microstudy on Concrete Creep Under the Biaxial Compression

2.1 General

The numerical computation programs for creep are mainly based on the uniaxial creep tests in the past[2,3]. The microstructure of the cement paste is the basis of the creep mechanism. There were many creep hypotheses but no agreement has been totally achieved until now. No direct relations are constructed between the micro-experiments and the macro-tests, though we have made great improvement in the creep model and the numerical calculations[4].

本文选自《Cement and Concrete Research》32(2002)1865～1870,作者还有 Gao Hu,Chen Fengqi。

The biaxial apparatus in this paper provides the rigidity displacement load as shown in Fig.1. The load frame is made of steel, the modulus of which is approximately 10 times that of concrete. With the help of the high magnification optical microscope (QHS-2005C), it is possible for us to observe the creep changes especially the crack deformation inside the mortar and those between the interfaces of the aggregates. The dimension of the concrete slice is 100mm × 100mm × 10mm.

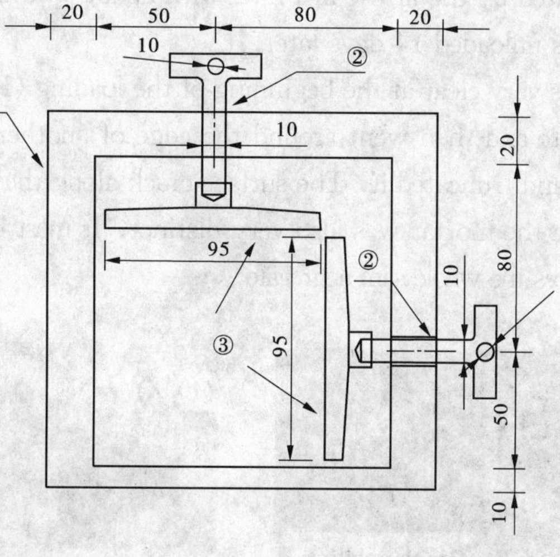

Fig. 1 Sketch plane figure of the loading apparatus (unit: mm)

①Load frame; ②Screw; ③Load slab

The formation and development of the cracks have a very important influence on the mechanical properties of concrete. People sometimes keep the idea that creep deformations will cause interior damage on the concrete. Damage comes from the increasing cracks from the point view of the macro behavior. So we focused our attention on the changes of the cracks in the whole loading process.

2.2 Introduction of the Experiments

The specimen was a cube with the dimension of 100mm. We cut it to slices of 10mm thick at the age of 10 and 6 days, respectively. The mixture is listed in Table 1.

Table 1 Material mixture (unit: kg/m^3)

Water	Cement	Flyash	Sand	Aggregate			Admixture	
				Small	Middle	Large	DH9	JG4
78	60	100	673	465	620	465	3.2	4.8

DH9 and JG4 were the water reducer and the retarder, respectively.

The large and middle gravels were picked off after mixing.

There were three groups of experiment. The specimens were loaded at the same day after slicing. We applied several rigid-displacement loads manually in case the loads were relaxed. The screw pushes the load slab forward and ensures biaxial load on the concrete slice. We added the load in one direction slowly then in another direction. Thus, the biaxial loads were increased alternately. The surface of the specimen was always kept wet.

2.3 Experiment Results

2.3.1 Crack A

The first specimen was cut into slices at the age of 9 days and loaded at 10 days. Crack A originated as indicated by the arrow in Fig.2 with about 44μm long and 3～4μm wide at the beginning. It was unloaded 14 days later.

(1) Crack A was very clear at the beginning of the loading (Fig.3). It started from the bottom of an aggregate and then went around the edge of another aggregate. It ended by a third slim aggregate and truncated it. The surface crack along the second aggregate was very clear. The part inside the mortar was also very distinct. It must be the outer load that created the crack for it ran across the whole slim aggregate.

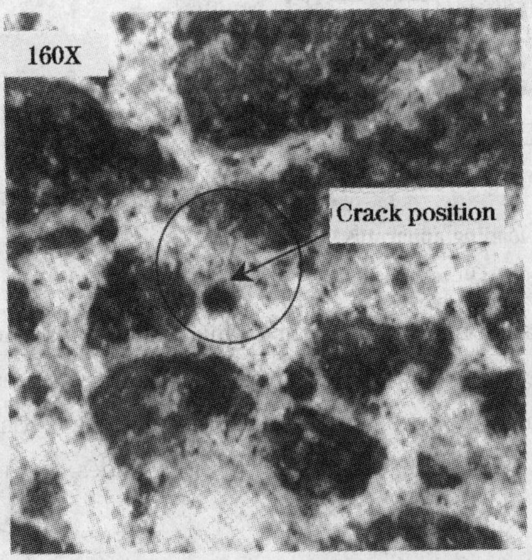

Fig.2 Position of Crack A

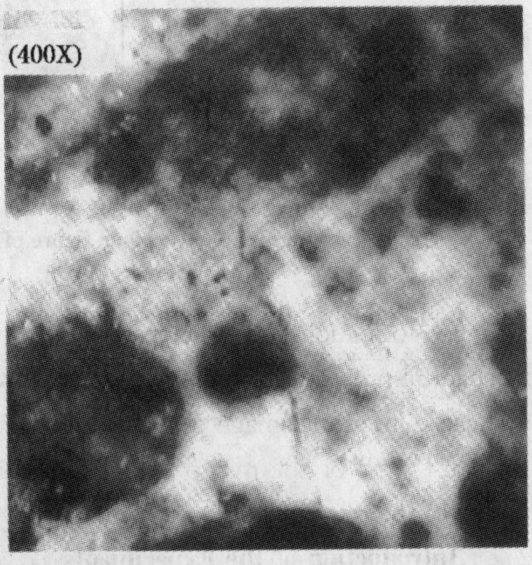

Fig.3 Original crack loaded at the age of 10 days

(2) In Fig.4, the crack was thinner than the one in Fig.3 after the 6h biaxial load. The width of the crack in the mortar diminished more than the crack around the edge of the aggregate, though both of them were still very clear.

(3) The crack continued to close up as the load held for 1 day (Fig.5). However, the trail could still be observed. The interface crack around the aggregate did not close in the same degree.

(4) After 14 days, the crack diminished so much that the lower part of the crack could hardly be identified (Fig.6). Only the upper one could still be observed. The middle part of it around the aggregate also closed more than before.

(5) The load was removed after 14 days. Six days later, the specimen was reloaded

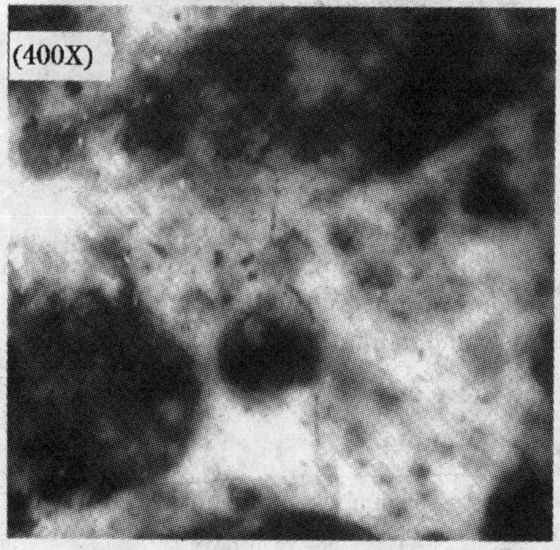

Fig.4 Biaxial load for 6h at the age of 10 days

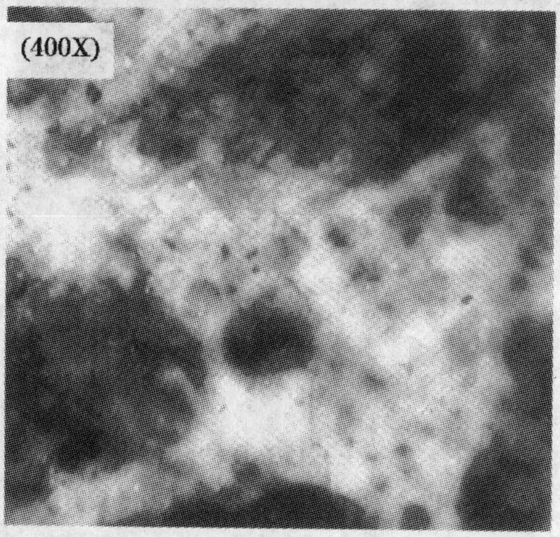

Fig.5 Biaxial load for 24h at the age of 10 days

again. From Fig.7, we can find that the crack did not open again. In fact, we could not identify the former crack. Those cracks in the mortar disappeared entirely from the surface.

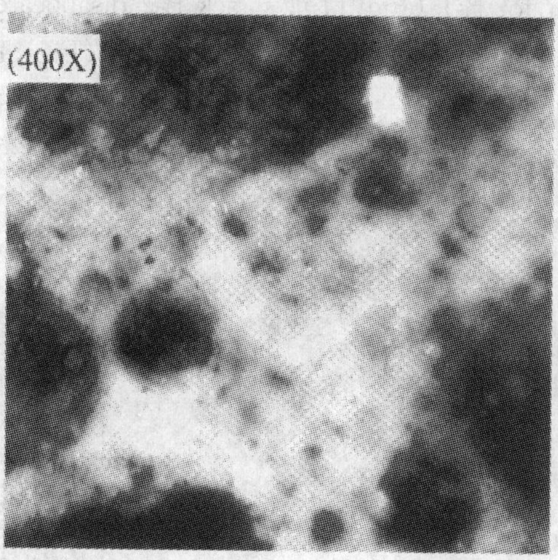

Fig.6 Biaxial load for 14 days at the age of 10 days

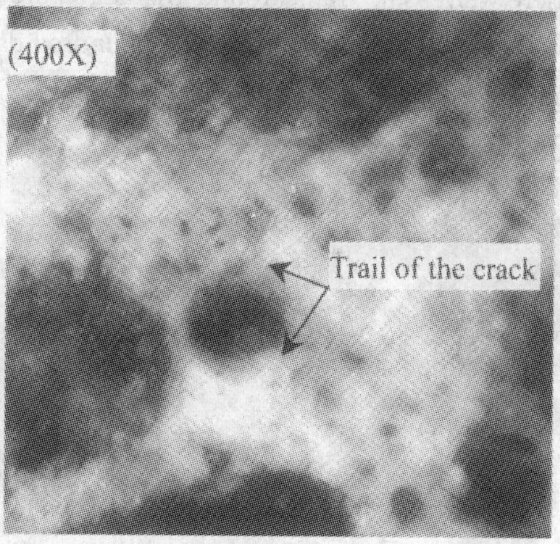

Fig.7 Biaxial load for 14 days then unloaded for 6 days. Reload no cracks

2.3.2 Crack B

The second specimen was sawn to slices at the age of 6 days. It was loaded at the same day and was held for 100 days. Two cracks, B-1 and B-2, were studied with the original dimensions by $80\mu m \times 8\mu m$(B-1) and $50\mu m \times 5\mu m$ (B-2).

(1) The age of this specimen was only 6 days. There were two cracks that were shown in Fig.8. Crack B-1 was near a big aggregate. It was a little broad with some microcracks dispersed around it (Fig.9). Crack B-2 was inside the mortar (Fig.13).

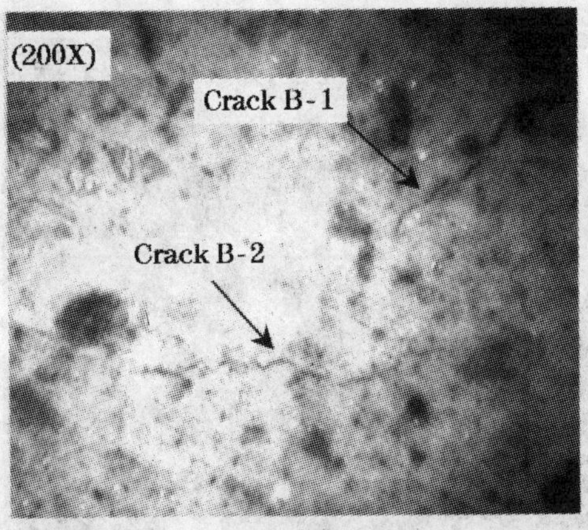

Fig.8 Position of Crack B at the age of 6 days

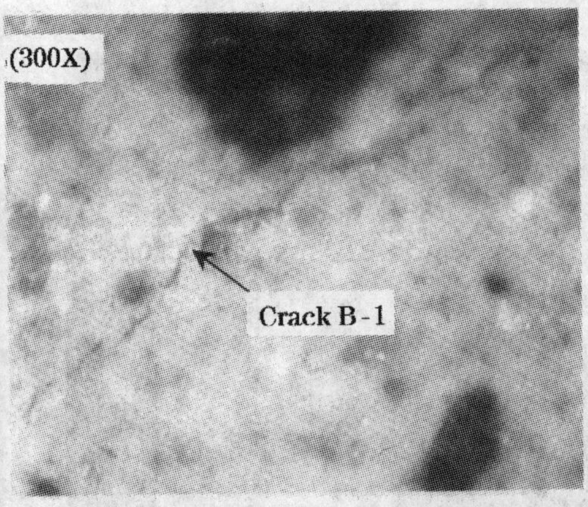

Fig.9 Original crack when loaded at the age of 6 days

(2) In Fig.14, both Crack B-1 and Crack B-2 closed up a lot after 4 days biaxial load just like the aforementioned Crack A although there were some trails left (see details in Fig.10 and Fig.15 for Crack B-1 and Crack B-2, respectively).

(3) Forty days later with the biaxial load, Cracks B-1 and B-2 tended to fade out. There were some trails around the aggregate left for B-1 (Fig.11). Crack B-2 disappeared totally in the mortar (Fig.16). A hundred days later, the cracks were very blurry (Figs.12 and 17).

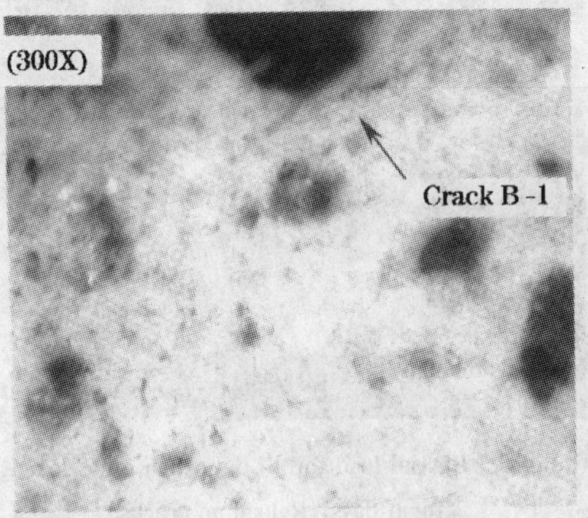

Fig.10 Biaxial load for 4 days at the age of 6 days

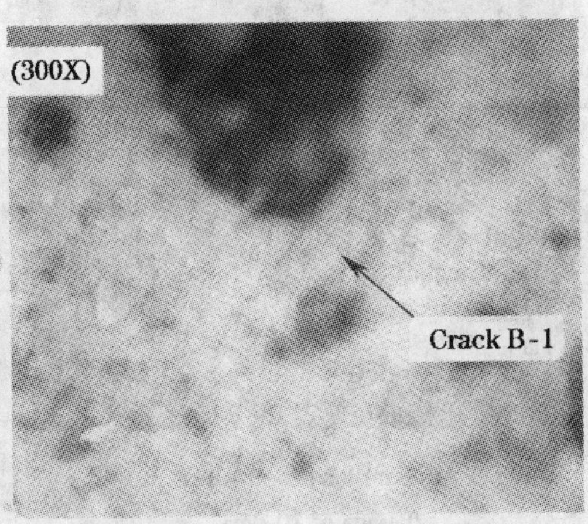

Fig.11 Biaxial load for 40 days at the age of 6 days

3 Analysis

There were two types of cracks presented by Cracks A and B in the mortar and around the surface of the aggregate. Evidently, the aforementioned tests show that with time, the two types of cracks tend to disappear under the biaxial compression load especially in the

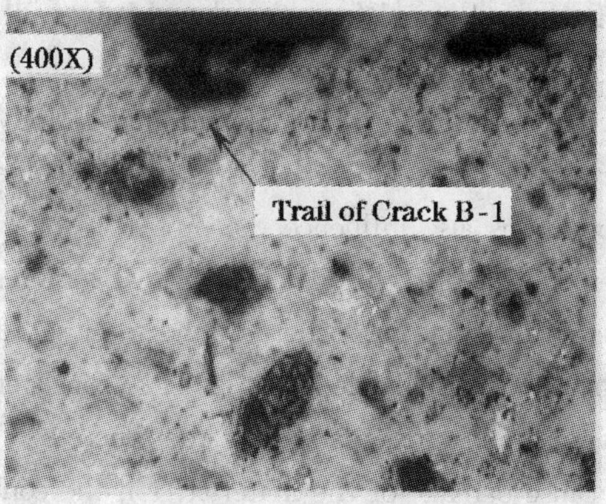

Fig.12 Biaxial load for 100 days then unload for 8 days

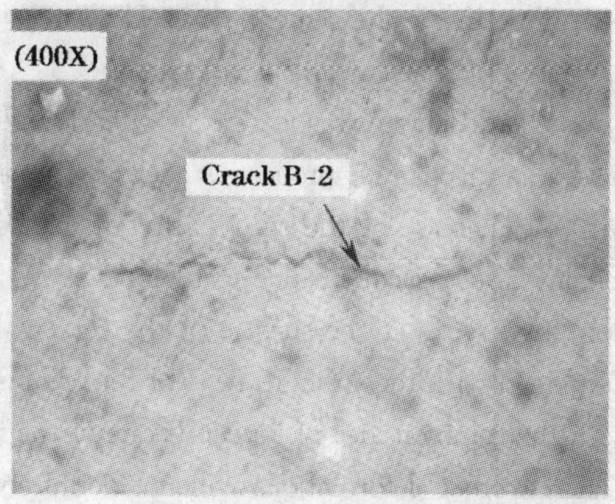

Fig.13 Original crack when loaded at the age of 6 days

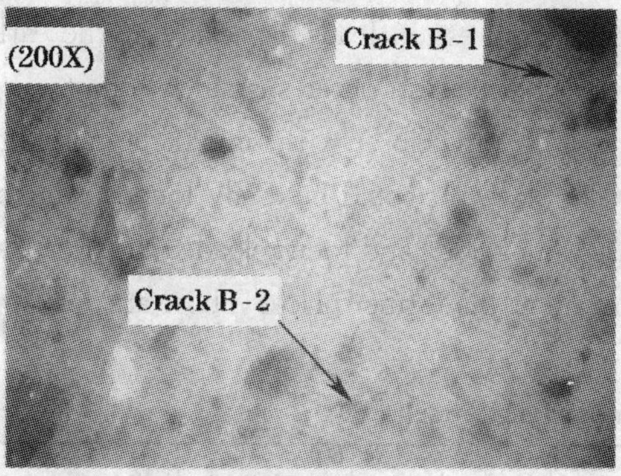

Fig.14 Biaxial load for 4 days at the age of 6 days

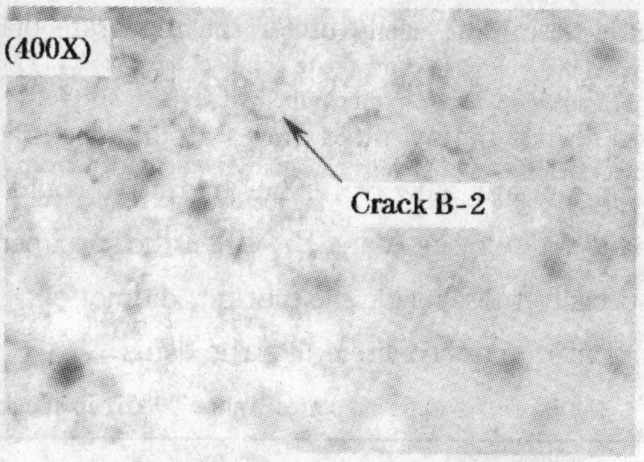

Fig.15 Biaxial load for 4 days after the age of 6 days

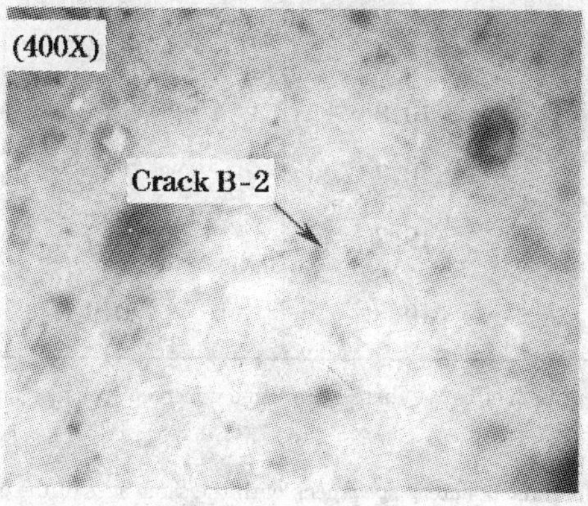

Fig.16 Biaxial load for 40 days at the age of 6 days

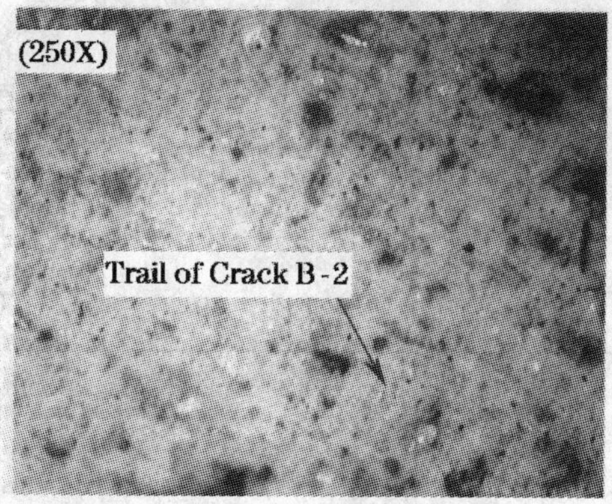

Fig.17 Biaxial load for 100 days then unload 8 days

mortar. For example, the lower part of Crack A faded out entirely even with no trails left. The interface crack closed obviously at the beginning though by a smaller degree compared with those inside the cement part. However, if the load lasted for more than 14 days, the interface crack also nearly disappeared.

When concrete was loaded at an early age, the cement part had not hydrated entirely. Also, the mechanical properties such as the strength of the cement-based material changed with the increase of the age. Different load conditions also influence the properties of the cement-based specimens due to hydration. When subjected to the sustained biaxial compression, the cracks at the surface of the cement-based material like concrete tend to close up. Combined with the strength tests of the creep specimens (see Table 2), it is not so consistent with the common idea of "creep is one of the reason causing the damage of the concrete"[5]. Concrete creep deformations will not definitely cause damage of the material. On the contrary, the sustained compression load at an early age can increase the strength of the cement-based material which is different from that of the other materials[6]. Hydration products may come close more easily under the moderate biaxial compression loads especially at the early age. Moreover, the cracks could close if they are subject to an outer sustained compression load. Since the hydrated grains around the cracks will come closer with time if the humidity is appropriate, new or further hydration could take place. It could be easily found from the changes of Cracks A and B. When the specimen was unloaded and then reloaded, the cracks, especially those inside the mortar, did not open again at the former place. Those are very important in mass concrete like the dams.

Table 2 Creep specimen strength results

No.	Creep type	Load age (days)	Load duration (days)	Strength of creep specimen (MPa)	Strength of noncreep specimen (MPa)
A-1	Biaxial	14	45		8.2
A-2	Biaxial	60	90	14.4	11.3
B-1	Biaxial	30	28	10.8	5.5
B-2	Biaxial	60	30	10.7	7.0
C-1	Uniaxial	60	12	19.7	18.3
C-2	High stress uniaxial	90	18	19.8	20.9

All the stress levels were 30% of the ultimate strength except C-2(60%). There were three noncreep specimens in every group.

The values of the last column are the average strengths of the three noncreep specimens with the same ages of the corresponding creep specimens.

4 Strength Results of Preloaded Specimens

Both uniaxial and biaxial creep machines were applied in the creep tests. The specimens were 100mm × 100mm × 100mm. They were unloaded after a certain period of sustained loading (more than 3 weeks). Then they were subjected to strength tests of which the results are shown in the following table. The noncreep specimen strengths are also listed for comparison.

As shown in the table, those creep specimens which were subjected to a sustained load at an early age (30 days) have higher strengths than those specimens with no sustained loading at the same age (e.g., B-1). When the age of creep loading is higher (60 days), the increase of the strengths is a little smaller (e.g., A-2 and B-2). When the concrete is older (90 days), this phenomenon will then weaken.

5 Conclusions

The long distance optical microscope with variable focus and high magnification can reveal new physical phenomena of the concrete hydration process. They connect the relation between the microchanges in concrete with the macromechanical properties such as the strength of the concrete.

The micro-observations indicate that cracks inside the concrete under biaxial sustained loads will fade out. Combined with the strength tests of the creep specimens, it is shown that biaxial compression load would help the cementbased material at an early age to compact the whole cement gel framework and to promote the hydration. It also formed the new cementation, which led to the restoration of the crack. Those deformations caused by compression creep at an early age will not always induce damage to the cementbased materials.

Acknowledgements

The present work is supported by the “985” Technique Fund of Tsinghua University.

References

[1] K. van Breugel. *Simulation of Hydration and Formation of Structure in Hardening Cement-Based Materials*. Delft University Press, Delft, 1997

[2] Z.P. Bazant, F.H. Wittmann. *Creep and Shrinkage in Concrete Structures*. Wiley, Chichester, 1982, pp.3~18

[3] A.M. Neville, W.H. Dilger, J.J. Brooks. *Creep of Plain and Structural Concrete*. Contribution Press, London, 1983, pp.158~179

[4] Z.P. Bazant, S. Prasannan. *Solidification theory for concrete creep: I. Formulation*. J. Eng. Mech. (8)(1989) 1691~1703

[5] X.Z. Yu, C.X. Qiao, Q.L. Zhou. *Fracture Mechanics of Rock and Concrete (in Chinese)*. Central South China University of Technology Press, Changsha, 1991, pp.395~410

[6] S.Coutinho. *A contribution to the mechanism of concrete creep*. Mater. Constr. 10(55)(1977)3~16

无限域波动问题的有限元模型

摘　要　本文基于半解析波动方程,推导了无限域黏弹性人工边界单元。在有限元波动模型中,统一了节点计算稳定性问题;提出了合理的人工边界反射系数公式,为有限元模型提供了理论基础。SH 波数值分析表明,本文有限元模型具有多向波动透射能力。

关键词　半解析法　波动反射　无限域　有限元

高坝结构抗震关键问题之一是模拟无限域地基波动问题。目前,除应用边界元法[1]外,结合适当的人工边界,采用有限元法更为有效[2,3]。

人工边界的研究一直吸引着众多研究者,其中具有局部特性的透射边界获得了广泛的应用[4]。但是对于波大角度入射情况,单向透射边界反射系数较大;多向透射边界虽精度有了明显提高,但反射系数计算问题仍未得到圆满解决[5]。另一类局部边界是等效黏弹性边界[6~8],在时域计算中具有一定的精度,而边界反射问题也同样需要解决。

本文首先基于半解析法和单侧波动方程,建立黏弹性人工边界单元。在有限元法框架下,统一了内节点与边界点两类计算稳定性问题。为解决人工边界反射这一关键问题,本文提出一种合理的边界反射系数计算方法。最后通过算例说明本文有限元模型与人工边界单元具有多向波动透射能力。

1　人工边界单元列式

本文人工边界单元不同于常规边界元,而是基于半解析方法与单侧波动方程,建立的边界力与位移关系。人工边界点坐标(x,y)可由人工边界单元节点坐标$\{x\}$与$\{y\}$插值为(见图 1)

$$\begin{aligned} x(\eta) &= [N(\eta)]\{x\} \\ y(\eta) &= [N(\eta)]\{y\} \end{aligned} \tag{1}$$

式中:$[N(\eta)]$为人工边界单元形函数;η为单元局部坐标。

半无限域内任意点$\hat{P}(\hat{x},\hat{y})$可由相似边界单元表示为

$$\begin{aligned} \hat{x}(\xi,\eta) &= [N(\eta)]\{x(\xi)\} \\ \hat{y}(\xi,\eta) &= [N(\eta)]\{y(\xi)\} \end{aligned} \tag{2}$$

式中:$\{x(\xi)\}$与$\{y(\xi)\}$为相似边界单元节点坐标,是无量纲ξ的函数,依比例相似边界法[9]可表示为$\{x(\xi)\}=\xi\{x\}$和$\{y(\xi)\}=\xi\{y\}$。当$\xi=1$时,相似边界即为人工边界。

任意$\hat{P}(\hat{x},\hat{y})$点位移采用半解析等参方法表示为

$$\{\hat{u}(\xi,\eta)\}=[N(\eta)]\{u(\xi)\} \tag{3}$$

式中:$\{u(\xi)\}$为相似边界单元节点未知位移函数,当$\xi=1$时即为人工边界单元节点

本文选自《工程力学》2002 年第 2 期,作者还有刘天云、刘颖黎。

位移。

考虑平面外 SH 波动，ξ 方向应变为

$$\varepsilon = [B^1]\{u(\xi)\}_{\xi} \tag{4}$$

式中忽略了 η 方向应变的影响，但可以形成有效的辐射边界。其中

$$[B^1] = \frac{1}{|J|}[y_{,\eta} - x_{,\eta}]^{\mathrm{T}}[N(\eta)] \tag{5}$$

式中：$|J| = xy_{,\eta} - yx_{,\eta}$。

人工边界单元平面外运动方程可以简化为

$$[E^0]\xi^2\{u\}_{,\xi\xi} + [E^0]\xi\{u\}_{,\xi} = [M^0]\xi^2\{\ddot{u}\} \tag{6}$$

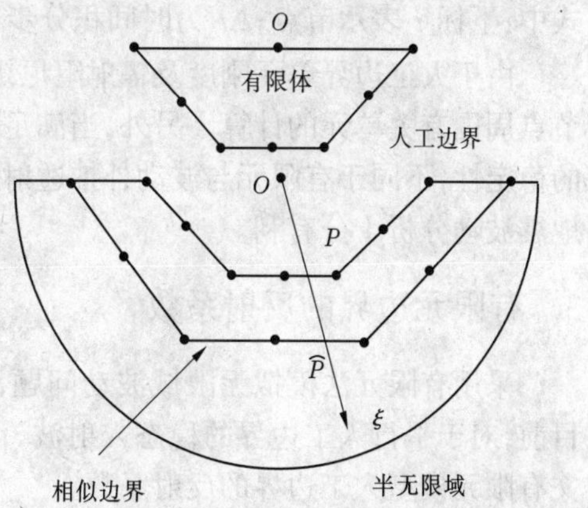

图 1 无限域人工边界单元

式中：$[E^0] = \int_{-1}^{+1}[B^1]^{\mathrm{T}}G[B^1]|J|\mathrm{d}\eta$，$[M^0] = \int_{-1}^{+1}[N(\eta)]^{\mathrm{T}}\rho[N(\eta)]|J|\mathrm{d}\eta$，其中 G、ρ 分别为剪切模量与密度。

引入下面位移关系式[5] $\nu(\xi) = \frac{1}{\sqrt{\xi}}u(\xi)$，并代入式(6)，得简化标准波动方程

$$[E^0]\{\nu\}_{,\xi\xi} = [M^0]\{\ddot{\nu}\} \tag{7}$$

根据虚位移原理，人工边界界面反力为

$$\{W(\xi)\}^{\mathrm{T}}\{R(\xi)\} = \int_s w(\xi,\eta)t(\xi,\eta)\mathrm{d}s \tag{8}$$

式中：$t(\xi,\eta)$、$w(\xi,\eta)$是 ξ 为任意值的相似人工边界分布面力和权函数；$R(\xi)$、$W(\xi)$为相应离散函数，当 $\xi=1$ 时，得人工边界界面反力

$$\{R\} = \frac{1}{2}[E^0]\{u\} + [C^0]\{\dot{u}\} \tag{9}$$

式中：$[C^0] = [M^0][C]$，$[C][C] = [M^0]^{-1}[E^0]$，式(9)为弹簧阻尼系统，具有 0 阶精度。

由此可见，$[E^0]$和$[C^0]$为人工边界单元的刚度与阻尼矩阵，这是不同文献[6]的分布参数边界。在单元尺寸较小，单元节点位移相同时，式(9)才为等效分布参数的黏弹性边界[6,7]；不考虑弹性性质，式(9)为有名黏性边界[8]。可见这几种边界是本文人工边界单元的特例。

2 有限元时域波动稳定性

对无限域波动问题，近场采用有限元离散，附加人工边界单元，整体运动平衡方程为

$$[M]\{\ddot{u}\} + [C]\{\dot{u}\} + [K]\{u\} = \{P\} \tag{10}$$

式中：$[M]$、$[C]$、$[K]$分别为质量、阻尼、刚度矩阵；$\{\ddot{u}\}$、$\{\dot{u}\}$和$\{u\}$分别为加速度、速度和位移向量；$\{P\}$为输入节点荷载向量，对于远场入射波激励，应采用文献[7]方法计算。

式(10)已将无限域波动问题转化为有限域的振动问题，同时将一般内节点与边界点两类复杂的数值稳定性问题转化为统一的时域积分稳定性问题。采用解耦的中心差分法，节点位移积分显式格式为

$$\left(\frac{1}{\Delta t^2}m_i + \frac{1}{\Delta t}c_i\right)u_i^{t+\Delta t} = p_i^t - r_i^t + \frac{2}{\Delta t^2}m_i u_i^t - \left(\frac{1}{\Delta t^2}m_i - \frac{1}{2\Delta t}c_i\right)u_i^{t-\Delta t} \tag{11}$$

式中：下标 i 表示节点；Δt 为时间积分步长；r_i 为节点恢复力，由节点相关单元集成。

由于人工边界单元刚度及辐射阻尼矩阵具有时空局部特性，计算节点恢复力时仅是节点周围有关单元的计算。另外，当满足数值积分稳定性条件时，全部节点计算具有相同的稳定性，不同于有限元与波动外推透射边界结合方法[2]。因此，本文有限元法对长时间地震波动分析十分有利。

3 有限元边界的反射系数

采用有限元法模拟无限域波动问题，人工边界反射系数体现了边界透射误差程度。目前，对于平行人工边界的稳态入射波，计算的边界反射系数均等于 1[2,5]。下面研究本文有限元模型人工边界的反射系数。

考虑图 2 中 SH 波以任意角度入射时，人工边界节点 0 解耦的平面外运动平衡方程

$$m_0 \ddot{w}_0 + c_0 \dot{w}_0 + \sum_{i=0}^{5} k_i w_i = 0 \tag{12}$$

式中：m_0、c_0 和 k_0 为边界节点 0 的质量、辐射阻尼和刚度（包括人工边界单元）；k_i 为与节点 0 相关单元节点刚度，由刚度矩阵相应行确定。

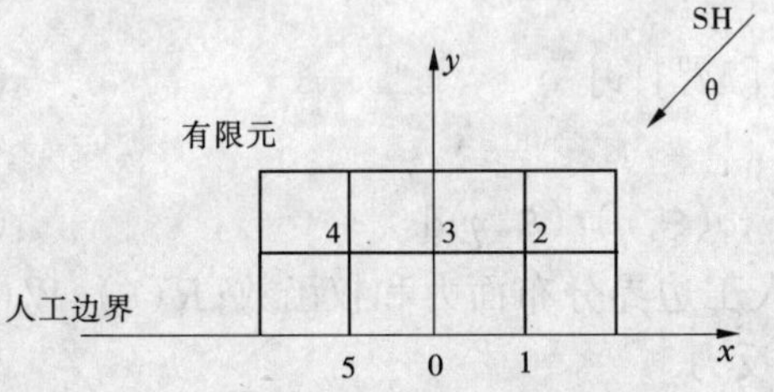

图 2 人工边界节点 0 及局部有限元节点

式(12)计算边界点 0 的频域解为

$$W_0^c = H(\omega)^{-1} \sum_{i=1}^{5} k_i W_i^I \tag{13}$$

式中：$H(\omega) = k_0 - \omega^2 m_0 + j\omega c_0$；$W_i^I$ 为 i 点的入射波幅值；W_0^c 是根据内节点计算的人工边界 0 点幅值。

由于式(13)计算误差，式(13)可表示为

$$W_0^I + W_0^R = H(\omega)^{-1} \sum_{i=1}^{5} k_i W_i^I \tag{14}$$

式中：W_0^I 为人工边界节点的精确值；W_0^R 为计算误差或反射波。

相应的反射系数为

$$R_A = \left| \frac{W_0^R}{W_0^I} \right| = \left| 1 - H(\omega)^{-1} \sum_{i=1}^{5} k_i b_i^I \right| \tag{15}$$

式中：b_t^I 为人工边界节点 0 附近节点 i 的入射波幅值系数[5]。

对于稳态情况，计算模型内节点位移同时包括入射波 W_i^I 及人工边界反射波 W_i^R。此时式(13)计算的人工边界点 0 入射波幅值应修改为

$$(W_0^I + W_0^R)^c = H(\omega)^{-1} \sum_{i=1}^{5} k_i (W_i^I + W_i^R) \tag{16}$$

同样考虑上式的计算误差，得稳态情况的人工边界节点位移幅值

$$W_0^I + 2W_0^R = H(\omega)^{-1} \sum_{i=1}^{5} k_i (W_i^I + W_i^R) \tag{17}$$

相应的反射系数为

$$R_B = \left| \frac{W_0^R}{W_0^I} \right| = \left| (1 - H(\omega)^{-1} \sum_{i=1}^{5} k_i b_i^I) / (2 - H(\omega)^{-1} \sum_{i=1}^{5} k_i b_i^R) \right| \tag{18}$$

式中：b_i^R 为反射波在人工边界节点 0 附近节点 i 的幅值系数[5]。

式(15)与式(18)是人工边界瞬态与稳态两种情况的反射系数。为了清楚地认识人工边界单元这种边界的反射特性,图3是两种情况反射系数与入射角关系曲线。

由图可见,本文有限元模型的人工边界具有以下特点:

(1)波以任何角度入射,边界反射系数较小,且均匀。

(2)稳态反射系数与瞬态反射系数接近,不同于以往分析结果。

(3)沿节点入射方向的波并不能完全透射。

(4)计算反射系数仅与有限元刚度系数有关,有利于分析二维和三维的各种入射波动问题。

4 算例

为了说明本文有限元法模拟近场波动模拟能力,考虑固定基底均匀弹性层上作用出平面简谐线荷载产生的波动。这一模型根据激振频率可以在弹性层内产生行进波与削减波[2,10]。有限元模型取如图4所示的区域,采用正方形四节点单元和两节点的人工边界单元,$H/\Delta x=10$。图5给出了节点$(x,y)=(H,0)$处位移计算结果与精确解[10]的比较。

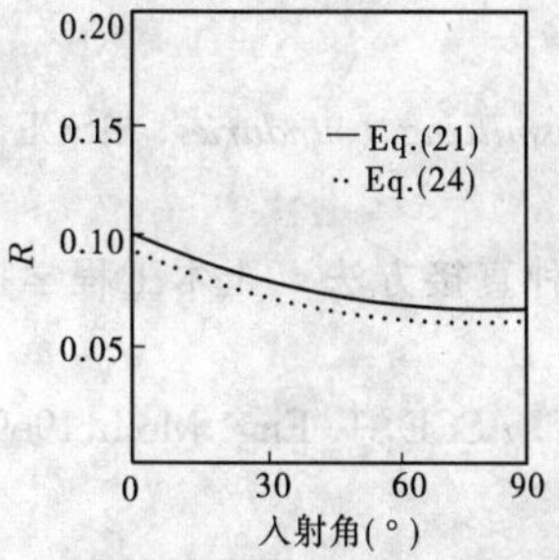

图3 反射系数与入射角曲线

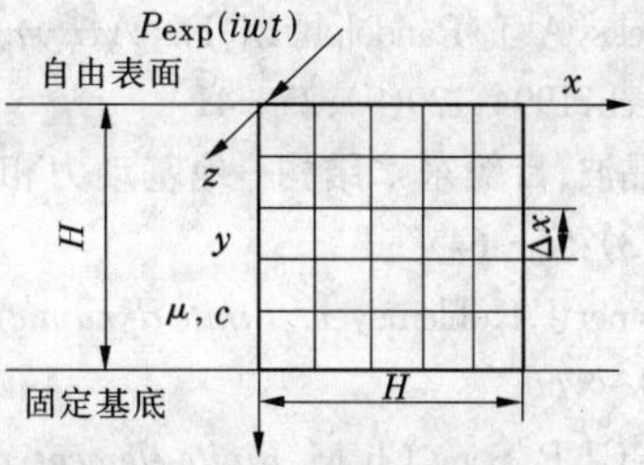

图4 弹性层有限元模型

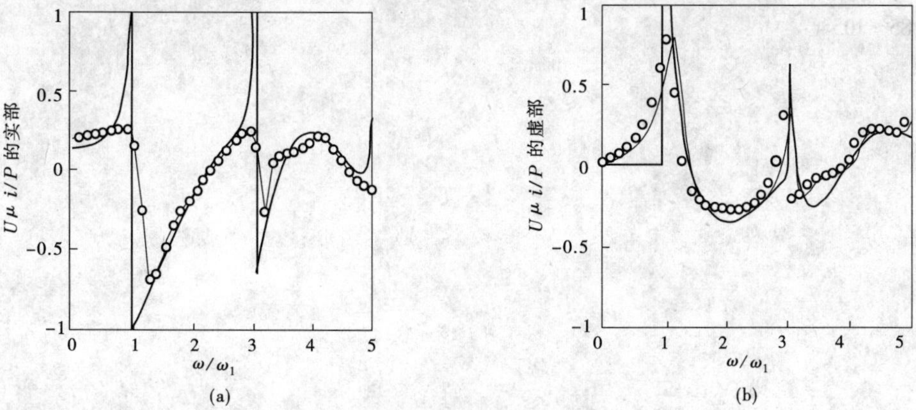

图5 数值解与解析解比较

由图5可见,本文有限元模型计算结果具有一定的精度,但对于削减波($\omega\leqslant\omega_1$)与共振频段($\omega=\omega_2,\omega_3,\cdots$)模拟误差较大。这主要是人工边界单元不能很好模拟具有静力特性的削减波,而共振频段也同时包含削减波。考虑两种波动现象,进一步提高模拟精度有待深入研究。

5 结语

本文为了建立无限域波动的有限元分析方法,推导了人工边界单元。结果有限元内节点与边界点的计算稳定性得到统一,且人工边界具有多向波动透射能力。新提出的边界稳态反射系数计算方法,为波动问题的有限元模型提供了坚实的理论基础。开发高精度的人工边界单元应做深入探讨。

参考文献

[1] 林皋,关飞．用边界元法研究地震波在不规则地形处的散射问题．大连理工大学学报,1990,30(2):145～151

[2] 廖振鹏．工程波动理论导引．北京:科学出版社,1996

[3] 陈厚群．当前我国水工抗震中的主要问题和发展动态．振动工程学报,1997,10(3):253～257

[4] 邵振海,洪伟,周健义．透射边界条件的统一理论．中国科学,2000,30(1):64～69

[5] Liao Zhenpeng, G. Yang. *Multi-directional transmitting boundaries for steady-state SH waves*. Earthq. Eng. Struct. Dyn., 1995, 24:361～371

[6] Deeks A J, Randolph M F. *Axisymmetric timedomain transmitting boundaries*. ASCE, J.Eng. Mech.1994,120(9):25～41

[7] 刘晶波,吕颜东．结构—地基动力相互作用问题分析的一种直接方法．土木工程学报,1998,31(3):55～64

[8] Lysmer J, Kuhlemeyer. *Finite dynamic model for infinite media*. ASCE, J. Eng. Mech.1969,95(4):859～877

[9] Wolf J P, Song Ch M. *Finite-element modelling of unbounded media*. John Wiley & Sons Lid, England, 1996

[10] Lysmer J, Wass G. *Shear waves in plane infinite structures*. ASCE, J.Eng.Mech.1972,98(1):85～105

软化砂砾岩上的拱坝新结构

摘　要　为在砂砾软岩上经济、快速地修建拱坝，针对软岩强度低、变形大的特点，分析了水压和累积自重作用下软岩上的拱坝受力和变形规律，提出了以下工程策略：上游坝面周边设置人工拱面缝释放岩石拉应力，缝端用槽钢止裂；下游布置推力墩增强坝肩，限制变位；扩大基础均化坝体由自重产生的压应力集中。结果表明：在软岩上采取上游面设置人工拱面缝释放拉应力，下游面设置推力墩限制变位的措施后，拱坝及其周边岩石能够满足内应力及承载力要求。

关键词　拱坝设计　软弱基础　人工拱面缝　推力墩

通常认为在基础地质条件较差的坝址上不宜修建拱坝。但实践中也有在岩石强度较低的坝基上修建拱坝的工程实例。比如 1995 年建成的四川雅安铜头电站[1]，拱坝坝高 75m，坝基坝肩均为下三系砾岩，湿抗压强度仅 16～36MPa，变形模量仅 1.8～3.1GPa。2001 年完成施工的塔西河石门子拱坝坝高 109m，中下部岩石湿抗压强度为 20MPa，蠕变变形模量仅 2.0GPa，采用柔性拱[2,3]和分温度缝[4,5]的措施，以基础处理为代价，实现了在弱基上修建拱坝。

新疆某工程方案比选中，在砂砾岩上修拱坝由于将溢洪道、泄水孔都合并在拱坝坝体上，从而比土坝方案有更大的经济优势。为此，需要研究能够适应弹模仅为 0.5GPa 的软弱岩石的拱坝新结构。

该拱坝坝址区分布的地层为第四系下更新统西域砾岩（Q_1^L），砾石层具粗粒状结构，块状构造泥沙质、钙质胶结或半胶结，遇水易软化。砾石成分以花岗岩、辉绿岩为主。工程区岩体成岩作用及胶结程度欠佳，根据钻孔及平硐（PD2 和 PD3）资料，在清水钻进情况下岩芯难以成柱状，岩石质量指标 RQD 为零；采用植物胶钻进方能取得部分柱状岩芯，RQD 值为 46%。岩体原位应力—弹模试验结果见表 1。

表 1　岩体原位应力—弹模试验结果　　（单位：MPa）

σ	E_{PD2}	E_{PD3}
0.7	294.1	349.6
1.4	508.2	537.3
2.1	445.0	586.4
2.8	619.9	743.7
3.5	589.8	752.6

1　软岩上修建拱坝存在的问题

按梯级开发规划，该坝为中厚拱坝，坝顶▽1 385m，河床▽1 286m，坝高 118m。泄洪

本文选自《清华大学学报（自然科学版）》2003 年第 11 期，作者还有刘颖黎、陈强、李鹏辉。

量为 1 700m^3/s,基础弹性模量取为 0.5GPa。

本文选用了两个计算模型。整体模型 1 是原型拱坝计算模型。由模型 1 计算结果可知,在纯水压作用下,拱坝表现为明显的向下游的刚体位移,位移量约为 3cm,而且坝体的剪应力不大,均在 1MPa 以内。因此,截取拱坝的最大受力拱圈(▽1 282 ~ 1 283m)为模型 2。

整体模型 1:节点总数为 17 223,单元总数为 14 068,八节点等参元。约束边界条件为上下游岩石 y 方向支承,左右岸岩石 80m 处 x 方向支承,岩石底部▽1 150m 为 z 方向支承。水压作用在上游坝面和上游两岸岩石面上,水位取为▽1 384m。利用模型 1 的施工累积结果来说明软弱岩石的承载力问题。

平面模型 2:节点总数为 1 156,单元总数为 500,八节点等参元。约束边界条件为上下游岩石 y 方向支承,左右岸岩石 80m 处 x 方向支承。水压作用在上游坝面和上游两岸岩石面上,水位仍取为▽1 384m。如图 1 所示,字母 a、b、c、d 以及 a′、b′、c′、d′为上游坝肩处网格节点,位置 1、2、3 表示下游不同长度推力墩的位置。利用模型 2 来分析水压作用下软弱岩石上的拱坝变位和受力规律。首先讨论以下两种情况的水压结果:①弹性模量为 0.5GPa 的软弱地基;②弹性模量为 10.0GPa 的坚硬地基。

结果分析如下。

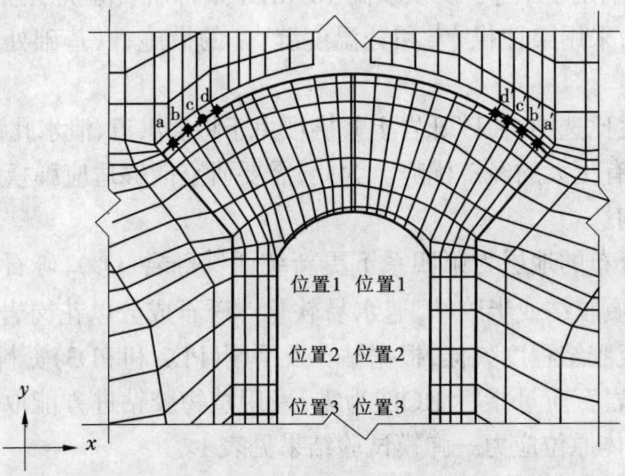

图 1　平面拱圈网络

1.1　位移

如图 2(a)、图 2(b)所示,正值表示向下游位移,可见坚硬岩石对坝肩有着较强的约束变形能力,而软弱岩石对刚性体的约束作用很小,软岩平面拱圈的位移量是坚硬岩石的 5 倍左右。

1.2　应力

软弱岩石上的拱坝与岩石的弹模比值为 1/40,刚体向下游变位较大,造成上游坝肩与岩石、坝踵与河床基岩之间产生较大的局部拉应力,影响坝肩的稳定,如图 3(a)、图 3(b)所示,而且软岩的拱端应力集中大,但软岩 y 方向拉应力范围小。图 3(c)表明,坝肩下游软弱岩石提供的 x 方向支承力不够而在拱冠附近产生接近 0.4MPa 的拉应力。

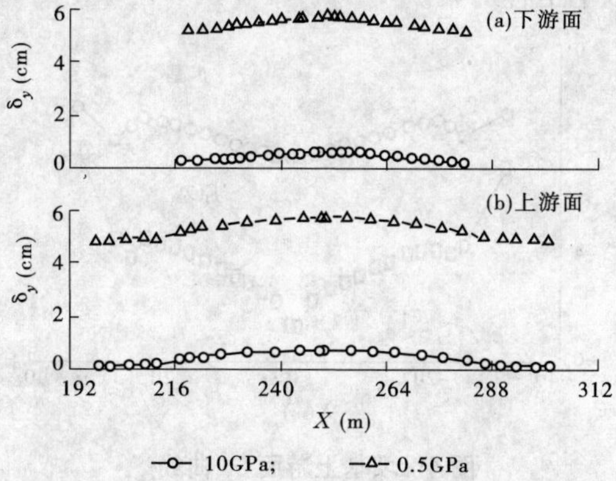

图 2 不同弹模地基拱圈上下游面 δ_y 曲线

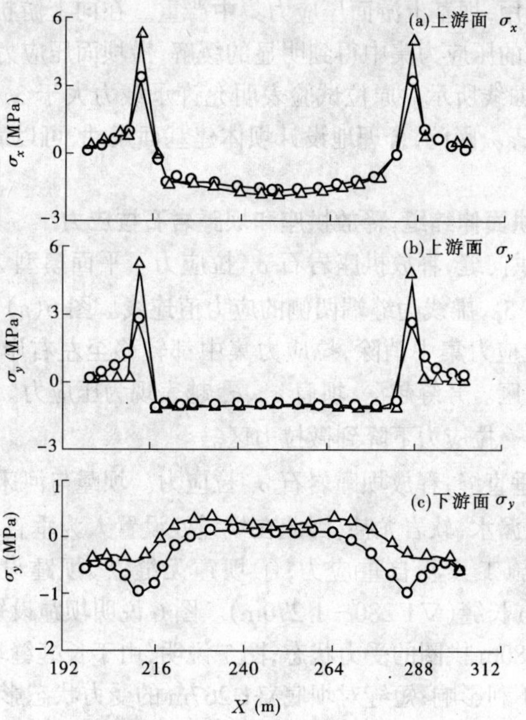

图 3 不同弹模地基拱圈上下游面正应力曲线

1.3 地基承载力

拱坝未蓄水前，在累积自重作用下，上游坝踵压应力过大，软岩基础面最大压力区 σ_z 应力曲线如图 4“原基”曲线所示，地基难以承受 5.5MPa 的压应力。

2 软岩上拱坝设计的对策分析

在弹性模量仅为 0.5GPa 岩石基础上修建拱坝，针对岩石抗压强度低以及软弱岩石的大变形性能,提出了以下工程对策。

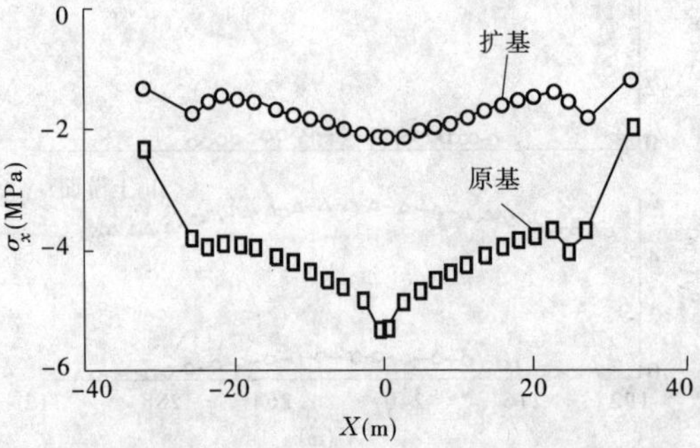

图 4 坝基上游面 σ_z 曲线

2.1 扩大基础,缓解累积自重引起的坝踵局部压应力集中

由于累积自重的作用,坝基上游面压应力集中严重。在向上游扩大基础 3m 后,累积自重在坝基上游面产生的压应力集中得到明显的缓解,沿坝面压应力非常均匀,最大只有 2.2MPa,如图 4"扩基"曲线所示。原位试验表明允许承载力大于 3.5MPa,埋深 100m 也表明侧压力大于 2.3MPa。因此,合理地设计坝体建基面尺寸,可以满足软岩地基的承载力要求。

2.2 上游坝面设人工拱面伸缩缝,释放拱座和坝踵岩石拉应力

(1)坝肩设置人工拱向缝,释放拱座岩石 σ_y 拉应力。平面模型 2 水压作用下不同开缝深度的计算结果见图 5。虚线为缝端两侧的应力值连线。图 5(a)、图 5(b)说明开缝后 x、y 方向的坝肩混凝土应力集中消除,拉应力集中都转移至左右岸缝端,坝肩基础上处于低应力区甚至压应力区。开缝越深,坝肩 σ_x、σ_y 越表现为压应力。因此,设缝后大大改善了坝肩应力,尤其是 σ_y 拉应力下降到微拉力区。

(2)坝踵设置人工垂直缝,释放坝踵岩石 σ_y 拉应力。坝踵与河床岩石的拉应力,易使得上游岩石因被拉开而漏水,软岩尤甚,因此在坝踵处设置人为垂直缝。选取整体模型 1 计算以下 3 种方案的施工累积自重应力:①坝踵无缝;②坝踵设 3m 短缝▽1 280～1 277m);③坝踵设 10m 长缝(▽1 280～1 270m)。图 6 说明坝踵设短缝有效地释放了岩石拉应力,改善了▽1 280m 拱圈的受力状态;图 7 说明,由于长缝缝端离坝底仅 3m,对坝底▽1 267m 受力造成不利影响;短缝对坝底▽1 267m 的受力状态影响甚微。

(3)从设置人工拱面缝改善应力的效果和缝端本身的稳定性来加以分析。以上分析说明拱面缝的设置改善了平面拱的应力分布,降低了平面拱受力后的拉力值,使应力集中区转移至缝端。

缝端的稳定性需用应力强度因子[6]判别。作者计算了整体模型 1 坝踵和坝肩处的缝端应力强度因子(见表 2),负值为拉缝,正值为压缝,混凝土抗裂韧性 $K_{IC}=2.0\text{MN/m}^{3/2}$。荷载单独作用时,应力强度因子皆大于抗裂韧性,而荷载综合作用的结果,应力强度因子小于抗裂韧性。因此,在施工过程中,可以提前蓄水以减小前期应力强度因子。为安全起见,在缝端设止裂槽钢以防万一。

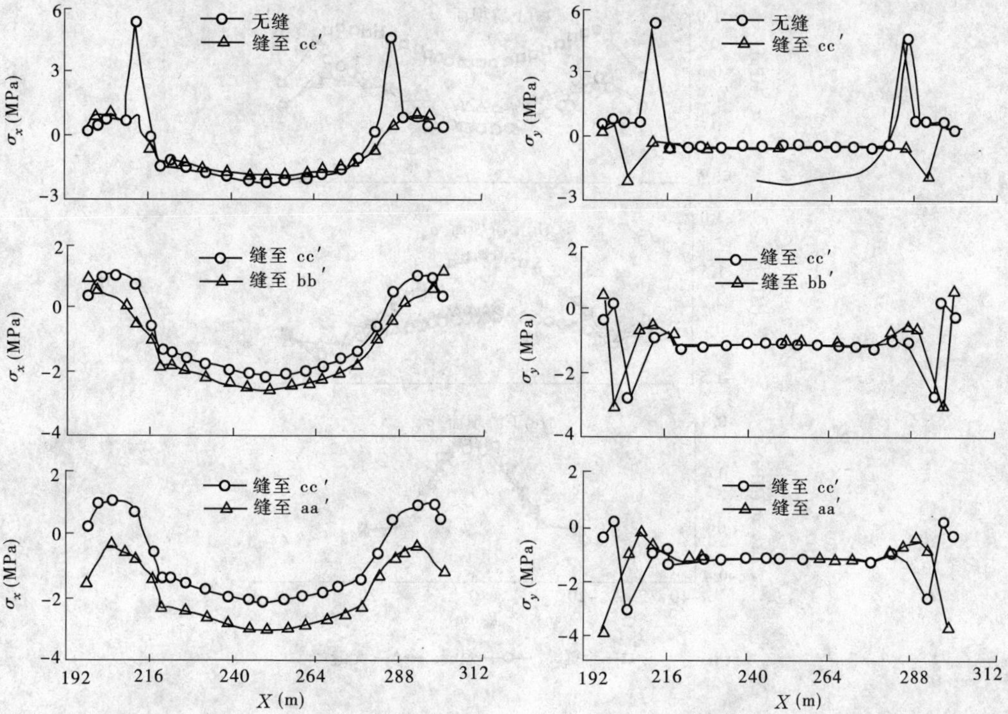

(a)开缝深度对上游坝面 σ_x 的影响　　(b)开缝深度对上游坝面 σ_y 的影响

图 5　不同坝肩开缝深度的正应力曲线

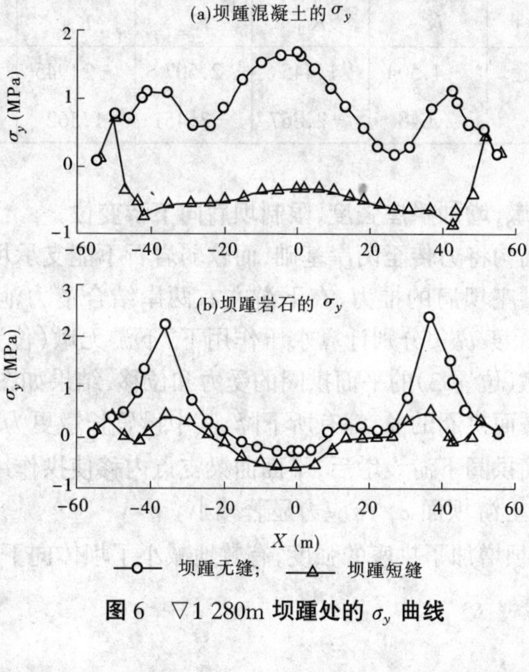

图 6　▽1 280m 坝踵处的 σ_y 曲线

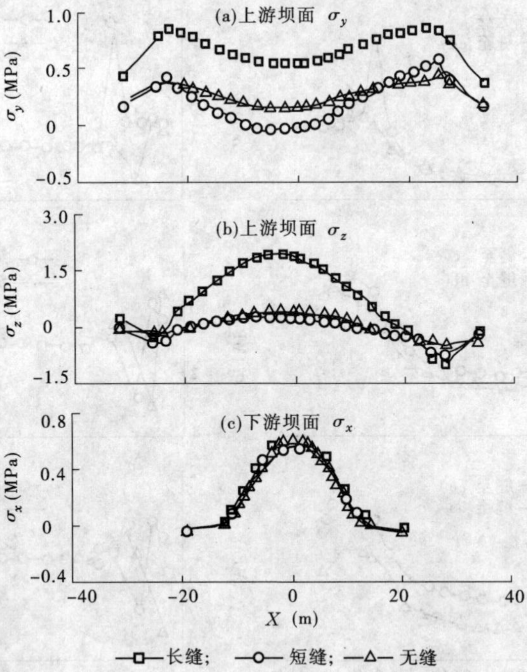

图 7　▽1 267m 上下游坝面的正应力

表 2　缝端应力强度因子计算结果　　(单位:MN /$m^{3/2}$)

缝端位置	水压荷载		温度和累积自重		水压+温度和累积自重	
	K_{I}	K_{II}	K_{I}	K_{II}	K_{I}	K_{II}
▽1 282m 右岸坝肩拱向缝	-4.504	1.445	2.507	-2.945	-1.997	-1.500
▽1 277m 坝踵垂直缝	2.648	-2.867	-3.451	1.562	-0.805	-1.305

2.3　下游坝肩设推力墩,增加拱座强度,限制坝肩向下游变位

拱坝主要靠拱体结构将力传至两岸基础,而软弱岩石不能支承坝肩推力,从而产生较大的变形。为了增强拱座坝肩的推力,在下游左右两岸结合消力池结构设置了推力墩。选用平面模型 2,开缝深度 bb',分别计算水压作用下,下游无墩(位置 1)、下游设 23m 短墩(位置 2)和 40m 长墩(位置 3)的平面拱圈的受力和位移,结果如图 8、图 9 所示。

图 8 说明加墩后平面拱圈的 σ_y 都有所下降,其中设置长墩更为有效地减小了向下游的位移。图 9 说明平面拱圈下游设墩后,平面曲梁支点内移使拱作用有一定加强,下游坝面 y 方向支承力增加,上游坝面 σ_x 压应力显著减小。

因此,加墩后的拱坝增加了拱座的强度,有效地减小了坝体向下游的位移。

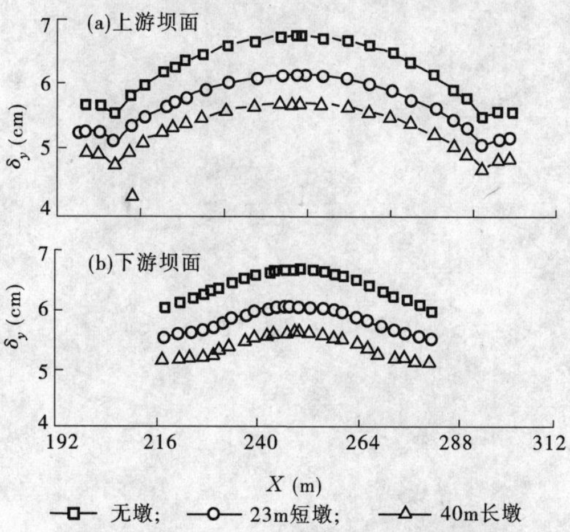

图8 加墩后上下游坝面的 δ_y 曲线

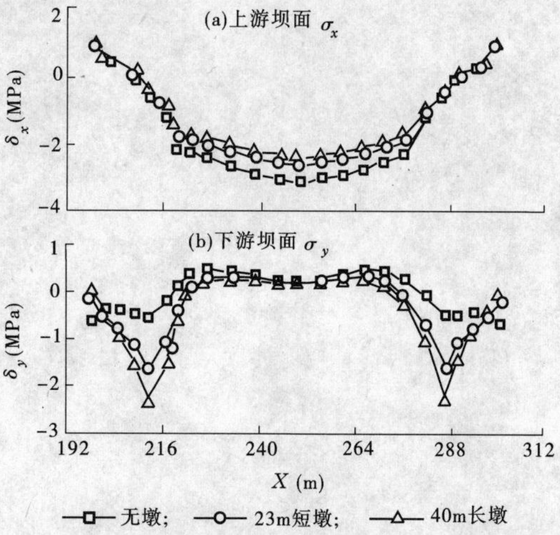

图9 加墩后上下游面的正应力曲线

3 结论

本文提出了在软化砂砾岩上建拱坝的新的结构和构造措施:一方面,上游坝面设置人工拱面缝释放岩石拉应力,容许软岩与坝体之间变形协调;另一方面,下游两岸坝肩设置推力墩增强坝肩强度,限制 y 方向位移。以上两种措施并举,同时扩大地基基础尺寸以满足地基承载力要求,使得在软岩上修建拱坝其结构上的可行性得到了保证。

参考文献

[1] 辜明清,纪洪华. 第三系砾岩建筑拱坝的工程地质问题分析与评价. 四川水力发电,2001,20(4):33～35

[2] 刘光廷,李鹏辉,谢树南,等. 碾压混凝土拱坝的铰结拱研究. 水利学报,2002(6):27～31

[3] 刘光廷,徐增辉,李鹏辉. 柔性拱和软弱地基上的碾压混凝土拱坝. 清华大学学报(自然科学版),2002,42(10):1365～1368

[4] 刘光廷,谢树南,李鹏辉,等. 碾压混凝土拱坝设人工短缝的应力释放及止裂作用. 水利学报,2002(6):9～14

[5] 刘光廷,胡昱,王恩志,等. 石门子碾压混凝土拱坝温度场实测与仿真计算. 清华大学学报(自然科学版),2002,42(4):539～542

[6] Liu Guangting, Lin Guoyu. *Study on the curved and branch cracks in massive concrete structures*. Proc of the International Conference on Dam Fracture.. Boulder: Electric Power Research Institue, 1991

四、湿热传导和干裂问题

石门子碾压混凝土拱坝采用聚氨酯硬质泡沫保温保湿的效果分析

关键词 聚氨酯保温层 高寒地区 碾压混凝土拱坝 保温保湿 石门子坝

1 工程简介

新疆塔西河石门子碾压混凝土拱坝最大坝高 109m，坝顶高程 1 394.00m，建基面高程 1 285.00m，溢洪道及泄水孔布置在拱坝中部主河道上，以便泄洪时水流顺畅。坝体混凝土总方量为 21.1 万 m^3。

坝址地区冬季寒冷，月平均气温在零度以下长达 5 个月，多年平均气温 4.1℃，极端最高气温 33.2℃，极端最低气温 −31.5℃，日气温波动较大，属典型的高寒剧变气温地区。坝基岩石为泥钙质胶结砾岩，且部分棕红色砾岩遇水软化，左右坝肩均存在软弱夹层和断层，地质条件非常恶劣。坝址地区地震烈度高达 8 度。总之，该工程是一座修建在高寒弱基强震地区的百米以上碾压混凝土拱坝工程。

本工程为减少温度梯度变化及干缩造成的裂缝，经研究在众多的保温材料中选取了工艺简单的新型聚氨酯硬质泡沫。该保温材料在保温、保湿和经济性方面均优于传统的保温材料，可满足西北地区大坝保温、隔热和保湿要求，防止大坝因温度梯度及干缩等变化而产生裂缝。该保温材料的研究和应用取得了良好的经济效益和社会效益。

2 聚氨酯的主要理化性能

在大坝上采用聚氨酯硬质泡沫喷涂进行保温保湿，经过长期研究表明：与其他保温材料如聚氯乙烯和聚苯乙烯相比较，它具有外形美观、保温隔热及保湿性优良、施工简单等优点，其保温隔热及保湿性能不因气候影响而发生较大的波动。其主要理化性能见表 1。

表 1 聚氨酯硬质泡沫保温保湿材料的主要理化性能

项目	密度(kg/m^3)		尺寸稳定性	吸水率	抗压强度	导热系数	耐燃性(离火
	内部密度	表皮密度	(%)	(g/m^2)	(MPa)	(W/(m·K))	自熄时间)(s)
性能	29～60	35～50	＜2.0	＜150	＞0.17	0.019＋0.003	＜3

保温材料和混凝土之间的黏结直接影响其保温性能。聚氨酯在没有加入发泡剂之前本身是一种强度极高的黏合剂，在加入发泡剂制成泡沫后，其黏结力仍然很强，仍能和混凝土连为一体。而且水对于聚氨酯基本没有溶解腐蚀作用，即水与聚氨酯不发生反应，水淹后不会脱落，亦可用于坝体水位变动区的保温保湿。

本文选自《水利水电技术》2002 年第 6 期，作者还有李鹏辉、杜彬、徐增辉。

从现场可看到,要将混凝土表面喷涂的聚氨酯保温层清除非常困难,需用铁铲等利器连同混凝土表层一起清除,清除下来的聚氨酯保温层上还黏结有大约 1mm 厚的混凝土,聚氨酯已渗入混凝土。

3　聚氨酯保温、保湿效果分析

新疆塔西河石门子水库整个坝体的聚氨酯分两个阶段喷涂施工,第一阶段从 1 323.50～1 365.00m 高程,第二阶段从 1 365.00～1 394.00m 高程。设计要求坝前喷涂 3cm 厚聚氨酯,坝后喷涂 5cm 厚聚氨酯,喷涂前将坝面清理干净。为保持干燥,选用自上而下、从左右坝肩至拱坝中缝的喷涂顺序,选用的聚氨酯密度为 $40kg/m^3$,导热系数控制在 0.03W/(m·K)以下。

3.1　聚氨酯的保温效果

在坝体表面设置用导热系数较低的聚氨酯材料所制成的保温层,当外界气温变化时,混凝土内部不直接与大气进行热交换,使表面由于大幅度降温、温度梯度急剧增大的部分仅仅在保温层里发生,从而使混凝土温度梯度平缓,起到降低表层温度拉应力的效果。从图 1 可以看出:在 2000 年 10 月 26 日～2001 年 2 月 22 日整个冬季的外界气温在 -20℃左右时,下游1 336.50m高程坝体内部温度由 25℃降至 20℃,而聚氨酯保护层下混凝土表面的温度从约 8℃降到 6.0℃左右稳定,均在零度以上,使第一年冬季坝体混凝土的内外温差从 40℃减小到 14℃,内外温差削减率达 65%,保温效果显著。考虑运行期由于混凝土内部发热量逐渐减少,混凝土内部稳定温度场为 6℃,聚氨酯保护层下混凝土表面的温度仍会远远高于外界 -20～-30℃的气温(若仍按 14℃的温差考虑,估计在 -8℃左右),大大降低混凝土内外温差,仍能起到良好的保温作用。

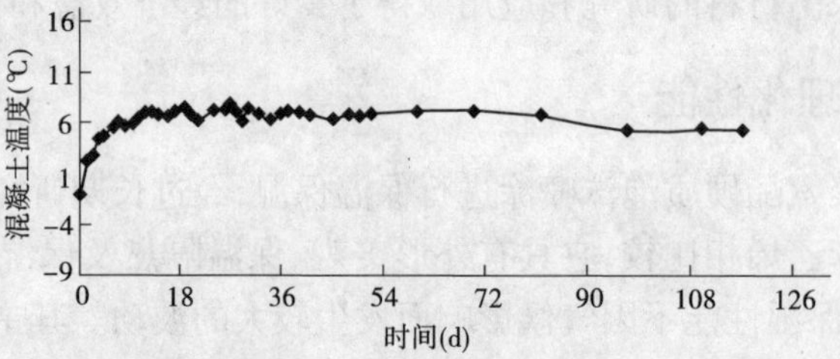

图 1　2000 年 10 月 26 日～2001 年 2 月 22 日 1 336.50m 高程
左坝肩下游面聚氨酯保温层下混凝土表面温度变化曲线

为考察聚氨酯保温层在夏季的保温作用,在 1 335.00～1 337.00m 高程坝下游面混凝土表层钻孔,同时在该处附近强行剥下聚氨酯保温层并钻孔进行对比试验。

由 2000 年 7 月的观测结果可知,有聚氨酯保温层的混凝土温度基本不随外界温度变化,无聚氨酯保温层的混凝土温度随外界气温变化较大。当外界气温为 30℃的高温时,聚氨酯保温层下 5cm 深(不计 5cm 厚的聚氨酯保温层厚度)处混凝土温度基本保持在 17℃不变,1cm 深处混凝土温度为 20℃,测得混凝土与聚氨酯保温层交界面上的温度为 22℃;而无聚氨酯保温层的 5cm 深处混凝土温度为 25℃,1cm 深处混凝土温度为 27℃,表面基本和外界气温同步变化,有时较外界气温还高,这是由于外界气温变幅较大时混凝土温度有滞后现象。相比而言,有聚氨酯保温层的 5cm 深处混凝土温度较无聚氨酯保温层的温度降低 8℃,有聚氨酯保温层的 1cm 深处混凝土温度较无聚氨酯保温层的降低 7℃,表面降低更多,总的看来,喷涂聚氨酯保温层后,在夏季高温情况下混凝土内外温差可降低 7℃左右,大大削减了混凝土内外温差应力。

聚氨酯保温层的耐久性较好,从现场强行剥落的聚氨酯来看,经过一年时间,聚氨酯保温层内部聚氨酯完好无损,无老化迹象。即使聚氨酯保温层在很多年后老化,届时由于外部表层为抗冻混凝土,混凝土的抗冻性能已随抗冻混凝土强度的提高而增强了,可以抵抗聚氨酯老化后的坝体抗冻性。

综上所述,在混凝土内部水化至最高温度值时喷涂聚氨酯保温层,不会增加坝体混凝土温度,只会减缓混凝土散热时间,减小混凝土表面的温度梯度,降低混凝土内外温差值,削减坝体混凝土的温度应力。

3.2　聚氨酯的保湿效果

有资料表明,由于湿度变化而引起的干缩裂缝占大坝表面裂缝的 60%～70%,因此坝面的保湿十分重要,聚氨酯保温层还有保湿的作用。

从湿度的实测资料可以看出:当大气湿度为 40%的情况下,喷涂聚氨酯保温层下 5cm 深处混凝土的湿度不随外界湿度变化而变化,湿度基本保持在 97%,1cm 深处混凝土的湿度为 89%。无喷涂聚氨酯保温层的 5cm 深处混凝土湿度为 96%,与喷涂聚氨酯保温层的 5cm 深处混凝土的湿度基本相同,这是由于混凝土本体的湿传导性能很差的缘故;无喷涂聚氨酯保温层 1cm 深处混凝土湿度仅为 60%,较喷涂聚氨酯保温层相同深度处混凝土的湿度减少约 30%。强行剥开聚氨酯保温层没发现任何表面干缩裂缝。由此可见,聚氨酯保温层施工期保湿效果良好,防止了表面干缩裂缝。

4　结语

在寒冷地区石门子坝坝面喷涂聚氨酯保温材料,第一年冬季在外界气温约 -20℃时,聚氨酯保温层下混凝土表面温度为 6～8℃,第二年夏季聚氨酯保温层可降低 7℃的内外温差,保温效果良好,可大大减少高寒地区拱坝温度应力。聚氨酯保温层还有良好的保湿作用,至第二年夏季尚未发现表面干缩裂缝。该保温材料的研究和首次在大坝中应用取得了良好的效益。

参考文献

[1] 张超然,郑守仁,彭启友,等.三峡水利枢纽混凝土工程温度控制研究.北京:中国水利水电出版社,2001

混凝土湿热传导与湿热扩散特性试验研究(Ⅰ)

——试验设计原理

摘　要　了解不同含湿状态下混凝土的热物性与湿物性,对研究混凝土坝在不同时期的温度控制与表面保护措施具有重要意义。论述了"常功率平面热源法"测定混凝土湿热传导与湿热扩散特性的原理和方法,对影响测试精度的各个参数进行了误差传递分析,讨论了进行加热片热容修正的必要性,使整个试验能在设计的试验精度范围内展开,避免了试验安排的盲目性。

关键词　平面热源法　混凝土　导温系数　导热系数

无论是在混凝土坝的施工期,还是在运行期,大体积混凝土的温度应力问题总是备受工程界的关注。目前在工程中采用的各种消解或削弱混凝土温度应力的措施,都离不开对混凝土内部的导热性能与其边界的散热性能的深刻理解。一般而言,混凝土是一种导热性能不良的材料,所以,最高温升常常出现在混凝土坝的坝体中部,消散坝体内部温升的方法常为预埋冷却水管法。这种措施会给那些不设横缝或仅少量设缝的碾压混凝土拱坝的施工带来一些麻烦。文献[1]报道了利用碾压混凝土薄层碾压的特点,施工期间,在碾压层之间浸泡缓缓流动的冷水,以消散或缓解内部高温问题的工程措施。这一工程措施的理论背景涉及到两个方面:其一为在水化过程中混凝土的热学参数与完全硬化后混凝土的热学参数的比较问题;其二为新浇混凝土与外表流水在温度、湿度两方面的相互作用问题。这正是本文开展含湿混凝土热传导与湿扩散研究的出发点。

同时,在水工结构与建筑结构的许多场合都涉及到混凝土湿热传导与湿热扩散问题。如北方寒冷地区,冬夏季温差与昼夜温差都比较大,混凝土内外湿度差更大,大坝混凝土表面裂缝问题十分突出。尤其是在夏季,当水库在防洪限制水位附近运行时,已经蓄水饱和的混凝土受日照辐射作用,将会使坝体上游面混凝土产生大量的干缩裂缝,影响坝体的正常蓄水与安全运行。又如建筑楼板的干燥过程[2]、建筑墙体的吸潮量计算[3]、拆模后混凝土的冷击机理[4]等,都牵涉到混凝土温度与湿度的相互作用问题,必须慎重对待。

在我国目前的混凝土坝温度应力计算与温控措施设计中,基本上都只涉及到了混凝土的导热传热性质[5],对大坝混凝土温度场与渗流场的耦合问题、温度场与湿度场的耦合问题还没有予以足够的重视[6],其主要原因是混凝土湿度场的测量问题比较困难[7],耦合计算方法也比较复杂。随着高性能湿敏电容传感器进入市场,各种型号与规格的温度计已被开发出来,为在实验室中系统地研究温、湿度的耦合作用提供了条件。

本文采用"常功率平面热源法"[8]对不同含湿状态下混凝土的导温系数、导热系数进行了试验研究。该方法是一种"非稳定"试验方法,在试验数据的处理上比较麻烦,需要对试验所依赖的原理进行仔细研究,对整个试验过程进行完整的控制与记录;需要对加热片

本文选自《三峡大学学报(自然科学版)》2002年第1期,作者还有黄达海。

的热容量进行标定与补偿。

1 试验设计原理

在图1中,A、B、C是仅仅厚度不同的试件。A为主试件,B、C试件构成A的边界,只要测量的时间合适(即充分利用混凝土导热性能不良的特点,选择恰当的测量时机),主试件A就可以看做是“无限大平板”。在对内含高热敏电阻丝的铜板加热时,主试件两表面中央地区都将在整个升温期间各保持为等温面。随着时间的延长,A试件紧挨铜板的部分首先开始升温,逐渐向远离加热片的两边延伸,直到 $\tau=\tau_{\lim}$ 时,辅助试件B的上表面与C的下表面也将开始升温。在 $0<\tau<\tau_{\lim}$ 期间,试件A、B叠合在一起,以及试件C都将表现为半无限大物体,而铜板热源也将均等地向两侧供热,每侧均为 q_0 kcal/(m²·h),即

$$2q_0 = q = Q/S \quad (\mathrm{kcal/(m^2 \cdot h)}) \tag{1}$$

式中:Q 为铜板热源的热功率,kcal/h;S 为铜板的面积,m²。

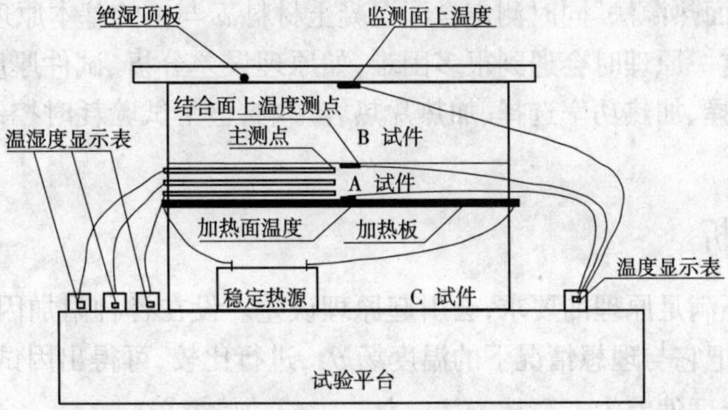

图1 试验装置简图

在初始温度 t_i 分布均匀的半无限大物体内部,从 $\tau=0$ 起,半无限大物体表面,受均匀分布的平面热源 q_0 的作用,在常物性条件下,离加热片表面 x 处混凝土的温升 $\theta_{x,\tau}=(t_{x,\tau}-t_i)$ 为[2]

$$\theta_{x,\tau} = (2q_0/\lambda)\sqrt{a\tau}\,\mathrm{ierfc}(x/2\sqrt{a\tau}) \tag{2}$$

式中 ierfc(ξ)代表变量 ξ“高斯误差补函数的一次积分”,其值可以从数学函数表中查到。

当 $\tau>0$ 但 $x=0$ 时,$\mathrm{ierfc}(0)=1/\sqrt{\pi}$,由式(2)知

$$\theta_{0,\tau} = (1/\sqrt{\pi})(2q_0/\lambda)\sqrt{a\tau} \tag{3}$$

这样,如果用两个温度计或热电偶分别测定 τ_0 时刻图1所示主试件A与加热片接触面上中心区温升 $\theta_{0,\tau_0}=(t_{0,\tau_0}-t_i)$,以及 τ_{x_1} 时刻A与B接触面上的中心区温升,则根据式(2)、式(3)有

$$\frac{\theta_{x_1},\tau_{x_1}}{\theta_{0,\tau_0}}\sqrt{\frac{\tau_0}{\tau_{x_1}}} = \sqrt{\pi}\,\mathrm{ierfc}\left(\frac{x_1}{2\sqrt{a\tau_{x_1}}}\right) \tag{4}$$

令 $\phi=\frac{\theta_{x_1},\tau_{x_1}}{\theta_{0,\tau_0}}\sqrt{\frac{\tau_0}{\tau_{x_1}}}$，$\xi_{x_1}=\frac{x_1}{2\sqrt{a\tau_{x_1}}}$，那么 $\phi=\sqrt{\pi}\cdot\mathrm{ierfc}\left(\frac{x_1}{2\sqrt{a\tau_{x_1}}}\right)$ 的值就可以求得；反查函数表(实际计算中以程序方式实现，$\xi\sim\phi$ 关系见图 2(a)，即可得 $\xi_{x_1}=\frac{x_1}{2\sqrt{a\tau_{x_1}}}$ 的值，从而计算出相应于该测试温度范围 $t_{0,\tau_0}-t_{x_1,\tau_{x_1}}$ 的平均温度 $t=\frac{1}{2}(t_{0,\tau_0}+t_{x_1,\tau_{x_1}})$ 时混凝土的导温系数为

$$a=\frac{x_1^2}{4\xi_{x_1}^2\tau_{x_1}} \tag{5}$$

将 a 代入式(2)就求得试件的导热系数 λ 为

$$\lambda=\frac{2q_0}{\sqrt{\pi}\theta_{0,\tau_0}}\sqrt{a\tau_0} \tag{6}$$

这就是"常功率平面热源法"同时测定含湿混凝土材料 a 与 λ 的基本原理。

在实际应用这一原理时会遇到很多困难，如原理误差分析、试件厚度选择、温度测点布置、计算时刻选择、加热功率选择、加热片热容影响、整个试验耗时控制等，需要仔细斟酌。

2 原理误差分析

当试验条件不满足原理的要求，会引起原理误差。设在各种附加因素影响下试样中的温度场为 $\theta_{x,\tau}^*$，把它与理想情况下的温度场 $\theta_{x,\tau}$ 进行比较，可得出因试验条件偏离原理的要求而引起的温度偏差为

$$\Delta\theta_{x,\tau}/\theta_{x,\tau}=(\theta_{x,\tau}^*-\theta_{x,\tau})/\theta_{x,\tau} \tag{7}$$

由此引起 a 的偏差为

$$\frac{\Delta a}{a}=-2\frac{\Delta\xi}{\xi}=\frac{2\mathrm{ierfc}(\xi)}{\xi\mathrm{erfc}(\xi)}\frac{\Delta\phi}{\phi} \tag{8}$$

其中，$\frac{2\mathrm{ierfc}(\xi)}{\xi\mathrm{erfc}(\xi)}$ 随 $\xi=\frac{x}{2\sqrt{a\tau}}$ 的变化见图 2(b)。由于 q_0，τ_0 的误差与测试原理无关，由式(6)可得混凝土导热系数的试验误差为

$$\frac{\Delta\lambda}{\lambda}=-\frac{\Delta\theta_{0,\tau_0}}{\theta_{0,\tau_0}}+\frac{1}{2}\frac{\Delta a}{a} \tag{9}$$

3 试件厚度选择

如果把温度、湿度测点布置在主、辅试件之间，就难以克服主、辅试件之间可能存在的缝隙对测量结果的影响(虽然试验前对主、辅试件接触面进行了"人工对磨"处理，但仍嫌接触面不够平整)。因此，把主试件中主测点布置在试件中部离加热片 45mm 的地方，这样做，一方面可以减少辅助试件的厚度尺寸，另一方面更可以使测点的温湿度基本不受试验环境的影响。由材料因素确定了主试件几何厚度 Δ 为 60mm 的基础上，主试件测点厚

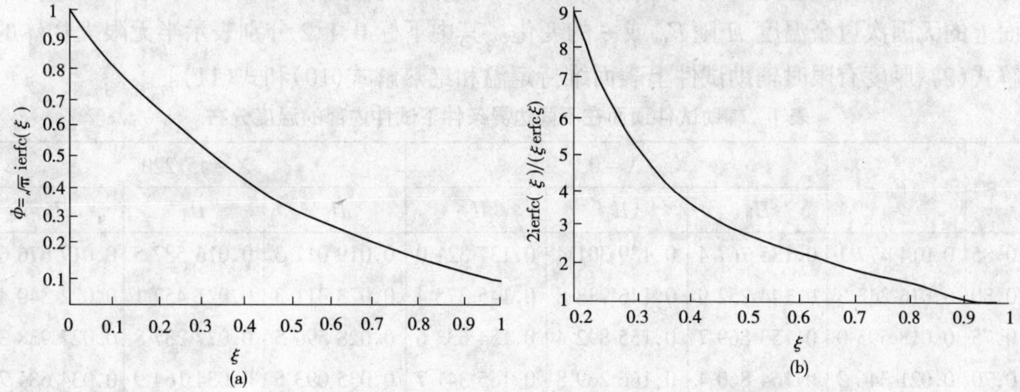

图 2　误差传递关系

度 $x_1=45$mm,辅助试件 B 几何厚度 δ 为 160mm,实际上覆厚度为 175mm,约为主试件测点厚度 x_1 的 4 倍,辅助试件 C 的厚度 $\delta+\Delta=220$mm。

式(2)是半无限平面的理论解答,对于有限厚度的试样所引起的原理误差可以做如下分析。

参考图 3,设在初始时刻,厚度为 L 的试样与介质处于热平衡。从 $\tau=0$ 的时刻起,试样的一个表面受恒定热流加热,热流率为 q_0,试样表面(即辅助试样上表面)向周围介质散热,放热系数为 β。$\beta=0$ 和 $\beta=\infty$是两种极端情况。显然,实际温度变化情况介于这两者之间。

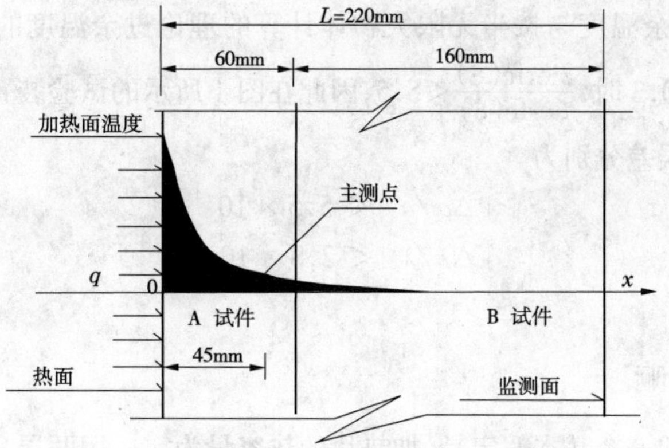

图 3　加热中试件内部温度分布

当 $\beta=\infty$时,试样中的过余温度场为

$$\theta_1=\frac{q_0L}{\lambda}\left\{1-\frac{x}{L}-\sum_{n=0}^{\infty}\frac{8}{(2n+1)^2\pi^2}\mathrm{e}^{-\left(\frac{2n+1}{2}\pi\right)^2\frac{a\tau}{L^2}}\cos\left(\frac{(2n+1)\pi}{2}\frac{x}{L}\right)\right\}\tag{10}$$

而当 $\beta=0$ 时,试样中的过余温度场为

$$\theta_2=\frac{q_0L}{\lambda}\left\{\frac{1}{3}+\frac{1}{2}\left(\frac{x}{L}\right)^2-\frac{x}{L}+\frac{a\tau}{L^2}-\sum_{n=0}^{\infty}\frac{2}{n^2\pi^2}\mathrm{e}^{-n^2\pi^2\frac{a\tau}{L^2}}\cos\left(n\pi\frac{x}{L}\right)\right\}\tag{11}$$

取无因次温度为 $\Pi=\theta\lambda/q_0L$,无因次厚度为 $X=x/L$,无因次时间为 $F_0=a\tau/L^2=$

$X^2/4\xi^2$,计算结果见表1。表中给出了3种不同边界条件下,$X=0$ 和 $X=45/220$ 这两个面上的无因次过余温度 Π 随 F_0 或 ξ 的变化。其中下标0、1、2分别表示半无限大物体的解式(2)、厚度有限时辅助试件上表面维持定温和绝热解式(10)和式(11)。

表1 辅助试件顶面在不同边界条件下试件内部的温度分布

ξ	F_0	$X=0$			$X=45/220$		
		Π_0	Π_1	Π_2	Π_0	Π_1	Π_2
0.85	0.014 477 1	0.135 767 4	0.139 301 4	0.137 321 0	0.019 011 3	0.016 587 5	0.017 676 6
0.80	0.016 343 3	0.144 252 9	0.146 988 8	0.145 375 4	0.023 311 3	0.021 457 1	0.022 349 4
0.75	0.018 595 0	0.153 869 7	0.155 892 4	0.154 633 6	0.028 590 5	0.027 237 8	0.027 938 3
0.70	0.021 346 3	0.164 860 4	0.166 269 8	0.165 341 7	0.035 093 5	0.034 164 9	0.034 684 7
0.65	0.024 756 7	0.177 542 0	0.178 450 9	0.177 816 2	0.043 140 8	0.042 552 0	0.042 909 7
0.60	0.029 054 8	0.192 337 1	0.192 866 0	0.192 473 7	0.053 159 6	0.052 824 1	0.053 046 0
0.55	0.034 577 6	0.209 822 3	0.210 089 8	0.209 879 1	0.065 731 9	0.065 567 5	0.065 686 1
0.50	0.041 838 8	0.230 804 6	0.230 916 4	0.230 823 2	0.081 671 2	0.081 607 1	0.081 657 6
0.45	0.051 652 9	0.256 449 5	0.256 486 3	0.256 454 4	0.102 151 0	0.102 134 7	0.102 149 0
0.40	0.065 373 2	0.288 505 7	0.288 516 1	0.288 507 4	0.128 928 6	0.128 928 8	0.128 929 4
0.35	0.085 385 4	0.329 720 8	0.329 725 4	0.329 722 2	0.164 761 4	0.164 763 9	0.164 763 6
0.30	0.116 219 0	0.384 674 3	0.384 671 4	0.384 682 5	0.214 239 5	0.214 220 5	0.214 263 6

从表1中可以看出,当 $\xi \geqslant 0.3$ 时,三者的计算值非常接近。在实际测试中,$0<\beta<\infty$,试样中的实际过余温度与按半无限大物体计算的理论过余温度的相对偏差应更小。由图2可知,当 $\xi \geqslant 0.3$ 时,$\dfrac{2\mathrm{ierfc}(\xi)}{\xi\mathrm{erfc}(\xi)}<5.5$,因此在图1所示的试验装置中,由于试样的有限厚度引起的原理误差分别为

$$\begin{aligned} |\Delta a/a| &< 5.5\times10^{-4} \\ |\Delta\lambda/\lambda| &< 2.8\times10^{-4} \end{aligned} \tag{12}$$

完全可以忽略不计。

4 加热片热容影响

上述计算原理的一个基本假定是:加热片的热容量为零。用两层3mm厚的铜板把薄模型加热片夹在其中,并用若干螺钉紧置,解决了加热方式问题。但由此引起的加热片热容量影响问题,仍必须慎重对待。

设单位面积加热片(连同绝缘薄膜)的热容量为 W,对试样的热表面可以写出热平衡方程

$$W\frac{\partial\theta}{\partial\tau}(0,\tau)-\lambda\frac{\partial\theta}{\partial x}(0,\tau)=q \tag{13}$$

试样中的导热过程可用如下数学模型描述:

$$\left.\begin{aligned}&\partial\theta^*/\tau = a\partial^2\theta^*/\partial x^2,(0\leqslant x,0\leqslant\tau\leqslant\infty)\\&\theta^*(x,0)=0\\&\theta^*(L,\tau)=0\\&W\frac{\partial\theta^*}{\partial\tau}(0,\tau)-\lambda\frac{\partial\theta^*}{\partial x}(0,\tau)=q\end{aligned}\right\}\tag{14}$$

用拉普拉斯变换法可以解得[3]

$$\theta^*_{x,\tau}=\frac{qL}{\lambda}\left\{1-\frac{x}{L}-\sum_{n=0}^{\infty}\frac{2\sin\left[\mu_n(1-\frac{x}{L})\right]}{\mu_n^2(k^2\mu_n^2+k+1)\sin(\mu_n)}\cdot\exp(-\mu_n^2\frac{a\tau}{L^2})\right\}\tag{15}$$

其中,$k=Wa/L\lambda$,是加热片的热容量与试样的热容量之比,μ_n 为特征方程

$$\cot\mu = k\mu\tag{16}$$

的第 n 个正根。

当忽略加热片的热容量后,$k=0$,$\mu_n=\pi(2n+1)/2(n=0,1,2,\cdots)$,式(15)事实上就演变为式(10),经无因次化后,考虑加热片热容量时的无因次温度 $\Pi^*_{x,\tau}$ 与不考虑加热容量时的无因次温度 $\Pi_{x,\tau}$ 分别表示为

$$\Pi_{x,\tau}=1-X-\sum_{n=1}^{\infty}\frac{2\sin[\mu_n(1-X)]}{\mu_n^2(k^2\mu_n^2+k+1)\sin(\mu_n)}\exp(-\mu_n^2F_0)\tag{17}$$

$$\Pi_{x,\tau}=1-X-\sum_{n=1}^{\infty}\frac{8\cos[(2n+1)\pi X/2]}{(2n+1)^2\pi^2}\exp\left[-(\frac{2n+1}{2})^2\pi^2F_0\right]\tag{18}$$

表 2～表 4 显示:对于所设计的试验装置,加热片的热容量对试样内温度场的影响是不容被忽视的。当测点离加热片的距离过小,如 x_1 小于 0.03m,容易受材料不均匀性的影响;当测点离加热片的位置超过 0.09m 时,加热片对测点温度的影响很不稳定,这说明测点与加热片的距离应当适中。同时,观测时间离开始加热时间越近,误差也越大,最大误差发生在导温系数最小、观测时间最短的情况($\theta^*/\theta=0.63$)。进一步研究发现:对表 2所选的时间范围内,当测点离加热片的位置不超过 0.09m 时,θ^*/θ 总是小于 1。所以,不考虑加热片的影响,用本文设计的试验装置,按式(2)计算的 λ^* 值要比混凝土实际的 λ 值大;相反地,按式(2)计算的 a^* 值要比混凝土实际的 a 值小(表 2 中的黑体字即为实际测点对应的温度比值)。因此,需要对加热片的热容量问题进行修正。当测点位置

表 2 加热片热容量对不同时间、不同位置无因次温度场的影响(1)

($k=0.7,a=3.2\times10^{-3}\text{m}^2/\text{h}$)

x (m)	τ=0.5(h)			τ=1.0(h)			τ=1.5(h)		
	θ^*	θ	θ^*/θ	θ^*	θ	θ^*/θ	θ^*	θ	θ^*/θ
0.030	0.070 5	0.097 0	0.726 7	0.138 0	0.173 9	0.796 3	0.194 7	0.235 5	0.826 8
0.045	0.044 6	0.062 1	**0.717 5**	0.102 2	0.130 3	**0.784 5**	0.153 7	0.187 6	**0.819 3**
0.060	0.027 2	0.037 8	0.718 1	0.074 1	0.095 4	0.776 7	0.119 6	0.147 2	0.812 2
0.090	0.009 6	0.012 2	0.789 6	0.036 4	0.047 5	0.767 3	0.069 1	0.086 4	0.799 6
0.120	0.003 7	0.003 4	1.076 8	0.016 4	0.021 3	0.771 7	0.037 4	0.047 4	0.790 0
0.150	0.001 4	0.000 7	1.922 7	0.006 8	0.008 6	0.798 7	0.018 8	0.023 9	0.784 4

一定($x_1=0.045$m)时,对本文的试验装置,修正公式为[9]

$$a = 1.1a^* \tag{19}$$

$$\lambda = 0.87\lambda^* \tag{20}$$

应用式(19)、式(20)修正加热片热容量引起的误差见文献[9]。

表3 加热片热容量对不同时间、不同位置无因次温度场的影响(2)

($k=0.7, a=2\times3.2\times10^{-3}\text{m}^2/\text{h}$)

x (m)	$\tau=0.5$(h)			$\tau=1.0$(h)			$\tau=1.5$(h)		
	θ^*	θ	θ^*/θ	θ^*	θ	θ^*/θ	θ^*	θ	θ^*/θ
0.030	0.138 0	0.138 0	0.793 6	0.244 4	0.288 3	0.847 8	0.329 7	0.377 2	0.873 9
0.045	0.102 2	0.102 2	**0.784 5**	0.200 1	0.237 7	**0.841 6**	0.281 1	0.323 4	**0.869 3**
0.060	0.074 1	0.074 1	0.776 7	0.162 0	0.193 9	0.835 4	0.237 8	0.275 0	0.864 8
0.090	0.036 4	0.036 4	0.767 3	0.102 4	0.124 3	0.823 8	0.165 6	0.193 5	0.855 9
0.120	0.016 4	0.016 4	1.771 7	0.061 4	0.075 5	0.813 4	0.110 3	0.130 1	0.847 8
0.150	0.006 8	0.006 8	1.798 7	0.034 3	0.042 6	0.804 7	0.068 2	0.081 2	0.840 9

表4 加热片热容量对不同时间、不同位置无因次温度场的影响(3)

($k=0.7, a=0.5\times3.2\times10^{-3}\text{m}^2/\text{h}$)

x (m)	$\tau=0.5$(h)			$\tau=1.0$(h)			$\tau=1.5$(h)		
	θ^*	θ	θ^*/θ	θ^*	θ	θ^*/θ	θ^*	θ	θ^*/θ
0.030	0.030 4	0.047 7	0.637 4	0.070 5	0.097 0	0.726 7	0.106 0	0.138 1	0.767 4
0.045	0.013 8	0.021 9	**0.630 5**	0.044 6	0.062 1	**0.717 5**	0.074 2	0.097 9	**0.757 7**
0.060	0.005 9	0.008 2	0.728 6	0.027 2	0.037 8	0.718 1	0.050 5	0.067 3	0.750 9
0.090	0.003 4	0.001 4	2.413 8	0.009 6	0.012 2	0.789 6	0.021 6	0.028 7	0.753 5
0.120	0.003 7	0.002 3	1.629 1	0.003 7	0.003 4	1.076 8	0.008 5	0.010 7	0.798 2
0.150	0.001 1	0.000 5	2.292 2	0.001 4	0.000 7	1.922 7	0.003 2	0.003 4	0.928 6

5 对有效测试时间 $\tau_{\lim}$ 的界定

按照半无限平面的假设,在整个试验过程中,辅助试件上表面不能有温度变化。假设在 $\tau=\tau_{\lim}$ 时控制加热片温升不超过100℃,辅助试件上表面的温升不超过0.5℃,那么,由式(2)有

$$\frac{0.5}{100} = \sqrt{\pi}\,\mathrm{ierfc}\left(\frac{x_1+\delta}{2\sqrt{a\tau_{\lim}}}\right) \tag{21}$$

由 $\phi\sim\mathrm{ierfc}(\xi)$ 关系,得

$$\frac{0.22}{2\sqrt{a\tau_{\lim}}} = 1.545 \tag{22}$$

所以

$$\tau_{\lim} = 0.005\,1/a \tag{23}$$

就本文设计的试验装置,对于导温系数较大的混凝土材料,$\tau_{\lim}$ 约为80min,对于导温系数

一般的混凝土材料，$\tau_{\lim}$在120min左右。实际操作时，连续在30～115min内，每隔5min读数一次，最后以17个测点的计算平均值作为该混凝土的试验值。

6 温度测点布置

从表2～表4中可以看出，当测点离加热片的距离加大时，加热片热容量引起的试验误差将增加。所以，主试件厚度不宜超过60mm。由于所用试件尺寸较大，虽然已经制造了一批专用试模，但仍然难以确保主辅试件的接触面完全平整，即使是采取了“人工对磨”措施，测试点也应以布置在主试件之内为好。另一方面(见图2)，测点也不能离加热片太近。因为，当$\xi \leqslant 0.3$时，由厚度因素引起的误差将显著加大，所以测点布置在离加热片45～50mm的地方最为合适。考虑到需要在同一试件上完成传热物性参数与传质物性参数的联合试验，所以，选择$x_1 = 0.045$m，当$x_1 = 0.045$m时，整个温度测量过程中，ξ的近似值基本在图2允许范围之内。不然，当$\xi \geqslant 0.6$之后，ϕ的测量误差在反求ξ时将显著放大。

7 试验误差的总体分析

如果热源功率完全不变，测试开始前各试样温度分布均匀且数值相等，按公式(5)测定导温系数a的最大相对误差将是

$$\left|\frac{\Delta a}{a}\right| = 2\left|\frac{\Delta x_1}{x_1}\right| + 2\left|\frac{\Delta \xi_{x_1}}{\xi_{x_1}}\right| + \left|\frac{\Delta \tau_{x_1}}{\tau_{x_1}}\right| \tag{24}$$

式中：$|\Delta x_1/x_1|$为布点位置偏离误差；$|\Delta \tau_{x_1}/\tau_{x_1}|$为时间记录误差；$|\Delta \xi_{x_1}/\xi_{x_1}|$为无因次时间的相对误差。

一般规格的手表的精度大约为0.05s，人工操作误差0.1s，在几十分钟的过程中，$|\Delta \tau_{x_1}/\tau_{x_1}|$完全可以忽略不计。本次试验的尺寸很大，试模难免有些变形，试样表面不可能很平整，预留孔的位置也有一定的误差，所以$|\Delta x_1/x_1|$的精度很难控制在2%以内。因此，要使$|\Delta a/a| \leqslant 10\%$。那么，必须设法使$|\Delta \xi_{x_1}/\xi_{x_1}| \leqslant 3\%$。事实上，由式(4)有

$$\Delta \xi_{x_1} = \frac{d\xi_{x_1}}{d\phi}\Delta\phi = \frac{1}{\frac{d}{d\xi_{x_1}}\left[\sqrt{\pi}\,\mathrm{ierfc}(\xi_{x_1})\right]}\Delta\phi = \frac{1}{(\sqrt{\pi})\mathrm{erfc}(\xi_{x_1})}\Delta\phi \tag{25}$$

也就是

$$\frac{\Delta \xi_{x_1}}{\xi_{x_1}} = \frac{\phi}{\xi_{x_1}(\sqrt{\pi})\mathrm{erfc}(\xi_{x_1})}\frac{\Delta\phi}{\phi} = \frac{\mathrm{ierfc}(\xi_{x_1})}{\xi_{x_1}\mathrm{erfc}(\xi_{x_1})}\frac{\Delta\phi}{\phi} \tag{26}$$

τ_0，τ_{x_1}的误差可以忽略不计，按ϕ的定义有

$$\xi_{x_0} < \tau < \tau_{\lim}$$

$$\frac{\Delta\phi}{\phi} = \frac{\Delta\theta_{x_1,\tau_{x_1}}}{\theta_{x_1,\tau_{x_1}}} + \frac{\Delta\theta_{0,\tau_0}}{\theta_{0,\tau_0}} \tag{27}$$

$\theta_{x_1,\tau_{x_1}}$、θ_{0,τ_0} 是用同一块温湿表进行测量的，因此可认为 $\Delta\theta_{x_1,\tau_{x_1}}=\Delta\theta_{0,\tau_0}=\Delta\theta$，于是

$$\frac{\Delta\phi}{\phi}=\frac{\Delta\theta}{\theta_{0,\tau_0}}(\frac{\theta_0}{\theta_{x_1}}+1)=\frac{\Delta\theta}{\theta_{0,\tau_0}}\left[\frac{1}{(\sqrt{\pi})\mathrm{ierfc}(\xi_{x_1})}\sqrt{\frac{\tau_0}{\tau_{x_1}}}+1\right] \tag{28}$$

将式(28)代入式(26)，得到

$$\frac{\Delta\xi_{x_1}}{\xi_{x_1}}\Big/\frac{\Delta\theta}{\theta_{0,\tau_0}}=\frac{1}{(\sqrt{\pi})\mathrm{ierfc}(\xi_{x_1})}\sqrt{\frac{\tau_0}{\tau_{x_1}}}+\frac{\mathrm{ierfc}(\xi_{x_1})}{\xi_{x_1}\mathrm{erfc}(\xi_{x_1})} \tag{29}$$

式(29)右边的两项均不可能出现负值，所以，先测量 θ_0，后测量 θ_{x_1}，即维持 $\tau_0\leqslant\tau_{x_1}$ 时，将使 $\Delta\xi_{x_1}/\xi_{x_1}$ 减小。于是，当 $\tau_0\leqslant\tau_{x_1}$ 时，有

$$\frac{\Delta\xi_{x_1}}{\xi_{x_1}}\Big/\frac{\Delta\theta}{\theta_{0,\tau_0}}\leqslant\frac{1}{(\sqrt{\pi})\mathrm{ierfc}(\xi_{x_1})}+\frac{\mathrm{ierfc}(\xi_{x_1})}{\xi_{x_1}\mathrm{erfc}(\xi_{x_1})} \tag{30}$$

当 $\tau_0=\tau_{x_1}$ 时，等号成立。容易证明，当 $\xi_{x_1}=0.573$ 时，$\frac{\Delta\xi_{x_1}}{\xi_{x_1}}/\frac{\Delta\theta}{\theta_{0,\tau_0}}$ 取得极值，即

$$\min\left(\frac{\Delta\xi_{x_1}}{\xi_{x_1}}\Big/\frac{\Delta\theta}{\theta_{0,\tau_0}}\right)=2.51\qquad(\xi_{x_1}=0.573) \tag{31}$$

当 $0.3\leqslant\xi_{x_1}\leqslant0.6$ 时，$\frac{\Delta\xi_{x_1}}{\xi_{x_1}}/\frac{\Delta\theta}{\theta_{0,\tau_0}}\leqslant3.22$。因此，为使 $|\Delta\xi_{x_1}/\xi_1|\leqslant6\%$ 成立，必须使

$$\frac{\Delta\theta}{\theta}\leqslant\frac{3\%}{3.2}=0.94\% \tag{32}$$

从芬兰进口的温湿度表的温度测量精度在0.5%之内，所以，式(32)的精度是能够满足的。式(32)还说明，加大加热片的热功率，提高加热面上混凝土的温升，有助于控制试验误差。

式(5)是计算混凝土导热系数的理论依据。根据误差分析理论

$$\left|\frac{\Delta\lambda}{\lambda}\right|=\left|\frac{\Delta q}{q}\right|+\left|\frac{\Delta\theta}{\theta_{0,\tau_0}}\right|+\left|\frac{\Delta x_1}{x_1}\right|+\left|\frac{\Delta\xi_{x_0}}{\xi_{x_0}}\right| \tag{33}$$

式中：$\xi_{x_0}=\xi_{x_1}\sqrt{\tau_{x_1}/\tau_0}$；$\left|\frac{\Delta\xi_{x_0}}{\xi_{x_0}}\right|=\left|\frac{\Delta\xi_{x_1}}{\xi_{x_1}}\right|+\frac{1}{2}(\left|\frac{\Delta\tau}{\tau_{x_1}}\right|+\left|\frac{\Delta\tau}{\tau_0}\right|)$。

上述已经说明 $\frac{1}{2}(\left|\frac{\Delta\tau}{\tau_{x_1}}\right|+\left|\frac{\Delta\tau}{\tau_0}\right|)\ll1\%$，而现有万用表标定热功率的精度大约为1%，即 $\left|\frac{\Delta q}{q}\right|\leqslant1\%$，结合前文关于 $\left|\frac{\Delta\xi_{x_0}}{\xi_{x_0}}\right|=\left|\frac{\Delta\xi_{x_1}}{\xi_{x_1}}\right|\leqslant3\%$，$\left|\frac{\Delta x_1}{x_1}\right|\leqslant2\%$，$\left|\frac{\Delta\theta}{\theta_{0,\tau_0}}\right|\leqslant1\%$ 等的分析，从总体上讲，可以将混凝土导热系数的测量误差控制在7%左右。结合上述关于混凝土导温系数的分析，如果不考虑加热片热容量的影响，整个试验从原理、测试技术到成果整理的总误差大致为

$$\left|\frac{\Delta\lambda}{\lambda}\right|\leqslant7\%\qquad\left|\frac{\Delta a}{a}\right|\leqslant10\% \tag{34}$$

前面虽然用经验公式(19)、式(20)对加热片热容量引起的误差进行了修正,但公式本身的误差是难以避免的。式(19)、式(20)的计算不仅依赖对混凝土与加热片的热容量的标定,而且对混凝土的物性参数的范围进行了估计。事实上,要对加热片的热容、混凝土的热容进行标定是一件很困难的事,又涉及到相应的试验误差。所以,即使对加热片的热容量进行了修正,混凝土导温系数与导热系数的试验误差仍然应该考虑此项。理论计算已经表明,不考虑加热片热容的无因次温度的最大误差小于13%,在此,如果认为进行热容修正之后的热源误差与测试的随机误差相当,按5%考虑,那么,本次试验的综合误差应在式(35)、式(36)控制的范围,即

$$|\Delta\lambda/\lambda| \leqslant \sqrt{0.07^2 + 0.05^2} = 8.6\% \tag{35}$$

$$|\Delta a/a| \leqslant \sqrt{0.1^2 + 0.05^2} = 11.2\% \tag{36}$$

这对土木工程与水利工程中的混凝土材料试验,一般情况下,还是可以接受的。

8 加热片热功率的选择

上述分析表明,加大热源功率,既可使加热片热容效应减小,又可使温度测试的相对误差降低,有助于减少总的试验误差。但另一方面,也提高了试验本身的难度,对试验环境的要求也将更加严格,特别对含湿量较大的试样,过大的热功率将使选定的试件的有效测试时间 $\tau_{\lim}$ 缩短。因此,要综合考虑加热片热功率的选择问题。由于本试验以铜板内夹薄膜电阻丝的方式提供热功率,加热片的热容量较大(约为混凝土试样热容量的7%),因此在加热开始的前20～30min,混凝土试件所接收到的热功率并不稳定。试验中也表明,当20～30min以后,近热测点与远热测点的温度变化很有规律,说明热功率基本稳定。为保证测试的时间范围比较大,设混凝土热物性参数在正常范围内取值,按式(6),在时间 τ 变化(30～120min)的情况下,计算了一组可能的热功率值,最后综合考虑了试验的精度与难度,选定加热片的设计总功率为 $Q = 2\ 512.08$kJ,实测加热片总功率为 $Q = 2\ 524.64$kJ。

9 结语

本文采用较大尺寸的混凝土试件,构造的半无限平面试验方法,设备简单,操作方便,具有满意的试验精度。与现行的混凝土试验规程相比,具有如下优点:①可以同时测定混凝土的导温系数与导热系数;②可以测定不同含湿量的混凝土热物性;③可以降低实验室温湿度控制标准;④试验误差一般不超过10%,具有广泛的实用性。

参 考 文 献

[1] Liu Guangting, Li Penghui, Zhang Fude. *Simulating Analysis and Temperature Control for High RCC Arch Dam*. Proceeding of International Symposium on RCC Dam, Chengdu, China, 1999

[2] Jana S, Antonio C, Sousa M. *Moisture and Heat Flow in Concrete Walls Exposed to Fire*. Journal of Engineering Mechanics, 1993, 120(10):2028～2043

[3] Christopher H, Hoff W D, Skeldon M. *The Sorptivity of Brick: Dependence on the Initial Water*. Journal

of Phys. D Appl. phys, 1983(16): 1875～1880
[4] Paul U J. *Plastic Shrinkage Cracking and Evaporation*. ACI. J, 1998, 95:365～375
[5] 朱伯芳.大体积混凝土温度应力与温度控制.北京:中国水利水电出版社,1999
[6] 柴军瑞.混凝土坝渗流场与温度场耦合计算的数值方法.水力发电学报,2000(1):48～55
[7] 孙宁,杜小兵.智能湿度测量仪.武汉水利电力大学学报,1999(1):56～58
[8] 王补宣,任泽霈.利用平板导热仪测定热缘材料导温系数的探讨.工程热物理学报,1981(8):262～268
[9] 王补宣.常功率平面热源法加热片热容量的影响.工程热物理学报,1983(1):38～43

混凝土湿热传导与湿热扩散特性试验研究(Ⅱ)

——试验成果及其分析

摘　要　利用5组组合试件,测试了不同含湿状态下混凝土的导温系数,并采用原理部分的公式对实测结果进行了修正;用修正后的混凝土热物性参数,计算了试验条件下主测点与加热面上的温度变化过程。试验表明计算值与实测值吻合良好,误差在6%以内。由本试验方法得到的饱和混凝土试件的导温系数为干燥试件导温系数的1.6倍。

关键词　相对温度　混凝土　导温系数　导热系数　热容修正

1　不同湿度混凝土试件的制备

以表1所示的配比,制作了400mm×400mm×60mm(A)、400mm×400mm×160mm(B)、400mm×400mm×220mm(C)混凝土试件各5个,分为5组(每组A、B、C试件各1个):第一组拆模后在室内静置7d后放入干燥箱干燥;第二组拆模后置于室外大气环境;第三组拆模后置于养护室($RH=80\%$,$t=20℃$)内养护;第四组置于室内潮湿环境(表面有保护);第五组拆模后放入水中养护。

表1　混凝土配合比($d_{max}=20$mm)

水灰比	试件	水(kg/m³)	水泥(kg/m³)	砂子(kg/m³)	石子(kg/m³)
0.6	5组×3个	180	300	677	1 255

对于干燥箱中的试件,设定恒定的加热温度(80℃),加热约12d,然后关掉电源,让其在干燥箱中自然冷却。冷却5d后,打开干燥箱,测量厚度最大的试件中部的相对湿度。如果RH小于10%,就认为A、B、C组件内部水分已经完全干燥,否则,继续加热,直至满足要求。打开干燥箱的密封门,到安装好试件,到正式加热测量,直至试验结束,时间不超过5h。其中3h用于平衡温湿度计的响应时间,2h用于加热测量。

对于超饱和试件,拆模后就放在水箱中养护。试验前2d从水箱中搬出,周围罩上潮湿的布袋,静置于水箱旁,其目的是为了除去试件表面的明水,又使其表面保持潮湿状态,温度也基本不变。试验前3h将温湿度计探针插入预留孔。由于试验环境的湿度及温度与环境的温湿度差别显著(试验环境温度基本在22℃上下波动,幅度不超过1℃,相对湿度在25%上下波动,幅度不超过2%,而水箱中的温度基本维持16℃不变,探针插入混凝土3h后混凝土湿度基本不变,一般稳定在100%～105%)。一旦把试件搬入实验室,立即开始试验,以尽量保持试件内部温度的均匀性。

混凝土在拆模后,内部的相对湿度基本为100%,对第四组试件,拆模后立即开始试

本文选自《三峡大学学报(自然科学版)》2002年第2期,作者还有黄达海。

验比较妥当。但考虑要屏蔽早期水化热的影响，仍需要将试件放入潮湿环境静置一段时间，并在此期间对其表面进行保护。将养护室的相对湿度设定为80%，温度设定为20℃，即可在拆模后进行第三组试件的养护。第二组试件的准备比较复杂，首先放在室外进行干燥试验，待中心点湿度下降到60%后，搬入养护室养护，并同时进行湿度监测，试验安排在中心点湿度开始变化之前进行。

试验前，对加热片的热功率进行了实测，其比热与密度是从文献[1]中查出的。在确定由于加热片热容影响而采用的修正公式(21)、公式(22)时，需用到混凝土的导温系数与导热系数，而这两个参数正是待求的。实际应用时，均以修正前试验值的平均值代入。

2 试验数据的有效范围

图1是相对湿度为100%试件的升温过程与降温过程。监测面温度的测量非常关键。当监测面温度开始上升时，说明试件已与环境进行了热交换，装置已不在半无限平面原理所要求的范围了，应该立即停止加热。从图1中可以看出，在加热前期，热面温度上升非常迅速，而混凝土主测点的温度具有明显的滞后；大约15min之后，热面温升与主测点温升均处于调整状态，30min后，二者的升温速度基本接近。所以，有效记录应以30min（包括30min）以后为准。

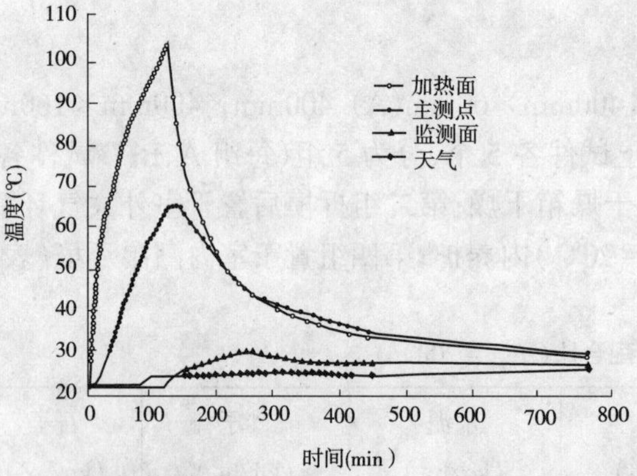

图1 加热与自然冷却过程中各点的温度过程

根据试验过程与表2记录，可以看出：

(1)不同含湿状态下的混凝土试件均能获得比较宽裕的观测时间。从开始加热，到辅助试件上表面开始产生温度变化，加热时间均在2h左右（超饱和状态试件最短，约105min；干燥试件时间最长，约155min）。为了方便比较，在计算混凝土的导温系数与导热系数时，均取30～105min时段内15个测点的平均值。

(2)不同含湿状态混凝土试件的升温过程有较大的差别。总的说来，干燥试件热表面升温快，饱和试件热表面升温较慢。

(3)在加热过程中，不同试件内部湿度变化规律比较复杂。有的基本没有湿迁移（如超饱和试件），有的变化明显（如 $RH=80\%$，$RH=60\%$时），有的呈现逐步干燥的趋势（$RH=100\%$时），有的则湿分逐步增加（如 $RH=10\%$）。

(4)加热片热容量的影响比较严重。刚开始加热的前0.5h，加热片热容的存在，使试件热面温度受到很大影响，在此以后，加热片热容的影响减弱，热面温升与主测点温升均呈现良好的规律性。因此，在数据整理时，以开始加热后0.5h到停止加热的这段时间为准。

表2　不同试验组的温度过程与湿度过程

时间	$RH=10\%$			$RH=60\%$			$RH=80\%$			$RH=100\%$			$RH>100\%$		
(min)	θ_{0,τ_0}	$\theta_{x_1,\tau_{x_1}}$	RH	θ_{0,τ_0}	$\theta_{x_1,\tau_{x_1}}$	RH	θ_{0,τ_0}	$\theta_{x_1,\tau_{x_1}}$	RH	θ_{0,τ_0}	$\theta_{x_1,\tau_{x_1}}$	RH	θ_{0,τ_0}	$\theta_{x_1,\tau_{x_1}}$	RH
5	15.5	0	11.4	15	0	61.7	12	0.6	79.4	13	0.2	101.9	12.8	0.3	104.4
10	27	0.7	11.8	24	0.7	62.8	20	1.6	80.1	21	1.4	101.9	20.9	1.5	104.3
15	34.5	2.5	12.5	29	2.2	63.6	25	3.5	81.5	26	3.4	101.7	25.8	3.6	104.8
20	39.5	4.9	13.2	34	4.0	64.7	29	5.7	82.6	30	5.7	101.5	29.4	6.0	104.1
25	44.5	7.4	13.8	40	6.9	65.9	32	8.2	83.0	33	8.1	101.1	32.8	8.8	104.8
30	49	10.3	14.5	43	9.4	66.5	35	10.6	83.8	37	11	100.5	36.5	11.4	104.3
35	52.5	13.2	15.1	47	12.0	67.0	38	12.6	84.2	40	13.4	100.5	39.5	13.9	104.7
40	56	16.2	15.7	50	14.4	68.2	40	15.2	85.0	42	15.7	100.4	41.3	16.5	104.3
45	59.5	18.7	16.3	53	17.9	69.4	43	17.6	86.4	45	18.3	99.9	44.5	18.7	104.6
50	63	21.2	16.8	55	19.1	70.5	46	19.6	87.1	48	21.0	99.4	47.0	21.3	103.6
55	65.5	23.6	17.3	58	21.4	71.0	48	21.2	88.0	50	23.3	99.1	49.5	23.7	103.6
60	68	26.1	17.8	60	23.5	72.1	50	22.9	88.5	52	25.6	98.8	51.0	25.9	103.0
65	70	28.1	18.2	62	25.1	73.3	51	24.2	90.3	55	28.3	98.5	53.9	28.7	103.2
70	72.0	30.2	18.6	64	27.5	74.9	53	25.8	92.3	57	30.2	98.3	55.9	30.5	104.0
75	74.0	32.2	18.9	66	29.3	76.0	55	27.8	93.5	58.5	31.5	98.2	57.7	31.8	104.9
80	75.5	34.2	19.2	68	31.3	77.0	56	28.9	94.2	60	32.9	98.0	58.9	33.7	104.0
85	77	36.2	19.5	70	33.1	78.8	57	30.2	95.4	61.5	34.8	98.0	60.8	35.9	104.6
90	79.5	38.2	19.7	72	34.7	80.0	59	31.5	96.4	63	36.4	97.9	62.0	37.0	104.5
95	81	40.0	19.9	73	36.5	81.9	61	32.7	96.9	64.5	37.8	97.8	62.7	38.4	103.5
100	83	41.6	20	75	38.9	83.3	62	34.1	97.3	65	38.9	97.7	63.8	39.6	104.7
105	84.5	43.1	20.2	76	39.3	85	63	35.2	97.9	66.5	39.9	97.8	64.5	40.2	103.7
110	86	44.5	20.3	78	40.2	88.9	65	26.3	98.2	66.9	40.3	97.7	—	—	—
115	88.0	45.9	20.4	79	41.8	90.2	66.5	27.6	98.5	—	—	—	—	—	—

3　混凝土的导温系数与导热系数

按前文所述的原理,整理了各组试件的导温系数与导热系数,其结果见表3。分析表3可知:

(1)各组试件的 ξ_{x_1} 值基本处于0.3~0.6之间,保证了试验的精度在原理部分所要求的范围之内。

(2)各组试件的混凝土导温系数与导热系数的一致性比较好,最大的离差系数 $C_v=8.16\%$。这说明在30~105min时段内,任取一个时间测量混凝土的 θ_{0,τ_0}、$\theta_{x_1,\tau_{x_1}}$,都可以取得较好的试验结果。

(3)含湿量(相对湿度)RH 的80%附近,混凝土的导温系数与导热系数的变化均比较大。因此,对大坝上游面混凝土而言,无论是计算其寒潮袭击,还是日照影响,导温系数与导热系数的取值,都要与其他部位的混凝土区别对待。

(4)超饱和状态下的混凝土的导温系数与导热系数分别是干燥状态下混凝土导温系数、导热系数的 1.64、1.62 倍。

表 3 各组试件的导温系数 a(m^2/h)与导热系数 λ(4.186 8kJ/(m·h·℃))

项目	$RH=10\%$		$RH=60\%$		$RH=80\%$		$RH=100\%$		$RH>100\%$	
	a	λ	a	λ	a	λ	a	λ	a	λ
修正前	0.002 5	3.562 9	0.002 57	3.976 8	0.003 5	5.625 3	0.004 1	5.782 4	0.004 2	5.788 5
修正后	0.003 25	2.850 3	0.003 34	3.181 4	0.004 6	4.500 2	0.005 3	4.625 9	0.005 5	4.638 8
C_v	3.96%	2.14%	4.08%	3.88%	3.63%	4.41%	8.16%	4.78%	7.44%	4.11%
ϕ_{max}	0.520 1		0.524 1		0.565 7		0.605 5		0.612 0	
ϕ_{min}	0.254 6		0.258 4		0.333 3		0.335 3		0.335 6	
$\xi_{x_1,max}$	0.618 0		0.612 0		0.513 0		0.511 0		0.510 2	
$\xi_{x_1,min}$	0.323 0		0.320 0		0.285 0		0.253 0		0.252 1	

4 考虑加热片热容量影响后混凝土导温系数与导热系数的修正

前文中已经分析过加热片对混凝土温度场的影响,并给出了相应的修正公式。对表 2中的试验结果,按公式(21)、公式(22)对上面 5 组数据进行修正,得到的结果如表 3 所示。由于公式(21)、公式(22)中的系数是固定不变的,因此不同含湿状态下混凝土的导温系数与导热系数的比并不改变。修正后的导温系数的图形显示见图 2。

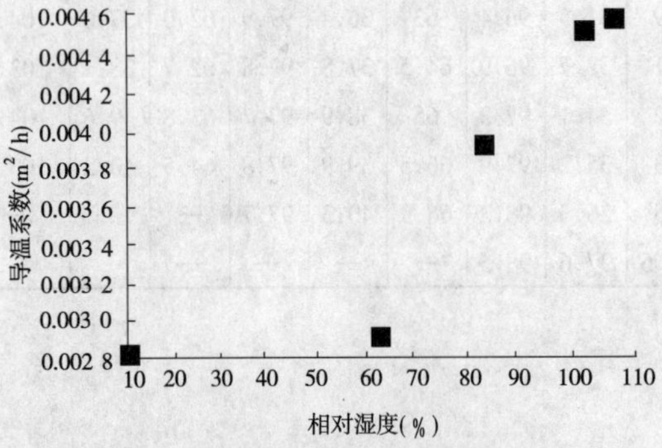

图 2 混凝土相对湿度与导温系数关系

5 预测温度与实测温度的对比

对混凝土导温系数与导热系数进行修正后,利用公式(2)对试验结果进行预测。预测值与实测值的比较见图 3、图 4,修正后主测点温度的计算值与实测值相近,最大误差不超过 6%。

图 3、图 4 中还有两个比较明显的特征:其一,对不同含湿量的试件,预测结果的误差也不一致。对含湿量大的试件,不论热面,还是主测点,拟合的效果始终不理想;其二,预测值在多数情况下略低于实测值。

同时,从图 2 中可以看出:当混凝土的含湿量 $RH<60\%$时,导温系数基本没有变化,说明气体的迁移对热传导速度的贡献有限,导热系数的大小主要受控于混凝土中的干燥孔隙,这与文献[2]的研究结果一致;当混凝土的含湿量 $RH>60\%$时,导温系数变化剧烈,说明非饱水孔隙已经基本连通,干燥孔隙的数量大大减少,气体迁移量达到一定规模;当 $RH>100\%$以后,气体迁移量又显著下降,导温系数的增加缓慢。有关其中的汽液相变机制及迁移量的计算有待进一步研究。

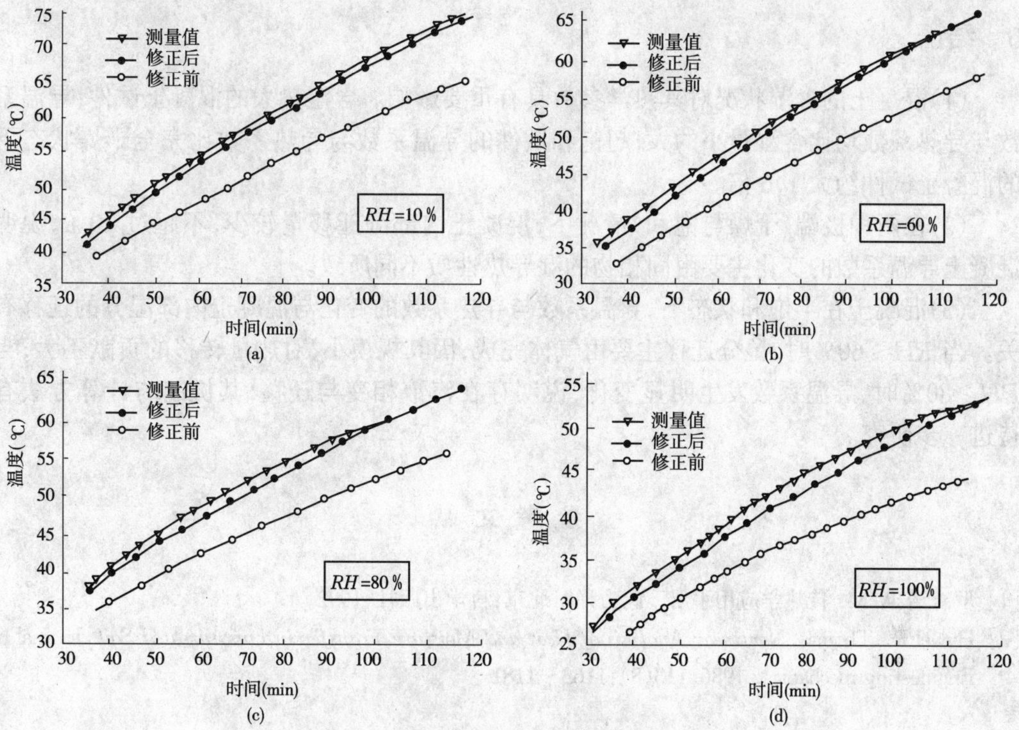

图 3 主测点实测温度与计算温度比较

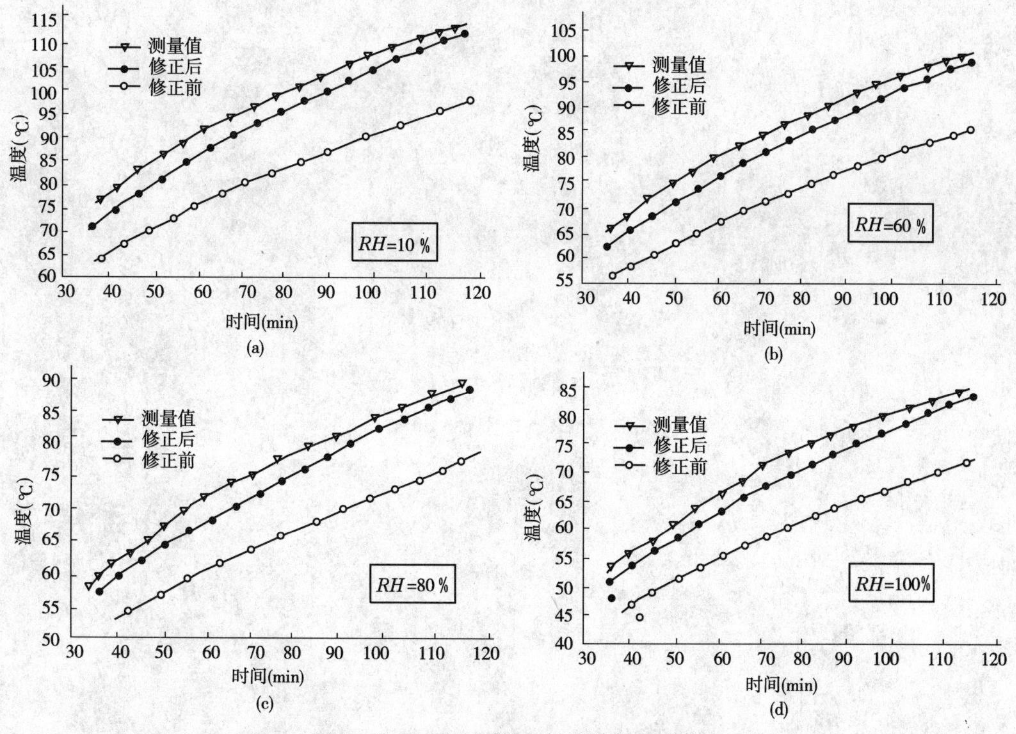

图 4 加热面实测温度与计算温度比较

6　结语

(1)混凝土的含湿状况对其热学参数具有重要影响。含湿量大的混凝土试件,导温系数与导热系数均比含湿量小的大;超饱和试件的导温系数与导热系数比完全干燥状态下的混凝土试件约大1.6倍。

(2)在两种极端(干燥与饱和)情况下,混凝土内部湿迁移量较少,不超过10%,说明混凝土导温系数的变化主要由固相物的湿导热性质不同所致。

(3)混凝土在半饱和状态下,导温系数与导热系数的变化与混凝土内部湿分的迁移有关。当 $RH \leqslant 60\%$ 时,湿分迁移主要由气体完成,因其规模小,对热量转移的贡献不大;当 $RH \geqslant 80\%$ 时,导温系数发生明显变化,说明存在汽液相变与迁移,其机制与计算方法有待进一步研究。

参考文献

[1] 罗森诺 W M. 传热学应用手册 . 谢力译 . 北京:科学出版社,1992

[2] Hywel R. Thomas. *Nonlinear Analysis of Heat and Moisture Transfer in Unsatureated Soil*. Journal of Engineering mechanics, 1986,113(8):1163~1181

混凝土等温传湿过程的试验研究

摘　要　利用 400mm×400mm×160mm 块状试件,构造了混凝土内部湿分迁移的半无限平面模型。在等温环境下,测量了第一饱和状态下混凝土向非饱和空气介质传湿的全过程。利用 Boltzmamn 变量 η,导出了混凝土湿度控制方程的常微分形式,并将其中的质扩散系数 D_m 表示为显函数,便于试验确定。研究表明:Boltzmamn 变量与混凝土的相对湿度 H 具有良好的规律性,$\eta \sim H$ 可以用四次多项式拟合;混凝土的质扩散系数严重地依赖于当前状态下的相对湿度 H,且均可以用三次多项式表达;在同一湿度条件下,碾压混凝土的质扩散系数为常态混凝土的 4~12 倍。研究成果可为混凝土表面保护与抗裂设计提供参考。

关键词　混凝土　相对湿度　Boltzmamn 变量　质扩散系数

产生混凝土表面裂缝的一个重要因素是混凝土表面的干缩应力或湿差应力。混凝土表面的湿度梯度,以及由此而产生的湿差应力,取决于混凝土的湿扩散速度。由于混凝土的湿扩散速度(以质扩散系数 D_m 表示)强烈地依赖于混凝土本身的湿度状态[1],且由于混凝土的含湿状态难以准确地测量,所以,长期以来,混凝土湿度控制方程的求解进展缓慢,混凝土的表面裂缝问题在理论上并没有得到很好的解决。本文利用混凝土内部的相对湿度 H 与混凝土的体积含湿率 ω(或重量含湿率)在一定湿度范围内的线性关系 $H = f(\omega) = K\omega + B$(见图 1)[2],在等温环境下,测试了第一饱和状态下混凝土与碾压混凝土向非饱和空气介质传湿的全过程,得到了相对湿度从 70% 到 100% 范围内,两种混凝土的质扩散系数,为进一步研究混凝土的温湿度耦合作用打下基础。

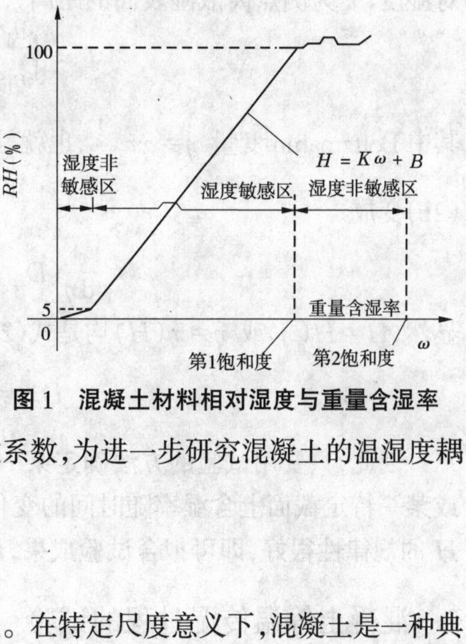

图 1　混凝土材料相对湿度与重量含湿率

1　混凝土湿度扩散方程与 Boltzmamn 变量

文献[3]研究了多孔介质温湿度耦合控制方程。在特定尺度意义下,混凝土是一种典型的多孔介质。忽略重力的影响,并将孔隙中蒸汽压力与毛细吸力转化为温度与湿度的函数后,混凝土的湿度扩散方程可以简单地表示为[3]

$$\frac{\partial \omega}{\partial \tau} = \nabla (D_m \nabla_{\omega}) + \nabla (D_t \nabla_t) \tag{1}$$

式中:D_m 为在没有温度变化的情况下混凝土湿分迁移的质扩散系数,m^2/h,它是混凝土散湿能力与保湿能力的综合表示,表明物体内部湿度趋于一致的能力,它实际上是含湿度的函数,即 $D_m = D_m(\omega)$,正是由于这一关系,使得式(1)成为了经典的非线性微分方程,

本文选自《水利学报》2002 年第 6 期,作者还有黄达海。

使理论解法几乎失去可能；D_t 为温度变化引起湿分迁移的质扩散系数，简称热质扩散系数，$m^2/(h\cdot℃)$。

为了使问题得到简化，假设介质与环境的初始温度是均匀的，且在等温环境中湿分扩散引起的混凝土温度改变可以忽略不计[3]，那么式(1)可变为

$$\frac{\partial \omega}{\partial \tau} = \nabla(D_m \nabla \omega) \tag{2a}$$

基于混凝土湿分表示的线性假定，$H = K\omega + B$，式(2a)的另一种表达式为

$$\frac{\partial H}{\partial \tau} = \nabla(D_m \nabla H) \tag{2b}$$

相应地，$D_m = D_m(\omega)$ 变成 $D_m = D_m(H)$。一种求质扩散系数的方法是 Bruce 和 Klute 在研究土壤的入渗问题时提出来的[4]。其基本思路是：在一维情况下，假定混凝土干燥前沿的推进速率反比于 $\tau^{1/2}$，那么，单位面积混凝土的累计散湿量 I 就正比于 $\tau^{1/2}$，即 $I = S\tau^{1/2}$（S 为混凝土的干燥度）。事实上，按物理意义，从 τ_0 时刻到 τ 时刻，单位面积混凝土的累计散湿量 $I = \int_{H_1}^{H_0} x\mathrm{d}H$（$H_1$ 为 τ 时刻混凝土的相对湿度，H_0 为 τ_0 时刻混凝土的初始相对湿度，x 为测点离散湿表面的距离），于是

$$I = \int_{H_1}^{H_0} x\mathrm{d}H = \tau^{1/2}\int_{H_1}^{H_0} \eta \mathrm{d}H \tag{3}$$

其中 Boltzmamn 变量 $\eta = x\tau^{-\frac{1}{2}}$，也就是 $S = \int_{H_1}^{H_0} \eta \mathrm{d}H$。根据复合函数求导规则，可将式(2b)变成

$$\frac{\mathrm{d}}{\mathrm{d}\eta}\left(D_m \frac{\mathrm{d}H}{\mathrm{d}\eta}\right) + \frac{1}{2}\eta \frac{\mathrm{d}H}{\mathrm{d}\eta} = 0 \tag{4}$$

显然，$H = H(\eta)$ 或 $\eta = \eta(H)$ 均是式(2b)的解。由式(4)经代数运算即可以得

$$D_m = \frac{-1}{2}\frac{\mathrm{d}\eta}{\mathrm{d}H}\int_{H_1}^{H_0} \eta \mathrm{d}H \tag{5}$$

因此，只要用试验的方法确定某一时刻混凝土试件中含湿率随坐标 x 的分布规律，或某一特定截面上含湿率随时间的变化规律，就可以得到 η 与 H 的离散关系。如果 η 与 H 的规律性很好，即可拟合试验成果，形成 $\eta = \eta(H)$ 的函数关系，按式(5)确定 D_m。

2　混凝土等温传湿过程的试验

图 2 为混凝土等温传湿的试验装置。混凝土与碾压混凝土试件相对而立，环境温湿度探头介于两试件的中央。4 支直径为 4mm 的温湿度探头分别插于深 200mm、直径为 5mm 的预留孔中（每个试件各预留 1 个边孔与 1 个中孔，具体位置见图 2）。试件置于钢筋混凝土平台上，台的上方设有顶面带孔的有机玻璃罩，以尽量保持试验期间试件周围的温度恒定不变。试件成型后 1d 拆模，随即置于试验平台上养护。试件的四周表面涂有一层清漆，以维持四周的绝湿边界。整个试件，尤其是两个主散湿面在养护期间以湿布覆盖，以维持混凝土表面与内部的湿度平衡。14d 后，混凝土内部的温度与环境温度基本达到平衡，试件的湿度分布基本一致，试验随即开始。为了建立混凝土相对湿度与其重量含

湿率之间的关系，试验前对两种试件称重，试验后放入干燥箱内干燥。干燥箱的温度稳定在80℃，干燥约18d后再一次称重。在称重的同时，也测量了对应状态下中孔的相对湿度。所用混凝土与碾压混凝土的配比及其试件干湿重见表1。试验成果见表2。

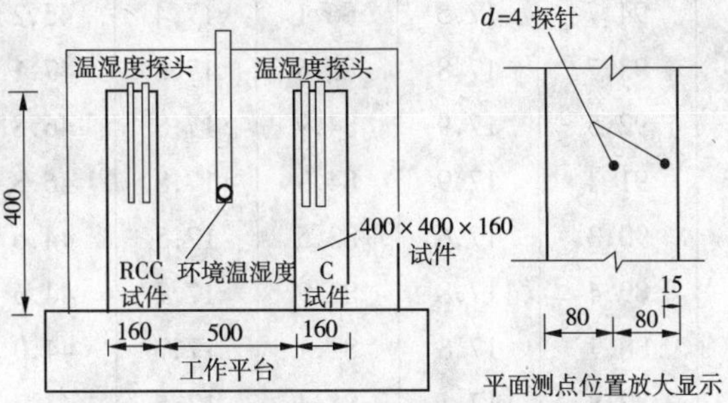

图2　混凝土等温传湿试验装置　(单位:mm)

表1　混凝土与碾压混凝土配比及其试件干湿重　(单位:kg/m^3)

材料	水	水泥	粉煤灰	砂	小石	中石	木钙	DH_9S	试件湿重(kg)	试件干重(kg)	初始湿度(%)	干燥湿度(%)
C	170.4	340.8	—	682.5	1 224	—	0.6	0.5	61.33	58.00	103.5	7.1
RCC	120.4	100.8	140.0	506.6	714	824.2	1.1	0.9	58.13	51.60	99.5	4.3

表2　混凝土准等温传湿试验成果

日期(月·日)	常规混凝土中孔湿度(%)	RCC中孔湿度(%)	常规混凝土边孔		RCC边孔		环境	
			温度(℃)	湿度(%)	温度(℃)	湿度(%)	温度(℃)	湿度(%)
3.21	103.5	99.5	23.0	103.5	23.9	97.4	23.3	19.0
3.22	103.3	99.2	22.5	103.4	22.1	93.7	22.8	30.6
3.23	104.1	99.4	23.2	103.3	23.6	89.4	24.0	27.4
3.24	103.5	99.2	23.3	103.1	23.3	86.2	24.1	24.0
3.25	103.0	99.3	23.5	102.5	23.4	78.0	23.4	19.4
3.26	102.5	99.4	22.5	101.4	22.5	73.8	23.0	23.5
3.27	102.2	99.2	22.1	99.8	22.0	69.2	23.6	22.1
3.28	102.0	99.3	22.0	98.6	22.1	64.5	22.3	22.8
3.29	101.7	99.1	22.3	96.9	22.2	59.7	24.2	22.6
3.30	101.4	99.0	23.8	95.3	23.8	54.9	22.2	26.1
3.31	101.2	98.8	22.1	93.7	21.0	51.2	20.9	22.9
4.1	101.1	98.3	19.8	92.7	18.8	48.5	19.0	26.1
4.2	100.9	98.0	19.0	91.5	18.8	48.4	19.0	29.2
4.3	100.6	97.6	18.1	90.4	18.1	46.6	18.1	28.5
4.4	100.9	96.7	17.7	89.3	17.6	45.4	17.7	28.0
4.5	100.5	96.3	17.5	88.4	17.4	45.8	17.5	32.7
4.6	100.1	95.9	17.4	87.7	17.3	45.9	17.3	39.1
4.7	99.8	95.3	17.5	86.8	17.4	45.2	17.5	37.1

续表 2

日期（月·日）	常规混凝土中孔湿度（%）	RCC 中孔湿度（%）	常规混凝土边孔		RCC 边孔		环境	
			温度（℃）	湿度（%）	温度（℃）	湿度（%）	温度（℃）	湿度（%）
4.8	100.1	94.7	17.5	86.1	17.4	45.2	17.5	37.1
4.9	100.0	93.7	17.8	85.6	17.6	47.1	17.7	31.5
4.10	100.4	92.5	17.9	84.9	17.8	46.8	17.9	38.4
4.11	100.0	91.4	17.9	84.9	17.8	46.8	17.9	38.4
4.12	100.3	90.3	17.6	83.5	17.5	44.6	17.6	37.4
4.13	100.0	89.4	17.8	82.9	17.7	44.6	17.8	36.2
4.14	100.1	88.7	17.8	82.1	17.7	44.0	17.8	35.5
4.15	99.9	87.8	17.1	81.4	17.5	43.2	17.1	36.5
4.16	99.8	86.1	17.1	80.6	17.0	43.0	17.7	36.7
4.17	99.9	85.6	17.2	79.8	17.1	42.8	17.5	35.5
4.18	99.8	84.9	18.1	79.4	18.0	44.7	18.1	34.1
4.19	99.2	83.9	18.4	79.1	18.3	47.7	—	—
4.20	99.8	83.5	18.2	78.5	18.1	47.2	18.2	40.2
4.21	99.7	82.9	17.4	77.2	17.4	44.8	17.5	37.0
4.22	99.9	82.1	17.4	76.4	17.5	40.7	17.4	38.1
4.23	99.7	81.3	17.5	75.7	17.3	42.9	17.4	39.1
4.24	99.5	80.6	17.2	74.7	17.2	41.1	17.2	33.2
4.25	99.1	80.0	17.3	73.8	17.2	40.2	17.3	43.3
4.26	98.4	79.7	17.4	73.0	—	—	17.4	53.4
4.27	98.0	79.5	17.8	72.5	—	—	17.8	39.8
4.29	97.6	69.0	17.9	72.2	17.8	47.0	17.9	38.8
5.1	96.9	78.3	18.4	71.9	18.4	41.9	18.4	39.4
5.3	96.5	77.7	18.5	71.4	18.6	43.8	18.5	47.5
5.5	96.1	77.0	18.3	70.6	18.4	39.6	18.3	49.0
5.7	96.1	76.6	18.6	69.9	18.5	45.9	18.7	53.0

从表 2 中发现：设计环境温度为 20℃，实测环境温度最高 24.2℃，最低 17.1℃；实测混凝土与碾压混凝土边孔温度均随气温作微小波动，表明试验基本在等温环境中进行，同时也证明对耦合方程式(1)作近似处理是可行的。为了更直观地反映两种混凝土边、中孔湿度随大气的变化情况，将表 2 中的湿度数据用图 3 表示。从图 3 可以看出：在试验开始后 35d 之内，常规混凝土中孔湿度几乎没有变化，到试验结束时，其湿度变化也很小；而碾压混凝土则不然，其中孔湿度在试验开始后 10d 就开始有变化，边孔测点的湿度在第 16d 就基本与环境湿度达到平衡了。显然，为满足一维半无限平面扩散的条件，对常规混凝土，前 35～40d 的试验数据是可用的，对碾压混凝土而言，可用数据个数将减少，多项式拟合时要作一些处理。

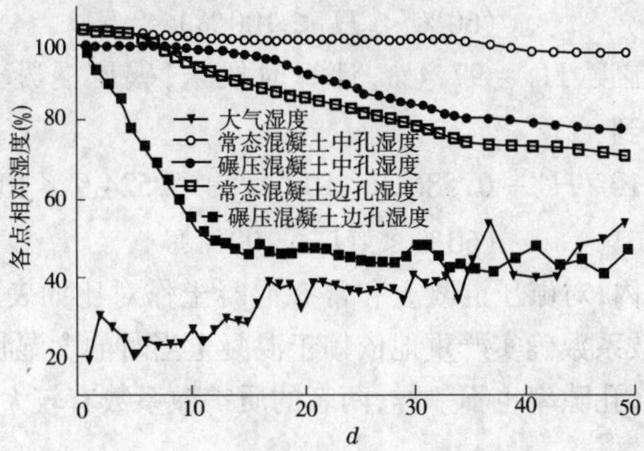

图 3 混凝土等温传湿试验结果

3 混凝土质扩散系数的确定

对于边孔,$x=0.015\text{m}$,Boltzmamn 变量 $\eta=x\tau^{-\frac{1}{2}}$ 实际上表达了一个时间因素。特定截面($x=0.015\text{m}$)的相对湿度 H 随时间因素 η 的变化规律如图 4 所示。

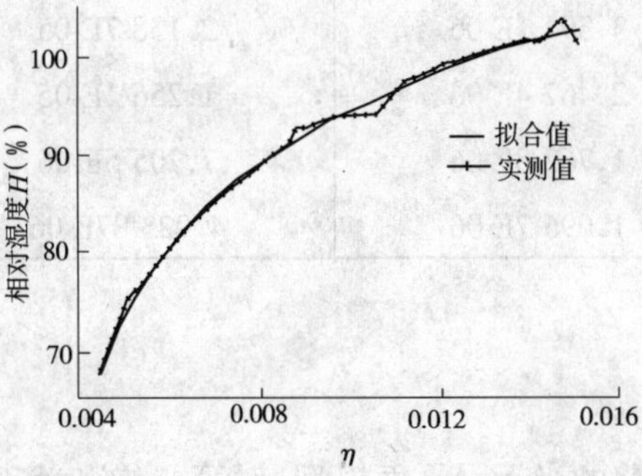

图 4 常规混凝土相对湿度 H 随时间因素 η 的变化规律

经比较,四次多项式对实测结果拟合较好,其具体表达式如式(6)。按式(5),混凝土质扩散系数应该可以表达成其相对湿度的三次多项式。混凝土相对湿度适用的范围为 70%<H<100%,环境相对湿度在 20%~50%之间。

$$\eta = 4.461\,3\times10^{-9}H^4 - 1.319\,7\times10^{-6}H^3 + 0.151\,1\times10^{-3}H^2 - 0.007\,8H + 0.155\,8 \quad (70\% < H < 100\%) \tag{6}$$

混凝土初始湿度 $H_0=103.5\%$,计算时刻末混凝土相对湿度 $H_1=70.6\%$,根据式(5)有:

$$D_m(H) = 2.448\times10^{-10}H^3 - 5.431\,8\times10^{-8}H^2 + 4.147\times10^{-6}H - 1.073\times10^{-4} \quad (70\% < H < 100\%) \tag{7}$$

对碾压混凝土,取前面 16 个(3 月 28 日以前)能够满足半无限平面要求的试验值,用四次多项式对其拟合,多项式如下:

$$\eta = 5.303\times10^{-9}H^4 - 0.775\,28\times10^{-6}H^3 + 0.010\,41\times10^{-3}H^2 + 0.002\,86H - 0.100\,21$$

$$(60\% < H < 100\%) \tag{8}$$

碾压混凝土初始湿度 $H_0 = 97.4\%$，计算时段末，碾压混凝土的相对湿度 $H_1 = 64.5\%$，由式(5)可以得到：

$$D_m^*(H) = 0.532\,8 \times 10^{-9}H^3 - 0.586\,3 \times 10^{-6}H^2 + 0.524\,9 \times 10^{-3}H + 7.211 \times 10^{-4}$$
$$(60\% < H < 100\%) \tag{9}$$

在常见的湿度范围内，对碾压混凝土和常态混凝土作对比如表 3 所示。从表 3 中可以看出，混凝土的质扩散系数确实严重地依赖于混凝土当时的含湿状态。不仅如此，由于两种混凝土的配比不同，孔隙率也不一样，两者的质扩散系数有较大的差别，湿度越大，差别也越大。

表 3　不同湿度条件下常态混凝土与碾压混凝土质扩散系数的比较

相对湿度 H(%)	常态混凝土 D_m(m^2/h)	碾压混凝土 D_m^*(m^2/h)	D_m^*/D_m
100	9.412 3E-06	11.741 2E-05	12.47
95	7.816 6E-06	7.134 6E-05	9.13
90	4.726 6E-06	3.408 6E-05	7.21
85	3.394 1E-06	2.138 7E-05	6.30
80	2.467 4E-06	1.256 1E-05	5.09
75	1.762 8E-06	7.205 5E-06	4.09
70	1.096 7E-06	4.923 87E-06	4.49

4　结语

构造了混凝土湿分迁移的半无限平面模型，对第一饱和状态下混凝土与碾压混凝土向非饱和空气介质传湿的全过程进行了测试。主要结论有：①Boltzmamn 变量($\eta = x\tau^{-1/2}$)与混凝土内部相对湿度具有良好的规律性，可以用四次多项式拟合；②两种混凝土的质扩散系数均严重地依赖于当前状态下的相对湿度，且均可以用三次多项式公式表达；③相对湿度在 70%～100%之间的常态混凝土的质扩散系数一般为 10^{-6}～10^{-5} m^2/h 量级，混凝土含湿量大时，质扩散系数也较大；④在同一内部湿度条件下，碾压混凝土的干燥速率为常态混凝土的 4～12 倍；⑤混凝土湿分迁移的温度效应与环境温湿度影响应成为下一步研究的重点。

参 考 文 献

[1] Christopher, Hall, Hoff W D. *The sorptivity of brick: dependence on the initial water content*. J. Phys. D: Appl. Phys., 1983, 16:129～135

[2] Bazant Z P, Joong-Koo Kim. *Consequence of diffusion theory for shrnkage of concrete*. Material and Structure, 1991, 24:346～349

[3] 方肇洪．测定多孔介质湿分迁移特性的积分效应法．北京：清华大学，1987

[4] Burce P R, Klute A. *The measurement of soil moisture diffusivity*. Soil Science Society, American Proceeding, 1956, 20:421～428

EXPERIMENTAL STUDY ON SURFACE CRACKING OF EARLY-AGE CONCRETE

Abstract This paper focuses on relative humidity (*RH*) and temperature (*T*) difference between the internal part and the surface of concrete caused by solar radiation and wind. An experimental model was set up with early-age concrete specimens under sun shinning, windy condition. The concrete specimens were shaped in the 400mm×400mm×160mm mold. One side of the specimen was exposed to air, while the other five sides were covered with adiabatic and impermeable material, so as to make up a semi-infinite plate model. Two groups of specimens were compared. Specimen in Group 1 was exposed to sunlight directly, and specimen in Group 2 was exposed to air but covered with a sunshield, so that the air temperature, wind velocity, as well as the relative humidity of air were nearly the same for the two groups. Hairline cracks were observed on the surface of the specimen in Group 1, but no cracks were found on the specimen of Group 2. Experimental results also indicated that both large relative humidity gradient and temperature variation did exist simultaneously in the drying zone. Evaporation rates and total weight loss during test for two groups were calculated, and the critical evaporation rate of concrete was discussed as well.

Key words moisture; temperature; early-age concrete; solar radiation; wind velocity; evaporation rate

Many factors may cause surface cracking of early age concrete[1]. Temperature stress and drying shrinkage stress are two of them that can not be ignored. From the later half of the last century, a large amount of work has been done to prevent concrete from drying cracking[2,3]. Unfortunately, surface cracks do happen in many projects all over of the world, especially for early-age concrete. As freshly placed concrete in an arid climate is exposed to hot sunlight, the water on the top will be evaporated. When the evaporation rate is greater than the rate at which water rise to the surface by bleeding, drying shrinkage of concrete occurs.

Because of bad thermal conductivity and moisture diffusivity of concrete, almost all the absorbed solar energy of the surface in sunlight is consumed in increasing the surface temperature, which in turn speeds up water evaporating[4]. In this case, the lasting time exposed to sun is very important. If the surface of fresh concrete can be protected ahead of the time when it suffers to the critical evaporating rate, surface cracks will be avoided. Practice in the Three Gorges Project in China has indicated that even in hot weather, as long as sunshield or atomization for the bin where concrete is placing is taken, much less surface cracking of concrete will happen in hot weather concreting[5]. This paper presents an experimental model to study the aforementioned phenomenon, with early-age concrete specimens under sun shinning and windy condition. Two groups of specimens with and without sunshield were com-

本文选自《应用基础与工程科学学报》2002 年第 4 期,作者还有 Huang Dahai。

pared. Experimental results indicate that both large *T* variation and *RH* gradient did exist in the sunbaked specimen, which made the surface dried and shrunk. This may be the dominant reasons for surface cracks of concrete.

1 Experimental Program

1.1 Composition of Concrete

The composite of concrete (C25) is shown in Table 1. The sand was dried natural river sand with a maximum grain size of 5mm, and the coarse aggregate was artificial one with a maximum size of 40mm. Ordinary Portland cement was used in all batches.

Table 1 Weight of the composite material (unit: kg/m^3)

Water	Cement	Sand(<5mm)	Aggregate(5~20mm)	Aggregate(20~40mm)	Water reducer
115	230	662	820	575	0.050

1.2 Test Specimens

The combined specimens were used, one of them named main specimen, and the other named assistant specimen which makes up the suitable boundary for the former. Specimens in two groups are the same. 4 pre-cast holes with metal rods in each main specimen were fixed at the exactly positions for measuring the *T* and *RH* of concrete. Before the test, all the holes were sealed by rubber rods. Five sides of the combined specimen in the test were covered by adiabatic and impermeable material, while the left one was exposed to air. The whole experimental program is presented in Table 2. The test devices are shown by Fig.1 and Fig.2.

Table 2 Experimental program

Specimens	7 days	
Cube specimen 100mm×100mm×100mm	Splitting test 2	Compression test 2
Main block specimen 400mm×400mm×160mm	Group 1 1	Group 2 1
Assistant block specimen 400×400mm×60mm	Group 1 1	Group 2 2
Prism specimen 100mm×100mm×400mm	2	

1.3 Curing

All specimens were immerged into a big box specially made for water curing of concrete after the formers were moved off. The curing water was heated by an electric heater so as to keep a uniform initial *T* field in all dimensions before test. At 6th-day, the specimens were picked up from the water and placed on a specially made plateform. The probes were inserted into the holes, which could test a more steady initial *T* and *RH* of the internal part of con-

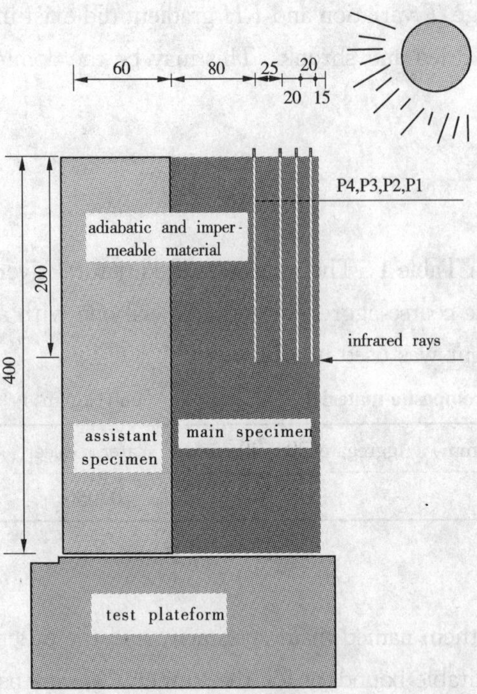

Fig. 1 **Sketch of the device**
(unit:mm)

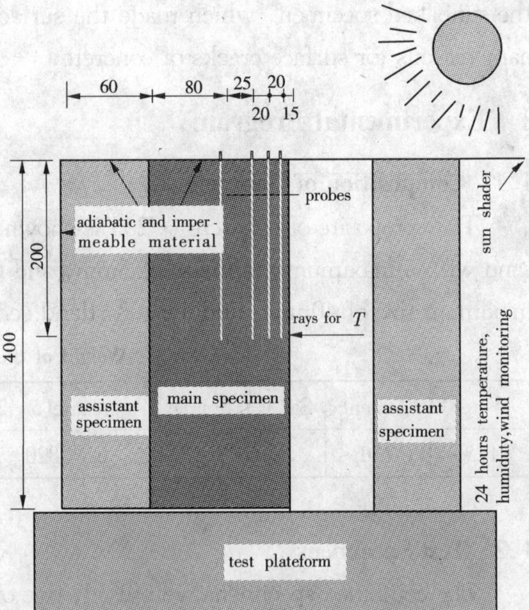

Fig. 2 **Sketch of the device without sunlight**
(unit:mm)

crete, and also eliminate the response time of the probes. Being demolded, cube specimens and prism specimens were placed in a curing room until test.

1.4 Measurement

T and *RH* of air, as well as the *T* and *RH* of inner part of concrete were recorded by 8 sensors named HMP42 with half an hour interval. The local wind velocity was recorded for two kinds of condition: one was completely open, and the other was somewhat shielded, and geographic variation of wind had been considered. Surface *T* of concrete was measured by infrared rays.

2 Experimental Results

2.1 Strength and Deformation Parameters

The basic information about the material parameters is shown in Table 3, which will be the basis to strain and stress calculation under different conditions.

2.2 *T* Variation

T processes at different positions are shown in Fig.3 and Fig.4 for the two groups specimens. In Fig.3 and Fig.4, it is found: ①The surface *T* of Group 1 changed sharply when sun was shining, but eased up quickly for cloudy time. Solar radiation could at least made the surface *T* of concrete 10℃ higher than the specimen taken shelter. ② Influenced by solar radiation, *T* of the Point 1 to Point 3 in Group 1 changed more obviously than in Group 2, especially for the Point 1 which was closer to the surface. ③ In the night, the internal T of two groups was basically uniform for all points, which implies that the T of the specimens could be thought as an uniform approximately. So if the specimens were placed outside 12 h. ahead of test, the uniform initial T could be guaranteed. ④ The farther of the position to the surface in Group 1, the lower range of the T variation was recorded, see Point 3 in Fig.3.

Table 3 Parameters of the concrete

Time	Compressive strength (MPa)	Poisson ratio	Elastic modulus (GPa)	Splitting strength (MPa)	Expansive ratio (10^{-6}/℃)
7days	20.31	0.182	21.1	1.62	8.25

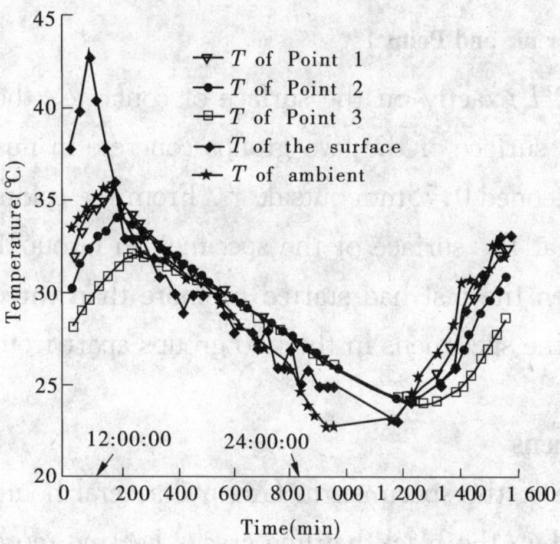

Fig.3 T variations for different positions in Group 1

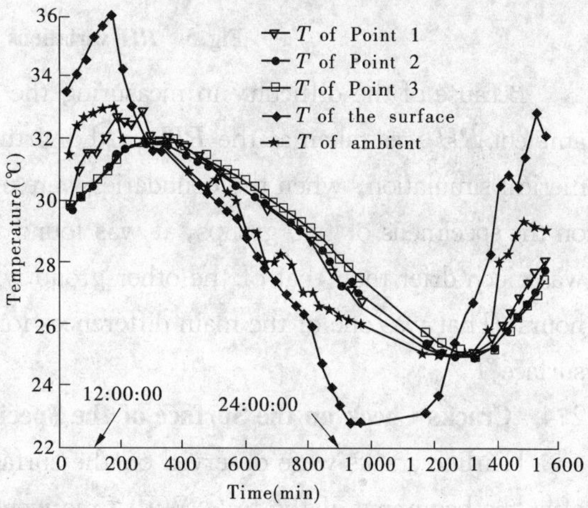

Fig.4 T variations for different positions in Group 2

2.3 *RH* Variation

Given a period of time, a part of free water of concrete in capillary pores will transform itself into water vapor and then escape out of the surface. But during a very short time, the *RH* of internal part cannot change evidently, while the *RH* on the surface may change rapidly. Especially, when the mass diffusion coefficient of concrete is very small and the mass exchange coefficient with ambient is relatively large, a great *RH* gradient may exist on a thin layer of the concrete. According to the test results in Fig.5, it can be seen: ① Although the *RH* of air was changed strongly, the *RH* of Point 1 for both groups was stable all the time, which illustrated that the evaporation process is completely focused on the surface of concrete. ② Accordingly, drying shrinkage in sunlight or shade occurs only on a thin layer on the surface of concrete. That means the drying shrinkage is quite localized, and there was definitely a huge *RH* gradient on the concrete surface.

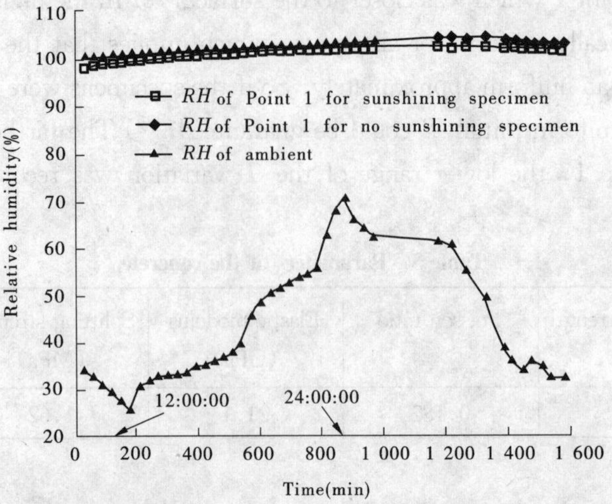

Fig.5 *RH* variations for air and Point 1

Because of the difficulty in measuring the *RH* exactly on the surface of concrete, the ambient *RH* was taken as the *RH* on the virtual surface of the two groups concrete in numerical simulation, when the boundaries were extended 0.75mm outside[2]. From the colors on the specimens of two groups, it was found that the surface of the specimen in Group 1 was much drier than that of the other group when the test had started no more than three hours. That was one of the main differences for the specimens in the two groups apart from surface T.

2.4 Cracks Check on the Surface of the Specimens

Hairline cracks were observed on the surface of the specimen in Group 1 several hours after the beginning of the test. With time went by, the black hairline cracks became more continuous, and their color changed from black to gray, and slowly to white. New cracks generated continuously until the next day, and then the cracks was formed and fixed. But nothing special was found on the surface of the specimen in Group 2. Through a careful checkup on the surfaces of the specimens in both groups when the test was finished, another three interesting phenomena were discovered: ① Water on the surface lost rapidly under solar radiation, then plastic shrinkage cracks occurred. Bleeding water from the inner part flew to the surface and carried with $Ca(OH)_2$. The later solidified in the cracks and made the color white. ② Hairline cracks occurred in the center of the surface, and less cracks were found along the circumjacent that implied a stronger restraint, such as two directions restraint, existed in the center of the surface. ③ More pores on the surface of concrete, the less cracks were found, which suggests that richer mortar will result in a flatter surface and therefore more hairline cracks because of a heavier water loss.

3 Problems Discussion

3.1 Evaluation Rate on the Surface of Concrete

Typical evaporation formula is given by Paul (1998):

$$E = (e_0 - e_a)(a + bu) \tag{1}$$

where, E is the weight (kg) of water evaporated per square meter of surface per hour ($kg/m^2 \cdot h^{-1}$), e_0 is the pressure of saturated vapor pressure at the T of the evaporating surface (kPa), e_a is pressure of air (kPa), a and b are experimental constant, and u is the average horizontal air or wind speed measured at a level about 0.5m higher than the evaporating surface (km/h).

Because of the difficulty in measuring vapor pressure, Paul[1] presented a simple formula for the T range of 10℃ to 40℃, which demonstrates a good relationship between T and vapor pressure as follow:

$$e_s = 0.61\exp[17.3T/(237.3 + T)] \tag{2}$$

where, e_s is the saturation vapor pressure (kPa), and T is temperature (℃) on the surface.

Considering air relative humidity and transferring the experimental constants, Paul found that Eq.(1) can be expressed as:

$$E = 0.313(e_{s0} - re_{sa})(0.253 + 0.06u) \tag{3}$$

where, e_{s0} is vapor pressure at concrete surface (kPa) from Eq.(2), e_{sa} is vapor pressure of air (kPa) from Eq.(2), r is RH.

In order to consider geographic variation of wind, according to Paul's suggestion, u in Eq. (3) can be simplified as:

$$u_e = 2/3(u_{std}) \tag{4}$$

where, u_e is equivalent wind velocity at 0.5m above the ground, u_{std} is wind velocity at the standard height of 10m.

Based on above formulas and the measured velocity of air duning test (see Table 4), surface evaporation rates were calculated. It shows that the evaporation rate changes with wind velocity synchronously, which imply that wind velocity is the most important factor in evaporation formula, and logically the accuracy of Eq.(4) can also significantly influent the reliability of Eq.(3). Apart from the large effect of wind velocity, other characters about evaporation rate, such as the maximum evaporation rate, minimum evaporation rate and the time-weighted evaporation rate for both groups, which are shown in Table 5, are also very important for the comparison between the two groups. If total water loss is studied, time-weighted average evaporation rate calculated is valuable to compare with average bleeding rate measured. The total water losses for both groups under different conditions are also including in Table 5.

Table 4　Characteristic T at different positions　(unit: ℃)

Item	Air	Group 1				Group 2			
		Sur.	P1	P2	P3	Sur.	P1	P2	P3
T_{max}	36.0	43.0	35.6	34.1	32.0	33.3	32.8	32.0	31.9
T_{min}	22.7	23.0	24.2	24.1	24.0	25.0	24.9	24.9	25.0
ΔT_{max}	13.3	20.0	11.4	10.0	8.0	8.3	7.9	7.1	6.9

Table 5　Wind velocity adopted　(unit: km/h)

12:30:00	19:30:00	24:00:00	7:00:00	12:30:00
24	18	36	12	18

It is also discovered that the time-weighted average evaporation rate calculated for two groups are almost the same. In Fig.4, it is found that sunlight had not sustained a long time, so the T on the surface of concrete increased quickly and fell down rapidly. The evaporated water in Group 1 was only a little more than that of the Group 2. But in the night, the evaporated water of Group 2 was greater because of the un-equilibrium time lasting longer than Group 1, so the total water loss in two groups did not differ much. Experimental results have confirmed this too.

Due to the wind velocity can change evaporation rate evidently, the trivial difference of environment between two groups can not be ignored. The front of the surface of Group 1 was open, but not so for Group 2 because of the shield, which means wind velocity for two groups could not be equal strictly. From Table 6 it can be seen that the minimum T on the surface of Group 1 is 23.0℃, which is very near to the T of air at the same time, but the minimum T on the surface of Group 2 is 25℃, 2℃ higher than air at the same time. That illustrates wind speed in Group 1 was higher than the specimen of Group 2, and it speeded up the T balance between the surface of Group 1 and air, while heat exchange between the Group 2 and air was much slower than the Group 1. On the other hand, if the difference of wind velocities between two groups is not so great, according to the experimental result (specimen in Group 1 cracked, in Group 2 did not), the reliability of Eq.(3) needs to be further proved in the future.

Table 6　Characteristics evaporation rate　(unit: $kg/m^2 \cdot h^{-1}$)

Item	Group 1	Group 2
Max. evaporation rate	1.49	1.18
Min. evaporation rate	0.15	0.34
Time-weighted average evap. rate	0.848	0.844

3.2 Plastic Shrinkage Cracking by Temperature Difference

If focus is put on the surface of the specimen (no more than 5mm), the experimental model can be approximately treated as a semi-infinite plate. Based on elastic theory, the maximum tensile stress on the surface of concrete can be approximately expressed as

$$\sigma_{max} = \frac{1\,000}{1-\mu} E\alpha\Delta T_{max} \tag{5}$$

where, σ_{max} is the maximum tensile stress on the surface of concrete (MPa), μ is Poisson rate of concrete, E is elastic modulus of concrete (GPa), α is expansive ratio (10^{-6}/℃), and ΔT_{max} is maximum T drop between surface concrete and core concrete (℃).

Actually, a clear day or a cloudy day can change the surface T rapidly. That means the T of the internal part of concrete, a few millimeters to the surface, still has no response while the T of air has changed a lot, so the ΔT_{max} in Eq.(5) can be approximately replaced by the scope of T change on the surface. If we ignore the compressive stress by T rise, based on table 6, ΔT_{max} is 20℃ for Group 1, and 8.3℃ for Group 2. Correspondingly, the maximum tensile stresses on the surfaces of concrete for Group 1 and Group 2 are 2.71MPa and 1.13MPa respectively by Eq.(5). Comparing with the splitting strength tested at 7thday in Table 3, it is very helpful to understand why the specimen of Group 1 cracked and the other group did not.

3.3 Bleeding Rate onto the Surface of Concrete

Bleeding rate onto the surface of concrete is involved in coupled heat and mass transfer in saturated and unsaturated media. Many researchers have done a great deal of work in this field. As to concrete media, Huang's work[6] is oe of the most important of them. If the T and moisture on the free surface of concrete are settled, theoretically no actual difficulty does exist in numerical method to simulate the change processes of T and moisture in the specimens following Huang's approach. But a lot of parameters related to the formulas educed by Huang are difficult to determinate in the test, such as heat transfer coefficient and mass transfer coefficient. To analyze the bleeding rate onto the surface, the mass transfer coefficient at an average level is useful. Table 7 shows the average bleeding rate $\overline{B}$ for both groups calculated by weight losses (WL) during the evaporation test.

Table 7 Water loss and average bleeding rate (unit: kg)

Item	Group 1		Group 2	
	Before test	After test	Before test	After test
Weight	62.85	61.74	62.73	61.92
WL by Test	1.11($\overline{B}$=0.267)		0.81($\overline{B}$=0.195)	
WL by Eq.(3)	7.31		7.07	

It is surprise to found that the results of total water loss calculated by Eq.(3) present a huge difference to test. Comparison between the evaporation rates with and without considering wind velocity showed that it is reasonable that the effect of wind was enlarged impractically.

3.4 Discussion

How to understand the surface shrinkage and restrained cracking of concrete mechanically, and how to provide methods to predict the likelihood of plastic cracking due to evaporation have tempted researchers for almost a century. From the later half of the last century, lots of work have been done to prevent plastic cracking in concrete. Unfortunately surface cracks still exist in many projects all over of the world. Maybe what has been ignored by us is that the surface of concrete might crack just a few hours later than it was demolded, no protecting measurements could work in time. Paul[1] has summarized the work in this area comprehensively, and has presented a serial of new and easier formulas to calculate the evaporating rate of concrete, which serves as a critical value for estimating where plastic shrinkage cracking is likely to occur, but little attention has been paid to the time. The criterion is difficult to use because the evaporation rate largely depended on the velocity that changes strongly all the time.

Two key factors affect intensively the T and moisture on the surface of concrete: one is solar radiation, and the other is wind velocity. Under approximately the same wind condition and completely different solar radiation condition, two specimens were tested and obtained an entirely different results: one was cracked, and the other was not, which remind us that drying shrinkage cracking is more complicated than estimated. Further research on this topic is necessary.

Based on the test results, especially on the total water loss, see Table 7, the effect of solar radiation carried out by Eq.(3) was probably lessened, while the effect of wind was enlarged excessively. It seems for the block specimen Eq.(3) in a whole will over-estimate the evaporation rate and a composite criterion coupled T and moisture of concrete is greatly needed.

4 Conclusions

From the experimental results and previous understanding about the behavior of early-age concrete, the following conclusions are obtained:

(1) Surface temperature of concrete changes sharply when sunlight is shining on or drifting off. Solar radiation can at least make surface temperature of concrete 10℃ higher than the case taken shelter from sunlight.

(2) *RH* of internal part concrete can not change evidently, while the *RH* on the surface may change rapidly. A huge *RH* gradient does exist in a thin layer of concrete.

(3) More pores on surface of concrete, less cracks would be observed, which suggests that richer mortar will result in more hairline cracks because of a heavier water loss.

(4) The evaporation rate changes with wind velocity synchronously. The evaporation

rates calculated are higher than the bleeding rates tested, which indicated the prevailing formula in a whole over-estimates the evaporation rate of concrete.

References

[1] Uno Paul J. *Plastic shrinkage cracking and evaporation formulas*. ACI Material Journal, 1998, 95(4): 365~375

[2] Kim J K, Lee C S. *Prediction of differential drying shrinkage in concrete*. Cement and Concrete Research, 1998, 28(7): 985~994

[3] Pittman David W, Ragen Steven A. *Drying shrinkage of roller compacted concrete or pavement application*. ACI Material Journal, 1998, 95(1): 19~26

[4] Michanel Bartlett, Macgregor James G. *Effect of moisture on concrete core strength*. ACI Material Journal, 1993, 91(3): 227~236

[5] He Gong, Dai Huichao. *Temperature control in concrete construction of the Three Gorges Project*. China Three Gorges Construction, 1998, 9(2): 21~26

[6] Huang C L D. *Multi-phase moisture transfer in porous media subjected to temperature gradient*. International J. of Heat and Mass Transfer, 1979, 22: 1295~1307

STUDY ON MASS DIFFUSIVITY OF CONCRETE UNDER ISOTHERMAL CONDITION

Abstract Mass diffusivity is one of the moisture properties of concrete, which represents the capacity of concrete scattering internal moisture to its environment. Under isothermal condition, mass diffusivity of concrete depends on micro-pore structure, initial moisture content and its spatial distribution. For early-age concrete, mass diffusivity varies strongly with moisture. Recurring to the concept of average moisture loss, the relationship between average mass diffusivity and moisture diffusion moment is educed. With average mass diffusivity instead of mass diffusivity, the transfer tendency of concrete moisture is numerically simulated. Drying rate, shrinkage strain and restrained stress based on two kinds of mass diffusion theories are compared. At last, the maximum drying stress and maximum cracked depth of massive concrete are calculated in a case study. The results indicate that the surface stress of early-age concrete is larger than estimated by linear diffusion theory, and the drying cracks concentrate in a very localized place compared with that by temperature change. That information may be useful to surface protection design of early-age concrete.

Key words concrete; mass diffusivity; initial moisture; moisture diffusion moment; free drying strain

The main reasons of surface cracking of concrete are drying stress and temperature stress[1~3]. For early-age concrete, when the former is demolded, the moisture difference between the surface and environment will be very high, and will result in great shrinkage stress. The moisture gradient on the surface of concrete and its sequential stress depends on drying rate[4] which is based on the mass diffusivity. The latter is strongly related to its moisture condition. Because the moisture condition is very difficult to measure, there is no distinct progress in solution of moisture control equation for a long time[5,6]. The surface cracking caused by drying shrinkage in engineering does exist widely.

It is known that the control equation of moisture diffusion is completely the same as the heat transfer equation of concrete assuming mass diffusivity were constant[7]. It was assumed that the mass diffusivity is about 1 200～1 600 times less than temperature diffusion coefficient under certain condition, but the process of moisture transfer is quite different from that of heat[8]. Relatively, there is less discussion on how to simplify moisture diffusion coefficient of concrete, and what is the problem brought out by simplification. This paper defines a new concept (moisture diffusion moment, MDM) for the drying shrinkage of concrete at early-age. Based on the MDM, the relationship between mass diffusivity and its average val-

本文选自《应用基础与工程科学学报》2002 年第 4 期，作者还有 Huang Dahai。

ue is educed. With average mass diffusivity instead of mass diffusivity, the transfer tendency of concrete moisture is numerically simulated. Drying rate, as well as shrinkage strain and restrained stress caused by two kinds of mass diffusion theory are compared. At last, the maximum stress and maximum cracked depth of mass volume concrete in North-China are calculated, which not only may serve as a reference to the design of surface protection of concrete, but also may be a basis for exploring the effect due to coupled temperature and moisture of early-age concrete[9].

1 Mass Diffusivity of Concrete

1.1 Nonlinear Diffusion Equation

As to the problem coupled temperature and moisture, the control equation is as follow[4]:

$$\frac{\partial \omega}{\partial \tau} = \nabla(D_m \nabla \omega) + \nabla(D_t \nabla t) \tag{1}$$

where, D_m is the mass diffusivity of concrete under isothermal condition (m^2/h). It is a function of moisture content ω, such as $D_m = D_m(\omega)$. D_t is the mass transfer coefficient by temperature gradient. Under isothermal condition, formula(1) can be simplified as:

$$\frac{\partial \omega}{\partial \tau} = \nabla(D_m \nabla \omega) \tag{2}$$

Among certain range, moisture content behaves linearly with relative humidity[6,12], such as $H = k_r\omega + B$. Then another form of Eq.(2) is as:

$$\frac{\partial H}{\partial \tau} = \nabla(D_m \nabla H) \tag{2a}$$

where, k_r and B are coefficients, which can be determined by experiments. Accordingly, $D_m = D_m(\omega)$ becomes as $D_m = D_m(H)$.

For one dimensional diffusion problem, the drying front x of concrete advances proportionally with $\tau^{1/2}$, the square root of elapsed time, so the accumulative dried volume of moisture I also changes proportionally with $\tau^{1/2}$, which can be expressed as $I = S\tau^{1/2}$. Here, S is the dried degree. From τ_0 to τ, the accumulative dried volume can be expressed as $I(x) = \int_H^{H_i} x\mathrm{d}H$ (H is the relative humidity of concrete at τ, H_i is the initial relative humidity of concrete at τ_0, x is the drying front.), so

$$I(x) = \int_H^{H_i} x\mathrm{d}H = \tau^{1/2}\int_H^{H_i} \eta \mathrm{d}H \tag{3}$$

where, Boltzmann variable is set as $\eta = x\tau^{-1/2}$, then $S = \int_H^{H_i} \eta \mathrm{d}H$. From Eq.(2a), we get:

$$\frac{\mathrm{d}}{\mathrm{d}\eta}\left(D_m \frac{\mathrm{d}H}{\mathrm{d}\eta}\right) + \frac{1}{2}\eta\frac{\mathrm{d}H}{\mathrm{d}\eta} = 0, \qquad \left(H|_{\eta\to\infty} = H_i\ \left.\frac{\mathrm{d}H}{\mathrm{d}\eta}\right|_{\eta\to\infty} = 0\right) \tag{4}$$

So, $H = H(\eta)$ or $\eta = \eta(H)$ is the solution of Eq.(2a). From Eq.(4), it arrives:

$$D_m = -\frac{1}{2}\frac{\mathrm{d}\eta}{dH}\int_H^{H_i} \eta \mathrm{d}H \tag{5}$$

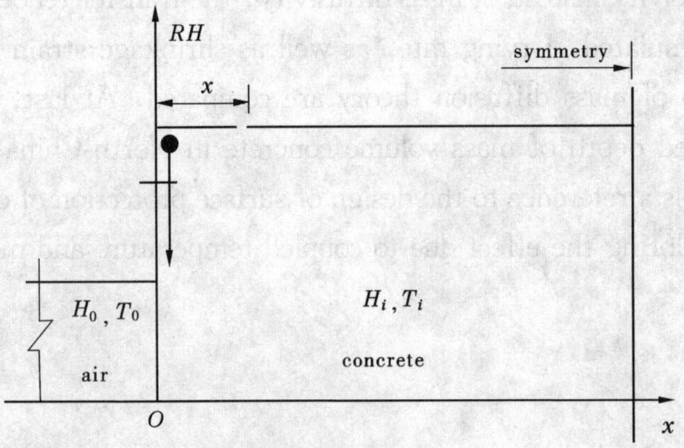

Fig. 1 Sketch of the model

1.2 $\overline{D}_m$ Educed from MDM

Take Fig. 1 as the typical model of surface drying problem of concrete, and assume environment relative humidity H_0 keeping constant, and the MDM at τ can be expressed as:

$$V(\tau) = \rho_d k_r \int_0^{\infty} (H_i - H) x \mathrm{d}x \tag{6}$$

where, ρ_d is the density of concrete at dried condition (kg/m^3), k_r is a coefficient transferring water content and relative humidity. Considering $x=0$, $H=H_0$, as well as $x=\infty$, $H=H_i$, and setting $h=\dfrac{H_i-H}{H_i-H_0}$, we have:

$$V(\tau) = \frac{1}{2}\rho_d k_r \int_{H_0}^{H_i} x^2 \mathrm{d}H = \frac{1}{2}\rho_d k_r \tau \int_{H_0}^{H_i} \eta^2 \mathrm{d}H = \frac{1}{2}\rho_d k_r (H_i - H_0)\tau \int_0^1 \eta^2 \mathrm{d}h \tag{7}$$

Defining $\overline{D}_{m,v}$ as the average mass diffusivity upon MDM, then the MDM at τ can also be expressed as:

$$V(\tau) = \rho_d k_r (H_i - H_0)\overline{D}_{m,v}\tau \tag{8}$$

Comparing Eq.(7) and Eq.(8), it has:

$$\overline{D}_{m,v} = \frac{1}{2}\int_0^1 \eta^2 \mathrm{d}h \tag{9}$$

According to Eq.(4), we have:

$$\int_0^1 \frac{1}{2}\eta^2 \mathrm{d}h = -\int_{h=0}^{h=1} \eta \mathrm{d}\left(D_m \frac{\mathrm{d}h}{\mathrm{d}\eta}\right) = -\left(\eta D_m \frac{\mathrm{d}h}{\mathrm{d}\eta}\right)\Big|_{\eta=\infty}^{\eta=0} + \int_{\infty}^{0} D_m \frac{\mathrm{d}h}{\mathrm{d}\eta}\mathrm{d}\eta = \int_0^1 D_m \mathrm{d}h \tag{10}$$

so:

$$\overline{D}_{m,v} = \frac{1}{2}\int_0^1 \eta^2 \mathrm{d}h = \int_0^1 D_m \mathrm{d}h = \overline{D}_m \tag{11}$$

It can be seen from Eq.(11), the average mass diffusivity of concrete upon MDM is equivalent to the average value arithmetically, which is sketched in Fig. 2. Another possible method to simplify the mass diffusivity is impulse function[9], see Fig. 2. No matter which simplification method is used, huge error will be involved in Eq.(2a).

2 Drying Processes and Drying Stress

2.1 Actual Mass Diffusivity

According to experimental results, when $H_0 = 30.0\%$, and $H_i = 100.0\%$, the mass

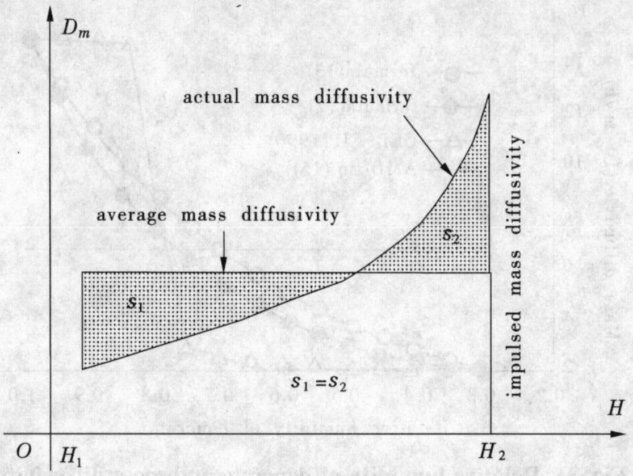

Fig.2 Average mass diffusivity upon MDM

diffusivity can be expressed as follows:

Polynomial form[10]:

$$D_m = a_3(H - H_0)^3 + a_2(H - H_0)^2 + a_1(H - H_0) + a_0 \tag{12}$$

where, $a_3 = 30.12 \times 10^{-7}$, $a_2 = 0.684\,6 \times 10^{-7}$, $a_1 = 2.738\,5 \times 10^{-7}$, $a_0 = 2.028\,5 \times 10^{-7}$.

Exponential form[10]:

$$D_m = b_1 \exp[b_2(H - H_0)] \tag{13}$$

where, $b_1 = 2.07 \times 10^{-7}$, $b_2 = 2.81$.

CEB-FIP(1990) formula[11,12]:

CEB-FIP(1990) presented another formula of mass diffusivity from $H=0$ to $H=1.0$:

$$D_m(H) = D_1 \left\{ \alpha + \frac{1 - \alpha}{1 + [(1 - H)/(1 - H_c)]^n} \right\} \tag{14}$$

where, D_1 is the maximum mass diffusion coefficient when $(H=1.0)$. D_0 is the minimum mass diffusion coefficient when $(H=0)$. H_c is the characteristic moisture content, which is set as $H_c = 0.8$ while $D_m(H_c) = 0.5D_1$. $\alpha = D_0/D_1$ is the rate of the maximum and minimum coefficient. It is assumed that $\alpha = 0.05$ for ordinary concrete. n is the increasing exponent of mass diffusivity. It is about 15.

As a matter of fact, no moisture would transfer when $H = 0$. So another form about mass diffusivity of concrete is presented in the Fig.3 among $H = 0.3 \sim 1.0$, and it is compared with formula (12) and formula (13). It can be seen that all simplified forms existed only for convenience. Actually, mass diffusivity of concrete just behaves the style with formula (14), but does not change so acutely as formula (14). So as a represent of non-linear diffusion theory, formula (13) is chosen to compare with formula (15) in simulating the drying process of concrete.

2.2 Average Mass Diffusivity (AMD)

From formula (11), $\overline{D}_m = \int_0^1 D_m(H)\,dH$, and connecting formula (13), we have

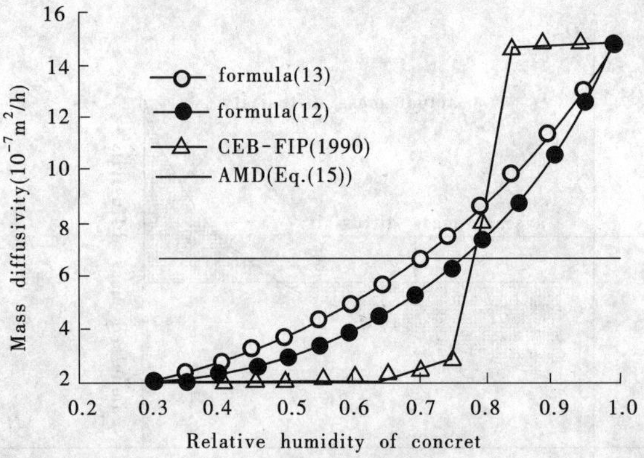

Fig.3 Relative humidity of concrete and mass diffusivity

$$\overline{D}_{m,v} = \overline{D}_m = \frac{1}{1-0.3}\int_0^1 D_m(H)\mathrm{d}H = \frac{1}{0.7}\int_{0.3}^1 b_1\left\{\exp[b_2(H-H_0)]\right\}\mathrm{d}H \quad (15)$$

By formula(15), we get $\overline{D}_m = 6.471\times10^{-7}(\mathrm{m}^2/\mathrm{h})$. According to experimental results[13], the thermal diffusivity a of saturated concrete is $5.3\times10^{-3}(\mathrm{m}^2/\mathrm{h})$, and for dried concrete is about $3.2\times10^{-3}(\mathrm{m}^2/\mathrm{h})$, they are about 5 000～8 000 times higher than the average mass diffusivity of concrete, and 3 600～15 000 times higher than the mass diffusion coefficient at the related moisture content, see Fig.3. Therefore, the mass diffusion coefficient of concrete is quite different from its thermal diffusion coefficient. When its internal temperature of inner part concrete changes, its moisture can hardly be changed synchronously. If the surface of concrete is exposed to a dry and windy environment, the restrain effect by inner part will be very strong.

2.3 Drying Processes Comparison Between Linear Diffusion and Non-linear Diffusion Theory

The linear diffusion equation can be written as:

$$\frac{\partial H}{\partial \tau} = \overline{D}_m \nabla(\nabla H) \quad (16)$$

For the isothermal drying process in Fig.1, linear and non-linear diffusion processes will be numerically simulated.

Taking the surface zone of massive concrete as an infinite plate, the initial condition and boundary condition are the same as that in Fig.1. The time step is small at early stage and is large at later stage. The grid is uniform, and the element size is 0.5mm.

Assuming the age of concrete is 7d($\tau_0 = 7$). Before drying process begins, $\tau \geqslant \tau_0$, $T = T_i = T_0$ and $H_0 = 0.3$. No wind and solar radiation are considered. Because the drying time is very long, the creep of concrete should be calculated. The most difficult problem is to determine the moisture exchange coefficient between air and concrete. According to Bazant[12], if we extend the numerical boundary 0.75mm outwards, the third kind boundary can be approximately treated as the first boundary. In this paper, Bazant's approach is used.

It can be seen in Fig.4 to Fig.6 that the non-linear equation implies a notable pattern which is dried at a very local zone near the surface of concrete. But the linear equation does not. Apart from the time scale, the drying process calculated by linear Eq. (16) is almost the same in patterns as that by temperature control formula (8). Therefore, the drying rate obtained by linear equation is smaller than that simulated by non-linear equation. If we compare the drying rate between formula(13) and formula (14), it can be seen that the drying rate by CEB − FIP(90) is faster than formula(13). See Fig.4 to Fig.6.

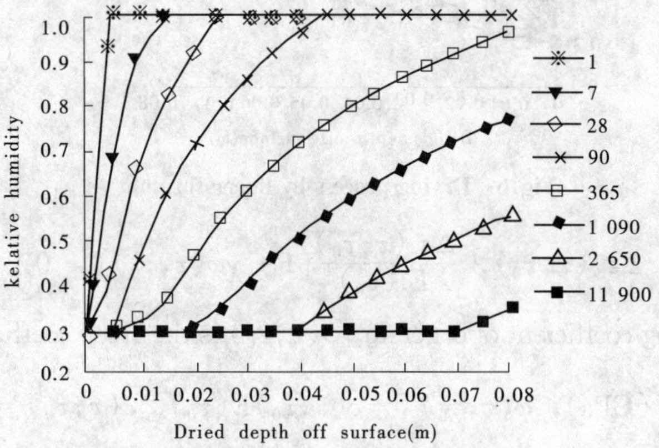

Fig.4 Drying process by non-linear theory (Eq.(13))

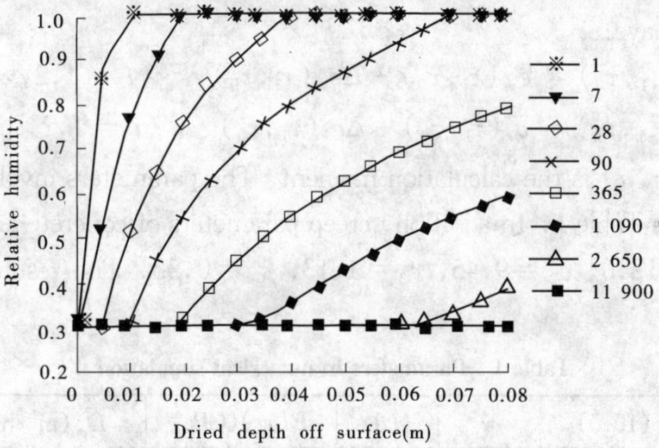

Fig.5 Drying process by CEB-FIT formula

2.4 Drying Shrinkage Strain and Stress

Supposing that the shrinkage strain is proportional to its internal moisture loss[12], then we have

$$\Delta\varepsilon_{sh}(\tau,\tau_0) = k_{sh}(1-H) \tag{17}$$

where, k_{sh} is the shrinkage coefficient of concrete. Because the drying shrinkage is inconsistent between external and internal concrete, restrained stress generates. For infinite surface, the shrinkage is completely restrained. So the strain increment by stress increment $\Delta\sigma_r(\tau,\tau_0)$ at period $(\tau-\tau_0)$ should satisfy the following formula:

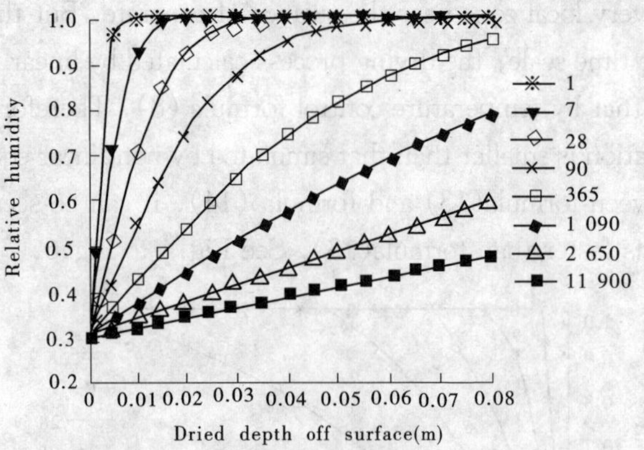

Fig.6　Drying process by linear formula

$$\Delta\varepsilon_{sh}(\tau,\tau_0)+\frac{\Delta\sigma_r(\tau,\tau_0)}{E_c(\tau_0)}[1+\chi\varphi(\tau,\tau_0)]=0 \qquad (18)$$

where, χ is the aging coefficient of concrete, $\varphi(\tau,\tau_0)$ is the creep coefficient, $E(\tau_0)$ is the elastic module at τ_0 (GPa), $\varphi(\tau,\tau_0)=c(\tau,\tau_0)E(\tau_0)$, $c(\tau,\tau_0)=\left(c_1+\frac{c_2}{\tau^{c_3}}\right)\left\{1-\exp[-c_4(\tau-\tau_0)]\right\}(10^{-6}\text{MPa}^{-1})$. By difference method, connecting formula(17),(18) to formula (2a), we have:

$$\varepsilon_{sh}(\tau_{i+1},\tau_0)=\varepsilon_{sh}(\tau_i,\tau_0)+\Delta\varepsilon_{sh}(\tau_i,\tau_0)\qquad(i=1,2,\cdots,n) \qquad (19)$$

$$\sigma_r(\tau_{i+1},\tau_0)=\sigma_r(\tau_i,\tau_0)+\Delta\sigma_r(\tau_i,\tau_0)\qquad(i=1,2,\cdots,n) \qquad (20)$$

where, $(i=1,2,\cdots,n)$ is the calculation moment. The parameters involved in the numerical simulation are as Table 1. In addition, creep parameters of concrete are picked up in reference [8], $c_1=112.0$, $c_2=9.45$, $c_3=1.13$, $c_4=0.35$. The results are expressed in Fig.7 and Fig.8.

Table 1　Parameters in numerical simulation

L(mm)	$k_{sh}(10^{-6})$	χ	τ(d)	$E(\tau_0)$(GPa)	$\overline{D}_m$(m^2/h)	D_1(m^2/h)
80	480.0	0.8	7.0	20.0	6.5×10^{-7}	1.4×10^{-6}

According to the first boundary condition, there are no differences in shrinkage strains between the linear diffusion equation and its non-linear counterpart. So the positions off surface 5.0mm, 15.0mm and 30.0mm are chosen to show the shrinkage strains and shrinkage restrained stresses.

Fig.7 indicates the free shrinkage of concrete at different positions. It can be seen that the drying strain based on linear theory is smaller than the non-linear one. At $x=5.0$mm, the response times for two theories are almost the same. When drying time is less than 3d, the free drying strain for linear formula is only slightly less than that by non-linear theory,

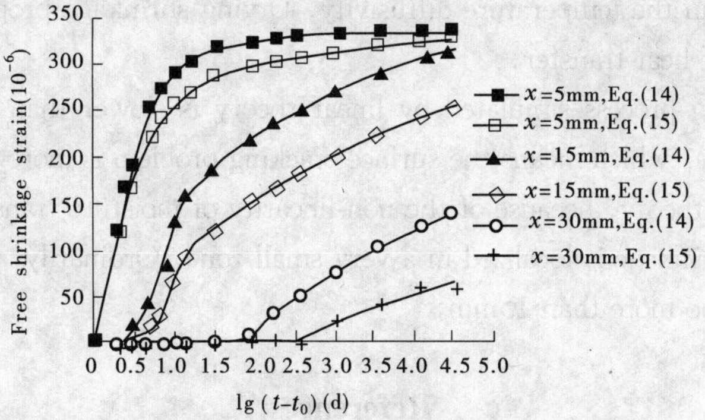

Fig.7 Shrinkage strain comp. between two theories

but when drying time goes to 10d, the difference between them reaches the maximum value, which is about 45×10^{-6}. When drying time exceeds 100d, the difference in free shrinkage strain between them, on the contrary, falls down and then goes to zero. As for the points at $x = 15.0$mm and $x = 30.0$mm, the response times of them are quite different, and the shrinkage strain by linear formula lags obviously. In the view of free drying shrinkage, the strain by linear theory and non-linear theory differs a little, a lot, and then a little again when time goes on. That can be explained by the characteristics of mass diffusion coefficient with moisture content in Fig.3.

Fig.8 indicates the processes of drying shrinkage stress by two kinds of theories. For the point $x = 5$mm, the maximum stress reaches 3.21MPa at 7d according to non-linear theory. By linear diffusion formula, the stress at the same time and the same point is 2.67MPa. So, linear formula would give us a virtual safer impression about the surface stress condition. For the point at $x = 15$mm, the developing processes of shrinkage stress are much more complex than the point $x = 5$mm. It is difficult to evaluate under which theory the shrinkage stress is bigger. That phenomenon implies that the drying depth would be quite limited, no more than 15.0mm before 100d. As to the point at $x = 30$mm, the restrained stresses are the same for the two kinds of theory, and both are in compressive stress condition, which implies that the drying problem is a quite localized one.

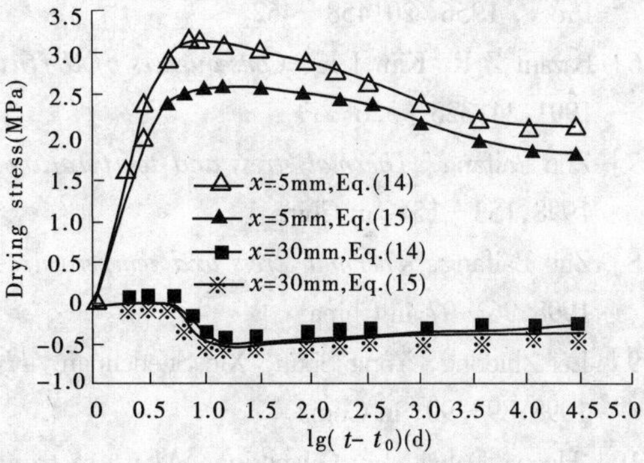

Fig.8 Drying stress comp. with two diffusion theories

3 Conclusions

Based on the analytical results of two kinds of diffusion theory, we have the following conclusions:

(1) The average mass diffusivity conducted by moisture transfer moment is about 5 000 ~

8 000 times less than the temperature diffusivity. Drying shrinkage properties are quite different from those of heat transfer.

(2) The drying process simulated by linear theory is slower than non-linear diffusion theory at early stage, which means the surface cracking problem is more dangerous than that estimated by linear theory, because of the non-linearity of moisture transfer.

(3) Drying shrinkage is localized in a very small zone. Ordinarily, the depth of drying shrinkage crack is no more than 15mm.

References

[1] Jana Selih, Sousa Antonio C M. *Moisture and heat flow in concrete walls exposed to fire*. Journal of Engineering Mechanics, 1993, 120(5):2028~2043

[2] Michanel Bartlett, Macgregor James G. *Effect of moisture on concrete core strength*. ACI Material Joural, 1993,91(3):227~236

[3] Huang C L D. *Multi-phase moisture transfer in porous media subjected to temperature gradient*. International J. of Heat and Mass Transfer, 1979,22:1295~1307

[4] Yu Weiping. *Heat and mass transfer properties in moist porous media*. Tsinghua University, 1987,65~68, in China

[5] Bruce P R, Klute A. *The measurement of soil moisture diffusivity*. Soil Science Society, American Proc., 1956, 20:458~462

[6] Bazant Z P, Kim J K. *Consequences of diffusion theory for shrinkage of concrete*. Mat. and Struc, 1991,24:323~326

[7] Zhu Baifang. *Thermal stress and temperature control of mass concrete*. China Electric Power Press, 1998,153~154, in China

[8] Zhu Baifang. *Thermal stress and temperature control of mass concrete*. China Electric Power Press, 1998,96~97,in China

[9] Lei Zhidong, Yang Sixiu, Xie Shenchuan. *Hydraulic dynamics of soil*. Tsinghua University Press, 1998,89~90, in China

[10] Huang Dahai, Liu Guangting. *Moisture transfer of concrete under isothermal condition*. Journal of Hydraulic Engineering, 2002,34(6):97~101,in China

[11] CEB-FIP Model Code. Comite Euro-International du Beton, Miland, Italy, 1990

[12] Kim J K, Lee C S. *Prediction of differential drying shrinkage in concrete*. Cement and Concrete Research, 1998,28(2):985~994

[13] Liu Guangting, Huang Dahai. *Experimental study on thermal conductivity and thermal diffusivity*. J.of Three Gorges University, 2002,24(2):1~7,in China

节理岩体的渗透系数与应变、应力的关系

摘　要　根据岩体裂隙渗流试验成果，采用机械隙宽的概念并根据节理岩体的力学本构关系，导出了含一组或多组节理的岩体的等效渗透系数与复杂应变的耦合关系式，以一组节理为例，以 Z 为法线的节理等效渗透系数为：$k_z = k_{0z}D_i(A_z\varepsilon_z + 1)^{n_i}(C_{\tau z}\cdot\sqrt{\gamma_{xz}^2+\gamma_{yz}^2} - 1)^2$（式中 A_z、$C_{\tau z}$ 为 ε_z、γ_{xy}、γ_{yz} 的耦合作用系数，D_i、n_i 为与应力、应变有关的修正系数）。公式说明节理岩体的等效渗透系数是复杂应变的函数，并且受裂隙面几何形态、节理面力学参数、间距、隙宽、应力加载和卸载条件的影响，是复杂岩基在复杂应变条件下考虑力学—渗流耦合关系的一种新的探索。

关键词　裂隙渗流　力学—渗流耦合作用　等效渗透系数　复杂应变

人们从工程实践和经验认识到存在于岩体中的渗透水流对岩体具有力学的、物理的和化学的等各方面作用，这些作用不但影响和改变了岩体的强度和变形特性，而且在岩体内形成了一个渗透力场。另一方面，水工建筑物的修建又改变了原来岩体的应力场和变形状况，导致节理岩体的水力特性发生改变，最终又导致渗流场发生变化。这就是近年来日益受到工程科技人员重视的力学—渗流耦合作用。已有的研究成果多数是从应力影响渗透系数的关系给出的，例如 C. L. Louis 根据现场试验和室内试验给出关系式。

近年来国内外不少学者研究耦合作用分析问题。有些人继续从应力角度研究问题，有些人继续引用立方定理研究结构面受荷变形后的渗透系数。为深入探索研究，本文根据裂隙渗流试验成果，从应变、应力改变裂隙的水力特性出发，研究节理岩体的等效渗透系数与复杂应变和应力条件的关系。

1　含有一组节理的岩体的渗透系数与应变、应力的关系

1.1　单裂隙的水力特性与变形的关系

根据文献[1]各种不同几何形态的裂隙面在零应力、压应力条件下的渗流量 Q 与机械隙宽 E（裂隙上下两个中面的距离）的关系曲线，可以示意性地将零应力条件的小开度、中开度、大开度以及压应力条件下加、卸载等5条曲线绘于图1，曲线1、2为压应力条件下加、卸载，曲线3、4、5分别为零应力条件下的小、中和大开度曲线。E_0 为初始隙宽，E_1 为小开度（层流）最大隙宽，E_2 为大开度（紊流）最小隙宽。

总结试验可以写出5条曲线的渗流量经验公式：$Q_i = A_iE^{n_i}$（$i=1,2,3,4,5$），以及相应的5条曲线的渗透系数 $K_i = B_iE^{n_i-1}$（$i=1,2,3,4,5$），式中 A_i、B_i、n_i 为与曲线和裂隙面几何形态有关的常数，其中 A_i、B_i 分别为标准流量系数和标准渗透系数，具有相应量纲，E 为无量纲相对机械隙宽。

本文选自《清华大学学报（自然科学版）》1996年第1期，作者还有耿克勤、陈兴华。

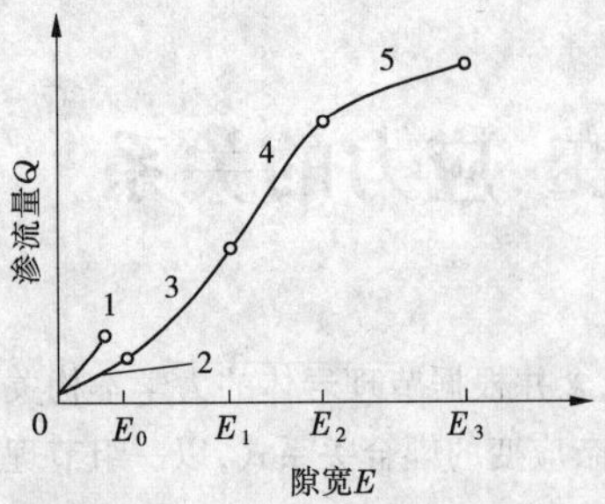

图1 压应力、零应力条件的 $Q \sim E$ 曲线

假设可以通过节理几何统计调查、压水试验等确定含一组节理的岩体的某一压应力条件下初始的当量渗透系数 K_{0j}，节理平均间距为 l，则利用第一条曲线公式有

$$K_{0j} = B_1 E_0^{n_1-1} E_0 l^{-1} = B_1 E_0^{n_1} l^{-1} \tag{1}$$

$$E_0 = \sqrt[n_1]{K_{0j} l / B_1} \tag{2}$$

式中：n_1、B_1 为由试验确定的常数；E_0 为初始隙宽。

根据文献[1]压剪应力条件下渗透系数 K 与剪切变形 S 有关系

$$K = AS^2 - BS + C = A\left(S - \frac{B}{2A}\right)^2 + \frac{4AC - B^2}{4A} \tag{3}$$

由试验知，当 $S = B/(2A)$ 时，有 $K \approx 0$，式(3)简化为

$$K = A\left(S - \frac{B}{2A}\right)^2 \tag{4}$$

令 $S_0 = B/(2A)$，则式(4)为

$$K = A(S - S_0)^2 \qquad \begin{cases} \text{当 } S \leqslant R \text{ 时，} & S = S \\ \text{当 } S > R \text{ 时，} & S = R \end{cases} \tag{5}$$

式中：A、B、C、S_0 为与压应力、裂隙面几何形态有关的常数；R 为裂隙面自相关长度（用数理统计方法求得的裂隙面凸起的平均长度）[1]。

1.2 结构面变形与应变的关系

图 2 表示含有一组节理的岩体单元，节理平均张开度（隙宽）为 e，间距为 l，设受法向压应力 σ_n（设压应力为负值）作用，沿节理面法线变形由单元中的岩块和节理共同产生，设 $\Delta = \Delta_f + \Delta_r$，式中 Δ_f、Δ_r 分别为结构面和岩块的变形，定义

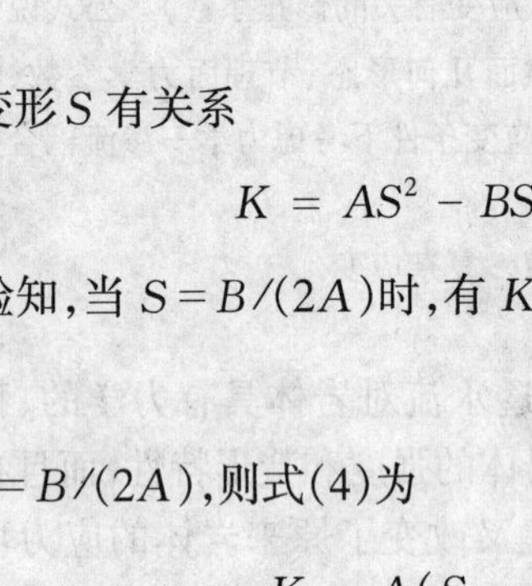

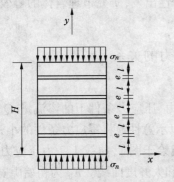

图2 含一组节理的岩体单元

$$\alpha = \frac{e_0}{l} = \frac{ne_0}{H} = \frac{H}{l}\frac{e_0}{H}$$

式中：e_0 为节理初始张开度，H 为单元总长，单元沿节理面法线应变为

$$\varepsilon_n = \Delta / H = \varepsilon_f \alpha + \varepsilon_r (1 - \alpha)$$

式中：ε_f、ε_r 分别为节理和岩块的法向应变。定义 $\beta = E_f / E_r$，式中 E_f、E_r 分别为节理面和岩石法向弹模，解出

$$e = e_0 + \Delta e = e_0\left[1 + \frac{\varepsilon_n}{\alpha + (1 - \alpha)\beta}\right]$$

仿照上面过程，可以获得节理剪切变形与单元剪应变的关系。图 2 中设节理沿 x 方向剪切位移为 δ_1，岩石为 δ_2，有 $\gamma_f = \delta_1 / e_0$，$\gamma_r = \delta_2 / l$，节理岩体总剪应变为

$$|\gamma_{xy}| = \frac{\delta_1 + \delta_2}{e_0 + l} = \frac{e_0\gamma_j + l\gamma_r}{e_0 + l} = \alpha\gamma_f + (1-\alpha)\gamma_r$$

令 $\eta = G_f/G_r$ 为节理剪切模量与岩石剪切模量之比，解出 $\delta_1 = e_0|\gamma_{xy}|/[\alpha + \eta(1-\alpha)]$，用 S_{xy} 代替 δ_1，代表以 y 为法线的节理面沿 x 方向的剪切位移值，有

$$S_{xy} = e_0|\gamma_{xy}|/[\alpha + \eta(1-\alpha)] \tag{6}$$

1.3 节理岩体的渗透系数与应变的关系

结合前述公式即可导出各种应力条件下的渗透系数公式。

(1)压应力条件下加载，即 $\sigma_n < 0, \Delta\varepsilon_n < 0$，节理面渗透系数为

$$k_1 = B_1E^{n_1-1} = k_0(1 + \frac{\varepsilon_n}{\alpha + \beta(1-\alpha)})^{n_1-1} \tag{7}$$

式中 $k_0 = B_1E_0^{n_1-1}$。将 k_1 化为节理岩体的当量(等效)渗透系数:

$$k_{1j} = k_1\frac{E}{l} = k_{0j}(1 + \frac{\varepsilon_n}{\alpha + \beta(1-\alpha)})^{n_1} \tag{8}$$

式中 $k_{0j} = B_1E_0^{n_1}/l$，为初始时节理岩体的当量渗透系数。

(2)压应力条件下卸载，即 $\sigma_n < 0$, $\Delta\varepsilon_n > 0$，节理岩体的当量渗透系数为

$$k_{2j} = k_2\frac{E}{l} = k_{0j}(1 + \frac{\varepsilon_n}{\alpha + \beta(1-\alpha)})^{n_2}\frac{B_2E_0^{(n_2-n_1)}}{B_1} \tag{9}$$

式中 E_0 为式(2)值，B_1、B_2、n_1、n_2 均为试验常数，$B_2E_0^{(n_2-n_1)}/B_1$ 可看做修正系数。

(3)零应力条件下小开度层流状态时，$\sigma_n = 0, E < E_1$，节理岩体的当量渗透系数为

$$k_{3j} = \frac{B_3}{l}E^{n_3} = k_{0j}(1 + \frac{\varepsilon_n}{\alpha})^{n_3}\frac{B_3E_0^{(n_3-n_1)}}{B_1} \tag{10}$$

(4)零应力条件下中开度过渡状态时，$\sigma_n = 0, E_1 < E < E_2$，节理岩体当量渗透系数为

$$k_{4j} = \frac{B_4}{l}E^{n_4} = k_{0j}(1 + \frac{\varepsilon_n}{\alpha})^{n_4}\frac{B_4E_0^{(n_4-n_1)}}{B_1} \tag{11}$$

(5)零应力条件大开度紊流状态时，$\sigma_n = 0, E \geqslant E_2$，节理岩体当量渗透系数为

$$k_{5j} = \frac{B_5}{l}E^{n_5} = k_{0j}(1 + \frac{\varepsilon_n}{\alpha})^{n_5}\frac{B_5E_0^{(n_5-n_1)}}{B_1} \tag{12}$$

(6)压剪条件下的渗透系数。由式(5)有 $k = A(S - S_0)^2$，其中 $S_0 = B/2A$，由文献[1]表示裂隙面几何形状的三维指标可导出 $S_0 = RE_0/2\delta$，这里 δ 为均方差，R 为裂隙面的自相关长度。

当 $S = 0$ 时，$k_0 = AS_0^2$，$k\cdot k_0^{-1} = [(S - S_0)\cdot S_0^{-1}]^2 = (S\cdot S_0^{-1} - 1)^2$，引入式(6)，有

$$k_{xy} = k_{oy}(\frac{S_{xy}}{S_{oxy}} - 1)^2 \quad \begin{cases} \text{当 } S_{xy} \leqslant R_{xy} \text{ 时，} & S_{xy} = S_{xy} \\ \text{当 } S_{xy} > R_{xy} \text{ 时，} & S_{xy} = R_{xy} \end{cases} \tag{13}$$

式中：k_{xy} 为以 y 为节理面法线的节理沿 x 方向的渗透系数；k_{0y} 为以 y 为法线的节理面没有剪应变时初始渗透系数；S_{oxy} 为以 y 为法线的节理沿 x 方向剪切时式(5)中 S_0 值；S_{xy} 为以 y 为法线的节理沿 x 方向剪切位移值；R_{xy} 为以 y 为法线的节理沿 x 方向的自相关长度。

由于 k_{xy}、k_{oy} 分别乘以 E_0/l 就是当量渗透系数，因此式(13)也就是节理岩体的当量

渗透系数公式。利用式(6)和 $S_0 = RE_0/2\delta$,并令

$$A = \frac{1}{\alpha + \beta(1-\alpha)}, \quad B = \frac{1}{\alpha + \eta(1-\alpha)} \tag{14}$$

若 A_y、B_y 是以 y 为法线的节理组上式之值,有

$$\frac{S_{xy}}{S_{oxy}} = \frac{2\mid\gamma_{xy}\mid\delta_{xy}B_y}{R_{xy}} \tag{15}$$

式中 δ_{xy}、R_{xy} 代表以 y 为法线之节理面沿 x 方向的均方差和自相关长度,式(13)变为

$$k_{xy} = k_{oy}(C_{xy}\mid\gamma_{xy}\mid - 1)^2 \tag{16}$$

式中 $C_{xy} = 2\delta_{xy}B_y/R_{xy}$。

同理 γ_{zy} 也会引起节理面的 k_{jy} 发生变化,可以认为合成剪应变引起的变化规律同式(16),设 γ_{xy}、γ_{zy} 的合成应变方向为 τ,同样定义 $C_{\tau y}$,则有

$$k_{jy} = k_{oy}\left(\frac{\sqrt{S_{xy}^2 + S_{zy}^2}}{S_{o\tau y}} - 1\right)^2 = k_{oy}\left(C_{\tau y}\sqrt{\gamma_{xy}^2 + \gamma_{zy}^2} - 1\right)^2 \tag{17}$$

式(17)反映了 γ_{xy}、γ_{zy} 对渗透系数的影响,如果再计入 ε_y 的影响,合并式(8)、式(17),有

$$k_{jy} = k_{oy}(1 + A_y\varepsilon_y)^{n_1}\left(C_{\tau y}\sqrt{\gamma_{xy}^2 + \gamma_{zy}^2} - 1\right)^2 \tag{18}$$

式(18)适用于压应力加载条件。

2 含有多组节理系的岩体和断层的渗透系数与应变、应力的关系

先研究含有三组正交节理系的岩体,见图 3,取三组正交节理面的法线为坐标轴 x、y、z,由渗透张量理论可得

$$K = \begin{bmatrix} k_{ey} + k_{ez} & 0 & 0 \\ 0 & k_{ex} + k_{ez} & 0 \\ 0 & 0 & k_{ey} + k_{ex} \end{bmatrix} = \begin{bmatrix} k_x & 0 & 0 \\ 0 & k_y & 0 \\ 0 & 0 & k_z \end{bmatrix} \tag{19}$$

式中 k_{ex}、k_{ey}、k_{ez} 分别为以 x、y、z 轴为法线的节理系的当量渗透系数,根据式(19),有渗透张量主值

$$\left.\begin{aligned} k_x &= k_{ey} + k_{ez} = k_{xy} + k_{xz} \\ k_y &= k_{ex} + k_{ez} = k_{yx} + k_{yz} \\ k_z &= k_{ey} + k_{ex} = k_{zy} + k_{zx} \end{aligned}\right\} \tag{20}$$

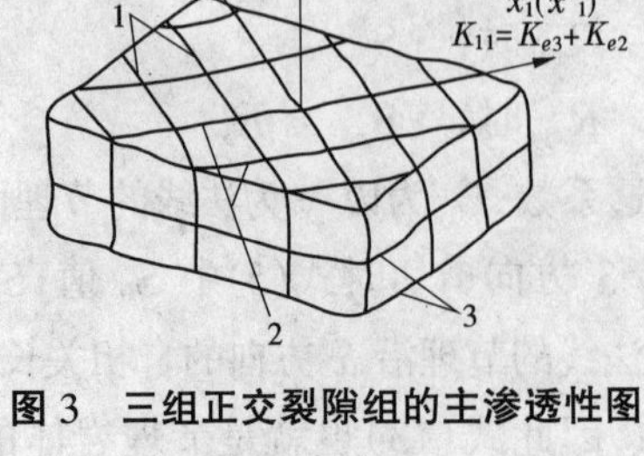

图 3 三组正交裂隙组的主渗透性图

为方便推导耦合公式,式(20)引入了 6 个渗透参数。只需分别研究 k_{xy}、k_{xz}、k_{zy} 在不同应力状态、不同隙宽条件下受法向应变和剪应变影响所产生的变化即可。式(8)~式(18)对 k_{xy}、k_{xz}、k_{zy} 仍然合适。由此可以写出不同条件下的式(20)各分量值,例如对压应力条件加载时,即有条件:$\sigma_x < 0$, $\sigma_y < 0$, $\sigma_z < 0$, $\Delta\varepsilon_y < 0$, $\Delta\varepsilon_z < 0$,则

$$k_x = k_{xy} + k_{xz} = k_{oy}(1 + A_y\varepsilon_y)^{n_1}\left(C_{zy}\sqrt{\gamma_{xy}^2 + \gamma_{zy}^2} - 1\right)^2 + k_{oz}(1 + A_z\varepsilon_z)^{n_1}\left(C_{\tau z}\sqrt{\gamma_{xz}^2 + \gamma_{yz}^2} - 1\right)^2 \quad (21)$$

同理,可以写出 k_y、k_z 的关系式。

对于含有多组斜交节理的岩体,根据渗透张量理论,总渗透张量等于各组节理系的渗透张量之和。利用多组节理岩体的本构关系,可求得每一组节理系的隙宽变化 Δw、剪切位移 Δu 和 Δv,套用式(8)~式(18),同样可求得该组节理系的渗透系数。如对压应力条件下加载,某组节理系的渗透系数为

$$k_{1j} = k_{0j}\left(\frac{E_0 + \Delta w}{E_0}\right)^{n_1} \quad (22)$$

压剪条件下加载时有

$$k_{6j} = k_{0j}\left(\frac{E_0 + \Delta w}{E_0}\right)^{n_1}\left(\frac{\sqrt{\Delta u^2 + \Delta v^2}}{S_0} - 1\right)^2 \quad (23)$$

式(22)、式(23)中 E_0 为初始隙宽,S_0 按式(5)取值。按这一思路可写出全部应力、应变条件下的 7 个公式,从而解决了含多组斜交节理的岩体的渗透系数与应变、应力的关系。

断层厚度一般较大,由于构造原因和岩性成分的不同,其内部导水裂隙的状况也各不相同,为了耦合分析方便起见,可借用三组正交导水裂隙的概念,即假定式(19)成立,x、y、z 可取为断层的法向、走向和倾向。这样,可获得类似式(21)一样的一套公式。主干裂隙可以看做是断层的特例,仿照处理。于是,同样解决了导水断层和主干裂隙的渗透系数和应变、应力的关系。

3 结论

本文根据岩石裂隙渗流试验成果,采用机械隙宽的概念并根据节理岩体的力学本构关系,导出了含一组或多组节理的岩体的等效渗透系数与复杂应变的关系。以一组节理为例,以 z 为法线的节理岩体等效渗透系数为

$$k_{jz} = k_{oz}D_i(A_z\varepsilon_z + 1)^{n_i}\left(C_{\tau z}\sqrt{\gamma_{xz}^2 + \gamma_{yz}^2} - 1\right)^2$$

式中:A_z、$C_{\tau z}$ 为 ε_z、γ_{xz}、γ_{yz} 的耦合作用系数;D_i 为与分段有关的修正系数;$C_{\tau z} = B_z 2\delta_{\tau z}/R_{\tau z}$,$R_{\tau z}$、$\delta_{\tau z}$分别为节理面 τ 方向的自相关长度和起伏差;B_z 为剪切位移耦合作用系数。

上式说明节理的等效渗透系数是复杂应变 ε_z、γ_{xy}、γ_{yz} 的函数,也受裂隙面几何形态、节理面力学参数、间距、隙宽、应力状态、加卸载条件的影响。利用上式可解决导水主干裂隙、三组正交节理、断层和斜交节理的渗透系数求解问题,它反映了耦合作用的内部机理,是复杂岩基在复杂应变条件下考虑力学—渗流耦合关系的一种新的探索。

采用本文研究的复杂岩基的力学—渗流耦合分析模型,成功地完成了建筑在复杂岩基之上的龙羊峡重力拱坝和两岸坝肩岩体的力学、渗流和耦合分析,初步实测验证表明,本文提出的模型和计算方法是合理实用的。

参 考 文 献

[1] 耿克勤,刘光廷.岩体裂隙渗流水力特性的实验研究.清华大学学报,1996,36(1):102～106
[2] 耿克勤.复杂岩基的渗流、力学及其耦合分析研究以及工程应用:[学位论文].北京:清华大学水利水电工程系,1994

岩体裂隙渗流水力特性的试验研究

摘　要　根据数理统计原理,从随机平稳过程理论出发,提出了一套描述裂隙空间曲面几何形态的三维指标和方法。在一套特制的岩石裂隙渗流试验装置上系统地研究了不同几何形态的裂隙在不同应力、应变条件下的水力特性,探讨了渗透系数与机械隙宽、剪切变形、几何形态、应力条件、加卸载条件的关系,并得出了各种不同情况下的的试验数据拟合方程式。

关键词　裂隙渗流　水力特性　力学—渗流耦合作用

单条裂隙作为岩体裂隙网络的基本单元,决定了地下水在岩层中的基本渗透特征,是各种渗透理论模型的基础。早期研究均以两片光滑平行板构成的缝隙为前提,根据Navier-Stocks公式推导出裂隙过流能力与隙宽立方成正比,即立方定理。由于平行板模型与实际裂隙相差太远,许多学者提出了不同的修正公式。

前人对单裂隙渗流进行了大量室内和野外试验以及计算机模拟试验,取得了丰硕的成果。但对压应力条件下的试验研究较多,零应力、大隙宽和剪切变形对渗流的影响研究较少,对天然粗糙裂隙研究较少。研究压应力、剪应力与水力特性的关系较多,从隙宽、剪切变形角度研究对渗流量的影响较少,定性的描述多,定量的规律总结较少。本文针对上述薄弱环节选取4种不同几何形态的裂隙,进行了多组全面试验研究,获得了一系列定量的试验规律。

试件平面尺寸为26cm×24.5cm。光滑平行裂隙试件系采用具有光滑平面的硬塑料板用环氧树脂黏结剂粘贴在砂浆混凝土块上制成。粗糙度规则的人工齿形裂隙试件是用经过机械加工过的具有规则齿形的有机玻璃板粘贴在砂浆混凝土块上制成的。天然裂隙面试件是用采自龙羊峡水电站G_4断裂带两种不同粗糙度的天然原状岩样作模子,用砂浆混凝土浇筑而成。

1　用数理统计原理确定的裂隙曲面几何形态的三维指标

裂隙面的水力特性受其形状、水力、应力应变条件的影响,对于无充填物的岩石裂隙,裂隙壁面的几何形态显然与渗流性质有很重要的关系。

裂隙面上任一点相对于某一基准面的高度$H_i(X_i, Y_i)$是一个随机变量,采用随机变量的数字特征概念可以反映其统计特征。对任一裂隙面可以选取某一方向为X方向,另一垂直方向为Y方向。平行于X方向可切取许多剖面,任一裂隙剖面的起伏程度可用均方差$\sigma_x(H)$表示,同理可求得平行Y轴的某剖面的均方差$\sigma_y(H)$。若在整个裂隙面上采样求H_i,同样可求得整个裂面上的均方差(本文用均方差σ表示整个裂隙面上的起伏程度):

本文选自《清华大学学报(自然科学版)》1996年第1期,作者还有耿克勤、陈凤翔、陈兴华。

$$\sigma(H)=\sqrt{D(H)}=\sqrt{E\{[H_i-E(H)]^2\}} \tag{1}$$

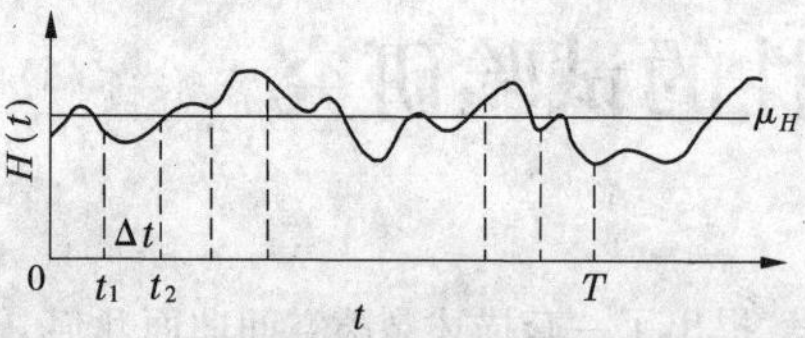

图1　裂隙不平剖面示意图

图1为裂隙面上沿 X 方向切取的某一剖面，把横坐标看成时间轴 t，裂隙剖面高低不平的图形就可视为一随机过程 $H(t)$。前后的环境和主要条件都不随时间变化，裂隙面剖面的粗糙不平曲线显然可看做一种平稳随机过程。设 $H(t_1)$ 和 $H(t_2)$ 是随机过程 $H(t)$ 在任意时刻 t_1 和 t_2 的状态，称二阶原点混合矩 $R_{HH}(t_1,t_2)=E[H(t_1)H(t_2)]$ 为随机过程 $H(t)$ 的自相关函数，简称相关函数。

根据平稳随机过程的自相关函数各态历经定理，可以一次试验所得到的样本函数 $H(t)$ 来确定该过程的均值和自相关函数，即

均值　$$\mu_H=\frac{1}{T}\int_0^T H(t)\mathrm{d}t \tag{2}$$

自相关函数　$$R_H(\tau)=\frac{1}{T-\tau}\int_\tau^T H(t)H(T-\tau)\mathrm{d}t\quad(0\leqslant\tau\leqslant T) \tag{3}$$

由于在实际量测中难以得到 $H(t)$ 的表达式，可用数学方法计算式(2)和式(3)，根据图1把 $[0,T]$ 等分为 N 个长为 $\Delta t=T/N$ 的小区间，然后在时刻 $t_k=(K-\frac{1}{2})\Delta t$，$K=1,2,\cdots,N$，对 $H(t)$ 取样，得 N 个函数值 $H_k=H(t_k)(k=1,2,\cdots,N)$，积分式(2)可得 $\hat{\mu}_H=\frac{1}{N}\sum_{k=1}^{N}H_K$，为了方便，将式(3)中 $H(t)$ 用 $(H(t)-\hat{\mu}_H)$ 代替，式(3)可变为 $\hat{R}_H(\tau_r)=\frac{1}{N-r}\sum_{k-1}^{N-r}(H_k-\hat{\mu}_H)\cdot(h_{k+r}-\hat{\mu}_H)(r=0,1,2,\cdots,m(m<N))$，可算出相关函数的一系列近似值，该值有正有负。定义若方程 $\hat{R}_H(\tau_r)=0$ 有解 $\tau_r=R$，则称 R 为该随机变量的自相关长度。计算平行于 X 方向的多个剖面可得一组 R_x 值，同理可得一组 R_y 值，取其平均值即可得裂隙曲面二维方向起伏频率大小的代表性数值 $\overline{R}_x$ 和 $\overline{R}_y$。R 值越小，表明相距很近的两点相关程度越小，起伏频率越高，起伏角越大，表面越粗糙。

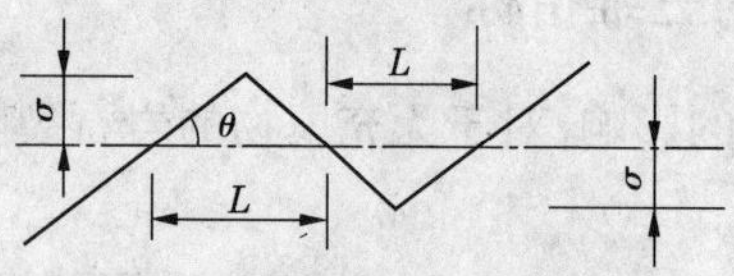

图2　裂隙面起伏差图

综合上述裂隙面的二维自相关长度和起伏程度的概念，可获得裂隙曲面几何形态的三维指标表示方法。如图2所示，可以从统计意义上认为均方差 σ（起伏程度或起伏差）是突起的平均高度，自相关长度 L 是突起的平均长度，则统计意义上的起伏角（或平均坡度）可为 $\theta=\arctan(2\sigma/L)$。

对整个裂隙曲面而言，可求得代表整个曲面的均方差 σ 和 X、Y 两个方向的平均自相关长度 $\overline{R}_x$、$\overline{R}_y$，由此可求得代表整个裂隙曲面几何形态的三维指标 σ、$\overline{R}_x$、$\overline{R}_y$。

若定义 $\overline{\theta}_x=\arctan(2\sigma\sqrt{R_x})$，$\overline{\theta}_y=\arctan(2\sigma\sqrt{R_y})$，$\overline{\theta}_x$、$\overline{\theta}_y$ 为裂隙曲面统计意义上的 X、Y 两个方向上的平均起伏角，显然也可用 σ_1、$\overline{\theta}_x$、$\overline{\theta}_y$ 代表整个裂隙曲面几何形态的三维指标。

用断面的实测值经过计算机程序处理，可十分快捷地获得给定裂隙曲面的起伏差和二维起伏角及二维的自相关长度。

2 裂隙渗流试验成果与分析

由于天然应力作用下产生的裂隙壁面大多是不规则的，裂隙上下两个面都有一个中面，假定这两个中面平行，中面的距离定义为机械隙宽 a_m。试验表明，对相当粗糙的天然裂隙，立方定理并不成立。本文选取的天然裂隙 G_4 的隙面起伏差为 2.3～2.8mm，机械隙宽最大为 3mm 左右，其表面起伏差与裂隙开度大致相当，在这样的条件之下本文讨论其水力特性。本文采用机械隙宽的概念研究问题，文中隙宽、图上裂隙开度 E 均指机械隙宽 a_m。

2.1 裂隙开度与渗流量和渗透系数的关系

通过多组试验研究了不同几何形态的裂隙面，当水力坡降为一定值，法向应力和剪应力均为零，但机械隙宽逐渐增大或逐渐减小时，裂隙开度与渗流量和渗透系数之间的关系。渗透系数 K 是根据实测流量 Q 和隙宽 E，及水力坡降 J，并假定达西定律成立时，依据

$$K = Q/(EbJ) \tag{4}$$

计算出的名义数值。式中 b 为试件流水宽度。

图 3～图 5 表示平行光滑人工裂隙、G_4-1 不同几何形态的裂隙零应力条件下渗流量、渗透系数与隙宽的关系。由图可以得出以下结论：

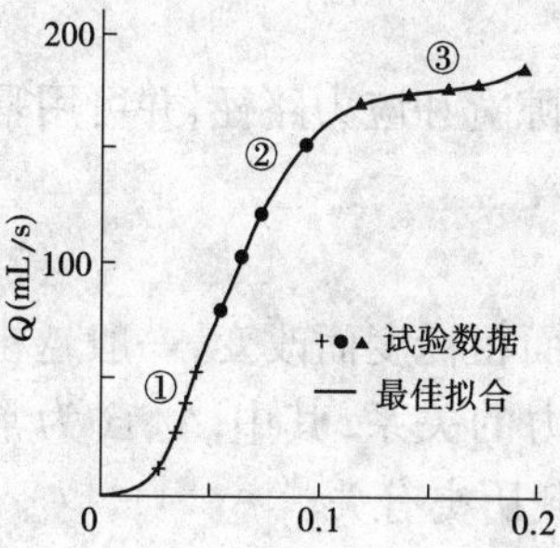

① $Q=1\,021.430E^{3.062}$

② $Q=2\,065.22E^{1.143\,14}$

③ $Q=277.368E^{0.243\,7}$

图 3 光滑平行裂隙隙宽减少时 Q～E 三段幂函数

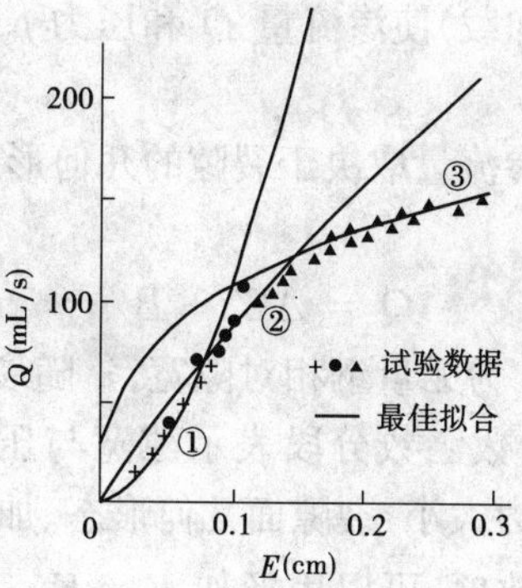

① $Q=5\,776.9E^{1.71}$

② $Q=591.6E^{0.822}$

③ $Q=288.7E^{0.322}$

图 4 试件 G_4-1Q～E 三段幂函数

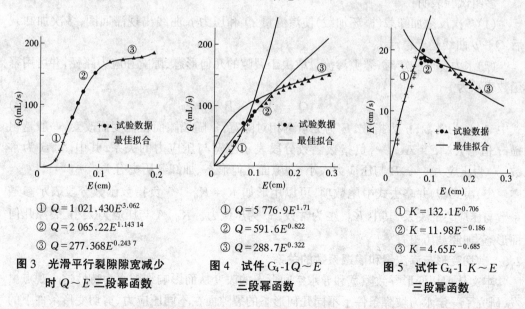

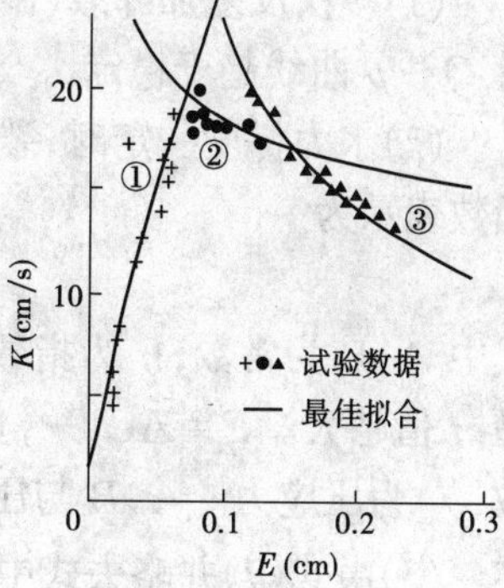

① $K=132.1E^{0.706}$

② $K=11.98E^{-0.186}$

③ $K=4.65E^{-0.685}$

图 5 试件 G_4-1 K～E 三段幂函数

(1)一定水力坡度下裂隙渗流量取决于裂隙面几何形态和隙宽。

(2)不管隙宽是逐渐减少还是增加，Q～E 和 K～E 是一条相当光滑的曲线，可用高次多项式拟合。

(3)根据曲线变化趋势，可采用幂函数形式 $Q_i = A_iE^{n_i}$ 分小开度、中开度、大开度三段

很好地拟合试验点，n_i 随段数增加而递减，反映渗流流态从层流、过渡状态到紊流的变化过程。

(4) $Q_i = A_i E^{n_i}$ 中指数 n_i 的规律是：小开度层流时，$1.71 \leqslant n_i \leqslant 3.0$，裂隙面几何形态越光滑，$n_i$ 值越大；对中等开度过渡状态 $0.8 \leqslant n_i \leqslant 1.4$，对大开度紊流 $0.3 \leqslant n_i \leqslant 0.48$。

(5)名义渗透系数 $K \sim E$ 曲线也可分三段用幂函数拟合，即

$$Q_i = A_i E^{n_i} \qquad (i = 1,2,3) \tag{5}$$

从式(4)又可得

$$K_i = B_i E^{m_i} \qquad (i = 1,2,3) \tag{6}$$

式中 B_i、m_i 为与分段有关的常数，并有 $m_i = n_i - 1 (i = 1,2,3)$。为使式(5)、式(6)左右两边量纲一致，本文定义：E 为无量纲相对隙宽比值，等于实际隙宽除以模型隙宽的比值；A_i 为标准流量系数；B_i 为标准渗透系数。下文类似公式均采用这里有关 E、A、B 的定义。

进一步的研究表明，式(5)中的 A_i、n_i 都是裂隙面起伏角的函数，对粗糙裂隙而言，裂隙的水力特性取决于机械隙宽和其本身的粗糙程度等因素，而不仅仅是绝对突起高度与隙宽之比。

2.2 压应力、应力路径和裂隙开度与渗流量的关系

针对不同几何形态的裂隙面在一定的水力坡降条件下研究了压应力、应力路径与渗流量的关系，给出了试验数据的拟合方程式。

多组试验表明：

(1)多次反复加卸载(循环加载)使渗流量 Q 和压力 p 曲线出现滞回圈，多次加卸载后 $Q \sim p$ 曲线趋于稳定。

(2)水力梯度一定时，裂隙渗流量取决于裂隙的几何形态、隙宽和应力路径，并可用幂函数表示为

$$Q = AE^n + B \tag{7}$$

式中 A、B 为常数，n 为指数，E 为无量纲相对隙宽，n 随裂隙面粗糙度而改变，一般越粗糙 n 值越大。$E = Ae^{-B\sigma_n}$，负指数函数分段表示隙宽与压应力的关系，其中 A、B 为常数，σ_n 为压应力。A、B 与压应力大小、裂隙面几何形态、加卸载历史有关。

(3)由式(7)并略去式中尾数项，可以用形如 $K = K_0 e^{-A\sigma_n}$ 负指数函数分段表示渗透系数与压应力的关系，其中 K_0、A 为常数，σ_n 为压应力。K_0、A 与压应力大小、裂隙几何面形态、加卸载历史有关。

2.3 剪切变形与渗流量和渗透系数的关系

本文从剪切变形导致隙宽和导水空间形态的改变从而影响裂隙水力特性这一观点出发，研究了一定水力坡降条件下不同几何形态的裂隙面在不同压应力、剪切变形条件下的渗流量和渗透系数以及剪切变形和法向变形的关系、法向变形和水力特性的关系。图6给出了部分试验成果。图中 E 表示由于剪切变形产生的隙宽，K 表示根据达西定律算出的渗透系数，拟合方程式中 x 表示横坐标的变量，即剪切变形。

对光滑平行裂隙在有一定隙宽和受到某一恒定压力的条件下进行试验，发现剪切位

移对流量没有什么影响,显然这是由平行光滑裂隙的几何形状所决定的。

对 G_4-1、G_4-2 多组试件进行的不同压应力、不同剪切变形的试验结果如下:

(1)在不同压应力作用下裂隙面由于剪切变形会使渗流量发生先减少,后来又逐渐加大的变化,$Q \sim S$ 试验点可用 4~5 次多项式很光滑地拟合。最大剪切位移达 6mm,最大流量达 $43cm^3/s$。法向压应力越大,同样大的剪切变形产生的渗流量越小。

(2)不同压应力作用下,剪切变形使隙宽先变小(剪缩),而后又随剪切变形一同增大(剪胀)。

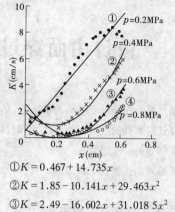

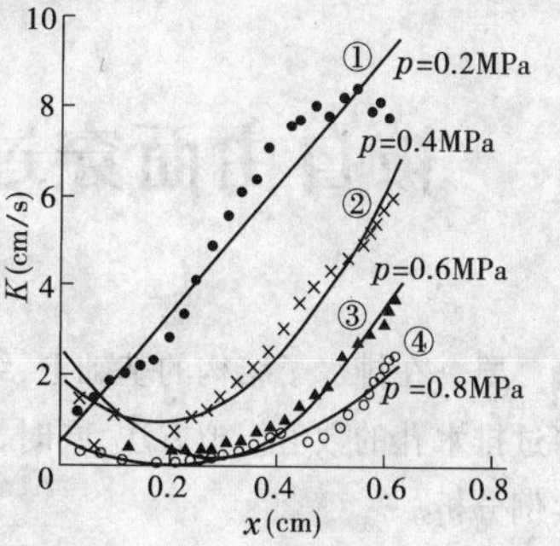

①$K = 0.467 + 14.735x$

②$K = 1.85 - 10.141x + 29.463x^2$

③$K = 2.49 - 16.602x + 31.0185x^2$

④$K = 0.563 - 5.1045x + 12.63x^2$

图 6　G_4-2 $K \sim x$ 综合方程式

(3)渗流量与由于剪切变形产生的隙宽 E 之间的试验点可以用二次多项式拟合。

(4)渗透系数与剪切位移试验点可以用二次多项式拟合:$K = AS^2 - BS + C$。式中 A、B、C 是与裂隙面几何形态、压应力有关的常数。随压应力增大,同样的剪位移导致渗透系数绝对值减小,但随剪位移增大导致渗透系数的相对变化较大,说明水力特性不只取决于剪切变形、隙宽,还与法向应力有关,法向应力的大小将影响剪变形所产生的裂隙上下面之间的导水通道的空间形状。

(5)裂隙面剪切变形对渗流量、渗透系数的影响取决于裂隙面几何形态、剪切位移和法向应力的大小。

3　结论

天然粗糙裂隙面的渗透水流一般是完全三维的。本文根据数理统计原理,从随机平稳过程理论出发,提出了一套描述裂隙曲面几何形态的三维指标和方法,即均方差和二维方向的自相关长度,为研究天然粗糙裂隙的复杂应变对水力特性的影响创造了条件。

在特制的一套岩石裂隙渗流试验装置上研究了不同几何形态的裂隙在零应力、压应力和剪应力作用下不同裂隙开度或应变条件下的水力特性,探讨了渗透系数与机械隙宽、剪切变形、几何形态、应力条件、加卸载条件和水力梯度的关系,为定量研究裂隙的水力特性和力学的耦合关系进行了很有价值的探索。本项研究的成果已成功地应用于建筑在复杂岩基上的龙羊峡重力拱坝和两岸肩岩体的力学—渗流耦合分析。

参 考 文 献

[1] Esaki J. *Shear-flow coupling test on rock joints*. Proc 7th Int Conf ISRM,1992

[2] 于冰. 裂隙渗流与应力耦合关系的实验研究:[学位论文]. 北京:清华大学水利水电工程系,1993

[3] 耿克勤. 复杂岩基的渗流、力学及其耦合分析研究以及工程应用:[学位论文]. 北京:清华大学水利水电工程系,1994

被自由面穿过排水孔的数值模拟方法

摘　要　在排水子结构的基础上,结合求解无压渗流场的调整传导矩阵法,给出了被自由面穿过排水孔的数值模拟方法,同时,对渗流量也提出了一种简单的计算方法,最后给出了一个实例分析。

关键词　排水孔　自由面　排水子结构　调整传导矩阵法　渗流量

排水孔是水利工程中常用的排水设施,它对渗流场水头分布影响很大,如何正确有效地对其渗流行为进行数值模拟就显得十分重要。但由于排水孔尺寸很小,若将其作为内边界处理,会导致有限元计算网格过于复杂。目前工程上一般是以给定水头的结点来代替排水孔,这种处理没有反映孔的尺寸效应。文献[1]首次提出了排水子结构算法,避免了模拟排水孔时复杂的网格的划分,但无法模拟穿过自由面时排水孔的排水情况,文献[2]在文献[1]的基础上进行了改进,但没有给出排水孔内边界的具体处理方法。本文在排水子结构的基础上,结合求解无压渗流的调整传导矩阵法,对排水孔与自由面相交的情况给出了具体的算法,有效地解决了排水孔的数值模拟问题,同时对渗流量的计算提出了一种简单的方法。

1　求解无压渗流场的调整传导矩阵法

用调整传导矩阵法求解无压渗流场就是在每次迭代中修正渗透传导矩阵,使其逐步逼近真实的渗流区域。i 次迭代后,对于自由面以上的单元,在下次计算中遗弃;自由面以下的单元,其传导矩阵保持不变;被自由面穿过的单元,其传导矩阵须修正,修正的思路为:单元中水面以上的高斯点渗透系数取原值的千分之一,水面以下的高斯点渗透系数取原值,以此原则重新计算单元传导矩阵,得 $i+1$ 次迭代方程为

$$[K]_{i+1}[H]_{i+1} = \{Q\}_{i+1} \tag{1}$$

式中$[K]_{i+1}$、$[H]_{i+1}$、$[Q]_{i+1}$分别为 $i+1$ 次计算的传导矩阵、待求水头列阵、等效结点流量列阵。

2　排水子结构被自由面穿过时的出口传导矩阵及右端项

对于含有一个排水孔的六面体八结点等参元中的子结构,其内部单元划分(内部分层以 2~4 层为宜[1])如图 1 所示。

对子结构可建立如下渗流平衡方程:

$$[K]^z[H]^z = [Q]^z \tag{2}$$

式中$[K]^z$、$[H]^z$、$[Q]^z$ 分别为子结构的传导矩阵、水头列阵、等效结点流量列阵(含子结

本文选自《武汉大学学报(工学版)》2001 年第 2 期,作者还有朱军、陆述远。

构邻近单元的结点流量贡献)。子结构传导矩阵由其内部各单元传导矩阵叠加而成,即$[K]^z=\sum[K]_e^z$,子结构中单元传导矩阵$[K]_e^z$中的元素k_{ij}的高斯积分可表示为

$$k_{ij}=\sum_l A_l\,|J|_l[B_i]_l^{\mathrm T}[k]_l[B_j]_l \tag{3}$$

式中:$[k]_l=\begin{bmatrix}k_x & & \\ & k_y & \\ & & k_z\end{bmatrix}_l$,为高斯点渗透系数矩阵;

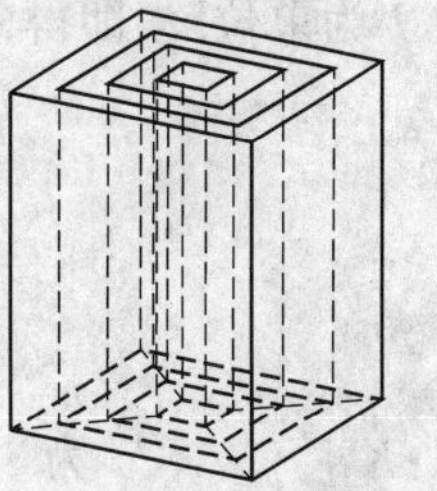

图 1　排水子结构内部单元划分

$[B_i]_l^{\mathrm T}=\left[\dfrac{\partial N_i}{\partial x},\dfrac{\partial N_i}{\partial y},\dfrac{\partial N_i}{\partial z}\right]$;$A_l$为高斯点的权系数;$|J|_l$为高斯点雅可比行列式值;$N_i$为单元形函数。

设子结构的出口结点水头及右端项为H_1、Q_1,排水孔内边界点水头及右端项为H_3、Q_3,其余内部结点水头及右端项为H_2、Q_2,故平衡方程用分块矩阵可表示为

$$\begin{bmatrix}K_{11} & K_{12} & K_{13}\\ K_{21} & K_{22} & K_{23}\\ K_{31} & K_{32} & K_{33}\end{bmatrix}\begin{bmatrix}H_1\\ H_2\\ H_3\end{bmatrix}=\begin{Bmatrix}Q_1\\ Q_2\\ Q_3\end{Bmatrix} \tag{4}$$

根据上次(设为i次)迭代计算出的水头值可判断子结构与自由面的相对位置,当子结构与自由面相交时,其内部单元高斯点压力水头有的大于零,有的小于零。对于压力水头小于零的高斯点,相应渗透系数取原值的千分之一,压力水头大于等于零的高斯点,渗透系数取原值,以此原则计算各单元传导矩阵,叠加后可得$i+1$次计算的子结构传导矩阵,如式(6)。

当子结构与自由面相交时,其部分内边界(正压力水头内边界,见图 2)排水,可由上次迭代计算出的子结构结点水头值求出排水孔内边界中正压力水头部分的边界流量q,再由式(5)等效到排水孔内边界结点上,以修正子结构的等效结点流量列阵,表达式为

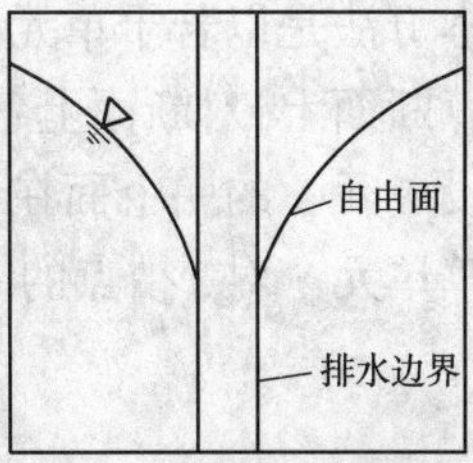

图 2　被自由面穿过的排水子结构

$$\Delta Q_3^{i+1}=\int[N]^{\mathrm T}q\,\mathrm d\Gamma \tag{5}$$

则$i+1$次迭代计算的子结构渗流平衡方程为

$$\begin{bmatrix}K_{11}^{i+1} & K_{12}^{i+1} & K_{13}^{i+1}\\ K_{21}^{i+1} & K_{22}^{i+1} & K_{23}^{i+1}\\ K_{31}^{i+1} & K_{32}^{i+1} & K_{33}^{i+1}\end{bmatrix}\begin{bmatrix}H_1^{i+1}\\ H_2^{i+1}\\ H_3^{i+1}\end{bmatrix}=\begin{Bmatrix}Q_1\\ Q_2\\ Q_3+\Delta Q_3^{i+1}\end{Bmatrix}=\begin{Bmatrix}A_1^{i+1}\\ A_2^{i+1}\\ A_3^{i+1}\end{Bmatrix} \tag{6}$$

利用高斯—约当法可将式(6)消元成如下形式:

$$\begin{bmatrix}K_{11}^{i+1^*} & 0 & 0\\ K_{21}^{i+1^*} & I & 0\\ K_{31}^{i+1^*} & 0 & I\end{bmatrix}\begin{bmatrix}H_1^{i+1}\\ H_2^{i+1}\\ H_3^{i+1}\end{bmatrix}=\begin{Bmatrix}A_1^{i+1^*}\\ A_2^{i+1^*}\\ A_3^{i+1^*}\end{Bmatrix}$$

式中 I 为单位阵,即得

$$K_{11}^{i+1^*} H_1^{i+1} = A_1^{i+1^*} \tag{7}$$

$$H_2^{i+1} = A_2^{i+1^*} - K_{21}^{i+1^*} H_1^{i+1} \tag{8}$$

$$H_3^{i+1} = A_3^{i+1^*} - K_{31}^{i+1^*} H_1^{i+1} \tag{9}$$

其中:$K_{11}^{i+1^*}$、$A_1^{i+1^*}$ 为 $i+1$ 次子结构凝聚后的出口传导矩阵及右端项。

自由面以上的子结构,在下次计算中遗弃;自由面以下的子结构,内边界结点水头给定[1],传导矩阵及右端项不用修正。

将子结构凝聚后的出口传导矩阵叠加到整体传导矩阵$[K]_{i+1}$上,同时右端项也叠加到整体等效结点流量列阵$[Q]_{i+1}$上,利用方程(1)计算出结点水头值,由子结构的出口水头值,再利用式(8)、式(9)可计算出子结构内部结点水头值,如不满足收敛精度,则按以上思路进行下一轮的迭代计算。

3 计算渗透流量的方法

对于渗透流量的计算,一般方法是先求出计算断面(由于流速在单元面上不连续,计算断面一般由若干单元中截面组成)上的法向流速,再在断面求积分即得。本文提出的方法避开法向流速的求解,而仅利用调整传导矩阵法计算的最终传导矩阵与结点水头值加上较简单的运算即可得出渗透流量。

本方法是以若干单元面组成的面为计算断面,算出计算断面同边的单元(且有一个面在计算断面上)对断面上各结点的流量贡献之和,即为该断面的渗透流量。

设单元 j 的一个面在计算断面上,i 结点为单元 j 的一结点且在计算断面上,用下式可计算单元 j 对 i 结点的结点流量贡献:

$$Q_{ij} = \sum_{k=1}^{l} a_{m_i,k} \times h_k \tag{10}$$

式中:m_i 为 i 结点在 j 单元中的局部编号,$a_{m_i,k}$ 为 j 单元最终传导矩阵$[K]_j^e m_i$ 行 k 列的元素,h_k 为 j 单元水头列阵$[H]_j^e k$ 行的元素,l 为 j 单元的结点个数。

计算断面同边单元对 i 结点总的结点流量贡献为 $Q_i = \sum_{j=1}^{m} Q_{ij}$,$m$ 为在断面同边与 i 结点公点且一个单元面在断面上的单元总数,则通过计算断面的渗流量为

$$Q = \left| \sum_{i=1}^{n} Q_i \right| \tag{11}$$

n 为计算断面上的结点总数。用该方法计算过流量时不用求出法向流速,比常规法简单。

4 算例

某混凝土重力坝,坝高 100m,底宽 70m,顶宽 10m,上游水位为 89m,下游水位为 11m,在坝体中距上游面 3m 处设孔径为 15cm、孔距为 5m 的垂直排水孔幕,坝基也设有深 30m 的垂直排水孔幕,其孔距、孔径与坝体排水孔相同,主要几何尺寸如图 3 所示。图中 A—B、B—B 为计算渗流量的两个断面。坝体、坝基的渗透系数分别为 1.0×10^{-8}m/s、

1.0×10^{-7}m/s。有限元计算网格如图 4 所示,计算区域沿厚度方向取 5m,坝体、坝基各设一排水孔,排水孔的中心在厚度方向 2.5m 处。

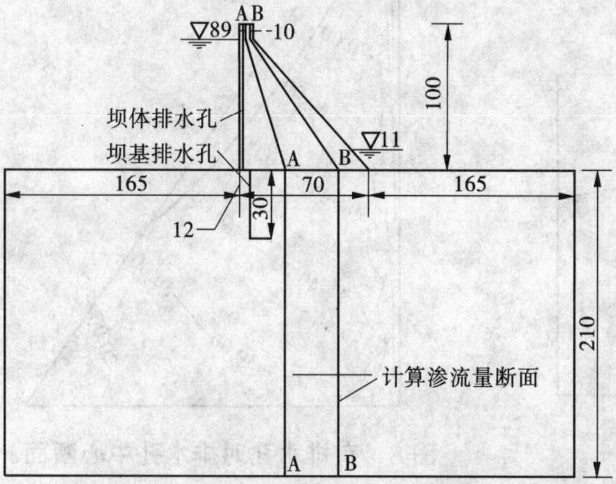

图 3　计算区域主要尺寸　(单位:m)

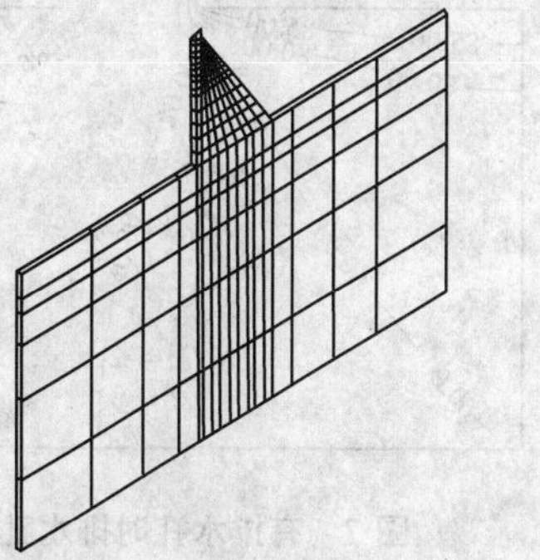

图 4　有限元计算网格

图 5、图 6 为不设排水孔时水头等值线图,图 7、图 8 为设排水孔时沿排水孔中心断面水头等值线图。由图 6、图 8 对比可知,在坝体,由于排水孔的作用,使自由面位置大幅下降,并使坝体中的渗流水头主要集中消耗在排水孔附近,降压作用十分显著。由表 1 可知排水孔的排水作用也是很明显的,在不设排水孔时,A—A 断面的渗流量为:$3.478\,998\times10^{-5}$m^3/s,而设排水孔后其渗流量减小为 $2.028\,225\times10^{-5}$m^3/s,其余渗透水量通过排水孔排出了坝外。由图 9 可以看出,坝基排水孔的设置有效地降低了坝基面的扬压力,这对维持坝体整体稳定十分有利。

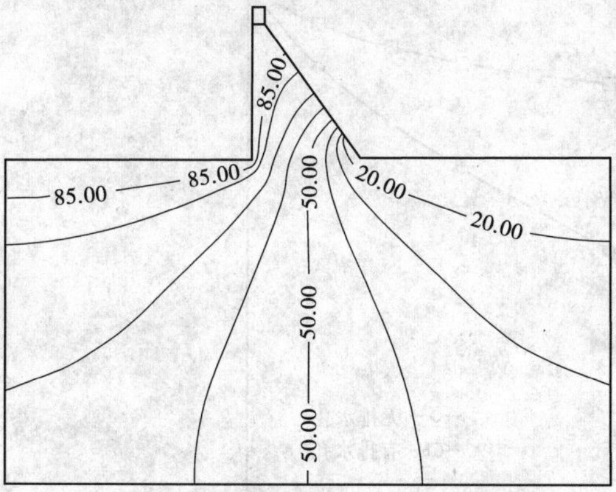

图 5　无排水孔时坝体坝基等水头线

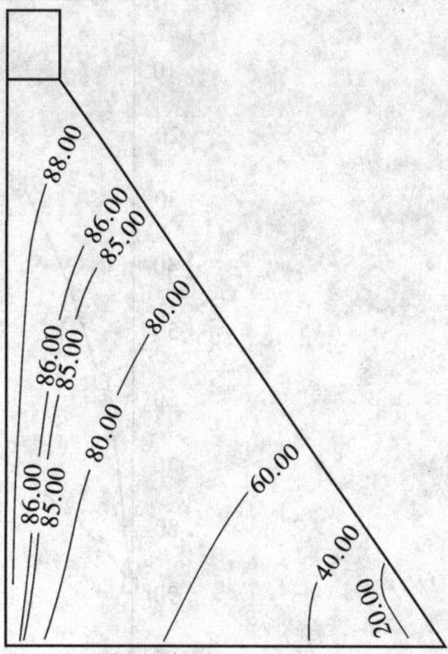

图 6　无排水孔时坝体等水头线

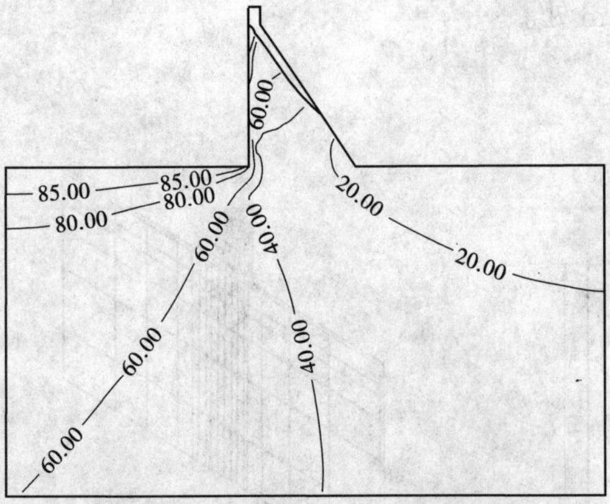

图7　有排水孔时排水孔中心断面坝体坝基等水头线

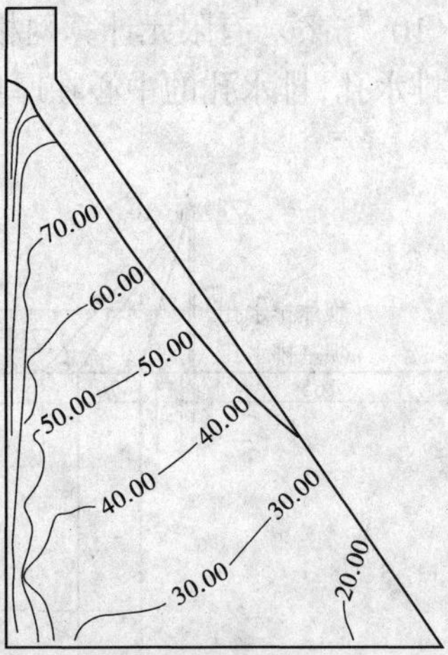

图8　有排水孔时排水孔中心断面坝体等水头线

表1　两个断面渗流量计算结果　（单位：m^3/s）

断　面	无排无孔	有排水孔
A—A	$3.478\,998\times10^{-5}$	$2.028\,225\times10^{-5}$
B—B	$3.478\,915\times10^{-5}$	$2.026\,718\times10^{-5}$
是否满足渗流连续性	是	是

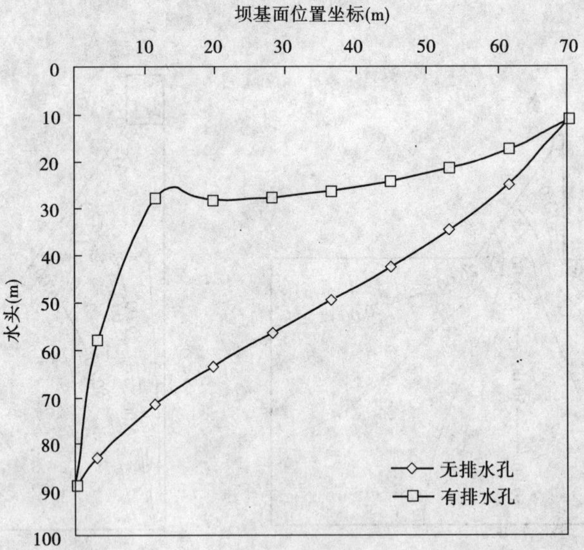

图9　坝基有无排水孔时坝基面水头分布对比

（沿排水孔中心断面）

5 结语

本文对排水孔与自由面相交的情况给出了具体的算法,有效地解决了排水孔的数值模拟问题,实例的计算结果符合工程实际规律。文中同时对渗流量的计算也提出了一种简单的方法,该方法的计算结果满足渗流连续性要求。这些研究成果对工程有一定的实用价值。

参考文献

[1] 王镭,刘中,张有天.有排水孔幕的渗流场分析.水利学报,1992(4):15~20
[2] 朱岳明,张燎军.渗流场求解的改进排水子结构法.岩土工程学报,1997(3):69~76

改进的单元渗透矩阵调整法求解无压渗流场

摘　要　针对现有单元渗透矩阵调整法解决无压渗流问题的不足,本文提出了改进算法。该法在调整渗透矩阵时对单元不同高斯点取不同的渗透系数,水上高斯点取原值的千分之一,水下高斯点取原值,以此原则计算单元渗透矩阵,从而避免了单元被自由面切割部分的体积求解。文中同时对溢出面的处理提出了新的见解。经实例证明,本方法是有效可行的。

关键词　有限元　无压渗流　自由面　溢出面

在许多水利工程中存在着无压渗流问题,这类问题的关键在于求解渗流场的边界,即确定事先不知道其位置的自由面和溢出面,属于非线性边界问题。用有限元求解时,常采用的方法有两种:固定网格法与变网格法。但变网格法容易产生网格畸形,并难以处理渗流介质水平分层的情况,尤其在渗流场与应力场耦合分析中,更加显出其局限性。所以自从 Neuman[1] 于 1973 年提出求解自由面的 Calerkin 法以后,国内外许多学者致力于固定网格法的研究[2~6],提出了许多有效的方法,这些方法解决了不少问题,但也不同程度存在着缺陷。本文在 Bathe[3] 提出的单元渗透矩阵调整法的基础上,对其进行了改进,改进后的方法具有编程简单、计算效率和精度高等特点。

1　渗流的连续性方程及边界条件

根据 Darcy 定理及水流连续性条件,当渗透系数主方向与坐标方向一致时,稳定渗流满足如下微分方程:

$$\frac{\partial}{\partial x}\left(k_x\frac{\partial H}{\partial x}\right)+\frac{\partial}{\partial y}\left(k_y\frac{\partial H}{\partial y}\right)+\frac{\partial}{\partial z}\left(k_z\frac{\partial H}{\partial z}\right)+Q_0=0 \tag{1}$$

式中:$H=h+z$,其中 $h=\frac{p}{\gamma}$为压力水头(p 为水压力;γ 为水的比重);z 为位置水头;k_x、k_y、k_z 为 3 个主渗透系数;Q_0 为域内源密度。

其中边界条件常见有如下几类:

(1)第一类边界条件。即边界(Γ_1)的水头已知

$$H|_{\Gamma_1}=\varphi(x,y,z) \tag{2}$$

(2)第二类边界条件。即边界(Γ_2)的流量已知

$$k\frac{\partial H}{\partial n}\bigg|_{\Gamma_2}=q(x,y,z) \tag{3}$$

(3)自由面及溢出面边界。

自由面 Γ_3:

本文选自《水利学报》2001 年第 8 期,作者还有朱军。

$$H|_{\Gamma_3} = Z(x,y), \quad k\frac{\partial H}{\partial n}\bigg|_{\Gamma_3} = 0 \tag{4}$$

溢出面 Γ_4：

$$H|_{\Gamma_4} = Z(x,y), \quad k\frac{\partial H}{\partial n}\bigg|_{\Gamma_4} \leqslant 0 \tag{5}$$

2 改进的单元渗透矩阵调整法

2.1 基本原理

Bathe 等提出的单元渗透矩阵调整法中，需每次迭代求出自由面的位置，再求出穿越自由面单元的水上、水下部分的体积。水上部分的渗透系数取 k/μ（μ 一般取 1 000），水下部分的渗透系数取 k。可见，要确定穿越自由面单元的水上、水下部分的体积，需先确定自由面与单元的切割情况，判断切割两部分的几何形状，这对三维而言其计算效率是很低的。而本文所提出的方法不需确定穿越自由面单元的水上、水下部分的体积，可高效地求解无压渗流场。

将计算区域划分为 3 个子区 Ω_1、Ω_2、Ω_3，其中 Ω_1 由自由面以下的单元组成，单元的渗透矩阵不用调整；Ω_3 由自由面以上的单元组成，在迭代计算中丢去；Ω_2 由自由面穿过的单元组成，问题的关键在于这个区域单元的渗透矩阵的调整。

由有限元方法可知，单元渗透矩阵中的元素可表示为

$$k_{ij} = \iiint_{\Omega^e} [B_i]^{\mathrm{T}}[k][B_j]\,\mathrm{d}x\mathrm{d}y\mathrm{d}z \tag{6}$$

式中：$[k]=\begin{bmatrix} k_x & & \\ & k_y & \\ & & k_z \end{bmatrix}$为单元渗透系数矩阵；$[B_i]^{\mathrm{T}}=\left[\frac{\partial N_i}{\partial x},\frac{\partial N_i}{\partial y},\frac{\partial N_i}{\partial z}\right]$，其中 N_i 为单元形函数。

式(6)的高斯积分公式为

$$k_{ij} = \sum_l A_l\,|J|_l[B_i]_l^{\mathrm{T}}[k]_l[B_j]_l \tag{7}$$

式中：A_l 为高斯点的权系数；$|J|_l$ 为高斯点雅可比行列式值。

在进行 i 次迭代计算后，对所有节点压力水头均小于零的单元（Ω_3），在下次计算中丢去；所有节点压力水头大于或等于零的单元（Ω_1），其单元渗透矩阵不用调整；对于自由面穿过的单元（Ω_2），通过单元节点水头可求出其高斯点压力水头 h。对于 $h\geqslant 0$ 的高斯点，渗透系数取原值 k；对 $h<0$ 的高斯点，渗透系数取 $k/1\,000$，代入式(7)计算单元渗透矩阵，这样达到调整的目的（避免了求解穿越自由面单元的水上、水下部分的体积）。为避免迭代中产生振荡，可将自由面穿过的单元加密高斯点，经对比研究表明，当高斯点加密至 64 个时（三维情况），迭代中振荡现象消除，然后重新组成总渗透矩阵，得 $i+1$ 次的有限元计算公式

$$[K_{i+1}][H_{i+1}] = \{Q\} \tag{8}$$

及计算区域

$$\Omega^{i+1} = \Omega_1^{i+1} + \Omega_2^{i+1} \tag{9}$$

式(8)中$[K_{i+1}]$为 $i+1$ 次迭代计算的总渗透矩阵；$[H_{i+1}]$为待求节点水头；$\{Q\}$为自由项。

当前后两次迭代计算的节点水头差小于允许误差时，停止计算，然后利用压力水头等于零原则求出自由面位置。

2.2 溢出面的处理

在无压渗流计算中，溢出面的处理一直没有得到很好的解决。本文将溢出面转化成第二类边界处理，取得了满意的结果。在 i 次迭代计算后，可求出溢出面单元外表面的外法向流量 q_1，在 $i+1$ 次迭代时，通过下式将其转化为第二类边界：

$$Q = \int_{\Gamma_3} [N]^{\mathrm{T}} q_1 \mathrm{d}\Gamma \tag{10}$$

相应修改式(8)中的自由项$\{Q\}$，这样可提高计算精度及加快迭代速度。

3 算例

3.1 算例 1

在图 1 的 10m×10m×10m 正方体均质挡水建筑物渗流分析中(上游水位是 10m，下游水位是 2m)，采用八节点六面体等参单元来划分网格，迭代计算只要 5 次即达到所需的精度(误差 $\varepsilon=0.01$)。自由面计算结果与解析结果吻合较好(见图 2)，证明了本方法的正确性。在与改进的方法计算对比中发现，两者水头结果差小于 3%，但计算时间上，改进前的方法为 4s，而改进后的方法为 2s，这主要是因为改进前的方法要花大量的时间用于确定自由面与单元的切割情况进而求出穿越单元的水上、水下部分的体积。笔者认为，改进方法的另一优越性在于编程简单。

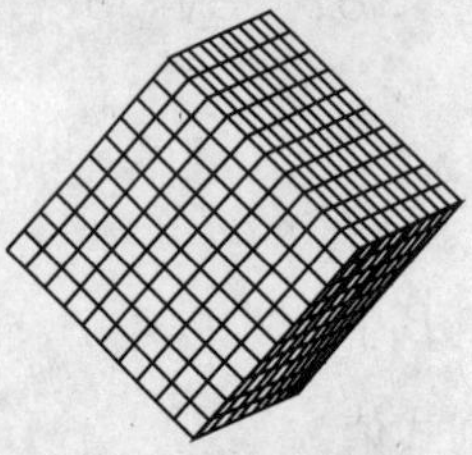

图 1　三维网格

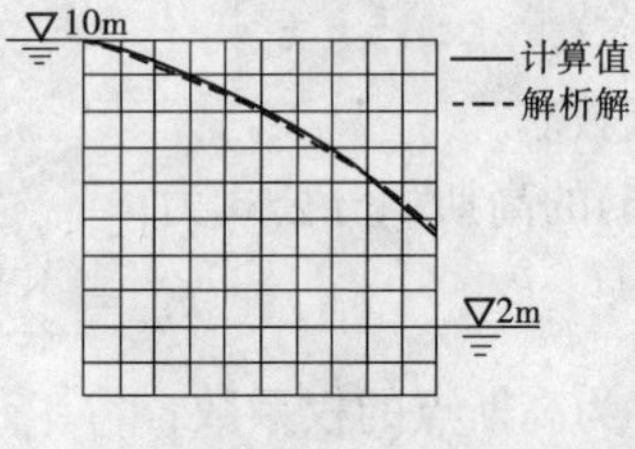

图 2　自由面计算与解析结果的对比

3.2 算例 2

某水平分层渗流介质(见图 3)，自上而下共分 5 层，各层为均匀各向同性，渗透系数分别是 10^{-7}m/s、10^{-6}m/s、10^{-5}m/s、10^{-4}m/s、10^{-3}m/s，上、下游水位分别是 25.5m、6m。有限元网格如图 4 所示，计算发现水头等值线在介质界面发生偏转，这与渗流的折射现象相符，如图 3 所示。

3.3 算例 3

某坝上游水位高程 200m，下游高程 120m，河谷对称。取一半区域计算，坝体按不透水材料处理，坝肩岩体的渗透系数为：$k_x = k_y = 1\times10^{-4}$m/s，$k_z = 4\times10^{-5}$m/s，自由面的出露面如图 5 所示，$z=160$m 及 $x=195$m 断面压力水头等值线如图 6、图 7 所示。

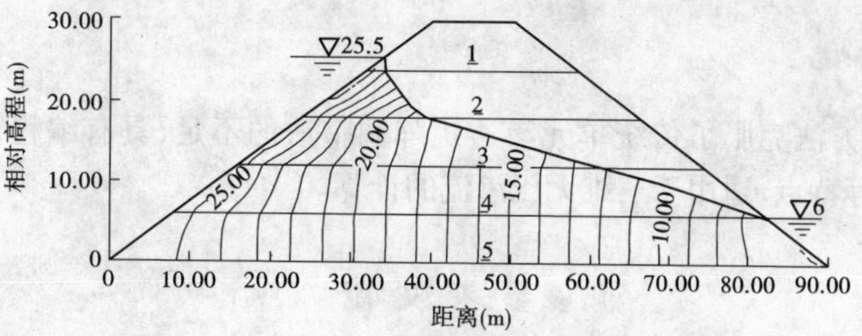

图 3 水平分层介质水头等值线 (单位:m)

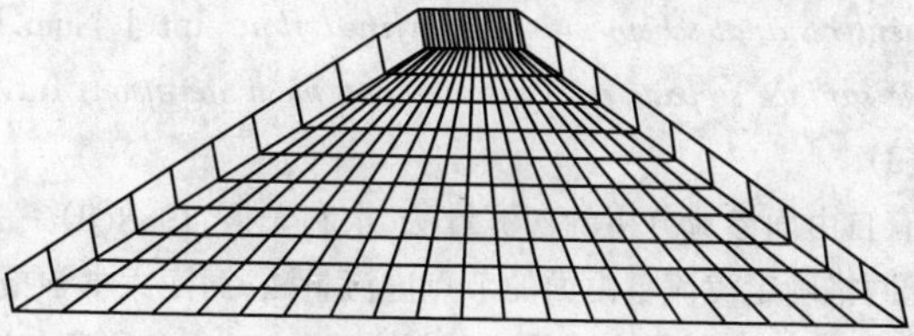

图 4 水平分层介质的有限元网格

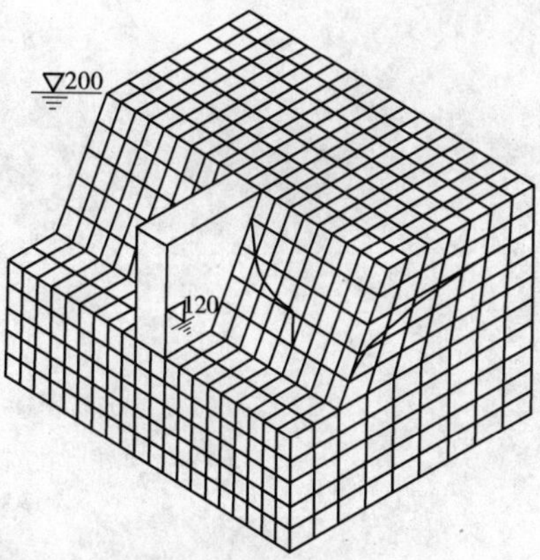

图 5 自由面出露面的位置 (单位:m)

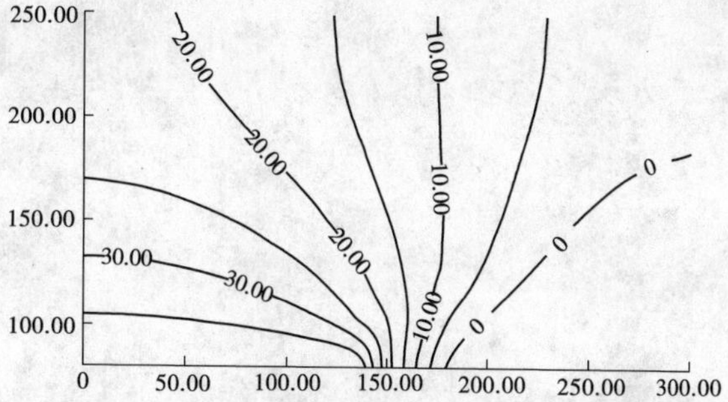

图 6 $z=160$m 断面压力水头等值线 (单位:m)

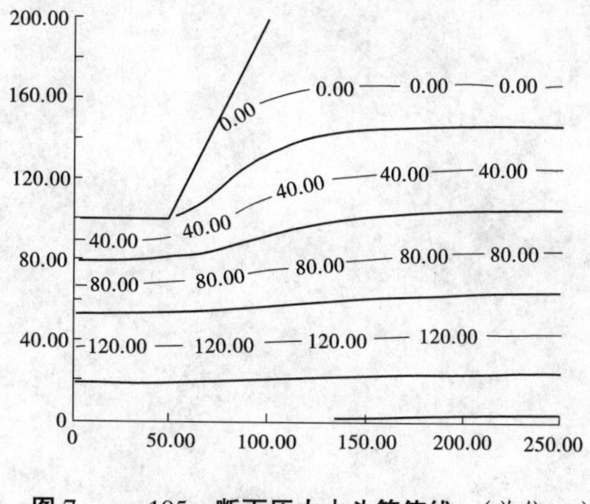

图 7 $x=195$m 断面压力水头等值线 (单位:m)

4　结语

本文提出的方法克服了传统单元渗透矩阵调整法的不足，具有编程简单、收敛速度快、计算精度高等特点，适用于三维无压渗流的计算。

参考文献

[1] Neuman S P. *Saturated-unsaturated seepage by finite elements*. Hydraulic Div., ASCE, 1973, 99(12)

[2] Desai C S. *Finite element residual schemes for unconfined flow*. Int. J. Num. Meth. Engng., 1976(10)

[3] Bathe K J. *Finite free surface seepage analysis without mesh iteration*. Int. J. Num. Anal. Methods in Geomechanics, 1979(3)

[4] 张有天，陈平，王镭.有自由面渗流分析的初流量法.水利学报，1988(8)

[5] 速宝玉，朱岳明.不变网格确定渗流自由面的节点虚流量法.河南大学学报，1991(9)

[6] 周创兵，熊文林，梁业国.求解无压渗流场的一种新方法.水动力学研究与进展，1996(10)

饱和非饱和三维多孔介质非稳定渗流分析

摘　要　对常用的饱和非饱和三维多孔介质非稳定渗流的有限元算法提出了改进，经实例证明，本方法是有效可行的。

关键词　非饱和　非稳定渗流　自由面　溢出面　有限元

土壤、沙层、砾石层等松散岩石以及具有裂隙的坚硬岩石均属于多孔介质，多孔介质的渗流属于饱和非饱和渗流，研究它的运动规律对工程有重要意义。

1　多孔介质饱和非饱和渗流的微分方程及有限元公式

1.1　渗流微分方程及定解条件

当主渗透系数方向与坐标方向一致时，多孔介质饱和非饱和渗流满足如下微分方程：

$$\frac{\partial}{\partial x}\left(k_x(h)\frac{\partial H}{\partial x}\right)+\frac{\partial}{\partial y}\left(k_y(h)\frac{\partial H}{\partial y}\right)+\frac{\partial}{\partial z}\left(k_z(h)\frac{\partial H}{\partial z}\right)=\frac{\partial \theta}{\partial t} \tag{1}$$

式中：$H=h+z$，其中 h 为压力水头（饱和区为正，非饱和区为负），z 为位置水头；$k_x(h)$、$k_y(h)$、$k_z(h)$为渗透系数，在饱和区，主渗透系数为饱和值，与 h 无关，在非饱和区，是压力水头 h 的函数[1]；$\theta=n\cdot s$ 为体积含水量（n 为空隙率，s 为饱和度，s 在饱和区等于 1，在非饱和区是 h 的函数[1]），在饱和区等于介质空隙率，与 h 无关，在非饱和区，$\frac{\partial \theta}{\partial t}=n\frac{\partial s}{\partial t}+s\frac{\partial n}{\partial t}$，不考虑介质骨架变形对渗流的影响时，$\frac{\partial \theta}{\partial t}=n\frac{\partial s}{\partial h}\frac{\partial H}{\partial t}$，故(1)式又可写为

$$\frac{\partial}{\partial x}\left(k_x(h)\frac{\partial H}{\partial x}\right)+\frac{\partial}{\partial y}\left(k_y(h)\frac{\partial H}{\partial y}\right)+\frac{\partial}{\partial z}\left(k_z(h)\frac{\partial H}{\partial z}\right)=n\frac{\partial s}{\partial h}\frac{\partial H}{\partial t} \tag{2}$$

多孔介质饱和非饱和渗流微分方程的定解条件由初始条件与边界条件构成。

初始条件：

$$H(x,y,z,0)=\varphi(x,y,z,0)$$

边界条件通常有如下几类：

(1)第一类边界条件。即已知水头边界 Γ_1

$$H(x,y,z,t)\mid_{\Gamma_1}=\gamma(x,y,z,t)\quad(t>0) \tag{3}$$

(2)第二类边界条件。即已知流量边界 Γ_2

$$K\cdot\frac{\partial H(x,y,z,t)}{\partial l}\bigg|_{\Gamma_2}=q(x,y,z,t)\quad(t>0) \tag{4}$$

式中 l 为边界 Γ_2 外法向向量。

(3)自由面及溢出面边界。

本文选自《武汉大学学报(工学版)》2001 年第 3 期，作者还有朱军、陆述远。

自由面 Γ_3：

$$H(x,y,z,t)\mid_{\Gamma_3} = Z(x,y,z,t), K \cdot \left.\frac{\partial H(x,y,z,t)}{\partial l}\right|_{\Gamma_3} = 0 \quad (t>0) \tag{5}$$

溢出面 Γ_4：

$$H(x,y,z,t)\mid_{\Gamma_3} = Z(x,y,z,t), K \cdot \left.\frac{\partial H(x,y,z,t)}{\partial l}\right|_{\Gamma_4} \leqslant 0 \quad (t>0) \tag{6}$$

1.2 渗流有限元法

微分方程(2)的定解问题等价于如下泛函的极值问题：

$$I(H) = \iiint\limits_V \left\{ \frac{1}{2}\left[k_x(h)\left(\frac{\partial H}{\partial x}\right)^2 + k_y(h)\left(\frac{\partial H}{\partial y}\right)^2 + k_z(h)\left(\frac{\partial H}{\partial z}\right)^2 \right] + n\,\frac{\partial s}{\partial h}\frac{\partial H}{\partial t}H \right\} \mathrm{d}V - \int\limits_{\Gamma_2} qH\mathrm{d}\Gamma \tag{7}$$

根据研究区域的结构特性,将计算区域离散为多个单元,某单元的水头插值函数为

$$H(x,y,z,t) = \sum N_i(\xi,\eta,\zeta)H_i$$

式中：$N_i(\xi,\eta,\zeta)$为单元的形函数；H_i 为节点水头；(ξ,η,ζ)为基本单元的局部坐标。

对式(7)取其变分等于零,并对各单元叠加,可得有限元方程

$$[K][H]_{t_0+\Delta t} + \frac{[S]\{[H]_{t_0+\Delta t} - [H]_{t_0}\}}{\Delta t} = [P]_{t_0+\Delta t} \tag{8}$$

式中：矩阵$[K]$由各单元矩阵$[K]^e$ 叠加而得,矩阵$[K]^e$ 的元素可表示为

$$K_{ij} = \iiint\limits_{v^e} [B_i]^{\mathrm{T}} \begin{bmatrix} k_x(h) & & \\ & k_y(h) & \\ & & k_z(h) \end{bmatrix} [B_j]\mathrm{d}v \tag{9}$$

其中$[B_i]^{\mathrm{T}} = \left[\frac{\partial N_i}{\partial x}, \frac{\partial N_i}{\partial y}, \frac{\partial N_i}{\partial z}\right]$；矩阵$[S]$由各单元矩阵$[S]^e$ 叠加而得,矩阵$[S]^e$ 的元素可表示为

$$S_{ij} = \iiint\limits_{v^e} n\,\frac{\partial s}{\partial h}N_iN_j\,\mathrm{d}v \tag{10}$$

矩阵$[P]_{t_0+\Delta t}$为$t_0+\Delta t$ 时的节点等效流量列阵(Δt 为时间步)；$[H]_{t_0+\Delta t}$、$[H]_{t_0}$分别为时间 $t_0+\Delta t$、t_0 时的节点水头列阵。

2 多孔介质饱和非饱和非稳定渗流的有限元改进算法

在非稳定渗流计算的每个时间步中须进行迭代,迭代的过程就是根据压力水头确定单元的渗透系数 k 及$\frac{\partial s}{\partial h}$,进而修正矩阵$[K]$、$[S]$。在一般的有限元算法中,单元的压力水头取各节点值的平均,但当单元划分的尺寸较大时,上述处理方法就显得比较粗糙。本文所提出的方法是以高斯点为研究对象,在单元中不同的高斯点有不同的压力水头,进而可得到不同的渗透系数 k 及$\frac{\partial s}{\partial h}$,这样修正得的矩阵$[K]$、$[S]$比一般方法更合理。

式(9)、式(10)的高斯积分公式分别为

$$K_{ij} = \sum_l A_l [B_j]^{\mathrm{T}} \begin{bmatrix} k_x(h) & & \\ & k_y(h) & \\ & & k_z(h) \end{bmatrix} |J|_l \tag{11}$$

$$S_{ij} = \sum_l A_l n \frac{\partial s}{\partial h} N_i N_j |J|_l \tag{12}$$

在时间 $t_0+\Delta t$ 中 i 次迭代计算后,可得各节点的压力水头 h,进而可求出单元各高斯点的压力水头。对于压力水头大于或等于零的高斯点,处于饱和区,渗透系数取饱和值;对于压力水头小于零的高斯点,处于非饱和区,渗透系数取值可由试验所测定的渗透介质 $k\sim h$ 曲线得出,$\frac{\partial s}{\partial h}$也可由实测得的 $s\sim h$ 曲线得出。在计算单元矩阵$[K]^e$、$[S]^e$时,由上述方法确定各高斯点上的渗透系数 k 及$\frac{\partial s}{\partial h}$,代入式(11)、式(12)求出单元矩阵$[K]^e$、$[S]^e$;再将各单元叠加,得矩阵$[K]$、$[S]$。于是时间 $t_0+\Delta t$ 的$i+1$ 次有限元计算公式为

$$[K]_{t_0+\Delta t}^{i+1}[H]_{t_0+\Delta t}^{i+1} + \frac{[S]_{t_0+\Delta t}^{i+1}\left\{[H]_{t_0+\Delta t}^{i+1} - [H]_{t_0}\right\}}{\Delta t} = [P]_{t_0+\Delta t} \tag{13}$$

式中:$[K]_{t_0+\Delta t}^{i+1}$、$[S]_{t_0+\Delta t}^{i+1}$ 分别为矩阵$[K]$、$[S]$在时间 $t_0+\Delta t$ 的 $i+1$ 次迭代的值;$[H]_{t_0+\Delta t}^{i+1}$、$[H]t_0$分别为时间 $t_0+\Delta t$ 的$i+1$ 次迭代及时间 t_0 时的节点水头列阵。

当前后两次迭代计算的节点水头差小于允许误差时,停止本时间步的计算。

3 有限元计算中的几个问题

3.1 时间步

在计算中,时间步的取值不能太小,否则将产生过大的累积误差;时间步也不能太大,否则计算将不收敛。由于在实际工程中不同研究对象的渗透性相差很大,故对所研究对象首先应进行一定量的试算,根据计算的收敛情况,来确定可行时间步的数量级(秒、时、天),然后选定一初始时间步进行计算,如收敛,则取此值为该时段的步长,否则,时间步减半,直到获取收敛的时间步为止。

3.2 溢出面的处理

在渗流计算中,溢出面的处理一直没有得到很好的解决。本文将溢出面转化为第二类边界处理,取得了满意的结果。

在 i 次迭代计算后,可求出溢出面单元外表面的外法向流量 q_1,在 $i+1$ 次迭代时,通过下式将其转化为第二类边界:

$$Q = \int_{\Gamma_4} [N]^{\mathrm{T}} q_1 \mathrm{d}\Gamma \tag{14}$$

相应修改式(13)中的$[P]_{t_0+\Delta t}$,这样可提高计算精度及加快迭代速度。

3.3 计算参数的处理

在实际工程中 $k\sim h$、$s\sim h$ 的函数关系是以试验离散点的形式给出,它们的函数关系

可由离散点线性插值得来。$s \sim h$ 的线性插值造成$\frac{\partial s}{\partial h}$呈阶梯状，在计算中将产生振荡，本文将文献[2]中对$\frac{\partial s}{\partial h}$的处理方法加以改进，得出下式：

$$\frac{\partial s}{\partial h}=\frac{s(h)-s(h_0)}{A\cdot h-B\cdot h_0} \tag{15}$$

式中：h 为本时间步的压力水头；h_0 为上一时间步的压力水头；

$$A=\begin{cases}1 & (h<0)\\ 0 & (h\geqslant 0)\end{cases};B=\begin{cases}1 & (h_0<0)\\ 0 & (h_0\geqslant 0)\end{cases};$$

$$s(h)=\begin{cases}1 & (h\geqslant 0)\\ \text{由 } s\sim h \text{ 的离散点线性插值} & (h<0);\end{cases}$$

$$s(h_0)=\begin{cases}1 & (h_0\geqslant 0)\\ \text{由 } s\sim h \text{ 的离散点线性插值} & (h_0<0)。\end{cases}$$

采用上述方法可有效地消除计算振荡。

4　算例

4.1　砂槽模型试验

文献[3]介绍的砂槽模型长 315cm、宽 23cm、高 33cm。模型材料为均匀砂，孔隙率为 0.44，饱和渗透系数为 3.3×10^{-3}m/s，非饱和砂土的饱和度、负压、相对渗透系数关系如表 1 所示。初始条件采用上下游水位均为 10cm 的平衡态，在时间 0s，上游水位骤升至 30cm，自由面计算结果与试验对比如图 1 所示，两者吻合较好，证明了本方法的正确性。

表 1　砂土的土水特性曲线

饱和度	负压(kPa)	相对渗透系数
1	0	1
0.82	0.325	0.97
0.64	0.65	0.94
0.50	0.91	0.20
0.45	1.00	0.13
0.18	10.0	0.01

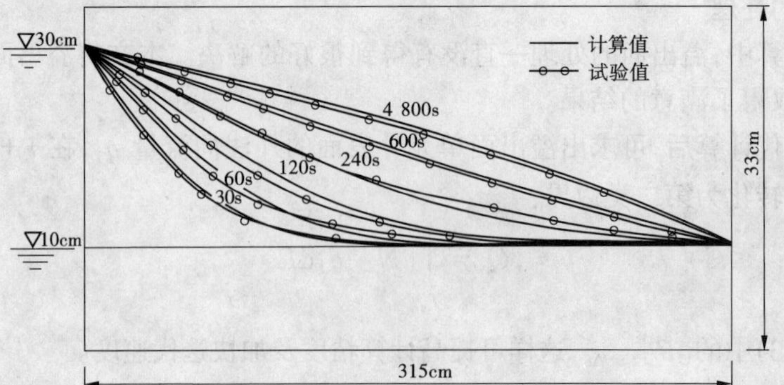

图 1　砂槽模型自由面的计算解与试验结果对比

4.2 工程实例

某均质土坝，坝高 50m，顶宽 10m，上游坝坡 1∶2，下游坝坡 1∶1.5。饱和渗透系数为 3.4×10^{-6}m/s，孔隙率为 0.464，土水特性参数见表 2。坝体竣工时土体的饱和度为 80%，上下游无水。取沿轴线方向 10m 长的坝段为计算对象，三维网格如图 2 所示。

(1)水位上升工况自由面的变化情况：上下游水位在 30d 内分别均匀升至 45m、5m。各时间段自由面的位置如图 3 所示。

表 2　土的土水特性曲线

饱和度	负压(kPa)	相对渗透系数
1	0	1
0.989 2	21.19	9.80e－1
0.976 3	31.00	9.10e－1
0.939 6	39.44	4.80e－1
0.631 5	47.87	1.00e－1
0.528 0	51.31	6.00e－2
0.379 3	61.12	1.00e－2
0.286 6	72.89	2.00e－3
0.212 5	92.02	2.00e－4
0.177 6	115.07	2.00e－5
0.154 7	138.12	3.00e－6

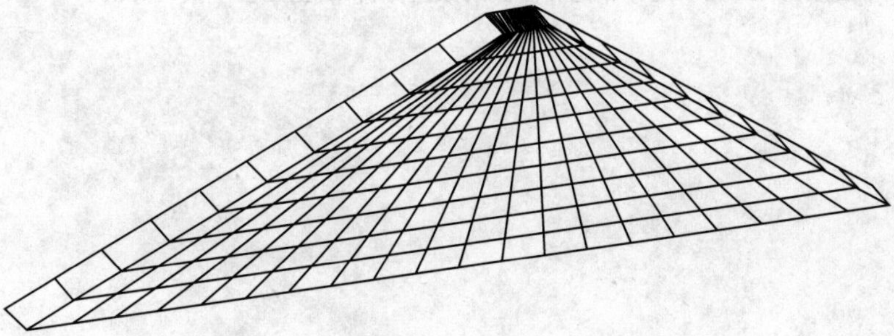

图 2　三维网格图

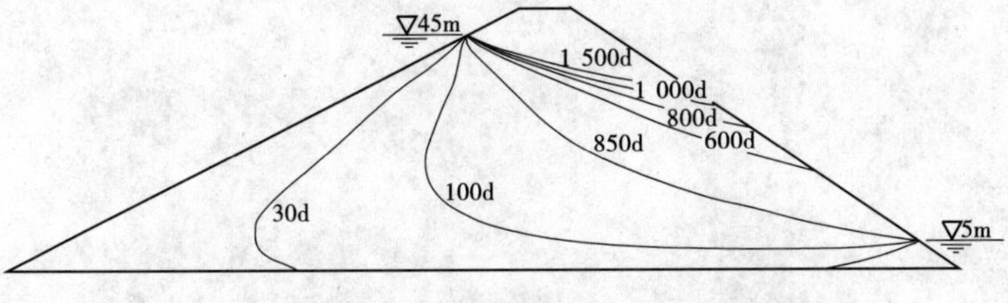

图 3　水位上升工况各时间段自由面的位置

(2)水位下降工况自由面的变化情况：水位上升 1 500d 后上游水位在 10d 内均匀降至 5m，下游水位不变。各时间段自由面的位置如图 4 所示。

由图(3)、图(4)可知,自由面在两种工况的初期变化很快,随着时间的推移,变化逐渐变慢,直到趋于稳定。在上游水位骤降时,坝内的水位滞后于坝外水位的降落,在上游面附近形成"倒流",这会严重危及上游坝坡的稳定。

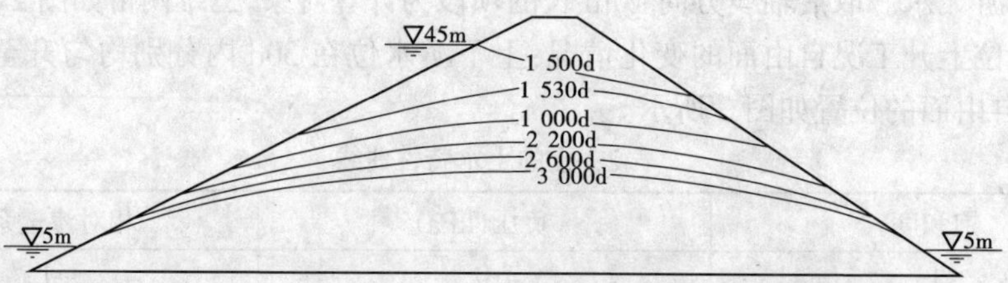

图 4　水位下降工况各时间段自由面的位置

5　结语

本文提出了饱和非饱和三维多孔介质非稳定渗流的有限元算法,对溢出面本文也提出了处理方法。该方法的计算结果是符合工程实际规律的,具有使用价值。

参 考 文 献

[1] Fredlund D G, Rahardio H.非饱和土力学.陈仲颐等译.北京:中国建筑工业出版社,1997

[2] 吴梦喜,高莲士.饱和非饱和土体非稳定数值分析.水利学报,1999(12)

[3] 高骥,雷光耀,张琐春.堤坝饱和非饱和渗流的数值分析.岩土工程学报,1988(6)

饱和模型非定常渗流的数值求解方法

摘　要　提出了饱和模型非稳定流的有限元算法，并对自由面流量补给项提出了一种简单的处理方法，从而避免了在迭代中求解自由面的位置，最后给出了计算实例。

关键词　饱和模型非定常渗流　有限元　自由面

渗透介质的非定常渗流模型现在主要有两种：饱和模型及饱和非饱和模型。饱和非饱和模型非定常渗流的数值计算方法相对而言比较简单，对于饱和模型非定常渗流，由于存在自由面流量补给项问题，处理起来比较复杂。现有的计算方法是采用变网格法在自由面上加流量补给项（见文献[1]～文献[3]），但该方法难以处理三维问题。本文利用高斯公式提出了一种简单的处理方法，有效地解决了饱和模型非稳定渗流的数值计算问题。

1　饱和模型非定常渗流的微分方程及边界条件

根据Darcy定理及水流连续性条件，当渗透系数主方向与坐标方向一致时，非定常渗流满足如下微分方程：

$$\frac{\partial}{\partial x}\left(k_x\frac{\partial H}{\partial x}\right)+\frac{\partial}{\partial y}\left(k_y\frac{\partial H}{\partial y}\right)+\frac{\partial}{\partial z}\left(k_z\frac{\partial H}{\partial z}\right)+Q_0=S_s\frac{\partial H}{\partial t} \tag{1}$$

式中：$H=h+z$，其中 $h=\dfrac{p}{\gamma}$ 为压力水头（p 为水压力，γ 为水的比重），z 为位置水头；k_x、k_y、k_z 为三个主渗透系数；Q_0 为域内源密度；S_s 为单位储水系数(1/m)，即在单位体积的饱和渗流介质内，在单位水头改变下，由于渗流介质压缩和土体的膨胀所释放的储存水量，在一般的情况下由于自由面下降所引起的介质压缩或弹性释放水量比因自由面下降而排出的水量小得多，在计算中常忽略不计。

微分方程只有与其特定的边界条件和初始条件一起才能构成一个适定的定解问题，初始条件和边界条件表述如下。

初始条件：

$$H(x,y,z,t)\mid_{t=0}=H_0(x,y,z) \tag{2}$$

边界条件一般有如下几种：

(1)第一类边界。即边界(Γ_1)的水头已知

$$H\mid_{\Gamma_1}=\varphi(x,y,z,t) \tag{3}$$

(2)第二类边界。即边界(Γ_2)的流量已知

$$k\frac{\partial H}{\partial n}\mid_{\Gamma_2}=q(x,y,z,t) \tag{4}$$

(3)自由面及溢出面边界。

本文选自《岩土力学》2002年第3期，作者还有朱军、蓝青松、钟砥宁。

自由面 Γ_3：

$$H|_{\Gamma_3} = Z(x,y),\quad k\frac{\partial H}{\partial n}\bigg|_{\Gamma_3} = \mu\frac{\partial H}{\partial t}n_z \tag{5}$$

溢出面 Γ_4：

$$H|_{\Gamma_4} = Z(x,y),\quad k\frac{\partial H}{\partial n}\bigg|_{\Gamma_4} \leqslant 0 \tag{6}$$

式(5)中的 $\mu\frac{\partial H}{\partial t}n_z$ 为自由面上由于自由面变动而引起的流量补给；μ 为给水度，它表示自由面改变单位高度时，从含水层单位截面积上吸收或排出的水量，是无量纲数；n_z 是自由面外法线方向向量 $n=\{n_x,n_y,n_z\}$ 的第三分量。

2　渗流有限元方程

微分方程(1)的定解问题等价于如下泛函的极值问题：

$$I(H) = \iiint\limits_V \left\{\frac{1}{2}\left[k_x\left(\frac{\partial H}{\partial x}\right)^2 + k_y\left(\frac{\partial H}{\partial y}\right)^2 + k_z\left(\frac{\partial H}{\partial z}\right)^2\right] + S_s\frac{\partial H}{\partial t}H\right\}\mathrm{d}V - \int\limits_{\Gamma_2}\mu\frac{\partial H}{\partial t}n_z H\mathrm{d}\Gamma \tag{7}$$

根据研究区域的结构特性，将计算区域离散为有限个单元，任一单元的水头插值函数为

$$H(x,y,z,t) = \sum N_i(\xi,\eta,\zeta)H_i$$

式中：$N_i(\xi,\eta,\zeta)$ 为单元的形函数；H_i 为结点水头；(ξ,η,ζ) 为基本单元的局部坐标。

对式(7)取其变分等于零，并对各单元叠加，可得有限元方程：

$$[K][H] + [S]\left[\frac{\partial H}{\partial t}\right] - [G]\left[\frac{\partial H}{\partial t}\right] = [P] \tag{8}$$

式中：渗透矩阵 $[K]$ 由各单元渗透矩阵 $[K]^e$ 叠加而得，矩阵 $[K]^e$ 的元素可表示为

$$K_{ij} = \iiint\limits_{V^e}[B_i]^{\mathrm{T}}\begin{bmatrix}k_x & & \\ & k_y & \\ & & k_z\end{bmatrix}[B_j]\mathrm{d}v\quad (i=1,2,\cdots,n;\ j=1,2,\cdots,n) \tag{9}$$

其中 $[B_i]^{\mathrm{T}} = \left[\frac{\partial N_i}{\partial x},\frac{\partial N_i}{\partial y},\frac{\partial N_i}{\partial z}\right]$，$n$ 为单元结点数；储水矩阵 $[S]$ 由各单元储水矩阵 $[S]^e$ 叠加而得，矩阵 $[S]^e$ 的元素可表示为

$$S_{ij} = \iiint\limits_{V^e}S_sN_iN_j\mathrm{d}v \tag{10}$$

流量补给矩阵 $[G]$ 由自由面穿过各单元流量补给矩阵 $[G]^e$ 迭加而得，矩阵 $[G]^e$ 的元素可表示为

$$G_{ij} = \iint\limits_{\Gamma_3}\mu N_iN_jn_z\mathrm{d}\Gamma \tag{11}$$

其中 Γ_3 为单元与自由面的交截面。

3　有限元算法

非稳定渗流的计算由多个时间步组成，而在每个时间步中又需要进行多次迭代，在迭

代中根据压力水头修正渗透矩阵[K]、储水矩阵[S],并计算流量补给矩阵[G],详述如下。

3.1 渗透矩阵[K]、储水矩阵[S]的修正

由式(9)、式(10)可得单元$[K]^e$,$[S]^e$ 矩阵的元素高斯积分公式为

$$K_{ij} = \sum_{l=1}^{ng} |J|_l H_l [B_i]^{\mathrm{T}} \begin{bmatrix} k_x(h) & 0 & 0 \\ 0 & k_y(h) & 0 \\ 0 & 0 & k_z(h) \end{bmatrix}_l [B_j] \tag{12}$$

式中$|J|_l$、H_l 为高斯点雅可比行列式及权系数。

根据上次计算的单元高斯点压力水头 h,由下式修正渗透系数及单位储水系数:

$$\left.\begin{aligned} k_x(h) &= \begin{cases} k_x & (h \geqslant 0) \\ 10^{-3} k_x & (h < 0) \end{cases} \\ k_y(h) &= \begin{cases} k_y & (h \geqslant 0) \\ 10^{-3} k_y & (h < 0) \end{cases} \\ k_z(h) &= \begin{cases} k_z & (h \geqslant 0) \\ 10^{-3} k_z & (h < 0) \end{cases} \end{aligned}\right\} \tag{13}$$

$$S_s(h) = \begin{cases} S_s & (h \geqslant 0) \\ 10^{-3} S_s & (h < 0) \end{cases} \tag{14}$$

3.2 流量补给矩阵[G]的计算

为了求[G]矩阵,一般要先确定单元与自由面的交截面,再在交截面上求面积分,这对三维问题而言其计算效率是很低的。为此,可利用高斯公式将式(11)转化为单元体积分与各表面积分之差。

$$G_{ij} = \iint_{\Gamma_3} \mu N_i N_j n_z \, \mathrm{d}\Gamma = \iiint_{V^e} A(h) \mu \left(\frac{\partial N_i}{\partial z} N_j + \frac{\partial N_j}{\partial z} N_i \right) \mathrm{d}v - \sum_{l=1}^{m} \iint_{\Gamma_l} A(h) \mu N_i N_j n_z \, \mathrm{d}\Gamma \tag{15}$$

式中:$A(h)$为示性函数,$A(h) = \begin{cases} 1 & (h \geqslant 0) \\ 0 & (h < 0) \end{cases}$;$m$ 为单元表面个数;Γ_l 为单元的第 l 个表面。

利用上式可方便地计算出 G_{ij},而不用确定单元与自由面的交截面。

文献[1]中试验渗透介质的渗透系数 $k = 0.1$cm/s,给水度 $\mu = 0.4$,单位储水率 $S_s = 0$。基于上述理论与算法,对文献[1]中的试验进行计算,得出自由面的变化过程及位置如图 1 所示,计算结果与试验解吻合较好。

4 算例

某拱坝,河谷对称,取一半区域计算。坝体按不透水材料处理,坝肩坝基岩体的渗透系数为:$k_x = k_y = k_z = 10^{-7}$m/s,单位储水率 $S_s = 0$,给水度 $\mu = 0.03$。初始状态是上游水位高程为 138m,下游水位为 125m 的平衡态,在 150d 中,上游水位均匀上升至 195m 高程,然后,在 30d 内,上游水位又均匀降至 138m 高程。有限元网格如图 2 所示,$y = 44$m

断面各时间的压力水头等值线如图3所示。

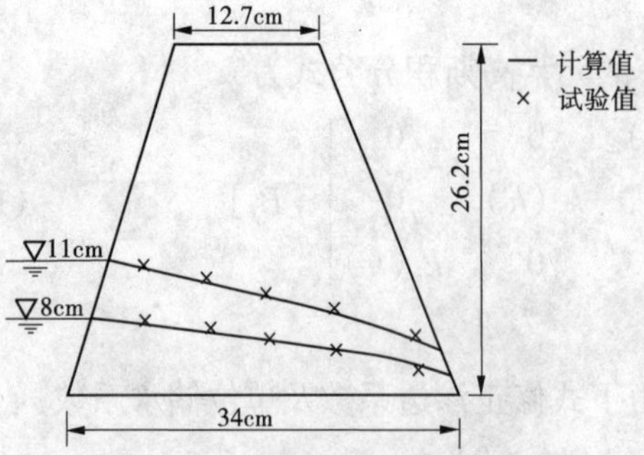

图1 计算解与试验值对比

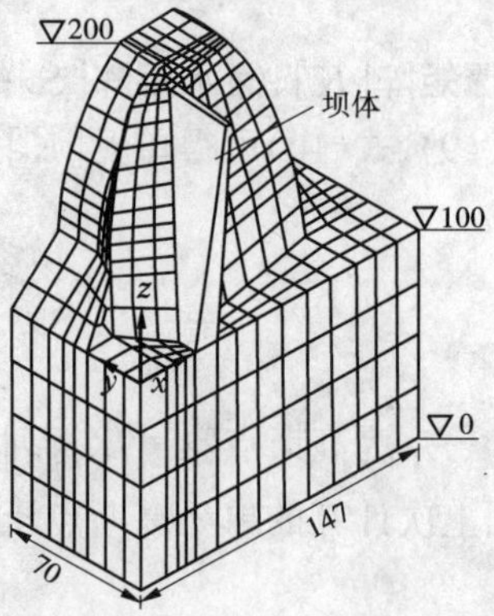

图2 有限元网格 (单位:m)

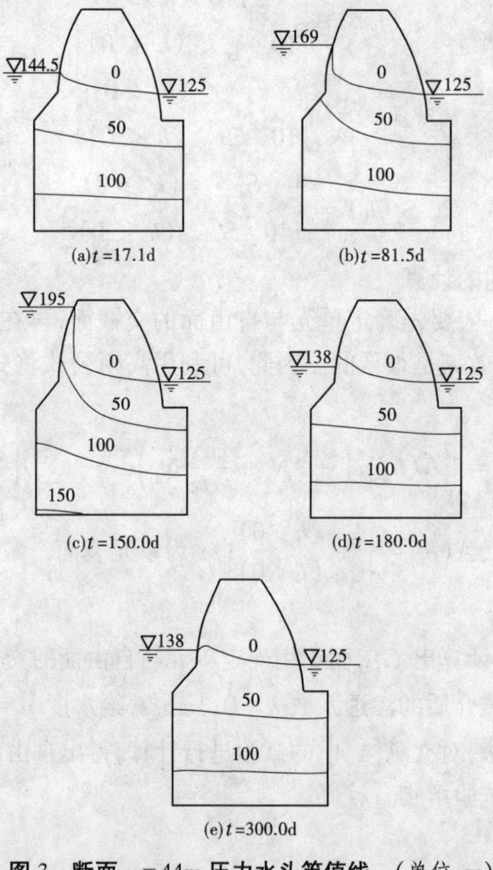

图3 断面 $y=44$m 压力水头等值线 (单位:m)

由图3可以看出在上游水位变动过程中自由面(即压力水头为零的面)的变化过程，计算出的自由面位置及溢出点符合工程规律,为工程实际提供了有益的参考。

5 结语

本文提出了饱和模型非定常渗流的有限元算法,并对自由面流量补给项给出了一种简单可行的处理方法。该有限元算法的计算结果与试验解吻合较好,对实例的计算结果是符合工程实际规律的,对工程具有一定的实用价值。

参考文献

[1] Desai C S. *A numerical procedure for three-dimensional transient free surface seepage*. Adv. Water Resources, 1983,9(6):175~181

[2] Neuman S P. *Saturated-unsaturated seepage by finite elements*. Hydraulic Div., ASCE, 1973,99(12):2233~2250

[3] Desai C S. *Finite element residual schemes for unconfined flow*. Int. J. Num. Meth. Engng., 1976, 6(10):175~181

[4] Bathe K J. *Finite free surface seepage analysis without mesh iteration*. Int. J. Num. Anal. Methods in Geomechanics, 1979, 3(1):2~22

[5] 张有天,陈平,王镭.有自由面渗流分析的初流量法.水利学报,1988,13(8):18~26

饱和软岩受压硬化、强度折减及本构模型

摘　要　单轴压试验验证了常见低渗透的饱和软岩受压前期刚度加大、强度减小。引进孔隙水影响因子建立了饱和软岩本构模型。有限单元法计算结果表明，该本构关系的计算结果和试验相似，也反映了孔隙水承担部分压力荷载，并在材料中产生了横向拉应力，以及软岩的饱和强度折减现象。

关键词　强度折减　本构关系　孔隙水影响因子　饱和软岩

软岩等材料处于自然干燥状态（湿度＜30％）和饱和状态时二者的强度差别相当显著，有些岩石的饱和状态强度仅为干燥状态的一半左右。对建于软岩基础上的拱坝，拱座基础由于受地下水位上下波动的影响，即处于干燥和饱和的往复交替状态之中，地基岩石的强度也在不断变化，将直接影响地基和上部结构物的稳定与安全。

饱和状态时，岩石材料强度的降低[1~3]首先是由于水对岩石胶质的溶解作用，使得岩粒之间的黏合力降低；其次，水和岩石中的某些成分发生了化学反应，生成物失去了原来反应物和其他颗粒的黏结作用，有些生成物体积发生膨胀，产生较大的内应力，造成岩石的崩解；再有，饱和岩石受力时，岩石的孔隙率变小，产生较大的孔隙水压力。一般来说，岩石的受力是有方向性的，在岩石的受压方向上，岩石的刚性增大，表现为弹性模量增大，但孔隙压力在各个方向上是一致的，主受力方向上的垂直水压力使岩石受到附加的拉力，而岩石的抗拉能力远小于抗压能力。因此，即使是不大的孔隙水压力也会引起软岩的破坏。岩石在形成后的漫长年代里，经历了反复多次水的浸泡，因此其浸水时的化学物理作用已趋平缓并减弱，而孔隙水的力学效应就成为影响软岩强度降低的重要因素。

为了研究新疆石门子坝软岩地基浸水软化性能，对坝基红色软岩进行了单轴压试验。同时，为模拟饱和软岩中水的力学作用，建立了饱和软岩的线弹性本构模型，并进行验证计算。

1　红色软岩单轴压试验

用新疆石门子水库坝基泥钙质胶结砾岩做试验，试件尺寸为 10cm×10cm×10cm。试件共分成3组，每组两个。其中，一个放在和原状态相近的环境（温度20℃、湿度＜30％）下，备作干燥状态试件；另一个长时间浸泡在水中，使其饱和。考虑到岩石性状的复杂、不均匀性，以及每组两个试件的可比性，在切割加工试件时，使每组的两个试件均出自同一块岩石的相邻部分。为了体现饱和软岩中孔隙水压力的影响，采用长春试验机研究所生产的试验机以最大加载速度 200kN/min 加载，3组试件的单轴压强度见表1。可见，饱和状态下软岩的单轴压强度明显低于干燥状态。

本文选自《水利水运工程学报》2002年第4期，作者还有周飞平。

表1　红色软岩单轴压强度

试件组	单轴压强度(MPa)		强度下降率(%)
	干燥状态	饱和状态	
1	47.8	31.8	33.5
2	48.4	37.1	23.3
3	48.0	35.4	26.3

第一、三组红色软岩试件两种状态下的应力—应变关系见图1。

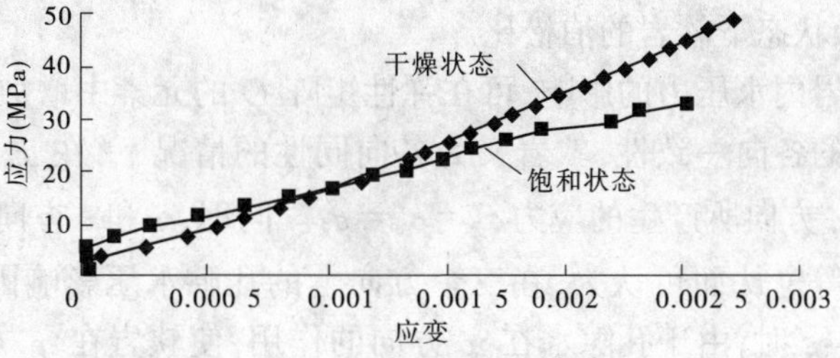

(a)第一组试件

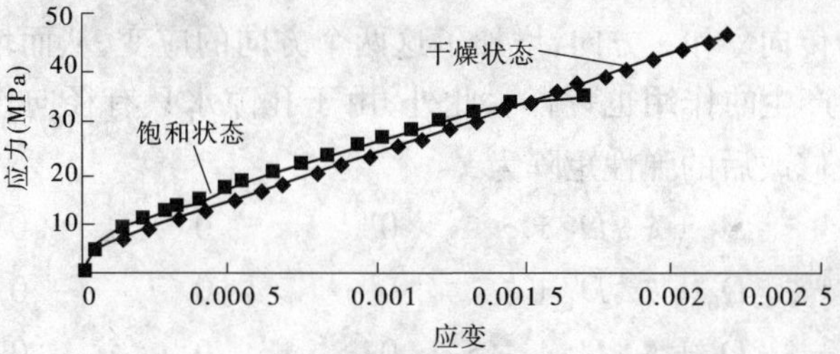

(b)第三组试件

图1　红色软岩两种状态的应力—应变关系

由图1可见,软岩在两种状态下的加载过程中,应力—应变大体保持线性关系,尤其是干燥状态更具线性特性。在加载初始阶段附近的某个区域,饱和状态软岩的弹性模量大于干燥状态,这表明饱和时的孔隙水虽有提高软岩刚度的作用,但饱和岩石的最终强度低于干燥岩石。

2　饱和软岩的线弹性本构模型

2.1　模型的建立

在多孔隙材料中,其孔隙的分布和大小极不规则,当孔隙中充满水而未能顺利排出时,由孔隙水和材料共同来承担外荷载。因此,在建立饱和软岩的本构模型时,宏观上将其作为一种均质材料来处理。同时也考虑到水只产生径向压力,而不产生剪应力。

软岩在干燥状态下的本构关系为

$$\sigma = D\varepsilon \tag{1}$$

式中:弹性矩阵

$$D=\begin{bmatrix} D_0 & D_1 & D_1 & 0 & 0 & 0 \\ D_1 & D_0 & D_1 & 0 & 0 & 0 \\ D_1 & D_1 & D_0 & 0 & 0 & 0 \\ 0 & 0 & 0 & \frac{E}{2(1+\mu)} & 0 & 0 \\ 0 & 0 & 0 & 0 & \frac{E}{2(1+\mu)} & 0 \\ 0 & 0 & 0 & 0 & 0 & \frac{E}{2(1+\mu)} \end{bmatrix}$$

其中：$D_0=E(1-\mu)/(1+\mu)(1-2\mu)$；$D_1=E\mu/(1+\mu)(1-2\mu)$；$E$ 为干燥状态下软岩的弹性模量；μ 为干燥状态下软岩的泊松比。

为了计及饱和软岩内水压力的影响，可在弹性矩阵 D 的元素中增加孔隙水压的影响因子。由于静水压力的各向一致性，软岩又为各向同性的情况下，在 x 方向产生应变 ε_x 时，则静水在 x、y 和 z 方向所产生的应力 $\sigma_x=\sigma_y=\sigma_z$。同理，$y$ 和 z 方向有应变时所产生的静水应力也各自相等。从而可认为，在三个方向上的孔隙水压影响因子应是相等的。当在 x 方向施加应变 ε_x 时，由于孔隙水在 x 方向的作用，使软岩在 x 方向的受力增加，进而体现为软岩弹性模量的提高，总体上并不产生附加力，而在 y 和 z 方向，由于孔隙水将在 x 方向受到的力传向 y 和 z 方向，增加了这两个方向的应变，从而增加了附加应力；同理，施加 ε_y 和 ε_z 所产生的作用也一样。此外，由于孔隙水只有径向作用，孔隙水的剪应力影响系数为 0，故修改后的弹性矩阵为

$$D=\begin{bmatrix} D_0+\xi & D_1+\xi & D_1+\xi & 0 & 0 & 0 \\ D_1+\xi & D_0+\xi & D_1+\xi & 0 & 0 & 0 \\ D_1+\xi & D_1+\xi & D_0+\xi & 0 & 0 & 0 \\ 0 & 0 & 0 & \frac{E}{2(1+\mu)} & 0 & 0 \\ 0 & 0 & 0 & 0 & \frac{E}{2(1+\mu)} & 0 \\ 0 & 0 & 0 & 0 & 0 & \frac{E}{2(1+\mu)} \end{bmatrix} \tag{2}$$

式中：ξ 为孔隙水影响因子。

2.2　孔隙水影响因子合理性证明

由式(2)可知：

$$\sigma_x+\sigma_y+\sigma_z=(D_0+2D_1+3\xi)(\varepsilon_x+\varepsilon_y+\varepsilon_z)$$

则饱和软岩的体积模量

$$K_s=D_0+2D_1+3\xi=\frac{E}{1-2\mu}+3\xi \tag{3}$$

可得

$$\sigma_x=(D_0-D_1)\varepsilon_x+(D_1+\xi)\frac{\sigma_x+\sigma_y+\sigma_z}{D_0+2D_1+3\xi}$$

从而有

$$(D_0 - D_1)\varepsilon_x = \frac{1}{D_0 + 2D_1 + 3\xi}[(D_0 + D_1 + 2\xi)\sigma_x - (D_1 + \xi)\sigma_y - (D_1 + \xi)\sigma_z] \quad (4)$$

现以 y 方向单独加载，考虑其对 ε_x 的影响。干燥状态下($\xi=0$)，由式(4)得

$$\varepsilon_x = \frac{-D_1\sigma_y}{(D_0 - D_1)(D_0 + 2D_1)}$$

令

$$C_0 = \frac{D_1}{(D_0 - D_1)(D_0 + 2D_1)}$$

饱和状态下($\xi>0$)，由式(4)得

$$\varepsilon_x = \frac{-(D_1 + \xi)\sigma_y}{(D_0 - D_1)(D_0 + 2D_1 + 3\xi)}$$

令

$$C_s = \frac{D_1 + \xi}{(D_0 - D_1)(D_0 + 2D_1 + 3\xi)}$$

要证明孔隙水影响因子的合理性，只需证明$(C_s - C_0)>0$即可。

$$C_s - C_0 = \frac{1}{D_0 - D_1}\left(\frac{D_1 + \xi}{D_0 + 2D_1 + 3\xi} - \frac{D_1}{D_0 + 2D_1}\right)$$

由于 $D_0 > D_1$，故只需要证明$\dfrac{D_1 + \xi}{D_0 + 2D_1 + 3\xi} - \dfrac{D_1}{D_0 + 2D_1} > 0$。设 $D_1 = a$，$D_0 + 2D_1 = b$，可得

$$\frac{D_1 + \xi}{D_0 + 2D_1 + 3\xi} - \frac{D_1}{D_0 + 2D_1} = \frac{(b - 3a)\xi}{b(b + 3\xi)}$$

则只要证明$(b - 3a)>0$：

$$b - 3a = D_0 + 2D_1 - 3D_1 = D_0 - D_1 > 0$$

因此，$(C_s - C_0)>0$，说明孔隙水影响因子 $\xi(\xi>0)$可反映软岩饱和时孔隙水对其强度的影响。

2.3 孔隙水影响因子的确定

设软岩为线弹性材料，其中的孔隙分布为随机分布，根据 Betti - Rayleigh 相关性理论[4]，可得出在外压不变的条件下，软岩在干燥和饱和状态下的压缩性公式[3]分别为

$$\frac{1}{K_d} = \frac{1}{K_0} + \frac{\varphi}{K_\varphi}, \frac{1}{K_s} = \frac{1}{K_0} + \frac{\varphi}{\overline{K_\varphi}} \quad (5)$$

式中：K_d、K_s 分别为软岩在干燥和饱和状态下的体积模量；K_0 为软岩本体矿物的体积模量；φ 为软岩的孔隙比；K_φ 为干燥状态下的“孔隙刚度”，且$\dfrac{1}{K_\varphi} = \dfrac{1}{\upsilon_p}\dfrac{\partial \upsilon_p}{\partial \sigma}\Big|_p$；饱和状态下的“孔隙刚度”$\overline{K_\varphi} = K_\varphi + \dfrac{K_0 K_f}{K_0 - K_f}$，其中 υ_p 为软岩的孔隙体积，σ 为外界压应力，P 为软岩内的孔隙水压力(保持不变)，K_f 为孔隙水的体积模量。

根据式(5)可以得出干燥、饱和状态下软岩体积模量的差：

$$\frac{1}{K_d} - \frac{1}{K_s} = \frac{\varphi}{K_\varphi} - \frac{\varphi}{\overline{K_\varphi}} \quad (6)$$

通常，岩石矿物本体的体积模量大于水的体积模量，即 $K_0 > K_f$，则有

$$\frac{K_s - K_d}{K_s K_d} = \varphi \frac{\dfrac{K_0 K_f}{K_0 - K_f}}{K_\varphi \overline{K}_\varphi} > 0$$

亦即

$$K_s - K_d > 0$$

可见,从一般的理论推导也可得出软岩饱和状态的体积模量大于干燥状态的结论。

对于式(6),设$\dfrac{\varphi}{K_\varphi} - \dfrac{\varphi}{\overline{K}_\varphi} = C_\varphi$,可得

$$\frac{1}{K_s} = \frac{1}{K_d} - C_\varphi$$

最终可得

$$K_s = K_d + \frac{C_\varphi K_d^2}{1 - C_\varphi K_d}$$

同前面所得的饱和材料的体积模量式(3)对比,得

$$\xi = \frac{C_\varphi K_d^2}{3(1 - C_\varphi K_d)} \tag{7}$$

3 饱和状态下软岩内应力数值计算

根据上述干燥和饱和状态下软岩的本构关系,采用有限单元法计算了外荷载和平面尺寸如图2所示的软岩模型(平面应变)应力分布。干燥状态的软岩弹性模量为3 000MPa,泊松比为0.2,ξ为600MPa。计算中采用平面四节点等参单元,且不计软岩的重度。

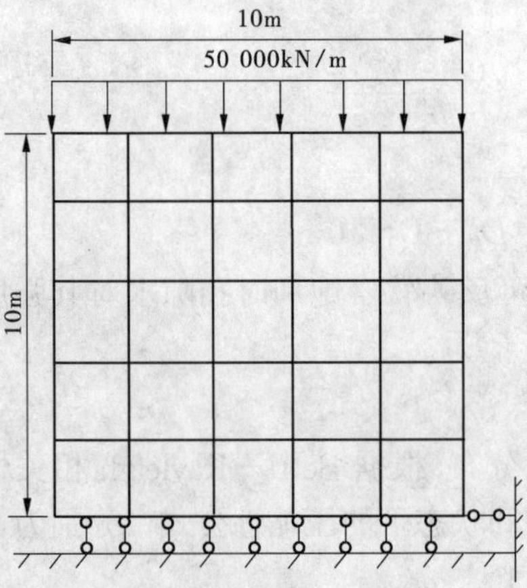

图2 平面有限元模型

该单轴压模型的内部应力呈均匀分布。干燥和饱和状态下软岩某一水平截面上的水平、竖向应力见图3。

由图3可见,干燥状态时,软岩内的水平应力为0,这是因为水平方向无约束;饱和状态时,在水平向产生了8.1MPa的拉应力,这相对外荷载50 000kN/m来说,是相当大的。同时,在干燥状态时,竖向应力为-50MPa,可见,外荷载完全由软岩本体承担;饱和状态时,竖向应力为-41.9MPa,剩下的-8.1MPa就由孔隙水承担。饱和状态时产生的横向拉应力恰好为8.1MPa,这体现了静水压力的各向一致性,也反映了饱和状态时软岩内的拉应力是由孔隙水压力造成的。

4 结语

(1)红色软岩在干燥、饱和状态下的单轴压试验表明,低渗透的软岩浸水饱和后,有初始硬化现象,但强度有所降低。

(2)根据水的涨胀力学效应建立的饱和软岩线弹性本构模型,验证了饱和软岩的体积弹性模量高于干燥状态。

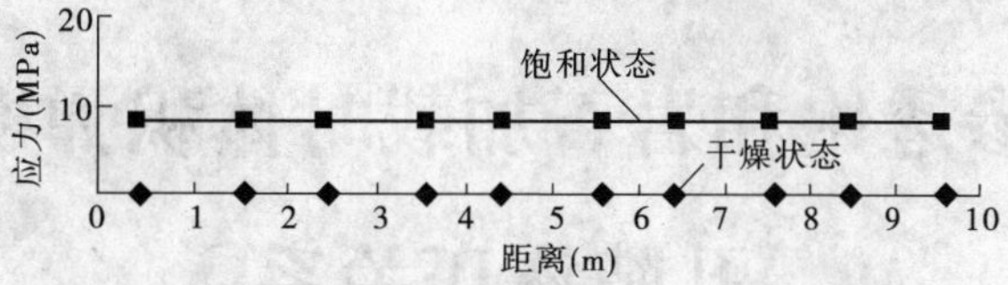

(a)水平应力

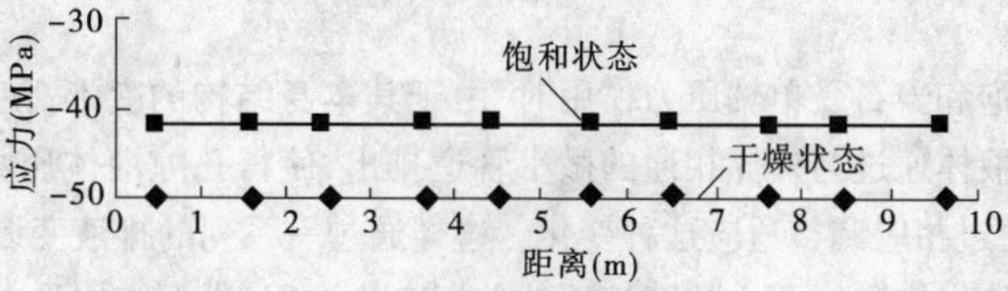

(b)竖向应力

图3　软岩内的应力分布

(3)对一个简单软岩模型进行数值计算的结果表明,饱和软岩的孔隙水确实能使软岩的强度折减。

参 考 文 献

[1] 曾云．盘道岭隧洞软弱岩石浸水软化对强度和变形特性的影响．陕西水力发电,1994,10(1):29～33

[2] 冯启言,韩宝平,隋旺华．鲁西南地区红层软岩水岩作用特征与工程应用．工程地质学报,1999,7(3):266～271

[3] Gary Mavko, Tapan Mukerji. *Seismic pore space compressibility and Gassmann's relation*. Geophysics, 1995,60(6):1743～1749

[4] Walsh J. *The effect of cracks on the compressibility of rock*. Journal of Geophysical Research, 1965,70: 381～389

低渗透饱和岩石加载时体积弹模与孔隙液压关系

摘　要　低渗透率饱和岩石受单轴压力作用时,由于其本身结构的变形,使得孔隙的液体也受压。受压的孔隙液体通过与外界相通的微小管道排出,使得孔隙液体压力降低,于是外力转嫁给固体结构,通过相应调整适应这种变化。这样通过一系列的排液变形和调整后最终达到平衡。本文定量给出饱和岩石内孔隙液压的前期变化过程、岩石结构受力过程以及饱和体体积弹模的变化过程,并通过试验验证了这一现象的变化过程的合理性。试验也展示了岩石由于结构浸水胶质软化而后期刚度下降。

关键词　饱和体　体积弹模　孔隙液压

新疆石门子碾压混凝土拱坝的坝肩基岩为红色泥钙质砾岩,质软;受水的影响较大,红色软岩饱和时受压变形大,强度也只有干燥状态的一半左右。因此,库内蓄水后,随着库水位的升高,坝肩基岩大变形和岩体受力稳定与否成为大坝安全的关键,需要对岩石饱和时力学性状进行分析研究。实际上,岩石的饱和状态最终强度小于干燥状态的现象(以后我们称之为饱和强度折减)早就已经提出[4,5],在安康、小浪底、万家寨工程中都遇到岩石的饱和强度折减问题,由于当时折减后还有足够强度或通过以对地基要求低的土坝代替混凝土坝的方式来解决。随着碾压混凝土技术的运用,筑坝的成本大幅度降低,有时即使在软弱岩基上修建碾压混凝土拱坝不仅速度快,而且花费相当费用来进行地基处理的总的造价也比修筑其他传统坝型的造价要低。再加上柔性拱之类的新的结构形式的提出[1],使得软弱岩石上的碾压混凝土拱坝变得实际可行。饱和软岩强度折减[6]和刚度变化问题就被正式摆到研究的议程上来。

饱和砾岩的刚度变化主要有两个原因:一是砾岩胶质的软化,二是孔隙水受压时产生内压而引起的涨胀效应[6]。冯启言等[5]讨论了溶解、崩解和膨胀等在红层软岩遇水失稳中所起的作用;曾云[4]对第三系软岩进行试验,得出软岩浸水强度下降,变形加大的特性。他们都只涉及到岩石胶质软化对后期强度折减的定性作用。下面我们研究软岩孔隙水的前期宏观刚化力学作用,试图建立孔隙水的力学模型。饱和体孔隙中充满了液体,其孔隙通过微小缝管与外界相通,在饱和体受到外界荷载时,饱和体本体受到压力,同时也挤压孔隙中的液体,从而使孔隙中的液体通过微小缝管向外界排出。对于饱和岩石一般受外载来说,由于外载加载很快,在加载过程中,孔隙水还来不及排出。从而我们可以观测到,对于饱和岩石在加载时,其体积弹模以及孔隙水压力的变化过程分两个阶段如下:第一阶段,饱和岩石在加载过程中,由于加载速度较快,孔隙水来不及迅速排出,因此在加载过程饱和岩石是无液体排出的[6];第二阶段,在加载完毕之后,岩石在恒定外压下,孔隙水徐徐排出,荷载也逐渐更多地转移到岩石本体上,随着孔隙水的排出,孔隙液压下降,岩石本体

本文选自《岩石力学与工程学报》2004 年 6 月第 23 卷第 11 期,作者还有周飞平。

通过应力的重新调节,继续向孔隙水施压,这样随着孔隙水的排出,重复着上述过程,直到孔隙水压下降到由于毛细作用而引起孔隙水压而止。从宏观上来看,在上面过程中,在孔隙水压下降的过程中,同时也伴随着岩石的体积模量的下降过程。但是要注意到,这个体积模量的下降是只考虑孔隙水压的减少而引起的,在实际工程中,在孔隙水的排出过程中,其压力水同时也施压于岩石本体颗粒,给岩石本体造成破坏,也使岩石的体积模量降低。图 1 为一般状态和饱和状态各自的微元的受力模式图。

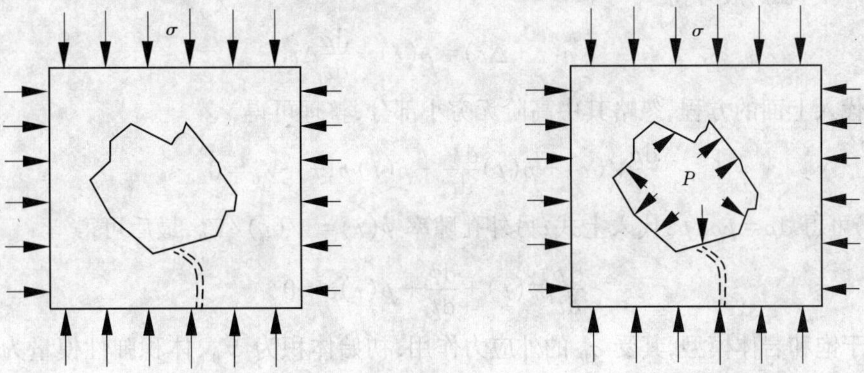

(a)一般状态　　(b)饱和状态

图 1　微元受力状态

1　数学模型的建立

下面我们研究饱和体受载后第二阶段的体积弹模、孔隙水压力以及孔隙率的相互关系。

在孔隙水受压而排出时,单位体积出水能力即出水流量与孔隙压差成正比,因此在时间间隔 Δt 内,排出水体积 ΔV 为

$$\Delta V = p(t)cV_0\Delta t \tag{1}$$

式中:$p(t)$为孔隙水压差,其随时间而变化;c 为孔隙出水系数;V_0 为岩石总体积。

另外,液体的体积压缩系数 $\beta = -\dfrac{\mathrm{d}V}{V\mathrm{d}p}$,液体受压时质量保持恒定,即

$$\rho V = C$$

其中 C 为常数。对上式两边微分整理得

$$\frac{\mathrm{d}\rho}{\rho} = -\frac{\mathrm{d}V}{V}$$

代入 β 的关系式中可得

$$\beta = \frac{\mathrm{d}\rho}{\rho\mathrm{d}p} \tag{2}$$

t 时刻孔隙中的水量为 $m(t) = \rho(t)V(t)$,$t+\Delta t$ 时刻的水量为 $m(t+\Delta t) = \rho(t+\Delta t)V(t+\Delta t)$,$V(t)$为 t 时刻的孔隙体积,$\rho(t)$为 t 时刻的孔隙水密度,在 Δt 时段内,从孔隙内流出的水量为 $\Delta m = \rho(t)\Delta V = \rho(t)p(t)cV_0\Delta t$。那么根据物质守恒定律,它们应

该满足以下关系：

$$m(t)=m(t+\Delta t)+\Delta m$$

把各表达式代入后可得

$$\rho(t)V(t)=\rho(t+\Delta t)V(t+\Delta t)+\rho(t)p(t)cV_0\Delta t$$

对 $V(t+\Delta t)$进行级数展开,忽略其高阶部分得 $V(t+\Delta t)=V(t)+\frac{\mathrm{d}V}{\mathrm{d}t}\Delta t$

同理把 $\rho(t+\Delta t)$展开得

$$\rho(t+\Delta t)=\rho(t)+\frac{\mathrm{d}\rho}{\mathrm{d}t}\Delta t$$

把它们代入上面的方程,忽略其中高阶无穷小部分,整理可得

$$\frac{\mathrm{d}\rho}{\mathrm{d}t}V(t)+\rho(t)\frac{\mathrm{d}V}{\mathrm{d}t}+\rho(t)p(t)cV_0=0$$

由式(2)可得 $\mathrm{d}\rho=\beta\rho\mathrm{d}p$,代入上式,另外孔隙率 $\phi(t)=V(t)/V_0$,最后可得

$$\frac{\mathrm{d}p}{\mathrm{d}t}\beta\phi(t)+\frac{\mathrm{d}\phi}{\mathrm{d}t}+p(t)c=0 \tag{3}$$

对于饱和岩体模型,其受 σ_0 的外应力作用,初始体积为 V_0,体积弹性模量为 $k(t)$,在 t 时刻,其体积变化量为

$$V_1=\frac{\sigma_0 V_0}{k(t)}$$

在 $t+\Delta t$ 时刻,其体积变化量为

$$V_2=\frac{\sigma_0 V_0}{k(t+\Delta t)}$$

由于此时荷载已经加载完毕,也就是说,岩石本体的弹性变形已经完成,V_2 和 V_1 的差值就是孔隙体积的变化 ΔV:

$$\Delta V = V_2 - V_1$$

$$\Delta V = \sigma_0 V_0\left[\frac{1}{k(t+\Delta t)}-\frac{1}{k(t)}\right] \tag{4}$$

对 $k(t+\Delta t)$进行一阶展开并整理得

$$\Delta V=\sigma_0 V_0\left(\frac{-\frac{\mathrm{d}k}{\mathrm{d}t}\Delta t}{k^2(t)+k(t)\frac{\mathrm{d}k}{\mathrm{d}t}\Delta t}\right)$$

由于相对于 $k^2(t)$,$k(t)\frac{\mathrm{d}k}{\mathrm{d}t}\Delta t$ 为高阶无穷小,可忽略不计,另外 $\Delta\phi=\Delta V/V_0$,最后整理可得

$$k^2(t)\frac{\mathrm{d}\phi}{\mathrm{d}t}+\sigma_0\frac{\mathrm{d}k}{\mathrm{d}t}=0 \tag{5}$$

另外,对于一般线弹性的饱和岩石,在没有液体渗出时,其体积模量 K_{sat} 可以写成[2,3]

$$\frac{1}{K_{sat}}=\frac{1}{K_0}+\frac{\phi}{\tilde{K}_\phi} \tag{6}$$

这里
$$\widetilde{K_\phi}=K_\phi+\frac{K_0K_f}{K_0-K_f}$$

$$\frac{1}{K_\phi}=\frac{1}{V_p}\frac{\partial V_p}{\partial \sigma}\bigg|_p \tag{7}$$

式中:K_0 为岩石本体体积弹模;K_f 为孔隙液体体积弹模;V_p 为孔隙体积;ϕ 为孔隙率。

对于饱和岩石受力,而孔隙液体渗出时,由于孔隙液体渗出的过程比较缓慢,因此我们可以认为在每个渗出的瞬间,岩石都处于一种平衡状态。因此,对于一个非渗出的饱和岩石受力时的体积弹模和孔隙率的关系同样也适用于缓慢渗出状态的岩石,只是缓慢渗出饱和岩石的体积弹模以及孔隙率是随时间变化的,其关系如下:

$$\frac{1}{K_{sat}(t)}=\frac{1}{K_0}+\frac{\phi(t)}{\widetilde{K_\phi}(t)} \tag{8}$$

这里 $\widetilde{K_\phi}(t)=K_\phi(t)+\dfrac{K_0K_f}{K_0-K_f}$

$$\frac{1}{K_\phi(t)}=\frac{1}{V_p(t)}\frac{\partial V_p}{\partial \sigma}\bigg|_p \tag{9}$$

在这个液体渗出过程中,$p(t)$和 $\phi(t)$的关系如下式所示[3]($\phi(t)$隐含在 K_ϕ 之中):

$$p(t)=\frac{\dfrac{1}{K_\phi}}{\dfrac{1}{K_\phi}+\dfrac{1}{K_f}-\dfrac{1}{K_0}}\sigma_0 \tag{10}$$

下面考虑一下 K_ϕ 和 ϕ 的关系,在式(7)中,$\dfrac{1}{K_\phi}=\dfrac{1}{V_p}\dfrac{\partial V_p}{\partial \sigma}\bigg|_p=\dfrac{1}{\phi(t)V_0}\dfrac{\partial V_p}{\partial \sigma}\bigg|_p$,考虑岩石为线弹性的,在岩石受恒压力 σ_0 的作用时,其孔隙率 ϕ 越小,岩石本体所承受的压力越大,孔隙水所承受的压力越小。因此,从式(10)可以看出,$\dfrac{1}{K_\phi}$应该随着 ϕ 减小而变小。为了简单起见,我们可以认为$\dfrac{\partial V_p}{\partial \sigma}\bigg|_p$ 在整个过程中与孔隙率 ϕ 的平方成正比,即 $C_\phi\phi^2(t)$(C_ϕ 为一常数)。因此可得

$$K_\phi=\frac{V_0}{C_\phi\phi(t)} \tag{11}$$

把式(11)代入式(10),同时令$\dfrac{1}{K_f}-\dfrac{1}{K_0}=K'_{f0}$,可得

$$p(t)=\frac{\phi(t)}{\phi(t)+\dfrac{K'_{f0}V_0}{C_\phi}}\sigma_0 \tag{12}$$

这样,由式(3)、式(5)和式(12),我们就得到饱和岩石在受恒外力状态时的关于体积弹模 $k(t)$、孔隙率 $\phi(t)$和孔隙液体压力 $p(t)$函数关系的方程组:

$$\left.\begin{aligned}&\frac{\mathrm{d}p}{\mathrm{d}t}\beta\phi(t)+\frac{\mathrm{d}\phi}{\mathrm{d}t}+p(t)c=0\\&k^2(t)\frac{\mathrm{d}\phi}{\mathrm{d}t}+\sigma_0\frac{\mathrm{d}k}{\mathrm{d}t}=0\\&p(t)=\frac{\phi(t)}{\phi(t)+\dfrac{K'_{f0}V_0}{C_\phi}}\sigma_0\end{aligned}\right\}\tag{13}$$

可以根据相应的初始边界条件来解这一方程组。

把方程组(13)的第三式带入第一式,令$\dfrac{K'_{f0}V_0}{C_\phi}=\gamma$,可得

$$\frac{\phi'(t)\phi(t)\sigma_0\gamma\beta}{[\phi(t)+\gamma]^2}+\phi'(t)+\frac{\phi(t)\sigma_0 c}{\phi(t)+\gamma}=0\tag{14}$$

整理上式可得

$$\frac{\phi'(t)\sigma_0\gamma\beta}{\phi(t)+\gamma}+\frac{\phi'(t)[\phi(t)+\gamma]}{\phi(t)}+\sigma_0 c=0\tag{15}$$

解方程(15)可得

$$\phi(t)+(\sigma_0\gamma\beta\ln\gamma+\gamma)\ln\phi(t)=-\sigma_0 ct+C_1$$

上式中令 $\sigma_0\gamma\beta\ln\gamma+\gamma=\alpha$,简化得

$$\phi(t)+\alpha\ln\phi(t)=-\sigma_0 ct+C_1\tag{16}$$

这就是 $\phi(t)$和时间 t 的关系式,$\phi(t)$是一隐函数。从式(16)可以看出,当 $t=0$ 时, $C_1=\phi(0)+\alpha\ln\phi(0)$;当 $t\to\infty$时,$\phi\to0$。

对于一般岩石来说,ϕ 相对较小,远小于 1。因此,对于式(16),忽略第一项 $\phi(t)$后,可以表示成

$$\phi(t)=C_0\mathrm{e}^{-B_0 t}\tag{17}$$

式中:$C_0=\mathrm{e}^{C_1/\alpha}$;$B_0=\dfrac{\sigma_0 c}{\alpha}$。

把式(17)代入式(12)可得

$$p(t)=\frac{C_0\mathrm{e}^{-B_0 t}}{C_0\mathrm{e}^{-B_0 t}+\gamma}\sigma_0$$

最后整理可得

$$p(t)=\frac{C_0\sigma_0}{C_0+\gamma\mathrm{e}^{B_0 t}}\tag{18}$$

这样,我们就得到了在外界恒压下,饱和岩石内水压力 $p(t)$随时间 t 的变化过程,由式(18)可知,$p(t)$随着时间的延伸而衰减,当 $t\to\infty$时,$p(t)\to0$。

把式(17)代入式(8)可得饱和岩石在恒压下体积弹模 $k(t)$随时间 t 的变化过程:

$$\frac{1}{k_{sat}(t)}=\frac{1}{K_0}+\frac{K'\mathrm{e}^{-2B_0 t}}{1+K''\mathrm{e}^{-B_0 t}}\tag{19}$$

式中: $K'=\dfrac{C_\phi C_0^2}{V_0}$;$K''=\dfrac{K_0K_fC_\phi C_0}{V_0(K_0-K_f)}$。

这样，由式(17)～式(19)，得出了饱和岩石在恒压下的体积模量 $k(t)$、孔隙水压 $p(t)$ 以及孔隙率 $\phi(t)$ 各自随时间 t 的变化函数关系。

由上面所推导的式(19)可以看出，在加载刚开始，即 $t=0$ 时，饱和岩石的体积模量 $k(t)$ 是大于一般干燥状态时的体积模量 K_0 的，随着时间的延伸，孔隙水的排出，饱和岩石的体积模量 $k(t)$ 逐渐降低，慢慢地逼近 K_0。以下的单轴压试验验证了上述过程。

2 试验验证

为了验证孔隙水的排出过程，特地设计了软岩在恒载下的饱和状态和干燥状态的对比试验。采用新疆石门子坝基红色软岩，长春试验机研究所生产的试验机。试件的尺寸为10cm×10cm×10cm，试件共分成3组，每组两个：一个放在和原状态相近的环境(温度20℃、湿度<30%)下，备作一般干状态试件；另外一个放在水中长时间浸泡，使其饱和。另外，考虑到岩石性状的复杂性和不均匀性，为了使每组的两个试件具有可比性，在切割加工试件时，使每组的两个试件均出自同一块岩石的相邻两部分。加载速度为200 kN/min，最终荷载为120kN。

观测了试件48h内的位移，以大概每5s一次的频率记录位移数据点。由于数据点数目太多，因此在下面的时间—位移图上，不再标识数据点的位置，而只是画出数据点的连线。

三组试件的初始时段内饱和状态和干燥状态时间—位移曲线对比图见图2、图3、图4。

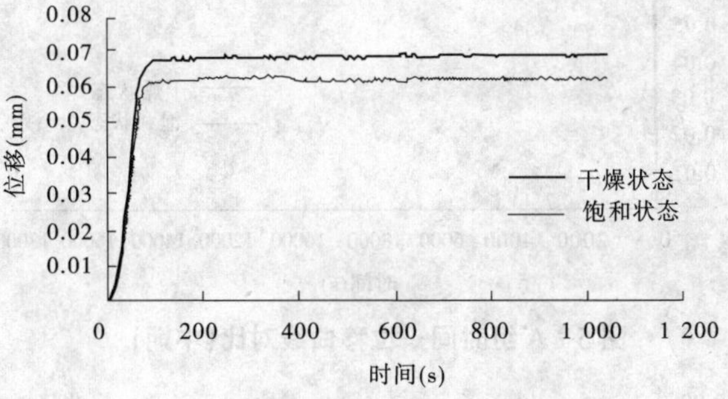

图2 A组时间—位移曲线对比

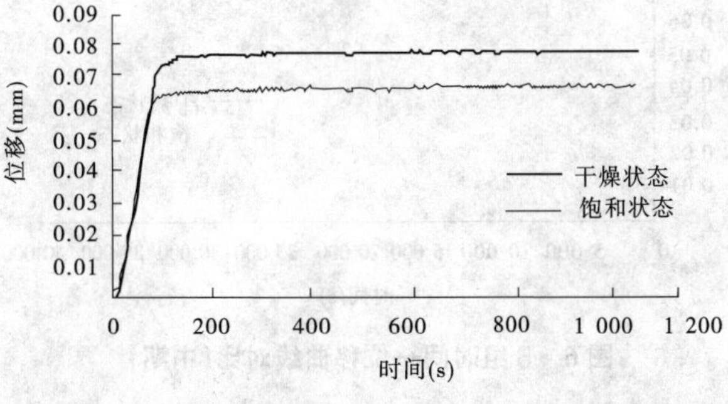

图3 B组时间—位移曲线对比

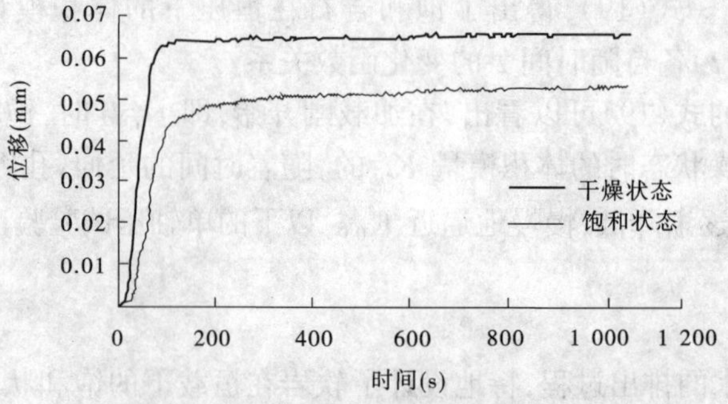

图 4　C 组时间—位移曲线对比

由这三幅图可以看出，随着时间的递增，荷载的增加，位移也跟着呈线性增加，当达到预定荷载后，曲线拐向水平方向，因此在此荷载下岩石还是弹性阶段。另外，在达到预定荷载后，饱和曲线都在干燥曲线下面，这说明预定荷载下，当孔隙水还没有排出时，干燥岩石的位移要比饱和岩石的大，这也说明了孔隙水在受压后增大岩石弹模的作用。随着孔隙水的排出，岩石的弹模也随着降低，因此饱和位移线向干燥位移线逼近，这也验证了前面理论推导的饱和软岩的体积弹模 $k(t)$ 逐渐降低逼近干燥体积弹模 K_0 的结论。而且由于岩石胶质的软化，饱和体积弹模最终低于干燥状态弹模，饱和位移曲线也越过干燥位移曲线，如图 5、图 6、图 7 所示。

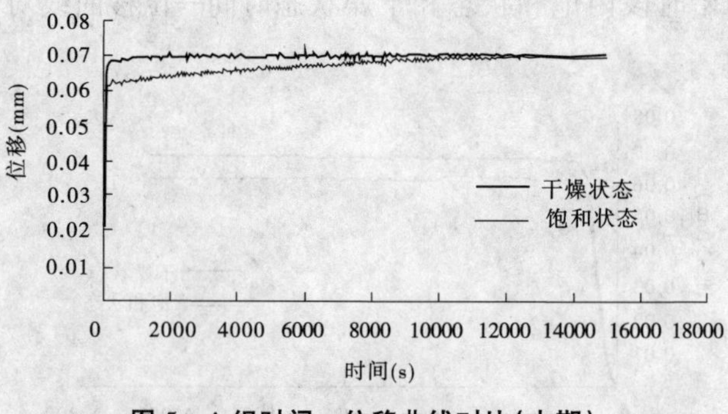

图 5　A 组时间—位移曲线对比(中期)

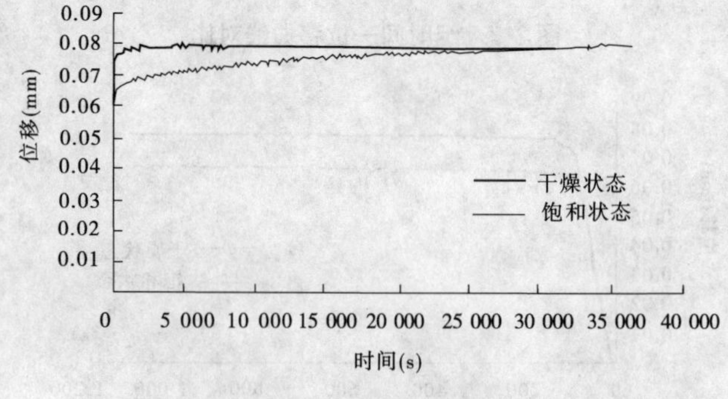

图 6　B 组时间—位移曲线对比(中期)

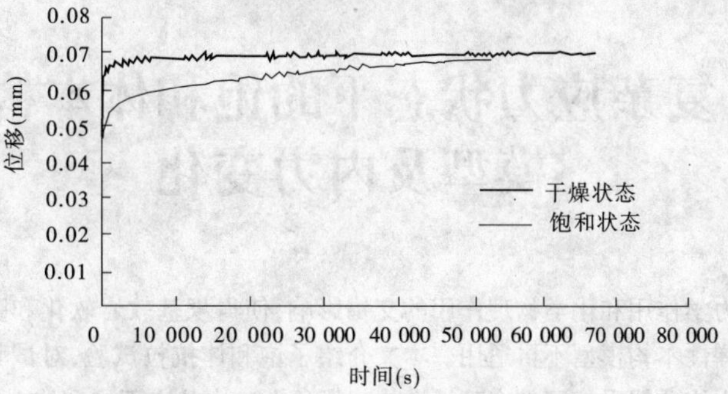

图 7 C组时间—位移曲线对比(中期)

3 结语

(1)饱和软岩在外界荷载作用下,孔隙水缓慢地排出,使软岩的弹模也随之降低。

(2)通过质量守恒等一系列的定律推导出孔隙水压在外界恒荷载下的变化规律。

(3)红色软岩的单轴恒载试验验证了孔隙水的力学作用,以及孔隙水的排水过程。

参 考 文 献

[1] 刘光廷,徐增辉,李鹏辉. 柔性拱和软弱地基上的碾压混凝土拱坝. 清华大学学报,2002(11)

[2] Walsh J. *The effect of cracks on the compressibility of rock*. Journal of. Geophysical Research,1965,70:381~389

[3] Gary Mavko, Tapan Mukerji. *Seismic pore space compressibility and Gassmann's relation*. GEOPHYSICS,1995,60(6): 1743~1749

[4] 曾云. 盘道岭隧洞软弱岩石浸水软化对强度和变形特性的影响. 陕西水力发电,1994,10(1):29~33

[5] 冯启言,韩宝平,隋旺华. 鲁西南地区红层软岩水岩作用特征与工程应用. 工程地质学报,1999,7(3):266~271

[6] 周飞平,刘光廷. 饱和软岩受压硬化、强度折减及本构模型. 水利水运工程学报,2002(4)

复杂应力状态下的饱和体本构模型及内力变化

摘　要　水的力学作用和化学物理作用的交错影响,使得坝基软岩软化和受力更为复杂,也使一般固体线弹性本构模型不再适用。本文介绍了饱和体抗拉试验,对试验结果进行拟合,用试验验证了本构曲线受拉区的合理性。构建了复杂应力状态下饱和体本构模型,实现了复杂应力饱和体计算的有限元算法,并验证了算法的可行性和收敛性。根据新构建的本构模型和算法,给出了相应的三维有限元计算程序,其计算算例的结果验证了本构模型的合理性和算法的正确性。

关键词　岩石性质及测定　饱和体　本构模型　复杂应力

软岩等材料处在自然干燥状态(湿度<30%)时和孔隙内充满水时二者的强度差别很大[1~3],有些岩石的饱和状态的抗压强度仅为干燥状态的一半左右。对于软岩基础上的拱坝,拱座基础由于受地下水位的上下波动的影响,即处于干燥和饱和的往复交替状态之中,地基岩石的强度也在不断地变化,将直接影响地基和上部结构物的稳定和安全。孔隙水对岩石的影响大致分为两部分:首先是孔隙水对岩石的化学物理作用,降低岩石的刚度[1,2];其次是孔隙水在受压未能排出时产生的涨胀效应[3~4]。

在本文中,饱和体是以软岩为代表的一类有复杂闭合孔隙,而孔隙水又对其结构产生软化作用的材料。因此,是以软岩为代表来研究孔隙水对饱和体的力学性能的影响。

1　软岩拉伸试验

1.1　试件的制备

结合某工程坝基泥钙质胶结砾岩与仿真计算来进行岩石测试,试件的尺寸选为10cm×10cm×10cm。试件共分成3组,每组两个,一个放在和原状态相近的环境(温度20℃、湿度<30%)下,备作一般干状态试件,另外一个放在水中长时间浸泡,使其饱和。另外,由于岩石性状的复杂性和不均匀性,为了使每组岩石的两个试件具有可对比性,在试件的切割加工时,使每组的两个试件出自同一块岩石的相邻两部分。采用把试件黏结到拉伸头,然后通过拉伸头接到试验机的加载头的方式来实施拉伸加载。

1.2　试验结果与分析

3组试件的抗拉强度如表1所示。首先,由于软岩干燥状态的单轴抗压强度大于40MPa,而饱和状态的单轴抗压强度也大于10MPa[3],从表1可以看出,软岩的单轴抗拉强度远低于其单轴抗压强度;其次,饱和状态的抗拉强度要小于干燥状态时,其中相差最大的A组的饱和状态的抗拉强度仅只有干燥状态的27.3%;再有,这3组岩石同样都是红色软岩,但由于它们来自不同的部位,水的化学物理作用效果不同,它们的抗拉强度差

本文选自《清华大学学报(自然科学版)》2003年第11期,作者还有周飞平、李鹏辉。

别也显著，这也说明了开始在进行试件选材时“同组同部位”的必要性。

表 1　干燥、饱和状态抗拉强度对比表

σ(MPa)(A组)		σ(MPa)(B组)		σ(MPa)(C组)	
干燥	饱和	干燥	饱和	干燥	饱和
1.776	0.484	0.696	0.547	0.572	0.179

下面以B组的为例介绍试件两种状态荷载—位移对比曲线图，如图1所示，饱和状态的荷载位移曲线都在干燥状态之下，这说明孔隙水确实对软岩的整体结构起到了削弱作用。

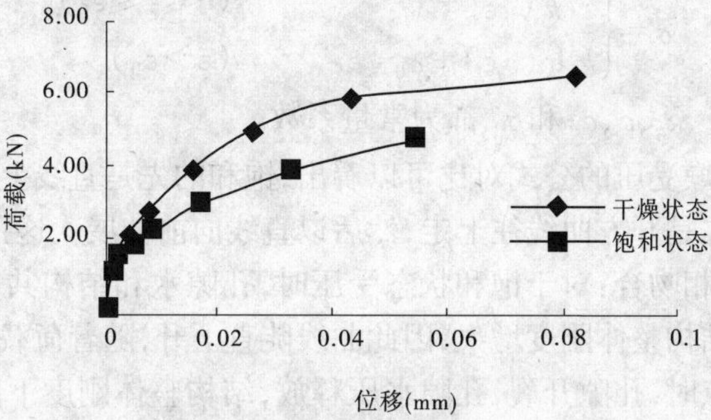

图 1　B 组荷载—位移曲线对比图

2　本构曲线及其拟合

对于复杂应力下的饱和体，当处于受压状态时，材料受到孔隙水化学物理作用削减刚度的同时还受到孔隙水涨胀增大刚度作用，由于涨胀效应大于化学物理作用而使初始刚度增大[3]；当处于受拉状态时，只受化学物理作用而刚度降低。把抗拉试验和抗压试验的结果[3]综合起来，得到了应力—应变曲线如图2所示。

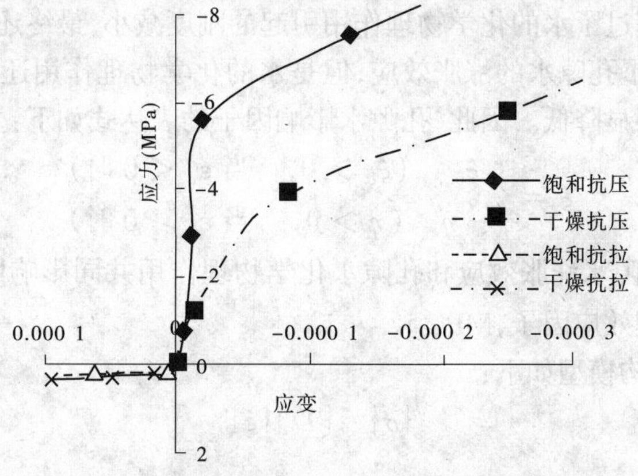

图 2　软岩干燥和饱和状态应力—应变曲线图

下面，用最小二乘法对上述试验得到的应力—应变曲线进行拟合，得到如下公式。

(1)饱和受压状态:

$$\sigma=\begin{cases}k\varepsilon & (0\leqslant\varepsilon\leqslant\varepsilon_0)\\ k_s\sqrt{c\varepsilon}+\sigma_0 & (\varepsilon>\varepsilon_0)\end{cases}\tag{1}$$

这里,整个曲线分为两个阶段,从 0 至 ε_0 是直线上升段,当 ε 大于 ε_0 后,上升趋势有所减缓,成为开方曲线。

(2)干燥受压状态:

$$\sigma=\begin{cases}k\sqrt{c\varepsilon} & (0\leqslant\varepsilon\leqslant\varepsilon_0)\\ k_s\varepsilon+\sigma_0 & (\varepsilon>\varepsilon_0)\end{cases}\tag{2}$$

(3)受拉时,干燥和饱和状态的形式一致:

$$\sigma=\begin{cases}k\sqrt{c\varepsilon} & (0\leqslant\varepsilon\leqslant\varepsilon_0)\\ k_s\ln(c_s\varepsilon)+\sigma_0 & (\varepsilon>\varepsilon_0)\end{cases}\tag{3}$$

式(1)、(2)、(3)中的 k、k_s、c、c_s 和 σ_0 都为常量系数。

由饱和受压和干燥受压的公式对比可以看出,饱和的先是直线上升,然后以开方曲线向上延伸;而干燥的先是开方曲线往上走,然后以直线向前伸展。这正好和软岩的受压过程以及孔隙水的作用相吻合:对于饱和状态受压时,孔隙水和结构共同承担荷载,孔隙水产生涨胀效应,使得结构整体刚度增大,因此曲线陡直上升,随着荷载增加,孔隙水压力增大,当达到某一临界点时,孔隙开裂,孔隙水压释放,结构整体刚度下降,曲线以相对平缓的开方曲线延伸;而对于干燥状态,在压力作用下,结构先对其孔隙等进行整合[7],曲线以开方曲线扩展,当整合完毕后,结构刚度变得稳定,因而曲线以直线延伸。

对于受拉时,由于孔隙水只对结构的整体刚度产生弱化影响,并没有改变结构的力学性能整体趋势,因此饱和和干燥的应力—应变曲线的形式相似。

3　模型的建立

在单向荷载作用时考虑用孔隙水影响因子来体现孔隙的涨胀作用[3],下面以其为基础来构造复杂应力状态下的本构模型。由以上分析可知,在受压状态时,孔隙水的涨胀效应产生的刚度增加超过了水的化学物理作用引起的刚度减小,最终还是使其刚度增大;而在受拉状态时,没有了孔隙水的涨胀效应,但是水的化学物理作用还继续起着作用,这样受拉状态时的刚度明显降低。因此,孔隙水影响因子的表达式如下:

$$\xi=\begin{cases}\xi_0 & (\xi_0>0,\quad 当\ \varepsilon_v<0\ 时)\\ -\eta & (\eta>0,\quad 当\ \varepsilon_v\geqslant0\ 时)\end{cases}\tag{4}$$

式中:ξ_0 为受压时孔隙水涨胀效应和孔隙水化学物理作用共同影响因子,MPa;$-\eta$ 为受拉时孔隙水化学物理效应因子,MPa。

因此,相应的本构模型如下:

$$\{\sigma\}=[D]\{\varepsilon\}\tag{5}$$

其中:

$$[D]=\begin{bmatrix} D_0+\xi & D_1+\xi & D_1+\xi & 0 & 0 & 0 \\ D_1+\xi & D_0+\xi & D_1+\xi & 0 & 0 & 0 \\ D_1+\xi & D_1+\xi & D_0+\xi & 0 & 0 & 0 \\ 0 & 0 & 0 & \dfrac{E}{2(1+\mu)} & 0 & 0 \\ 0 & 0 & 0 & 0 & \dfrac{E}{2(1+\mu)} & 0 \\ 0 & 0 & 0 & 0 & 0 & \dfrac{E}{2(1+\mu)} \end{bmatrix} \tag{6}$$

式中:

$$E=\begin{cases} E_p(\varepsilon_v\leqslant 0) & \text{抗压弹模} \\ E_t(\varepsilon_v>0) & \text{抗拉弹模;} \end{cases}$$

$$\mu=\begin{cases} \mu_p(\varepsilon_v\leqslant 0) & \text{抗压泊松比} \\ \mu_t(\varepsilon_v>0) & \text{抗拉泊松比;} \end{cases}$$

ξ 为孔隙水影响因子;

$$D_0=\frac{E(1-\mu)}{(1+\mu)(1-2\mu)};$$

$$D_1=\frac{E\mu}{(1+\mu)(1-2\mu)}。$$

4 有限元算法的实现

由于事先并不知道结构的应力分布,因此也并不知道结构中饱和水孔隙因子的分布,在整个加载的过程中,结构的整体刚度是变化的,是非线性的。关于此本构模型的有限元计算实现方式,可以考虑在初始计算时,每一个都考虑为受压单元,其 ξ、E 和 μ 都为受压状态时的预定值,然后加载计算,根据计算的结果统计受拉的单元,并把其相应的 ξ 设为 $-\eta$,E 为 E_t,μ 为 μ_t;再重新计算总刚,再解方程……这样经过多次迭代,直到所有的受拉区的都为 $-\eta$、E_t 和 μ_t 为止。这样,在饱和体结构的受压区,由孔隙影响因子来体现孔隙水的涨胀效果,而在受拉区,孔隙水影响因子为 $-\eta$。因此,最终的计算结果体现了孔隙水的影响。算法的流程图如图 3 所示。

5 迭代的收敛性证明

首先,由于荷载是静力恒载,在整个加载过程中,由于受拉区的卸载,导致受拉区的扩张,扩张后的受拉区再卸载,受拉区再扩张……经过多次卸载扩张之后,最终达到平衡。通过这个过程可以看出,随着受拉区的扩大,结构的整体刚度也随着降低,因此在静力恒载作用下,结构的整体刚度是下降的。可见荷载位移曲线应该是上凸的。

其次,在迭代过程中,把虚拟的由水所承担的那部分拉应力转移到材料本体来承担时,由于被转移区未被转移的主要拉应力依然由材料本体所承担,因此被转移区不会在这个转移过程中实现其性质的改变,也就是不会由受拉区突然转变为受压区。可见,在迭代

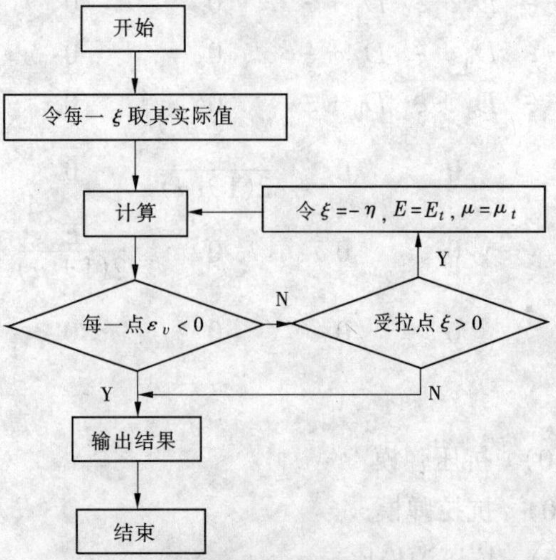

图 3　迭代求解过程流程图

过程中，材料中不会出现反复拉压变化的区域，因此在迭代过程中，每一次统计到的孔隙水影响因子 ξ 大于零的受拉区域和当次迭代所产生的新的受拉区域是等价的。从而，在迭代过程中以统计 ξ 大于零的受拉区域作为当次迭代所产生的新的受拉区是合适的。

在迭代过程中，每一次根据所求得的位移进行刚度修正，最后逼近收敛到结构实际刚度，迭代的过程如图 4 所示，最终收敛 P—U_0 处。

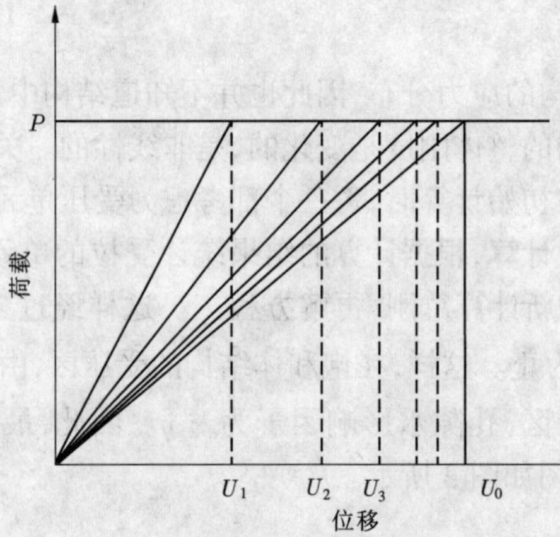

图 4　迭代过程示意图

6　计算实例

根据上述复杂应力状态本构关系以及迭代求解方式编写了三维有限元计算程序，用 ANSYS 来完成有限元模型的建立，并对模型进行优化，最后在进行后处理时，根据需要可实现饱和—干燥状态等值线的对比图。

所建模型如图 5 所示，模型尺寸 10m×6m×10m，顶部受 100kN/m^2 压荷载Ⅰ和左侧上部受 100kN/m^2 荷载Ⅱ。材料弹模 $E_p = 3\ 000$MPa，$E_t = 800$MPa，泊松比 $\mu_p = 0.2$，

$\mu_t=0.24$,孔隙水影响因子 ξ 为 600MPa,η 为 0。单元采用三维 20 节点等参元,一共有 600 个单元。竖向为 y 轴方向,横向为 x 轴方向,纵向为 z 轴方向。

工况 1:单向均匀受压。单独受荷载Ⅰ作用,约束为底部和地基接触部分竖向约束。

工况 2:单向均匀受拉。所受荷载大小和位置与荷载Ⅰ一致,但是方向与其相反,为竖向均布拉力,约束与工况 1 一样。

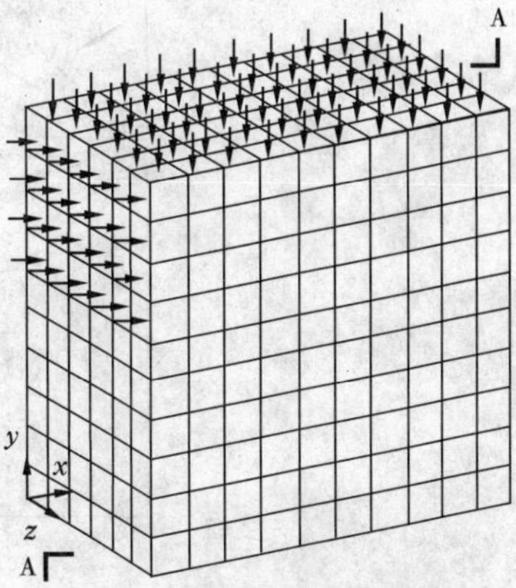

图 5 计算模型图

可以看出,工况 1 在结构中产生一个均匀压力场,而工况 2 产生了一个均匀拉力场,计算结果如表 2 所示。由表 2 可以看出,在均匀压力场中,干燥状态时,荷载完全被结构本体所承担,由于在 x 和 y 方向没有约束,因此 σ_x、σ_z 为 0;饱和状态时,竖向荷载被结构本体和孔隙水分别承担,各自为 -91.1 kN/m^2 和 -8.9 kN/m^2,而结构本体的 σ_x 和 σ_z 为 8.9kN/m^2,正好和孔隙水所承担的竖向荷载的大小相等。这就说明了孔隙水在承担竖向荷载时,产生涨胀效应,把所受荷载向各个方向传递,最终被结构本体承担。在均匀拉力场中,饱和状态和干燥状态的受力状态完全一致,孔隙水对结构的受力分布并没有产生影响。这些与前面所作的孔隙水所起的力学涨胀效应的分析完全吻合。

表 2 两种工况应力计算结果

状 态	饱和状态 σ(kN/m^2)			干燥状态 σ(kN/m^2)		
方 向	x 向	y 向	z 向	x 向	y 向	z 向
受压	8.9	−91.1	8.9	0	−100	0
受拉	0	100	0	0	100	0

工况 3:复杂外荷载。荷载为图 5 所示的两组荷载Ⅰ和Ⅱ,边界约束为底部与地基接触部分固结约束。进行了饱和、干燥对比计算,在其计算结果中,取了截面 $z=3.0$m(图 5 中的 A—A 截面)的 σ_x 应力分布等值线分布如图 6 所示。

由图 6 应力 σ_x 分布图可以看出,干燥状态和饱和状态应力分布差别较大,除了左下角的 16.63kN/m^2 的等值线外,饱和状态的等值线都向左上方有一定的偏移。如在干燥状态左上侧等值线 -25.05kN/m^2 位置,其相应饱和状态的值为 -15kN/m^2 左右,而且在右下角形成一个 16.63kN/m^2 的拉力区,可见孔隙水的确引起结构受力状态的恶化。

由此可见,饱和状态和干燥状态的应力分布差别的确是显著的,而且出现了干燥状态时没有的拉力区。因此,有必要对饱和状态时孔隙水的涨胀作用进行考虑和关注。

7 结语

本文对软岩进行饱和状态和干燥状态的抗拉对比试验,根据抗拉试验结果和抗压试

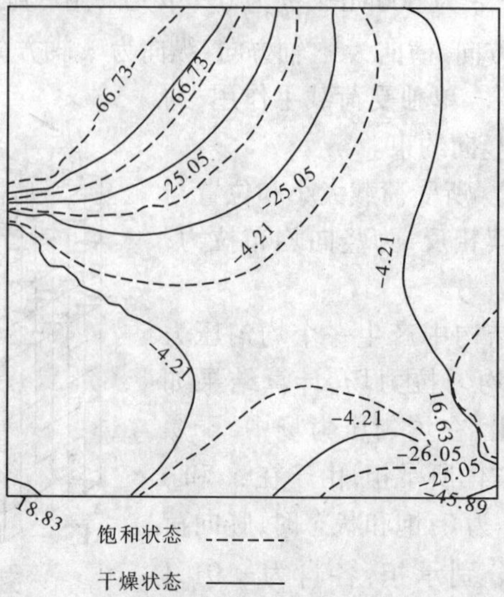

图 6　应力 σ_x 等值线分布图　（单位:kN/m²）

验的结果得到软岩在饱和、干燥状态的应力—应变曲线对比图,并对试验结果进行了曲线拟合,得到了复杂受力状态的饱和状态线弹性本构模型。给出了复杂受力状态下有限元计算迭代方法,并验证了迭代的收敛性。给出了饱和体复杂受力状态的有限元计算程序,计算分析了实例。计算结果表明了在复杂应力状态下,通过孔隙水影响因子来考虑孔隙水的涨胀效应是有效合理的,考虑饱和体孔隙水的涨胀作用是必须的。

参 考 文 献

[1] 曾云．盘道岭隧洞软弱岩石浸水软化对强度和变形特性的影响．陕西水力发电，1994,10(1):29～33

[2] 冯启言,韩宝平,隋旺华．鲁西南地区红层软岩水岩作用特征与工程应用．工程地质学报,1999,7(3):266～271

[3] 周飞平,刘光廷．饱和软岩受压硬化、强度折减及本构模型．水利水运工程学报,2002,(4):39～43

[4] 刘光廷,周飞平．低渗透饱和岩石加载时体积弹模与孔隙液压关系．岩石力学与工程学报,2004 年 6 月,23(11):1792～1796

[5] Walsh J. *The effect of cracks on the compressibility of rock*. J of Geophysical Research. 1965,70:381～389

[6] Gary Mavko, Tapan Mukerji. *Seismic pore space compressibility and Gassmann's relation*. GEOPHYSICS,1995,60(6):1743～1749

[7] 周维垣．高等岩石力学．北京:水利电力出版社,1994

软弱地基上的碾压混凝土拱坝应力与位移分析

摘　要　某工程在软弱基础上修建碾压混凝土拱坝,以加快速度,合并挡水、溢洪和泄洪建筑物,减少投资。但坝高大于百米,基础软弱,应力和位移大,尤其是坝肩向下游位移大。提出设置推力墩新结构来增强拱座受力,限制其变形。示例对水压荷载作用下坝体的应力和位移进行三维仿真分析,表明仅设置 30m 长的推力墩即可使坝体应力普遍下降 50%,位移减小 20%;坝肩基岩几乎处于微压状态,水压应力向推力墩转移,加大坝基底面减小坝体沉陷。由于推力墩结构减小了拱跨度,增强了拱坝的整体性,分担了主要的坝肩荷载,可使拱坝应力得到改善,位移得到控制。

关键词　碾压混凝土拱坝　推力墩　软弱基础

通常修建拱坝理想的条件是河谷狭窄,基岩性能良好(均匀、完整、足够强度、透水性小等)的刚性基础上。在软弱基础上修建拱坝尤其是较薄的、较高的碾压混凝土拱坝易使坝体的变位过大,局部应力集中恶化,以至于造成坝体不稳定和坝体破坏。因此,尽管修建碾压混凝土拱坝工程量少,工艺简化,施工速度快,但在软弱基础上建造碾压混凝土拱坝还有很多技术难题尚待解决。本文通过改进坝体结构以及局部加固基础,以改善坝体应力和位移,使软岩上修建拱坝成为可行的且是经济的。

1　软弱基础上的某碾压混凝土拱坝

某工程主坝前期为高 108m 的碾压混凝土拱坝,坝址区广泛分布砂砾岩(Q_1^L),岩体较完整,泥钙质、钙质胶结或半胶结,成岩作用差,拱肩钻孔取不出岩芯,需以植物胶取样。强度低,原位饱和砂砾岩弹模仅为 0.5~0.7GPa。河床覆盖层厚 3m 左右,左坝肩发育有 2 个阶地,右坝肩边坡为倒坡。河谷接近 U 形河谷。

在该工程的设计过程中,由于基础弹模过低,坝体变位大,坝身和坝肩都出现很大的应力集中现象。采用在坝肩下游设置推力墩(见图 1(a))、下游面设人工短缝等措施,坝体变位得到控制,坝肩和坝身应力得到改善,推力墩的作用比较明显。

计算以坝轴线中点为原点,横河向(指向左岸为正)为 x 轴,顺河向(逆水流方向为正)为 y 轴,铅直方向(向上为正)为 z 轴(如图 1(a)所示)。整体工程共划分单元 13 151 个,节点 16 084 个。

自重用含中缝拱的累积自重;水压用整体拱含构造缝,水库校核洪水位 107m,上游考虑 60m 的淤沙压力,下游水深 13m。整体三维有限元计算结果,本文取典型高程 1 310m 的应力和位移进行比较讨论。

本文选自《清华大学学报(自然科学版)》2004 年第 44 卷第 3 期,作者还有陈强、李鹏辉。

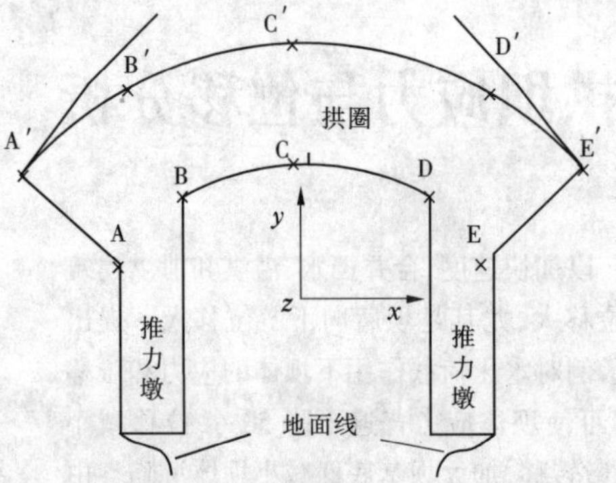

(a)拱圈平面布置示意图(有推力墩)

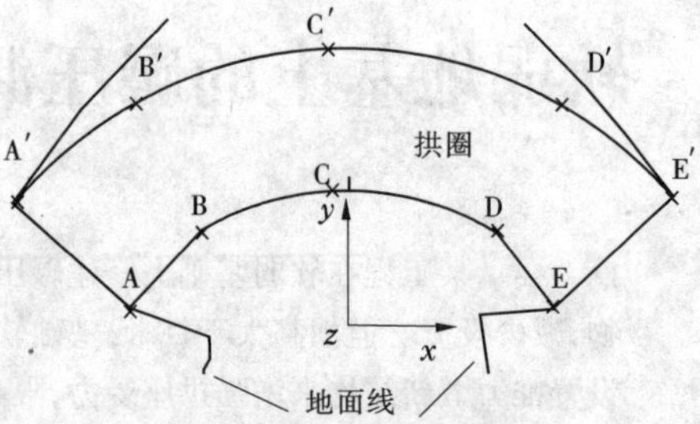

(b)拱圈平面布置示意图(无推力墩)

图1　拱坝平面布置示意图

2　基础软弱对坝身应力和位移的影响及设置推力墩后的效果

2.1　基础软弱对坝身位移和应力的影响

从图2可以清楚地看出,在水压作用下,比较拱座基岩弹模0.5GPa和弹模5GPa,拱坝坝体顺河向位移峰值由35.3mm变成9.5mm,平均差别为3～4倍(见图2(c))。

A、C两点间顺河向位移差,在基础弹模为0.5GPa情况下是7.7mm,基础弹模为5GPa情况下位移5.5mm。这表明基础差的情况下拱圈自身变形也比较大。

当基岩弹模为0.5GPa时,B点和D点之间的区域存在较大的拱向拉应力集中,应力峰值1.53MPa(C点附近因为设人工短缝,拱向拉应力峰值下降);当基岩弹模为5GPa时,B点和D点之间的拱向拉应力峰值0.48MPa(见图2(a)),且BD间应力比较均匀。

上游面拱向应力基本为压力区(图2(b)),在基岩弹模为0.5GPa和5GPa情况下压应力峰值相差约1MPa,且后者A′E′之间应力值和应力变幅都小于前者。

此外,弹模的不同对下游面 σ_z 影响也比较大,如图2(d)所示,弹模5GPa情况下的 σ_z 小于弹模0.5GPa的 σ_z 值,且沿AB的 σ_z 变幅小。坝身下游面的 σ_y 随弹模变化较小,数值也在±0.2MPa之间,故图2中没有列出。

可见,弹模降低使拱坝应力普遍恶化,变位加大。

2.2　推力墩结构对坝身位移和应力的影响

设置推力墩后(见图2(a)),B点和D点之间的拱向拉应力 σ_x 峰值从1.53MPa降低到0.8MPa,且整个坝体下游面的应力水平普遍降低50%;靠近坝头附近的拉应力 σ_x 略有上升,但最大值不超过0.5MPa,如图2(b)所示,坝体上游面的拱向应力在设置推力墩结构后普遍下降,应力峰值由-2.6MPa下降至-2MPa。以上结果表明,在设置推力墩后坝体应力明显改善,其应力大小基本接近基础弹模提高到5GPa的情况。

如图2(d)所示,基础0.5GPa不变,设置推力墩后,σ_z 应力降低50%,和基础弹模5GPa的情况下 σ_z 大小非常接近。

由位移(见图2(c))可见,设推力墩后坝身顺河向位移降低,整体下降约20%,但是与基础弹模5GPa的情况相比,位移还是比较大。这表明推力墩结构只是在一定程度上改

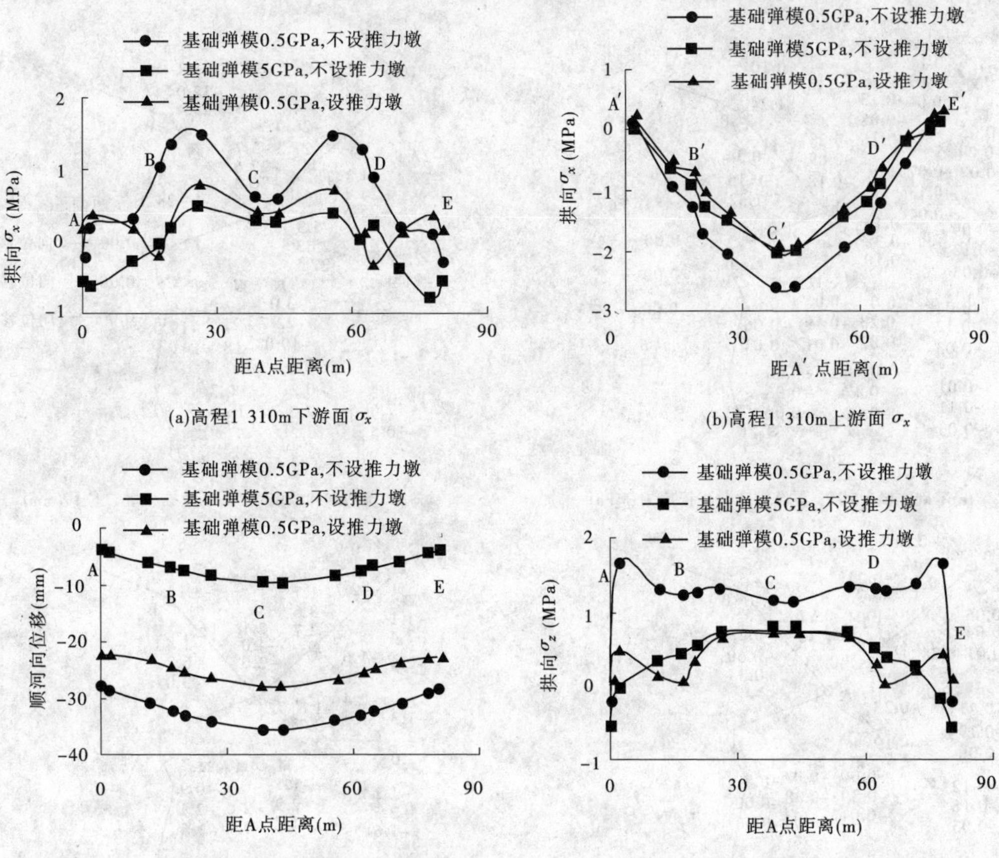

(a)高程1 310m下游面 σ_x　　(b)高程1 310m上游面 σ_x

(c)高程1 310m下游面顺河向位移图　　(d)高程1 310m下游面 σ_z

图2　水压荷载下坝体的拱向 σ_x、σ_z 和顺河向位移图

善坝身位移。

在基础 0.5GPa 不设推力墩情况下 AC 两点间位移差是 7.7mm，设推力墩后为 5.5mm。这表明设推力墩后拱圈自身变形减小。

3　基础软弱对坝肩基岩应力和位移的影响及设置推力墩后的效果

3.1　基础软弱对坝肩基岩位移和应力的影响

如图 3(a)、图 3(c)所示，基岩弹模不同，水压作用下坝肩应力分布规律也相应变化。在弹模为 0.5GPa 的情况下，沿 A′A 拱向应力 σ_x 从微拉应力渐变成压应力，变幅为 0.37MPa，沿 A′A 拱向应力 σ_y、σ_z 也存在微拉力区；在弹模为 5GPa 的情况下，σ_x、σ_y、σ_z 微拉力区范围缩小。这表明软岩对拱肩应力分布不利。

在低弹模情况下，在 A 点下游的岩石区域 σ_y 值比较大(见图 3(a))，这反映了坝肩岩石向下游位移的趋势，而 σ_x 和 σ_z 都比较小。

下面看位移分布规律。基础弹模为 0.5GPa 情况下，顺河向(y 向)位移和垂直河向(x 向)位移比较大，拱座以下很大范围内的岩石向下游位移达 16.0mm 以上(见图 3(b))。

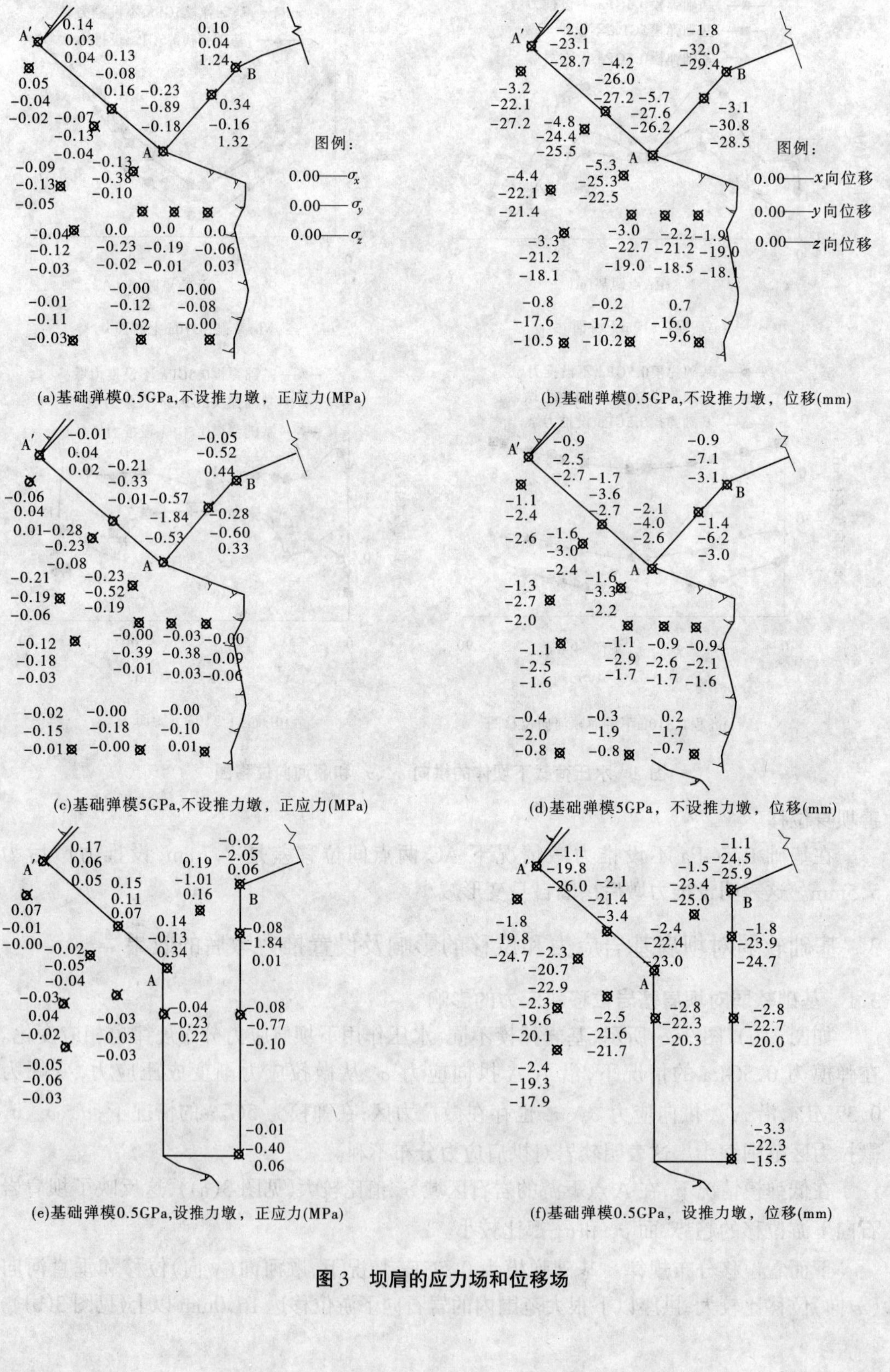

(a)基础弹模0.5GPa,不设推力墩，正应力(MPa)

(b)基础弹模0.5GPa,不设推力墩，位移(mm)

(c)基础弹模5GPa,不设推力墩，正应力(MPa)

(d)基础弹模5GPa，不设推力墩，位移(mm)

(e)基础弹模0.5GPa,设推力墩，正应力(MPa)

(f)基础弹模0.5GPa，设推力墩，位移(mm)

图 3　坝肩的应力场和位移场

对比图 3(b)和图 3(d)沿 A′A 的 x 向位移,可以发现基础软弱时坝体向两侧山体挤压更明显。

由以上应力和位移分布规律可知,基础软弱时,坝体向下游和两侧的山体的变位比较明显,坝肩下游大范围岩石区变形加大。

3.2 推力墩结构对坝肩基岩位移和应力的影响

设置推力墩以增强拱座的抗力,减小水压作用下坝体和拱座附近局部岩体向下游的变位。

由图 3(e)可见,设置推力墩后 A′A 下游基岩区压应力普遍下降,推力墩混凝土结构本身应力增大,但远小于混凝土抗压强度,在 B 点附近存在顺河向的压应力集中,峰值约 −2.0MPa,且整个推力墩结构顺河向压应力普遍比基岩应力大,这表明,应力向推力墩结构转移。而且注意到在设置推力墩结构后,基岩几乎全部处于受压状态,应力值不大,有利于基岩的稳定。

对比图 3(a)、图 3(e),发现设置推力墩后,减小了 B 点附近较大区域的坝体的 σ_z 值,表明这一区域的应力恶化得到缓解。

如图 3(b)、图 3(f)所示,设置推力墩后坝肩附近拱向位移减小一半,顺河向位移减小 10%。需要指出的是,B 点附近的顺河向位移值由 32.0mm 降低至 24.5mm,这表明推力墩减小了坝体向下游位移的趋势。推力墩结构整体向下游位移和坝体保持协调,这说明拱的内应力很小。

3.3 组合应力(自重+水压)条件下的推力墩效果

软弱基础上混凝土坝体及推力墩自重大,引起沉降变形大,可通过加大基础来减小变形量。

如图 4(a)所示,自重荷载作用下,因整个坝体结构重心偏上游,坝肩向上游转动。水压、自重荷载叠加后的位移场如图 4(b)所示,顺河向(y 向)位移普遍小于 15mm。

推力墩结构有利于改善坝体和基岩的应力,减小坝体整体向下游变位。

从受力特点来分析,设置推力墩前,坝体跨度 AE 为 67m(图 1(b)),设置推力墩后跨度 BD 为 46m(图 1(a)),减小 30%的跨度;而在计算模型中,拱坝上游面弧线 A′E′保持不变,可以认为水压荷载基本不变。因此,在相同的荷载下,拱圈跨度减小应力亦会减小。注意到设置推力墩前后拱圈底部混凝土和基岩的接触面积由 2 569m^2 增大到 3 711m^2(见图 1),这增强了供坝抗滑能力。实际情况是应力水平普遍降低 20%~40%,坝体位移也得到控制。

比较“基岩取弹模 5GPa,不设推力墩”和“基岩弹模取实测弹模 0.5GPa,设推力墩”这两种情况,如图 2 所示,二者上游面拱向应力大小非常接近,下游面拱向应力差别不大,竖直方向的应力 σ_z 也非常接近。因此,从应力的角度看,设置推力墩后,接近于把坝体建在一个弹模是 5GPa 的较好基岩上。

4 结语

基岩弹模低,导致坝体应力恶化,但是其主要影响还是坝体变位过大。坝肩基岩有向横河向挤压、顺河大变位,坝体沉降比较大。

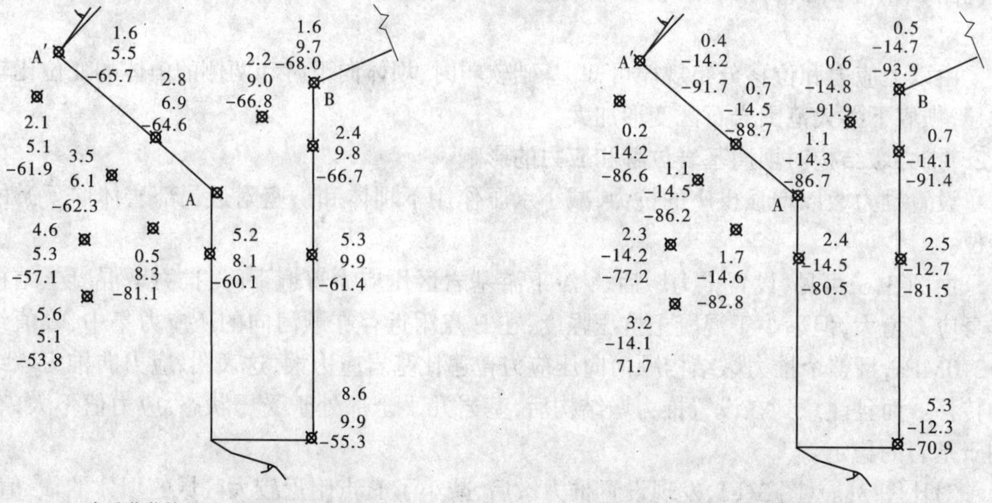

(a)自重荷载情况下，位移(mm)　　(b)水压和自重荷载叠加情况下，位移(mm)

图4　基础弹模0.5GPa情况下坝肩位移场

为解决应力过大,控制坝体向下游变位,从改进坝体结构的角度入手,提出设置推力墩结构。推力墩结构大大减小拱圈跨度,增大拱坝底部混凝土和基岩的接触面积,增强拱坝顺河向抗力。计算表明,坝体应力得到很大改善,坝肩应力得到有效控制;整个结构变位得到控制,尤其是向下游变位的趋势得到改善。经过计算分析,推力墩结构对改善应力的作用,近似于把坝体建在弹模是5GPa的较好基岩上。

参考文献

[1] 刘光廷,徐增辉,胡昱．侧约束对拱坝坝体应力和位移的影响．清华大学学报(自然科学版),2002,42(11):1537～1540

[2] 刘光廷,徐增辉,李鹏辉．柔性拱和软弱地基上的碾压混凝土拱坝．清华大学学报(自然科学版),2002,42(10):1365～1368

[3] Zeng Zhaoyang, Ma Qian. *Study on the structural joints in the high RCC arch dam*. Shuili Fadian/Water Power, 1998,1:273～285

[4] 李守义,杜效鹄,王选平．拱圈形状对应力和坝肩稳定的影响．西安理工大学学报,1998(1):75～79

[5] 董羽蕙．香溪口工程坝肩软弱夹层的处理及其应力分布．贵州工学院学报,1995,24(2):34～37

[6] Liu Guangting, Lin Guoyu. *Study on the curved and branch cracks in massive concrete structures*. Proceedings of Int conf on Dam Fracture, 1991, 11:19～28

软岩多轴流变特性及其对拱坝的影响

摘　要　文中尝试利用多轴非线性流变模型,将砾岩在多轴应力条件下的流变试验成果应用于实际工程,使仿真数值计算结果更接近实际情况。与干燥状态相比,泡水后软岩除了瞬时变形模量大幅度降低外,流变也很显著,这会对坝体应力带来明显的影响。文中还考虑了侧压对岩石流变的影响。由于侧压作用,软岩流变减少,拱坝拉应力区域缩减,拉应力值也有一定程度降低。

关键词　软岩　多轴试验　流变　数值计算

在软弱的沉积岩上修拱坝[1],除了要考虑基岩瞬时变形,还需考虑软岩的时间效应。大量的现场量测和室内试验都表明,软岩的流变属性是非常显著的,尤其是软岩泡水之后。所以如何准确地描述拱座处软岩的时间效应,将会给拱坝的设计和建造带来重要的影响。

在目前国内[2~5]、外[6~8]岩石流变研究领域,人们对岩石在单轴压缩、常规三轴等受力条件下的流变属性已经做了一些室内试验研究。但研究对象多集中在岩石的轴向流变,而对侧向流变以及侧(围)压对岩石流变影响研究甚少[9,10]。而这些影响对构造一个真正反映软岩流变特性的本构关系是十分重要的。

本文结合新疆某拱坝,采用坝区软弱砾岩,进行单、双轴流变试验。坝址区出露侏罗系中、上统,白垩系下统地层,为一套连续沉积的河湖相碎屑岩,产出状态以中厚层至块状为主,层理发育,具有明显的沉积韵律。其中对拱坝结构影响最大的是侏罗系上统客拉扎组,岩石为泥、铁及钙质混合胶结,呈棕红色,强度较低,厚度58m。室内试验表明,坝区岩体尤其是泥、铁及钙质混合胶结的红色砾岩,具有浸水软化及显著的时间效应,也是本文研究的主要对象。通过试验,构造出能更真实反映软岩时间效应的本构模型,并将其应用于非线性仿真计算中。

1　试验及成果

1.1　试验仪器及选用试件

红色砾岩的单、双轴流变试验在CSS－283型混凝土、岩石双轴徐变试验机完成。CSS－283型混凝土、岩石双轴徐变试验机为长春试验机研究所与清华大学水利系共同设计,并由前者开发制造出来的。该机器由主机(见图1)、电控箱和计算机控制处理系统三大部分组成。

试验机采用机电伺服机构提供垂直与水平方向的荷载。加载能力:垂直方向为500kN(压),水平方向为300kN(压)。试验机加载系统具有锁定功能,当意外断电时,荷载变化平均速率每小时小于1%。另外试验机还配备有UPS外挂电源,以保证停电时候

本文载刊于《岩石力学与工程学报》2004年4月第23卷第8期,作者还有胡昱、陈凤岐、徐增辉。

图 1　双轴徐变仪主机

计算机和主机能正常工作,满足了流变试验中荷载要长期稳定的试验要求。

采用轮幅式测力传感器测量垂直和水平方向的轴向荷载,精度为±1%示值;采用差动式位移传感器测量垂直和水平方向变形,测量分辨率达到 0.1μm。

为了减少垂直轴与水平轴加载之间的相互影响,水平轴具有浮动功能,并且水平轴加载头与压板之间采用滚动连接。

流变实验室配备有两台 Mcway 冷暖空调,温度基本控制在 20℃ ±0.5℃。

砾岩试件由坝区运回的岩样切割而成,试件尺寸为 100mm×100mm×100mm。干燥试件在自然环境下干燥,泡水试件则是将试件在清水中泡水 30 天。

1.2　试验成果

流变试验包括以下几个方面的内容:①干燥和泡水砾岩流变对比;②砾岩流变泊松图 2 是干燥、泡水条件下,红色砾岩比与弹性泊松比对比;③侧压对砾岩流变的影响。

1.2.1　干燥、泡水砾岩流变

流变曲线对比图。各种条件下砾岩试件瞬时变形和流变变形见表 1。

表 1　各种条件下砾岩变形($\sigma_1=8$MPa)

状态	瞬时变形 (10^{-6})	流变变形 (10^{-6})
干燥	556	131
泡水	2 787	1 243

注:表中流变变形对应时间为 1.5×10^6s。

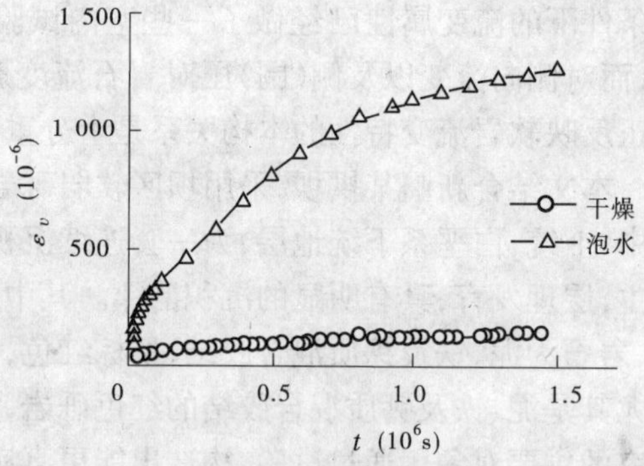

图 2　干燥、泡水条件砾岩流变曲线对比($\sigma_1=8$MPa)

从图 2、表 1 可以看出,泡水后,红色砾岩流变特性更显著,相同应力条件下,泡水砾岩流变相当于干燥状态的 1/10。干燥情况下,砾岩流变相当于瞬时弹性变形的 25%,而泡水后,流变与瞬时变形之比为 1∶2。

1.2.2　流变泊松比

软岩单轴受压流变试验中,轴向流变(受力方向)与侧向流变化趋势既有相似之处,也有不同的地方。相似之处是,它们都经历流变的两个阶段:初期流变和二期流变。初期流变过程,变形速率递减;二期流变过程,变形速率恒定。不同的地方是,侧向流变在开始的阶段变化很快,而在后期变形趋于平缓;轴向流变,在后期仍有一定的变形速率。这种现象与软岩瞬时变形有一定差别,瞬时变形中,无论是轴向还是侧向,它们的应力—应变曲线均是直线(干燥状态),瞬时泊松比(侧向瞬时变形与轴向瞬时变形比值的绝对值)是定值。而对于单轴流变试验,如果将某一时刻侧向流变与轴向流变比值的绝对值定义成流变泊松比，那么如图3所示，流变泊松比将不再是一个定值，而是时间的函数，并且其值将随时间的增长而减少，最后趋近于一个定值。在工程中，为了分析方便，取流变时间为1×10^6s时的侧向流变与轴向流变比值的绝对值作为单轴条件下的流变泊松比。

图4比较了几个单轴流变试验中，瞬时弹性泊松比与流变泊松比之间的区别。在单轴压缩条件下，干燥砾岩的瞬时弹性泊松比一般较小，在0.2～0.3范围内浮动，而其流变泊松比则较大。从图中可以看出，在单轴压缩条件下，流变泊松比一般是瞬时弹性泊松比的两倍。所以在进行拱坝坝肩时间效应分析时，如果用瞬时弹性泊松比代替流变泊松比，将会给计算带来一定差别。

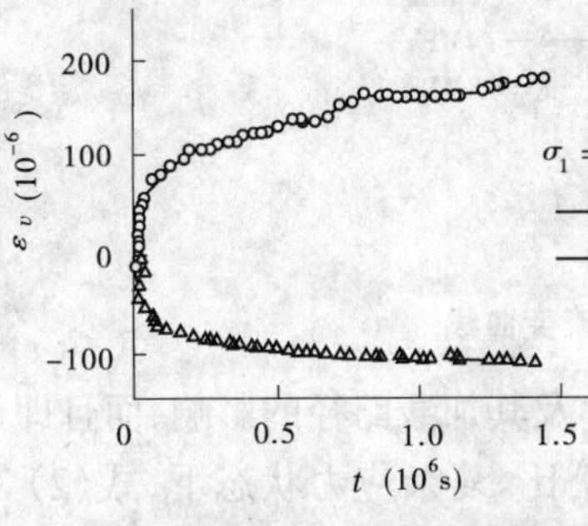

图3 砾岩轴向、侧向流变曲线

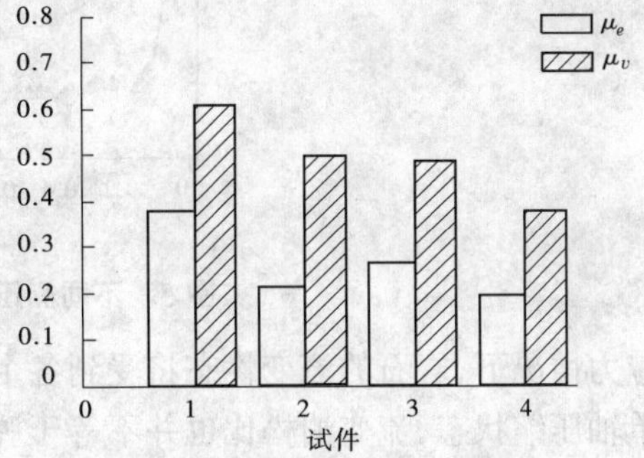

图4 弹性泊松比和流变泊松比对比

1.2.3 侧压对砾岩流变的影响

以上考虑的仅是单轴受压情况，并没有考虑侧压对软岩流变的影响。事实上，在实际工程中，有侧压和围压的情况才是最普遍的，所以有必要研究侧压对软岩轴向和侧向流变的影响。

试验过程：先进行侧向加载，待变形基本稳定之后（时间7～14d），保持侧压不变，轴向施压（$\sigma_1=8$MPa），开始软岩流变试验，试验结果见图5。

由图5可以看出，侧压对软岩的轴向流变和侧向流变均有影响。两者均变小，尤其是侧向流变，有无侧压影响很大。

2 黏弹性本构方程

在本文中，采用Kelvin-Voigt模型来描述棕红色砾岩受力变形的时间效应。

在Kelvin模型中，总应变ε分解成弹性应变ε_e、黏弹性应变ε_{ve}，总应变率表示为

$$\dot{\varepsilon}=\dot{\varepsilon}_e+\dot{\varepsilon}_{ve} \tag{1}$$

其中黏弹性应变率$\dot{\varepsilon}_{ve}$可由下式得到：

$$\dot{\varepsilon}_{ve}=\frac{\sigma}{\eta}-\frac{E_2}{\eta}\varepsilon_{ve} \tag{2}$$

式中：E_2是黏弹性模量；η是黏弹性系数。

在将上述单轴应力状态公式推广到多维应力状态的时候，通常做法是假定黏性变形的泊松比μ_{ve}是常量，与时间、应力状态等没有关系，并且其值等于弹性变形的泊松比μ_e。这样做固然可以简化模型，减少计算量，但上述试验结果表明，在双轴和三轴压缩的复杂

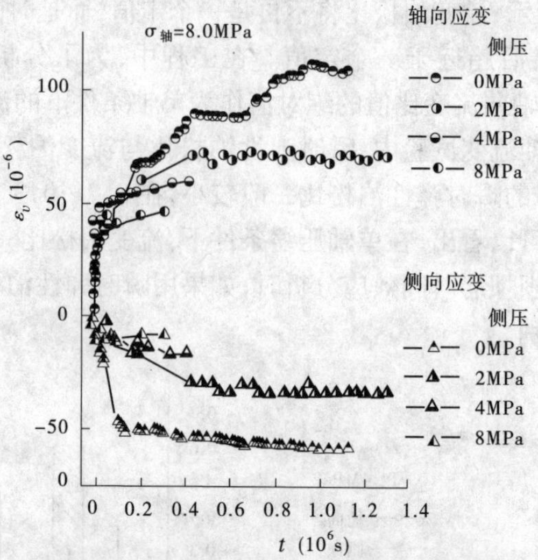

图 5　不同侧压砾岩轴向、侧向流变曲线

应力情况下，岩石的流变性态将受到各个方向应力大小及其加载路径的影响，而且即使是单轴压缩状态，流变泊松比也并不等于弹性变形的泊松比。复杂应力状态下，式(2) 写成式(3) 的形式。

$$\{\dot{\varepsilon}_{ve}\} = \frac{[A]\{\sigma\}}{\eta} - \frac{E_2}{\eta}\{\varepsilon_{ve}\} \tag{3}$$

式中的黏弹性模量 E_2、矩阵$[A]$中的流变泊松比 μ_v 均是侧压$\sigma_{侧}$ 的函数。根据干燥砾岩试验结果(图 5)，函数写成如下形式：

$$\frac{E_2}{E_{20}} = -0.022\,39\left(\frac{\sigma_{侧}}{\sigma_0}\right)^2 + 0.383\,2\frac{\sigma_{侧}}{\sigma_0} + 1.0 \tag{4}$$

$$\mu_v = \frac{1}{-0.088\,7\left(\frac{\sigma_{侧}}{\sigma_0}\right)^2 + 1.597\frac{\sigma_{侧}}{\sigma_0} + 2.161} \tag{5}$$

其中 $\sigma_0 = 1.0$MPa，E_{20} 是无侧压($\sigma_3 = 0$) 时的黏弹性模量。计算材料力学参数见表 2。

表 2　计算材料力学参数($\sigma_3 = 0$)

材料	状态	容重 (kN/m³)	变形模量 E_{10} (GPa)	瞬时弹性泊松比 μ_{e0}	黏弹性模量 E_{20} (GPa)	黏弹性系数 η (GPa·s)	流变泊松比 μ_{v0}
砾岩	干	24.9	14.58	0.28	74.64	1.73×107	0.48
	泡水	25.7	2.01	0.36	6.43	3.46×106	0.6

由于岩石自重作用，随着拱圈高程不同，$\sigma_{侧}$ 会不同。这意味着在不同高程，砾岩流变程度不一样。深层坝基，$\sigma_{侧}$ 越大，砾岩流变程度就越小。

在下文的数值计算中，将包括流变泊松比对流变的影响、比较干燥和泡水情况下的砾岩流变以及考虑侧压对流变影响等几方面内容。由于试验中得到的是自然干燥条件下侧压对砾岩流变影响的试验曲线,所以在数值计算中,参照干燥情况下的公式,修改式(4)、式(5) 后得到与泡水情况相应的公式,用于数值计算。

3 计算及成果

示例如图 6(新疆某工程 1 335m 高程平面拱圈网格剖分图) 所示。计算以横河向(指向左岸为正)为 x 轴,顺河向(逆水流方向为正)为 y 轴。为保证计算精度,共划分 280 个单元,344 个节点。并选用控制点 C 点的位移和应力进行分析。如图所示:点 C 位于拱冠的下游面处,当拱坝受水压作用时,这部分属于拉应力区域。

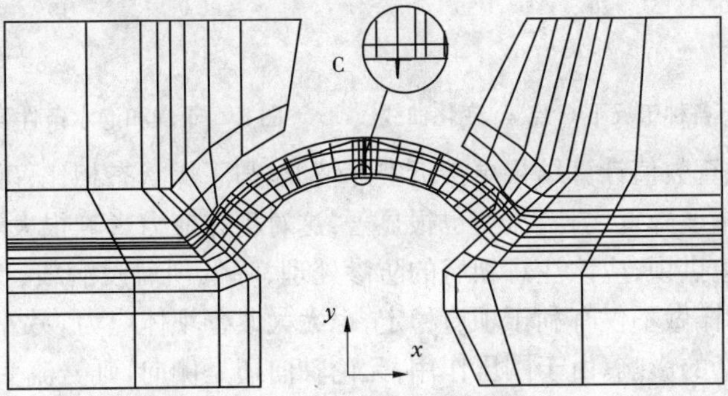

图 6 1 335m 高程平面拱圈网格剖分

水库正常蓄水高程 1 390m,所以此时拱圈承受上游水压荷载 0.55MPa。计算结构采用柔性拱结构。

在计算中,混凝土弹性模量取 20.0GPa,泊松比为 0.16,材料参数来自工程的实测。砾岩参数见表 2。

图 7 是干燥条件下,各种工况 C 点 σ_x 应力变化曲线图。从图中可以得到以下几条结论:

(1) 对于干燥情况,砾岩流变对坝体应力影响不显著,C 点的拉应力从 0.29MPa 上升到 0.33MPa。

(2) 比较 $\mu_v = 0.28$、$\mu_v = 0.48$ 两条曲线,两条曲线值相差不大。说明流变泊松比对应力的影响也不大。

(3) 在计算中,考虑黏弹性模量 E_2、流变泊松比 μ_v 均是侧压 $\sigma_{侧}$ 的函数后,C点拉应力经过流变只上升到 0.32MPa,略小于没有考虑侧压的情况,其原因仍是干燥条件下砾岩流变不显著。

图 8 是干燥、泡水两种条件下坝体应力对比图。相对于干燥条件下砾岩流变的不显著,在泡水后,砾岩流变显著,而且对坝体应力影响很大。C 点应力从 1.31MPa 上升到 1.60MPa。已经从较安全状态转变为较不安全状态。如果不考虑侧压对砾岩流变的影响,则应力会上升到 1.83MPa,结果会更不安全。

4 结论

本文尝试利用多轴非线性流变模型,将砾岩在多轴应力条件下的流变试验成果应用

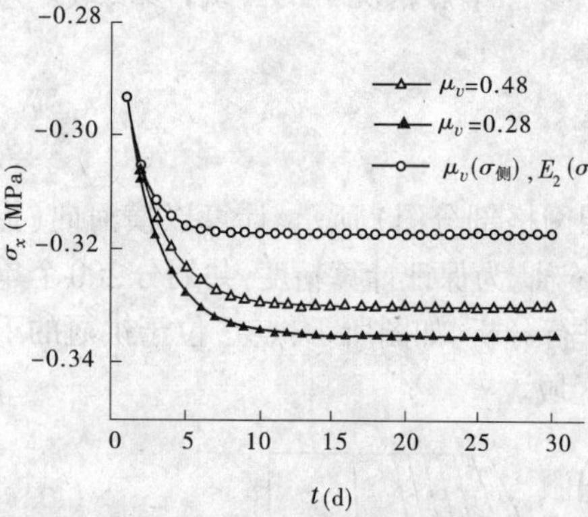

图7　干燥条件下各种工况下C点 σ_x 变化曲线

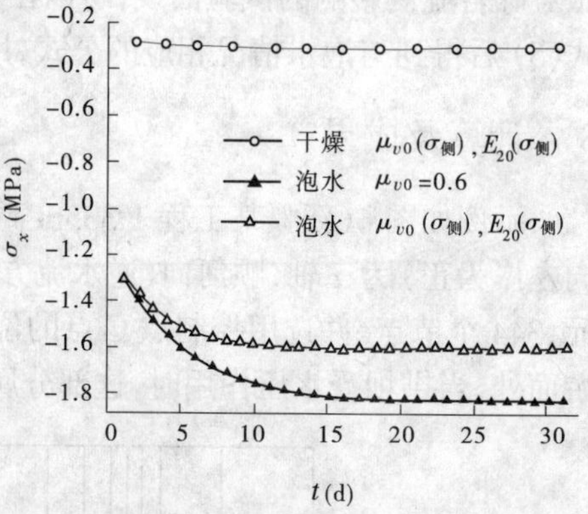

图8　干燥和泡水条件下C点 σ_x 变化曲线

于实际工程,使仿真数值计算结果更接近实际情况。与干燥状态相比,砾岩泡水之后,除了瞬时变形模量大幅度降低之外,流变也很显著,这对坝体应力影响很大。所以,在浸水软化的软弱基础上修建拱坝,应该注意坝肩的防渗处理,降低坝肩浸润线,保持和加大部分坝肩岩体的干燥。这样做不仅有利于坝肩稳定,也大大改善坝体应力。另外在本文中,还分析了围压对岩石流变的影响。由于围压作用,无论轴向还是侧向,砾岩流变均减少,从而使拱座岩石位移减少,拱圈拉应力区域缩减,拉应力值也有一定程度的降低。

参 考 文 献

[1] 刘光廷,徐增辉,李鹏辉．柔性拱和软弱地基上的碾压混凝土拱坝．清华大学学报,2002,42(10):1365~1368

[2] 杨春和,白世伟,吴益民．应力水平及加载路径对盐岩时效的影响．岩石力学与工程学报,2000,19(3):270~275

[3] Li Yongsheng, Xia Caichu. *Time-dependent tests on intact rocks in uniaxial compression*. Int.J.rock Mech. & Min. Sci.,2000,37(3):467~475

[4] 邓荣贵,周德培,张倬元,等．一种新德岩石流变模型．岩石力学与工程学报,2001,20(6):780~784

[5] 范广勤．岩土工程流变力学．北京:煤炭工业出版社,1992

[6] Boitnott G N. *Experimental characterization of the nonliear rheology of rock*. Int. J. rock Mech. & Min.Sci., 1997,34(3~4):33

[7] Malan D F, Vogler U W, Drescher K. *Time-dependent behaviour of hard rock in deep level gold mines*. Journal of the South African Institute of Mining and Metallurgy, 1997,97:135~147

[8] Maranini E, Brignoli M. *Creep behaviour of a weak rock: experimental characterization*. Int.J.rock Mech. & Min.Sci., 1999,36(1):127~138

[9] Gerstle K H. *Simple formulation of biaxial concrete behavior*. ACI, 1981,78(5):62~68

[10] 揽生瑞,过镇海．定侧压下混凝土二轴受压变形特性的试验研究．土木工程学报,1996,29(2):28~36